Greenland
(Kalatdlit-Nunat)
Alaska
Yukon
N.W.T.
Nunavut
[Labrador]
B.C.
Alta.
Sask.
Man.
Ont.
Que.
Nfld.
St.Pierre
and Miquelon
P.E.I.
N.B.
N.S.
Vt.
Maine
N.H.
Mass.
R.I.
Conn.
N.J.
Del.
Md.
Wash.
Oreg.
Idaho
Mont.
Wyo.
N.Dak.
S.Dak.
Minn.
Wis.
Mich.
N.Y.
Pa.
Iowa
Nebr.
Nev.
Utah
Colo.
Kans.
Mo.
Ill.
Ind.
Ohio
W.Va.
Va.
Ky.
Calif.
Ariz.
N.Mex.
Okla.
Ark.
Tenn.
N.C.
S.C.
Ga.
Ala.
Miss.
La.
Tex.
Fla.
Mexico

Flora of North America

Contributors to Volume 11, Parts 1 and 2

Daniel Adams
Zoya V. Akulova-Barlow
Robert J. Alier
Jenna M. Annis
Peter W. Ball
Julie A. Ballenger
David J. Bogler
Alice Broadhead
Steven L. Broich
Luc Brouillet
Rachel K. Clark
Alfonso Delgado-Salinas
Óscar Dorado
Matthew L. Duley
John E. Ebinger
Ashley N. Egan
Paul R. Fantz
Frank T. Farruggia
Gabriel Flores-Franco
John M. Gillett†
Douglas H. Goldman
Rosaura Grether
Zachary E. Guthrie

Richard R. Halse
Neil A. Harriman†
Héctor M. Hernández
Denis M. Kearns
Brian R. Keener
Alexander Krings
Thomas G. Lammers
Matt Lavin
Carolyn K. Levings
Alan W. Lievens
Melissa A. Luckow
Brigitte Marazzi
Robert H. Mohlenbrock
Guy L. Nesom
Hiroyoshi Ohashi
Matthew A. Parker
Derick B. Poindexter
Jay A. Raveill
James L. Reveal†
María de Lourdes Rico-Arce
Brant W. Riegel
Rhonda Riggins
Erin Thais Riley
Velva E. Rudd†

David S. Seigler
Teresa Sholars
Leila M. Shultz
Beryl B. Simpson
Ernest Small
Solange Sotuyo
Shannon C. K. Straub
Lawrence R. Stritch
James C. Sugar
David M. Sutherland
Ralph L. Thompson
Leticia Torres-Colín
Debra K. Trock
Gordon C. Tucker
Billie L. Turner†
L. J. G. van der Maesen
Michael A. Vincent
Wade Wall
Alan S. Weakley
Stanley L. Welsh
Martin F. Wojciechowski
Michael Woods
Richard P. Wunderlin

Editors for Volume 11, Parts 1 and 2

David E. Boufford
Assisting Taxon Editor for Fabaceae

Tammy M. Charron
Managing Editor

Kanchi Gandhi
Nomenclatural and Etymological Editor

Martha J. Hill
Senior Technical Editor

Robert W. Kiger
Bibliographic Editor

Thomas G. Lammers
Assisting Taxon Editor for Fabaceae

Geoffrey A. Levin
Lead Editor (2019–2021)

Jay A. Raveill
Assisting Taxon Editor for Fabaceae

John L. Strother
Reviewing Editor

Michael A. Vincent
Lead Taxon Editor for Fabaceae

James L. Zarucchi†
Editorial Director and Lead Editor (to 2019)

Volume 11, Parts 1 and 2 Composition

Tanya Harvey
Layout Artist and Editorial Assistant

Kristin Pierce
Compositor and Editorial Assistant

Trifolium macrocephalum

Flora of North America

North of Mexico

Edited by FLORA OF NORTH AMERICA EDITORIAL COMMITTEE

VOLUME 11

Magnoliophyta: Fabaceae, part 2

SUBFAMILY FABOIDEAE, TRIBES ROBINIEAE TO FABEAE

NEW YORK OXFORD • OXFORD UNIVERSITY PRESS • 2023

Oxford University Press is a department of the University of Oxford.
It furthers the University's objective of excellence in research,
scholarship, and education by publishing worldwide.

Oxford New York
Auckland Cape Town Dar es Salaam Hong Kong Karachi Kuala Lumpur
Madrid Melbourne Mexico City Nairobi New Delhi Shanghai Taipei Toronto

With offices in
Argentina Austria Brazil Chile Czech Republic France Greece Guatemala Hungary Italy
Japan Poland Portugal Singapore South Korea Switzerland Thailand Turkey Ukraine Vietnam

Published by Oxford University Press, Inc.
198 Madison Avenue, New York, New York 10016
www.oup.com

Library of Congress Cataloging-in-Publication Data
(Revised for Volume 11)
Flora of North America North of Mexico
edited by Flora of North America Editorial Committee.
Includes bibliographical references and indexes.
Contents: v. 1. Introduction—v. 2. Pteridophytes and gymnosperms—
v. 3. Magnoliophyta: Magnoliidae and Hamamelidae—
v. 22. Magnoliophyta: Alismatidae, Arecidae, Commelinidae (in part), and Zingiberidae—
v. 26. Magnoliophyta: Liliidae: Liliales and Orchidales—
v. 23. Magnoliophyta: Commelinidae (in part): Cyperaceae—
v. 25. Magnoliophyta: Commelinidae (in part): Poaceae, part 2—
v. 4. Magnoliophyta: Caryophyllidae (in part): part 1—
v. 5. Magnoliophyta: Caryophyllidae (in part): part 2—
v. 19, 20, 21. Magnoliophyta: Asteridae (in part): Asteraceae, parts 1–3—
v. 24. Magnoliophyta: Commelinidae (in part): Poaceae, part 1—
v. 27. Bryophyta, part 1—
v. 8. Magnoliophyta: Paeoniaceae to Ericaceae—
v. 7. Magnoliophyta: Salicaceae to Brassicaceae—
v. 28. Bryophyta, part 2—
v. 9. Magnoliophyta: Picramniaceae to Rosaceae—
v. 6. Magnoliophyta: Cucurbitaceae to Droseraceae—
v. 12. Magnoliophyta: Vitaceae to Garryaceae—
v. 17 Magnoliophyta: Tetrachondraceae to Orobanchaceae—
v. 10 Magnoliophyta: Proteaceae to Elaeagnaceae—
v. 11 Magnoliophyta: Fabaceae, parts 1 and 2

ISBN: 9780197619803 (v. 11, set); ISBN: 9780197577974 (v. 11, part 1); ISBN: 9780197577981 (v. 11, part 2)
1. Botany—North America.
2. Botany—United States.
3. Botany—Canada.
I. Flora of North America Editorial Committee.
QK110.F55 2002 581.97 92-30459

1 2 3 4 5 6 7 8 9

Contents

Contributors to Volume 11, Parts 1 and 2

Daniel Adams
The University of North Carolina at Chapel Hill
Chapel Hill, North Carolina

Zoya V. Akulova-Barlow
El Cerrito, California

Robert J. Alier
Eastern Illinois University
Charleston, Illinois

Jenna M. Annis
Eastern Illinois University
Charleston, Illinois

Peter W. Ball
University of Toronto
Mississauga, Ontario

Julie A. Ballenger
Columbus State University
Columbus, Georgia

David J. Bogler
Missouri Botanical Garden
St. Louis, Missouri

Alice Broadhead
North Carolina State University
Raleigh, North Carolina

Steven L. Broich
Oregon State University
Corvallis, Oregon

Luc Brouillet
Université de Montréal
Montréal, Québec

Rachel K. Clark
North Carolina State University
Raleigh, North Carolina

Alfonso Delgado-Salinas
Universidad Nacional Autónoma de México
Mexico City, Mexico

Óscar Dorado
Centro de Educación Ambiental e Investigación Sierra de Huautla
Universidad Autónoma del Estado de Morelos
Cuernavaca, Mexico

Matthew L. Duley
Miami University
Oxford, Ohio

John E. Ebinger
Eastern Illinois University
Charleston, Illinois

Ashley N. Egan
Utah Valley University
Orem, Utah

Paul R. Fantz
North Carolina State University
Raleigh, North Carolina

Frank T. Farruggia
Smithsonian Institution,
National Museum of Natural History
Washington, DC

Gabriel Flores-Franco
Universidad Autónoma del Estado de Morelos
Cuernavaca, Mexico

John M. Gillett†
Nepean, Ontario

Douglas H. Goldman
United States Department of Agriculture
Greensboro, North Carolina

Rosaura Grether
Universidad Autónoma Metropolitana-Iztapalapa
Mexico City, Mexico

Zachary E. Guthrie
Eastern Illinois University
Charleston, Illinois

Richard R. Halse
Oregon State University
Corvallis, Oregon

Neil A. Harriman†
University of Wisconsin Oshkosh
Oshkosh, Wisconsin

Héctor M. Hernández
Instituto de Biología
Universidad Nacional Autónoma de México
Mexico City, Mexico

Denis M. Kearns
Bakersfield, California

Brian R. Keener
The University of West Alabama
Livingston, Alabama

Alexander Krings
North Carolina State University
Raleigh, North Carolina

Thomas G. Lammers
University of Wisconsin Oshkosh
Oshkosh, Wisconsin

Matt Lavin
Montana State University
Bozeman, Montana

Carolyn K. Levings
Oklahoma Panhandle State University
Goodwell, Oklahoma

Alan W. Lievens
Texas Lutheran University
Seguin, Texas

Melissa A. Luckow
L. H. Bailey Hortorium
Cornell University
Ithaca, New York

Brigitte Marazzi
Natural History Museum of Canton Ticino
Lugano, Switzerland

Robert H. Mohlenbrock
Southern Illinois University
Carbondale, Illinois

Guy L. Nesom
Academy of Natural Sciences of Drexel University
Philadelphia, Pennsylvania

Hiroyoshi Ohashi
Tohoku University
Sendai, Japan

Matthew A. Parker
State University of New York
Binghamton, New York

Derick B. Poindexter
The University of North Carolina at Chapel Hill
Chapel Hill, North Carolina

Jay A. Raveill
Central Missouri State University
Warrensburg, Missouri

James L. Reveal†
Cornell University
Ithaca, New York

María de Lourdes Rico-Arce
Royal Botanic Gardens
Kew, Richmond, Surrey, England

Brant W. Riegel
Eastern Illinois University
Charleston, Illinois

Rhonda Riggins
San Luis Obispo, California

Erin Thais Riley
Montana State University
Bozeman, Montana

Velva E. Rudd†
National Museum of Natural History
Smithsonian Institution
Washington, DC

David S. Seigler
University of Illinois
Urbana, Illinois

Teresa Sholars
Mendocino, California

Leila M. Shultz
Utah State University
Logan, Utah

Beryl B. Simpson
The University of Texas at Austin
Austin, Texas

Ernest Small
Ottawa Research and Development Centre
Agriculture and Agri-Food Canada
Ottawa, Ontario

Solange Sotuyo
Instituto de Biología
Universidad Nacional Autónoma de México
Mexico City, Mexico

Shannon C. K. Straub
Hobart and William Smith Colleges
Geneva, New York

Lawrence R. Stritch
United States Forest Service
Washington, D.C.

James C. Sugar
North Carolina State University
Raleigh, North Carolina

David M. Sutherland
University of Nebraska
Omaha, Nebraska

Ralph L. Thompson
Berea College
Berea, Kentucky

Leticia Torres-Colín
Universidad Nacional Autónoma de México
Mexico City, Mexico

Debra K. Trock
California Academy of Sciences
San Francisco, California

Gordon C. Tucker
Eastern Illinois University
Charleston, Illinois

Billie L. Turner†
The University of Texas at Austin
Austin, Texas

L. J. G. van der Maesen
Wageningen Agricultural University
Wageningen, The Netherlands

Michael A. Vincent
Miami University
Oxford, Ohio

Wade Wall
North Carolina State University
Raleigh, North Carolina

Alan S. Weakley
The University of North Carolina at Chapel Hill
Chapel Hill, North Carolina

Stanley L. Welsh
Brigham Young University
Provo, Utah

Martin F. Wojciechowski
Arizona State University
Tempe, Arizona

Michael Woods
Troy University
Troy, Alabama

Richard P. Wunderlin
University of South Florida
Tampa, Florida

Fabaceae subfamilies, tribes, and genera. Subfamilial classification follows the Legume Phylogeny Working Group (2017), with the sequence of genera adapted from G. P. Lewis at al. (2005).

Volume 11, Part 1

Volume 11, Part 2

Key to Subfamilies

David J. Bogler
Michael A. Vincent

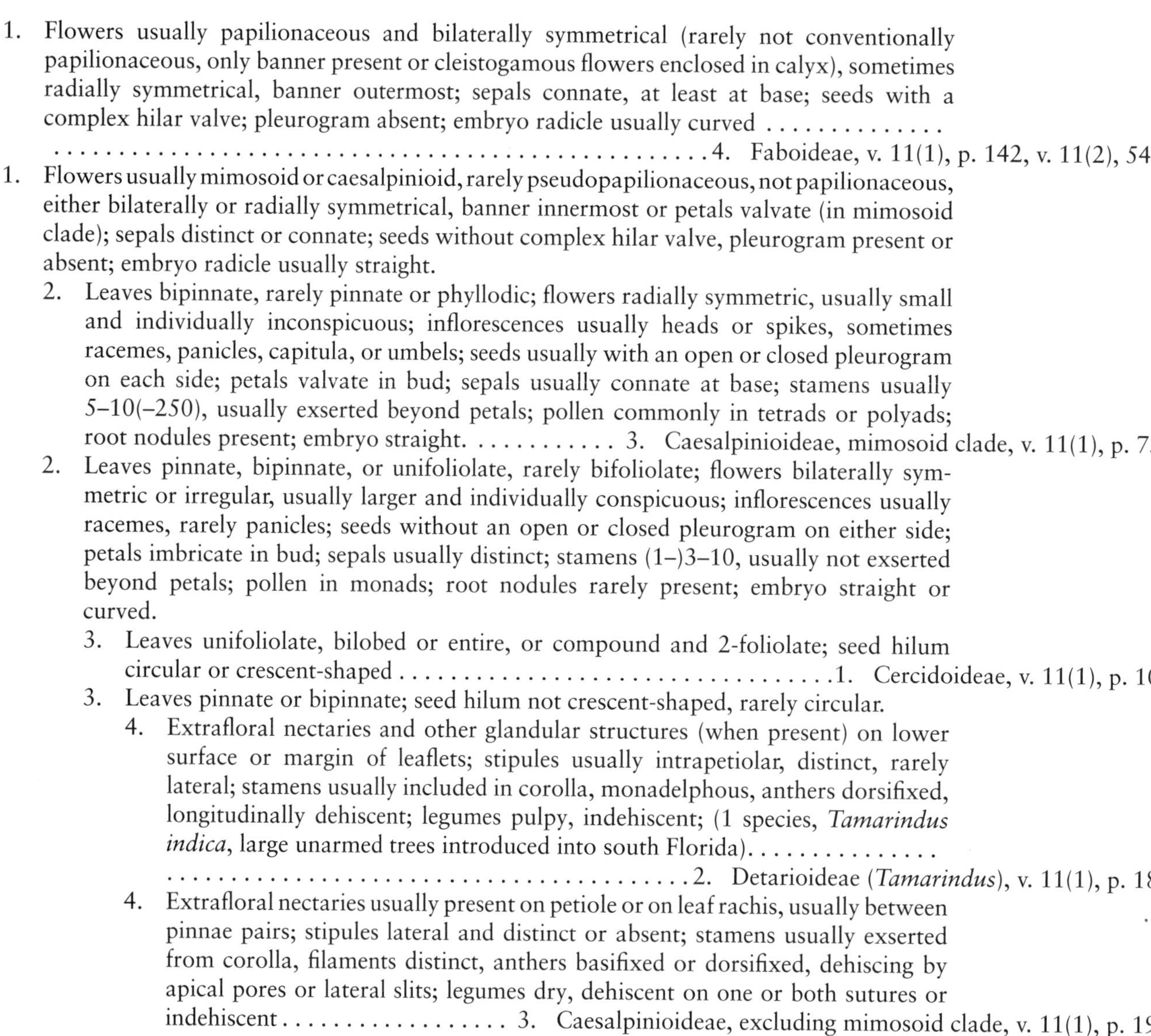

1. Flowers usually papilionaceous and bilaterally symmetrical (rarely not conventionally papilionaceous, only banner present or cleistogamous flowers enclosed in calyx), sometimes radially symmetrical, banner outermost; sepals connate, at least at base; seeds with a complex hilar valve; pleurogram absent; embryo radicle usually curved . . . . 4. Faboideae, v. 11(1), p. 142, v. 11(2), 543
1. Flowers usually mimosoid or caesalpinioid, rarely pseudopapilionaceous, not papilionaceous, either bilaterally or radially symmetrical, banner innermost or petals valvate (in mimosoid clade); sepals distinct or connate; seeds without complex hilar valve, pleurogram present or absent; embryo radicle usually straight.
    2. Leaves bipinnate, rarely pinnate or phyllodic; flowers radially symmetric, usually small and individually inconspicuous; inflorescences usually heads or spikes, sometimes racemes, panicles, capitula, or umbels; seeds usually with an open or closed pleurogram on each side; petals valvate in bud; sepals usually connate at base; stamens usually 5–10(–250), usually exserted beyond petals; pollen commonly in tetrads or polyads; root nodules present; embryo straight. . . . . 3. Caesalpinioideae, mimosoid clade, v. 11(1), p. 73
    2. Leaves pinnate, bipinnate, or unifoliolate, rarely bifoliolate; flowers bilaterally symmetric or irregular, usually larger and individually conspicuous; inflorescences usually racemes, rarely panicles; seeds without an open or closed pleurogram on either side; petals imbricate in bud; sepals usually distinct; stamens (1–)3–10, usually not exserted beyond petals; pollen in monads; root nodules rarely present; embryo straight or curved.
        3. Leaves unifoliolate, bilobed or entire, or compound and 2-foliolate; seed hilum circular or crescent-shaped . . . . 1. Cercidoideae, v. 11(1), p. 10
        3. Leaves pinnate or bipinnate; seed hilum not crescent-shaped, rarely circular.
            4. Extrafloral nectaries and other glandular structures (when present) on lower surface or margin of leaflets; stipules usually intrapetiolar, distinct, rarely lateral; stamens usually included in corolla, monadelphous, anthers dorsifixed, longitudinally dehiscent; legumes pulpy, indehiscent; (1 species, *Tamarindus indica*, large unarmed trees introduced into south Florida). . . . . 2. Detarioideae (*Tamarindus*), v. 11(1), p. 18
            4. Extrafloral nectaries usually present on petiole or on leaf rachis, usually between pinnae pairs; stipules lateral and distinct or absent; stamens usually exserted from corolla, filaments distinct, anthers basifixed or dorsifixed, dehiscing by apical pores or lateral slits; legumes dry, dehiscent on one or both sutures or indehiscent . . . . 3. Caesalpinioideae, excluding mimosoid clade, v. 11(1), p. 19

d. FABACEAE Lindley subfam. FABOIDEAE Rudd, Rhodora 70: 496. 1968

Papilionoideae de Candolle

Trees, shrubs, lianas, herbs, or vines, unarmed or armed. **Extrafloral nectaries** absent on petiole and rachis, sometimes stipular, stipellar, or bracteal, rarely on sepals. **Stipules** lateral, free, or absent. **Leaves** pinnate, palmate, unifoliolate, or 3-foliolate, rarely 2 or 4-foliolate, not bipinnate. **Flowers** usually papilionaceous, rarely nonpapilionaceous (in *Amorpha*, *Parryella*, sometimes *Clitoria*), bilateral, rarely asymmetrical, or radial; sepals connate at least basally; petals 5(or 6), rarely only 1 (banner) present or 0; stamens (1–9)10(+), filaments connate, or adaxial filament ± distinct, rarely all filaments distinct, usually heteromorphic, anthers basifixed or dorsifixed; pollen in monads. **Fruits** legumes, dehiscent or indehiscent, or loments, drupes, or samaroid. **Seeds** with complex hilar valve, hilum elongate, pleurogram absent; embryo usually curved, rarely straight. x = 5, 6, 7, 8, 9, 10, 11, 12.

Genera ca. 503, species ca. 14,000 (111 genera, 1162 species in the flora): nearly worldwide.

SELECTED REFERENCES Allan, G. J. and J. M. Porter. 2000. Tribal delimitation and phylogenetic relationships of Loteae and Coronilleae (Faboideae: Fabaceae) with special reference to *Lotus*: Evidence from nuclear ribosomal ITS sequences. Amer. J. Bot. 87: 1871–1881. Endo, Y. and H. Ohashi. 1997. Cladistic analysis of phylogenetic relationships among tribes Cicereae, Trifolieae, and Vicieae (Leguminosae). Amer. J. Bot. 84: 523–529. Heyn, C. C. 1981. Trifolieae. In: R. M. Polhill and P. H. Raven, eds. 1981. Advances in Legume Systematics. Parts 1 and 2. 2 vols. Kew. Vol. 1, pp. 383–385. Lassen, P. 1989. A new delimitation of the genera *Coronilla*, *Hippocrepis*, and *Securigera* (Fabaceae). Willdenowia 19: 49–62. Lavin, M. and M. Sousa S. 1995. Phylogenetic systematics and biogeography of the tribe Robinieae. Syst. Bot. Monogr. 45. McMahon, M. 2005. Phylogenetic relationships and floral evolution in the papilionoid clade Amorpheae. Brittonia 57: 397–411. McMahon, M. and L. Hufford. 2004. Phylogeny of Amorpheae (Fabaceae, Papilionoideae). Amer. J. Bot. 91: 1219–1230. Rydberg, P. A. 1924. Genera of North American Fabaceae. II. Tribe Galegeae (continued). Amer. J. Bot. 11: 470–482. Steele, K. P. and M. F. Wojciechowski. 2003. Phylogenetic analyses of tribes Trifolieae and Vicieae, based on sequences of the plastid gene, *matK* (Papilionoideae: Leguminosae). In: B. B. Klitgaard and A. Bruneau, eds. 2003. Advances in Legume Systematics. Part 10. Kew. Pp. 355–370. Wojciechowski, M. F. et al. 2000. Molecular phylogeny of the "temperate herbaceous tribes" of papilionoid legumes: A supertree approach. In: P. S. Herendeen and A. Bruneau, eds. 2000. Advances in Legume Systematics. Part 9. Kew. Pp. 277–298.

Key to Genera of Subfamily Faboideae

1. Trees, shrubs (sometimes suffrutescent), or woody vines.
   2. Leaves palmately foliolate or appearing so, or all or mostly unifoliolate, or reduced to phyllodes.
      3. Leaves reduced to spinelike phyllodes; corollas yellow; fruits legumes, partly enclosed by persistent calyx, densely villous . . . . 59. *Ulex*, v. 11(1), p. 256
      3. Leaves not reduced to spinelike phyllodes; corollas white, creamy white, pink, reddish to blue-purple, orange-yellow, or yellow; fruits legumes or loments, usually visible, glabrous, glabrate, or pubescent.
         4. Leaves all unifoliolate, often reduced or deciduous and absent.
            5. Shrubs or small trees with erect or scandent stems; leaflet blades 25–80 mm, elliptic or ovate; corollas white, creamy white, or yellowish, sometimes pinkish; fruits indehiscent; Florida . . . . 73. *Dalbergia* (in part), v. 11(1), p. 327
            5. Trees or shrubs with erect stems; leaflet blades 2–35 mm, sometimes early deciduous; corollas white, yellow, pink to reddish purple, or blue to violet-purple; fruits dehiscent or indehiscent; sw, w United States.
               6. Stems green, rushlike, unarmed; corollas yellow; fruits dehiscent with twisting valves; introduced, w United States . . . . .58. *Spartium* (in part), v. 11(1), p. 256
               6. Stems brownish green, branched, armed; corollas pinkish, blue, or purplish, sometimes white; fruits indehiscent; desert Southwest.

7. Fruits legumes, enclosed in calyx or exserted, plump to compressed, gland-dotted; seeds usually 1; corollas blue to purple or violet, sometimes white; stems gland-dotted . . .64. *Psorothamnus* (in part), v. 11(1), p. 274
7. Fruits loments, exserted, terete, moniliform (constricted between seeds), not gland-dotted, glabrous; seeds (1 or)2–8(–10); corollas pinkish to reddish purple; stems not gland-dotted. . . . . .141. *Alhagi*, v. 11(2), p. 907

[4. Shifted to left margin.—Ed.]

4. Leaves palmate or appearing palmate, sometimes unifoliolate (sometimes mixed with pinnate leaves).
  8. Leaves unifoliolate (sometimes mixed with pinnate leaves), or appearing palmate.
    9. Leaves unifoliolate or odd-pinnate; stipules subspinescent; stems broomlike, green; inflorescences mostly solitary flowers in axils of distal unifoliolate leaves; legume valves elastically dehiscent; trans-Pecos Texas. . . . . 131. *Genistidium*, v. 11(2), p. 554
    9. Leaves appearing palmate; stipules and leaf rachis spinescent or spine-tipped; stems not broomlike, brownish; inflorescences 1–4(or 5)-flowered, flowers solitary or in fascicles; legume valves twisting in dehiscence; Alaska, B.C., Alberta, Quebec, c, e United States. . . . . 139. *Caragana* (in part), v. 11(2), p. 903
  8. Leaflets 1–11(–17).
    10. Leaves (1–)5–11(–17)-foliolate; stipules adnate to petiole; keel attenuate; stamens monadelphous . . . . 53. *Lupinus* (in part), v. 11(1), p. 193
    10. Leaves 1–5-foliolate; stipules usually not adnate to petiole or absent; keel not attenuate; stamens distinct or monadelphous.
      11. Stamens distinct; corollas reddish purple; shrubs with thorn-tipped stems; rarely fruiting; California native. . . . . .49. *Pickeringia*, v. 11(1), p. 169
      11. Stamens monadelphous; corollas white or yellow; shrubs or trees, unarmed; introduced widely.
        12. Trees or large shrubs; inflorescences axillary, pendulous racemes; leaves palmately trifoliolate; corollas yellow; legumes pendulous, constricted between seeds; introduced, British Columbia, California, Maine, Massachusetts, Oregon, Utah,Washington. . . . . 54. *Laburnum*, v. 11(1), p. 248
        12. Shrubs; inflorescences axillary or terminal, racemes or glomerules or flowers solitary, or clustered on short axillary shoots; distal leaves often reduced and unifoliolate; corollas yellow or white; legumes pendulous or erect, not constricted between seeds; introduced widely.
          13. Calyx cylindric, 8–9 mm; corollas white; twigs erect becoming pendent . . . . 55. *Cytisus* (in part), v. 11(1), p. 250
          13. Calyx campanulate, 3–7(–15) mm; corollas yellow or white; twigs erect or ascending, sometimes becoming pendent.
            14. Corollas white; styles incurved; calyx bilabiate, adaxial lip 2-lobed; stems nearly leafless . . . . .56. *Retama*, v. 11(1), p. 253
            14. Corollas yellow or white; styles abruptly incurved; calyx bilabiate or barely or scarcely lobed; stems generally leafy; seeds with appendage.
              15. Styles abruptly curved near middle; calyx lobes connate most of their length, shallowly lobed; leaves not caducous; corollas yellow or white; legumes laterally compressed or inflated, explosively dehiscent . . . . 55. *Cytisus* (in part), v. 11(1), p. 250
              15. Styles abruptly incurved distally; calyx abaxial lip 3-lobed, adaxial lip 2-lobed; leaves often caducous; corollas yellow; legumes inflated, not explosively dehiscent. . . . . . . .57. *Genista*, v. 11(1), p. 253

[2. Shifted to left margin.—Ed.]

2. Leaves pinnate, not reduced, rarely unifoliolate; leaflets 3–61(–96+).
 16. Leaves pinnately 3-foliolate, usually not unifoliolate or reduced to spines.
  17. Vines trailing, twining and high climbing, or creeping; inflorescences pseudoracemes.
   18. Calyx 5.5–7.5 mm; leaflet margins entire, not lobed or sinuate; stipules 2.5–3 mm; legumes indehiscent; lianas to 5 m. . . . . 84. *Lackeya*, v. 11(1), p. 370
   18. Calyx 6–18 mm; leaflet margins usually lobed, toothed, or sinuate, sometimes entire; stipules 5–16(–25) mm; legumes dehiscent; vines 2–30 m.
    19. Herbaceous vines, 2–5(–10) m; stipules linear-lanceolate, 5–11 mm; inflorescence bracts setaceous; introduced, Florida . . . . 93. *Pachyrhizus* (in part), v. 11(1), p. 396
    19. Woody or coarsely herbaceous vines, climbing and creeping, to 30 m; stipules peltate, 8–16(–25) mm; inflorescence bracts ovate to lanceolate; introduced widely . . . . 94. *Pueraria* (in part), v. 11(1), p. 397
  17. Shrubs, suffrutescent subshrubs, or trees, not creeping; inflorescences pseudoracemes or racemes.
   20. Fruits indehiscent; seeds 1.
    21. Shrubs; stems and leaves not gland-dotted; fruits loments with 1 article, elliptic to suborbicular, pubescent, without swordlike beak; inflorescences pseudoracemes (each cluster 2–4-flowered), rarely capitate; widespread . . . . 108. *Lespedeza* (in part), v. 11(1), p. 431
    21. Suffrutescent subshrubs; stems and leaves gland-dotted; fruits legumes, ovoid, with swordlike beak; inflorescences dense, headlike racemes; introduced, California . . . . 117. *Aspalthium*, v. 11(1), p. 494
   20. Fruits dehiscent or indehiscent; seeds 1–12.
    22. Shrubs or subshrubs; inflorescences axillary racemes, 8–60+-flowered, often appearing spicate; hairs biramous (2-branched); legumes not constricted between seeds . . . . 76. *Indigofera* (in part), v. 11(1), p. 335
    22. Trees or shrubs; inflorescences terminal or axillary racemes or pseudoracemes, 1–80[–100]-flowered; hairs not biramous; legumes depressed or constricted between seeds.
     23. Shrubs, short-lived, unarmed; stipels setiform; leaflet blades gland-dotted abaxially; corollas yellow, orange, red, or purplish; legumes depressed between seeds; seeds white to cream and brown, purplish, or almost black, sometimes mottled . . . . 90. *Cajanus*, v. 11(1), p. 390
     23. Trees or shrubs, armed with recurved prickles; stipels swollen, glandlike; leaflet blades not gland-dotted; corollas red; legumes regularly or irregularly constricted between seeds; seeds red to orange-red or orange, sometimes with black markings . . . . 91. *Erythrina* (in part), v. 11(1), p. 391

[16. Shifted to left margin.—Ed.]

16. Leaves odd- or even-pinnate, rarely subpinnate or unifoliolate, leaflets (1–)3–96+.
 24. Flowers apetalous or corollas with banner only; surfaces gland-dotted; inflorescences terminal, racemes or spikes; seeds 1 or 2.
  25. Corollas with banner only, blue, purple, or white. . . . . 61. *Amorpha* (in part), v. 11(1), p. 258
  25. Corollas absent or only banner present, yellow.
   26. Leaflet blades linear-filiform or oblong-elliptic; calyx tube not 10-ribbed; corolla absent; legumes prominently gland-dotted; seeds 1 or 2; sw United States (Colorado Plateau) . . . . 60. *Parryella*, v. 11(1), p. 258
   26. Leaflet blades suborbiculate to oblong-ovate; calyx tube 10-ribbed; corolla absent or vestigial banner present, yellow; legumes with scattered glands; seed 1; ne Arizona . . . . 62. *Errazurizia*, v. 11(1), p. 270
 24. Flowers with corollas; surfaces glandular or not; inflorescences terminal or axillary, usually racemes, panicles, fascicles, or flowers solitary, rarely pseudoracemes, corymbs, or spikes; seeds 1–40.

27. Stamens distinct or connate proximally.
28. Legumes indehiscent; bracteoles present; corollas purple, blue-purple, lilac, lavender, yellow, pink, or white; seeds usually red, dull red, reddish brown, or black, rarely orange or yellow.
29. Leaflet blades not leathery; inflorescences racemes or panicles; calyx truncate; corollas usually white or yellow, rarely pink or purple; stamens 8; legumes fleshy, straight to curved, moniliform; seeds black . . . . 44. *Styphnolobium*, v. 11(1), p. 160
29. Leaflet blades leathery; inflorescences racemes; calyx with obvious lobes; corollas usually shades of purple, rarely white; stamens 10; legumes papery, leathery, or woody, torose to torulose, straight to slightly curved or subglobose to cylindric; seeds usually red or dull red to reddish brown, rarely orange or yellow . . . . 45. *Dermatophyllum*, v. 11(1), p. 162
28. Legumes dehiscent; bracteoles present or absent; corollas white, creamy white, or yellow; seeds light brown to yellow.
30. Leaflet blades densely villous, sericeous, or glabrescent adaxially (in *S. tomentosa*); stipules usually present, caducous; legumes not compressed, narrowly oblong-moniliform; coastal near beaches . . . 46. *Sophora* (in part), v. 11(1), p. 164
30. Leaflet blades glabrous adaxially; stipules absent; legumes compressed laterally, elliptic to linear or lanceolate, not moniliform; inland in forests.
31. Leaflets alternate; axillary buds enclosed in petiole base; inflorescences pendulous panicles; calyx tubular, slightly zygomorphic; legumes not winged along margin; seeds 5–8, reniform, brown . . . . . . 43. *Cladrastis*, v. 11(1), p. 159
31. Leaflets opposite or subopposite; axillary buds exposed; inflorescences erect racemes; calyx campanulate; legumes winged along one suture; seeds 1–3, ellipsoidal, yellow. . . . . 47. *Maackia*, v. 11(1), p. 167

[27. Shifted to left margin.—Ed.]

27. Stamens monadelphous, submonadelphous, diadelphous, or connate at least ½ their length.
32. Stamens monadelphous, submonadelphous, or connate ½ their length (vexillary stamen may be distinct at base or absent).
33. Trees, shrubs, or vines; stamens 9 or 10; seeds 1 or 3–8; Florida.
34. Woody or suffrutescent vines; leaves even-pinnate; seeds red, black, red and black, black and white, or whitish; stamens 9 (vexillary stamen absent); fruits legumes, curved, beaked, elastically dehiscent; seeds (1–)3–7 . . . . 81. *Abrus*, v. 11(1), p. 355
34. Shrubs or trees; leaves odd-pinnate; seeds reddish brown to dark brown; stamens 10; fruits legumes or loments, straight, not beaked, indehiscent or tardily dehiscent; seeds 1 or 3–8.
35. Fruits loments, leathery, wings papery (10–20 mm wide); calyx with 5 short lobes; seeds 3–8; s Florida coastal hammocks . . . . .78. *Piscidia*, v. 11(1), p. 345
35. Fruits legumes, woody or rigidly leathery, without wings; calyx truncate, lobes obsolete; seed 1; introduced in Florida, waste places and thickets . . . . 79. *Millettia*, v. 11(1), p. 346
33. Shrubs or subshrubs; stamens (4 or)5, 9, or 10; seeds 1(or 2); widespread, including Florida.
36. Flowers papilionaceous, petals all arising from receptacle (hypanthium rim), wings and keel not epistemonous; banner reflexed less than 90°; shrubs, subshrubs, or trees, armed or unarmed, sterile shoots sometimes sharp-tipped; deserts, sw United States . . . . .64. *Psorothamnus* (in part), v. 11(1), p. 274
36. Flowers conventionally papilionaceous or not, only banner arising from receptacle (hypanthium rim), wings and keel epistemonous, arising laterally or terminally from stamen column; banner reflexed 90°; herbs, shrubs, or subshrubs, usually unarmed (rarely thorns present in *Dalea*); widespread.

37. Calyx ribs not anastomosing; leaflet blades with pale sinuous lines, single gland between petiolules; trichomes stiff, short, not spirally twisted; fruits loments, stipitate; se Arizona . . . . 65. *Marina* (in part), v. 11(1), p. 280
37. Calyx ribs usually anastomosing, forming closed arches; leaflet blades without sinuous lines, 2 adaxial intrapetiolular glands and 2 abaxial postpetiolular glands often present between opposing leaflets; trichomes spirally twisted; fruits legumes, sessile; widespread . . . . . 66. *Dalea* (in part), v. 11(1), p. 283

32. Stamens diadelphous (vexillary stamen sometimes slightly proximally attached to others).
38. Leaves mostly even-pinnate, rarely odd-pinnate (or leaflets irregularly arranged).
39. Trees or shrubs, armed with spine-tipped, persistent leaf rachises, or sometimes with spinescent stipules.
40. Trees to 10 m; stipules 4–10 mm, spinescent; leaves even- or odd-pinnate, leaflets (8 or)9–21(–24); corollas whitish to purplish; styles with pollen brush surrounding distal ½; legumes stipitate-glandular; Arizona, California . . . . 127. *Olneya*, v. 11(2), p. 544
40. Shrubs 1–3 m; stipules 1–4 mm, sometimes spinescent; leaves even-pinnate, leaflets 2 or 4(–10); corollas purple to lilac or white; styles without pollen brush; legumes glabrous; introduced, Saskatchewan, California, Utah. . . . . 140. *Halimodendron*, v. 11(2), p. 906
39. Shrubs, usually unarmed, sometimes weakly prickly or spiny.
41. Inflorescences fascicles or short racemes of 1–5 flowers.
42. Corollas mostly whitish, sometimes tinged pinkish; styles tufted with pollen brush; stipules 3–5 mm, subulate; legumes constricted between seeds; s Texas . . . . 129. *Coursetia* (in part), v. 11(2), p. 549
42. Corollas yellow; styles without pollen brush; stipules 5–9 mm, sometimes spine-tipped; legumes not constricted between seeds; introduced widely . . . . 139. *Caragana* (in part), v. 11(2), p. 903
41. Inflorescences longer racemes or panicles, with 1–40+ flowers.
43. Calyx lobes shorter than tube; corollas white, pale yellow to orange or red, with or without purple spots; styles with spreading hairs; leaflets folding closed at night; legumes not glandular, with spongy mesocarp, bladdery-inflated, sometimes winged. . . . . 118. *Sesbania* (in part), v. 11(1), p. 496
43. Calyx lobes equal to or longer than tube; corollas mostly whitish; styles with tufted or lateral pollen brush; leaflets not folding; legumes glandular, not spongy, inflated, or winged. . . . . 129. *Coursetia* (in part), v. 11(2), p. 549

[38. Shifted to left margin.—Ed.]

38. Leaves odd-pinnate (sometimes irregularly so).
44. Inflorescences racemes, flowers fascicled or in viscid-glandular racemes; Arizona . . . . 129. *Coursetia* (in part), v. 11(2), p. 549
44. Inflorescences racemes, panicles, corymbs, or solitary flowers, glandular or eglandular.
45. Corollas not typically papilionaceous, petals scarcely differentiated, subequal, white, sometimes becoming purple; stamens visible; inflorescences spikelike racemes; legumes indehiscent; seeds 1(or 2) . . . . 63. *Eysenhardtia*, v. 11(1), p. 271
45. Corollas papilionaceous, white, creamy, yellow, pink to purple, azure, or rose; stamens generally hidden within keel; inflorescences racemes, panicles, corymbs, or solitary flowers; legumes dehiscent or indehiscent; seeds 1–10(–16).
46. Legumes sessile, laterally compressed, tardily dehiscent; trees or shrubs, often armed with spinescent stipules; corollas whitish or pinkish . . . . . . 128. *Robinia*, v. 11(2), p. 545
46. Legumes stipitate, inflated or compressed, dehiscent or indehiscent; trees, shrubs, or vines, unarmed; corollas yellow, white, creamy white, pink to purple, reddish purple, azure, or rose.

47. Legumes bladdery-inflated; corollas bright yellow, banner sometimes with red markings . . . . .136. *Colutea*, v. 11(2), p. 901
47. Legumes flattened, compressed, slightly inflated, plump, or cylindric, not bladdery-inflated; corollas yellow, white, creamy white, pink to purple, reddish purple, azure, or rose.
48. Inflorescences axillary, flowers solitary; leaflets (19–)23–59; corollas yellow; seeds 1 or 2; sw Texas .48. *Brongniartia*, v. 11(1), p. 168
48. Inflorescences axillary or terminal, racemes; leaflets 1–25; corollas yellowish, white, creamy white, pink to purple, reddish purple, azure, or rose; seeds 1–14; Arizona and se United States.
49. Racemes 4–7-flowered; peduncles and pedicels glandular-hirsute; calyx tubular; corollas usually yellowish; legumes oblong, slightly inflated; s Arizona. . . . . 75. *Diphysa*, v. 11(1), p. 334
49. Racemes 10–100-flowered; peduncles and pedicels eglandular (except sometimes *Wisteria* pedicels with clavate glands); calyx campanulate; corollas yellowish, white, creamy white, pink to purple, reddish purple, azure, or rose; legumes linear, oblong to elliptic, oblanceolate, subreniform, or subglobose, plump, cylindric, compressed, or flattened; c, e, s United States.
50. Legumes narrowly ellipsoid to oblong, compressed, often winged, samaroid; seeds 1 or 2(–4); leaflets 3 or 5; trees; introduced, s Florida . . . . 73. *Dalbergia* (in part), v. 11(1), p. 327
50. Legumes linear, ovoid, linear-oblong, oblong-elliptic, oblanceolate, or subglobose, not narrowly ellipsoid, not winged; seeds 1–10; leaflets (7 or)9–21(–25); trees or vines, rarely shrubs; c, e, s United States.
51. Legumes drupaceous, pendent, indehiscent; trees; introduced, Florida . . . . 67. *Andira*, v. 11(1), p. 316
51. Legumes not drupaceous, erect, dehiscent; trees or woody vines; c, s, e United States.
52. Twining woody vines; inflorescences terminal, pendent racemes; calyx obviously lobed; legumes flattened or cylindric, torulose; c, e, s United States . . . 77. *Wisteria*, v. 11(1), p. 342
52. Trees; inflorescences axillary racemes; calyx lobes inconspicuous; legumes laterally compressed, linear, not torulose; introduced, Florida. . . . . . 126. *Gliricidia*, v. 11(2), p. 543
1. Herbs or herbaceous vines, stems annual, biennial, or perennial.
53. Leaves all or mostly unifoliolate (or leaflets obsolescent).
54. Stamens monadelphous.
55. Suffrutescent subshrubs, gland-dotted when young, sterile shoots usually sharp-tipped; inflorescences loosely 1–20+-flowered, with thornlike tip; corollas usually blue to blue-purple, rarely white, banner with yellow eye; legumes gland-dotted; seeds usually 1, rarely 2; sw deserts . . .64. *Psorothamnus* (in part), v. 11(1), p. 274
55. Herbs, not gland-dotted when young, short shoots absent; inflorescences loose or not, 1–100-flowered, unarmed; corollas usually blue, pink, rose, yellow, or white, rarely orangish or lavender, banner spot white, cream, pink, maroon, or dark blue; legumes not gland-dotted; seeds 1–70; widespread.
56. Stems persistently green, photosynthetic, glabrous, rushlike; leaves unifoliolate or obsolescent; corollas yellow; legumes linear-oblong; seeds 6–18; introduced, California, Oregon, Texas, Washington. . . . . .58. *Spartium* (in part), v. 11(1), p. 256
56. Stems not persistently green and photosynthetic, glabrous or pubescent, not rushlike; leaves palmately compound or unifoliolate; corollas usually blue, pink, rose, yellow, or white, rarely orangish or lavender; legumes oblong, ovoid, ellipsoid, cylindric, or globose; seeds 1–70; widespread.

57. Leaflet blades 5–150 mm; corollas usually yellow, sometimes orangish, rarely white, blue, or lavender; legumes usually inflated; seeds 1–70, oblique-cordiform to oblong-reniform; widespread .... 52. *Crotalaria* (in part), v. 11(1), p. 185

57. Leaflet blades (10–)20–270 mm; corollas pink, rose, or purple; legumes usually oblong, not inflated; seeds 2–7, spheric, lentiform or angulate; Florida .... 53. *Lupinus* (in part), v. 11(1), p. 193

54. Stamens diadelphous (except *Orbexilum* sometimes monadelphous proximally).

58. Herbs, annual; leaves sessile; inflorescences axillary, flowers solitary; corollas pinkish; seeds 4-angled with vertical constriction; Arizona...132. *Sphinctospermum*, v. 11(2), p. 555

58. Herbs, annual, perennial, or suffrutescent, or vines; leaves petiolate; inflorescences axillary, terminal, or leaf-opposed, usually pseudoracemes, racemes, or spikes, rarely panicles; corollas purple, blue, pink, red, orange, or yellow; seeds reniform, oblong, subglobose, ovoid to ellipsoid, obovate, or 4-angled, without constriction; c, e, se United States.

59. Herbs, not gland-dotted; stems uncinulate-pubescent; corollas red to reddish blue, reddish violet, orange, orange-buff, pink, pinkish lavender, or white; fruits loments; seeds 2–8; introduced, Alabama, Florida, Georgia, Louisiana, Mississippi, North Carolina, Texas...........111. *Alysicarpus*, v. 11(1), p. 465

59. Herbs or vines, mostly gland-dotted; stems not uncinulate-pubescent; corollas yellow, yellow-orange, violet, purple, or purplish blue; fruits legumes; seeds 1 or 2; c, e, se United States.

60. Legumes dehiscent, not rugose; corollas yellow or yellow-orange; herbaceous vines; inflorescences usually axillary, rarely terminal, usually racemes, sometimes heads or clustered, 1–3-flowered; c, e, se United States ....89. *Rhynchosia* (in part), v. 11(1), p. 382

60. Legumes indehiscent, rugose; corollas violet, purple, or purplish blue; erect herbs; inflorescences terminal, spikes, 5–50-flowered; Florida, Georgia .... 112. *Orbexilum* (in part), v. 11(1), p. 467

[53. Shifted to left margin.—Ed.]

53. Leaves 3–96+-foliolate, distalmost leaves sometimes reduced and unifoliolate.

61. Herbs, sometimes subshrubs; leaves mostly palmately compound; leaflets (1–)3–11(–17), sometimes unifoliolate or pseudopalmate, rarely phyllodic.

62. Stamens distinct.

63. Legumes laterally compressed, valves papery, slowly dehiscent; ovaries short-stipitate; corollas yellow...............................50. *Thermopsis*, v. 11(1), p. 170

63. Legumes inflated, valves leathery, indehiscent; ovaries long-stipitate; corollas white, yellow, violet, or blue............................. 51. *Baptisia*, v. 11(1), p. 177

62. Stamens monadelphous or diadelphous.

64. Stamens monadelphous.

65. Fruits bristly loments (with 2–15 segments); leaflets 2 or 4, blade surfaces sometimes punctate; corollas yellow or orange-yellow; inflorescences subtended by enlarged bracts; filaments equal .... 68. *Zornia*, v. 11(1), p. 317

65. Fruits legumes, not bristly; leaflets 1–11(–17), blade surfaces not punctate; corollas yellow, white, purple, or blue, sometimes orangish, lavender, or rose; inflorescence bracts present but not enlarged; filaments alternately long and short.

66. Legumes usually inflated; corollas yellow, sometimes orangish; leaflets 1 or 3; seeds 1–70, oblique-cordiform to oblong-reniform, becoming loose at maturity; aril sometimes conspicuous; mostly e United States ....52. *Crotalaria* (in part), v. 11(1), p. 185

66. Legumes laterally compressed; corollas blue to purple, sometimes white, yellow, pink, or rose; leaflets (1–)5–11(–17); seeds 2–12, spheric, lentiform, or angulate, not becoming loose; aril absent; mostly w North America .... 53. *Lupinus* (in part), v. 11(1), p. 193

64. Stamens diadelphous.
  67. Fruits spirally coiled. . . . . 149. *Medicago* (in part), v. 11(2), p. 983
  67. Fruits straight or curved.
    68. Herbs, especially leaves, calyx, and fruits, usually gland-dotted or glandular-pubescent.
      69. Calyx not enlarging as fruit matures; leaves sometimes deciduous by anthesis except basally, leaflets (1 or)3–5 . . . . 115. *Ladeania*, v. 11(1), p. 475
      69. Calyx enlarging, often somewhat inflating with fruit maturation; leaves persistent, leaflets (1–)3–7(or 8).
        70. Fruits rugose, glabrous, sometimes glandular-punctate, well exserted beyond the calyx; calyx campanulate in fruit . . . . 112. *Orbexilum* (in part), v. 11(1), p. 467
        70. Fruits not rugose, usually pubescent, included in calyx except for beak; calyx gibbous-campanulate in fruit . . . . 116. *Pediomelum* (in part), v. 11(1), p. 476
    68. Herbs not gland-dotted.
      71. Fruits enclosed within calyx or corolla, or slightly exserted.
        72. Hairs silvery, dolabriform (branched in middle); leaflet blade margins entire; herbs subacaulescent and tufted, or prostrate or cushion-forming; flowers in short racemes of 2–6(–10) flowers . . . . .135. *Astragalus* (in part), v. 11(2), p. 584
        72. Hairs not dolabriform; leaflet blade margins usually toothed or entire, rarely lobed; herbs caulescent or acaulescent, usually erect or ascending, sometimes decumbent to prostrate, rarely mat-forming; flowers in umbels, headlike racemes, or spikes, rarely solitary.
          73. Stipules absent or glandular. . . . . . 123. *Acmispon* (in part), v. 11(1), p. 507
          73. Stipules conspicuous, not glandular . . . . 145. *Trifolium* (in part), v. 11(2), p. 914
      71. Fruits well exserted from calyx or corolla.
        74. Stipules absent or glandular . . . . 123. *Acmispon* (in part), v. 11(1), p. 507
        74. Stipules conspicuous, not glandular.
          75. Fruits elliptic or broadly ovate to ± globose, not reniform; leaflet blade margins entire throughout; inflorescences small, axillary clusters (pseudoracemes), with 1–4 flowers; corollas with pink-purple banner, white wings, keel apex purple . . . . 107. *Kummerowia*, v. 11(1), p. 429
          75. Fruits falcate to reniform-incurved; leaflet blade margins partly serrate; inflorescences cylindrical heads with (5–)15–50 flowers; corollas yellow. . . . 149. *Medicago* (in part), v. 11(2), p. 983

[61. Shifted to left margin.—Ed.]

61. Vines, herbs, or subshrubs; leaves usually pinnate, rarely unifoliolate or phyllodic; leaflets (1 or)3–80(–96+).
  76. Leaves mostly unifoliolate or 3-foliolate.
    77. Herbs with separate foliose and flowering stems.
      78. Corollas red; leaves alternate; fruits legumes; s United States . . . . 91. *Erythrina* (in part), v. 11(1), p. 391
      78. Corollas usually pink, rarely white; leaves usually 4–7-whorled, sometimes scattered on stems; fruits loments; North America, Great Plains and eastward . . . . 110. *Hylodesmum* (in part), v. 11(1), p. 462
    77. Vines, herbs, or subshrubs without separate foliose and flowering stems.

[79. Shifted to left margin.—Ed.]

79. Stamens monadelphous at anthesis (vexillary stamen becoming distinct in *Hoita*).
   80. Wings and keel epistemonous, attached terminally or laterally to stamen tube.
      81. Ovule 1; stems eglandular; leaflet blade surfaces with sinuous lines (lineolate); calyx ribs not anastomosing; trichomes stiff, short; California . . 65. *Marina* (in part), v. 11(1), p. 280
      81. Ovules 2; stems gland-dotted; leaflet blade surfaces not lineolate; calyx ribs anastomosing distally; trichomes flexuous, spirally twisting; widespread . . . . 66. *Dalea* (in part), v. 11(1), p. 283
   80. Wings and keel not epistemonous, attached below staminal tube.
      82. Fruits indehiscent, not exserted from calyx, apiculate or beaked, eglandular or sparsely glandular; seed 1; Pacific States, British Columbia.
         83. Corollas purple or purplish-tinged; calyx not enlarging in fruit, becoming papery; fruits with secondary internal wall of sclereids; California. . . 113. *Hoita*, v. 11(1), p. 470
         83. Corollas cream or yellow; calyx enlarging and concealing fruit, not becoming papery; fruits without secondary internal wall of sclereids; Pacific states, British Columbia . . . . 114. *Rupertia*, v. 11(1), p. 472
      82. Fruits dehiscent or indehiscent, exserted from calyx, apiculate-beaked or not, eglandular; seeds 1–15; widespread.
         84. Fruits loments, indehiscent.
            85. Stipules amplexicaul, adnate to petioles for most of its length; inflorescences short spikes or solitary flowers, 1–15-flowered; bracts foliaceous, persistent; corollas yellow or orange-yellow . . . . 71. *Stylosanthes*, v. 11(1), p. 322
            85. Stipules free from petioles; inflorescences simple or compound racemes or pseudoracemes, or long spikes, (1 or)2–51-flowered; bracts not foliaceous, persistent or deciduous; corollas usually pink, blue, shades of purple, or white, rarely yellow.
               86. Stipels present, persistent; calyx lobes longer than tube; loments with (1 or)2–10 segments, stipitate or sessile. . . . . 109. *Desmodium* (in part), v. 11(1), p. 442
               86. Stipels absent or early-deciduous; calyx lobes shorter than tube; loments with 2–5 segments, distinctly stipitate . . . . 110. *Hylodesmum* (in part), v. 11(1), p. 462
         84. Fruits legumes, dehiscent or indehiscent.
            87. Herbs, thorns present or absent; stipules adnate to petiole; leaflet margins usually serrulate at least distally, rarely entire; inflorescences racemes, with 1–3 flowers; legumes usually not exceeding calyx . . . . 146. *Ononis*, v. 11(2), p. 975
            87. Vines, trailing or climbing, or herbs, unarmed; stipules not adnate to petiole; leaflet margins entire or lobed; inflorescences pseudoracemes or panicles, with 8–50 flowers; legumes larger, well exceeding calyx.
               88. Stipules caducous, deltate, or obsolete; ventral margin of fruit 3–5 ribbed; inflorescences panicles, with 8–50 flowers . . . . 82. *Canavalia*, v. 11(1), p. 356
               88. Stipules present, conspicuous, peltate; ventral margin of fruit not ribbed; inflorescences pseudoracemes, with 15–40 flowers . . . . 94. *Pueraria* (in part), v. 11(1), p. 397

[79. Shifted to left margin.—Ed.]

79. Stamens usually diadelphous, rarely distinct (except becoming diadelphous in *Pueraria* as fruit expands).
   89. Corollas large (20–60+ mm); banners much larger than wings and keel (more than 2 times); inflorescences 1 or 2(–4)-flowered, axillary pseudoracemes; flowers resupinate.
      90. Calyx funnelform, lobes shorter than tube; wings extending beyond the keel; styles geniculate distally; fruits 6–11 mm wide, convex and depressed between seeds or flat . . . . 85. *Clitoria* (in part), v. 11(1), p. 371
      90. Calyx campanulate, lobes equal to or longer than tube; wings subequal to keel; styles incurved, broadly U-shaped; fruits 3–6 mm wide, flat with raised rib near margin . . . . 86. *Centrosema*, v. 11(1), p. 376

89. Corollas smaller, or if not, then banner not much larger than other petals; inflorescences 1–500+-flowered, axillary or terminal racemes, pseudoracemes, fascicles, panicles, umbels, heads, or flowers solitary; flowers not resupinate.
91. Leaflet margins usually at least partly dentate or serrate, lateral vein tips slightly exserted; fruits indehiscent (or breaking crosswise or irregularly), sometimes prickly and spirally coiled; seeds 1–few; corollas 2–27 mm.
92. Fruits spirally coiled, sometimes only falcate, with or without prickles . . . . 149. *Medicago* (in part), v. 11(2), p. 983
92. Fruits not spirally coiled, without prickles.
93. Fruits included in marcescent corolla or slightly exserted, usually papery or membranous; flowers usually in umbellate racemes. . . . . 145. *Trifolium* (in part), v. 11(2), p. 914
93. Fruits exserted beyond corolla remnants, thickly leathery; flowers in slender or short racemes.
94. Stems usually erect or ascending, sometimes decumbent; inflorescences elongate, axillary racemes; seeds 1 or 2(or 3) . . . . 147. *Melilotus*, v. 11(2), p. 977
94. Stems usually decumbent, procumbent, or prostrate, sometimes ascending or erect; inflorescences racemes or heads, sometimes umbellate, or flowers solitary; seeds 1–30.
95. Corollas 5.5–18 mm, banner without major veins; legumes linear to ovoid or rhomboid-obovoid; seeds oblong to ovoid . . . . .148. *Trigonella*, v. 11(2), p. 981
95. Corollas 2–4(–6) mm, banner with major basal vein; legumes terete, compressed, or flat; seeds mostly reniform . . . . 149. *Medicago* (in part), v. 11(2), p. 983

[91. Shifted to left margin.—Ed.]

91. Leaflet margins entire, rarely lobed, or if dentate, vein tips not exserted (sometimes exserted in a few teeth in *Pachyrhizus*); fruits dehiscent through sutures or indehiscent; seeds 1–25 (–30); corollas often greater than 27 mm.
96. Keel incurved 90–180° or spirally coiled.
97. Stipules auriculate or peltate; corollas yellow, purple, or white; legumes resupinate by twisting of pedicel; seeds mostly with a white aril (protruding hilum) . . . . 99. *Vigna* (in part), v. 11(1), p. 405
97. Stipules not auriculate or peltate; corollas usually pink, purple, red, or orange, rarely yellow or white; legumes not resupinate; seeds usually without aril.
98. Hairs finely uncinate, minutely hooked; floral nodes not swollen; pedicels equal to or longer than calyx tube; keel beaked, apex laterally and tightly coiled 1.5–2 turns. . . . . 104. *Phaseolus*, v. 11(1), p. 414
98. Hairs not uncinate, straight, loosely tangled, or glandular; floral nodes swollen; pedicels mostly shorter than calyx tube; keel incurved or rarely coiled but not laterally.
99. Wing petals oblong, not projected beyond distal bend of keel; hilum elongated ½ length of seed or longer.
100. Keel petals connate along upper margin without forming a gibbosity or hump proximal to the beak; banner with two prominent appendages on inner face; calyx 5-lobed; inflorescences pseudoracemes with 50–60+ flowers; bracts and bracteoles usually caducous; corollas greenish yellow to purple; introduced, Texas. . . . . . 103. *Oxyrhynchus*, v. 11(1), p. 412
100. Keel petals connate along upper margin where a gibbosity or hump forms proximal to the beak; banner without appendages on inner face; calyx with 4 acute-attenuate lobes; inflorescences pseudoracemes, on long peduncle, with 1–12(–22) flowers; secondary bracts and bracteoles persistent, bracteoles conspicuous, equal to or longer than the calyx tube; corollas pink; c, e United States. . . . . 105. *Strophostyles* (in part), v. 11(1), p. 423

99. Wing petals oblong, obovate, ovate, or spatulate, conspicuously projected beyond distal bend of keel; hilum not elongated.
101. Petals connate, keel beak hooked, tip of beak hidden by wing petals; corollas salmon-orange, red, or purple-black; one wing petal directed upward to adopt function of banner . . . . 106. *Macroptilium*, v. 11(1), p. 426
101. Petals distinct, keel beak widely curved, openly hooked, or sigmoidally curved, tip of keel not hidden by wing petals; corollas usually pink to purple, lilac, or white, rarely lavender; wings not directed upward.
102. Keel beak gradually twisted into a hook shape, with conspicuous interlocking marginal hairs, distalmost portion of keel beak folded back on itself; legumes short-beaked distally, mostly erect . . . . .100. *Ancistrotropis*, v. 11(1), p. 408
102. Keel beak sigmoid-curved or tightly coiled, not folded back distally.
103. Keel beak very tightly coiled distally, projected downward rather than laterally; inflorescences with 50 flowers; corollas usually light pink to purple, sometimes white becoming yellowish, wings with purple pattern; introduced, Florida . . . . .101. *Leptospron*, v. 11(1), p. 409
103. Keel beak distinctly sigmoid-curved (S-shaped); inflorescences with 2–10 flowers; corollas light to deep purple or deep lilac, wings without purple pattern; Florida. . . . . 102. *Sigmoidotropis*, v. 11(1), p. 410

[96. Shifted to left margin.—Ed.]

96. Keel incurved to ca. 90°, not coiled.
104. Leaflets evidently stipellate at maturity.
105. Fruits loments; inflorescence rachis mostly uncinate-pubescent . . . . 109. *Desmodium* (in part), v. 11(1), p. 442
105. Fruits legumes; inflorescence rachis not uncinate-pubescent.
106. Stems usually twining or trailing, prostrate, or rarely ascending or erect; calyx tubular; keel and style slightly to strongly incurved; cleistogamous flowers (with reduced corollas and stamens) usually present along with purple or purplish blue chasmogamous flowers; sw, sc United States . . . . .92. *Cologania* (in part), v. 11(1), p. 393
106. Stems ascending, erect, spreading, climbing to prostrate, twining, or procumbent; calyx usually campanulate, rarely 2-lipped or tubular; keel and style incurved or not; cleistogamous flowers usually absent (except *Amphicarpaea*) and chasmogamous present with corollas yellow to orange, shades of purple, pink, blue, or white; widespread.

[107. Shifted to left margin.—Ed.]

107. Herbs, subshrubs, or vines, gland-dotted; legumes pubescent; corollas yellow or yellow-orange; seeds 1 or 2; sc, se United States . . . . .89. *Rhynchosia* (in part), v. 11(1), p. 382
107. Herb, shrubs, lianas, or vines, not gland-dotted; legumes glabrous or pubescent; corollas usually violet, pink, blue, lavender, purple, greenish yellow, or white, rarely yellow; seeds 1–25; widespread.
108. Stipules persistent and conspicuous.
109. Herbs; stems erect, pilose-pubescent; inflorescences short racemes, flowers 5–8; corollas 4.5–7(–10) mm; seeds 2–4. . . . . .96. *Glycine*, v. 11(1), p. 401
109. Vines; stems prostrate, twining, or creeping, glabrous or pubescent; inflorescences racemes or pseudoracemes, flowers 1–40; corollas 3.6–30 mm; seeds 1–25.
110. Calyx (6–)10–18 mm (including lobes); leaflet blades 8–20(–26) cm, margins usually 3-lobed; vines coarse, climbing or creeping, to 30 m . . . . 94. *Pueraria* (in part), v. 11(1), p. 397
110. Calyx 1.3–8 mm; leaflet blades 1.3–5.6(–7.2) cm, margins usually entire, sometimes shallowly deeply incised or lobed; vines prostrate, climbing, or trailing, 1–3 m.

111. Bracteoles obsolescent or absent; flowers 6–24, distributed along axis; styles glabrous . . . . 95. *Amphicarpaea*, v. 11(1), p. 399
111. Bracteoles calyx-like, usually persistent to anthesis; flowers 1–4 distally congested on long peduncle or rachis much contracted; styles bearded.
112. Corollas 25–30 mm; stipules conspicuously retrorse-auriculate . . . . 99. *Vigna* (in part), v. 11(1), p. 405
112. Corollas 3.6–15 mm; stipules entire, without retrorse lobe.
113. Corollas pale yellow with reddish veins; bracteoles minute or deciduous; legumes pendulous; Florida . . . . 99. *Vigna* (in part), v. 11(1), p. 405
113. Corollas pink or pinkish, keel beak dark purple; bracteoles persistent; legumes held horizontally or somewhat drooping; widespread . . . . 105. *Strophostyles* (in part), v. 11(1), p. 423
108. Stipules small, relatively inconspicuous, or obsolescent.
114. Corollas 30–65 mm; legumes often with stinging hairs, compressed between seeds; seeds 10–20 mm diam., with conspicuous lateral hilum; se United States . . . . 88. *Mucuna*, v. 11(1), p. 380
114. Corollas 6–15(–17) mm; legumes without stinging hairs, not compressed between seeds; seeds 3–13 mm, lateral hilum inconspicuous or absent; c, e, s, se, sw United States.
115. Styles glabrous; bracteoles generally caducous; herbs, from a woody taproot . . . . 83. *Galactia* (in part), v. 11(1), p. 358
115. Styles bearded or with 2 lines of hairs; bracteoles present; vines (from a woody base) or herbs.
116. Vines (from a woody base); stems twining and climbing; pedicels longer than calyx tube; banners with 1 prominent appendage at base; styles with 2 lines of hairs; bracteoles lanceolate, persistent; legumes 3–5 cm, ventral suture not verrucose; seeds 4–7 mm, black or brown, hilum 2.5–3 mm with aril. . . . . .97. *Dipogon*, v. 11(1), p. 402
116. Herbs; stems climbing or suberect; pedicels shorter than calyx tube; banners with 2 prominent appendages at base; styles bearded; bracteoles elliptic-rounded, subpersistent; legumes 5–10 cm, ventral suture verrucose; seeds 9–13 mm, white or reddish brown to black, hilum and large white aril extending more than ½ seed length . . . . 98. *Lablab*, v. 11(1), p. 404
[104. Shifted to left margin.—Ed.]
104. Leaflet stipels absent or deciduous.
117. Fruits dehiscent, (1 or)2–numerous-seeded.
118. Fruits 6–15 cm; corollas 14–22 mm . . . . 93. *Pachyrhizus* (in part), v. 11(1), p. 396
118. Fruits 1–4 cm; corollas 2.5–12(–14) mm.
119. Herbs, with pilose hairs; corollas salmon reddish, 5 mm; seeds 3–6 . . . . .76. *Indigofera* (in part), v. 11(1), p. 335
119. Herbs or vines, without pilose hairs; corollas yellow, orange-yellow, or green-yellow, (4–)6–12(–14) mm; seeds 1 or 2. . . .89. *Rhynchosia* (in part), v. 11(1), p. 382
117. Fruits indehiscent or irregularly dehiscent, either 1-seeded loments or legumes or several-seeded and -segmented loments.
120. Loments with (1 or)2–10 segments, with 1 seed per segment, splitting between indehiscent segments . . . . 109. *Desmodium* (in part), v. 11(1), p. 442
120. Loments or legumes with a single segment, 1-seeded, indehiscent or irregularly dehiscent.
121. Bodies of fruits included in enlarged calyx except for projecting beak . . . . 116. *Pediomelum* (in part), v. 11(1), p. 476
121. Bodies of fruits usually not included in calyx, subequal to calyx lobes or exserted above them.

122. Loment walls papery; bracteoles present; herbs or shrubs, not gland-dotted . . . . 108. *Lespedeza* (in part), v. 11(1), p. 431
122. Legume walls thickly leathery; bracteoles absent; herbs, commonly gland-dotted . . . . 112. *Orbexilum* (in part), v. 11(1), p. 467

[76. Shifted to left margin.—Ed.]

76. Leaves mostly 3–96-foliolate (reduced leaves may have only 2 or 3 leaflets).
123. Leaves even-pinnate; herbs annual, perennial, or biennial.
124. Fruits geocarpic, ± indehiscent; stamens monadelphous, with 8 functional anthers and 2 sterile filaments . . . . 72. *Arachis* (in part), v. 11(1), p. 324
124. Fruits borne above ground, dehiscent or indehiscent; stamens diadelphous, uniform.
125. Leaflets all 2 and/or 4 in number.
126. Styles terete, with a dense ring of hairs just proximal to stigma; corollas 2–8 mm (8–12 mm in *V. ocalensis*); leaflets usually both 2 and 4 . . . . 150. *Vicia* (in part), v. 11(2), p. 994
126. Styles abaxially compressed; corollas 10 mm or more; leaflets all either 2 or 4.
127. Leaflets 2, usually with several longitudinal veins in addition to midrib; inflorescence bracts absent . . . . . 152. *Lathyrus* (in part), v. 11(2), p. 1008
127. Leaflets 4, without major longitudinal veins in addition to midrib; inflorescence bracts present, caducous . . . . 153. *Pisum* (in part), v. 11(2), p. 1030
125. Leaflets (0 or)2–30(–96+), if mostly 2 or 4, some leaves with more than 4 leaflets.
128. Tendrils absent, rachis slightly or evidently extended as a short bristle or mucronate tendril; legumes bladdery-inflated, terete, or flattened, dehiscent or indehiscent.
129. Calyx undulate-truncate or with 5 short lobes ¼-⅓ as long as tube; stipules narrowly triangular, caducous; legumes terete, elliptic, or 4-angled, flat, inflated, or winged, glabrous; leaflets 10–96+, folding forward to close at night. . . . . 118. *Sesbania* (in part), v. 11(1), p. 496
129. Calyx 2 lipped with some or all lobes at least ½ as long as tube; stipules foliose, persistent; legumes linear, sparsely pubescent; leaflets 2–6, not folding . . . . 150. *Vicia* (in part), v. 11(2), p. 994
128. Tendrils present on some or all leaves; legumes laterally compressed (-turgid), dehiscent.
130. Stipules foliaceous, usually larger than leaflets; leaflets 4 or 6; styles folded longitudinally, bearded laterally; stems not winged . . . . 153. *Pisum* (in part), v. 11(2), p. 1030
130. Stipules foliaceous or inconspicuous, not larger than leaflets; leaflets 2–30; styles not longitudinally folded, either laterally bearded or with apical tuft of hairs; stems angled or winged.
131. Calyx lobes 2–4 times longer than tube; herbs conspicuously pilose; flowers 10–15 mm, 1–3 at or near apex of axillary racemes; stems angled, not winged . . 151. *Lens*, v. 11(2), p. 1007
131. Calyx lobes all or some less than 2 times as long as tube, usually shorter than tube; herbs glabrous or pubescent, rarely pilose; flowers 2–35 mm, mostly axillary; stems angled or winged.
132. Styles terete with a distal tuft of hairs (rarely absent) on abaxial side or encircling; stems angled . . . . 150. *Vicia* (in part), v. 11(2), p. 994
132. Styles abaxially compressed, laterally to apically bearded on adaxial side; stems angled and/or winged . . . . 152. *Lathyrus* (in part), v. 11(2), p. 1008

[123. Shifted to left margin.—Ed.]

123. Leaves odd-pinnate; herbs, subshrubs, or vines, usually perennial.

133. Flowers not papilionaceous, wing and keel petals epistemonous, arising from apex of the stamen tube or laterally from it, or wings and keel absent, corolla then consisting only of banner; herbs or shrubs often conspicuously gland-dotted.

134. Corollas consisting only of banner, keel and wings absent; suffrutescent herbs, mostly canescent . . . . 61. *Amorpha* (in part), v. 11(1), p. 258

134. Corollas with 5 petals, epistemonous keel and wings either scarcely differentiated, ovate-oblong to lanceolate and arising from apex of stamen tube, or differentiated and arising laterally from stamen tube; herbs or shrubs, not canescent.

135. Ovules 1 and seed 1; inflorescences racemes; leaflet blades with sinuous lines; calyx ribs not anastomosing distally; sw United States . . . . 65. *Marina* (in part), v. 11(1), p. 280

135. Ovules 2 and seeds 1 or 2; inflorescences spikes; leaflet blades without sinuous lines; calyx ribs anastomosing distally; widespread. . . . . 66. *Dalea* (in part), v. 11(1), p. 283

133. Flowers papilionaceous (-subpapilionaceous), wings and keel arising from receptacle, all petals present; herbs, shrubs, vines, or trees, glandular or eglandular.

136. Stamens distinct or proximally connate; corollas white, creamy white, yellow, or purple; perennial herbs . . . . 46. *Sophora* (in part), v. 11(1), p. 164

136. Stamens monadelphous or diadelphous, usually basally connate; corollas white, yellow, pink to salmon, orange, shades of purple, blue, or red; usually annual or perennial herbs, vines, or subshrubs.

137. Subshrubs, armed, glandular nearly throughout; inflorescence rachis with thornlike tip in anthesis; Nevada . . . . .64. *Psorothamnus* (in part), v. 11(1), p. 274

137. Herbs, subshrubs, or vines, usually unarmed (except *Peteria* armed, stipules and stipels spinescent and bracts spine-tipped), usually eglandular; inflorescence rachis without thornlike tip; widespread.

138. Fruits loments.

139. Inflorescences umbels.

140. Leaflets 11–25; corollas white, pink, purple, or bicolored; perennial herbs; introduced, widespread. . . . . .119. *Securigera*, v. 11(1), p. 501

140. Leaflets 5–7; corollas yellow; shrubby herbs; introduced, California . . . . 120. *Coronilla*, v. 11(1), p. 502

139. Inflorescences fascicles, racemes, panicles, spikes, or heads, rarely solitary flowers.

141. Flowers sub-papilionaceous, wings much smaller than other petals; loments indehiscent, coarsely reticulate, winged, prickly edged; seed 1. . . . . 143. *Onobrychis*, v. 11(2), p. 912

141. Flowers papilionaceous, wings not significantly smaller than other petals; loments dehiscent or indehiscent, not coarsely reticulate, not or moderately winged, not prickly edged (surfaces sometimes prickly in *Hedysarum boreale*); seeds 1–9.

[142. Shifted to left margin.—Ed.]

142. Vines, twining; distal segment of loment sterile, flat, winglike (except *N. wislizeni*); sw United States . . . . 69. *Nissolia,* v. 11(1), p. 319

142. Herbs, not twining; distal segment of loment not produced into a wing; se United States or widespread.

143. Loments geocarpic, ± indehiscent; stamens monadelphous, with 8 functional anthers and 2 sterile filaments . . . . 72. *Arachis* (in part), v. 11(1), p. 324

143. Loments not geocarpic, dehiscent or indehiscent; stamens monadelphous or diadelphous, 10, all functional.

144. Plants annual; inflorescences umbellate heads; loment segments oblong or elliptic-oblong; flowers with inconspicuous keel. . . . . .122. *Ornithopus,* v. 11(1), p. 505

144. Plants annual or perennial; inflorescences racemes (sometimes subcapitate) or panicles, rarely solitary flowers; loment segments flattened, subglobose, subquadrate, or cylindric; flowers with conspicuous or inconspicuous keel.

145. Inflorescences terminal and axillary panicles; stipules petiolate . . . . .70. *Chapmannia,* v. 11(1), p. 320

145. Inflorescences axillary racemes; stipules sessile.

146. Stipules peltate; inflorescences with 1–5(–15) flowers; keel acute, included, bent, or curved; corollas yellowish; stems often with glandular hairs; se, sw United States . . . . 74. *Aeschynomene,* v. 11(1), p. 329

146. Stipules ± connate-sheathing, lanceolate; inflorescences with 5–60 flowers; keel broadly truncate, much exceeding other petals; corollas usually pink, reddish, or purple, or yellow, rarely white; stems without glandular hairs; w, ne United States, Canada . . . . .142. *Hedysarum,* v. 11(2), p. 908

[138. Shifted to left margin.—Ed.]

138. Fruits legumes.

147. Leaflet margins conspicuously dentate; legumes inflated and densely glandular-pubescent; seeds 1 or 2, ovoid-globular . . . . .144. *Cicer,* v. 11(2), p. 913

147. Leaflet margins entire; legumes inflated or not, glabrous or pubescent, not glandular; seeds 1–77(–84), globose to cuboid, oblong, ovoid, obovoid, reniform, ellipsoid, or terete.

148. Inflorescences headlike racemes or umbels; flowers subtended by a reduced lobed bract (prophyll); corollas usually yellow; terminal leaflet usually considerably longer than laterals; legumes included in calyx; seeds 1 or 2, globose to ovoid. . . . . .121. *Anthyllis,* v. 11(1), p. 503

148. Inflorescences racemes or pseudoracemes or flowers solitary, rarely umbellate or fasciculate; flowers without prophylls; corollas purple to blue, pink, reddish, maroon, orange, yellow, cream, or white; terminal leaflets usually not considerably longer than laterals; legumes included in calyx or not; seeds 1–77 (–84), globose to cuboid, oblong, ovoid, obovoid, reniform, ellipsoid, or terete.

149. Leaflets 3(or 5); vines, twining; corollas usually purple to pink-purple or bluish, rarely magenta; keel slightly incurved; sw, sc United States . . . . .92. *Cologania* (in part), v. 11(1), p. 393

149. Leaflets 1–45(–70); herbs, rarely vines or shrubs, not twining (except *Apios*); corollas purple to blue, pink, reddish, maroon, orange, yellow, cream, or white; keel straight to suberect (except incurved in *Apios*); widespread.

150. Banners 40–55 mm, much larger than other petals and arising from lower side of resupinate flower; leaflets 5 or 7, stipellate; stipules persistent, striate; inflorescences usually bearing a single resupinate flower . . . . .85. *Clitoria* (in part), v. 11(1), p. 371

150. Banners 4–26 mm, nearly equal to or only moderately larger than other petals; leaflets 1–45(–70), stipellate or not; stipules persistent or deciduous, not striate; inflorescences without resupinate flowers.

[151. Shifted to left margin.—Ed.]

151. Inflorescences umbels or solitary flowers; legumes narrowly oblong or linear, subterete to quadrate; leaflets 3–25.
 152. Leaflets 3–19, proximal pair not in stipular position; stipules leafy and scarious; corollas yellow, cream, white, pink, purple, red, or lurid; w North America . . . . . . 124. *Hosackia*, v. 11(1), p. 532
 152. Leaflets 5, proximal pair in stipular position, others palmately arranged; stipules glandlike; corollas yellow, usually marked with red; introduced, widespread . . . . . 125. *Lotus*, v. 11(1), p. 538

151. Inflorescences racemes or pseudoracemes; legumes linear to oblong, cylindric, ellipsoid, ovoid, lanceoloid, or globose; leaflets 1–45(–70).
 153. Stipules deeply sagittate-lobed, persistent; bracts subulate, persistent after anthesis; stamens monadelphous; legumes linear-cylindric, torulose . . . . 138. *Galega*, v. 11(2), p. 902
 153. Stipules not sagittate, not lobed, persistent or deciduous; bracts when present usually deltate, lanceolate, linear, or setaceous, rarely subulate, persistent or caducous; stamens monadelphous or diadelphous; legumes linear to oblong, cylindric, ellipsoid, ovoid, lanceoloid, or globose, not torulose.
  154. Leaf blades glandular-punctate; legumes glabrous or with hooked setae; corollas yellow-white, purple-tinged, or bluish . . . . 133. *Glycyrrhiza*, v. 11(2), p. 556
  154. Leaf blades not glandular-punctate; legumes glabrous or pubescent, without hooked setae; corollas white, cream, yellow, pink, blue to purple, maroon, pale green, violet, lavender, or lilac.
   155. Hairs dolabriform (2-branched from middle) in part or throughout; stipules free, not connate; corollas pink to red, salmon to maroon, orange-mauve to orange, or greenish yellow to ochroleucous, rarely white; anthers apiculate and initially gland-tipped . . . . . . .76. *Indigofera* (in part), v. 11(1), p. 335
   155. Hairs basifixed; stipules adnate to petiole or free; corollas white, cream, yellow, pink, blue to purple, maroon, pale green, violet, lavender, or lilac; anthers not apiculate.
    156. Herbs or vines prostrate, twining, or clambering.
     157. Inflorescences terminal or leaf-opposed; leaflets (3 or)5–11 (or 13), with numerous (8–15) parallel, straight, lateral veins extending to margins . . . . 80. *Tephrosia* (in part), v. 11(1), p. 347
     157. Inflorescences axillary; leaflets 1–7(or 9), without numerous parallel, lateral veins.
      158. Keels carinate or moderately incurved; styles filiform, not coiled; inflorescences few-flowered at apex of peduncle or reduced to 1 or 2 flowers in leaf axils; leaflet blades 20–55 mm; rhizomes not tuber-bearing. . . . . . . 83. *Galactia* (in part), v. 11(1), p. 358
      158. Keels incurved to strongly incurved; styles spirally coiled; inflorescences many-flowered, nodose pseudoracemes, often flowering ½+ axis length; leaflet blades 47–100 mm; rhizomes tuber-bearing . . . . 87. *Apios*, v. 11(1), p. 378
    156. Herbs usually erect, ascending, prostrate, or decumbent, rarely scandent, not vining.
     159. Inflorescences pseudoracemes, usually leaf-opposed, with (1 or)2–45 flowers; legumes laterally compressed, flat; styles bearded (except *T. angustissima*) . . . . . . 80. *Tephrosia* (in part), v. 11(1), p. 347
     159. Inflorescences terminal or axillary racemes; legumes usually bladdery-inflated (except *Peteria* laterally compressed); styles glabrous, sometimes bearded distally.

[160. Shifted to left margin.—Ed.]

160. Stipules spinescent; inflorescences leaf-opposed racemes, appearing terminal; styles slightly bearded; seeds cylindric; w, sc United States . . . . 130. *Peteria*, v. 11(2), p. 552

160. Stipules not spinescent; inflorescences racemes, not leaf-opposed, axillary or terminal; styles glabrous or bearded; seeds reniform; widespread.

  161. Plants with both conspicuously beaked (porrect) keel tips and scapose racemes, often spikelike; plants usually cespitose; styles glabrous. . . . . .134. *Oxytropis*, v. 11(2), p. 557

  161. Plants not with both beaked keels and scapose racemes; styles bearded or glabrous.

    162. Styles glabrous; legumes dehiscent throughout or apically, compressed to bladdery-inflated; corollas violet, blue-purple, purple, red-purple, pink-purple, pink, lilac, reddish, whitish, yellowish, cream, ochroleucous, or greenish; plants with or without creeping rhizomes; widespread, especially in w United States . . . . .135. *Astragalus* (in part), v. 11(2), p. 584

    162. Styles distally bearded; legumes indehiscent, bladdery-inflated; corollas orange-red or brick-red; plants without creeping rhizomes; introduced, w, c North America . . . . .137. *Sphaerophysa*, v. 11(2), p. 902

126. GLIRICIDIA Kunth in W. G. Walpers, Repert. Bot. Syst. 1: 679. 1842 • Madre de cacao [Latin *glires*, dormouse, and *cidi*, kill, alluding to use of bark as rodent poison] I

Matt Lavin

Trees, [rarely shrubs], unarmed. **Stems** usually erect to ascending, less commonly scandent, young growth glabrate to sericeous, peduncles and pedicels eglandular. **Leaves** alternate to subopposite, odd-pinnate; stipules present, caducous; petiolate; leaflets (7–)13–21(–25)[–41], stipels absent or inconspicuous, blade margins entire, surfaces glabrate to strigose. **Inflorescences** 20–100-flowered, axillary, racemes; bracts present; bracteoles absent. **Flowers** papilionaceous; calyx campanulate, lobes 5 (inconspicuous); corolla pinkish [whitish or purplish]; stamens 10, diadelphous; anthers basifixed; style glabrous, without pollen brush distally; stigma terminal, capitate, ciliate. **Fruits** legumes, short-stipitate, erect, laterally compressed, linear, elastically dehiscent, glabrous. **Seeds** [2 or] 3–10[–15], lenticular; with apical hilum. x = 10, 11.

Species 5 (1 in the flora): introduced, Florida; Mexico, Central America, nw South America; introduced also in West Indies (Puerto Rico, Virgin Islands), s Asia, Africa, Pacific Islands.

Gliricidia is native to lowland, seasonally dry and upland pine-oak woodlands in Mesoamerica and coastal Ecuador and adjacent Peru (M. Lavin and M. Sousa S. 1995; Lavin et al. 2003).

Gliricidia is not readily distinguished from other woody papilionoid genera even though the monophyly of the genus and its sister relationship to the Antillean genus *Poitea* Ventenat are well supported by molecular and, secondarily, morphological characters in a phylogenetic analysis (M. Lavin et al. 2003). All five species of the genus produce showy flowers, with most along a single rachis reaching anthesis nearly simultaneously. Of the related woody papilionoid genera that share this flowering habit, *Gliricidia* has a calyx that is fairly distinctive in being either tubular or campanulate but usually persisting with the maturing or mature fruit and having relatively short to inconspicuous lobes.

1. Gliricidia sepium (Jacquin) Kunth in W. G. Walpers, Repert. Bot. Syst. 1: 679. 1842 • Quickstick F I

Robinia sepium Jacquin, Enum. Syst. Pl., 28. 1760

Trees to 15 m. **Leaves** (15–)19–30(–35) cm; stipules triangular, ca. 0.5–2 × 1 mm; petiole 1.5–3 cm, glabrate; rachis canaliculate; petiolules 1–3 mm, glabrate; leaflet blades narrowly elliptic to elliptic, 44–83 × (17–)21–42(–48) mm, base attenuate to rounded, apex often broadly pointed. **Racemes:** rachises with 30–100 nodes mostly 0.1–2 mm apart, axis mostly glabrate to sparsely strigose; bracts persistent, triangular, 0.8–1.2 × 1 mm. **Pedicels** 5–11(–15) mm. **Flowers:** calyx tube (5.5–)6–9 mm, glabrous or sparsely strigose, lobes equal, inconspicuous, 0.1–0.2 mm; corolla 15–23 mm, glabrous; filaments subequal; anthers relatively small, dehiscing longitudinally. **Legumes** light to dark brown, 100–170(–230) × 14–22 mm, base blunt, apex acute, often terminating in persistent style base. **2*n*** = 20, 22.

Flowering year-round. Disturbed areas; 0–50 m; introduced; Fla.; Mexico; Central America; nw South America; introduced also in West Indies (Puerto Rico, Virgin Islands); widely elsewhere in tropical and subtropical areas.

Gliricidia sepium is native to seasonally dry neotropical forests of Mesoamerica and is now widely introduced in tropical regions (M. Lavin and M. Sousa S. 1995).

Economic uses of *Gliricidia sepium* were reported by C. E. Hughes (1987). The wood is used in construction, the leaves for medical purposes and livestock fodder, and the tree is cultivated as an ornamental, as shade for coffee and cacao trees, and as part of a living fence system. Common names in Latin America, including madricacao, madriado, and mataratón, reflect the broad economic importance of this species.

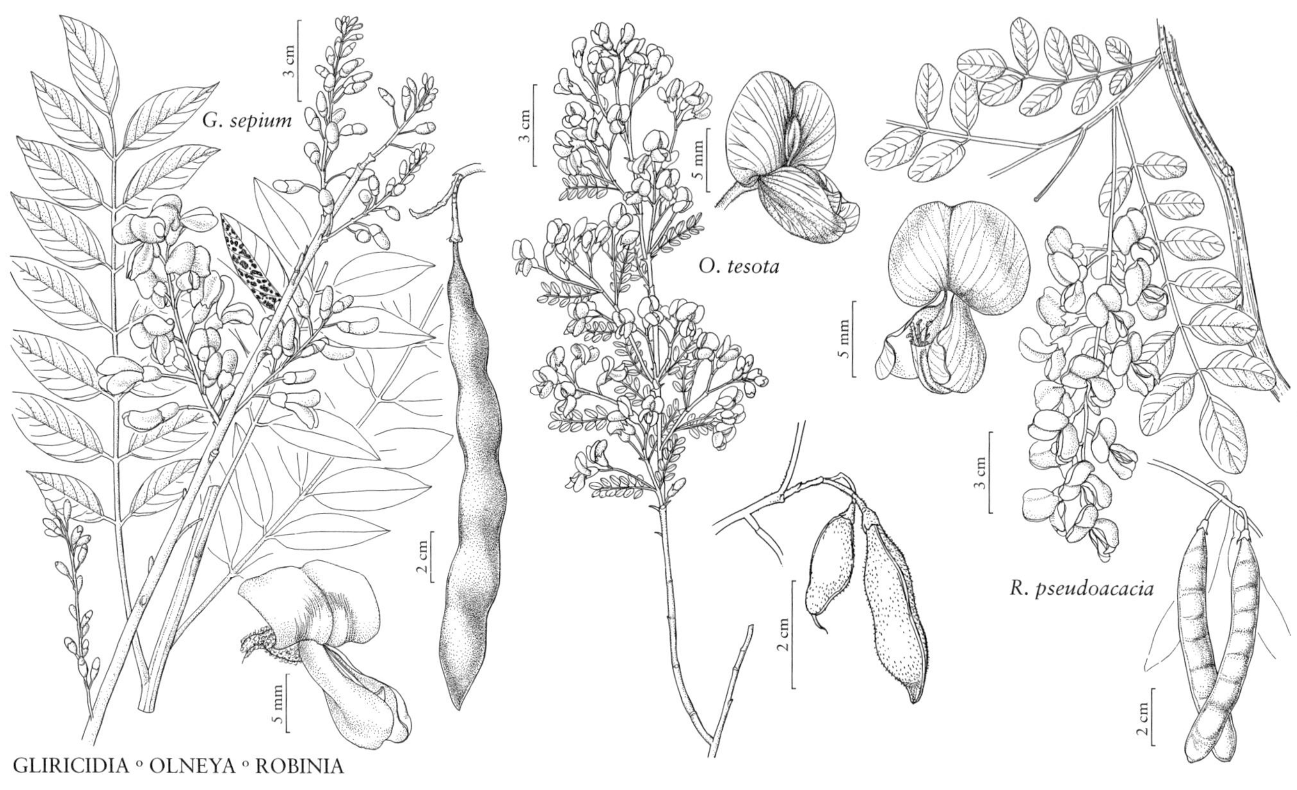

GLIRICIDIA ◦ OLNEYA ◦ ROBINIA

127. OLNEYA A. Gray, Pl. Nov. Thurb., 328. 1854 • Desert ironwood [For Stephen Thayer Olney, 1812–1878, American botanist]

Matt Lavin

Trees, to 10 m, armed, stipules spinescent. **Stems** usually erect to ascending, rarely scandent, young growth densely sericeous to woolly. **Leaves** alternate, even- or odd-pinnate; stipules present, caducous or persistent, 4–10 mm; petiolate; leaflets (8 or)9–21(–24), usually alternate, rarely opposite, stipels absent, blade margins entire, surfaces sericeous. **Inflorescences** 3–29-flowered, terminal, often congested into panicles; bracts present; bracteoles absent. **Flowers** papilionaceous; calyx zygomorphic, campanulate, lobes 5; corolla whitish to purplish, wing petals and keel tips usually purple; stamens 10, diadelphous; anthers basifixed; style glabrous proximally, with pollen brush surrounding distal ½; stigma terminal, capitate, ciliate. **Fruits** legumes, stipitate, terete, fusiform, elastically dehiscent, sparsely to densely stipitate-glandular, pubescent. **Seeds** 1 or 2(–5), spheroidal; hilum subapical. $x = 9$.

Species 1: sw United States, nw Mexico.

Olneya is native to the Sonoran Desert in Arizona and adjacent California, and to northwestern Mexico.

Olneya is readily distinguished from other woody papilionoid genera by the combination of broadly triangular calyx lobes, banner and wing petals tomentose abaxially, leaf rachises terminated by a spinose seta but that also usually bear an odd number of leaflets in alternate arrangement, and spinescent stipules that are especially prominent on the younger twigs.

1. Olneya tesota A. Gray, Pl. Nov. Thurb., 328. 1854 F

Leaves 2–10 cm; stipules subulate, 4–10 × 1 mm, spinescent; petiole 0.5–1 cm, strigose; rachis canaliculate; petiolules 1 mm, sericeous or glabrescent; leaflet blades narrowly obovate to elliptic, (5–)7–21 × 2.5–7(–9) mm, base attenuate to rounded, apex rounded. **Inflorescences** with fewer than 30 nodes, internodes mostly 0.5–6 mm, axis tomentose to woolly, stipitate glands absent or sparse; bracts persistent to caducous, 1 × 1 mm, blunt. **Pedicels** 3–6 mm. **Flowers:** calyx tube (1.5–)2–4 mm, sericeous to tomentose, lobes equal, broadly triangular, 7–11 mm; corolla 10–14 mm, glabrous or sericeous; filaments subequal; anthers small, dehiscing longitudinally; ovary with stipitate glands, densely sericeous. **Legumes** light to dark grayish or brownish, 2–5(–6) × 1.1–1.3 cm, base blunt, apex acute, often terminating in persistent style base, usually sparsely covered with stipitate glands. **2*n*** = 18.

Flowering early summer. Open, dry, shrubby sites; 0–1300 m; Ariz., Calif.; Mexico (Baja California, Baja California Sur, Sonora).

Olneya tesota is economically important to the Seri Indians of the Sonoran Desert (R. S. Felger and M. B. Moser 1985). The many uses include nutritional (seeds and unripe pods) and medical ones, and production of firewood, tools, weapons, musical instruments, and artistic sculptures from the wood. Tinctures have been made from the green wood and used by the Seris in vision quests, which they believed gave them power.

128. ROBINIA Linnaeus, Sp. Pl. 2: 722. 1753; Gen. Pl. ed. 5, 322. 1754 • Locust [For Jean Robin, 1550–1629, Royal Gardener in Paris]

Matt Lavin

Thomas G. Lammers

Trees or shrubs, armed [unarmed], stipules spinescent. **Stems** erect to ascending, often root-sprouting, young growth glabrous, sericeous, tomentose, or hispid, hairs sometimes stipitate-glandular. **Leaves** alternate, odd-pinnate; stipules present, caducous, or persistent becoming spinescent; rachis canaliculate; petiolate; leaflets 7–45, usually opposite to subopposite, rarely alternate, stipels present, blade margins entire, surfaces glabrate or strigose to sericeous. **Inflorescences** (3 or)4–25-flowered, axillary, racemes; bracts present, caducous; bracteoles absent. **Flowers** papilionaceous; calyx zygomorphic, campanulate, lobes 5, abaxial longer than laterals, adaxial more connate than laterals; corolla whitish or pinkish, glabrous; stamens 10, diadelphous, filaments subequal; anthers basifixed, relatively small, dehiscing longitudinally; style glabrous, with pollen brush loosely scattered along 1 side distally; stigma terminal, capitate, ciliate. **Fruits** legumes, sessile, laterally compressed, linear, placental margin not winged (narrowly winged in *R. pseudoacacia*), tardily, elastically dehiscent, not constricted between seeds, glabrous, hispid, or glandular-hispid. **Seeds** 3–10(–16), lenticular; hilum slightly recessed. *x* = 10.

Species 4 (4 in the flora): North America, n Mexico; introduced in South America (Chile), Eurasia, Australia.

Robinia often colonizes disturbed settings in temperate deciduous and conifer forests, woodlands, and shrubby vegetation (D. Isely and F. J. Peabody 1984; M. Lavin and M. Sousa S. 1995). *Robinia pseudoacacia* is planted as a landscape and timber tree far outside its natural range, from which it has naturalized extensively; the remaining shrubby species are also cultivated as ornamentals, though less commonly and with less tendency to naturalize (Isely 1998)

Robinia is distinguished from other legume genera in the flora area by its fruits that are tardily dehiscent and not very elastically (or explosively) so. Seeds are transversely arranged; the hilum faces toward the base of the fruit rather than toward the placental margin. The placental (upper) margin is usually not winged except narrowly so in *R. pseudoacacia*. Each seed is borne from an elongate funiculus. The *Robinia* raceme also differs from that of its closest relatives in originating from leaf axils of the current season's growth and in producing flowers that reach anthesis simultaneously.

Fossil wood that is indistinguishable from that of *Robinia pseudoacacia* is encountered from the Late Eocene to Miocene in the south-central and western United States (U. Prakash et al. 1962; Prakash 1968; L. C. Matten et al. 1977; M. Lavin et al. 2003). Fossil leaves dating to the Oligocene have been attributed to the genus with less confidence (D. Isely 1998; Lavin et al.).

Robinia represents one of relatively few temperate North American lineages to have evolved from neotropical ancestry (as in *Strophostyles*; E. T. Riley-Hulting et al. 2004). Most temperate North American legume groups (such as *Astragalus*, *Lupinus*, and *Vicia*) originate from Eurasia. Similar to neotropical relatives, *Robinia* species primarily occupy disturbance-prone habitats and often root-sprout on unstable or exposed soils; they can form dense colonies that stabilize loose soil. Their growth habit ranges from shrubs to trees; *R. pseudoacacia* generally adopts a large-tree habit most consistently. Variation in such growth form is likely a function of disturbance. The smaller the stature of the plant, the more likely the habitat disturbance is regular or recent. Growth of *Robinia* species also appears to be regulated more by temperature than day length, which could be a result of a recent tropical ancestry. Consequently, *Robinia* seems outcompeted in undisturbed settings and is prone to die back related to cold temperatures. Apart from a variable shrub to tree growth form, this may explain the generally crooked stems and unkempt appearance of many *Robinia* individuals and populations.

With exception to the predominantly white-petaled and outcrossing *Robinia pseudoacacia* (B. C. Bongarten 1992), the three predominantly pink-petaled species (*R. hispida*, *R. neomexicana*, and *R. viscosa*) harbor much interpopulation variation that is often recognized formally at the species or infraspecific level (W. W. Ashe 1922). This variation is often the result of hybridization (for example, *R. viscosa* var. *hartwigii*), clonal variation due partially to reproduction involving triploidy (as in segregates of *R. hispida*), plasticity of growth form (*R. hispida* var. *nana*), or geographic structuring (*R. neomexicana* var. *rusbyi*) (D. Isely and F. J. Peabody 1984). None of the historically recognized intraspecific variation is treated formally here. The taxonomy of *Robinia* would be better served with genetic data and analyses that bear on the origins of asexual races rather than application of formal taxonomic names to every variant and intermediate form.

1. Corollas usually whitish, rarely pinkish, 15–20 mm; racemes pendent, (10–)15–25-flowered; legumes glabrous, placental margin narrowly winged; raceme rachises eglandular; calyx sericeous, lobes shorter than tube . . . . .3. *Robinia pseudoacacia*
1. Corollas pinkish, 20–25 mm; racemes lax to ascending or erect, (3 or)4–20-flowered; legumes hispid or glandular-hispid, placental margin not winged; raceme rachises sericeous, tomentose, or hispid, sometimes glandular; calyx sericeous, tomentose, or hispid, sometimes glandular, lobes slightly longer to slightly shorter than tube.
    2. Branches and leaf axes tomentose to sericeous, eglandular; leaflet surfaces strigose to sericeous . . . . .2. *Robinia neomexicana*
    2. Branches and leaf axes hispid or glandular; leaflet surfaces: abaxial glabrate and adaxial strigose to sericeous, or abaxial sericeous and adaxial glabrate.
        3. Branches and leaf axes hispid, hairs conspicuous or indurate, 1–5 mm, or without sessile or stipitate glands; floral bract margins entire; leaflets 7–13, surfaces glabrate abaxially, strigose to sericeous adaxially. . . . . 1. *Robinia hispida*
        3. Branches and leaf axes glandular, glands sessile or stipitate; floral bract margins toothed; leaflets 13–25, surfaces sericeous abaxially, glabrate adaxially . . . . 4. *Robinia viscosa*

1. Robinia hispida Linnaeus, Mant. Pl. 1: 101. 1767 • Bristly locust [E]

Robinia albicans Ashe; *R. boyntonii* Ashe; *R. elliottii* (Chapman) Ashe; *R. fertilis* Ashe; *R. hispida* var. *elliottii* Chapman; *R. hispida* var. *fertilis* (Ashe) R. T. Clausen; *R. hispida* var. *kelseyi* (J. F. Cowell ex Hutchinson) Isely; *R. hispida* var. *nana* (Elliott) de Candolle; *R. hispida* var. *rosea* Pursh; *R. kelseyi* J. F. Cowell ex Hutchinson; *R. leucantha* Rehder; *R. michauxii* Sargent; *R. nana* Elliott; *R. pallida* Ashe; *R. pauciflora* Ashe; *R. pedunculata* Ashe; *R. unakae* Ashe

Shrubs, 1–3(–10) m; branches hispid, hairs conspicuous or indurate. **Leaves** 15–30 cm; stipules 5–9 mm; petiole 0.9–2 cm, hispid, petiole and axis often with conspicuous or indurate hairs; petiolules 1–2 mm, glabrate; leaflets 7–13, blades broadly elliptic, 15–50 × 10–35 mm, surfaces glabrate abaxially, strigose to sericeous adaxially. **Racemes** (3 or)4–11(–15)-flowered, lax to ascending, 5–13 cm, rachis sericeous or hispid; bracts lanceolate, 8–10 × 1–2 mm, margins entire. **Pedicels** 4–7 mm. **Flowers:** calyx tube 5–6 mm, sericeous, lobes 4–7 mm; corolla pinkish, 20–25 mm. **Legumes** rarely forming, dark to reddish brown, 4–8 × 1–1.2 cm, hispid. **Seeds** 3–5.

Flowering spring–early summer. Open, often disturbed areas, temperate deciduous forests, roadsides; 0–1300 m; B.C., N.S., Ont.; Ala., Ark., Calif., Colo., Conn., Del., Fla., Ga., Ill., Ind., Kans., Ky., La., Maine, Md., Mass., Mich., Minn., Miss., Mo., Nebr., N.H., N.J., N.Mex., N.Y., N.C., Ohio, Okla., Oreg., Pa., R.I., S.C., Tenn., Tex., Utah, Vt., Va., Wash., W.Va., Wis.; introduced in Eurasia.

The conspicuously hispid leaf axes and branches distinguish the common forms of *Robinia hispida* from other pink-petaled species of *Robinia*. Forms of *R. hispida* lacking such a hispid indument are distinguished from *R. viscosa* by leaf axes and branches without glands, and by leaves with 13 or fewer, and usually broadly elliptic, leaflets.

Robinia hispida appears to be native in Alabama, Georgia, North Carolina, South Carolina, Tennessee, and Virginia (D. Isely 1998), and should be considered introduced in other areas.

In addition to the synonyms above, the following are also considered synonymous with *Robinia hispida*: *R. grandiflora* Ashe (1922) is an illegitimate later homonym of *R. grandiflora* Linnaeus (1753); *R. rosea* Marshall (1785) and *R. rosea* Elliott (1822) are illegitimate later homonyms of *R. rosea* Miller (1768); and *R. speciosa* Ashe (1923) is an illegitimate later homonym of *R. speciosa* Swartz ex Besser (1816).

Robinia hispida varies in chromosome number: some plants are diploid, $2n = 20$, others are triploid, $2n = 30$. Only diploids in the mountains set fertile seed on a regular basis. Triploids as well as diploids of the Coastal Plain and adjacent Piedmont are sterile or nearly so, propagating almost exclusively by root-suckering. Morphology varies considerably within the species, particularly in habit and in the amount and distribution of pubescence; due to the predominance of asexual reproduction, populations in many cases are clones and quite uniform in these features (D. Isely and F. J. Peabody 1984; Isely 1998).

To accommodate this variation, *Robinia hispida* has been divided into five varieties (D. Isely and F. J. Peabody 1984; Isely 1998). The sterile diploids of the Coastal Plain and adjacent Piedmont are perhaps the most distinctive: subshrubs 5–8 cm, with unbranched, zigzag stems that are glabrous or slightly hispid. These have been called *R. hispida* var. *nana*. From the Piedmont into the mountains are found shrubs and small trees 1–8 m that resemble the last in their reduced pubescence but which have branched, straight stems and are sterile triploids; these have been called *R. hispida* var. *rosea*. Sympatric with both varieties are shrubs 0.6–3 m that differ in their obviously prickly-hispid stems. The widespread, sterile triploids with this morphology are *R. hispida* var. *hispida*, while the fertile diploids, endemic to the mountains of western North Carolina and adjacent Tennessee, are *R. hispida* var. *fertilis*. The fifth variety, *R. hispida* var. *kelseyi*, does not exist in nature but likely represents a horticultural selection of *R. hispida* var. *fertilis* with narrower leaflets.

Interspecific hybridization exacerbates the complex variation patterns seen in *Robinia hispida*. Nothospecies resulting from putative hybridizations involving *R. hispida* and *R. pseudoacacia* (*R.* ×*margaretta* Ashe, *R.* ×*oconeensis* Ashe) are found in Georgia, North Carolina, and Tennessee; *R. hispida* and *R. viscosa* (*R.* ×*longiloba* Ashe, *R.* ×*ashei* Schallert) are found in North and South Carolina.

2. Robinia neomexicana A. Gray, Pl. Nov. Thurb., 314. 1854 (as neo-mexicana) • New Mexico locust

Robinia breviloba Rydberg; *R. luxurians* (Dieck ex E. Goeze) Silva Tarouca & C. K. Schneider; *R. neomexicana* var. *rusbyi* (Wooton & Standley) W. C. Martin & C. R. Hutchins ex Peabody; *R. rusbyi* Wooton & Standley; *R. subvelutina* Rydberg

Shrubs or trees, 1–5(–15) m; branches tomentose to sericeous, eglandular. **Leaves** 10–25 cm; stipules 8–11 mm; petiole 0.5–1.6 cm, tomentose to sericeous; axis tomentose to sericeous, eglandular;

petiolules 2–3 mm, tomentose to sericeous; leaflets 13–23, blades elliptic, 25–35 × 15–20 mm, surfaces strigose to sericeous. **Racemes** 10–20-flowered, lax to erect, 3–10 cm, rachis tomentose to sericeous or hispid, sometimes with stipitate glands; bracts lanceolate, 9–12 × 2–3 mm, margins entire. **Pedicels** 3–5 mm. **Flowers:** calyx tube 6–7 mm, tomentose to sericeous, sometimes with stipitate glands, lobes 5–7 mm; corolla pinkish, 20–25 mm. **Legumes** light to dark brown, 4–8 × 0.9–1.1 cm, hispid. **Seeds** 4–10(–15).

Flowering spring–early summer. Open, disturbed settings, exposed rocky outcrops, steep slopes, pine forests and woodlands; 1500–2000 m; B.C.; Ariz., Calif., Colo., Nev., N.Mex., Tex., Utah, Wyo.; Mexico (Chihuahua, Sonora).

Robinia neomexicana is native in the United States and Mexico, and is introduced in British Columbia.

The tomentose to sericeous leaf axes and branches, often stipitate-glandular inflorescence rachises, often conspicuously hispid fruits, and distribution in southwestern United States and adjacent Mexico distinguish *Robinia neomexicana* from other pink-petaled *Robinia* species. Forms of *R. neomexicana* without the hispid indument and glandular hairs on the inflorescence rachises and fruits retain the relatively abundant tomentose to sericeous indument on the leaves and branches.

D. Isely and F. J. Peabody (1984) and Isely (1998) recognized two weakly differentiated and largely sympatric varieties of *Robinia neomexicana*: var. *neomexicana* with ovaries and fruits sparsely hispid to strongly glandular-hispid and var. *rusbyi* with ovaries and fruits glabrous at maturity.

Nothospecies based on putative hybrids involving *Robinia neomexicana* and *R. pseudoacacia*, *R.* ×*holdtii* Beissner and *R.* ×*coloradensis* Dode, are found in the range of *R. neomexicana* where *R. pseudoacacia* has been planted.

3. Robinia pseudoacacia Linnaeus, Sp. Pl. 2: 722. 1753 • Black locust, robinier faux-acacia [E] [F]

Robinia pringlei Rose

Trees, (1–)4–25 m; branches finely pubescent or glabrate, eglandular. **Leaves** 20–30 cm; stipules 5–10 mm; petiole 0.7–2.5 cm, strigose; petiolules 2–3 mm, glabrate; leaflets (7–)15–19, blades elliptic, 25–45(–65) × 10–20(–25) mm, surfaces glabrate. **Racemes** (10–)15–25-flowered, pendent, 5–19 cm, rachis sericeous; bracts lanceolate, 8–10 × 1 mm, margins entire. **Pedicels** 7–12 mm. **Flowers:** calyx tube 5–6 mm, sericeous, lobes 1–2 mm; corolla usually whitish, rarely pinkish, 15–20 mm. **Legumes** light to dark brownish, 4–10 × 1–1.5 cm, placental margin narrowly winged, glabrous. **Seeds** 4–8(–16).

Flowering spring–early summer. Temperate, deciduous forests and woodlands, disturbed areas; 0–2000 m; B.C., N.B., N.S., Ont., Que.; Ala., Ariz., Ark., Calif., Colo., Conn., Del., D.C., Fla., Ga., Idaho, Ill., Ind., Iowa, Kans., Ky., La., Maine, Md., Mass., Mich., Minn., Miss., Mo., Mont., Nebr., Nev., N.H., N.J., N.Mex., N.Y., N.C., N.Dak., Ohio, Okla., Oreg., Pa., R.I., S.C., S.Dak., Tenn., Tex., Utah, Vt., Va., Wash., W.Va., Wis., Wyo.; introduced in South America (Argentina, Chile), Eurasia, Australia.

Robinia pseudoacacia is native at least in the Appalachian and other mountainous regions of eastern North America; it is widely cultivated and escaped throughout North America and other temperate regions of the world. Black locust can be highly invasive and is considered a threat to native biodiversity in many areas (J. Heim 1990; B. M. Farris 2007; L. Derickx and P. M. Antunes 2013). Populations growing at latitudinal extremes (such as Canada) are sometimes more likely to be shorter (3 m or less).

The report of *Robinia pseudoacacia* from Prince Edward Island is based on a single old specimen, and the species is here excluded from that province.

The winged and glabrous fruits and flowers with white petals arranged on pendent racemes set *Robinia pseudoacacia* apart from other species of the genus.

Nothospecies based on putative hybrids involving *Robinia pseudoacacia* and *R. neomexicana* (*R.* ×*holdtii* Beissner, *R.* ×*coloradensis* Dode) are found in areas where the former has been planted; those involving *R. pseudoacacia* and *R. viscosa* (*R.* ×*ambigua* Poiret) are found in western North Carolina.

4. Robinia viscosa Ventenat, Bull. Sci. Soc. Philom. Paris 1(2): 161. 1799 • Clammy locust, robinier visqueux [E]

Robinia glutinosa Sims; *R. hartwigii* Koehne; *R. viscosa* var. *hartwigii* (Koehne) Ashe

Shrubs or trees, 1.5–4(–12) m; branches glandular, glands usually sessile, sometimes stipitate. **Leaves** 10–20 cm; stipules 3–6 mm; petiole 0.7–2 cm, with sessile glands, sometimes glands stipitate; axis glandular, glands usually sessile, sometimes stipitate; petiolules 1–2 mm, glabrate; leaflets 13–25, blades elliptic, 20–42 × 10–20 mm, surfaces sericeous abaxially, glabrate adaxially. **Racemes** 10–20-flowered, lax to ascending, 4–10 cm, rachis sericeous or hispid; bracts oblanceolate to obovate, 10–15 × 3–5 mm, margins 1–several-toothed (when 1, then with long-attenuate central tooth). **Pedicels** 3–6 mm.

Flowers: calyx tube 4–5 mm, sericeous, lobes 4–5 mm; corolla pinkish, 20–25 mm. **Legumes** rarely forming, dark brownish to purplish, 4–6 × 0.8–1 cm, glandular-hispid. **Seeds** 4–9.

Flowering spring–early summer. Open or disturbed areas, temperate deciduous forests, roadsides; 0–1600 m; N.B., N.S., Ont., P.E.I., Que.; Ala., Conn., Ga., Ill., Ind., Ky., Maine, Md., Mass., Mich., Minn., N.H., N.J., N.Y., N.C., Ohio, Pa., R.I., S.C., Tenn., Vt., Va., W.Va., Wis.

Robinia viscosa can be distinguished from other predominantly pinkish-petaled species by having glands while lacking a hispid indument, often in combination with leaves having more than 13 leaflets.

Robinia viscosa appears to be native in North Carolina, South Carolina, Tennessee, and Virginia (D. Isely 1998), and should be considered introduced in other areas.

D. Isely and F. J. Peabody (1984) and Isely (1998) distinguished two varieties of *R. viscosa*: var. *viscosa* with flat, sessile glands on young growth and inflorescences, and glabrous; and var. *hartwigii* without flat, sessile glands, and densely glandular-pubescent.

Nothospecies based on putative hybrids involving *Robinia viscosa* and *R. hispida* (*R.* ×*ashei* Schallert, *R.* ×*longiloba* Ashe) are found in North Carolina and South Carolina; those involving *R. viscosa* and *R. pseudoacacia* (*R.* ×*ambigua* Poiret) are found in western North Carolina.

129. COURSETIA de Candolle, Ann. Sci. Nat. (Paris) 4: 92. 1825 • Babybonnets [For George Louis Marie Dumont de Courset, 1746–1824, French botanist and agronomist]

Matt Lavin

Herbs, perennial, subshrubs, shrubs, or trees, rarely armed, stipules rarely spinescent. **Stems** usually erect to ascending, sometimes prostrate to decumbent [or scandent], young growth ± sericeous. **Leaves** alternate, odd- or even-pinnate; stipules present, ephemeral to persistent, subulate, 3–5 mm; petiolate; leaflets [3–]6–22[–27], usually opposite, rarely alternate, blade margins entire, surfaces pubescent or glabrous. **Inflorescences** 30–40-flowered, axillary, racemes [panicles] (flowers sometimes fascicled or in viscid-glandular racemes); bracts present; bracteoles absent. **Flowers** papilionaceous; calyx zygomorphic, campanulate, lobes 5, equal to or longer than tube; corolla whitish or yellowish, sometimes pinkish-tinged, [reddish, purplish, or yellow], usually glabrous; stamens 10, diadelphous; anthers basifixed, relatively small, dehiscing longitudinally; style glabrous, pollen brush tufted to loosely scattered along 1 side distally; stigma terminal, capitate, ciliate. **Fruits** legumes, sessile, laterally compressed, linear, elastically dehiscent, constricted between seeds or not, glabrous, pubescent, or glandular. **Seeds** 1–30, lenticular; hilum apical. $x = 8$.

Species ca. 42 (4 in the flora): sw, sc United States, Mexico, West Indies, Central America, South America.

Coursetia is distinguished from other legume genera in the flora area by the combination of racemes with acropetal maturation of flowers in which typically one flower per rachis reaches anthesis at a time (contrasting with *Olneya* and *Robinia*), styles each with a pollen brush borne laterally (latrorse), to the inside (introrse), or along the outer side (extrorse), and legumes with seed compartments evinced by lateral or abaxial constrictions in the pod margins or walls between seeds. Herbaceous *Coursetia* species are distinguished from other herbaceous legume genera by their pulvinate leaves. Otherwise, *Coursetia* is highly variable morphologically and not as readily diagnosed as related genera. Species of *Coursetia* are known from throughout the Neotropics, primarily in grass-poor, seasonally dry woodlands, and secondarily in savanna woodlands and pine-oak forests (M. Lavin 1988; Lavin and M. Sousa S. 1995; Lavin et al. 2003; R. Duno de Stefano et al. 2010; L. P. de Queiroz and Lavin 2011). In the flora area, *Coursetia* is found mainly in the Sonoran Desert of Arizona and in the Tamaulipan thorn-scrub of southern Texas.

SELECTED REFERENCE Lavin, M. 1988. Systematics of *Coursetia* (Leguminosae-Papilionoideae). Syst. Bot. Monogr. 21.

1. Shrubs or trees, 0.5–10 m; leaves even-pinnate; legumes dorsiventrally constricted between seeds, without linear transverse impressions between seeds on lateral surfaces; Arizona, Texas.
   2. Trees or shrubs, 1–10 m; legumes and axes of racemes stipitate-glandular; leaflets 8–22; Sonoran Desert, Arizona . . . . 1. *Coursetia glandulosa*
   2. Shrubs, 0.5–2 m; legumes and axes of racemes eglandular; leaflets 6–12; Tamaulipan thorn-scrub, s Texas . . . . 2. *Coursetia axillaris*
1. Herbs or subshrubs, 0.1–0.6 m; leaves odd-pinnate; legumes not dorsiventrally constricted between seeds, with linear transverse impressions between seeds on lateral surfaces; Arizona.
   3. Herbs, 0.1–0.3 m; stems prostrate to decumbent; corollas mostly yellowish; terminal leaflet not larger than laterals; leaflet surfaces: abaxial with reddish brown tannin deposits strictly along veins, especially at margins; legumes pilose to strigose; se Arizona . . .3. *Coursetia glabella*
   3. Subshrubs or, rarely, herbs, 0.1–0.6 m; stems erect to ascending; corollas mostly whitish; terminal leaflet distinctly larger than laterals; leaflet surfaces: abaxial with reddish brown tannin deposits concentrated toward center of blade between veins; legumes usually glabrous or woolly, rarely stipitate-glandular; s Arizona . . . . 4. *Coursetia caribaea*

1. Coursetia glandulosa A. Gray, Proc. Amer. Acad. Arts 5: 156. 1861 • Rosary babybonnets [F]

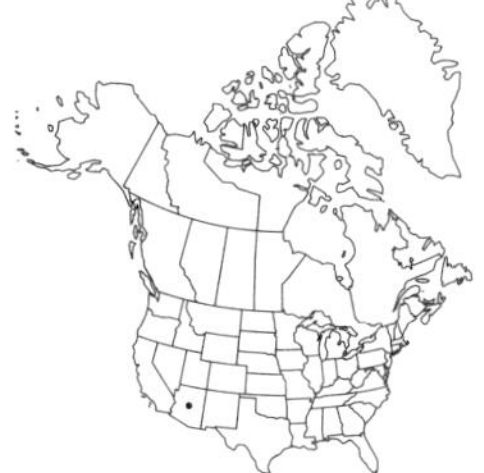

Coursetia microphylla A. Gray; *C. seleri* Harms

Shrubs or trees, 1–10 m. **Leaves** even-pinnate, (3–)4.5–15 cm; stipules subulate, 5–8 × 1 mm; petiole 0.5–2 cm, strigose; rachis canaliculate; leaflets 8–22, petiolules 1 mm, glabrate, blades narrowly to widely elliptic, (3–)5–17[–50] × 3–7[–22] mm, base rounded, apex rounded, usually mucronate, surfaces glabrate to strigose. **Racemes** often from short shoots of older twigs, nodes often 20–40, internodes usually 1–5 mm, axis sparsely to densely stipitate-glandular; bracts caducous, ovate to lanceolate, 1–3.5 × 1 mm. **Pedicels** 3–10(–12) mm. **Flowers:** calyx tube (2.5–)3–4 mm, stipitate-glandular, lobes 2–5 mm, abaxial longer than laterals, adaxial connate, more so than laterals; corolla mostly whitish, 12–15 mm; filaments subequal. **Legumes** light to dark brownish, 25–110 × 5–7 mm, base blunt, dorsiventrally constricted between seeds, without linear transverse impressions between seeds on lateral surfaces, apex acute, often terminating in persistent style base, glandular. **Seeds** 1–13. $2n = 16$.

Flowering spring–early summer. Open, dry shrubby sites, seasonally dry woodlands; 0–1800 m; Ariz.; Mexico.

In the flora area, *Coursetia glandulosa* is known from Gila, Maricopa, Pima, Pinal, Yavapai, and Yuma counties.

The range of variation in *Coursetia glandulosa* tends toward the larger end in the Pacific coastal dry forests of western to southern Mexico and the smaller end in Arizona. This variation, especially in leaflet size and plant height, is clinal. The long stems of *C. glandulosa* can bend to small angles without breaking and thus have been used by the Seri tribe for harpoon shafts, bows, and other tools (R. S. Felger and M. B. Moser 1985). The conspicuous, dark reddish, gummy resin found on the stems of *C. glandulosa* from throughout its range is the result of a symbiotic relationship between ants and the larvae of a scale insect. This lac exudate is highly prized by the Seri (Felger and Moser).

2. Coursetia axillaris J. M. Coulter & Rose, Bot. Gaz. 16: 180. 1891 • Texas babybonnets

Shrubs, 0.5–2 m. **Leaves** even-pinnate, 1.5–7 cm; stipules subulate, 3–5 × 1 mm; petiole 0.5–1 cm, strigose; rachis canaliculate; leaflets 6–12, petiolules 1 mm, glabrate, blades narrowly elliptic to obovate, 4–22 × 3–10 mm, base and apex rounded, surfaces usually glabrate to sparsely strigose. **Racemes** often from short shoots of older twigs, nodes often 3–11, internodes usually 1–4 mm, axis sericeous; bracts persistent, lanceolate, 0.5–2 × 1 mm. **Pedicels** 3–10 mm. **Flowers:** calyx tube 2–2.5 mm, sericeous, lobes 1.5–3 mm, abaxial longer than laterals, adaxial connate, more so than laterals; corolla mostly whitish, sometimes tinged pinkish, 9–11 mm; filaments subequal. **Legumes** light to dark brownish, 20–40 × 4–6 mm, base blunt, margins sinuous, dorsiventrally constricted between seeds, without linear transverse impressions between seeds on lateral surface, apex acute, often terminating in persistent style base, glabrous. **Seeds** 1–8. $2n = 16$.

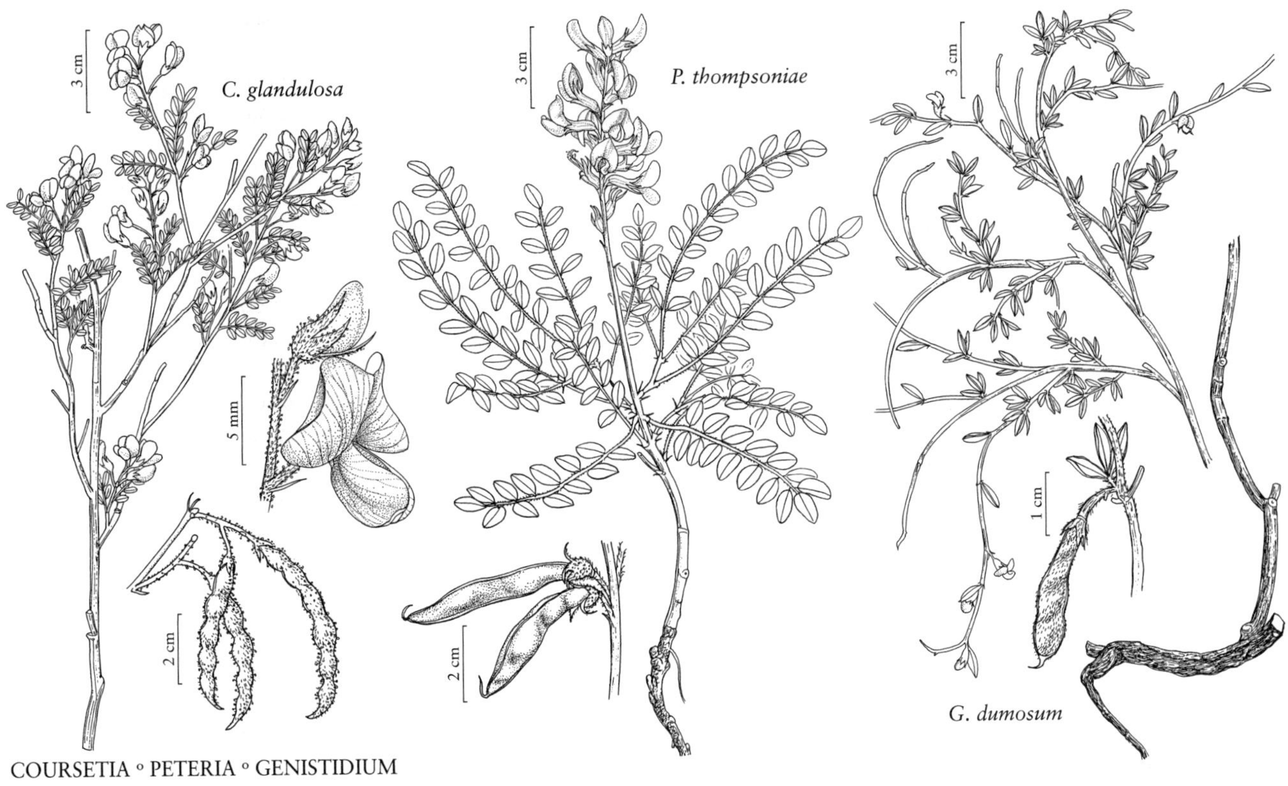

COURSETIA ◦ PETERIA ◦ GENISTIDIUM

Flowering spring. Open, dry shrubby sites, Tamaulipan thorn-scrub; 40–200[–3000] m; Tex.; Mexico (San Luis Potosí, Tamaulipas, Veracruz).

In the flora area, *Coursetia axillaris* is known from Duval, Hidalgo, Jim Hogg, Jim Wells, Kleberg, Nueces, Refugio, San Patricio, and Starr counties.

The much-branched shrubby growth form of *Coursetia axillaris* that contrasts with the long, slender stems of the close relative *C. glandulosa* is retained under greenhouse conditions (M. Lavin 1988). Thus, *C. axillaris* grows as a reliably compact ornamental.

3. **Coursetia glabella** (A. Gray) Lavin in C. H. Stirton, Advances Legume Syst. 3, 63. 1987 • Smooth babybonnets

Cracca edwardsii A. Gray var. *glabella* A. Gray, Proc. Amer. Acad. Arts 17: 201. 1882

Herbs, 0.1–0.3 m, stems prostrate to decumbent. **Leaves** odd-pinnate, 3–7.5 cm; stipules subulate, 3.5–5 × 1 mm; petiole 0.5–1 cm, glabrate; rachis canaliculate; leaflets 11–21, petiolules 1 mm, glabrate, blades elliptic, 5–15 × 2–11 mm, base and apex rounded, surfaces sericeous abaxially, glabrous adaxially, abaxial with reddish brown tannin deposits strictly along veins, especially at margins. **Racemes** from axils of leaves on young twigs, nodes often 5–15, internodes usually 3+ mm, axis sparsely pilose; bracts caducous, lanceolate, 2.5–4.5 × 1 mm. **Pedicels** 1.8–2.2 mm. **Flowers:** calyx tube 2–3 mm, pilose, lobes 3–5 mm, abaxial longer than laterals, adaxial connate, more so than laterals; corolla mostly yellowish, 9–12 mm; filaments subequal. **Legumes** light to dark brownish, 35–60 × 3–4 mm, base blunt, not dorsiventrally constricted between seeds, with linear transverse impressions between seeds on lateral surface, apex acute, often terminating in persistent style base, pilose to strigose. **Seeds** 7–15. $2n$ = 16.

Flowering summer. Open to closed understory of pine and oak forests; 1700–2200 m; Ariz.; Mexico (Chihuahua, Sonora).

Coursetia glabella is the northernmost species of the *C. pumila* (Rose) Lavin group (M. Lavin 1988) of four mainly Mexican species that are distinguished by an herbaceous habit, a generally decumbent growth form, and a predilection for pine-oak forests. The yellowish corollas that contrast with the large, reddish calyx lobes readily distinguish, in part, *C. glabella* from its close relatives to the south. The preferred pine-oak understory may include also an open, grass-poor, undisturbed setting. This contrasts with *C. caribaea*, which grows in the vicinity of *C. glabella* and appears to inhabit similar but more disturbed or grassy settings. *Coursetia glabella* appears to be rare in Arizona, occurring only in Pima and Santa Cruz counties.

4. Coursetia caribaea (Jacquin) Lavin in C. H. Stirton, Advances Legume Syst. 3, 63. 1987 • Anil falso

Galega caribaea Jacquin, Select. Stirp. Amer. Hist., 212, plate 125. 1763; *Cracca caribaea* (Jacquin) Bentham

Varieties 8 (1 in the flora): Arizona, Mexico, West Indies, Central America, South America.

Coursetia caribaea ranges from a shrub to subshrub or herb. Its form is associated with the extent of habitat disturbance; herbaceous forms are recent colonizers or results from individual perturbation, where resprouts from perennial rootstocks have yet to accumulate much woody tissue.

4a. Coursetia caribaea (Jacquin) Lavin var. **sericea** (A. Gray) Lavin, Syst. Bot. Monogr. 21: 122. 1988

Cracca edwardsii A. Gray var. *sericea* A. Gray, Proc. Amer. Acad. Arts 17: 201. 1882

Subshrubs or, rarely, herbs, 0.1–0.6[–3] m. **Roots** with fusiform-tuberous thickenings [diffuse and without thickenings]. **Leaves** odd-pinnate, 2.5–15 cm; stipules subulate, 3–12 × 1 mm; petiole 0.5–3 cm, sericeous; rachis canaliculate; leaflets [3–]7–13[–27], petiolules 1 mm, glabrate, blades narrowly to widely elliptic, 10–100 × 3–50 mm (terminal leaflet distinctly larger), base and apex rounded, surfaces glabrate to densely sericeous, abaxial with reddish brown tannin deposits concentrated toward center of blade between veins. **Racemes** from axils of leaves on young twigs, rachis 1.5–3.5 times length of subtending leaf [much shorter to as long as subtending leaf], nodes [1–]20–30, internodes usually 3+ mm, axis usually sericeous; bracts caducous, linear-lanceolate, 2–10 × 1 mm. **Pedicels** [1.5–]2–4[–8] mm. **Flowers:** calyx tube 2–3 mm, usually sericeous to hispid, rarely glandular, lobes 2–3[–11] mm, abaxial longer than laterals, adaxial connate, more so than laterals; corolla usually whitish, [tinged pinkish or yellowish], 5–12 mm; filaments subequal. **Legumes** light to dark brownish, 30–55[–95] × 3–4[–7] mm, base blunt, not dorsiventrally constricted between seeds, with linear transverse impressions between seeds on lateral surface, apex acute, often terminating in persistent style base, usually glabrous or woolly, rarely glandular. **Seeds** 5–30. $2n$ = 16.

Flowering mid–late summer. Open to closed understory of pine-oak forests; 1300–2300 m; Ariz.; Mexico (Chihuahua, Durango, Sinaloa, Sonora).

Variety *sericea* is distinguished geographically from var. *caribaea* by being the northernmost variety, confined to higher elevations in the understory of pine and oak woodlands of Arizona and adjacent Mexico in the Sierra Madre Occidental (M. Lavin 1988). Morphologically, var. *sericea* is distinguished by its often glandular inflorescence rachis, often with 20–30 nodes and a length of 1.5–3.5 times that of the subtending leaf. It is one of the forms of *Coursetia caribaea* that has leaves with more than seven leaflets, each of which forms distinctive reticulate tannin deposits abaxially; the tannin deposits in this variety are consistently present as dark purple reticulations concentrated towards the center of the leaflets.

Plants from Puerto Rico and the Virgin Islands are referred to as var. *caribaea*, which is morphologically variable and widespread in Mesoamerica (M. Lavin 1988). In contrast with var. *sericea* in Arizona and adjacent Mexico, var. *caribaea* in the Antilles produces eglandular inflorescences distinctly shorter than the subtending leaf and leaflets that do not accumulate tannin deposits. Notably, var. *caribaea* extends from northern South America through the Lesser Antilles into Puerto Rico, the Virgin Islands, and Hispaniola. This species has not yet been recorded from Cuba and Jamaica in spite of its abundance in the Yucatán Peninsula (R. Duno de Stefano et al. 2010).

130. PETERIA A. Gray, Smithsonian Contr. Knowl. 3(5): 50. 1852 • [For Robert Peter, 1805–1894, American naturalist in Kentucky]

Matt Lavin

Herbs, perennial, armed. **Stems** usually erect to ascending, rarely scandent, young growth ± sericeous. **Leaves** alternate, odd-pinnate; stipules present, persistent, spinescent; rachis canaliculate; petiolate; leaflets 7–31, usually opposite, rarely alternate, stipels absent, blade margins entire, surfaces glabrate to sericeous or strigose. **Inflorescences** 8–100+-flowered, leaf-opposed appearing terminal, racemes; bracts present, persistent, subulate, sometimes spine-tipped, bracteoles absent. **Flowers** papilionaceous; calyx tubular, lobes 5; corolla whitish, sometimes with purplish tinge, 14–22 mm, glabrous; stamens 10, diadelphous; anthers basifixed, relatively small, dehiscing longitudinally; style glabrous, with pollen brush tufted distally; stigma terminal, capitate, ciliate. **Fruits** legumes, sessile, laterally compressed, linear [elliptic], elastically dehiscent, glabrous. **Seeds** 2–5[–7], cylindric; hilum apical. x = 8, 9.

Species 4 (2 in the flora): w, sc United States, Mexico.

Peteria is native to the Chihuahuan and Great Basin deserts and nearby regions, and to Mexican pine forests (M. Lavin and M. Sousa S. 1995).

Peteria is distinguished from other temperate herbaceous legume genera by the combination of terminal racemes, spinescent stipels, and cylindric (or at least not strongly compressed) seeds. Plants in *Peteria* produce edible tubers borne from rhizomes.

1. Leaflet blades usually broadly elliptic to orbiculate, rarely narrowly elliptic, 12–21 mm; racemes congested, flowering internodes 1–5(–12) mm, usually with more than 2 consecutive flowers simultaneously at anthesis; banners 16–22 mm; n Arizona, Idaho, Nevada, adjacent California, Utah. . . . . 1. *Peteria thompsoniae*
1. Leaflet blades linear to narrowly elliptic, 3–6(–9) mm; racemes loose, flowering internodes (3–)5–35 mm, rarely with more than 1 flower reaching anthesis at a time; banners 14–16 mm; n Arizona, New Mexico, adjacent sw Colorado, Texas. . . . . 2. *Peteria scoparia*

1. Peteria thompsoniae S. Watson, Amer. Naturalist 7: 300. 1873 (as thompsonae) • Thompson's peteria [E] [F]

Peteria nevadensis Tidestrom

Herbs to 1 m. **Leaves** (5.5–)7–15.5 cm; stipules subulate, 4–6 × 1 mm; leaflets (9–)15–31, blades usually broadly elliptic to orbiculate, rarely narrowly elliptic, (6–)12–21 × (4–)7–13 mm, apex rounded, surfaces glabrate to sericeous. **Racemes** congested, usually with more than 2 consecutive flowers reaching anthesis simultaneously, nodes often 20–100+, internodes 1–5(–12) mm; bracts 5–11 × 0.5–1 mm. **Pedicels** 2–3 mm. **Flowers:** calyx tube (6–)7–11 mm, strigose to sericeous, lobes 7–11 mm; banner 16–22 mm. **Fruits** 40–65 × 6–7 mm. $2n$ = 16, 18.

Flowering early summer. Open, dry shrubby vegetation; 800–1800 m; Ariz., Calif., Idaho, Nev., Utah.

Peteria thompsoniae is found in the northeastern Mojave Desert, western Colorado Plateau, Great Basin Desert, and southeastern Columbia Plateau.

Populations of *Peteria thompsoniae* in northern Arizona (Mohave County) are distinctive in having a longer flowering season (end of April through August), leaflets usually more numerous (25–31), and leaflet surfaces consistently more glabrate and bearing more scattered tannin deposits than in populations from elsewhere. The flowers in these populations have a generally smaller calyx tube (6–7 mm) and a greater number of ovules per ovary (10–12). Populations from southern Utah (Kane and Washington counties) have leaves similar to those of the Arizona populations in that they tend to be more distinctly marked with finely scattered tannin deposits and have glabrate to sparsely strigose surfaces, but leaflet number per leaf is not as consistently high as in the Arizona populations. Populations from eastern Utah (Emery, San Juan, and Wayne counties) are distinct in having narrowly elliptic leaflets with at least adaxial surfaces glabrate (M. Lavin and M. Sousa S. 1995).

2. Peteria scoparia A. Gray, Smithsonian Contr. Knowl. 3(5): 50. 1852 • Rush peteria

Herbs to 0.8 m. **Leaves** 4–5 cm; stipules subulate, 3–5 × 1 mm; leaflets 11–13, blades linear to narrowly elliptic, 3–6(–9) × 1–2(–9) mm, apex acute, surfaces glabrate to strigose; terminal pinna often reduced to spinose seta. **Racemes** loose, rarely with more than 1 flower reaching anthesis simultaneously, nodes 8–20, internodes (3–)5–35 mm; bracts 3–5 × 0.5–1 mm. **Pedicels** 3–8 mm. **Flowers:** calyx tube 5.5–7 mm, glabrate to strigose, lobes 2–4 mm; banner 14–16 mm. **Fruits** 35–50(–62) × 5–6 mm. $2n$ = 18.

Flowering summer. Open, dry shrubby vegetation, shrub-grasslands; 1000–2000 m; Ariz., Colo., N.Mex., Tex.; Mexico (Chihuahua, Coahuila).

Peteria scoparia occurs in the Chihuahuan Desert, eastern Colorado Plateau, and intervening desert areas.

Peteria scoparia occasionally has even-pinnate leaves by the reduction of the terminal leaflet to a spine. Evenly pinnate leaves are also found in related legume genera including *Olneya* and *Sesbania* and in certain species of *Coursetia* and *Poitea* Ventenat; no spines are present in these genera. *Peteria scoparia* does not necessarily have early-deciduous leaflets. Specimens from southwestern Colorado and the northernmost populations in Arizona and New Mexico display more luxuriant foliage that approaches *P. thompsoniae*. Although these northernmost specimens of *P. scoparia* are vegetatively very similar to *P. thompsoniae*, they have inflorescences with widely spaced flowers, banners to 16 mm, and leaflets to 4 mm wide (M. Lavin and M. Sousa S. 1995).

131. GENISTIDIUM I. M. Johnston, J. Arnold Arbor. 22: 113. 1941 • Brushpea [Tribe *Genisteae* and Greek *-idion*, diminutive, alluding to resemblance in gross habit]

Matt Lavin

Shrubs, armed. **Stems** erect to ascending or scandent, broomlike, thorn-tipped, young growth sericeous. **Leaves** alternate, unifoliolate or odd-pinnate; stipules present, caducous or persistent, subspinescent; petiolate; leaflets 1 or 3, blade margins entire, surfaces usually sericeous, sometimes sparsely so. **Inflorescences** mostly solitary flowers, axillary, in distal unifoliolate leaves; bracts present; bracteoles absent. **Flowers** papilionaceous; calyx zygomorphic, campanulate, lobes 5; corolla yellowish; stamens 10, diadelphous; anthers basifixed; style glabrous basally, with pollen brush uniform in distal ½; stigma terminal, capitate, ciliate. **Fruits** legumes, sessile, laterally compressed, linear, elastically dehiscent, sericeous. **Seeds** 1–3(–6), lenticular; hilum apical. $x = 8$.

Species 1: Texas, n Mexico.

Genistidium is native to the Chihuahuan Desert in western Texas and adjacent Mexico. It is readily distinguished from other woody native North American papilionoid genera by the combination of trifoliolate vegetative leaves and unifoliolate leaves on young branch ends that often harbor a solitary flower. The brushy or broomlike growth habit also is distinctive (M. Lavin and M. Sousa S. 1995).

1. Genistidium dumosum I. M. Johnston, J. Arnold Arbor. 22: 113. 1941 C F

Shrubs to 1 m. **Leaves** 0.7–2(–3) cm; stipules subulate, 1–2 × 0.5 mm; petiole 0.2–0.6 cm, strigose; rachis canaliculate; petiolules 1 mm, glabrate; leaflet blades linear to narrowly oblanceolate, 5–20(–25) × 2–6(–8) mm, base attenuate to rounded, apex rounded. **Inflorescences:** bracts caducous, linear-lanceolate, 1–1.5 × 1 mm. **Pedicels** 1.5–2.5 mm. **Flowers:** calyx tube 2.5–3.5 mm, sericeous, lobes 3–4 mm, abaxial ones longer, adaxial 2 slightly more connate with each other than with laterals; corolla 6–8 mm, glabrous; filaments subequal; anthers to 1 mm, dehiscing longitudinally; pistil densely sericeous. **Fruits** light to dark grayish brown, 15–30 × 4–6 mm, base blunt, apex acute, often terminating in persistent style base. $2n = 32$.

Flowering summer. Open, dry shrubby vegetation; of conservation concern; 900–1200 m; Tex.; Mexico (Coahuila, Nuevo León).

Genistidium dumosum comprises three disjunct population centers, one in western Texas (Brewster County), the others in west-central Coahuila and southern Nuevo León (M. Lavin and M. Sousa S. 1995). By all indications, populations are few and small, and whether these three centers represent distinct taxa remains unsettled.

132. SPHINCTOSPERMUM Rose, Contr. U.S. Natl. Herb. 10: 107, plate 34. 1906 • Hourglass peaseed [Greek *sphinktos*, constricted, and *sperma*, seed, alluding to form resembling miniature vertebra]

Matt Lavin

Herbs, annual, unarmed. **Stems** erect to ascending, young growth strigose. **Leaves** alternate, unifoliolate; stipules present, persistent; sessile; blade margins entire, surfaces glabrate. **Inflorescences** solitary flowers, axillary, in leaf axils distally on branches; bracts present, caducous, bracteoles absent. **Flowers** papilionaceous; calyx campanulate, lobes 5; corolla pinkish; stamens 10, diadelphous; anthers basifixed; style glabrous basally, with pollen brush uniform distally; stigma terminal, capitate, ciliate. **Fruits** legumes, sessile, laterally compressed, linear, elastically dehiscent, glabrous. **Seeds** 3–12, 4-angled; with hilum recessed in a central constriction typically surrounding entire seed. $x = 8$.

Species 1: Arizona, Mexico.

Sphinctospermum is native to the Sonoran Desert in Arizona and adjacent Mexico and to Pacific coastal dry forests in Mexico, including southern Baja California, where it is locally abundant but not often collected (M. Lavin 1990; Lavin and M. Sousa S. 1995).

Sphinctospermum is readily distinguished by its annual habit, unifoliolate, linear-lanceolate leaves, and solitary flowers measuring less than 10 mm. Such morphological distinctions greatly obscured the relationships of the genus until the advent of molecular phylogenetics (M. Lavin and J. J. Doyle 1991).

SELECTED REFERENCES Lavin, M. 1990. The genus *Sphinctospermum* (Leguminosae): Taxonomy and tribal relationships as inferred from a cladistic analysis of traditional data. Syst. Bot. 15: 544–559. Lavin, M. and J. J. Doyle. 1991. Tribal relationships of *Sphinctospermum* (Leguminosae): Integration of traditional and chloroplast DNA data. Syst. Bot. 16: 162–172.

1. Sphinctospermum constrictum (S. Watson) Rose, Contr. U.S. Natl. Herb. 10: 107. 1906 [F]

Tephrosia constricta S. Watson, Proc. Amer. Acad. Arts 24: 46. 1889

Herbs to 8 dm. **Leaves** (1–)2–8(–9) cm; stipules subulate, 1–2 × 0.5 mm; blade linear-lanceolate. **Inflorescence bracts** linear-lanceolate, 1–2 × 0.5 mm. **Pedicels** 1–2 mm. **Flowers:** calyx tube 1.5–2.5 mm, glabrate, lobes 1.5–2.5 mm, proximalmost longer than lateral ones, adaxial 2 slightly more connate than lateral ones; corolla 5–6 mm, glabrous; filaments subequal; anthers relatively small, dehiscing longitudinally; pistil glabrous. **Legumes** light brown, terete, 20–30 × 2–3 mm, base blunt, apex acute, often terminating in persistent style base. $2n = 16$.

Flowering Aug–Nov. Disturbed areas; 50–1700 m; Ariz.; w, s Mexico.

In the flora area, *Sphinctospermum constrictum* is known from Cochise, Pima, Pinal, and Santa Cruz counties.

The inflorescence of a solitary flower of *Sphinctospermum constrictum* includes a very short rachis and floral bract subtending the pedicel. Sometimes, a short axillary shoot bearing a flower is borne from this same axil. This results in two flowers from a leaf axil along the main stem. The unifoliolate leaves and solitary flowers are superficially similar to those of 131. *Genistidium*, and molecular phylogenetic analysis suggests that these two are sister genera (R. Duno de Stefano et al. 2010).

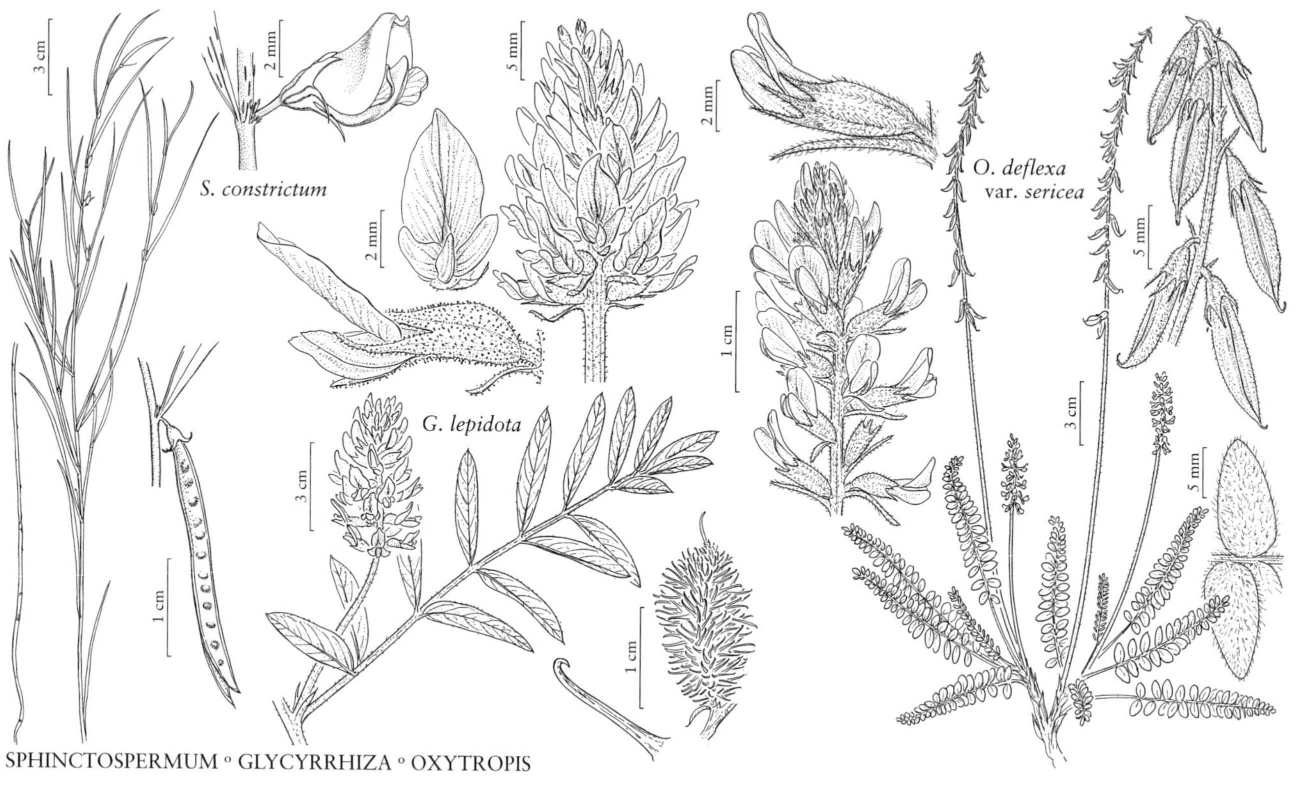

SPHINCTOSPERMUM ◦ GLYCYRRHIZA ◦ OXYTROPIS

133. GLYCYRRHIZA Linnaeus, Sp. Pl. 2: 741. 1753; Gen. Pl. ed. 5, 330. 1754 • Licorice [Greek *glykeros*, sweet, and *rhiza*, root, alluding to source of licorice]

Debra K. Trock

Herbs, perennial, unarmed, aromatic; rhizomes branched, roots deep, fleshy. **Stems** erect, single or several, unbranched or branched, sparsely pubescent, glandular, sometimes glutinous. **Leaves** alternate, odd-pinnate; stipules present, ovate to lanceolate, those of primary leaves broadly ovate; petiolate; leaflets 9–19, blade margins entire, surfaces pubescent, glandular-punctate. **Inflorescences** 15–50+-flowered, axillary, racemes; bracts present, lanceolate. **Flowers** papilionaceous; calyx campanulate, slightly bilabiate, lobes 5, 2 adaxial lobes partly connate; corolla yellow-white, purple-tinged, or bluish, banner erect to slightly recurved, lanceolate to narrowly ovate or oblong, 11–15 mm; wings oblong, adherent to subacute keel, both progressively shorter than banner; stamens 10, diadelphous; anthers dorsifixed, dimorphic, thecae of smaller ones often connate distally; ovary echinulate; style incurved, glabrous, stigma capitate. **Fruits** legumes, brown or purplish, stipitate, compressed, turgid, ellipsoid or oblong, indehiscent, glabrous or setaceous, setae hooked. **Seeds** 2–4, brown, obovoid, incurved proximal to hilum. $x = 8$.

Species ca. 18 (2 in the flora): North America, Mexico, South America, Europe, Asia, n Africa, Australia.

SELECTED REFERENCES Boe, A. and R. Wynia. 1985. Seed predation, seedling emergence, and rhizome characteristics of American licorice. J. Range Managem. 38: 400–402. Gibson, M. R. 1978. *Glycyrrhiza* in old and new perspectives. Lloydia 41: 348–354.

1. Leaflet blades broadly ovate, apices narrowly rounded to retuse; racemes 7–13+ cm; corollas mostly bluish purple-tinged; legumes glabrous. . . . . 1. *Glycyrrhiza glabra*
1. Leaflet blades narrowly ovate, lanceolate, or elliptic, apices mucronate; racemes 4–7 cm; corollas yellow-white or purple-tinged; legumes setaceous (setae hooked) . . . . .2. *Glycyrrhiza lepidota*

1. Glycyrrhiza glabra Linnaeus, Sp. Pl. 2: 742. 1753 • Cultivated or European licorice [I]

Herbs 5–10 dm, glabrous or finely pubescent along stems, petioles, and inflorescences. **Stems** with punctate glands. **Leaflet blades** broadly ovate, 25–50+ × 7–23 mm, apex narrowly rounded to retuse, surfaces usually glabrous, rarely sparsely pubescent along midvein. **Peduncles** 1/2 as long as racemes. **Racemes** open, 7–13+ cm. **Corollas** mostly bluish or purple-tinged. **Fruits** glabrous. 2*n* = 16.

Flowering late May–Jul. Moist, rocky hillsides, waste grounds, alkaline soils; 50–900 m; introduced; Calif., Nev., Utah; Europe; introduced also in temperate Asia, n Africa.

Glycyrrhiza glabra has been cultivated in Europe for over 2000 years. Theophrastus (371–287 BCE) mentioned that it is useful for treating asthma, coughs, and diseases of the lungs. European colonists probably introduced the species to the United States.

2. Glycyrrhiza lepidota Pursh, Fl. Amer. Sept. 2: 480. 1813 • American licorice [F] [W]

Glycyrrhiza glutinosa Nuttall; *G. lepidota* var. *glutinosa* (Nuttall) S. Watson

Herbs 3–12 dm, sparsely to densely glandular-pubescent. **Stems** with stipitate or punctate glands. **Leaflet blades** narrowly ovate, lanceolate, or elliptic, 25–50 × 5–15 mm, apex mucronate, surfaces sparsely tomentose. **Peduncles** nearly equal to racemes. **Racemes** compact, 4–7 cm. **Corollas** yellow-white or purple-tinged. **Fruits** setaceous. 2*n* = 16.

Flowering Apr–Aug. Disturbed sites, woodlands, prairies and meadows, damp, well-drained soils; 30–2300 m; Alta., B.C., Man., Ont., Sask.; Ariz., Ark., Calif., Colo., Conn., Idaho, Ill., Ind., Iowa, Kans., Maine, Mass., Minn., Mo., Mont., Nebr., Nev., N.Mex., N.Y., N.Dak., Okla., Oreg., Pa., R.I., S.Dak., Tex., Utah, Va., Wash., Wis., Wyo.; Mexico (Baja California).

Roots of *Glycyrrhiza lepidota* are edible raw or cooked; they contain glycyrrhizin, a compound that is said to be 50 times sweeter than sugar. Native Americans used this species for treatment of chest pains, coughs, diarrhea, earaches, fevers, stomachaches, and toothaches. The active ingredient may also increase blood pressure and, if excessively consumed, may cause hypertension and edema.

134. OXYTROPIS de Candolle, Astragalogia (qto.), 24, 66; (fol.), 19, 53, plates 2–8. 1802, name conserved • Locoweed, oxytrope [Greek *oxys*, sharp, and *tropis*, keel, alluding to pointed keel petals]

Stanley L. Welsh

Herbs, perennial, usually with very short internodes and appearing acaulescent, rarely caulescent, with 1 or more internodes apparent, unarmed or with spinescent leaf bases; usually cespitose, rarely pulvinate-cespitose or loosely matted; sometimes glandular-viscid, pubescent, hairs usually basifixed (malpighian in O. *lambertii*); from taproot or caudex. **Stems** spreading to ascending, usually pubescent, rarely glabrescent or glabrous. **Leaves** basally clustered or cauline, alternate, mostly odd-pinnate; stipules present, sometimes persistent, adnate to petiole, often connate-sheathing; petiolate, petiole sometimes persistent as marcescent thatch on caudex, rarely as pungent spines; leaflets 1–45(–70), usually opposite, subopposite, scattered (irregularly spaced), or fasciculate, rarely alternate or verticillate, usually jointed to rachis, blade margins entire, surfaces usually pubescent, sometimes glabrous. **Inflorescences** 1–50-flowered, axillary, racemes (sometimes subcapitate); bract 1; bracteoles usually absent, rarely 2. **Flowers** papilionaceous; calyx usually campanulate or cylindric, rarely inflated-urceolate, lobes 5, sometimes inflated and enclosing legumes, usually ruptured by legume; corolla pink to blue-purple or white to yellowish, 5–25 mm, keel petals shorter than wing petals, tip elongated into porrect beak; stamens 10, diadelphous; anthers dorsifixed; ovary enclosed in staminal sheath; style glabrous. **Fruits** legumes, sessile or stipitate, sometimes tumid or bladdery-inflated, straight, oblong to ellipsoid, ovoid, ovoid-ellipsoid, ovoid-oblong, lanceoloid-ovoid, cylindric, or subcylindric, abaxial suture usually rounded, adaxial suture often sulcate, dehiscent apically or throughout, unilocular or bilocular, or partially bilocular by intrusion of adaxial suture, usually pubescent, rarely glabrous. **Seeds** 3–25, light to dark brown or black, somewhat reniform. $x = 8$.

Species ca. 300 (22 in the flora): North America, Europe, Asia.

Separation of *Oxytropis* from *Astragalus* has long been argued, and the history of the discussion was outlined by R. C. Barneby (1952b) and S. L. Welsh (1989). The main distinctions lie in the inequilateral leaf bases of *Oxytropis* (as opposed to equilateral in *Astragalus*), and the porrect keel petals found in all species of *Oxytropis* and not in *Astragalus*. Molecular phylogenetic studies have supported the distinctness of the two genera (M. F. Wojciechowski 2005; A. D. Tekpinar et al. 2016).

Several relatively recent treatments of the taxonomy and nomenclature of *Oxytropis* differ greatly in their conclusions. Among these are the revision by S. L. Welsh (2001), publications by B. A. Jurtzev (1986, 1993b), J. M. Gillett et al. (2007), and the Pan-Arctic Flora (http://panarcticflora.org/).

At least some species of *Oxytropis* are highly toxic to grazing animals, due to the presence of swainsonine in their tissues (L. F. James et al. 1989).

Oxytropis revoluta Ledebour was attributed to Alaska by E. Hultén (1968) but has not yet been found in the flora area. It occurs in Russian islands immediately west of the United States/Russia border.

SELECTED REFERENCES Barneby, R. C. 1952b. A revision of the North American species of *Oxytropis* DC. Proc. Calif. Acad. Sci., ser. 4, 27: 177–312. Gray, A. 1884b. A revision of the North American species of *Oxytropis* DC. Proc. Amer. Acad. Arts 20: 1–7. Welsh, S. L. 2001. Revision of North American Species of *Oxytropis* de Candolle (Leguminosae). Orem.

1. Plants usually caulescent (1+ internodes apparent); legumes subsessile or stipitate, pendulous or spreading-declined.
   2. Leaflets 11–17, blades broadly lanceolate to oblanceolate, apices acute or subacute; racemes 20–40-flowered; introduced, Idaho, Montana, North Dakota, Utah, Wyoming . . . . 1. *Oxytropis riparia*
   2. Leaflets (9–)15–41, blades ovate, lanceolate, or lanceolate-oblong, apices acute to obtuse; racemes (2–)4–25[–30+]-flowered; native, widespread in w North America . . . . 2. *Oxytropis deflexa* (in part)
1. Plants acaulescent or appearing acaulescent (internodes concealed by leaf bases); legumes sessile, subsessile, or stipitate, erect, spreading, or spreading-declined.
   3. Legumes spreading-declined . . . . 2. *Oxytropis deflexa* (in part)
   3. Legumes erect or spreading.
      4. Base of herb sheathed with reddish, purplish, or purplish brown stipules.
         5. Corollas yellowish . . . . 20. *Oxytropis maydelliana*
         5. Corollas purplish.
            6. Racemes 1–3-flowered; legumes stipitate, reclining on ground at maturity, usually at least 3 times longer than wide . . . . 6. *Oxytropis kokrinensis*
            6. Racemes 5–8-flowered; legumes sessile, held aloft at maturity, to 3 times longer than wide . . . . 19. *Oxytropis kobukensis* (in part)
      4. Base of herb with light tan or grayish stipules, sometimes black in *O. campestris*).

[7. Shifted to left margin.—Ed.]

7. Leaflets usually 1 or 3, rarely 5, decurrent or obscurely articulated with rachis . . . . . 3. *Oxytropis mertensiana*
7. Leaflets (1–)5–45(–70), jointed to rachis.
    8. Plants glandular-viscid (especially stipules and calyces); bracts glabrous, except margins ciliate . . . . 14. *Oxytropis borealis*
    8. Plants not glandular-viscid; bracts pilose or villous.
        9. Racemes usually 1–5-flowered; corollas pink, purple, or bluish, not yellow, ochroleucous, or white (except in white morphs).
            10. Corollas (14–)16–22 mm; leaflets 9+, alternate, opposite, subopposite, widely scattered, or fasciculate; stipular margins with clavate processes mixed with cilia . . . . 21. *Oxytropis arctica* (in part)
            10. Corollas 6–20(–24) mm; leaflets 5–17, widely scattered or opposite, not fasciculate; stipular margins ciliate, without clavate processes (except in some *O. nigrescens*).
                11. Legumes erect, usually black-pilose, rarely glabrous or white-pilose; stipules usually prominent, glabrous or sparsely pilose abaxially, stramineous; interior Alaska, Yukon, Northwest Territories, British Columbia . . . . 4. *Oxytropis scammaniana*
                11. Legumes spreading to ascending, glabrous or pilosulous; stipules not especially conspicuous, pilose, silky-pilose, villous, or glabrous abaxially, whitish to light tan, grayish, or black; widespread.
                    12. Calyces usually conspicuously swollen or inflated at anthesis, investing legumes or nearly so (if not conspicuously inflated, *O. lagopus* var. *atropurpurea*, calyx villous to shaggy-villous); Alberta, Colorado, Idaho, Montana, Nebraska, South Dakota, Utah, Wyoming.
                        13. Legumes strigose-canescent, leathery, rigid at maturity; Wyoming . . . . 17. *Oxytropis nana* (in part)
                        13. Legumes villous, papery, not rigid at maturity; Alberta, Colorado, Idaho, Montana, Nebraska, South Dakota, Utah, Wyoming.
                            14. Bracts ovate to broadly lanceolate, flat; plants pulvinate-cespitose; Colorado, Nebraska, Utah, Wyoming. . . . . . . 11. *Oxytropis multiceps*
                            14. Bracts ovate-lanceolate to lanceolate, margins involute; plants cespitose but not pulvinate; Alberta, Idaho, Montana, South Dakota, Wyoming . . . . 12. *Oxytropis lagopus* (in part)
                    12. Calyces slightly inflated at anthesis, not investing legume at maturity; n Canada to sw United States.
                        15. Legumes 10–18(–23) mm, sessile or subsessile, glabrous or minutely strigose or strigulose, unilocular; racemes 1 or 2 (or 3)-flowered; Alaska, British Columbia, Yukon . . . . 8. *Oxytropis huddelsonii*
                        15. Legumes (7–)9–38(–40) mm, sessile, subsessile, or stipitate, usually pilose, pilosulous, villous, villous-pilose, hirtellous, strigulose, or strigose-pilosulous, rarely glabrous, unilocular, subunilocular, sub-bilocular, or bilocular; racemes 1–12-flowered; widespread.
                            16. Legumes ovoid-ellipsoid or bladdery-inflated, stipitate; leaflet blades falcate . . . . 5. *Oxytropis podocarpa*
                            16. Legumes oblong, oblong-ellipsoid, lanceoloid-ovoid, ovoid, or bladdery-inflated, usually sessile, subsessile, or short-stipitate (stipitate in *O. nigrescens* var. *lonchopoda*); leaflet blades not falcate.
                                17. Corollas 12–20 mm; leaflet surfaces usually silky- or silvery-canescent, villous, strigose, or loosely pilose, rarely glabrous; n North America . . . . 7. *Oxytropis nigrescens*
                                17. Corollas usually 6–12.5 mm (to 17 mm in *O. oreophila* var. *jonesii*); leaflet surfaces pilose, villous-pilose, or silky-pilose; w United States.

18. Racemes 3–5-flowered; legumes ellipsoid, cylindroid, bladdery-inflated . . . . 9. *Oxytropis oreophila* (in part)
18. Racemes 1–3 (or 4)-flowered; legumes oblong to lanceoloid-ovoid or ovoid, not bladdery-inflated . . 10. *Oxytropis parryi*

[9. Shifted to left margin.—Ed.]

9. Racemes usually 6–many-flowered; corollas pink, pink-purple, lavender, bluish purple, blue, purple, pinkish violet, if racemes fewer-flowered, then corollas yellow, ochroleucous, or white.
    19. Hairs malpighian; corollas usually pink-purple, rarely white. . . . . 18. *Oxytropis lambertii*
    19. Hairs basifixed; corollas pink, pink-purple, lavender, bluish purple, blue, purple, pinkish violet, white, whitish, yellowish, or creamy white.
        20. Corollas usually 6–12.5 mm (to 17 mm in var. *jonesii*); legumes bladdery-inflated; Arizona, California, Nevada, Utah . . . . 9. *Oxytropis oreophila* (in part)
        20. Corollas (10–)12–27(–28) mm; legumes cylindric, subcylindric, ovoid, ovoid-oblong, or ovoid-acuminate, not bladdery-inflated; Canada, w United States, not including Arizona or California.
            21. Calyces swollen at anthesis, accrescent and enclosing fruit.
                22. Calyces villous to shaggy-villous, hairs mixed blackish and white, appearing gray; legumes villous, papery to nearly membranous; Alberta, Idaho, Montana, South Dakota, Wyoming . . . . 12. *Oxytropis lagopus* (in part)
                22. Calyces densely shaggy-hirsute and subtomentose, hairs white; legumes strigose-canescent, firm; Wyoming. . . . . 17. *Oxytropis nana* (in part)
            21. Calyces not or slightly swollen in fruit, usually ruptured by fruit.
                23. Corollas white or yellowish.
                    24. Corollas (10–)12–20(–23) mm; leaflets 7–45; legumes papery to leathery or membranous . . . . 15. *Oxytropis campestris* (in part)
                    24. Corollas (14–)16–27(–28) mm; leaflets 7–19(–21); legumes fleshy when fresh, becoming leathery or almost woody and rigid, or thinly papery.
                        25. Leaflets 7–19(–21), blade surfaces sericeous, often densely so; racemes subcapitate to elongate, 5–20+-flowered; legumes fleshy when fresh, becoming leathery or almost woody and rigid . . . . 16. *Oxytropis sericea*
                        25. Leaflets 11–17, blade surfaces pilose; racemes relatively short to subcapitate, 2–10-flowered; legumes thinly papery . . . 21. *Oxytropis arctica* (in part)
                23. Corollas pinkish or purplish (rarely creamy white in *O. splendens*).
                    26. Calyces with blackish hairs and long, white hairs, appearing gray; leaves 1–10 cm; Alberta, Idaho, Montana, South Dakota, Wyoming. . . . . 12. *Oxytropis lagopus* (in part)
                    26. Calyces with white hairs, if with both blackish and white, then not from Wyoming or adjacent states; leaves 1.5–28 cm; Alaska east to Newfoundland and Labrador, south to New Mexico.
                        27. Corollas 17–25 mm; stipules papery or membranous, light tan or pale gray; Colorado, Idaho, Montana, Nevada, Saskatchewan, Utah, Wyoming. . . . . .13. *Oxytropis besseyi*
                        27. Corollas 11–22(–23) mm; stipules rigid, fragile, or membranous, purplish, yellowish, or grayish; widespread.
                            28. Corollas (14–)16–22 mm; stipular margins ciliate, with clavate processes; n, w Alaska, Manitoba, Northwest Territories, Nunavut, Yukon.
                                29. Stipules firm, usually purplish, usually well separated on elongate caudex branches; leaflets not fasciculate; Kobuk River drainage, Alaska. . . . . 19. *Oxytropis kobukensis* (in part)
                                29. Stipules fragile, grayish or yellowish, strongly imbricate; leaflets usually fasciculate; Alaska, Manitoba, Northwest Territories, Nunavut, Yukon . . . . 21. *Oxytropis arctica* (in part)

[28. Shifted to left margin.—Ed.]

28. Corollas 11–20(–23) mm; stipular margins ciliate or not, with or without clavate processes; n, nw North America, seldom in arctic.
    30. Leaflets fasciculate or not; corollas 11–20(–23) mm, calyces tubes (3.7–)4–9 mm; stipules glabrous, strigose, or pilose abaxially becoming glabrate, with or without marginal clavate processes; Alaska, se, n Yukon, Alberta, n, c British Columbia, North Dakota . . . . 15. *Oxytropis campestris* (in part)
    30. Leaflets usually fasciculate, rarely verticillate; corollas 12–16 mm, calyces tubes 5–6.5 mm; stipules silky-pilose abaxially, without marginal clavate processes; e Alaska, s Yukon, e to Hudson Bay, s to Colorado . . . . .22. *Oxytropis splendens*

1. **Oxytropis riparia** Litvinov, Sched. Herb. Fl. Ross. 6: 98. 1908 • Riparian oxytrope [I]

Plants coarse, cespitose, clumps to 1 m diam., caulescent, (20–) 60–100 cm, herbage minutely strigose; stems with 1 or 2+ internodes. **Leaves** subsessile, 5–15 cm; stipules foliaceous, light tan or grayish proximally, green distally, well separated on stem, 5–10 mm, sparsely to densely appressed to spreading pilose abaxially, margins ciliate; leaflets 11–17, alternate to subopposite, blades broadly lanceolate to oblanceolate, 10–38 × 3–12 mm, apex acute or subacute, surfaces sparsely to densely appressed to spreading-pilose abaxially, margins ciliate. **Peduncles** 8–15 cm, surpassing leaves, axis 3–20 cm in fruit, sparsely strigose to moderately pilose; bract linear-lanceolate, sparsely to densely pilose. **Racemes** (18–) 20–50-flowered, elongate, lax, subsecund. **Calyces** scarcely enlarging in fruit, campanulate, white-strigose; tube 2–2.5 mm, lobes 1.2–1.5 mm. **Corollas** purplish, 6–7 mm. **Legumes** pendulous, stipitate, stipe 1–2.5 mm, sulcate adaxially, narrowly oblong, 15–20 × 4–5 mm, unilocular, papery, white- and/or black-strigulose. 2*n* = 16, 32.

Flowering early–mid summer. Saline riparian lowlands with rush, greasewood, and cottonwood; 1100–2300 m; introduced; Idaho, Mont., N.Dak., Utah, Wyo.; Asia (Turkmenistan).

Oxytropis riparia evidently was first discovered on ranches near Waterloo and Twin Bridges, in the valleys of the Jefferson and Ruby rivers in Madison County, Montana. The species is currently spreading and is to be expected at widely distributed locations throughout much of the American West. Plants at the Seedskadee National Wildlife Refuge, Wyoming, are eaten by sage grouse; they seem to prefer the flower buds but eat all parts of the plant.

2. **Oxytropis deflexa** (Pallas) de Candolle, Astragalogia (qto.), 28, 96; (fol.), 22, 77. 1802 • Stemmed oxytrope, oxytrope à fruits retombants [F]

Astragalus deflexus Pallas, Acta Acad. Sci. Imp. Petrop. 2: 268, plate 15. 1779; *Aragallus deflexus* (Pallas) A. Heller; *Spiesia deflexa* (Pallas) Kuntze

Plants cespitose, caulescent or subacaulescent, sometimes appearing acaulescent, (5–)7–48 cm, herbage pilose, villous-pilose, long-villous, or sericeous, hairs spreading or retrorse; stems flexuous, with (0 or)1–7 internodes. **Leaves** 2–22 cm; stipules subherbaceous, light tan, grayish, or purplish, well separated on stem, 7–20 mm, ± pilose abaxially, margins ± ciliate; leaflets (9–)15–41, opposite or subopposite, blades ovate, lanceolate, or lanceolate-oblong, 3–25 × 1–8(–11) mm, apex acute to obtuse, surfaces pilose or glabrous adaxially. **Peduncles** 3.5–32(–36) cm, axis 3.5–10 cm in fruit, villous-pilose; bract linear to lanceolate-oblong, pilose. **Racemes** (2–)4–25[–30+]-flowered, extending beyond leaves. **Calyces** campanulate, 3–8 mm, villous-pilose, hairs stiff, black; tube 2–3.5(–4.5) mm, lobes 1.5–5 mm. **Corollas** bright pink-purple, purple, or whitish and sometimes suffused with purple, [lilac or blue-purple], 5–10.5 (–12) mm. **Legumes** spreading-declined, subsessile to short-stipitate, oblong to ellipsoid, 8–18 × 3–4.5 mm, subunilocular, thinly papery, pilosulous, hairs white and/or black. 2*n* = 16.

Varieties 5 (3 in the flora): North America, Europe (Norway), n Asia.

Two European and Asian varieties are known: var. *lapponica* (Wahlenberg) B. Boivin is known from northern Europe; var. *deflexa* is found in Siberia, and can be distinguished from var. *pulcherrima* by elongate racemes, smaller flowers, and slender fruits (S. L. Welsh 1995b).

1. Corollas usually dirty white or variously suffused with purple; racemes usually 10–25-flowered, subcylindric, usually much elongate in fruit; herbage usually conspicuously long-villous; usually of open sites .... 2c. *Oxytropis deflexa* var. *sericea*
1. Corollas bright pink-purple or purple; racemes (2–)4–20-flowered, hemispheric or subcapitate to shortly subcylindric, slightly elongate in fruit; herbage pilose, villous-pilose, or sericeous; often of woods, thickets, or tundra.
   2. Racemes usually 10–20-flowered; herbage copiously and loosely villous-pilose or sericeous .... 2a. *Oxytropis deflexa* var. *pulcherrima*
   2. Racemes usually (2–)4–10-flowered; herbage sparsely pilose, not sericeous .... 2b. *Oxytropis deflexa* var. *foliolosa*

2a. Oxytropis deflexa (Pallas) de Candolle var. **pulcherrima** S. L. Welsh & A. Huber, Great Basin Naturalist 55: 277. 1995 E

Astragalus retroflexus Pallas

Plants caulescent, subacaulescent, or appearing acaulescent; herbage copiously and loosely villous-pilose or sericeous. **Racemes** densely 10–20-flowered, hemispheric or subcapitate to shortly subcylindric, 20–27 mm wide when pressed, usually 1.5–6 cm in fruit, slightly elongate in fruit. **Corollas** bright pink-purple or purple.

Flowering summer. Alpine tundra, spruce-fir, and aspen communities, gravel, meadows; 500–4600 m; Colo., Utah.

2b. Oxytropis deflexa (Pallas) de Candolle var. **foliolosa** (Hooker) Barneby, Leafl. W. Bot. 6: 111. 1951 • Foliose locoweed, oxytrope à folioles nombreuses E

Oxytropis foliolosa Hooker, Fl. Bor.-Amer. 1: 146. 1831; *Aragallus foliolosus* (Hooker) Rydberg; *Astragalus deflexus* Pallas var. *foliolosus* (Hooker) Tidestrom; *O. deflexa* subsp. *foliolosa* (Hooker) Cody

Plants appearing acaulescent, sometimes with 1(or 2) developed internodes; herbage sparsely pilose. **Racemes** densely (2–)4–10-flowered, hemispheric or subcapitate to shortly subcylindric, slightly elongate in fruit, with more flowers. **Corollas** usually bright pink-purple or purple. $2n = 16$.

Flowering summer. Tundra, conifer, aspen, birch, and alder communities, gravel bars, roadsides; 0–3700 m; Alta., B.C., N.B., Nfld. and Labr., N.W.T., Nunavut, Ont., Que., Yukon; Alaska, Idaho, Mont., Nev., Utah, Wyo.

Though usually appearing acaulescent in alpine and shore situations, plants of var. *foliolosa* frequently have one or two evident internodes in lower elevation habitats along stream systems. Specimens intermediate between this and var. *sericea* are not uncommon. Assignment of all specimens to one or the other of the varieties is not always possible. The Pan-Arctic Flora (http://panarcticflora.org/) treats var. *foliolosa* as *Oxytropis deflexa* subsp. *dezhnevii* (Jurtzev) Jurtzev.

2c. Oxytropis deflexa (Pallas) de Candolle var. **sericea** Torrey & A. Gray, Fl. N. Amer. 1: 342. 1838 • Silky locoweed E F

Oxytropis deflexa subsp. *retrorsa* (Fernald) Á. Löve & D. Löve; *O. deflexa* var. *culminis* Jepson; *O. retrorsa* Fernald; *O. retrorsa* var. *sericea* (Torrey & A. Gray) Fernald

Plants caulescent or appearing acaulescent; herbage usually conspicuously long-villous. **Racemes** usually 10–25-flowered, subcylindric, usually much elongate in fruit. **Corollas** usually dirty white or variously suffused with purple.

Flowering summer. Spruce-fir, aspen, willow, alder, and meadow communities; 0–3200 m; Alta., B.C., Man., N.W.T., Nunavut, Ont., Sask., Yukon; Alaska, Calif., Colo., Idaho, Mont., N.Mex., N.Dak., Oreg., Utah, Wash., Wyo.

Variety *sericea* is the common phase of *Oxytropis deflexa* south of the Arctic. The variety is highly variable, especially in size and aspect of flowers. Flowers of some of the variants appear not to open, as if they were cleistogamous. The Pan-Arctic Flora (http://panarcticflora.org/) treats var. *sericea* as *O. deflexa* subsp. *retrorsa*.

3. Oxytropis mertensiana Turczaninow, Bull. Soc. Imp. Naturalistes Moscou 13: 68. 1840 • Mertens's oxytrope

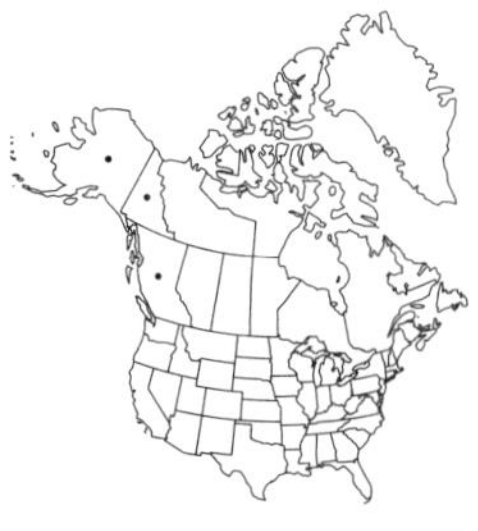

Aragallus mertensianus (Turczaninow) Greene; *Spiesia mertensiana* (Turczaninow) Kuntze

Plants cespitose, appearing acaulescent; caudex subterranean; branches elongate, to 11 cm, covered with persistent stipules. **Leaves** 1–7 cm; stipules membranous, light tan or grayish, glabrous abaxially; leaflets 1 or 3(or 5), mostly continuous with rachis, decurrent or obscurely articulated with rachis, blades elliptic to oblong, 7–25 × 2–5 mm, apex acute, surfaces glabrous abaxially, sparsely pubescent adaxially. **Peduncles** 3–8 cm, sparsely villous-pilose; bract linear, 3–6 mm, black-hirsute. **Racemes** 1- or 2-flowered. **Calyces** campanulate, densely black-pilose; tube 4.8–6.2 mm, lobes 2.1–4.1 mm. **Corollas** pink-purple, 12–16 mm. **Legumes** borne aloft, erect, stipitate, stipe 1.5–2 mm, ovoid- or lanceoloid-oblong, 13–20 × 4–5 mm, subunilocular, pilose, hairs black. $2n = 16$.

Flowering summer. Moist arctic tundra, alpine; 0–1900 m; B.C., Yukon; Alaska; Asia (Russia).

Oxytropis mertensiana is easily distinguished by its unifoliolate primary and trifoliolate secondary leaves, in conjunction with the few-flowered, densely black-pilose inflorescences. The British Columbia record may be an introduction.

4. Oxytropis scammaniana Hultén, Ark. Bot. 33B(1): 4, fig. 2. 1947 • Scamman's oxytrope [E]

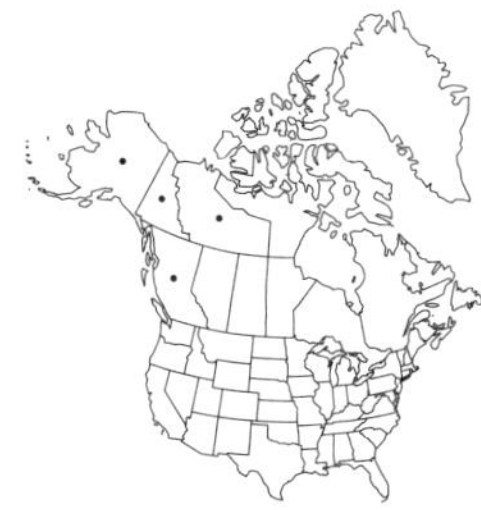

Plants cespitose, low-growing, appearing acaulescent; caudex usually subterranean; branches elongate, often with persistent, stramineous stipules. **Leaves** 2–9 cm; stipules membranous, stramineous, glabrous or sparsely pilose, margins ciliate; leaflets 9–13, opposite, blades lanceolate to elliptic, 4–15(–22) × 1–4(–6) mm, apex acute to obtuse, surfaces sparsely pilose or glabrous. **Peduncles** 2–8 cm, sparsely appressed-pilose, hairs may be black distally; bract lanceolate, black-pilose. **Racemes** (1 or)2 or 3(–5)-flowered. **Calyces** campanulate, densely spreading black-pilose; tube 4.5–6 mm, slightly enlarging, covering less than 1/8 of fruit, lobes 1.5–4(–5.5) mm. **Corollas** usually purplish, rarely white, 12–17(–20) mm. **Legumes** borne aloft, erect, sessile, oblong-ellipsoid, 11–18(–20) × 5–7 mm, subunilocular, membranous, black-pilose or, sometimes, white-pilose, rarely glabrous. $2n = 32$.

Flowering summer. Moist arctic and alpine tundra, heathlands, rocky slopes, talus, scree; 500–2200 m; B.C., N.W.T., Yukon; Alaska.

The inflorescences and fruits of *Oxytropis scammaniana* resemble those of *O. mertensiana*, possibly its nearest ally in North America. *Oxytropis scammaniana* is a species of conservation concern in British Columbia.

5. Oxytropis podocarpa A. Gray, Proc. Amer. Acad. Arts 6: 234. 1864 • Gray's oxytrope, oxytrope à gros fruits [E]

Aragallus inflatus (Hooker) A. Nelson; *A. podocarpus* (A. Gray) A. Nelson; *Oxytropis arctica* R. Brown var. *inflata* Hooker; *O. inflata* (Hooker) Steffen; *Spiesia inflata* (Hooker) Britton; *S. podocarpa* (A. Gray) Kuntze

Plants cespitose, appearing acaulescent; caudex subterranean or superficial; branches sometimes elongate, with persistent, pale stipules and leaf bases. **Leaves** 0.5–6 cm; stipules membranous, stramineous, 7–13 mm, glabrous, margins ciliate; leaflets (5–)9–13, opposite, blades linear-lanceolate to linear, (4–)5–8.5(–12) mm, usually involute and falcate, apex acute, surfaces greenish, sparsely hirsute. **Peduncles** 0.5–5 cm, pubescent; bract ovate to lanceolate, pilose. **Racemes** 1–3-flowered, subcapitate. **Calyces** campanulate, pilose; tube 5–7 mm, lobes (1–)2–3 mm. **Corollas** often purple, sometimes white, 12–15(–19) mm. **Legumes** spreading, stipitate, stipe 1.5–3 mm, ovoid-ellipsoid or bladdery-inflated, 15–25(–38) × 10–17(–20) mm, subunilocular, thin-papery, strigose-pilosulous.

Flowering summer. Rocky alpine ridges, coastal shores; 0–3900 m; Alta., B.C., Nfld. and Labr. (Labr.), Nunavut, Que.; Colo., Mont., Wyo.

Plants with flowers alone are difficult to separate from *Oxytropis nigrescens*; the folded, typically falcate leaflets of *O. podocarpa* are diagnostic. *Oxytropis podocarpa* is a species of conservation concern in Montana.

6. Oxytropis kokrinensis A. E. Porsild, Rhodora 41: 251, plate 553. 1939 • Kokrines oxytrope [E]

Plants cespitose, appearing acaulescent; caudex branches with persistent, purplish brown or reddish purple stipules and petiole bases. **Leaves** 1–5 cm; stipules membranous, purplish brown or reddish brown, sparsely pilose but early glabrate, margins ciliate; leaflets 7 or 9, blades elliptic to lanceolate, 4–6 × 1–2 mm, flat, margins revolute or folded, apex acute, surfaces sparsely hirsute. **Peduncles** 0.5–5 cm, sometimes slightly exceeding leaves, sparsely pilose; bract ovate to lanceolate, hispidulous. **Racemes** 1–3-flowered. **Calyces** campanulate, villous-pilose, hairs white or black; tube 4–6 mm, lobes 2–4 mm. **Corollas** purplish, 12–15(–16) mm. **Legumes** reclining on ground at maturity, stipitate, stipe 1.5–6 mm, inflated, 20–35 × 5–8(–15) mm (usually at least 3 times longer than wide), ± bilocular, short-pilose.

Flowering summer. Ridge tops, alpine fellfields, mountain-avens meadows; 300–1000 m; Alaska.

Oxytropis kokrinensis is a distinctive but obscure species known from about 20 sites in the Kokrines Mountains, the western Brooks Range, and scattered populations across west-central Alaska.

7. **Oxytropis nigrescens** (Pallas) Fischer in A. P. de Candolle and A. L. P. P. de Candolle, Prodr. 2: 278. 1825 • Blackish oxytrope, oxytrope noirâtre

Astragalus nigrescens Pallas, Sp. Astragal., 65, plate 53. 1800

Plants pulvinate-cespitose to loosely matted, appearing acaulescent, herbage silvery-canescent, villous, silky-villous, strigose, pilose, or glabrous; caudex branches erect or ascending to prostrate-spreading. **Leaves** 0.5–5 cm; stipules membranous, whitish or with light tan or grayish herbaceous tips, 5–14 mm, usually ± pilose, rarely glabrous abaxially, margins often long-ciliate, with clavate processes; leaflets 5–15, blades elliptic to ovate, 2–10 × 1–2(–3) mm, flat, margins involute but not falcate, apex acute or obtuse, surfaces silky- or silvery-canescent, villous, strigose, or loosely pilose, rarely glabrous. **Peduncles** 0.3–4[–5] cm, pubescent; bract narrowly lanceolate to linear, pilose. **Racemes** 1 or 2(–5)-flowered. **Calyces** campanulate, usually black-pilose, sometimes villous, strigose, or glabrous; tube 3–6 mm, lobes 1.8–4 mm. **Corollas** bright pink-purple or blue-purple to white, 12–20 mm. **Legumes** spreading, subsessile to short-stipitate or stipitate, stipe 1.5–5 mm, oblong-ellipsoid, 18–38(–40) × 8–11 mm, unilocular or subunilocular, usually strigulose to pilose or villous, rarely glabrous.

The Pan-Arctic Flora (http://panarcticflora.org/) splits the *Oxytropis nigrescens* complex into multiple species. It does not recognize *O. nigrescens* in the narrow sense as present in North America, restricting that species to Asia; instead, *O. arctobia*, *O. bryophila* and *O. czukotica* Jurtzev (not treated here) are considered present in North America. The Pan-Arctic Flora does not address the status of *O. nigrescens* var. *lonchopoda* because it grows outside the region they considered.

Varieties 3 (3 in the flora): n North America, Asia.

1. Legumes long-stipitate, stipes 4–5 mm, subequal to calyx tube; Ogilvie Mountains, Yukon . . . . 7c. *Oxytropis nigrescens* var. *lonchopoda*
1. Legumes subsessile to short-stipitate, stipes 1.5–2 mm, shorter than calyx tube; Alaska, British Columbia, Northwest Territories, Nunavut, Quebec, Yukon.
   [2. Shifted to left margin.—Ed.]
2. Leaflets 9–15, blade surfaces silvery-canescent, villous, strigose, or glabrous; Alaska, British Columbia, Northwest Territories, Yukon . . . . 7a. *Oxytropis nigrescens* var. *nigrescens*
2. Leaflets 5–11, blade surfaces densely silky-canescent; alpine in s Yukon and n British Columbia, coastal from Mackenzie Delta eastward . . . . 7b. *Oxytropis nigrescens* var. *uniflora*

7a. **Oxytropis nigrescens** (Pallas) Fischer var. **nigrescens**

Aragallus nigrescens (Pallas) A. Heller; *Oxytropis bryophila* (Greene) Jurtzev; *O. glaberrima* Hultén; *O. nigrescens* subsp. *bryophila* (Greene) Hultén; *O. nigrescens* var. *bryophila* (Greene) Lepage; *O. nigrescens* subsp. *pygmaea* (Pallas) Hultén; *O. nigrescens* var. *pygmaea* (Pallas) Chamisso; *O. pygmaea* (Pallas) Fernald; *Spiesia nigrescens* (Pallas) Kuntze

Plants densely cespitose to loosely matted, herbage green to silvery-canescent, villous, strigose, or glabrous. **Leaflets** 9–15, blade surfaces silvery-canescent, villous, strigose, or glabrous. **Peduncles** 1–4 cm. **Racemes** (1 or) 2(–5)-flowered. **Calyx tube** usually villous-pilose, hairs black. **Legumes** subsessile to short-stipitate, stipe 1.5–2 mm, shorter than calyx tube; body usually strigulose to pilose or villous, rarely glabrous, hairs black. **2*n*** = 16.

Flowering summer. Arctic and alpine tundra, coastal shores, gravel bars, rock outcrops; 10–1800 m; B.C., N.W.T., Yukon; Alaska; Asia (Kamchatka, Siberia).

Variety *nigrescens* is a highly variable taxon in which green or silvery, loose or compact, and villous to strigose or even glabrous, plants often grow intermingled. Morphological intermediates between this variety and vars. *lonchopoda* and *uniflora* occur.

7b. **Oxytropis nigrescens** (Pallas) Fischer var. **uniflora** (Hooker) Barneby, Proc. Calif. Acad., ser. 4, 27: 209. 1952 • One-flowered blackish locoweed, oxytrope du Nunavut [E]

Oxytropis arctica R. Brown var. *uniflora* Hooker in W. E. Parry, App. Parry J. Sec. Voy., 396. 1825; *Astragalus nigrescens* var. *arctobia* (Bunge) Tidestrom; *O. arctobia* Bunge; *O. nigrescens* subsp. *arctobia* (Bunge) Hultén; *O. nigrescens* var. *arctobia* (Bunge) A. Gray; *Spiesia arctobia* (Bunge) Kuntze

Plants densely cespitose or pulvinate, herbage densely silky-villous, caudex branches often becoming columnar.

Leaflets 5–11, blade surfaces densely silky-canescent. **Peduncles** 0.3–2.1 cm. **Racemes** 1- or 2-flowered. **Legumes** usually subsessile, sometimes short-stipitate, stipe to 2 mm, shorter than calyx tube; body usually variously strigulose to pilose or villous, rarely glabrous, hairs black.

Flowering summer. Arctic tundra, coastal shores, gravel bars, rock outcrops; 10–1500 m; B.C., N.W.T., Nunavut, Que., Yukon; Alaska.

Variety *uniflora*, as treated here, is a North American endemic and is of conservation concern in British Columbia; it was treated as *Oxytropis arctobia* by Z. Meyer (2012). *Oxytropis gorodkovii* Jurtzev from the Chukchi Peninsula of the Russian Far East matches it in every way. The Siberian specimens seem to represent ecological variants within var. *nigrescens*. The online Pan-Arctic Flora (http://panarcticflora.org/) considers the material treated here as var. *uniflora* to be two distinct species: *O. gorodkovii* and *O. arctobia*.

7c. **Oxytropis nigrescens** (Pallas) Fischer var. **lonchopoda** Barneby, Leafl. W. Bot. 10: 23. 1963 • Ogilvie Range locoweed [E]

Oxytropis nigrescens subsp. *lonchopoda* (Barneby) Cody

Plants loosely cespitose, herbage loosely pilose, caudex branches elongate and spreading. **Leaflets** 11–15, blade surfaces loosely pilose. **Peduncles** 0.3–2.1 cm. **Racemes** 2-flowered. **Legumes** stipitate, stipe 4–5 mm, subequal to calyx tube; body ellipsoid to cylindroid, villous.

Flowering summer. Alpine tundra; 1200–1700 m; Yukon.

There is considerable variation in stipe length through the range of *Oxytropis nigrescens*. The localization of an elongated stipe in var. *lonchopoda*, known only from the Ogilvie Mountains, demonstrates a coincidence of that feature with the similar *O. podocarpa*, whose fruit is much more inflated and in which the leaflets are usually falcate.

8. **Oxytropis huddelsonii** A. E. Porsild, Bull. Natl. Mus. Canada 121: 242, plate 17, fig. 5. 1951 • Huddelson's oxytrope [E]

Plants pulvinate-cespitose, appearing acaulescent; caudex branches prostrate. **Leaves** 1.5–5 cm, rachis obscurely purple, white-pilose; stipules firm, stramineous or suffused with red-purple or green, glabrous or sparsely pilose, margins long-ciliate; leaflets 7–13, blades lanceolate to elliptic or oblong, 3–6 × 1–2 mm, flat, margins involute, apex acute, surfaces sparsely pilose abaxially, pilose adaxially. **Peduncles** 1–4 cm, pubescent; bract narrowly lanceolate, pilose. **Racemes** 1 or 2(or 3)-flowered. **Calyces** campanulate, appressed-strigose to pilose; tube often suffused with purple, 4–6 mm, lobes 1.2–2.2 mm. **Corollas** pink-purple, 11–15(–17) mm. **Legumes** spreading, sessile or subsessile, ellipsoid, 10–18(–23) × 7–8 mm, unilocular, glabrous, minutely strigose, or strigulose. $2n$ = 16.

Flowering summer. Ridge tops, frost boils, alpine tundra, heathlands, woodlands; 500–2100 m; B.C., Yukon; Alaska.

Unilocular and glabrous or sparsely strigose fruits distinguish *Oxytropis huddelsonii* from *O. nigrescens*, with which it is mainly sympatric; it is without known intermediates.

9. **Oxytropis oreophila** A. Gray, Proc. Amer. Acad. Arts 20: 3. 1884 • Mountain oxytrope [E]

Plants cespitose, often densely pulvinate-cespitose, appearing acaulescent, herbage silky- to villous-pilose. **Leaves** 0.5–8.5 cm; stipules scarious, light tan, 4–12 mm, silky-pilose becoming glabrate, margins ciliate; leaflets 1–15(or 17), sessile, blades lanceolate, elliptic, ovate, lanceolate, or lanceolate-oblong, 1–15 × 0.5–4 mm, apex acute, surfaces pilose or villous-pilose. **Peduncles** (0–)1–14(–23) cm, axis to 1 cm in fruit, pilose to hirsute; bract narrowly lanceolate, pilose. **Racemes** 1–12-flowered, subcapitate. **Calyces** campanulate to short-cylindric, villous-hirsute; tube (3.2–)4–5.5 mm, lobes 1.3–3 mm. **Corollas** pink-purple or white, 6–16(–17) mm. **Legumes** erect, sessile or subsessile, ellipsoid-cylindroid, bladdery-inflated, (7–)9–25 × 5–14 mm, subunilocular to subbilocular, hirtellous to villous or villous-pilose.

Varieties 3 (3 in the flora): w United States.

1. Corollas (11–)14–16(–17) mm; leaflets 1–7; of shale and limestone in c, e, s Utah. . . . . 9c. *Oxytropis oreophila* var. *jonesii*
1. Corollas 6–12.5 mm; leaflets 7–15 (or 17); of shale, limestone, and various igneous substrates in w United States, including Utah.
    2. Peduncles 4–14(–23) cm; herbage often greenish; leaflets 9–15(–17); legumes (7–)9–17 × 6–14 mm; corollas usually 10–12.5 mm . . . . 9a. *Oxytropis oreophila* var. *oreophila*
    2. Peduncles 0.5–2(–5) cm; herbage silvery; leaflets 7–11; legumes 10–12 × 5–6 mm; corollas usually 6–10 mm . . . . 9b. *Oxytropis oreophila* var. *juniperina*

9a. Oxytropis oreophila A. Gray var. **oreophila** E

Aragallus oreophilus (A. Gray) A. Nelson; *Spiesia oreophila* (A. Gray) Kuntze

Plants densely to loosely cespitose, herbage often greenish. **Leaves** 2–8.5 cm; leaflets 9–15 (or 17). **Peduncles** 4–14(–23) cm. **Corollas** usually 10–12.5 mm. **Legumes** (7–)9–17 × 6–14 mm.

Flowering spring–summer. Alpine tundra, ridge tops, meadows, spruce-fir communities; 2200–3800 m; Ariz., Calif., Nev., Utah.

Variety *oreophila* is usually the taller and more robust phase of the species, more typical of higher elevations, where it often grows intermingled with *Oxytropis parryi*.

Astragalus oreophilus (A. Gray) Tidestrom is an illegitimate name that pertains here.

9b. Oxytropis oreophila A. Gray var. **juniperina** S. L. Welsh, Great Basin Naturalist 38: 339. 1978 E

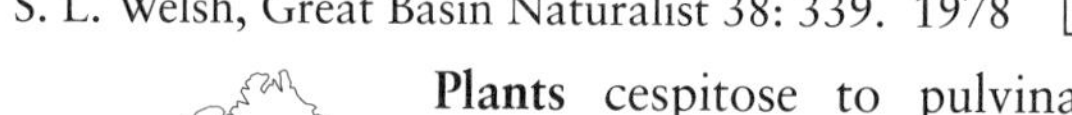

Plants cespitose to pulvinate, herbage silvery. **Leaves** 0.5–2 cm; leaflets 7–11. **Peduncles** 0.5–2(–5) cm. **Corollas** usually 6–10 mm. **Legumes** 10–12 × 5–6 mm.

Flowering spring-summer. Pinyon-juniper, mountain brush, fringed sagebrush, ponderosa pine, and bristlecone pine communities; 1900–2600 m; Ariz., Nev., Utah.

9c. Oxytropis oreophila A. Gray var. **jonesii** (Barneby) Barneby in A. Cronquist et al., Intermount. Fl. 3(B): 183. 1989 E

Oxytropis jonesii Barneby, Proc. Calif. Acad. Sci., ser. 4, 27: 215. 1952

Plants cespitose to pulvinate, herbage silvery. **Leaves** 0.7–3 cm; leaflets 1–7. **Peduncles** 0–3.5 cm. **Corollas** (11–)14–16(–17) mm. **Legumes** 14–25 × 8–13 mm.

Flowering spring–summer. Ponderosa pine, western bristlecone pine, and mixed desert shrub communities on limestone and shale formations; 1900–2500 m; Utah.

Variety *jonesii* is known from eastern, central, and southern Utah.

10. Oxytropis parryi A. Gray, Proc. Amer. Acad. Arts 20: 4. 1884 • Parry's oxytrope E

Aragallus parryi (A. Gray) Greene; *Spiesia parryi* (A. Gray) Kuntze

Plants cespitose, appearing acaulescent, 2–11 cm, herbage silky-pilose. **Leaves** 1.5–7 cm; stipules membranous or papery, light tan or pale gray, white-pilose, margins ciliate; leaflets 7–17, usually scattered, sometimes opposite, blades oblong to elliptic or lanceolate, 2–9(–12) × 0.8–3 mm, apex acute or obtuse, surfaces silky-pilose. **Peduncles** 1.2–8(–10) cm, axis 0.5–1 cm in fruit, pilose; bract lanceolate, pilose. **Racemes** 1–3(or 4)-flowered, clustered to slightly separated. **Calyces** somewhat accrescent and covering ¼ of fruit, campanulate to short-cylindric, 5–8 mm, densely white- and/or black-pilose; tube 3–5.5 mm, lobes 1.5–2.5 mm. **Corollas** usually pink-purple, rarely white, 7.5–12 mm. **Legumes** erect, sessile, oblong to lanceoloid-ovoid or ovoid, 13–22 × 4–8 mm, bilocular or sub-bilocular, pilosulous. $2n = 16$.

Flowering spring–summer. Alpine tundra, ridge tops, meadows; 2600–3800 m; Calif., Colo., Idaho, Mont., Nev., N.Mex., Utah, Wyo.

11. Oxytropis multiceps Nuttall in J. Torrey and A. Gray, Fl. N. Amer. 1: 341. 1838 • Rocky Mountain oxytrope [E]

Aragallus multiceps (Nuttall) A. Heller; *Oxytropis multiceps* var. *minor* A. Gray; *Spiesia multiceps* (Nuttall) Kuntze

Plants pulvinate-cespitose, appearing acaulescent, herbage silky-pilose. **Leaves** 1–5 cm; stipules membranous, light tan or pale gray, white-silky-pilose, margins ciliate; leaflets 5–9, opposite or scattered, blades lanceolate to elliptic, oblong, or oblanceolate, 3–13 × 1–4 mm, apex acute, surfaces silky-pilose. **Peduncles** 1–4 cm, axis 0.5–1 cm in fruit, long-villous; bract ovate to broadly lanceolate, sparsely pilose. **Racemes** 1–4-flowered, clustered. **Calyces** campanulate or already tumescent at anthesis, 7–13(–20) mm, densely white-pilose; tube 5.5–10 mm 8–18 mm in fruit, becoming bladdery-inflated and investing fruit, lobes 2–3 mm. **Corollas** bright pink to pink-purple, 17–24 mm. **Legumes** included within swollen calyx, erect or pendulous, stipitate, stipe 0.5–1.5 mm, ovoid-ellipsoid, 6–10 × 3–5 mm, subunilocular, papery, not rigid at maturity, short-villous.

Flowering spring–early summer. Gravelly summits and ridges, conifer and alpine communities; 1300–3200 m; Colo., Nebr., Utah, Wyo.

The dwarf habit, accrescent calyces, broad bracts, and relatively few flowers are characteristic of *Oxytropis multiceps*.

12. Oxytropis lagopus Nuttall, J. Acad. Nat. Sci. Philadelphia 7: 17. 1834 • Hare oxytrope [E] [F]

Plants cespitose, appearing acaulescent, herbage silky-pilose. **Leaves** 1–10 cm; stipules membranous, soon ruptured, light becoming dark in age, silky-pilose, margins ciliate; leaflets 5–17, scattered or congested, blades ovate-oblong to narrowly elliptic, 3–15 × 2–6 mm, apex acute or obtuse, surfaces pilose or sericeous. **Peduncles** 1–13 cm, axis 0.5–3(–4) cm in fruit, appressed-pilose to villous-hirsute; bract ovate-lanceolate to lanceolate, margins involute, shaggy-pilose. **Racemes** (3–)5–18-flowered, subcapitate or slightly elongate. **Calyces** deeply campanulate, villous to shaggy-villous, hairs mixed blackish and white, appearing gray, 2 mm; tube 5.5–7 mm, slightly swollen to strongly inflated, variably accrescent, ruptured by fruit or not, lobes 2–4.5 mm. **Corollas** bright pink-purple or bluish purple, 15–19(–20) mm. **Legumes** enclosed in or exserted from calyx, erect, sessile or short-stipitate, ovoid to narrowly oblong, turgid to inflated, 6–15(–20) × 4–6.5 mm, bilocular, papery to nearly membranous, white- or black-villous.

Varieties 3 (3 in the flora): w North America.

1. Leaflets 7 or 9(–13), congested on rachis, rachis about equaling longest leaflet; sw Alberta, w Montana . . . . . 12b. *Oxytropis lagopus* var. *conjugans*
1. Leaflets 11–17, well-distributed on rachis, rachis longer than longest leaflet; Idaho, Montana, South Dakota, Wyoming.
   2. Calyces becoming swollen, accrescent in fruit; legumes falling enclosed within calyx prior to dehiscence; Idaho, Montana, n Wyoming . . . . 12a. *Oxytropis lagopus* var. *lagopus*
   2. Calyces slightly swollen or not accrescent in fruit; legumes usually persisting on plant within calyx until after dehiscence; s Montana, South Dakota, Wyoming . . . . 12c. *Oxytropis lagopus* var. *atropurpurea*

12a. Oxytropis lagopus Nuttall var. **lagopus** [E] [F]

Aragallus lagopus (Nuttall) Greene; *Astragalus lagopus* (Nuttall) Tidestrom; *Spiesia lagopus* (Nuttall) Kuntze

Plants 5–15 cm. **Leaves** 1–10 cm, rachis longer than longest leaflet; leaflets 11–15, well distributed on rachis, blade surfaces sericeous. **Peduncles** erect, 2–15 cm, appressed-pilose, ascending-pilose, or villous-hirsute. **Racemes** 6–18-flowered. **Calyces** becoming swollen, accrescent in fruit, constricted at mouth, enclosing mature legume, 10–14(–18) mm. **Corollas** 15–18(–20) mm. **Legumes** falling enclosed within calyx prior to dehiscence, ovoid, 6–10 × 4–5 mm.

Flowering spring–early summer. Sandy and gravelly bluffs and slopes, with sagebrush; 1300–3300 m; Idaho, Mont., Wyo.

12b. Oxytropis lagopus Nuttall var. **conjugans** Barneby, Proc. Calif. Acad. Sci., ser. 4, 27: 227. 1952 • Hare's-foot locoweed [C] [E]

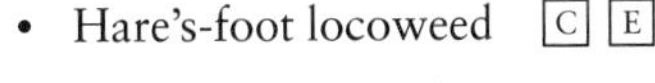

Plants 5–15 cm. **Leaves** 1–6 cm, rachis about equaling longest leaflet; leaflets 7 or 9(–13), congested on rachis, blade surfaces shaggy-pilose. **Peduncles** villous hairs spreading, horizontal, fine. **Racemes** 5–9-flowered. **Calyces** somewhat accrescent and inflated, ruptured in fruit or not, entirely or partially enclosing pod. **Corollas** 15–19 mm. **Legumes** usually not disarticulated from calyx, ovoid-oblong, 8–13 × 5 mm.

Flowering spring–early summer. Stony, calcareous ridge crests; 800–2000 m; of conservation concern; Alta.; Mont.

12c. Oxytropis lagopus Nuttall var. **atropurpurea** (Rydberg) Barneby, Leafl. W. Bot. 6: 111. 1951 E

Aragallus atropurpureus Rydberg, Bull. Torrey Bot. Club 34: 424. 1907

Plants 4–15 cm. **Leaves** 1.5–10 cm, rachis longer than longest leaflet; leaflets 11–17, well distributed on rachis, blade surfaces long-pilose. **Peduncles** usually villous, sometimes appressed-pilose. **Racemes** (3–)5–15-flowered. **Calyces** slightly swollen or not accrescent in fruit, ruptured by (but closely investing) base of exserted pod. **Corollas** 15–19 mm. **Legumes** usually persisting on plant within calyx until after dehiscence, swollen to inflated, oblong or ovoid, 8–15 × 4.5–6.5 mm.

Flowering spring–early summer. Gravelly plains, ridges, slopes; 1000–3200 m; Mont., S.Dak., Wyo.

13. Oxytropis besseyi (Rydberg) Blankinship, Sci. Stud. Montana Coll. Agric., Bot. 1: 80. 1905 • Bessey's locoweed E

Aragallus besseyi Rydberg, Mem. New York Bot. Gard. 1: 250. 1900

Plants cespitose, appearing acaulescent, herbage silky-pilose. **Leaves** 1.5–16 cm; stipules membranous or papery, light tan or pale gray, silky-pilose; leaflets 5–25, blades narrowly elliptic, lanceolate, or lanceolate-ovate, 4–21 × 1–4 mm, apex acute or obtuse, surfaces silky-pilose. **Peduncles** 2–19 cm, axis 0.5–8(–10) cm in fruit, hairs appressed or some ascending; bract ovate-rhombic to lanceolate or lanceolate-acuminate, silky-pilose, margins ciliate. **Racemes** 3–22-flowered, subcapitate to loosely racemose in flower, sometimes slightly elongate in fruit. **Calyces** cylindric-campanulate, hispid-hirsute, silky-hairy, silky-pilose, or appressed-silky, hairs white; tube (5–)6–8(–9.5) mm, lobes 2–6 mm. **Corollas** bright pink-purple, 17–25 mm, wing petals broadly expanded, often conspicuously 2-lobed apically. **Legumes** rupturing calyx but invested by it, erect or spreading, sessile or short-stipitate, stipe to 1.2 mm, cylindric, scarcely to strongly inflated or swollen, (5–)10–14(–20) × 2.5–10 mm, bilocular or semibilocular, papery, villous, hairs whitish, shiny, (1–)1.5–3 mm.

Varieties 6 (6 in the flora): w North America.

1. Legumes sessile; leaflets (5 or)7–25; peduncles surpassed by leaves (or leaves only to proximal-most flowers), axis 2.5–8(–10) cm in fruit; nw Colorado, adjacent Utah, s, c Wyoming . . . . 13f. *Oxytropis besseyi* var. *obnapiformis*
1. Legumes short-stipitate; leaflets 5–19; peduncles usually surpassing leaves, axis 0.5–5.5 cm (except 2–8 cm in var. *besseyi*) in fruit; Idaho, Montana, Nevada, Saskatchewan, Utah, Wyoming.
    2. Calyces silky-hairy or silky-pilose, hairs appressed, sometimes with few ascending hairs.
        3. Leaflets 5–9; racemes 7–10(–12)-flowered, axes 1–2.5 cm in fruit; Custer County, Idaho . . . 13d. *Oxytropis besseyi* var. *salmonensis*
        3. Leaflets 7–15; racemes 11–19-flowered, axes 2.5–5.5 cm in fruit; Montana, w Wyoming . . . 13e. *Oxytropis besseyi* var. *fallax*
    2. Calyces hispid-hirsute, hairs ascending-spreading.
        4. Racemes loose, axes 2–8 cm in fruit; peduncles 9–19 cm; leaflets 9–19, rachis 2–9 cm, longer than longest leaflet; n Wyoming, Carbon County, Montana, northward to s Saskatchewan. . . . . 13a. *Oxytropis besseyi* var. *besseyi*
        4. Racemes subcapitate (at least at anthesis), axes 0.5–2 cm in fruit; peduncles 2–9 (–12) cm; leaflets 5–9 (or 11), rachis to 0.5–1.4(–2) cm, usually shorter than longest leaflet; Idaho, Montana, Nevada, Utah, Wyoming.
            5. Leaflet blades (8–)10–21 mm; Green, Platte, and Wind river drainages, Wyoming and adjacent Montana, Utah . . . . 13b. *Oxytropis besseyi* var. *ventosa*
            5. Leaflet blades 3–10(–13) mm; w Montana and adjacent Idaho, disjunct in Nevada. . . . . 13c. *Oxytropis besseyi* var. *argophylla*

13a. Oxytropis besseyi (Rydberg) Blankinship var. **besseyi** E

Oxytropis nana Nuttall var. *besseyi* (Rydberg) Isely

Plants usually robust. **Leaves** 3–12 cm; rachis 2–9 cm, longer than longest leaflet; leaflets 9–19, 10–18 mm, scattered along rachis. **Peduncles** erect, 9–19 cm, usually surpassing leaves, axis 2–8 cm in fruit. **Racemes** 7–20-flowered, loose. **Calyces** 9–13 mm, hispid-hirsute, hairs ascending-spreading. **Corollas** 17–25 mm. **Legumes** short-stipitate, scarcely to strongly inflated.

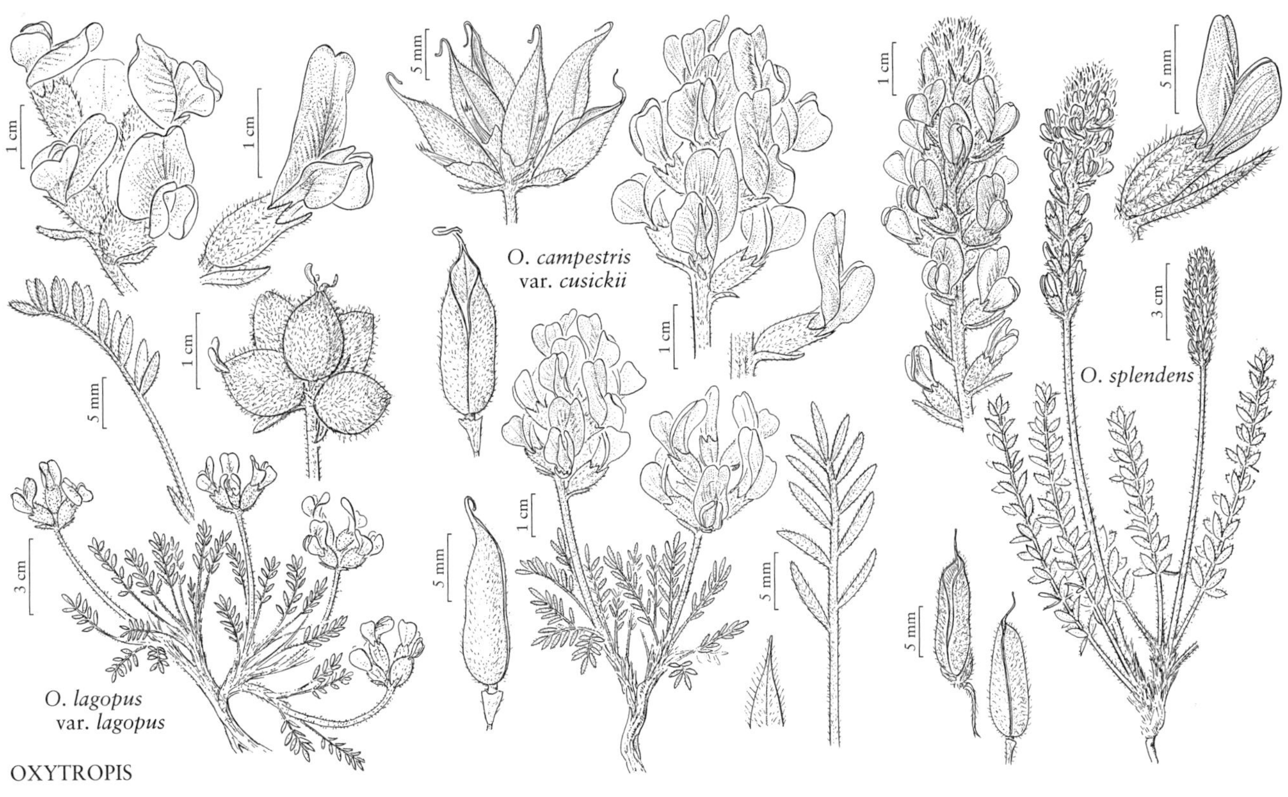

OXYTROPIS

Flowering spring–early summer. Hilltops, bluffs, banks, sagebrush, grasslands, sand, gravel; 1000–2900 m; Sask.; Mont., Wyo.

Variety *besseyi* is similar to *Oxytropis lambertii*, with which it is occasionally confused; it differs in its hispid-villous calyces, thin-walled fruits, and basifixed hairs.

13b. Oxytropis besseyi (Rydberg) Blankinship var. **ventosa** (Greene) Barneby, Leafl. W. Bot. 6: 111. 1951 E

Aragallus ventosus Greene, Proc. Biol. Soc. Wash. 18: 15. 1905; *Oxytropis nana* Nuttall var. *ventosa* (Greene) Isely

Plants usually robust. **Leaves** 3–7 cm; rachis 0.5–1.4 cm, usually shorter than longest leaflet; leaflets 5–9, congested on rachis, (8–)10–21 mm. **Peduncles** erect, 8–12 cm, usually surpassing leaves, axis usually 0.5–2 cm in fruit. **Racemes** 5–14-flowered, subcapitate at anthesis. **Calyces** 9–10.5 mm, hispid-hirsute, hairs ascending-spreading. **Corollas** 19–24 mm. **Legumes** short-stipitate, scarcely to strongly inflated.

Flowering spring–early summer. Hilltops, banks, bluffs; 1500–2500 m; Mont., Utah, Wyo.

Variety *ventosa* is restricted to the drainages of the Green, Platte, and Wind rivers of central and southern Wyoming and northeastern Utah, and northward to Clark's Fork, the drainage of the Bighorn River, and the Yellowstone River, Montana.

13c. Oxytropis besseyi (Rydberg) Blankinship var. **argophylla** (Rydberg) Barneby, Leafl. W. Bot. 6: 111. 1951 E

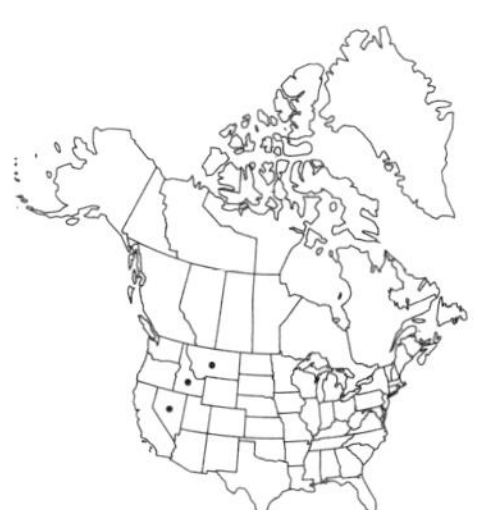

Aragallus argophyllus Rydberg, Mem. New York Bot. Gard. 1: 255. 1900; *Oxytropis nana* Nuttall var. *argophylla* (Rydberg) Isely

Plants low, densely cespitose, hairs silvery-white. **Leaves** 1.5–4 cm; rachis 0.5–1(–2) cm, usually shorter than longest leaflet; leaflets 5–9(or 11), congested on rachis, 3–10(–13) mm. **Peduncles** erect, ascending, or curved, 2–9 cm, usually surpassing leaves, axis 0.5–1.5 cm in fruit. **Racemes** 3–10-flowered, subcapitate at anthesis. **Calyces** 9–10.5 mm, hispid-hirsute, hairs ascending-spreading. **Corollas** 18–22 mm. **Legumes** short-stipitate, inflated.

Flowering spring–early summer. Hilltops, bluffs; 1300–3200 m; Idaho, Mont., Nev.

13d. Oxytropis besseyi (Rydberg) Blankinship var. **salmonensis** Barneby, Proc. Calif. Acad. Sci., ser. 4, 27: 234. 1952 [E]

Oxytropis nana Nuttall var. *salmonensis* (Barneby) Isely

Plants low, hairs appressed-silky. **Leaves** 4–8 cm; rachis 6–20 cm, shorter than or equaling longest leaflet; leaflets 5–9, crowded on rachis, 10–19 mm. **Peduncles** 6–10 cm, surpassing leaves, axis 1–2.5 cm in fruit. **Racemes** 7–10(–12)-flowered, subcapitate at anthesis. **Calyces** 9–12 mm, appressed silky-hairy, with few ascending hairs. **Corollas** 18–21 mm. **Legumes** short-stipitate, strongly inflated, subglobose.

Flowering spring–early summer. Clay slopes; 1600–1900 m; Idaho.

Variety *salmonensis* is restricted to the areas of Big Lost and Salmon rivers in Custer County.

13e. Oxytropis besseyi (Rydberg) Blankinship var. **fallax** Barneby, Proc. Calif. Acad. Sci., ser. 4, 27: 235. 1952 [E]

Oxytropis nana Nuttall var. *fallax* (Barneby) Isely

Plants usually robust. **Leaves** 4–16 cm; rachis 10–40 mm, shorter than longest leaflet; leaflets 7–15, scattered on rachis, 10–23 mm. **Peduncles** 10–15 cm, surpassing leaves, axis 2.5–5.5 cm in fruit. **Racemes** 11–19-flowered. **Calyces** 8.5–10.5 mm, appressed silky-pilose, sometimes with a few ascending hairs. **Corollas** 17–21 mm. **Legumes** short-stipitate, swollen to strongly inflated.

Flowering spring–early summer. Slopes, hilltops, on sandstone; 1200–2000 m; Mont., Wyo.

Variety *fallax* is restricted to an area west of the Bighorn River.

13f. Oxytropis besseyi (Rydberg) Blankinship var. **obnapiformis** (Ced. Porter) S. L. Welsh, Great Basin Naturalist 38: 337. 1978 [C] [E]

Oxytropis obnapiformis Ced. Porter, Madroño 9: 133, figs. 1–3. 1947; *O. nana* Nuttall var. *obnapiformis* (Ced. Porter) Isely

Plants usually robust. **Leaves** 4–11(–15) cm; rachis 3–9 cm, surpassing leaflets; leaflets (5 or) 7–25, distant and scattered on rachis, 6–18 mm. **Peduncles** 6–13 cm, surpassed by leaves or leaves reaching only to proximalmost flowers, axis 2.5–8(–10) cm in fruit. **Racemes** 8–22-flowered, dense. **Calyces** (7–)8–13 mm, subappressed-silky. **Corollas** 15–23 mm. **Legumes** sessile, strongly ovoid-inflated, rupturing calyx at maturity, densely gray-villous, hairs ascending.

Flowering spring–early summer. Sandhills, sandy bluffs; of conservation concern; 1600–2200 m; Colo., Utah, Wyo.

Variety *obnapiformis* is restricted to Moffat County, Colorado, Daggett County, Utah, and southwest Wyoming.

The fruit of var. *obnapiformis* is sessile or nearly so, not substipitate to short-stipitate as in other varieties of the species with inflated fruits. Plants from the type locality near Mayfield, Colorado, have 13–25 leaflets and racemes about equaling the leaves. Those from Daggett County, Utah, have 5–11 leaflets and racemes surpassing the leaves. Plants from elsewhere are intermediate and tie the two phases together.

14. Oxytropis borealis de Candolle in A. P. de Candolle and A. L. P. P. de Candolle, Prodr. 2: 275. 1825
• Boreal locoweed, oxytrope boréal

Plants cespitose, appearing acaulescent, 4–30 cm, glandular-viscid, especially stipules and calyces, herbage spreading-hairy. **Leaves** 1–25 cm; stipules membranous, light tan or grayish, 8–21 mm, often with debris adhering, usually prominently glandular, pilose or glabrous abaxially, margins ciliate; leaflets 17–39+, blades oblong to lanceolate or elliptic, 1.5–22 × 1–6 mm, apex acute or obtuse, surfaces pilose or glabrous, often glandular. **Peduncles** 1–27 cm, axis 0.5–19 cm in fruit, hirsute, pilose, or villous-pilose, hairs spreading; bract lanceolate to lanceolate-linear, shorter than or surpassing calyx, glandular or glabrous, margins ciliate. **Racemes** 3–19+-flowered, dense or nearly capitate. **Calyces** cylindric to shortly so, villous, hairs black and white; tube 4–7 mm, lobes 1–5(–8) mm, usually glandular. **Corollas**

whitish, yellowish, ochroleucous, lilac, purple, bluish, or pink-purple, keel tip maculate or not, (9–)11–18 (–21) mm. **Legumes** mostly erect, sessile, ovoid to subcylindric, 8–21(–30) × 4–7 mm, bilocular or incompletely so, glandular, strigose to pilose.

Varieties 5 (5 in the flora): North America, Asia.

Considerable confusion has existed over typification of *Oxytropis borealis* (S. L. Welsh 1990). The relationships of this species with several Eurasian taxa in sect. *Gloeocephala* Bunge are not well understood (R. C. Barneby 1952b).

1. Racemes subcapitate or nearly so, 5–10-flowered; wing petal blades dilated distally to 3.5–5 mm; leaflets (17 or)19–27(–37) . . . . 14a. *Oxytropis borealis* var. *borealis*
1. Racemes elongate, or subcapitate and elongating in fruit; wing petal blades not especially dilated distally, 2–3 mm, or if wider, then inflorescence not subcapitate; leaflets 17–39+.
    2. Peduncles 2.5–7 cm; calyx lobes 1–1.5 mm, not or obscurely tuberculate . . . . 14c. *Oxytropis borealis* var. *hudsonica*
    2. Peduncles (1–)4–27 cm; calyx lobes 1–4 (–4.5) mm, prominently tuberculate.
        3. Corollas white or bluish, keel tips maculate; inflorescence axis often (2–) 3–15 cm in fruit; se continental Alaska, n British Columbia, s Yukon . . . . 14d. *Oxytropis borealis* var. *sulphurea*
        3. Corollas white, ochroleucous, pink-purple, lilac, or yellowish, keel tips maculate or not; inflorescence axis often (1.5–)4–19 cm in fruit; Alaska to n, nc United States.
            4. Corollas pink-purple, lilac, whitish, or yellow; leaflet blades not thick or stiff; plants glandular . . . . 14b. *Oxytropis borealis* var. *viscida*
            4. Corollas usually white or ochroleucous, rarely fading bluish; leaflet blades thick and stiff; plants markedly viscid . . . . 14e. *Oxytropis borealis* var. *australis*

14a. Oxytropis borealis de Candolle var. **borealis**

Oxytropis uralensis (Linnaeus) de Candolle var. *subsucculenta* Hooker; *O. viscida* Nuttall var. *subsucculenta* (Hooker) Barneby

Plants usually 4–12(–18) cm. **Leaves** 1–18 cm; leaflets (17 or)19–27(–37), blade apex acute to obtuse or rounded. **Peduncles** 4–15 cm, subequal to or surpassing leaves, axis 0.5–2.5 cm in fruit, densely hirsute at least distally, hairs fuscous or mixed black and paler. **Racemes** 5–10-flowered, subcapitate or loose. **Calyces** 8–10(–12) mm, tube 5–6 mm, lobes (2–)3–4 (–8) mm. **Corollas** purple, lilac, or whitish, 13–17 mm; wing blades dilated distally to 3.5–5 mm. **Legumes** 10–18 × 5–7 mm. 2*n* = 48.

Flowering summer. Gravel bars, ridge crests, rocky sites; 0–1000 m; N.W.T., Yukon; Alaska; e Asia (Chukchi Peninsula).

Variety *borealis* is readily identified by the combination of relatively few leaflets, many flowers, and condensed, copiously hirsute inflorescences. Specimens from the interior, such as those in Denali National Park and at Black Rapids Glacier, Alaska, have racemes somewhat elongate and wing petals particularly widened near the apex.

14b. Oxytropis borealis de Candolle var. **viscida** (Nuttall) S. L. Welsh, Great Basin Naturalist 50: 358. 1991 • Sticky locoweed, oxytrope visqueux [E]

Oxytropis viscida Nuttall in J. Torrey and A. Gray, Fl. N. Amer. 1: 341. 1838; *Aragallus viscidus* (Nuttall) Greene; *Astragalus viscidus* (Nuttall) Tidestrom; *O. campestris* (Linnaeus) de Candolle var. *viscida* (Nuttall) S. Watson; *O. gaspensis* Fernald & S. L. Kelsey; *O. glutinosa* A. E. Porsild; *O. ixodes* Butters & Abbe; *O. leucantha* (Pallas) Persoon var. *depressa* (Rydberg) B. Boivin; *O. leucantha* var. *gaspensis* (Fernald & S. L. Kelsey) B. Boivin; *O. leucantha* var. *ixodes* (Butters & Abbe) B. Boivin; *O. leucantha* var. *magnifica* B. Boivin; *O. leucantha* var. *viscida* (Nuttall) B. Boivin; *O. sheldonensis* A. E. Porsild; *O. viscidula* (Rydberg) Tidestrom; *Spiesia viscida* (Nuttall) Kuntze

Plants usually 8–26+ cm, glandular. **Leaves** 2–21 cm; leaflets (19–)25–39+. **Peduncles** 4–27 cm, often some surpassing leaves, axis often (1.5–)4–19 cm in fruit, pubescent. **Racemes** 3–19+-flowered, subcapitate to elongate. **Calyces** 7–10.5 mm, tube 4–7 mm, lobes (1–)1.5–3.5 (–4.5) mm, prominently tuberculate. **Corollas** pink-purple, lilac, whitish, or yellowish, keel tips maculate or not, 11–16 mm; wing blades not especially dilated distally. **Legumes** (8–)12–21(–30) × (4–)5–7 mm.

Flowering spring–summer. Gravel bars, roadsides, ridge crests, talus slopes, pinyon-juniper slopes, sagebrush, boreal forest, tundra communities; 0–3900 m; Alta., B.C., N.W.T., Nunavut, Ont., Que., Yukon; Alaska, Calif., Colo., Idaho, Minn., Mont., Nev., Oreg., Utah, Wash., Wyo.

Variety *viscida* is quite variable, with numerous subunits held together by tenuous characteristics that are difficult to define or place in a key. Variation is often great in populations from adjacent hillsides or on a single gravel bar, especially in the Arctic. Dwarf plants far removed from the range of var. *hudsonica* are similar to that entity; the inflorescences become capitate, and the calyx lobes are often relatively very short. Further study might reveal the need for additional segregation. The Pan-Arctic Flora (http://panarcticflora.org/) recognizes *O. glutinosa* and *O. viscida* as distinct species.

14c. Oxytropis borealis de Candolle var. **hudsonica** (Greene) S. L. Welsh, Great Basin Naturalist 50: 357. 1991 • Hudson Bay locoweed, oxytrope de la baie d'Hudson [E]

Aragallus hudsonicus Greene, Proc. Biol. Soc. Wash. 18: 17. 1905; *Oxytropis hudsonica* (Greene) Fernald; *O. leucantha* (Pallas) Persoon var. *hudsonica* (Greene) B. Boivin; *O. leucantha* var. *leuchippiana* B. Boivin; *O. verruculosa* A. E. Porsild; *O. viscida* Nuttall subsp. *hudsonica* (Greene) Á. Löve & D. Löve; *O. viscida* var. *hudsonica* (Greene) Barneby

Plants usually to 8(–15) cm. **Leaves** mostly 1.5–8 cm; leaflets 19–33, blades 1.5–6 mm. **Peduncles** 2.5–7 cm, axis to 1 cm in fruit, sparsely villous-pilose. **Racemes** densely 3–6(–16)-flowered, subcapitate to short-spicate. **Calyces** 7.5–8 mm, tube 6–6.5 mm, lobes 1–1.5 mm, not or obscurely verrucose. **Corollas** purplish, 11–16 mm; wing blades not especially dilated distally. **Legumes** 8–15 × 5–7 mm. **2*n*** = 16.

Flowering summer. Arctic and subarctic shores; 100–400 m; N.W.T., Nunavut, Ont., Que., Yukon.

Variety *hudsonica* is closely allied to, and transitional with, var. *viscida*, from which it differs mainly in the usually smaller size, relatively short calyx lobes, and less marked glandularity. None of these characters is definitive in all instances, either alone or in combination.

14d. Oxytropis borealis de Candolle var. **sulphurea** (A. E. Porsild) S. L. Welsh, Great Basin Naturalist 50: 358. 1991 • Beringian locoweed [E]

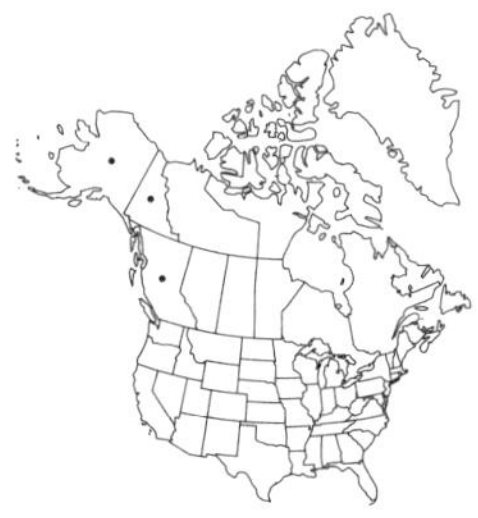

Oxytropis viscidula (Rydberg) Tidestrom subsp. *sulphurea* A. E. Porsild, Bull. Natl. Mus. Canada 121: 247. 1951

Plants usually 8–30 cm. **Leaves** 4–25 cm; leaflets 19–35, blades 4–18 mm. **Peduncles** 4–20+ cm, axis often (2–)3–15 cm in fruit, pilose. **Racemes** 8–25-flowered, compact to loose. **Calyces** 6–9 mm, tube 5–7 mm, lobes 2–4 mm, prominently tuberculate. **Corollas** white or bluish, keel tips maculate, 9–21 mm; wing blades not especially dilated distally. **Legumes** 8–15 × 5–7 mm.

Flowering summer. Roadsides, gravel bars, ridge crests in boreal forests, shrublands, meadows; 900–1300 m; B.C., Yukon; Alaska.

There are many transitional forms between vars. *sulphurea* and *viscida* in the broad sense. The materials included here are plottable in the herbarium and notable in the field. Many of the plants are small-flowered (ca. 12 mm) and, consequently, have narrow racemes. Large-flowered phases are present and, in some, the bracts are very long, surpassing the flowers at anthesis.

14e. Oxytropis borealis de Candolle var. **australis** S. L. Welsh, Great Basin Naturalist 50: 359. 1991 [E]

Plants usually 4–18 cm, markedly viscid. **Leaves** 4–17 cm; leaflets 17–27, blades thick and stiff, apex usually obtuse to rounded. **Peduncles** 1–15 cm, longer than or subequal to leaves, axis 4.5–5 cm in fruit, pubescent. **Racemes** usually 3–15-flowered, subcapitate to somewhat elongate. **Calyces** 5–7 mm, tube 3–4 mm, lobes 1–3 mm, prominently tuberculate. **Corollas** usually white or ochroleucous, keel tips maculate or not, rarely fading bluish, 15–18 mm; wing blades not especially dilated distally. **Legumes** erect-ascending, 12–16 × 4–6 mm.

Flowering spring–early summer. Pinyon-juniper, mountain brush, meadow communities; 2500–3500 m; Calif., Nev., Utah.

Variety *australis* is restricted to Emery, Sevier, and Wayne counties, Utah, Elko and Nye counties, Nevada, and Inyo and Mono counties, California.

15. Oxytropis campestris (Linnaeus) de Candolle, Astragalogia (qto.), 26, 74; (fol.), 20, 59. 1802 • Yellow locoweed, oxytrope des champs [F]

Astragalus campestris Linnaeus, Sp. Pl. 2: 761. 1753; *Aragallus campestris* (Linnaeus) Greene; *Spiesia campestris* (Linnaeus) Kuntze

Plants cespitose, appearing acaulescent, 4–86 cm, herbage pilose, silky-pilose, hirsute, or glabrescent. **Leaves** 2–40 cm; stipules membranous, stramineous to black, ovate to lanceolate, apex acuminate, glabrous, strigose, or pilose abaxially, margins usually ciliate, often with clavate processes; leaflets 7–45, opposite, subopposite, scattered, or fasciculate, blades oblong to lanceolate or obovate, 1–30(–33) × 1–9(–11) mm, surfaces ± pilose. **Peduncles** 2–36(–48) cm, axis 0.3–10(–23) cm in fruit, pilose, villous-pilose, or glabrate; bract narrowly lanceolate, longer than pedicel, sometimes surpassing calyx, pilose. **Racemes** 2–30+-flowered, ± lax in fruit. **Calyces** cylindric, 7–10 mm, hairs white, or black and white, loosely pilose; tube (3.7–)4–9 mm, lobes 0.5–3(–4) mm. **Corollas** white, whitish, yellowish, pink, pink-purple, lavender, blue, purplish-tinged, or purplish, keel tip maculate or not, (10–)12–20(–23) mm. **Legumes** erect, sessile or subsessile, cylindric, 8–27 × 3.5–7(–9) mm, partially bilocular (by intrusion of adaxial suture), papery to leathery or membranous, pilose.

Varieties ca. 15 (12 in the flora): North America, Eurasia.

Comparison of North American materials of the *Oxytropis campestris* complex with the Linnaean type and with other authentic specimens from Eurasia indicates a close relationship. The phases, as they occur in North America, are closely matched by their Eurasian counterparts. Such similarities are not easily discounted. An inclusive, rather than an exclusive, approach is indicated and is herein adopted.

1. Corollas usually purple, rarely white; east of 90th meridian.
    2. Racemes (3–)5–9-flowered, axis 0.3–1.5 cm in fruit, peduncles curved-ascending, 3–15(–18) cm; calyx lobes deltate, 0.5–1.5(–2) mm ..... 15j. *Oxytropis campestris* var. *minor*
    2. Racemes 7–12(–14)-flowered, axis 1.5–9(–11) cm in fruit, peduncles erect, (4–)8–36 cm; calyx lobes usually lanceolate, (1–)2–3 mm.
        3. Stipules glabrous or sparsely pilose abaxially; herbage silky-pilose becoming glabrate; legumes 14–27 mm; Maine, New Brunswick, Newfoundland, Nova Scotia, Ontario, Quebec........................ 15k. *Oxytropis campestris* var. *johannensis*
        3. Stipules pilose; herbage often loosely and copiously pilose; legumes 8–15 mm; Wisconsin................................15l. *Oxytropis campestris* var. *chartacea*
1. Corollas white, whitish, yellowish, purple, pink-purple, lavender, blue, bluish, pink, or polychrome; west of 90th meridian.
    4. Corollas mostly purple, lavender, blue, or pink-purple, sometimes polychrome.
        5. Plants 4–12(–16) cm; racemes 8–12(–14)-flowered, subcapitate or somewhat elongate; n Alaska, Northwest Territories, Yukon ....15c. *Oxytropis campestris* var. *roaldii*
        5. Plants (9–)12–45 cm; racemes (5 or) 6–15+-flowered, ± open or elongate; Alberta, British Columbia, Manitoba, Minnesota, North Dakota, Northwest Territories, Washington.
            6. Leaflets, at least some, fasciculate; corollas usually pink-purple or bluish, sometimes polychrome; sw Alberta, n British Columbia, Northwest Territories...15g. *Oxytropis campestris* var. *davisii*
            6. Leaflets scattered or subopposite; corollas purple, blue, pink, white, yellowish, or polychrome (in populations, rarely all one color); Manitoba, Minnesota, North Dakota, Washington.
                7. Leaflet blades ovate, linear-lanceolate, or narrowly oblong; Manitoba, Minnesota, North Dakota........15f. *Oxytropis campestris* var. *dispar*
                7. Leaflet blades linear to narrowly oblong; Grant County, Washington ....15i. *Oxytropis campestris* var. *wanapum*

[4. Shifted to left margin.—Ed.]

4. Corollas usually white, whitish, yellowish, or polychrome, rarely purplish.
    8. Racemes usually 2–9-flowered; plants 5–12(–18) cm; n Alaska, British Columbia, Mackenzie Mountains, Northwest Territories, Yukon ...... 15b. *Oxytropis campestris* var. *jordalii*
    8. Racemes (3–)8–30-flowered; plants (4–)12–55 cm; Alaska, Alberta, British Columbia, Colorado, Idaho, Manitoba, Montana, North Dakota, Northwest Territories, Oregon, Saskatchewan, South Dakota, Utah, Washington, Wyoming, Yukon.
        9. Stipule margins ciliate, with clavate processes; Alaska, n British Columbia to ne Manitoba, Northwest Territories, Yukon.... 15a. *Oxytropis campestris* var. *varians*
        9. Stipule margins ciliate or eciliate, usually without clavate processes; Alberta, British Columbia, Colorado, Idaho, Manitoba, Montana, North Dakota, Oregon, Saskatchewan, South Dakota, Utah, Washington, Wyoming.
            10. Leaflets (13–)17–33; elevations 1200–2300 m; Alberta, British Columbia, Colorado, Idaho, Manitoba, Montana, North Dakota, Oregon, Saskatchewan, South Dakota, Washington, Wyoming .... 15d. *Oxytropis campestris* var. *spicata*
            10. Leaflets 7–17(–19); elevations 300–3400 m; Alberta, British Columbia, Colorado, Idaho, Montana, Oregon, Utah, Washington, Wyoming.

[11. Shifted to left margin.—Ed.]

11. Plants 4–15(–21) cm; corollas whitish or yellowish, keel not maculate; subalpine or alpine; Alberta, British Columbia, Colorado, Idaho, Montana, Oregon, Utah, Washington, Wyoming ..... 15e. *Oxytropis campestris* var. *cusickii*
11. Plants (13–)19–30(–35) cm; corollas white, keel maculate; riparian; Flathead Lake, Montana, and Columbia River above Spokane, Washington.................................. 15h. *Oxytropis campestris* var. *columbiana*

15a. Oxytropis campestris (Linnaeus) de Candolle var. **varians** (Rydberg) Barneby, Proc. Calif. Acad. Sci., ser. 4, 27: 253. 1952 E

Aragallus varians Rydberg, Bull. New York Bot. Gard. 2: 176. 1901; *Oxytropis alaskana* A. Nelson; *O. campestris* subsp. *varians* (Rydberg) Cody; *O. hyperborea* A. E. Porsild; *O. tananensis* Jurtzev; *O. varians* (Rydberg) K. Schumann

Plants 5–55 cm, herbage silky-pilose to hirsute or glabrescent. **Leaves** 3–40 cm; stipules usually ± pilose abaxially, sometimes glabrous, margins ciliate, with clavate processes; leaflets (9–)15–45, scattered, subopposite, or fasciculate, blades 2–24 mm. **Peduncles** 3.5–35+ cm, axis 1.5–21 cm in fruit. **Racemes** (4–)10–25+-flowered. **Calyces** pilosulous, hairs black and pale, tube 4–7.5 mm, lobes (1.2–)1.5–3 mm. **Corollas** usually yellowish or whitish, rarely purplish in polychrome populations, sometimes fading purplish, keel tip sometimes maculate, usually 12–17(–19) mm. **Legumes** 12–19(–24+) × 3.5–6 mm. **2*n*** = 48, 96, 98.

Flowering spring–summer. Gravel bars, terraces, rock outcrops, roadsides, woods, heathlands, alpine meadows; 10–2000 m; B.C., Man., N.W.T., Yukon; Alaska.

Variety *varians* is a highly variable entity, with numerous plants with differing morphological phases often growing together on the same gravel bar or hillside in portions of Alaska and Yukon. Alpine phases of the variety, especially in southeastern Alaska, northern British Columbia, and southwestern Yukon, closely simulate high altitude materials of var. *cusickii* at its northern limits in Alberta and southern British Columbia. Specimens of var. *varians* appear to intergrade with materials of var. *jordalii* in montane sites near Juneau. Certainly, this is the northern counterpart of var. *spicata*, from which it differs in characters that are altogether tenuous. Some specimens from eastern Alaska show evidence of intermediacy between var. *varians* and *Oxytropis splendens*. These form the basis of *Oxytropis tananensis* Jurtzev (B. A. Jurtzev 1993b), which the Pan-Arctic Flora (http://panarcticflora.org/) recognizes as a distinct species.

15b. Oxytropis campestris (Linnaeus) de Candolle var. **jordalii** (A. E. Porsild) S. L. Welsh, Leafl. W. Bot. 10: 25. 1963 E

Oxytropis jordalii A. E. Porsild, Canad. Field-Naturalist 65: 77, plate 1. 1951; *O. campestris* subsp. *jordalii* (A. E. Porsild) Hultén; *O. leucantha* (Pallas) Persoon subsp. *jordalii* (A. E. Porsild) Jurtzev

Plants 5–12(–18) cm, herbage sparsely pilose, hairs subappressed. **Leaves** 1.5–9 cm; stipules glabrous or strigose abaxially, margins ± ciliate, apex often bristly; leaflets 9–19, scattered or opposite, blades 1–11 mm. **Peduncles** 3–12(–14) cm, axis 1–4.5 cm in fruit. **Racemes** usually 2–9-flowered, subcapitate or somewhat elongate. **Calyces:** tube (3.7–)4–5.5 mm, lobes 1–1.5 mm. **Corollas** whitish or yellowish, sometimes polychrome, 10–14(–15) mm. **Legumes** 9–12 × 3.5–5 mm. **2*n*** = 32.

Flowering spring–summer. Alpine tundra, heathlands, gravel bars, exposed ridges; 10–1300 m; B.C., N.W.T., Yukon; Alaska.

Variety *jordalii* is transitional to vars. *roaldii* and *varians*. Data from J. L. Jorgensen et al. (2003) give some support to *O. jordalii* and *O. varians* as distinct species.

15c. Oxytropis campestris (Linnaeus) de Candolle var. **roaldii** (Ostenfeld) S. L. Welsh, Great Basin Naturalist 51: 386. 1991 E

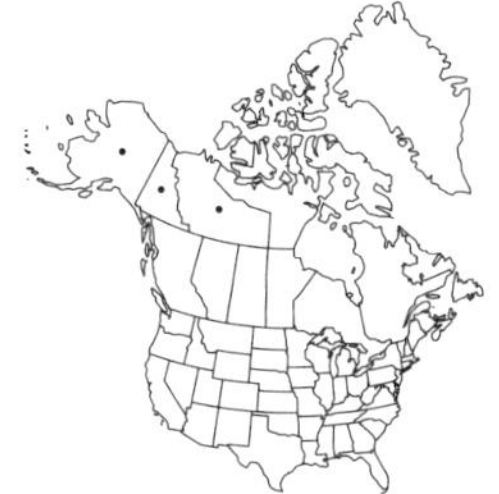

Oxytropis roaldii Ostenfeld, Skr. Vidensk.-Selsk. Christiana, Math.-Naturvidensk. Kl. 1909(8): 54, plate 3, fig. 16. 1910; *O. campestris* subsp. *roaldii* (Ostenfeld) Cody

Plants 4–16 cm, herbage sparsely pilose, hairs subappressed. **Leaves** 2–11 cm; stipules glabrous or strigose abaxially, margins ± ciliate, apex often bristly; leaflets 11–21, scattered or opposite, blades 4–8.5 mm. **Peduncles** 3–12 cm, axis 1.5–4.5 cm in fruit. **Racemes** usually 8–12(–14)-flowered, subcapitate or somewhat elongate. **Calyces:** tube (3.7–)4.5–5 mm, lobes (1–)1.2–2(–2.7) mm. **Corollas** lavender or pink-purple, sometimes polychrome, 13–16(–17) mm. **Legumes** 9–15 × 4–6 mm. **2*n*** = 64.

Flowering summer. Alpine and arctic tundra; 0–500 m; N.W.T., Yukon; Alaska.

Variety *roaldii* has flowers that are usually larger, calyx lobes that are usually longer, and other subtle differences aside from flower color that allow segregation from var. *jordalii*. However, there are intermediate specimens, and in some places, especially on gravel bars, flower color grades within populations. A similar pattern is to be noted between the partially sympatric vars. *davisii* and *spicata* in the mountains of Alberta, and between other varieties situated elsewhere. The Pan-Arctic Flora (http://panarcticflora.org/) recognizes *Oxytropis roaldii* as a distinct species.

15d. Oxytropis campestris (Linnaeus) de Candolle var. **spicata** Hooker, Fl. Bor.-Amer. 1: 147. 1831 E

Aragallus cervinus Greene; *A. spicatus* (Hooker) Rydberg; *Oxytropis campestris* var. *cervinus* (Greene) B. Boivin; *O. campestris* subsp. *gracilis* (A. Nelson) B. Boivin; *O. campestris* var. *gracilis* (A. Nelson) Barneby; *O. luteola* (Greene) Piper & Beattie; *O. monticola* A. Gray; *O. sericea* Nuttall subsp. *spicata* (Hooker) Cody; *O. sericea* Nuttall var. *spicata* (Hooker) Barneby

Plants 8–40 cm, herbage sparsely to densely silky-pilose. **Leaves** 6–23 cm; stipules glabrate to densely pilose abaxially, margins ciliate or eciliate, rarely with a few clavate processes; leaflets (13–)17–33, opposite, subopposite, or scattered, blades 3–23 mm. **Peduncles** (7–)8–30(–48) cm, axis 2–23 cm in fruit. **Racemes** 10–30-flowered. **Calyces:** tube 4.5–6.5 mm, lobes 1.5–3 mm. **Corollas** whitish or yellowish, fading yellowish, keel tip usually not maculate, 12–19.5 mm. **Legumes** 12–23 × 4–6 mm. **2*n*** = 32, 48.

Flowering spring–summer. Prairies, meadows, river terraces, woodlands; 1200–2300 m; Alta., B.C., Man., Sask.; Colo., Idaho, Mont., N.Dak., Oreg., S.Dak., Wash., Wyo.

Variety *spicata* is a highly variable taxon that closely resembles its counterpart var. *varians* farther to the north, but it presents differing facies and forms intermediate with other taxa. Morphological intermediates occur between vars. *davisii* and *spicata* in southwestern Alberta, and with var. *cusickii* through much of its range. Plants from British Columbia and Washington, known as var. *cervinus*, are similar to *Oxytropis sericea* var. *speciosa* in flower size (17–22 mm) and in number of leaflets (11–17). Occasional specimens of that entity do occur in British Columbia, and the most apparent diagnostic features, both tenuous, are the thick texture of the leaflets and the more conspicuously ochroleucous flowers of var. *speciosa*.

Examination of the type (S. L. Welsh 1995b) shows that the name var. *spicata* should be applied to the taxon that was previously known as var. *gracilis*. If var. *spicata* is recognized as a species, the name *Oxytropis spicata* (Hooker) Standley (1921) could not be used, since it is a later homonym of *O. spicata* O Fedtschenko & B. Fedtschenko (1909). The name *O. monticola* A. Gray would have priority. *Oxytropis spicata* (Hooker) Standley is an illegitimate name that applies here.

15e. Oxytropis campestris (Linnaeus) de Candolle var. **cusickii** (Greenman) Barneby, Leafl. W. Bot. 6: 111. 1951 E F

Oxytropis cusickii Greenman, Erythea 7: 116. 1899; *Aragallus alpicola* Rydberg; *Astragalus alpicola* (Rydberg) Tidestrom; *O. campestris* var. *rydbergii* (A. Nelson) R. J. Davis; *O. paysoniana* A. Nelson; *O. rydbergii* A. Nelson

Plants 4–15(–21) cm, herbage sparsely to densely pilose. **Leaves** 1.2–12 cm; stipules glabrous or sparsely pilose proximally, margins ciliate or eciliate; leaflets 7–15(–17), opposite, subopposite, or scattered, blades 4–23 mm. **Peduncles** prostrate to erect, 2–19 cm, glabrate, appressed-pilose, or villous-pilose, axis 0.5–3(–6) cm in fruit. **Racemes** 3–15-flowered, subcapitate to somewhat elongate. **Calyces:** tube 6–9 mm, lobes 1–3.5(–4) mm. **Corollas** whitish or yellowish throughout, keel tip usually not maculate, 14–18(–20) mm. **Legumes** 10–19 × 3.5–5(–6) mm. **2*n*** = 48.

Flowering summer. Talus slopes, ridge crests, alpine or subalpine meadows, usually above timberline; 2100–3400 m; Alta., B.C.; Colo., Idaho, Mont., Oreg., Utah, Wash., Wyo.

Variety *cusickii* is highly variable in flower size, especially where the large-flowered *Oxytropis sericea* var. *speciosa* occurs nearby. The existence of apparently transitional populations demonstrates the absence of consistent diagnostic features to separate what are, otherwise, rather distinctive taxa. The flowers seldom fade to a relatively bright yellowish on drying, as in *O. sericea* var. *speciosa*. It is not always possible to distinguish specimens of var. *cusickii* from var. *spicata*. Those materials traditionally passing as var. *cusickii* often occur in near proximity to var. *spicata*, which occurs at lower elevations on the same mountain ranges.

Oxytropis alpicola (Rydberg) M. E. Jones is an illegitimate name that pertains here.

15f. Oxytropis campestris (Linnaeus) de Candolle var. **dispar** (A. Nelson) Barneby, Leafl. W. Bot. 6: 111. 1951 [E]

Aragallus dispar A. Nelson, Erythea 7: 61. 1899; *Oxytropis dispar* (A. Nelson) K. Schumann; *O. monticola* A. Gray subsp. *dispar* (A. Nelson) Elisens & Packer

Plants 15–30 cm, herbage densely silky-pilose. **Leaves** strongly dimorphic, 5–21 cm; stipules usually concealed by vesture; leaflets 19–25, scattered or subopposite, blades primary ones crowded, ovate, shorter, distally linear-lanceolate or narrowly oblong, 4–20 mm. **Peduncles** 7–19(–26) cm, axis 3–8(–11) cm in fruit. **Racemes** 8–15-flowered, ± open to elongate. **Calyces:** tube 6–6.5 mm, lobes 2–2.7 mm. **Corollas** purple, blue, pink, white, yellowish, or polychrome (in populations), 17–19(–21) mm. **Legumes** 13–18 × 3.5–5 mm. **2*n*** = 32.

Flowering spring–summer. Grass and brush lands; 500–1000 m; Man., Sask.; Minn., N.Dak.

Variety *dispar* is closely allied to var. *spicata*, from which it differs in the flowers being polychrome within populations and in the somewhat firmer texture of the pods. It may well be that var. *dispar* is the somewhat stabilized product of previous hybridization involving the disjunct pale-flowered var. *spicata* and the purple-flowered *Oxytropis lambertii*, common in the same region. However, the presence of var. *johannensis*, not far distant to the northeast, might account for the occurrence of darker colored flowers in this region.

15g. Oxytropis campestris (Linnaeus) de Candolle var. **davisii** S. L. Welsh, Leafl. W. Bot. 10: 25. 1963 [E]

Oxytropis davisii (S. L. Welsh) Jurtzev; *O. jordalii* A. E. Porsild subsp. *davisii* (S. L. Welsh) Elisens & Packer

Plants 9–45 cm, herbage strigose, strigulose, or pilose. **Leaves** 3–17(–25) cm; stipules free ends 5–6 mm, sparsely pilose abaxially, margins ciliate, sometimes also with clavate processes; leaflets 25–39(–45), sometimes fasciculate, blades 4–20(–29) mm. **Peduncles** 5–35(–38) cm, axis 2–8(–14) cm in fruit. **Racemes** 10–30+-flowered, elongate in fruit. **Calyces:** tube 4.2–6(–6.5) mm, lobes 1.3–3 mm. **Corollas** usually pink-purple and fading dark purple, or bluish, sometimes polychrome, 14–19 mm. **Legumes** 10–14 × 3.5–5 mm. **2*n*** = 32.

Flowering spring–early summer. Gravelly sites in boreal forests; 900–1500 m; Alta., B.C., N.W.T.

Variety *davisii* is readily distinguished by the combination of its colorful flowers, fasciculate leaflets (or the tendency toward fasciculate leaflets), and elongate inflorescences. It forms apparent intermediates with *Oxytropis sericea* var. *speciosa* and at the southern portion of its range is more or less transitional to var. *spicata*. A relationship with var. *johannensis* cannot be discounted, especially with those portions of that variety with fasciculate leaflets. Specimens transitional to *O. splendens* make assignment of materials to one or the other difficult in particular instances.

15h. Oxytropis campestris (Linnaeus) de Candolle var. **columbiana** (H. St. John) Barneby, Leafl. W. Bot. 6: 111. 1951 [C] [E]

Oxytropis columbiana H. St. John, Proc. Biol. Soc. Wash. 41: 100. 1928

Plants (13–)19–30(–35) cm, herbage silky-pilose, greenish or canescent. **Leaves** (5–)8–17 cm; stipules usually pilose, sometimes glabrescent abaxially, margins sometimes ciliate; leaflets 11–17(or 19), opposite or subopposite, blades 9–30 mm. **Peduncles** (8–)12–30 cm, axis 2–10 cm in fruit. **Racemes** 10–28-flowered. **Calyces:** tube 5–6.5 mm, lobes (1.8–)2.5–4 mm. **Corollas** white, banner often veined, keel tip maculate with purplish blue, 15–20(–22) mm. **Legumes** 16–23 × 5–7 mm. **2*n*** = 48.

Flowering spring–summer. Gravel bars, stream banks, lake shores; of conservation concern; 300–1100 m; Mont., Wash.

Variety *columbiana* is distinguished by the combination of small number of leaflets, whitish flowers with maculate keels, and its soft, silky pubescence; it is very similar to var. *spicata*, with which it is somewhat transitional. It differs in about the same manner as other varieties in this complex group of infraspecific taxa. Most of the Washington populations appear to have been eradicated by storage water in a reservoir. This variety is known currently mainly from islands in, and points around, Flathead Lake, Lake County, Montana. The tendency toward relatively large flowers and only 11–17 leaflets is similar to the so-called cervinus phase of var. *spicata*, which is common some distance north of Flathead Lake and extending into British Columbia.

15i. Oxytropis campestris (Linnaeus) de Candolle var. **wanapum** Joyal, Great Basin Naturalist 50: 373, fig. 1. 1991 C E

Plants (10–)13–21 cm, herbage silky-pilose, canescent. **Leaves** (11–)14–18(–22) cm; stipules pilose abaxially, margins ciliate; leaflets (13–)19–25(–33), scattered or subopposite, blades linear to narrowly oblong, (8–)15–25(–33) mm. **Peduncles** (10–)17–21(–30) cm, axis (4–)6–8(–12) cm in fruit. **Racemes** (5 or)6–12-flowered. **Calyces:** tube 5–7 mm, lobes (1–)2–3 mm. **Corollas** pale lavender, banner veined, keel tip maculate with purplish blue, 14–20(–23) mm. **Legumes** 13–23 × 3.5–5 mm.

Flowering spring. Gravelly ridges above steep north-facing basalt talus; of conservation concern; 600 m; Wash.

Variety *wanapum* is restricted to xeric, basaltic gravels, talus, or outcrops in Grant County. Its flowers, suffused with purple, are diagnostic since no other varieties of the species in the Pacific Northwest typically have colored flowers. The narrow-bladed leaflets tend to be involute and to vary in number, usually 19–25. These vegetative features are unlike any of the other several varieties of *Oxytropis campestris* that occur elsewhere in North America and have lavender to purplish flowers.

15j. Oxytropis campestris (Linnaeus) de Candolle var. **minor** (Hooker) S. L. Welsh, Great Basin Naturalist 55: 277. 1995 • Oxytrope mineur E

Oxytropis uralensis (Linnaeus) de Candolle var. *minor* Hooker, Fl. Bor.-Amer. 1: 146. 1831; *O. campestris* var. *terrae-novae* (Fernald) Barneby; *O. terrae-novae* Fernald

Plants 5–20+ cm, herbage usually pilose, rarely silky-pilose hairs appressed, some ascending. **Leaves** (2–)3–10(–13) cm; stipules glabrous or glabrate abaxially, margins eciliate; leaflets 11–23(–27), opposite or subopposite, blades 2–10 mm. **Peduncles** curved-ascending, 3–15(–18) cm, axis 0.3–1.5 cm in fruit. **Racemes** (3–)5–9-flowered, subcapitate. **Calyces:** tube 5–6.5 mm, lobes deltate, 0.5–1.5(–2) mm. **Corollas** purple fading violet, 11–18 mm. **Legumes** 10–22 × 3.5–5 mm. $2n = 48$.

Flowering summer. Tundra near coasts; 0–600 m; Man., Nfld. and Labr., Nunavut, Ont., Que.

Putative reports of var. *minor* from the Mackenzie Mountains are probably referable to the purple-flowered var. *roaldii*, from which var. *minor* differs in its flowers that average larger, and in the longer calyx tube. There are several specimens from Churchill, Manitoba, that have been variously assigned to vars. *johannensis*, *minor*, or *varians*. Field studies of these populations need to be undertaken to resolve this problem. The Pan-Arctic Flora (http://panarcticflora.org/) treats this taxon as a distinct species, *Oxytropis terrae-novae* (with *O. campestris* var. *johannensis* as a synonym).

15k. Oxytropis campestris (Linnaeus) de Candolle var. **johannensis** Fernald, Rhodora 1: 88. 1899 • Oxytrope du fleuve Saint-Jean E

Aragallus campestris (Linnaeus) Greene var. *johannensis* (Fernald) J. M. Macoun; *A. johannensis* (Fernald) A. Heller; *Astragalus campestris* (Linnaeus) Greene var. *johannensis* (Fernald) Tidestrom; *Oxytropis campestris* subsp. *johannensis* (Fernald) Blondeau & Gervais; *O. johannensis* (Fernald) Fernald

Plants 4–86 cm, herbage silky-pilose, hairs subappressed, often becoming green and glabrate. **Leaves** 4–26 cm; stipules glabrous or sparsely pilose abaxially, margins ciliate; leaflets 15–29, opposite or subopposite, blades 3–29 mm. **Peduncles** erect, (4–)8–36 cm, axis 1.5–9(–11) cm in fruit. **Racemes** 7–12(–14)-flowered. **Calyces:** tube 5–6 mm, lobes usually lanceolate, (1–)2–3 mm. **Corollas** usually purple, rarely white, 12–18.5 mm. **Legumes** 14–27 × 5–9 mm. $2n = 48$.

Flowering summer. Rock outcrops, islands, gravel bars; 10–400 m; N.B., Nfld. and Labr. (Nfld.), N.S., Ont., Que.; Maine.

Plants of var. *johannensis* from south of James Bay, Ontario, have fasciculate leaves and relatively short fruits; the latter characteristic indicates a close relationship to var. *chartacea*. Some specimens appear to be transitional to *Oxytropis splendens*. The Pan-Arctic Flora (http://panarcticflora.org/) treats var. *johannensis* as a synonym of *O. terrae-novae*.

Variety *johannensis* is in the Center for Plant Conservation's National Collection of Endangered Plants.

15l. Oxytropis campestris (Linnaeus) de Candolle var. **chartacea** (Fassett) Barneby, Proc. Calif. Acad. Sci., ser. 4, 27: 269. 1952 C E

Oxytropis chartacea Fassett, Rhodora 38: 95. 1936

Plants 4–86 cm, herbage silky-pilose, hairs subappressed, often loosely and copiously pilose. **Leaves** 4–26 cm; stipules pilose, margins ciliate; leaflets 17–29, scattered, opposite, or subopposite, blades 3–29 mm. **Peduncles** erect, (4–)8–36 cm, axis 1.5–9(–11) cm in fruit. **Racemes** 7–12(–14)-flowered. **Calyces:** tube 5–6 mm, lobes usually lanceolate, (1–)2–3 mm. **Corollas** usually purple, rarely white, 12–18.5 mm. **Legumes** 8–15 × 4–6 mm. **2*n*** = 48.

Flowering summer. Sandy lake shores; of conservation concern; 300–400 m; Wis.

Variety *chartacea* is in the Center for Plant Conservation's National Collection of Endangered Plants.

16. Oxytropis sericea Nuttall in J. Torrey and A. Gray, Fl. N. Amer. 1: 339. 1838 E W

Plants cespitose, appearing acaulescent, 7–45 cm, herbage sparsely to densely silky-pilose, usually canescent. **Leaves** 6–28 cm; stipules membranous, light tan or grayish, 8–22 mm, free ends acuminate, pilose, villous, glabrate, or glabrous abaxially, margins ciliate or eciliate; leaflets 7–19(or 21), opposite, subopposite, or scattered, blades ovate to elliptic, oblong, or lanceolate, (4–)7–32(–40) × (1.5–)4–9(–10) mm, apex acute, surfaces sericeous, often densely so. **Peduncles** erect, 7–30 cm, sericeous; bract lanceolate, shorter than flowers, pilose. **Racemes** 5–20+-flowered, subcapitate to elongate. **Calyces** cylindric, 7–12 mm, pilose, hairs black and white, lobes dark hairy; tube 6.5–9 mm, lobes 2–4 mm. **Corollas** white to yellowish, keel tip maculate or not, 17–27(–28) mm. **Legumes** erect, sessile, subcylindric to ovoid-oblong, 15–24 × 4.5–7 mm, ± bilocular, fleshy when fresh, becoming leathery or almost woody and rigid, strigose or pilosulous.

Varieties 2 (2 in the flora): nw, c North America.

1. Corollas white or yellowish, fading whitish or yellowish, or polychrome, keel tips maculate; raceme axis 1.5–18 cm in fruit; s Montana and South Dakota southward . . . . 16a. *Oxytropis sericea* var. *sericea*
1. Corollas whitish or yellowish, fading yellowish, keel tips not maculate; raceme axis often compact, 3–12 cm in fruit; Idaho and n Wyoming northward. . . . . 16b. *Oxytropis sericea* var. *speciosa*

16a. Oxytropis sericea Nuttall var. **sericea** E

Aragallus lambertii (Pursh) Greene var. *sericeus* (Nuttall) A. Nelson; *A. sericeus* (Nuttall) Greene; *Oxytropis lambertii* Pursh var. *sericea* (Nuttall) A. Gray; *Spiesia lambertii* (Pursh) Kuntze var. *sericea* (Nuttall) Rydberg

Plants 14–45 cm. **Leaves** 6–28 cm; stipules glabrous or densely pilose abaxially; leaflets (9 or)11–19(or 21). **Peduncles** 7–30 cm, axis 1.5–18 cm in fruit. **Racemes** 5–20+-flowered. **Calyces** 9–12 mm, tube 6.5–9 mm, lobes 2.5–4 mm. **Corollas** white or yellowish, fading whitish or yellowish, or polychrome in populations, 18–27(–28) mm, keel tip maculate. **Legumes** 15–22 × 5–7 mm. **2*n*** = 24, 48.

Flowering spring–early summer(–fall). Plains, prairies, foothills to mountain summits; 600–3100 m; Colo., Idaho, Kans., Mont., Nebr., Nev., N.Mex., Okla., Oreg., S.Dak., Tex., Utah, Wyo.

Variety *sericea* forms hybrids with *Oxytropis lambertii* where the two entities come in contact, and occasionally where only one parent is known to occur. Especially impressive hybrid populations occur on the high plains and in outliers of the Rocky Mountains where *O. sericea* and the montane populations of *O. lambertii* are sympatric or nearly so. The swarms of hybrids, backcrosses, and derivatives at Nederland, Colorado, are especially distinctive, with floral colors and sizes not readily evident in either of the parental types. Such swarms occur widely at least in Colorado and Wyoming.

16b. Oxytropis sericea Nuttall var. **speciosa** (Torrey & A. Gray) S. L. Welsh, Great Basin Naturalist 55: 279. 1995 [E]

Oxytropis campestris (Linnaeus) de Candolle var. *speciosa* Torrey & A. Gray, Fl. N. Amer. 1: 341. 1838

Plants 8–36 cm. **Leaves** 6–18 cm; stipules densely pilose to villous, or glabrate abaxially; leaflets 7–17(–21). **Peduncles** 8–29 cm, axis often compact, 3–12 cm in fruit. **Racemes** 5–17-flowered. **Calyces** 7–10.5 mm, tube 6.5–7.5 mm, lobes 2–3 mm. **Corollas** whitish or yellowish, fading yellowish, 17–22 mm, keel tip not maculate. **Legumes** 16–24 × 4.5–6 mm. $2n = 48$.

Flowering spring–early summer. Gravelly and sandy bluffs, roadsides, stream gravel, plains, prairies, boreal forests; 700–3400 m; Alta., B.C., Man., Sask., Yukon; Idaho, Mont., Wyo.

Variety *speciosa* forms apparent hybrids with *Oxytropis campestris* var. *davisii* in northern British Columbia; exceptionally large-flowered plants traditionally placed with *O. campestris* var. *cusickii* may be little more than alpine disjuncts of var. *speciosa*. See also the discussion under 15d. *O. campestris* var. *spicata*.

17. Oxytropis nana Nuttall in J. Torrey and A. Gray, Fl. N. Amer. 1: 340. 1838 • Dwarf locoweed [E]

Aragallus collinus A. Nelson; *A. nanus* (Nuttall) Greene; *Astragalus tomae* Tidestrom; *Oxytropis lunelliana* A. Nelson; *Spiesia nana* (Nuttall) Kuntze

Plants densely cespitose, appearing acaulescent, herbage silky-pilose throughout, hairs usually silvery, sometimes greenish. **Leaves** 2–9(–11) cm; stipules membranous, stramineous, 8–15 mm, free blades 3–6 mm, silky-pilose abaxially, margins ciliate; leaflets 7–11(or 13), blades narrowly to broadly lanceolate-oblong or lanceolate to elliptic, 5–30 × 1–7 mm, apex acute, surfaces pubescent. **Peduncles** erect or curved-ascending, 3–15(–24) cm, axis 1.5–5(–7) cm in fruit, pubescent; bract narrowly ovate to lanceolate, 4–10(–15) mm, densely pilose. **Racemes** 4–19-flowered. **Calyces** cylindric-campanulate to inflated-urceolate, densely shaggy-hirsute and subtomentose, hairs white; tube 9–11 mm, becoming inflated and urceolate, enclosing fruit, lobes 1.5–2.5(–3) mm. **Corollas** purple or white, with purple-maculate keel, 18–22.5 mm. **Legumes** included in calyx and tardily deciduous with it, ascending, subsessile, ovoid, 7–10 × 4–5 mm, unilocular, leathery, firm, rigid at maturity, strigose-canescent.

Flowering spring–early summer. Bluffs, ridge crests; 1500–2100 m; Wyo.

Oxytropis nana is apparently intermediate between *O. multiceps* and *O. sericea*; it seems to form intermediates, occasionally, with both *O. lambertii* and *O. sericea*.

18. Oxytropis lambertii Pursh, Fl. Amer. Sept. 2: 740. 1813 • Lambert's locoweed [E] [W]

Plants cespitose, appearing acaulescent, (10–)14–50 cm, herbage pilose, silky-canescent, or strigose, hairs malpighian. **Leaves** (2–)4–25 cm; stipules persistent, connate opposite petiole at first, membranous becoming papery, light tan or grayish, pilose, silky, or glabrate; leaflets (3–)7–19, blades linear-lanceolate, lanceolate, ovate to oblong, linear, linear-oblong, or elliptic, 5–40 × 2–8 mm, apex acute, surfaces canescent. **Peduncles** erect, 4–25(–35) cm, usually surpassing leaves, axis 3–16 cm in fruit, strigose; bract lanceolate to ovate-acuminate, strigose to pilose. **Racemes** (6–)8–45-flowered. **Calyces** cylindric, (6.5–)7–10 mm, silky-strigose or -pilose, rarely with some dark or some loose hairs; tube purplish, (4.5–)5–8 mm, lobes 1.2–4 mm. **Corollas** usually pink-purple, rarely white, sometimes white and purple in populations, (5–)15–25 mm, wing petals 3.5–9 mm. **Legumes** erect or ascending, sessile or short-stipitate, cylindric or lanceolate-acuminate (in outline), 7–25 × 2.5–6 mm, bilocular, strigose to strigulose.

Varieties 3 (3 in the flora): w North America.

1. Legumes sessile or short-stipitate; leaflets (3–)7–15(–19), blades usually ovate, elliptic, or broadly lanceolate, rarely linear; Arizona, Colorado, New Mexico, Utah, Wyoming . . . . 18c. *Oxytropis lambertii* var. *bigelovii*
1. Legumes sessile; leaflets (5–)9–19, blades narrowly linear to linear-lanceolate or linear to narrowly oblong; Iowa, Kansas, Manitoba, Minnesota, Missouri, Montana, Nebraska, New Mexico, North Dakota, Oklahoma, Saskatchewan, South Dakota, Texas, Wyoming.
   2. Calyx lobes 1.5–4 mm; corollas 15–20 mm; legumes 8–15 mm (2+ times as long as calyx); Iowa, Kansas, Manitoba, Minnesota, Missouri, Montana, Nebraska, North Dakota, Oklahoma, Saskatchewan, South Dakota, Wyoming . . . . 18a. *Oxytropis lambertii* var. *lambertii*
   2. Calyx lobes 1.2–3(–4) mm; corollas 18–25 mm; legumes 7–10(–17) mm (less than 2 times as long as calyx); Kansas, New Mexico, Oklahoma, Texas . . . . 18b. *Oxytropis lambertii* var. *articulata*

18a. Oxytropis lambertii Pursh var. **lambertii** [E]

Aragallus angustatus Rydberg; *A. aven-nelsonii* Lunell; *A. formosus* Greene; *A. involutus* A. Nelson; *A. lambertii* (Pursh) Greene; *Astragalus lambertii* (Pursh) Sprengel; *Oxytropis angustata* (Rydberg) A. Nelson; *O. aven-nelsonii* (Lunell) A. Nelson; *O. bushii* Gandoger; *O. hookeriana* Nuttall; *O. involuta* (A. Nelson) K. Schumann; *O. plattensis* Nuttall; *Spiesia lambertii* (Pursh) Kuntze

Herbage usually silky-canescent, hirsute, sometimes ascending-hirsute, hairs appressed. **Leaves** (2–)5–17 (–23) cm; stipules thinly to densely pilose abaxially; leaflets (5–)9–19, blades linear, linear-lanceolate, or narrowly oblong, 5–40 mm. **Peduncles** 4.5–25 cm, axis 3–15 cm in fruit. **Racemes** 6–18-flowered. **Calyces** 7–10 mm, tube 5.5–8 mm, lobes 1.5–4 mm. **Corollas** usually pink-purple, rarely white, 15–20 mm. **Legumes** sessile, 8–15 mm, 2+ times as long as calyx, stiffly leathery or woody. $2n = 48$.

Flowering spring–early summer. Prairies, bluffs, badlands; 300–1500 m; Man., Sask.; Iowa, Kans., Minn., Mo., Mont., Nebr., N.Dak., Okla., S.Dak., Wyo.

18b. Oxytropis lambertii Pursh var. **articulata** (Greene) Barneby, Leafl. W. Bot. 6: 111. 1951 [E]

Aragallus articulatus Greene, Proc. Biol. Soc. Wash. 18: 13. 1905; *A. abbreviatus* Greene; *Astragalus lambertii* (Pursh) Sprengel var. *abbreviatus* (Greene) Shinners

Herbage finely pilose throughout. **Leaves** 4–25 cm; stipules glabrous or thinly or densely pilose abaxially, margins ciliate; leaflets (7 or) 9–19, blades narrowly linear to linear-oblong, 10–35 mm, usually thick, rigid. **Peduncles** 10–24 cm, axis 4–11(–13) cm in fruit. **Racemes** 12–28-flowered. **Calyces** 7–10 mm, tube 6–8 mm, lobes 1.2–3(–4) mm. **Corollas** usually pink-purple, rarely white, 18–25 mm. **Legumes** sessile, 7–10(–17) mm, included in calyx, less than 2 times as long as calyx.

Flowering spring–early summer. Prairies, bluffs, ravines; 600–2000 m; Kans., N.Mex., Okla., Tex.

18c. Oxytropis lambertii Pursh var. **bigelovii** A. Gray, Proc. Amer. Acad. Arts 20: 7. 1884 (as lamberti) [E]

Aragallus bigelovii (A. Gray) Greene; *Astragalus lambertii* (Pursh) Sprengel var. *bigelovii* (A. Gray) Tidestrom; *Oxytropis lambertii* subsp. *bigelovii* (A. Gray) W. A. Weber

Herbage pilose or silky-canescent, sometimes greenish. **Leaves** (2.5–)5–17(–24) cm; stipules silky or becoming glabrate abaxially, margins ciliate; leaflets (3–)7–15(–19), blades ovate, elliptic, broadly lanceolate, or, rarely, linear, 7–20(–32) mm. **Peduncles** (4–)7–25(–35) cm, axis (3–)5–16 cm in fruit. **Racemes** 8–28(–45)-flowered. **Calyces** (6.5–)8–10 mm, tube (4.5–)5–7(–7.5) mm, lobes (1.5–)2–4 mm. **Corollas** bright pink-purple or, occasionally, white and purple in populations, (5–)18–23(–25) mm. **Legumes** sessile or short-stipitate, 15–25 mm, ca. 2 times as long as calyx. $2n = 32$.

Flowering spring–early summer. Plains, prairies, mountain slopes, desert shrublands; 600–3100 m; Ariz., Colo., N.Mex., Utah, Wyo.

Populations of var. *bigelovii* from the canyon lands of Utah and adjacent Arizona have malpighian hairs with a very short attachment. Furthermore, the plants tend to be relatively tall and with features of the stem, inflorescence, and leaflets attenuated. The leaflets also tend to disarticulate readily from the rachis. If only the populations from Kane County, Utah, were seen, there might be a case for taxonomic recognition of those populations. In plants northward from there, the stem, inflorescence, and leaflets are not attenuated, even though the short branch of the malpighian hair is present. There does not seem to be sufficient correlation of the morphological features, however, to warrant taxonomic recognition for the plants from Kane County that appear to be transitional.

19. Oxytropis kobukensis S. L. Welsh, Iowa State J. Sci. 41: 286. 1967 • Kobuk locoweed [C] [E]

Plants cespitose, clump-forming, appearing acaulescent; caudex branches elongate. **Leaves** 6–10 cm; stipules persistent, well separated, firm, rigid, usually purplish or becoming purplish, free ends long-attenuate, pilose abaxially, or glabrate on free ends, margins scarious and ciliate, with clavate processes; leaflets 13–17, blades lanceolate to lanceolate-oblong, 6–16(–18) × 2–3.5 mm, base rounded, margins involute, apex obtuse to acute, surfaces strigose to pilose abaxially, pilose to glabrate adaxially. **Peduncles** 7–11 cm, strigose, hairs spreading, appressed; bract lanceolate, pilose, margins ciliate, with clavate processes. **Racemes** 5-8-flowered. **Calyces** purplish, short-cylindric to campanulate, minutely strigulose, hairs black and white; tube 5.8–7 mm, lobes 1.5–2.2 mm. **Corollas** blue or purplish, 16–18(–20) mm. **Legumes** held aloft at maturity, spreading, sessile, cylindric, 12–17 × 5–7 mm (to 3 times longer than wide), bilocular or sub-bilocular, pilose, hairs black or black and white. **2*n*** = 80.

Flowering summer. Sand dunes; of conservation concern; 0–100 m; Alaska.

Oxytropis kobukensis is restricted to the Kobuk River area in western Alaska.

20. Oxytropis maydelliana Trautvetter, Fl. Terr. Tschukt., 16. 1878 • Maydell's oxytrope, oxytrope de Maydell

Oxytropis campestris (Linnaeus) de Candolle var. *glabrata* Hooker; *O. campestris* var. *melanocephala* Hooker; *O. maydelliana* subsp. *melanocephala* (Hooker) A. E. Porsild

Plants cespitose, appearing acaulescent. **Leaves** 4–14 cm; stipules stiff, papery, becoming reddish brown, 12–20 mm, free ends caudate-acuminate, pilose to glabrate abaxially, margins ciliate; leaflets 11–21, blades ovate to lanceolate, elliptic, or oblong, 4–17 × 2–4 mm, apex acute or obtuse, surfaces pilose on midrib abaxially, pilose or glabrous adaxially. **Peduncles** erect or ascending, 4–15 cm, spreading-villous; bract lanceolate, shorter to longer than calyx, villous, margins ciliate. **Racemes** 6–10-flowered, subcapitate, slightly elongate in fruit. **Calyces** short-cylindric, villous, hairs intermixed black and white; tube 5–6 mm, lobes 1.5–3.2 mm. **Corollas** yellowish, keel tip not maculate, 13–17 mm. **Legumes** erect, sessile or subsessile, ovoid-ellipsoid, 15–21 × 5–7 mm, length less than or equal to 3 times width, partially bilocular, papery, sulcate adaxially, pilose, hairs black and white. **2*n*** = 96.

Flowering late spring–summer. Arctic and alpine tundra, heathlands, alluvial sands, gravels, dry rocky slopes; 0–1900 m; B.C., N.W.T., Nunavut, Que., Yukon; Alaska; e Asia (Chukotsk, Kamchatka).

Oxytropis maydelliana has yellowish flowers and reddish brown stipules, which easily characterize this arctic species.

21. Oxytropis arctica R. Brown, Chlor. Melvill., 20. 1823 • Arctic oxytrope [E]

Plants cespitose, appearing acaulescent. **Leaves** (3–)4–21 cm; stipules membranous, fragile, strongly imbricate, grayish or yellowish, 10–20 mm, pilose abaxially becoming glabrate, margins ciliate, with clavate processes; leaflets 3–21, alternate, opposite, subopposite, scattered, or fasciculate, blades lanceolate, elliptic, lanceolate-elliptic, or oblong, 4–40 × 2–5 mm, apex acute, surfaces pilose. **Peduncles** 4–15(–31) cm, strigulose to spreading-villous; bract linear-lanceolate, mostly longer than pedicel, pilose. **Racemes** 2–10+-flowered. **Calyces** cylindric, villous to shaggy-villous or pilose, hairs black and white; tube 5–8.7 mm, lobes 1.5–6 mm. **Corollas** usually pink-purple, pinkish violet, or bluish, rarely white or yellowish, (14–)16–22 mm, wing petals 4–6 mm wide apically. **Legumes** erect, spreading, or erect-ascending, sessile or short-stipitate, ovoid-acuminate, 10–25 × 5–7 mm, bilocular or sub-bilocular, thinly papery, pilose or short-villous.

The relationships among subspecific taxa of *Oxytropis arctica*, *O. campestris*, and *O. koyukukensis* were examined by J. L. Jorgensen et al. (2003) using molecular data.

Varieties 5 (5 in the flora): n North America.

1. Plants usually 15–45 cm; racemes 10 +-flowered; leaflets 11+, alternate, opposite, or fasciculate; disjunct from Anaktuvuk, Koyukuk, Northway, Shaktoolik, Umiat, and Wiseman, Alaska, and Kluane Lake, Yukon . . . . 21c. *Oxytropis arctica* var. *koyukukensis*
1. Plants 4–21 cm; racemes 2–8(–10)-flowered; leaflets 3–17+, alternate, opposite, subopposite, fasciculate, or scattered; Alaska, Manitoba, Nunavut, Yukon.
    2. Leaflets 11–17, alternate or opposite, blades broadly elliptic to oblong or lanceolate-elliptic; corollas white, fading cream; Kotzebue, Alaska, and eastward . . . . 21b. *Oxytropis arctica* var. *barnebyana*
    2. Leaflets 3–17+, alternate, subopposite, fasciculate, or scattered, blades narrowly lanceolate to lanceolate-elliptic, or lanceolate to elliptic or oblong; corollas pink-purple to bluish, pinkish violet, or, rarely, white or yellowish; Alaska, Manitoba, Northwest Territories, Nunavut, Yukon.

3. Leaves 2–17(–19) cm, leaflets alternate, subopposite, or fasciculate; n Alaska east to Hudson Bay . . . . 21a. *Oxytropis arctica* var. *arctica*
3. Leaves 3–13(–17) cm, leaflets usually fasciculate, sometimes opposite or scattered; Hudson Bay, sw Yukon.
   4. Calyces 3.5–4.5 mm wide when pressed, shaggy-pilose, hairs mostly dark; vicinity of Hudson Bay. . . . . .21d. *Oxytropis arctica* var. *bellii*
   4. Calyces 4–5 mm wide when pressed, shaggy-villous, hairs black and white; sw Yukon . . . . 21e. *Oxytropis arctica* var. *murrayi*

21a. Oxytropis arctica R. Brown var. **arctica** E

Aragallus arcticus (R. Brown) Greene; *O. uralensis* (Linnaeus) de Candolle var. *arctica* (R. Brown) Ledebour; *Spiesia arctica* (R. Brown) Kuntze

Plants 6–21 cm. **Leaves** 2–17 (–19) cm; leaflets (9 or)11–19 (or 21), alternate, subopposite, or fasciculate (sometimes in a single population), blades narrowly lanceolate to lanceolate-elliptic. **Peduncles** 4–15 cm. **Racemes** 2–10-flowered, subcapitate to elongate. **Calyces** villous to shaggy-villous. **Corollas** usually pink-purple to bluish, rarely white or yellowish. **Legumes** erect or spreading. $2n = 48, 64$.

Flowering summer. *Salix* heathlands, meadows, river terraces, stream bars and banks, ridge crests, talus slopes; 0–2300 m; Man., N.W.T., Nunavut, Yukon; Alaska.

Astragalus arcticus (R. Brown) Sprengel is an illegitimate name that pertains here.

21b. Oxytropis arctica R. Brown var. **barnebyana** S. L. Welsh, Great Basin Naturalist 28: 152, fig. 4. 1968 C E

Oxytropis sordida (Willdenow) Persoon subsp. *barnebyana* (S. L. Welsh) Jurtzev

Plants mostly 9–20 cm. **Leaves** 7–15 cm; leaflets 11–17, alternate or opposite, blades broadly elliptic to oblong or lanceolate-elliptic. **Peduncles** 7–15 cm. **Racemes** 2–10-flowered, subcapitate to elongate. **Calyces** villous to shaggy-villous. **Corollas** white, fading cream. **Legumes** erect-ascending, ovoid, beak slender, much elongated, 23 mm, pilosulous.

Flowering summer. *Salix* heathlands and meadows; of conservation concern; 10–800 m; Alaska.

Flower size, pilose stipules, and calyx features indicate an alliance to the sympatric *Oxytropis arctica* var. *arctica*. The racemes vary from subcapitate to somewhat expanded. In the expanded form the plants are a close match to much of *O. arctica* in a strict sense. The placement of var. *barnebyana* with *O. sordida*, a taxonomic entity considered by European authors (T. G. Tutin et al. 1964–1980) at infraspecific level within *O. campestris*, has considerable merit. However, the treatment by Jurtzev of var. *barnebyana* at infraspecific level within *O. sordida*, a highly variable taxonomic entity with both pale and colored flowers, would not solve the basic problem of the similarity of var. *barnebyana* to *O. arctica*, however well the placement elsewhere would indicate the similarity of this North American plant with the protean *O. campestris* complex. The calyx lobes of var. *barnebyana* vary from relatively short, as in some phases of *O. campestris*, to almost as long as some phases of *O. arctica*. The sympatry of var. *barnebyana* with *O. arctica* and its allopatry with respect to *O. campestris*, while not conclusive, weigh in the decision to keep the Kotzebue materials of var. *barnebyana* (which are at the type locality) with *O. arctica*. The absence of a stopping place for additional inclusions of North American taxa within an expanded *O. campestris* or *O. sordida* is likewise a consideration for keeping var. *barnebyana* with *O. arctica*.

21c. Oxytropis arctica R. Brown var. **koyukukensis** (A. E. Porsild) S. L. Welsh, Iowa State J. Sci. 41: 280. 1967 E

Oxytropis koyukukensis A. E. Porsild, Canad. Field-Naturalist 65: 78, plate 2. 1951

Plants mostly 15–45 cm. **Leaves** 5–26 cm; leaflets 11+, alternate, opposite, or fasciculate. **Peduncles** 8–31 cm. **Racemes** 10+-flowered, usually somewhat open to elongate. **Calyces** villous to shaggy-villous. **Legumes** erect or spreading, pilosulous. $2n = 48$.

Flowering spring–summer. Roadsides, tundra, meadows, dunes, gravel; 50–500 m; Yukon; Alaska.

Variety *koyukukensis* has been reported only from Anaktuvuk, Koyukuk, Northway, Shaktoolik, Umiat, and Wiseman, Alaska, and Kluane Lake, Yukon.

The specimens upon which var. *koyukukensis* is based vary considerably. They tend to be relatively tall plants with several-flowered racemes, but the specimens from Anaktuvuk approach, if not actually pass into, var. *arctica*. Leaflet arrangement varies from entirely fasciculate to merely scattered. Some specimens herein as assigned to var. *murrayi* approach this taxon in flower size, flower number, and leaflet arrangement. The Pan-Arctic Flora (http://panarcticflora.org/) recognizes *Oxytropis koyukukensis* as a distinct species.

21d. Oxytropis arctica R. Brown var. **bellii** (Britton) B. Boivin, Naturaliste Canad. 94: 73. 1967 [E]

Spiesia bellii Britton, Canad. Rec. Sci. 6: 148. 1894 (as belli); *Aragallus bellii* (Britton) Greene; *Astragalus bellii* (Britton) Tidestrom; *Oxytropis arctica* subsp. *bellii* (Britton) Á. Löve & D. Löve; *O. bellii* (Britton) Palibin

Plants 10–20 cm. **Leaves** 4–13 (–17) cm; leaflets 3 or 4, fasciculate 7–10 fascicles, blades narrowly lanceolate to elliptic or oblong, surfaces with simple hairs abaxially, pilose adaxially. **Peduncles** 7–18 cm; bract often longer than pedicel. **Racemes** (2–)4–8(–10)-flowered, elongate. **Calyces** deeply campanulate, 9–10 mm, shaggy-pilose hairs mostly black; tube 6–7.5 mm, 3.5–4.5 mm wide when pressed, lobes linear-lanceolate to triangular, 2.5–3 mm. **Corollas** usually pinkish violet, rarely white, 18–21 mm. **Legumes** erect or spreading, ovoid-acuminate, 12–20 mm, densely short-villous. $2n = 96$.

Flowering summer. Rocky and gravelly shores; 10–200 m; Man., Nunavut.

Variety *bellii* is found around bays and on islands on the northwestern side of Hudson Bay. The Pan-Arctic Flora (http://panarcticflora.org/) recognizes *Oxytropis bellii* as a distinct species.

21e. Oxytropis arctica R. Brown var. **murrayi** (Jurtzev) S. L. Welsh, Great Basin Naturalist 51: 383. 1991 [E]

Oxytropis sordida (Willdenow) Persoon subsp. *murrayi* Jurtzev in A. I. Tolmatchew, Fl. Arct. URSS 9: 179. 1986

Plants 4–16(–18) cm. **Leaves** 3–12 cm; leaflets 17+, usually fasciculate, sometimes opposite or scattered, blades narrowly lanceolate to lanceolate-elliptic. **Peduncles** 4–12(–14) cm. **Racemes** 2–7-flowered, subcapitate or slightly elongate. **Calyces** shaggy-villous hairs black and white; tube 4–5 mm wide when pressed. **Corollas** usually pink-purple to bluish, rarely white or yellowish. **Legumes** erect or spreading, 17–21 mm, pilose.

Flowering summer. Ridge crests, talus slopes, meadows; 700–1900 m; Yukon.

Variety *murrayi* presents variation that reflects the morphology of all portions of the *Oxytropis arctica* complex. It is similar in some of its aspects to var. *bellii*, from which it is distantly isolated, but it is probably most nearly allied to var. *koyukukensis*, which is much nearer geographically. The principal differences between vars. *bellii* and *murrayi* consist of the obviously larger flowers, broader calyces with mixed shaggy-villous vesture, and tendency to larger leaflets of the latter.

22. Oxytropis splendens Douglas ex Hooker, Fl. Bor.-Amer. 1: 147. 1831 • Showy oxytrope [E] [F] [W]

Aragallus splendens (Douglas ex Hooker) Greene; *Astragalus splendens* (Douglas ex Hooker) Tidestrom; *Spiesia splendens* (Douglas ex Hooker) Kuntze

Plants cespitose, appearing acaulescent. **Leaves** 3–28 cm; stipules membranous, stramineous, silky-pilose abaxially; leaflets fasciculate on rachis in 7–15 fascicles (32–70 leaflets), rarely with few verticillate, blades narrowly lanceolate, 4–25 × 2–6 mm, apex usually acute, rarely obtuse, surfaces villous. **Peduncles** 9–29(–36) cm, axis 3–16 cm in fruit, pilose; bract narrowly lanceolate, pilose. **Racemes** 9–35-flowered. **Calyces** cylindric, long-villous, hairs white; tube 5–6.5 mm, lobes 1.5–4(–6) mm. **Corollas** usually pink-purple, sometimes creamy white, 12–16 mm. **Legumes** ascending, minutely stipitate, ovoid to ovoid-oblong, 10–17 × 3–5 mm, subunilocular, both sutures sulcate, villous. $2n = 16$.

Flowering summer. Meadows, river banks, prairies, parklands; 300–4400 m; Alta., B.C., Man., N.W.T., Ont., Sask., Yukon; Alaska, Colo., Minn., Mont., N.Mex., N.Dak., Wyo.

Oxytropis splendens is readily identifiable by the combination of its copiously villous vesture, fasciculate leaflets, and petals that are short relative to calyx length. In the Alberta Rockies, intermediates between this species and phases of *O. campestris* vars. *davisii* and *spicata*, and perhaps also of var. *cusickii*, apparently occur. Materials from near James Bay, Ontario, appear to be intermediate between *O. campestris* var. *johannensis* and *O. splendens* in that they have less copious pubescence, a tendency for fasciculate leaflets, and ratio of petal length to calyx length that is intermediate between those of *O. campestris* var. *johannensis* and *O. splendens*.

135. ASTRAGALUS Linnaeus, Sp. Pl. 2: 755. 1753; Gen. Pl. ed. 5, 335. 1754 • Locoweed, milkvetch [Greek *astragalos*, ankle-bone or legume]

Stanley L. Welsh

Herbs, annual, biennial, or perennial, rarely suffruticose, unarmed (except with spines in *A. humillimus* and *A. kentrophyta*); hairs basifixed or malpighian; caudex aerial, superficial, or subterranean. **Stems** erect, ascending, prostrate, or decumbent, usually pubescent. **Leaves** alternate, unifoliolate, odd-pinnate, or reduced to phyllodia; stipules present, adnate to petiole or distinct, or connate opposite petiole; sessile, subsessile, or petiolate; leaflets 1–41(or 43), petiolulate or sessile, blade margins entire, surfaces glabrous or pubescent. **Inflorescences** 1–95(–125)-flowered, axillary or terminal, racemes, sometimes spikelike, subumbellate, or solitary; bracts present, often small, membranous, subtending pedicels; bracteoles 0–2, borne on calyx base. **Flowers** papilionaceous; calyx campanulate, cylindric, subcylindric, turbinate, or obconic-campanulate, lobes 5, lobes subequal or proximalmost longer; corolla violet, blue to purple, red, pink, lilac, whitish, yellowish, cream, ochroleucous, or greenish, petals mostly long-clawed, banner erect, wings oblong and apex entire or obscurely emarginate, keel suberect; stamens 10, diadelphous, alternate anthers of 2 different lengths; anthers dorsifixed; ovary sessile or stipitate; style straight or incurved, filiform, glabrous; stigma small, terminal. **Fruits** legumes, sessile (sometimes with gynophore), subsessile, or stipitate, deciduous from calyx or from abscission layer at gynophore apex and dehiscent on ground, or persistent and dehiscent on plant, body unilocular or partially or completely bilocular by intrusion of non-seed bearing suture, usually straight or incurved, rarely decurved or coiled inward, compressed to bladdery-inflated, linear, lanceoloid, oblong, ovoid, ellipsoid, orbicular, or suborbicular, dehiscent throughout or apically, glabrous or pubescent. **Seeds** 2–77(–84), reniform, 2-seriate, borne on slender funicles, sometimes connate basally by membrane or funicular flange simulating a septum, but issuing from seminal suture. x = 8, 11, 12 (13, 14).

Species ca. 3000 (357 in the flora): North America, Mexico, Central America, South America, Europe, Asia, Africa.

The following species were added to this treatment after *Astragalus* was finalized and do not appear in the key to species: 355. *A. tibetanus* (which will key to 180. *A. agrestis*), 356. *A. asotinensis* (which will key to 63. *A. sclerocarpus*), and 357. *A. kelseyae* (a very distinctive species in sect. *Kelseyani*, known only from the Wasatch Mountains, Weber County, Utah).

In *Astragalus*, the fruit may arise just above the calyx (like the corolla and androecium) or may be borne on a stalk, which consists of a gynophore and/or a stipe. The gynophore is derived from the receptacle, whereas the stipe is derived from the ovary itself. The gynophore and stipe are distinguished by the location of the abscission zone. A gynophore has an abscission zone at its apex, whereas a stipe has it at its base and remains attached to the rest of the fruit (as in *A. asclepiadoides*). In a few species, the base of the legume is narrowed and superficially stipelike, forming a pseudostipe; unlike a true stipe, a pseudostipe is hollow and not well differentiated from the rest of the fruit.

SELECTED REFERENCES Barneby, R. C. 1964. Atlas of North American *Astragalus*. Mem. New York Bot. Gard. 13. Welsh, S. L. 2007. North American Species of *Astragalus* Linnaeus, a Taxonomic Revision. Provo.

Key to Species of Group 1 and Other Groups

1. Leaflets usually 5 or 7, decurrent, blade apex spinulose; Great Plains westward . . . 76. *Astragalus kentrophyta*
1. Leaflets (0 or)1 or 3–39(–43), often not decurrent, blade apex not spinulose (except *A. detritalis*, sometimes *A. spatulatus*); widespread.

[2. Shifted to left margin.—Ed.]

2. Plants with malpighian hairs; leaflets usually 3, rarely 1 or 5, stipules (3–)4–18 mm, connate-sheathing, hyaline; legumes 3–10 mm, unilocular.
   3. Plants acaulescent and tuft-, cushion-, or mound-forming; flowers 12.3–29 mm; calyces cylindric.
      4. Flowers 16–29 mm, banner not differentiated into blade and claw, petals glabrous, rarely banner puberulent adaxially . . . . 352. *Astragalus gilviflorus*
      4. Flowers 12.3–17.5 mm, banner differentiated into blade and claw, with shoulder-like projections at middle, petals glabrous or villous abaxially.
         5. Petals glabrous abaxially; flowering May; Sweetwater County, sw Wyoming . . . . 353. *Astragalus proimanthus*
         5. Petals villous abaxially; flowering June–August; ne Colorado, Kansas, Montana, w Nebraska, North Dakota, South Dakota, Wyoming e of Continental Divide. . . . . 354. *Astragalus hyalinus*
   3. Plants caulescent and mat- or cushion-forming, or acaulescent or subacaulescent, and pulvinate and mat- or cushion-forming; flowers 5–16.7 mm; calyces usually campanulate, rarely subcylindric.
      6. Flowers 5–8 mm; calyces 2.4–4.2 mm.
         7. Plants cushion- or mat-forming; stems prostrate; stipules densely pilose abaxially; racemes (2 or) 3–5-flowered; flowers 5–6.2(–8) mm. . . . . .348. *Astragalus sericoleucus*
         7. Plants pulvinate, cushion-forming; stems not prostrate (obscured by stipules); stipules glabrous or glabrate abaxially (margins ciliate); racemes 2- or 3-flowered; flowers (5.8–)6.6–8 mm . . . . 349. *Astragalus aretioides*
      6. Flowers 8.2–16.7 mm; calyces 4.5–7.1 mm.
         8. Flowers 8.2–11.5 mm; keel petals 4.4–7.2 mm; calyx tubes 1.8–3.5(–3.8) mm; stipules (at least proximalmost) pilose abaxially. . . . . 350. *Astragalus tridactylicus*
         8. Flowers (9.5–)10.5–16.7 mm; keel petals 7.5–10.5 mm; calyx tubes 3.6–5.1 mm; stipules glabrous abaxially . . . . .351. *Astragalus barrii*

2. Plants with malpighian or basifixed hairs; leaflets usually 5–39(–43), rarely 0, 1, or 3 (seldom 3, with malpighian hairs); stipules 1–13(–20) mm, distinct, or sometimes connate-sheathing, foliose, herbaceous, papery, membranous, submembranous, scarious, or semi-leathery, not hyaline; legumes (0.9–)1–45(–75) mm, unilocular, bilocular, or semibilocular.
   9. Leaflets 1, blades ovate, orbiculate, or cordate . . . . .164. *Astragalus asclepiadoides*
   9. Leaflets (0 or)1 or 3–39(–43), if 1, then blades much longer than broad, usually spatulate.
      10. Plants perennial, from rhizomelike or stoloniferous caudex; leaflets (5 or)7–13 (or 15), pinnately veined; stipules of most proximal, leafless nodes connate, apex obtuse, distal stipules foliose; legumes simultaneously pendulous, stipitate, inflated, and unilocular.
         11. Plants 5–30(–36) cm; calyces campanulate to subcylindric, tubes 6.3–8 mm . . . . 1. *Astragalus umbellatus*
         11. Plants 25–90(–100) cm; calyces campanulate, tubes (4.3–)4.9–5.8 mm . . . . 2. *Astragalus americanus*
      10. Plants usually perennial, rarely annual, from a taproot or caudex; leaflets (0 or)1 or 3–39(–43), pinnate venation sometimes absent or inconspicuous; most proximal stipules distinct or connate, if connate, apex emarginate or bidentate, distal stipules rarely foliose; legumes not simultaneously pendulous, stipitate, inflated, and unilocular.
         12. Calyces obliquely ovoid, accrescent and inflated; legumes deciduous within accrescent calyces; Upper San Juan Valley, sw Colorado, adjacent New Mexico. . . . . 93. *Astragalus oocalycis* (in part)
         12. Calyces usually campanulate or cylindric, not accrescent and inflated; legumes not deciduous within calyces; widespread.
            13. Plants usually with malpighian hairs . . . . Group 2, p. 586
            13. Plants with basifixed hairs.

[14. Shifted to left margin.—Ed.]

14. Plants annual, short-lived perennials, or flowering first year . . . . Group 3, p. 590
14. Plants perennial (sometimes short-lived).
    15. Terminal leaflet of all or only distal leaves decurrent and not jointed to rachis . . . . Group 4, p. 594
    15. Terminal leaflet jointed to rachis.
        16. Stipules connate-sheathing proximally or throughout.
            17. Legumes stipitate, or sessile and gynophores (1–)1.3–11 mm . . . . Group 5, p. 597
            17. Legumes sessile or subsessile, stipe 0–1.7 mm, gynophore absent (except to 2 mm in *A. tennesseensis*). . . . . Group 6, p. 602
        16. Stipules distinct throughout.
            18. Legumes stipitate, or sessile and gynophores 0.3–5(–12) mm . . . . Group 7, p. 608
            18. Legumes sessile or subsessile, gynophores absent or to 1 mm.
                19. Plants acaulescent or subcaulescent and stem shorter than leaves or inflorescence . . . . Group 8, p. 616
                19. Plants caulescent, main stem longer than longest leaves or inflorescences . . . . Group 9, p. 620

Key to Species of Group 2

1. Plants short-lived perennial or flowering as annual; wc to se Arizona . . . . 310. *Astragalus arizonicus* (in part)
1. Plants usually long-lived perennial (except *A. amphioxys*, *A. lotiflorus*, and *A. piscator*); widespread.
    2. Leaves reduced to phyllodia proximally or throughout, leaflet blades, when present, oblanceolate, linear, linear-oblanceolate, or spatulate.
        3. Leaves 1–13(–17) cm; racemes loosely 7–23-flowered, in bud resembling grass spikelets; plants of sandstone hogbacks and cuestas in pinyon-juniper and mixed desert shrub communities; Uintah Basin, Utah . . . . 51. *Astragalus chloödes*
        3. Leaves 0.8–10 cm; racemes usually densely 1–11-flowered, in bud not resembling grass spikelets; plants of pinyon-juniper, sagebrush, and mountain brush communities, hilltops, exposed ridges, summits and gullied slopes of bluffs; Kansas to Utah, north to Saskatchewan and Alberta.
            4. Flowers 5.2–9.5 mm, keel petals 3.7–6 mm; legumes 4–8.5(–13) mm; fruiting calyces not prominently veined.
                5. Legumes laterally compressed; Kansas to Utah, north to Saskatchewan and Alberta . . . . 50. *Astragalus spatulatus*
                5. Legumes 3-sided compressed; Sublette County, Wyoming . . . . . 52. *Astragalus drabelliformis*
            4. Flowers 10.6–20 mm, keel petals 7–12.8(–13.4) mm; legumes 6–13(–15) mm and fruiting calyces prominently veined, or 15–38 mm and fruiting calyces not prominently veined.
                6. Leaves reduced to phyllodia; legumes 6–13(–15) × 2–5 mm, narrowly ovoid-ellipsoid to lanceoloid-ellipsoid; Carbon, Fremont, and Natrona counties, Wyoming . . . . .53. *Astragalus simplicifolius*
                6. Leaves 3–7-foliolate distally; legumes 15–38 × 2–3.5 mm, linear-oblong; Moffat and Rio Blanco counties, Colorado, Duchesne and Uintah counties, Utah. . . . . 54. *Astragalus detritalis*
    2. Leaves pinnate throughout, or reduced to phyllodia distally, leaflet blades filiform, oblong, elliptic, oblanceolate, obovate, linear, oblong-obovate, ovate, linear-oblong, suborbiculate-obcordate, oval, subrhombic, or rhombic.
        7. Leaves reduced to phyllodia distally or pinnate; terminal leaflet of distal leaves often not jointed to rachis and sometimes decurrent; plants caulescent.
            8. Peduncles and racemes together longer than stems, much surpassing subtending leaves; plants selenophytes; n Arizona, se Utah . . . . 89. *Astragalus moencoppensis* (in part)
            8. Peduncles and racemes together usually not or not much surpassing subtending leaves; plants not selenophytes; North Dakota to Idaho south to Kansas and Arizona.

9. Plants slender, not clump-forming, from rhizomelike, subterranean caudex; stems sprawling; stipules connate distally, subscarious or herbaceous; legumes sessile, subsessile, or stipitate, bladdery-inflated, purple-mottled, ellipsoid; e Montana, sw North Dakota south to Arizona, New Mexico, and Oklahoma, west to s Idaho, Utah . . . . 71. *Astragalus ceramicus*
9. Plants stout (coarse), clump-forming, from subterranean caudex, not rhizomelike; stems erect or ascending; stipules distinct, papery or foliaceous; legumes sessile, laterally compressed, not purple-mottled, narrowly oblong; e footslope of San Rafael Swell, Emery, Garfield, and Wayne counties, Utah . . . . 102. *Astragalus woodruffii* (in part)

[7. Shifted to left margin.—Ed.]

7. Leaves usually pinnate, sometimes unifoliolate; terminal leaflets jointed to rachis; plants caulescent or acaulescent.
   10. Plants from rhizomes, not clump-forming; legumes erect or narrowly ascending, oblong or cylindroid.
      11. Plants (10–)15–120(–160) cm, internodes not short or flexuous; plants of moist, though often summer-dry, communities; widespread in United States east of Sierra-Cascade axis and Canada . . . . .176. *Astragalus canadensis*
      11. Plants 6–20(–25) cm, internodes relatively short and strongly flexuous; plants of arid, sandy knolls or swales and talus; sc Wyoming to ne, sc Montana. . . . . 177. *Astragalus oreganus*
   10. Plants from superficial caudex, mat-, cushion-, or clump-forming; legumes declined-pendulous, ascending, spreading, erect, or reflexed, linear, ovoid, oblong, oblanceoloid, lanceoloid, or lanceoloid-ellipsoid.
      12. Legumes erect, ascending, reflexed, or declined, bilocular; plants caulescent.
         13. Flowers 4.5–6(–7) mm; plants villosulous, villous, or pilose, hairs basifixed, sub-basifixed, or malpighian; sc Idaho to e Oregon, and c, sc Washington. . . . . 335. *Astragalus caricinus* (in part)
         13. Flowers 8.7–19.5 mm; plants strigulose, hairs malpighian; Ontario to Alaska, south to Kansas, Arizona, and Oregon.
            14. Flowers ascending; raceme axis (1.5–)2.5–10 cm in fruit; wc to se Arizona . . . . 310. *Astragalus arizonicus* (in part)
            14. Flowers declined or ascending; raceme axis (0.6–)3–20 cm in fruit; Ontario to Alaska, south to Iowa, New Mexico, and Washington.
               15. Flowers declined; legumes deflexed; pedicels 3.2–6.5 mm; calyces 3.6–4.7 mm. . . . . .178. *Astragalus falcatus*
               15. Flowers ascending; legumes erect; pedicels to 0.8 mm; calyces 5.6 to 10.5 mm . . . . 179. *Astragalus laxmannii*
      12. Legumes mostly ascending or spreading, sometimes erect, rarely declined or pendulous, unilocular (except *A. anisus*, *A. calycosus*, and *A. terminalis*); plants acaulescent, subacaulescent, or caulescent.
         16. Plants acaulescent; wing petals with deeply cleft apex; peduncles scapelike; legumes bilocular . . . . .328. *Astragalus calycosus*
         16. Plants acaulescent or caulescent; wing petals with entire or obscurely emarginate apex; peduncles not scapelike; legumes mostly unilocular (bilocular in *A. anisus* and *A. terminalis*).
            17. Stipules mostly connate-sheathing, at least proximally.
               18. Stems prostrate; plants mat- or cushion-forming, caulescent.
                  19. Racemes 3–30-flowered; corollas greenish to ochroleucous or purple; leaflets (5–)9–17(or 19); habitats various, usually not sandstone escarpments . . . . .83. *Astragalus humistratus*
                  19. Racemes 1–4-flowered; corollas pink-purple; leaflets 7–11(–17); sandstone escarpments . . . . 84. *Astragalus sesquiflorus*
               18. Stems erect, ascending, decumbent, or prostrate; plants sometimes tuft- or mat-forming, caulescent or acaulescent.

[20. Shifted to left margin.—Ed.]

20. Legumes obovoid to ellipsoid, stipitate (stipes 0.5–1 mm); plants slender, delicate; New Mexico.
    21. Racemes 5–10(–14)-flowered; plants of escarpments; Sandoval County, New Mexico . . . . 122. *Astragalus knightii*
    21. Racemes (1 or) 2–4-flowered; plants of disturbed or compacted soils; Capitan Mountains, Lincoln County, New Mexico . . . . 123. *Astragalus kerrii* (in part)
20. Legumes ovoid, lanceoloid-ellipsoid, oblong, or ellipsoid, sessile (except *A. albulus*); plants robust, not or rarely slender or delicate; widespread.
    22. Plants caulescent or shortly so, not selenophytes; legumes declined-pendulous, linear, linear-oblong, linear-ellipsoid, or oblanceoloid, laterally compressed; plants usually of mountains or steppes; Alberta and British Columbia south to Washington, e Nevada, Utah, Wyoming . . . . 30. *Astragalus miser* (in part)
    22. Plants caulescent, selenophytes; legumes erect, ascending, declined, or pendulous, oblong, oblong-ellipsoid, or lanceoloid-ellipsoid, dorsiventrally or laterally compressed; plants usually of fine-textured desert substrates; Wyoming west to Nevada, south to Texas and Arizona.
        23. Peduncles (0.7–)1–3(–4) cm, racemes slightly surpassing subtending leaves; Coconino County, Arizona . . . . 88. *Astragalus sophoroides*
        23. Peduncles 1–23 cm, racemes shorter than or surpassing subtending leaves; Wyoming west to Nevada, south to Texas and Arizona.
            24. Peduncles (3–)5–23 cm, surpassing subtending leaves; plants flowering April–July (or September); wc, s Wyoming, south through w Colorado, northeast to sw Utah, s Nevada, n Arizona, nw New Mexico . . . . 87. *Astragalus flavus*
            24. Peduncles 1–4(–5.5) cm, much shorter than subtending leaves; plants flowering July–October; ne Arizona, sw Colorado, n New Mexico, w Texas . . . . 90. *Astragalus albulus*

[17. Shifted to left margin.—Ed.]

17. Stipules mostly distinct throughout (sometimes connate-sheathing proximally in *A. amphioxys*, distinct proximally but connate distally in *A. wittmannii*).
    25. Plants acaulescent or subacaulescent, mat-, tuft-, or cushion-forming; flowers 3.7–18 (–21) mm; leaves 0.3–9 cm; legumes 3–7.5 mm; rimrock at Grand Canyon and vicinity and Mogollon Rim, Arizona, sw Colorado, nw New Mexico.
        26. Plants tuft-forming, 6–25 cm; leaves (1.5–)2.5–9 cm; leaflets (7–)11–21(–25), blades (2–)3–12 mm; peduncles ± scapelike, (2.5–)3.5–15(–22) cm; racemes 17–26-flowered . . . . 304. *Astragalus gilensis*
        26. Plants tuft-, mat-, or cushion-forming, 0.5–3(–3.2) cm; leaves 0.3–3(–8) cm; leaflets (3 or)5–11, blades 1–5(–12) mm; peduncles axillary or obsolete, 0.2–0.6 cm; racemes 1–3-flowered.
            27. Caudex branches with spinose-persistent leaf bases; legumes laterally compressed; extreme sw Colorado and adjacent nw New Mexico . . . 308. *Astragalus humillimus*
            27. Caudex branches with non-spinose, marcescent leaf bases; legumes subterete, laterally compressed, or obcompressed; Grand Canyon and vicinity, Arizona, c New Mexico.
                28. Racemes 1-flowered; pedicels obsolete; calyces cylindric; Colfax, Harding, and Mora counties, New Mexico . . . . 306. *Astragalus wittmannii*
                28. Racemes (1 or) 2 (or 3)-flowered; pedicels 0.7–3.5 mm; calyces campanulate; Arizona, c New Mexico.
                    29. Flowers 9–11.5 mm, keel petals 7.5–8.7 mm; legumes 5–7.5 mm, laterally compressed; seeds 8–10; c New Mexico . . . . 305. *Astragalus siliceus*
                    29. Flowers 3.7–8 mm, keel petals 3.7–5.7 mm; legumes 3-4.5(–4.8) mm, slightly flattened or basally compressed abaxially; seeds 4–6; Grand Canyon area, Arizona . . . . 307. *Astragalus cremnophylax*
    25. Plants caulescent, subacaulescent, or acaulescent, usually loosely tuft-forming, or if somewhat mat-forming, then not with tiny leaves, legumes, and flowers; flowers (7–)8.5–28(–32) mm; leaves 1–17 cm; legumes (8–)9–40 mm; Manitoba to British Columbia, south to Missouri, Texas, and Arizona.

[30. Shifted to left margin.—Ed.]

30. Plants caulescent; stems erect, decumbent, or incurved-ascending, with 2–4 much-elongated internodes; peduncles 6–20 (–24) cm; corollas white except keel apex dark; flowers nodding; legumes erect . . . . 142. *Astragalus terminalis*
30. Plants subacaulescent to acaulescent, or short stemmed to caulescent (when short caulescent, then stems usually prostrate, *A. lotiflorus* sometimes erect); stems obsolete, reduced to crowns, prostrate, erect, ascending, or decumbent, internodes usually not elongated, often concealed by stipules; peduncles 0.4–15(–20) cm; corollas pink, purple, or white with or without dark keel apex; flowers erect to spreading; legumes ascending or spreading, or descending.
    31. Calyces shallowly campanulate, tubes 3.2–4.5 mm; flowers 8.5–14 mm . . . . 301. *Astragalus lotiflorus*
    31. Calyces cylindric, campanulate, vase-shaped, or cylindro-campanulate, tubes (3.4–) 4–14 mm; flowers (7–)10–32 mm.
        32. Leaflets (1 or)3 or 5.
            33. Leaflet blades 5–35(–47) mm; corollas pink-purple; caudex with thatch of persistent leaf bases . . . . 204. *Astragalus musiniensis* (in part)
            33. Leaflet blades 5–25 mm; corollas ochroleucous, greenish white, purple, or pink-purple; caudex with or without thatch of persistent leaf bases.
                34. Corollas purple or pink-purple; plants of alluvium, often on terraces of ancient Pleistocene lakes, ne Nye County, Nevada, Millard County, Utah . . . . 184. *Astragalus uncialis* (in part)
                34. Corollas ochroleucous or greenish white and keel tip purple; plants of igneous gravel, c Sevier County, Utah . . . . 203. *Astragalus loanus*
        32. Leaflets mostly 5–21, seedlings and early leaves with fewer.
            35. Leaflets usually 5–11(or 13) (to 18 in *A. cymboides*).
                36. Legumes plumply ovoid and moderately obcompressed, hirsute (hairs 2–2.5 mm); corollas ochroleucous or greenish white, often faintly purplish-tinged; Garfield, Iron, Kane, Millard, Piute, and Wayne counties, Utah . . . . 202. *Astragalus welshii*
                36. Legumes lanceoloid-ellipsoid or oblong to oblong-ellipsoid, laterally compressed or cylindroid becoming laterally compressed, strigose (hairs relatively short); corollas pink-purple or ochroleucous, sometimes suffused pink or purple, or lined purple; Colorado, Utah.
                    37. Flowers 18–24 mm . . . . .220. *Astragalus piscator*
                    37. Flowers 15–18.5 mm. . . . . .222. *Astragalus cymboides*
            35. Leaflets of at least some leaves 11–21.
                38. Legumes densely shaggy-hirsute; flowers 21–25 mm; Washington and adjacent Iron counties, Utah . . . . 205. *Astragalus concordius*
                38. Legumes usually strigulose or strigose, rarely glabrous; flowers 7–24 (–28) mm; Manitoba west to Alberta, south to Texas and Arizona.
                    39. Legumes obliquely globose, oblong-globose, or broadly obovoid, apex minutely cuspidate, not or scarcely beaked, bilocular (septum 3–6 mm wide); Gunnison County, Colorado. . . . . 225. *Astragalus anisus*
                    39. Legumes obliquely ovoid or oblong, lanceoloid-ovoid, ellipsoid, or crescentic, apex distinctly beaked, unilocular or subunilocular; Manitoba west to Alberta, south to Texas and Arizona.
                        40. Calyces 4.6–5.1 mm; flowers 7–8.3 mm, ochroleucous or purple-veined or -margined; legumes plumply ovoid or oblong-ellipsoid; Zuni Mountains, McKinley County, New Mexico . . . . . 224. *Astragalus accumbens*
                        40. Calyces 5–14.2(–14.3) mm; flowers 9.5–27(–28) mm; legumes obliquely ovoid or oblong, lanceoloid-ovoid, lunately ellipsoid, ellipsoid, oblong-ellipsoid, or crescentic; Manitoba west to Alberta, south to Texas and Arizona.

[41. Shifted to left margin.—Ed.]

41. Legumes fleshy becoming alveolate-spongy (walls 1+ mm thick, exocarp and endocarp separated by thick, pulpy mesocarp).
    42. Legumes oblong-ovoid or ellipsoid (not markedly thicker near base); Colorado, Montana, Utah, Wyoming (not in or near Henry Mountains) . . . . 218. *Astragalus chamaeleuce*
    42. Legumes turgidly lanceoloid-ovoid (broader proximally); near Henry Mountains, w Garfield and w Wayne counties, Utah . . . . 219. *Astragalus laccoliticus*
41. Legumes leathery or fleshy becoming leathery, papery, or subligneous (walls much less than 1 mm thick).
    43. Legumes obliquely ovoid, lanceoloid-ovoid, or lunately ellipsoid, (8–)9–20(–22) mm; flowers 10–18.5 mm; corollas usually whitish, ochroleucous, or tinged purplish, rarely purple; c, n Arizona, c Utah.
        44. Flowers (14.5–)15–18.5 mm; calyces 6–10.5 mm; herbage usually silky-strigose to strigulose (hairs lustrous); Arizona into e Kane County, Utah . . . . 216. *Astragalus castaneiformis*
        44. Flowers 10–15.5(–17.5) mm; calyces 5.5–8.9 mm; herbage strigulose (not especially lustrous); sc Utah . . . . 217. *Astragalus consobrinus*
    43. Legumes crescentic, subsymmetrically or obliquely oblong, oblong-ellipsoid, or ellipsoid, (11–)15–40 mm; flowers 9.5–27(–28) mm; corollas usually pinkish purple, rarely white; sc Canada to sc and sw United States.
        45. Legumes readily deciduous . . . . 221. *Astragalus amphioxys*
        45. Legumes persistent or tardily deciduous . . . . .223. *Astragalus missouriensis*

Key to Species of Group 3

1. Legumes (2–)2.3–4.2 mm; ovules 2.
    2. Flowers ascending becoming spreading or declined; racemes elongating in fruit; legumes strongly obcompressed; s Oregon southward . . . . 343. *Astragalus gambelianus*
    2. Flowers erect or ascending; racemes not elongating in fruit; legumes somewhat laterally compressed; San Joaquin Valley and s Coast ranges, California, s Nevada, s Arizona, southward . . . . 344. *Astragalus didymocarpus*
1. Legumes (0.9–)5–40 mm; ovules (3 or)4–38.
    3. Legumes spreading (in oblong or globose heads), coiled through 0.7–1.3 spiral into 6–8 mm diam. ring; Massachusetts . . . . 346. *Astragalus contortuplicatus*
    3. Legumes erect, ascending, spreading, reflexed, horizontal, declined, or pendulous (not in oblong or globose heads), straight, decurved, or incurved, not coiled more than 0.5 spiral; w and se United States.
        4. Legumes hirsute, hairs spreading-ascending, to 1.2–1.8 mm, lustrous; Alabama, Florida, Georgia, and South Carolina . . . . 300. *Astragalus villosus* (in part)
        4. Legumes strigose, strigulose, villosulous, hirsutulous, hirsute, or glabrous, when hirsute, then hairs less than 1 mm (except *A. sabulonum* hairs to 2.2 mm), not lustrous; w United States to Montana, Kansas, and Louisiana.
            5. Legumes reflexed, 5.5–9 mm, sessile with gynophores 0.1–0.5 mm; Texas . . . . 341. *Astragalus reflexus*
            5. Legumes erect, ascending, spreading, reflexed, horizontal, declined, or pendulous, (2.4–)5–50(–57) mm, sessile, stipitate, or with gynophores 0.4–2.5 mm; w United States including Texas.
                6. Legumes sessile, oblong to lanceoloid-oblong and without gynophores, or peltiform and with gynophores; Texas.
                    7. Legumes reflexed, peltiform, gynophores 1.5–2.3 mm; seeds 4; s Texas . . . . 342. *Astragalus brazoensis*
                    7. Legumes erect, oblong to lanceoloid-oblong, sessile; seeds 5–9; c, e Texas. . . . . 345. *Astragalus wrightii*
                6. Legumes sessile or stipitate, with or without gynophores, globose to linear or crescentic or oblong; w United States including Texas.

[8. Shifted to left margin.—Ed.]

8. Legumes ascending to erect, oblong-ellipsoid, stipitate (stipes 3–3.5 mm); selenophytes; San Juan County, Utah. . . . . 166. *Astragalus cutleri* (in part)
8. Legumes globose to linear or crescentic or oblong-ellipsoid, sessile or stipitate, sometimes with gynophores; not selenophytes; if legumes ascending to erect, oblong-ellipsoid and stipitate then not in San Juan County, Utah.
   9. Legumes obovoid to oblong-ellipsoid, 10–18 mm; flowers 4–6(–7) mm; banners abruptly recurved through 90°; Arizona, sw Colorado, New Mexico, se Utah . . . . .121. *Astragalus brandegeei* (in part)
   9. Legumes globose to linear or crescentic or oblong-ellipsoid; flowers (3.3–)3.7–12.5 (–13.2) mm; banners recurved through 90(–125)°, when flowers 4–7 mm, then banner curvature reflexed to 45°; w United States.
      10. Legumes semiellipsoid or lunately ellipsoid, slightly inflated, scarcely bladdery; racemes (3 or)4–9-flowered; flowers (3.3–)3.5–6.5 mm; Yuma County, Arizona, Imperial, Riverside, and San Diego counties, California . . . . 280. *Astragalus aridus*
      10. Legumes globose to linear or crescentic, bladdery or not; racemes 1–35-flowered; flowers (3.7–)5–18.5 mm; not simultaneously with legumes semiellipsoid or lunately ellipsoid, racemes with fewer than 9 flowers, and flowers less than 6.5 mm; sw United States north to Washington, Montana, east to Kansas, southeast to Louisiana.
         11. Legumes unilocular to subunilocular or semibilocular, generally obliquely ovoid to globose, inflated and often bladdery (± inflated in *A. sparsiflorus*), papery or papery-membranous.
            12. Legumes unilocular, subunilocular, or semibilocular, septum at least partial at base, often narrow.
               13. Leaflets (5 or)7 or 9; racemes 2–8-flowered; legumes bladdery-inflated, 6–12 mm wide; *Larrea* deserts in s Nevada, nw Arizona . . . . 279. *Astragalus geyeri* (in part)
               13. Leaflets 9–19; racemes (3–)7–15-flowered; legumes somewhat inflated, almost bladdery, 3–9 mm wide; e Oregon (formerly sc Washington) . . . . 283. *Astragalus diaphanus* (in part)
            12. Legumes unilocular, septum absent, even at base.
               14. Racemes mostly (3–)5–35-flowered.
                  15. Racemes and legumes in subglobose or oblong heads; plants of alkaline flats and seeps . . . . 284. *Astragalus hornii*
                  15. Racemes and legumes not in subglobose or oblong heads; plants not halophytic.
                     16. Plants annual or biennial, slender; John Day Valley and lower Columbia River, e Oregon (formerly sc Washington) . . . . 283. *Astragalus diaphanus* (in part)
                     16. Plants annual, biennial, or short-lived perennial, ± coarse; Texas and California north to Colorado and Washington.
                        17. Banner recurved through 90°; seeds 21–32; sandy desert shrublands . . . . 20. *Astragalus fucatus* (in part)
                        17. Banner recurved through 50°; seeds (10–)13–21; habitats various.
                           18. Legumes with strongly developed beak, clearly differentiated from body; Arizona to w Texas . . . . .263. *Astragalus allochrous* (in part)
                           18. Legumes with short and obscure beak, not well differentiated from body; e Mojave Desert, California, to w Texas . . . . 264. *Astragalus wootonii* (in part)
               14. Racemes (1 or)2–15-flowered.

[19. Shifted to left margin.—Ed.]

19. Legumes villosulous, villous, or hirsute, hairs spreading, curly.
    20. Plants short-lived perennials; legumes straight or slightly incurved, 13–21 × 7–11 mm; seeds 20–28 . . . . 273. *Astragalus pardalinus* (in part)
    20. Plants annuals or biennials; legumes lunately incurved or hooked, 9–17(–20) × (4–)5–8(–11) mm; seeds 10–19 . . . . 274. *Astragalus sabulonum*
19. Legumes strigulose, hairs appressed, straight.
    21. Legumes ± inflated, not bladdery; e slope of Colorado Rocky Mountains . . . . 282. *Astragalus sparsiflorus* (in part)
    21. Legumes mostly strongly inflated, bladdery; Montana, Wyoming, Utah west to Washington and California.
        22. Leaflets 7–11; legumes subsymmetric, 11–17 mm, seed-bearing flange 3–3.5 mm wide; seeds 28–30; lower Little Colorado River, Coconino County, Arizona . . . . 269. *Astragalus endopterus*
        22. Leaflets (3–)7–19(or 21), when 11+, then either flowers 6.3+ mm or purple or legumes strongly asymmetric and incurved or less than 11 mm wide; legumes sometimes similar in size and outline, usually smaller, seed-bearing flange to 2.5 mm wide; seeds (6 or)7–24; Montana to Washington, south to California, Arizona, and Utah.
            23. Leaflet blades mostly ovate or obovate-obcordate; legumes translucent . . . . 283. *Astragalus diaphanus* (in part)
            23. Leaflet blades mostly oblong-elliptic to linear; legumes translucent or not.
                24. Corollas usually whitish, purple in c Nevada; legumes green or suffused purple, becoming stramineous; n United States to s Nevada and adjacent Arizona, to Mono County, California . . . . 279. *Astragalus geyeri* (in part)
                24. Corollas pinkish purple or reddish purple; legumes pale green becoming stramineous, sometimes purple-suffused or -dotted; Panamint Mountains and Mojave Desert, California, to adjacent Arizona.
                    25. Flowers 7.8–10.4 mm; leaflets 7–13; legumes with seed-bearing flange 1–2.5 mm wide; seeds 19–24; Panamint Mountains and e Mojave Desert, south to Chuckwalla Mountains, Riverside County, California . . . . 275. *Astragalus nutans* (in part)
                    25. Flowers 5.5–7.4 mm; leaflets (9 or) 11–19 (or 21); legumes with seed-bearing flange 0.2–1.5 mm wide; seeds 7–12(–14); Colorado Desert, California, north to Chuckwalla Mountains, w Arizona southward . . . . 278. *Astragalus insularis*

[11. Shifted to left margin.—Ed.]

11. Legumes bilocular, generally oblong to linear or crescentic and not inflated, if broader than oblong or inflated, then valves fleshy becoming stiffly papery, leathery, or subligneous.
    26. Plants annual and perennial in same populations.
        27. Leaflet blade abaxially strigulose, adaxially glabrous or sometimes medially glabrate; legumes ascending; Arizona, New Mexico . . . . 309. *Astragalus nothoxys*
        27. Leaflet blade silvery-strigulose (appearing frosted); legumes declined, pendulous, or spreading; California, Nevada.
            28. Legumes 13–18 × 2.8–3.5 mm, thinly papery; seeds 8–11; east end of San Bernardino Mountains, California . . . . 311. *Astragalus albens*
            28. Legumes (13–)15–28(–32) × 3.5–8.5 mm, fleshy becoming leathery or subligneous; seeds 20–30; Mojave Desert, California, s Nevada . . . . 312. *Astragalus mohavensis*
    26. Plants annual (winter or spring).
        29. Legumes dehiscent while still attached to plants.
            30. Flowers (12–)13–18.5 mm; keel petals 9.5–13 mm; legumes 3.5–6(–6.5) mm wide, stipes (0.8–)1–2.6(–3) mm; styles puberulent proximal to stigmas; seeds 8–12(–14); Oklahoma, Texas . . . . 326. *Astragalus lindheimeri*
            30. Flowers 3.7–13(–13.2) mm; keel petals 3.7–7.8(–9.3) mm; legumes (1.6–)2.1–4.1 mm wide, stipes or gynophores 0–0.9 mm; styles glabrous; seeds 10–26; w United States east to Louisiana.

31. Flowers (5.2–)8.3–12(–13.2) mm; keel petals (4.5–)6–7.8(–9) mm, apex narrowly acute-triangular (beaklike); leaflet blade apex retuse or emarginate; legumes straight or slightly incurved, (17–)20–37 mm, glabrous; seeds 20–26 . . . . 325. *Astragalus leptocarpus*
31. Flowers 3.7–13 mm; keel petals 3.7–6.8(–9.3) mm, apex acute-triangular to obtusely rounded, beaklike or not; leaflet blade apex emarginate, retuse, truncate, rounded, obtuse or acute; legumes nearly straight, gently incurved, or incurved through 0.2–0.5 spiral, (7–)10–26 mm, strigulose, villosulous, hirsutulous, or glabrous; seeds 10–22.
    32. Legumes ascending, spreading, or declined, strigulose, villosulous, or glabrous, hairs straight; w United States east to Alabama . . . 323. *Astragalus nuttallianus*
    32. Legumes declined, hirsutulous, hairs curved; Inyo County, California, Clark and Nye counties, Nevada, and sw Washington County, Utah . . . . 324. *Astragalus nyensis*

[29. Shifted to left margin.—Ed.]

29. Legumes dehiscent after detaching from plant.
    33. Apex of keel bluntly deltate or narrowly triangular and ± acute; Texas to California, north to Utah.
        34. Legumes glabrous and apex of keel bluntly deltate; nw, se Arizona, New Mexico, Texas, sc Utah. . . . . 316. *Astragalus emoryanus*
        34. Legumes usually strigulose, sometimes glabrous, when glabrous, apex of keel acutely triangular; Arizona, s Nevada, se California . . . . 317. *Astragalus acutirostris*
    33. Apex of keel round or deltate; California North Coast Ranges, Great Valley, South Coast Ranges, along coast from Monterey to San Diego.
        35. Seeds borne in proximal 1/2 of legume; legume ovoid, ovoid-oblong, or fusiform, 5.5–10 mm, densely silvery-strigulose, apex abruptly contacted into a (glabrescent) spinelike beak; North Coast Ranges, Mendocino and Lake to Marin counties . . . . 322. *Astragalus breweri*
        35. Seeds borne near middle of legume; legume narrowly crescentic, linear, linear-oblong, or lanceoloid-oblong, (6–)10–50(–57) mm, strigulose, villosulous, or glabrous, usually not spinose-beaked; widespread in California, including North Coast Ranges.
            36. Keel petals 7.4–9.1 mm, wings 6.7–9 mm, keel petals subequal to or to 1.6 mm longer than wings; legumes crescentic and linear (base and apex acuminate), gynophore slender, 1.4–2.5 mm; Napa and Sonoma counties. . . . . 321. *Astragalus claranus*
            36. Keel petals 3.4–8.1 mm, wings 4.5–10.4 mm, keel petals shorter than wings; legumes linear-oblong, lanceoloid-oblong, narrowly crescentic, or narrowly linear, stipes (0–)2.7–5 mm; North Coast Ranges, South Coast Ranges, Great Valley, and along coast from Monterey to San Diego counties.
                37. Legumes (15–)18–57 mm, if less than 21 mm, then base cuneate-tapered or substipitate; North and South Coast ranges. . . . . 320. *Astragalus rattanii*
                37. Legumes 6–20 mm (to 50 mm in *A. tener* var. *ferrisiae*), base rounded; Great Valley and along coast from Monterey to San Diego.
                    38. Racemes 2–12-flowered, subcapitate, axis 0.2–0.8 cm in fruit, (when more than 5 mm, then 7–12-flowered); legumes green becoming stramineous; plants of low alkaline meadows and depressions along coast, bluffs or dunes; elevation 0–60 m . . . . 318. *Astragalus tener*
                    38. Racemes 2–5(–7)-flowered, axis (0.4–)0.7–2 cm in fruit; legumes mottled or suffused with purple, resupinate; plants of moist, open sites, foothill oak woodlands, treeless summits; elevation 40–1200 m . . . . 319. *Astragalus pauperculus*

Key to Species of Group 4

1. Legumes stipitate, stipes 2.5–15 mm (as short as 1 mm in *A. yoderwilliamsii*).
   2. Stipules distinct throughout.
      3. Legumes strongly laterally compressed, faces ± flattened.
         4. Corollas pink-purple; sw Wyoming to c, se Utah, ne Arizona, nw New Mexico, sw Colorado. . . . . 44. *Astragalus coltonii* (in part)
         4. Corollas pale lemon yellow; sc Colorado, nc New Mexico. . . . . 45. *Astragalus ripleyi*
      3. Legumes mostly dorsiventrally compressed, sometimes laterally compressed or subterete, faces convex or not.
         5. Flowers spreading-declined; corollas ochroleucous or nearly white, banner 13.5–24 mm; stipes 3–15 mm; Colorado and New Mexico west to Arizona and Nevada.
            6. Leaflets (1 or)3–9 (or 11), blades 0.5–4 mm wide; plants often on low-quality substrates; n Arizona, w, s Colorado, e Nevada, n New Mexico, s, w Utah, barely extending into Uinta Basin . . . . 48. *Astragalus lonchocarpus*
            6. Leaflets (1 or)3–7, blades 2–9(–13) mm wide; plants mainly on Cretaceous Mowry Shale and Tertiary Duchesne River and closely associated formations; Moffat County, Colorado, and Uinta Basin, Utah. . . . . 49. *Astragalus hamiltonii*
         5. Flowers ascending or declined; corollas pink-purple, banner 8–14 mm; stipes 2.5–6 mm; Utah.
            7. Plants 15–51 cm; leaves mostly pinnate; calyces (3.5–)3.8–7 mm; flowers (9–)10–15 mm; axis of raceme 1.5–28 cm in fruit; e Garfield, San Juan, and Wayne counties . . . . 42. *Astragalus nidularius* (in part)
            7. Plants 40–70 cm; leaves pinnate proximally, reduced to rachis with terminal leaflet distally; calyces 2.5–4.6 mm; flowers 8–10.5 mm; axis of raceme 5–40(–42) cm in fruit; Garfield and Wayne counties . . . . . . 43. *Astragalus harrisonii*
   2. Stipules connate-sheathing proximally, connate or distinct distally.
      8. Legumes bladdery-inflated, unilocular, papery-membranous (translucent); n Idaho, Malheur County, Oregon, Asotin County, Washington . . . . 69. *Astragalus cusickii* (in part)
      8. Legumes 3-sided and bilocular, or dorsiventrally or laterally compressed and unilocular, thin or fleshy becoming papery or leathery, or subligneous; British Columbia to Montana, south to Arizona.
         9. Legumes sharply 3-sided, bilocular.
            10. Plants caulescent and slender, 10–30 cm; stems spreading to ascending and diffuse; leaflet blades 1–11 mm; legumes 9–16 × 3–4.5 mm; elevation 600–900(–1000) m; Snake River and tributaries in sw Idaho and e Malheur County, Oregon. . . . . .115. *Astragalus mulfordiae* (in part)
            10. Plants short-stemmed and diminutive (densely tuft-forming), 1–3(–7) cm; stems erect or ascending; leaflet blades 1–3 mm; legumes 4–7 × 2–3 mm; elevation 1500–2200 m; sw Owyhee County, Idaho, ec Humboldt County, Nevada . . . . 118. *Astragalus yoderwilliamsii* (in part)
         9. Legumes dorsiventrally or laterally compressed, unilocular.
            11. Plants clump-forming, from elongated subterranean caudex with deeply set taproot; plants of sandstone soils; se Utah . . . . 42. *Astragalus nidularius* (in part)
            11. Plants clump-forming or not, from shallow subterranean or superficial caudex; plants often of seleniferous, basaltic, or pumice soils, not sandstone; California, Colorado.
               12. Leaflets of proximal leaves (5–)7–15, blades linear-oblong or oblanceolate, reduced distally, most distal leaves unifoliolate and filiform; legumes strongly laterally compressed, body linear-ellipsoid, 7–12-times longer than wide; corollas white; Grand County, Colorado . . .101. *Astragalus osterhoutii*
               12. Leaflets 5–21(–23), reduced distally, blades filiform to oblong-elliptic or oblanceolate; legumes laterally or dorsiventrally compressed or terete, body linear-oblong, linear-lanceolate, obliquely oblong, or clavate-ellipsoid, 4–9 times longer than wide; corollas pinkish red or greenish white, drying ochroleucous; California.

13. Leaflets 5–11; calyces 3.5–5 mm, lobes 0.6–1 mm; legumes strongly laterally compressed, 3–4 mm wide; seeds 13–17; n California . . . . .67. *Astragalus inversus* (in part)
13. Leaflets (11 or)13–21(or 23); calyces 8.1–10.1 mm, lobes 1.8–3.3 mm; legumes not compressed or somewhat obcompressed becoming dorsiventrally compressed, 5–8.5(–9) mm wide; s California . . . . 159. *Astragalus bicristatus* (in part)

1. Legumes sessile or subsessile, stipes or gynophores 0–1.7(–2) mm.
  14. Flowers (10–)14–30 mm (sometimes as small as 12 mm in *A. woodruffii* and 10 mm in *A. nelsonianus*); calyces cylindric (obliquely ovoid and accrescent in *A. oocalycis*), tubes (3.8–)4–10.2(–14) mm.
    15. Stipules at the most proximal nodes distinct (often obscurely connate in *A. woodruffii*).
      16. Legumes erect.
        17. Leaflet blades silvery-silky throughout; legumes narrowly oblong, 14–24 × 2.5–4.8 mm, laterally compressed, stiffly papery, strigulose; plants of sandy footslopes of the San Rafael Swell and environs, Utah. . . . . 102. *Astragalus woodruffii* (in part)
        17. Leaflet blades often silvery-canescent, more densely so adaxially; legumes obliquely ovoid or plumply oblong, 15–31 × 5–12 mm, subterete, fleshy becoming woody, glabrous; Death Valley, California, Lahontan Basin and environs, Nevada . . . . .152. *Astragalus serenoi* (in part)
      16. Legumes pendulous.
        18. Leaflets 9–23, blades linear, narrowly oblong, or elliptic, 1–33 × 0.3–3.2 mm (when linear, less than 20 mm); legumes sharply 4-sided compressed, 20–40 × 6–10 mm, strongly incurved or coiled; ne Arizona, sw Idaho, se, w, n Nevada, se Oregon, sw Utah. . . . . . . .247. *Astragalus tetrapterus* (in part)
        18. Leaflets 3–7(or 9), blades linear, 10–50 × 0.5–1.5 mm; legumes strongly obcompressed, (25–)30–45 × (11–)13–17(–23) mm, ± straight or obscurely sigmoid-arcuate; nc, nw Nevada . . . . .248. *Astragalus pterocarpus*
    15. Stipules at the most proximal nodes connate.
      19. Calyces accrescent, hirsute; legumes 6–7.5 mm, deciduous within calyces; Upper San Juan Valley, sw Colorado, adjacent New Mexico . . . 93. *Astragalus oocalycis* (in part)
      19. Calyces not accrescent, strigose, strigulose, or glabrate; legumes 9–35 mm, well exserted beyond persistent calyces; Manitoba to Alberta south to Kansas, Arizona, and Oregon.
        20. Corollas white, ochroleucous, or cream; leaves pinnate throughout, not reduced distally; e of Continental Divide except at 1900–2200 m in Montana, sw Wyoming, adjacent Utah.
          21. Stems ascending or erect; legumes erect or ascending; Carbon County, Montana, se to Carbon County, Wyoming . . . . 96. *Astragalus grayi*
          21. Stems decumbent, ascending, or erect; legumes declined or deflexed; Manitoba to Alberta south to Kansas and Utah, including Wyoming.
            22. Flowers (16–)21–24(–27) mm; calyx tubes 2.8–4.3 mm wide; leaflet blades involute, linear, filiform, or linear-oblanceolate, rigid; Alberta east to Manitoba, southward to Colorado and Kansas . . . . 94. *Astragalus pectinatus*
            22. Flowers 24–30 mm; calyx tubes 4.5–6.2 mm wide; leaflet blades flat (margins elevated), linear-oblong, not rigid; sw Wyoming to Moffat County, Colorado, and Daggett County, Utah . . . 95. *Astragalus nelsonianus*
        20. Corollas usually pink-purple with white or whitish wing tips, white with pink-purple keel tips, greenish yellow, rarely white throughout; leaves pinnate proximally and unifoliolate distally or all unifoliolate, sometimes reduced to naked rachis (phyllodia); plants of intermountain region, w Colorado to n Arizona, nw Nevada, se Oregon, and s Idaho.

23. Legumes erect; n Arizona, wc Colorado, nw Utah to Idaho, Nevada, Oregon.
   24. Corollas pink-purple with white wing tips, or greenish yellow, or whitish; racemes 7–35-flowered; n Arizona, Utah to Idaho, Nevada, Oregon . . . . 97. *Astragalus toanus* (in part)
   24. Corollas white with pink-purple keel tips; racemes 3–10-flowered; Delta and Montrose counties, Colorado . . . . 98. *Astragalus linifolius*
23. Legumes declined or deflexed; wc, nw Colorado, c, ne Utah.
   25. Corollas pale pink-purple, wing tips often paler or sometimes white; legumes oblong-ellipsoid, 12–25 × 5–7.5 mm, glabrous, terminal cusps 2.5–4 mm; San Rafael Swell, Utah, along lower Dolores River, wc Colorado . . . . 99. *Astragalus rafaelensis*
   25. Corollas usually pink-purple with white wing tips, rarely white throughout; legumes narrowly oblong, (15–)20–35 × 4.4–6(–7) mm, strigose or glabrate, terminal cusps 0.5–1 mm; Uinta County, Utah . . . . 100. *Astragalus saurinus*

[14. Shifted to left margin.—Ed.]

14. Flowers 4.3–13.5(–15.5) mm; calyces campanulate (except shortly cylindric in *A. episcopus*), tubes 1.2–5.6(–6) mm.
   26. Flowers 4.3–6.1 mm; calyx tubes 1.2–1.8 mm; legumes 9–12 × 2.5–3 mm, strongly laterally compressed; McKinley County, New Mexico . . . . 23. *Astragalus cliffordii*
   26. Flowers 5–13.5(–15.5) mm; calyx tubes (1.5–)1.8–5.6(–6) mm; legumes 5–35(–40) × (1.2–)1.9–9(–11) mm, 3-sided compressed, dorsiventrally compressed, obcompressed, bladdery-inflated, or laterally compressed, sometimes strongly so; w North America.
      27. Flowers 5–7.5 mm; calyx tubes 1.8–2.1 mm; legumes 5–8 × 1.9–3(–3.3) mm; Crook, Deschutes, and n Klamath counties, Oregon. . . . . 117. *Astragalus peckii*
      27. Flowers (5–)6.3–15.5 mm; calyx tubes (1.5–)2.3–5.6(–6) mm; legumes (5.5–)10–35(–40) × (1.2–)2–9 mm; w North America.
         28. Legumes linear-oblong, linear-oblanceoloid, or narrowly ellipsoid, 10–22 × 2.3–4.3 mm, subsessile or stipitate, stipes 0–2 mm (stipes concealed within calyces when present), dorsiventrally compressed; se California, sw Idaho, Nevada, e Oregon . . . . .119. *Astragalus atratus* (in part)
         28. Legumes linear to subglobose, 5.5–40 × (1.2–)2–11 mm, sessile, subsessile, or shortly stipitate, stipes 0–1.7 mm, laterally compressed, sometimes strongly so, obcompressed, or bladdery-inflated; w North America.
            29. Plants rushlike; leaflet blades mostly linear or reduced to a rachis (rarely elliptic or oblong).
               30. Legumes dorsiventrally compressed in proximal 1/2, laterally compressed distally . . . . .41. *Astragalus duchesnensis*
               30. Legumes laterally compressed throughout, sometimes strongly so.
                  31. Corollas ochroleucous; banners recurved through 100–130° . . . . 34. *Astragalus xiphoides*
                  31. Corollas pale pink or whitish to pink-purple or tinged purplish or pinkish; banners recurved through 40–45°.
                     32. Calyces shortly cylindric, suffused with purple or pale, white-strigose, tubes 3.4–5.2(–6) × 1.9–2.9(–3.4) mm; seeds 16–26 . . . . 39. *Astragalus episcopus*
                     32. Calyces campanulate, not suffused with purple, black-strigose, tubes 2.8–4.2 × 2.2–2.6 mm; seeds 8–14 . . . . 40. *Astragalus lancearius*
            29. Plants mostly not rushlike; leaflet blades of at least some leaves broader than linear.

[33. Shifted to left margin.—Ed.]

33. Plants selenophytes, 1–5 cm (dwarf) and densely clump-, cushion-, or tuft-forming, or 9–60 cm and clump-forming, from superficial or slightly subterranean caudex.
    34. Plants densely clump-, cushion-, or tuft-forming; leaves 1–4 cm; peduncles 0.5–3.5 cm; racemes 3–7-flowered; legumes spreading, bladdery-inflated, 10–17 × 7–11 mm; plants not scented .... 80. *Astragalus jejunus* (in part)
    34. Plants clump-forming; leaves 4–17 cm; peduncles 4–25 cm; racemes 6–34-flowered; legumes ascending-spreading, obcompressed (not bladdery), 5.5–8 × 2.3–3.4 mm; plants garliclike scented.......... 89. *Astragalus moencoppensis* (in part)
33. Plants not selenophytes, (1–)10–60(–80) cm, clump-forming or not, from subterranean or superficial caudex.
    35. Legumes ellipsoid to oblong, 9–15 mm; ne Arizona, w Colorado, nw New Mexico, e Utah (n to Uintah County) .... 22. *Astragalus wingatanus* (in part)
    35. Legumes linear, linear-oblong, linear-ellipsoid, oblanceoloid, or narrowly oblong, 10–50(–53) mm; w North America.
        36. Caudex superficial, with leafy spurs on caudex or base of stems forming basal tufts; Alberta, British Columbia, southward to Arizona and New Mexico, eastward to South Dakota .... 30. *Astragalus miser* (in part)
        36. Caudex subterranean or superficial, without leafy spurs on caudex or base of stems (without basal tufts); Montana to Colorado, west to Idaho and Arizona.
            37. Plants from deep subterranean caudex; leaves often nearly bladeless and rushlike; leaflet blades, when present, 5–30 × 0.5–4 mm; legumes 13–50(–53) × 2.3–5 mm; plants usually of dry or woodland habitats ....31. *Astragalus convallarius* (in part)
            37. Plants from shallow subterranean or superficial caudex (and a stout, tuberous taproot); leaves often expanded into flat, grasslike blades; leaflet blades 4–47(–67) × 1–5 mm; legumes 10–17 × 2.7–4 mm; plants usually of moist meadows and stream banks, in moist saline meadows and swales .....32. *Astragalus diversifolius* (in part)

Key to Species of Group 5

1. Plants caulescent, villous-hirsute or shaggy-villous, hairs minutely dilated at base; flowers nodding; corollas whitish or ochroleucous; legumes narrowly oblong to oblanceoloid, obscurely 3-sided compressed, glabrous, bilocular.......... 128. *Astragalus drummondii* (in part)
1. Plants subcaulescent to caulescent, mostly strigulose, villous to villosulous, or pilose; flowers nodding or not; corollas pink, purple, lavender, red, yellow, ochroleucous, cream, white, or greenish white; legumes, when oblong to lanceoloid, not bluntly 3-sided compressed, glabrous or pubescent, unilocular to bilocular.
    2. Legumes ovoid, leathery or stiffly papery, bilocular; corollas whitish tinged with violet; leaflet blades obovate-cuneate or suborbiculate, apex obtuse to emarginate; plants local in Rush and Skull valleys, Tooele County, Utah ....285. *Astragalus lentiginosus* (in part)
    2. Legumes, when ovoid, then cartilaginous, papery, papery-membranous, fleshy, or leathery, unilocular to bilocular; corollas pink, purple, lavender, red, yellow, ochroleucous, cream, white, or greenish white; leaflet blades filiform or narrowly elliptic to broadly obovate, apex acute to emarginate; widespread.
        3. Calyces obliquely ovoid, tubes accrescent, legumes enclosed, deciduous within accrescent calyx; upper San Juan Valley, sw Colorado, adjacent New Mexico ... . 93. *Astragalus oocalycis* (in part)
        3. Calyces usually campanulate or cylindric, when ovoid, tubes not accrescent, legumes not deciduous within calyx; widespread.
            4. Legumes obcompressed, bladdery-inflated, or terete, not laterally angled, unilocular.

[5. Shifted to left margin.—Ed.]

5. Legumes sessile on, and disjointing from, stipelike gynophore, 2.3–11 mm.
   6. Calyces 6–8.6 mm; leaflets 25–39; flowers 13–16 mm; gynophores 2.3–5.6(–6) mm; legumes bladdery-inflated, not laterally compressed, not bicarinate, 23–36 × 12–18 (–20) mm; coastal or near coastal California, San Luis Obispo County south to Santa Barbara County, on San Miguel and Santa Rosa isles . . . . 252. *Astragalus curtipes*
   6. Calyces (5.5–)8.7–10.3 mm; leaflets (11–)17–29(or 31); flowers 15.3–18(–19) mm; gynophores 3–11 mm; legumes bladdery-inflated and laterally compressed, bicarinate, (21–)25–45 × (6–)8–15.5 mm; South Coast Ranges, Stanislaus County, south to Santa Barbara, Kern, and San Luis Obispo counties, California . . . . 254. *Astragalus oxyphysus*
5. Legumes stipitate or, if sessile, then gynophore to 1 mm.
   7. Legumes erect, papery, stipes 7–19 mm; caudex subterranean; purple Triassic Chinle Formation in Kane and Washington counties, Utah, and Mohave County, Arizona.
      8. Stems prostrate-ascending; corollas ochroleucous, or pink-purple with white wing tips; e Washington and Kane counties, Utah, w of Cockscomb Segment of East Kaibab, and adjacent Mohave and Coconino counties, Arizona . . . . 162. *Astragalus ampullarius*
      8. Stems erect-ascending from decumbent base; corollas ochroleucous; sc, sw Washington County, Utah . . . . 163. *Astragalus ampullarioides* (in part)
   7. Legumes usually pendulous or declined, sometimes spreading or loosely ascending, cartilaginous or papery-membranous, stipes 1.5–12(–40) mm, or gynophores 0–1 mm; caudex subterranean or superficial; Alaska and w United States.
      9. Legumes sessile or articulate to short gynophore; caudex subterranean, rhizomatous; racemes 1–3(–6)-flowered; c, w Alaska. . . . . 78. *Astragalus polaris* (in part)
      9. Legumes subsessile or stipitate; caudex subterranean or superficial; racemes (3 or)4–45-flowered; Colorado and New Mexico west to Washington and California.
         10. Legumes cartilaginous becoming stiffly papery, somewhat fleshy, opaque; s Utah southward . . . . 26. *Astragalus hallii* (in part)
         10. Legumes papery-membranous, translucent; sc New Mexico to California and Washington.
             11. Stipes 14–40 mm; c, sc, w California . . . . 255. *Astragalus asymmetricus*
             11. Stipes 1.5–12 mm; New Mexico to California and Washington.
                 12. Stipes 1.5–3 mm; legumes ovoid, often red-mottled; sc New Mexico . . . . 28. *Astragalus castetteri*
                 12. Stipes 2–12 mm; legumes ovoid, semiobovoid, or semiellipsoid, red- or purple-mottled or not; Idaho and Washington south to Nevada and California.
                     13. Legumes ± obliquely obovoid, semiobovoid, or semiellipsoid, apex differentiated into broad, low-deltoid beak; wc, sw Idaho, e, se Oregon, sw Washington . . . . 69. *Astragalus cusickii* (in part)
                     13. Legumes subsymmetrically obovoid, apex broad, round, beak obsolete; s California to Washington, eastward to ne Nevada and c Idaho. . . . . 70. *Astragalus whitneyi*

[4. Shifted to left margin.—Ed.]

4. Legumes not inflated or, if swollen, then slightly bladdery or angled laterally or bluntly, unilocular or bilocular.
   14. Flowers nodding and retrorsely imbricate, (12.5–)14–23.5 mm; stipes (3.5–)4–22 mm.
       15. Corollas dull yellow; legumes fleshy becoming woody, unilocular, bicarinate by sutures; Sierra Nevada of California, Lake Tahoe n in Nevada . . . . 61. *Astragalus gibbsii*
       15. Corollas white, ochroleucous, or pink-purple; legumes papery or fleshy becoming thinly leathery, unilocular or bilocular, when unilocular, legumes 3-sided compressed or dorsiventrally compressed, sometimes abaxially bisulcate; widespread.
           16. Plants odorless; caudex subterranean; legumes 3-sided, abaxially sulcate, bilocular. . . . . 16. *Astragalus scopulorum*
           16. Plants with garliclike odor; caudex superficial; legumes dorsiventrally compressed or 3-sided, faces flat or bisulcate, unilocular.

17. Legumes with contrasting faces, adaxial face convexly rounded, abaxial face with suture forming a prominent ridge flanked by depressed grooves; corollas often pink-purple, sometimes white or ochroleucous; c Nevada eastward . . . . 91. *Astragalus bisulcatus* (in part)
17. Legumes sharply 3-sided, faces of subequal width and nearly flat; corollas usually white or ochroleucous, rarely suffused with purple or purple-veined; sw Wyoming, ne Utah to Texas north to Saskatchewan . . . . 92. *Astragalus racemosus*

[14. Shifted to left margin.—Ed.]

14. Flowers erect to nodding, if nodding, then often loosely and openly racemose (or becoming so) or, if flowers retrorsely imbricate, then mostly less than 14 mm; stipes 0–16 mm, or gynophores 0.3–11 mm.
18. Calyces 8.3–15.1 mm, sparsely white-hirsute, gibbous-saccate at base behind pedicel; legumes fleshy becoming spongy and honeycombed (walls 2.5–3 mm thick, translucent), bilocular . . . . 241. *Astragalus tennesseensis* (in part)
18. Calyces 2.3–10.1 mm, strigose or villous with white and/or black hairs, sometimes nearly glabrous, not gibbous-saccate behind pedicel (except *A. bisulcatus*); legumes mostly papery or papery-membranous, sometimes fleshy becoming leathery, unilocular to bilocular.
19. Legumes bilocular, 3-sided compressed; plants of woodlands, brushy, or open areas.
20. Plants 40–90 cm; flowers 11.5–13.5 mm; legumes incurved-ascending, linear-ellipsoid, (27–)30–37(–40) × 4–5 mm. . . . . 347. *Astragalus glycyphyllos*
20. Plants (1–)3–30(–55) cm; flowers 4.5–8.2 mm; legumes pendulous, linear-oblong or -oblanceolate, ellipsoid, or oblong-ellipsoid, 4–30 × 2–4.5 mm.
21. Plants (15–)20–55 cm; legumes 15–30 mm; ec, ne Arizona, wc New Mexico . . . . .14. *Astragalus egglestonii*
21. Plants 1–30 cm; legumes 4–16 mm; California, Idaho, Nevada, Oregon, Washington.
22. Plants 1–3(–7) cm; stems few to several, erect or ascending, densely tufted; caudex with thatch of persistent leaf bases; legumes 4–7 × 2–3 mm; Owyhee County, Idaho, ec Humboldt County, Nevada . . . . 118. *Astragalus yoderwilliamsii* (in part)
22. Plants 3–30 cm; stems several to numerous, prostrate, spreading, or ascending, not densely tufted, some internodes well developed; caudex without thatch of persistent leaf bases; not of Owyhee County, Idaho, Humboldt County, Nevada.
23. Legumes 9–16 × 3–4.5 mm; elevation 600–900(–1000) m; sw Idaho, Malheur County, Oregon . . . . .115. *Astragalus mulfordiae* (in part)
23. Legumes 6–10.5 × 2–3 mm; elevation 2100–2700 m; Mono County, California, adjacent Nevada . . . . 116. *Astragalus johannis-howellii*
19. Legumes mostly unilocular, subunilocular, or sub-bilocular (incompletely bilocular in *A. rusbyi*), laterally compressed, obcompressed, or flattened, if 3-sided, of mesophytic or alpine habitats.
24. Flowers nodding and retrorsely imbricate; legumes with contrasting faces, dorsal face with raised sutures between parallel depressions, ventral face convexly rounded; selenophytes; c Nevada eastward, Arizona north to British Columbia, east to Manitoba. . . . . 91. *Astragalus bisulcatus* (in part)
24. Flowers usually not nodding (except nodding in *A. leibergii*), not retrorsely imbricate and obviously racemose; legumes without contrasting faces; not selenophytes; Alaska to Newfoundland, south to Arizona.

[25. Shifted to left margin.—Ed.]

25. Legumes laterally compressed or flattened, unilocular.
   26. Legumes ascending, humistrate, coiled in 0.5–1 spiral, gynophores 4–10 mm; racemes 1–5-flowered; se Alaska, sw Yukon, British Columbia . . . . 79. *Astragalus nutzotinensis*
   26. Legumes pendulous, deflexed, or incurved-ascending, not humistrate, straight to slightly curved, or incurved through 0.25 spiral, stipes (0–)0.6–16 mm; racemes (1–)3–35-flowered; Yukon south to Arizona.
      27. Legumes incurved-ascending; leaflets 9–13, blades broadly obovate-cuneate or -flabellate; Lahontan Basin, Nevada . . . . 161. *Astragalus porrectus*
      27. Legumes pendulous or deflexed; leaflets (3 or)5–23, blades linear, narrowly oblong, elliptic, oblanceolate, oval, or obovate; not of Lahontan Basin, Nevada.
         28. Corollas purple or suffused with purple; stipules not blackened on drying; Montana, n Idaho, and British Columbia and Alberta, along Continental Divide . . . . 74. *Astragalus bourgovii*
         28. Corollas ochroleucous, or if purple (*A. inversus*, *A. wingatanus*, and some *A. multiflorus*) not near the Continental Divide in British Columbia, Alberta, Montana or Idaho; stipules blackened on drying or not.
            29. Stipules and ripe legumes commonly black or blackish; racemes often paired in leaf axils; flowers 6–9(–11) mm; legumes 7–17 × 2.5–4.5 mm . . . . 72. *Astragalus multiflorus*
            29. Stipules and ripe legumes brown, stramineous, or purplish; racemes 1 per leaf axil; flowers (5.5–)9.4–17.5 mm; legumes 9–43 × 3–6.5 mm.
               30. Herbage, pedicels, and calyx villous-villosulous with ascending, spreading and incurved, or curly hairs; calyx tube 5.2–7 × 3.5–4.5 mm; upper Sacramento and Klamath valleys, Shasta County, California to s Jackson County, Oregon. . . . . 68. *Astragalus californicus*
               30. Herbage, pedicels, and calyx strigulose with appressed or subappressed hairs, or subglabrous; calyx tube 1.5–5.5 × 1.2–3.5 mm (rarely longer and wider in *A. filipes*); widespread.
                  31. Stems often distinctly flexuous, from subterranean caudex; flowers 5.5–8 mm; ne Arizona, sw Colorado, nw New Mexico, se Utah . . . . 22. *Astragalus wingatanus* (in part)
                  31. Stems not or only indistinctly flexuous, caudex superficial; flowers 9.4–15 mm; w Utah to British Columbia southward.
                     32. Leaflets (5–)9–23; flowers whitish or cream, keel petals abruptly incurved through 95–120°, about as long as claws; legume body never mottled, glabrous or strigulose; British Columbia southward to California, eastward to Idaho and w Utah . . . . 66. *Astragalus filipes*
                     32. Leaflets 5–11; flowers pinkish red with whitish to buff banner and wing tips, keel petals incurved through 40–85°, longer than claws; legumes strigulose or, if glabrous, then mottled; Modoc to Siskiyou and Lassen counties, California . . . . 67. *Astragalus inversus* (in part)

25. Legumes usually 3-sided or dorsiventrally compressed, subterete, obcompressed, or laterally compressed, when laterally compressed, then swollen and subunilocular or incompletely bilocular.
   33. Racemes loosely (1 or)2–18(–20)-flowered; flowers ascending.
      34. Plants delicate (slender-stemmed); stems sprawling; racemes (1 or)2 or 3(–5)-flowered; moist montane meadows; Colorado, n Idaho, w Montana, Wyoming . . . . 4. *Astragalus leptaleus* (in part)
      34. Plants often somewhat coarse; stems prostrate to ascending; racemes (2–)4–20-flowered; forests, meadows, sandy soils, ridges, sagebrush flats; Alaska east to Newfoundland, south to Colorado.

35. Stipes 1–1.5 mm; stems prostrate (underground for 1–9 cm); flowers 9–9.8 mm; corollas yellowish (drying ochroleucous); legumes (13–)15–23 × 3.3–4 mm, 3-sided compressed; Little Kern River Basin, Tulare County, California . . .29. *Astragalus shevockii*
35. Stipes 4–12 mm (1–2 in *A. ertterae*) or gynophores 0.3–1 mm; stems prostrate to ascending; flowers (7–)10–19 mm; corollas greenish white, ochroleucous, or pink-purple and sometimes partly white; legumes (4.5–)16–40(–43) × (2.2–)5–12 mm, slightly obcompressed, 3-sided or dorsiventrally compressed, or terete; Alaska to Newfoundland, south to Colorado.
  36. Stipes or gynophores 0.3–2 mm.
    37. Corollas pink-purple or partly white; legumes ascending to spreading, (4.5–)7–10(–12) × (2.2–)3–4.5 mm, gynophores 0.3–1 mm; mesic sites; widespread, not in California . . . . 77. *Astragalus bodinii* (in part)
    37. Corollas ochroleucous; legumes pendulous (humistrate), 16–22 × 7–9 mm, stipes 1–2 mm; xeric habitats; Walker Pass, Kern County, California . . . . 160. *Astragalus ertterae*
  36. Stipes (4–)8–12 mm.
    38. Legumes obliquely ovoid or ovoid-acuminate, inflated but not bladdery, slightly obcompressed, (10–)13–24(–32) × 6–12 mm, set at an angle to the stipe; Sierra Nevada, California, adjacent Nevada . . . . 157. *Astragalus bolanderi*
    38. Legumes obliquely oblong or clavate-ellipsoid, subterete to somewhat obcompressed becoming dorsiventrally compressed, 20–40(–43) × 5–8.5(–9) mm, not set at an angle from the stipe; Los Angeles and San Bernardino counties, California. . . . . 159. *Astragalus bicristatus* (in part)

[33. Shifted to left margin.—Ed.]

33. Racemes (6–)10–45-flowered, at least some racemes with more than 16 flowers; flowers ascending to nodding.
  39. Legumes erect; corollas whitish (immaculate); flowers (10.8–)11.6–16.4 mm; peduncles and racemes together equaling or surpassing leaves; Columbia River valley in Chelan, Douglas, Grant, and Kittitas counties, Washington . . . . .156. *Astragalus leibergii*
  39. Legumes pendulous, spreading or descending; corollas usually purple, pink-purple, pink, or whitish and lilac- or lavender-tinged or -tipped, sometimes ochroleucous, rarely white; flowers 6–13.8(–14.8) mm; peduncles and racemes together usually shorter than stems; widespread.
    40. Corollas ochroleucous; leaflet blades of proximalmost leaves suborbiculate, broadly obovate, or oblong and apex often retuse-emarginate; Otero County, New Mexico . . . . 11. *Astragalus altus*
    40. Corollas usually purple, pink-purple, pink, or whitish, sometimes lilac- or lavender-tinged; leaflet blades of proximalmost leaves narrower, linear to ovate, oblong, elliptic or obovate, apex often obtuse to acute; widespread.
      41. Flowers 6–7.2 mm; racemes (7–)12–40-flowered, axis elongating to (2.5–)4–18 (–22) cm in fruit; seeds 6–13; nc Arizona, sw Colorado, c, nw New Mexico.
        42. Leaflets (11–)17–25; legumes black-strigulose, stipes 2.2–5 mm; nc Arizona . . . . 13. *Astragalus rusbyi*
        42. Leaflets 7–11; legumes glabrous, stipes (1–)1.2–2 mm; sw Colorado, New Mexico . . . . 19. *Astragalus proximus*
      41. Flowers 7–13.8(–14.8) mm (rarely as short as 6.2 mm in *A. alpinus*); racemes 3–26(–40)-flowered, axis elongating to (0.5–)1–15(–20) mm in fruit; seeds 5–25; widespread.
        43. Flowers 7–11 mm; racemes 7–26-flowered, axis elongated in fruit . . . . .17. *Astragalus flexuosus* (in part)
        43. Flowers (6–)7–14.5 mm; racemes 2–40-flowered, axis little or not elongated in fruit.

44. Caudex subterranean; keel somewhat longer than wings and subequal to banner; legumes sulcate abaxially . . . . 3. *Astragalus alpinus*
44. Caudex superficial or barely subterranean; keel shorter than wings; legumes flattened or depressed but not sulcate abaxially.
    45. Proximal stipules connate-sheathing; wing apex obtuse . . . . 7. *Astragalus robbinsii* (in part)
    45. Proximal stipules clasping but not connate or shortly connate proximally; wing apex bidentate. . . . . .8. *Astragalus australis* (in part)

Key to Species of Group 6

1. Legumes globose, subglobose, oblong-ellipsoid, or obliquely ovoid-oblong, fleshy, terete, slightly dorsiventrally compressed, or ± obcompressed, bilocular; stems sprawling-decumbent or ascending and radiating.
    2 Legumes glabrous, valves differentiated into double envelope separated by air space; Rutherford County, Tennessee . . . . 238. *Astragalus bibullatus*
    2. Legumes strigulose or pilosulous, valves not differentiated into double envelope; North Dakota and Montana south to Texas and Colorado . . . . .240. *Astragalus plattensis* (in part)
1. Legumes linear to globose, leathery to membranous, sometimes fleshy, 3-sided, dorsiventrally, or laterally compressed or flattened, or subterete, bilocular to unilocular; stems erect to prostrate, sometimes sprawling.
    3. Flowers ascending or erect, densely racemose (subcapitate); caudex subterranean.
        4. Stems 9–43 cm; corollas usually pink-purple, sometimes ochroleucous or nearly white; leaflets usually 13–23; legumes oblong-ellipsoid, scarcely swollen, obtusely 3-sided, sulcate abaxially . . . . 180. *Astragalus agrestis*
        4. Stems 30–90(–130) cm; corollas ochroleucous; leaflets 17–29(–31); legumes broadly obovoid or subglobose, inflated but firm, sulcate adaxially . . . . 181. *Astragalus cicer*
    3. Flowers erect to nodding, if erect then often soon spreading or declined and loosely racemosely arranged (dense heads in *A. austiniae*); caudex usually superficial.
        5. Flowers erect-ascending, in dense, ovoid or subglobose heads; legumes 5.5–7 × 3–3.5 mm, ± included in calyx; Lake Tahoe, El Dorado, Nevada, and Placer counties, California, and Washoe County, Nevada. 339. *Astragalus austiniae*
        5. Flowers erect to nodding, if erect-ascending then often soon spreading or declined and loosely racemose; legumes 4–60 × 1.2–35 mm, not usually included in calyx; widespread.
            6. Racemes loosely (rather densely in *A. ravenii*) (1–)3–6(–8)-flowered; plants from branched subterranean caudex; montane or arctic habitats.
                7. Underground stems 1–6 cm; corollas whitish, banners lilac-veined, recurved through 80–90°; Sierra Nevada, e Fresno, w Inyo, w Mono counties, California . . . . .289. *Astragalus ravenii*
                7. Underground stems 6+ cm (1.5–9 cm in *A. polaris*); corollas whitish, pink-purple, or lilac, banners recurved or reflexed through 50°; interior and n Alaska, Rocky Mountains, Colorado, Idaho, Montana, and Wyoming.
                    8. Legumes ovoid, turgid or bladdery, (15–)18–43 × 4.5–12(–15) mm; corollas usually pink-purple, rarely white; Alaska . . . . . . .78. *Astragalus polaris* (in part)
                    8. Legumes ovoid, lanceoloid, oblong, or ellipsoid, 3-sided compressed or obcompressed (not bladdery), 6.5–14 × 2.5–4 mm; corollas whitish, pink-purple, or lilac; Colorado, Idaho, Montana, Wyoming.
                        9. Corollas white, keel petals 6–7.5 mm; herbage green; legumes pendulous, oblong- or lanceoloid-ellipsoid, slightly decurved; moist montane meadows . . . . 4. *Astragalus leptaleus* (in part)
                        9. Corollas pink-purple, lilac, or whitish, keel petals 9–10 mm; herbage ashy gray; legumes ascending (humistrate), obliquely ovoid, lanceoloid-ovoid, or ovoid-ellipsoid, slightly incurved; alpine tundra. . . . . 5. *Astragalus molybdenus*

6. Racemes (1–)5–45(–125)-flowered; plants from branched or unbranched subterranean or superficial caudex, or from a taproot; widespread habitats.
   10. Flowers (initially) and legumes erect-ascending; proximal peduncles and racemes together much shorter than stems; e, ec Alaska, s Yukon . . . 10. *Astragalus williamsii*
   10. Flowers and legumes mostly pendulous, spreading, reflexed, deflexed, or ascending, when erect, peduncles and racemes together longer than stems; widespread.
   [11. Shifted to left margin.—Ed.]

11. Flowers ascending, sometimes spreading, and legumes erect, sometimes spreading, proximal peduncles and racemes together longer than stem, axis (2.5–)3–25 cm.
   12. Flowers 7–11 mm; corollas pink-purple, marcescent; legumes 5.5–8 × 2.3–3.4 mm; seeds 4–6; selenophytes; ne Arizona, se Utah. . . . . 89. *Astragalus moencoppensis* (in part)
   12. Flowers (13.2–)14–25.5 mm; corollas usually cream, white, or whitish, sometimes with purple tips, deciduous; legumes (10–)15–25 × 4.3–11 mm; seeds 15–35; not selenophytes; Pacific Northwest.
      13. Legumes usually villous-pilose or hirtellous, sometimes glabrescent; calyces (10–)11–15 mm, lobes (2.6–)4.6–6.7(–7.5) mm; within and near Columbia Gap, Wasco and Hood River counties, Oregon, and Klickitat County, Washington . . . . 154. *Astragalus hoodianus*
      13. Legumes glabrous or strigulose; calyces 4.9–9.2(–12.2) mm, lobes 1.3–5.1 mm; Idaho, Oregon, Washington.
         14. Banner recurved through 30–45°, oblanceolate or broadly rhombic-oblanceolate, 16–25.5 mm, apex emarginate; calyx lobes 1.3–3(–4) mm; legumes 4.3–8 mm wide; Benton County, Washington, and trans montane Oregon (Wasco to Baker County), se to sw Idaho . . . . 153. *Astragalus conjunctus*
         14. Banner recurved through 90°, oblong-oblanceolate, rhombic-oblanceolate, elliptic, oblong-ovate, or somewhat quadrately ovate-cuneate, (13.2–)14–20.7 mm, apex usually deeply notched; calyx lobes (2.4–)2.7–5.1 mm; legumes (5–)6–11 mm wide; Kittitas, Klickitat, and Yakima counties, Washington . . . . .155. *Astragalus reventiformis*

11. Flowers and/or legumes usually spreading or declined ultimately, racemes shorter or axis of longest peduncle and raceme together shorter than stem, axis 0.2–30 cm in fruit.
   15. Plants 2–9(–23) cm, tuft- or mat-forming, subacaulescent or short caulescent; sandy habitats; n Arizona, se Nevada, nw New Mexico, s Utah.
      16. Calyces 2–3.5 mm, tubes 1.2–2.5 mm; flowers 4–6.2 mm; New Mexico.
         17. Flowers 5–6.2 mm; legumes 8–14 mm, stipes 0.5–0.8 mm; Lincoln County . . . . .123. *Astragalus kerrii* (in part)
         17. Flowers 4–5 mm; legumes 9–9.8 mm, stipes 0.3–0.6 mm; McKinley County . . . . 124. *Astragalus heilii*
      16. Calyces 5.5–18 mm, tubes 3–13.5 mm; flowers 9–26 mm; Arizona, Nevada, New Mexico, Utah.
         18. Calyx tubes 6.5–13.5 mm; flowers 18–26 mm; keel petals concealing style; legumes obliquely ovoid-oblong, dorsiventrally compressed, fleshy becoming somewhat woody, unilocular; n Arizona, se Nevada, nw New Mexico, s Utah . . . . 185. *Astragalus zionis* (in part)
         18. Calyx tubes 3–4 mm; flowers 9–12 mm; keel petals not concealing style; legumes ellipsoid, bladdery-inflated, papery, bilocular; interdune valleys and sandy sites below White and Vermillion cliffs, Kane and Washington counties, Utah, and Coconino County, Arizona . . . . 293. *Astragalus striatiflorus*
   15. Plants (0.5–)3–80(–110) cm, usually strongly caulescent, sometimes acaulescent, subacaulescent, or short caulescent; marshy, desert, sandy, woodland, or mountain habitats; widespread.
      19. Racemes densely spikelike and flowers declined and retrorsely imbricate; axis 2.5–8(–9.5) cm in fruit; coastal California, Humboldt to Orange counties . . .253. *Astragalus pycnostachyus*
      19. Racemes loosely flowered, or if densely flowered then flowers not declined or retrorsely imbricate; axis 0.2–30 cm in fruit; n, w, s North America.

[20. Shifted to left margin.—Ed.]

20. Legumes laterally compressed or flattened, bicarinate and unilocular.
 21. Legumes 3.5–15 × 1.8–4.5 mm; seeds 4–8(–11).
  22. Apex of leaflets acute, obtuse, or retuse; legumes glabrous; ne Arizona, sw Colorado, nw New Mexico, se Utah . . . . 22. *Astragalus wingatanus* (in part)
  22. Apex of leaflets usually acute; legumes strigose; Saskatchewan to British Columbia south to South Dakota, Wyoming, and Idaho . . . . 73. *Astragalus vexilliflexus*
 21. Legumes 11–50(–53) × 2–9 mm; seeds (6–)8–26.
  23. Corollas pink-purple; flowers (13–)14–20 mm; legumes erect, stiffly leathery to somewhat woody; selenophytes . . . . 97. *Astragalus toanus* (in part)
  23. Corollas ochroleucous, whitish, or greenish white, often tinged or veined with purple or pink; flowers 5.3–13.5 mm; legumes ascending, pendulous, spreading, or declined, papery; not selenophytes.
   24. Flowering stems accompanied by short, sterile branches forming a tuft of sub-basal leaves; keel apex beaklike . . . . 30. *Astragalus miser* (in part)
   24. Flowering stems not with sub-basal tufts; keel apex broadly triangular.
    25. Plants from deep subterranean caudex; legumes (13–)25–50(–53) × 2.3–5 mm, linear, narrowly oblong, or oblanceoloid; dry communities . . . . 31. *Astragalus convallarius* (in part)
    25. Plants from shallow subterranean or superficial caudex (with tuberous taproot); legumes 10–17 × 2.7–4 mm, narrowly oblong; moist, saline meadows, ditches, swales. . . . . 32. *Astragalus diversifolius* (in part)
20. Legumes terete, 3-sided compressed, obcompressed, bladdery-inflated, or dorsiventrally compressed, or bilocular or sub-bilocular, when laterally compressed and unilocular, then valves convex or with a ridge parallel to the adaxial suture, or not bicarinate.
 26. Calyces 8.3–15.1 mm, sparsely white-hirsute, gibbous-saccate behind pedicels; legumes fleshy becoming spongy (walls 2.5–3 mm thick, alveolate-rugulose when ripe), bilocular; n Alabama, c Illinois, c Tennessee . . . . 241. *Astragalus tennesseensis* (in part)
 26. Calyces 2.1–8.2(–13) mm, strigose, pilosulous, villosulous, or glabrous, not gibbous-saccate behind pedicels; legumes papery, membranous, fleshy, or leathery, unilocular to bilocular; n, w, sw North America.
  27. Plants often densely gray-villosulous, stems sometimes more densely pubescent basally; legumes 3-sided, bilocular (except unilocular in *A. microcystis*).
   28. Flowers 9–17.5 mm; legumes 10–20 × 3–5.5 mm; seeds (10–)12–20; California, Nevada.
    29. Plants from superficial caudex, densely white-tomentose to base; calyces 6.2–8.2 mm; keel petals 6.6–9 mm; seeds (10–)12–16; California (Mono to Modoc counties), w Nevada . . . . 337. *Astragalus andersonii*
    29. Plants from subterranean caudex, underground for 0.5–5.5 cm where glabrous; calyces 8.6–13 mm; keel petals 10–12.2 mm; seeds (14–)16–20; e foothills, Sierra Nevada, near Lone Pine, Inyo County, California . . . . 338. *Astragalus sepultipes*
   28. Flowers 4.5–7.8(–8.3) mm; legumes 5–12(–15) × 2–4.2 mm; seeds 6–10; British Columbia to California, east to Montana.
    30. Legumes plumply ellipsoid, obovoid-ellipsoid, or subglobose, bladdery-inflated, 5–12(–14) × 4–7 mm; se British Columbia, n Idaho, wc Montana, ne Washington . . . . 75. *Astragalus microcystis* (in part)
    30. Legumes ellipsoid, lanceoloid-ellipsoid, or lenticular-oblong, 3-sided or laterally compressed, 5–8.5(–9) × 2–3 mm; California, Idaho, Oregon, Washington.

31. Stems erect or ascending, densely white-tomentose proximally; plants (10–)15–30 cm; leaves 3.5–9(–10.5) cm; leaflets 11–19(–23), blades (3–)5–15(–18) mm; racemes (5–)10–25-flowered, axis (1.5–)3–10.5 cm in fruit; sc Idaho to e Oregon, and c, sc Washington .... 335. *Astragalus caricinus* (in part)
31. Stems ascending and diffusely spreading, villosulous; plants 9–18 (–25) cm; leaves 1.2–3.5 cm; leaflets 7–15, blades 2–10 mm; racemes 5–10-flowered, axis 0.4–1.6 cm in fruit; ne California...... 336. *Astragalus lentiformis*

[27. Shifted to left margin.—Ed.]

27. Plants variously pubescent (including strigulose, strigose, pilosulous, villosulous, hirsutulous, hirtellous, or tomentulose) but not densely gray-villosulous; legumes unilocular or bilocular, when bilocular then not 3-sided-compressed.
32. Plants delicate, from a subterranean caudex; racemes loosely (1 or)2 or 3(–5)-flowered; montane Colorado, ec Idaho, disjunct in w Montana, Wyoming........ 4. *Astragalus leptaleus* (in part)
32. Plants usually slender or robust (delicate in *A. pulsiferae*), from a subterranean or superficial caudex; racemes (1–)5–90(–125)-flowered; n, w North America.
33. Legumes ovoid or ellipsoid, bladdery-inflated, 20–35 × 12–26 mm, bilocular; racemes (4–)6–10(–13)-flowered; flowers 6.4–8.3 mm; Custer and Lemhi counties, Idaho ....296. *Astragalus amblytropis*
33. Legumes linear to cylindroid-globose, including ovoid and ellipsoid, compressed, terete, or bladdery-inflated, 3.3–55(–60) × (1.5–)2.3–27(–35) mm, usually unilocular, sometimes subunilocular, sub-bilocular, or bilocular, when bilocular then not bladdery-inflated (*A. webberi* inflated but not bladdery); racemes 1–90(–125)-flowered; flowers 4.4–24 mm; not of Custer or Lemhi counties, Idaho.
34. Legumes strongly curved downward, linear-oblong or linear-ellipsoid, 13–25 × 2.3–3 mm, 3-sided compressed; flowers 5.2–7.7 mm; plants 10–28 cm; Coconino, Gila, and Yavapai counties, Arizona .... 12. *Astragalus recurvus*
34. Legumes usually straight or incurved or slightly so, when decurved usually broader (oblong, ellipsoid, ovoid-, clavate-, cylindroid-, or lanceoloid-ellipsoid, oblanceoloid, obovoid, lenticular, or subglobose), 3.3–55(–60) × (1.5–)2.3–27 (–35) mm, usually subterete, obcompressed, laterally or dorsiventrally compressed, or bladdery-inflated, when 3-sided then obscurely so; flowers (4.1–) 5.5–18.8 mm; plants 1–120 cm; n, w North America.
35. Plants from subterranean caudex, underground for 1.5–10(–18) cm; corollas whitish, tinged with dull lilac; legumes (7–)9–15 × 3–6 mm, ± bilocular; se Arizona, sw New Mexico ....15. *Astragalus cobrensis*
35. Plants from superficial or subterranean caudex, when subterranean then underground for 1–40 cm; corollas pink-purple, ochroleucous, yellowish, or white; legumes 3.5–55(–60) × 1.2–27 mm, usually unilocular, sometimes subunilocular, sub-bilocular or bilocular; n, w North America.
36. Plants acaulescent or subacaulescent, usually dwarf, forming mats, cushions, clumps, or tufts (except *A. pulsiferae*), 1–20(–30) cm.
37. Plants densely clump-, cushion-, or tuft-forming, caudex branches with thatch of marcescent leaf rachises; sagebrush communities .... 80. *Astragalus jejunus* (in part)
37. Plants loosely clump-forming (except densely in *A. platytropis*) or mat- or tuft-forming, caudex branches often without thatch of marcescent leaf bases; various communities.
38. Plants forming compact mats or cushions; slopes of degraded sandstone or base of sandstone buttes.
39. Leaves (1–)1.5–5.5 cm; leaflets (7 or) 9–15, not crowded, blades 0.7–10 mm; racemes 4–10-flowered ......85. *Astragalus chuskanus*
39. Leaves 0.4–1(–2) cm; leaflets (3 or)5–9, subpalmately crowded, blades 1–3.5(–6) mm; racemes 1–3(–5)-flowered.............................. 86. *Astragalus micromerius*
38. Plants loosely tuft-forming, or if densely so, not mat-forming; various habitats.

[40. Shifted to left margin.—Ed.]

40. Legumes deflexed, cylindroid-ellipsoid, 9–17 × 4–6 mm, obtusely 3-sided, strigulose; c New Mexico to w Texas . . . . 18. *Astragalus pictiformis*
40. Legumes ascending, spreading, or declined, sometimes humistrate, oblong, ovoid-ellipsoid or -lenticular, or subglobose, 3.3–20(–22) × 1.5–22 mm, usually bladdery-inflated or dorsiventrally compressed, sometimes slightly 3-sided compressed, villous, strigose, or strigulose; Montana to Colorado west to Washington and California.
    41. Racemes 2–5-flowered; legumes narrowly oblong, 12–20 × 3.5–5 mm, slightly 3-sided; plants 4–7(–10) cm, forming small tufts; Mesa Verde, Montezuma County, Colorado . . . . 232. *Astragalus deterior*
    41. Racemes (best developed) 5–13-flowered; legumes 3.5–33 × 1.5–22 mm, ovoid or subglobose and bladdery-inflated, sometimes lanceoloid-ovoid or obliquely ovoid-acuminate, if obscurely 3-sided then ovoid-lenticular; plants 1–25 cm, sometimes forming cushions or mats; Montana to Utah west to California and Washington.
        42. Flowers 10–13 mm; corollas whitish, tinged with pinkish lavender; Mono Lake in Mono County, California . . . . 288. *Astragalus monoensis*
        42. Flowers 4.4–10(–12) mm; corollas whitish, yellowish, ochroleucous, or pink-purple; w United States.
            43. Legumes 3.3–4.5 × 1.5–4.2 mm; Lassen County, California, Harney County, Oregon . . . . 290. *Astragalus tegetarioides*
            43. Legumes 8–33 × (5–)6–22 mm; w United States.
                44. Caudex subterranean or, if superficial, with many naked, slender branches below ground, stems underground for 2–9(–12) cm; corollas whitish or yellowish, banners and keel tips with lilac veins; legumes villosulous or hirtellous; Lassen to Sierra counties, California, adjacent Washoe County, Nevada, disjunct on Mt. Adams, Klickitat County, Washington . . . 292. *Astragalus pulsiferae*
                44. Caudex superficial (sometimes soboliferous in *A. limnocharis*); corollas pink-purple, whitish, or ochroleucous; legumes strigose or strigulose; w United States.
                    45. Legumes 15–33 × 10–22 mm, bilocular or semibilocular; montane summits; Montana to Utah west to Idaho, Oregon, and California . . . . 294. *Astragalus platytropis* (in part)
                    45. Legumes 9–18(–23) × 7–14(–15) mm, unilocular; plateaus, mountains, lakeshores; sc Utah.
                        46. Stipules connate-sheathing proximally, distinct distally; legumes thin and translucent, with gynophores 0.1–0.8 mm . . . . . . 271. *Astragalus perianus*
                        46. Stipules connate-sheathing throughout; legumes membranous and opaque, sessile.
                            47. Flowers 6.2–7.5 mm; corollas ochroleucous or pink-purple with purple wing tips . . . . 81. *Astragalus limnocharis*
                            47. Flowers 7.2–8 mm; corollas pink-purple with white wing tips . . . . 82. *Astragalus montii*

[36. Shifted to left margin.—Ed.]

36. Plants strongly caulescent, not forming mats, cushions, clumps, or tufts, (7–)20–100 (–120) cm.
    48. Racemes 2–18-flowered (to 33 in *A. praelongus*).
        49. Flowers 13–17.6 mm; Plumas and Sierra counties, California . . . . 158. *Astragalus webberi*
        49. Flowers 5.6–14(–16) mm; Arizona, Colorado, Utah.
            50. Flowers 11–14(–16) mm; corollas pale lemon yellow, keel petals immaculate; plants selenophytes; w Iron and Beaver counties, Utah . . . . . . 171. *Astragalus praelongus* (in part)
            50. Flowers 5.6–11 mm; corollas whitish tinged with lilac, or ochroleucous suffused with purple; plants not selenophytes; Arizona, Colorado.
                51. Flowers 5.6–5.8 mm; legumes ellipsoid or lanceoloid-ellipsoid, 6–9.5 mm, obcompressed, stipes ca. 0.4 mm; near Gunnison, Colorado . . . . 25. *Astragalus microcymbus*
                51. Flowers 8–11 mm; legumes oblong-ellipsoid, 21–34 mm, terete or dorsiventrally compressed, stipes to 1 mm; n Coconino County, Arizona . . . . 37. *Astragalus atwoodii* (in part)

[48. Shifted to left margin.—Ed.]

48. Racemes (3–)15–90(–125)-flowered.
52. Flowers (4.1–)5.3–8.4 mm; plants of Great Plains or montane and arctic.
53. Calyces 3.3–5.4 mm; legumes (4–)5–12(–13) mm, subsymmetrically or obliquely ovoid-ellipsoid, laterally compressed, strigose-pilosulous, sub-bilocular; montane or arctic, Colorado and Washington north to Alaska, east to Nova Scotia . . . 6. *Astragalus eucosmus*
53. Calyces 2.1–3.3 mm; legumes (4–)4.3–8(–9) mm, obliquely subglobose, plumply ovoid, or ovoid-ellipsoid, obcompressed, strigulose to villosulous, unilocular; high plains, Texas to Saskatchewan . . . . 24. *Astragalus gracilis*
52. Flowers (5.1–)8.4–21 mm; plants of woodlands, beach or lakeshores, desert scrub, rocky slopes, or mountain brush communities.
54. Legumes swollen, slightly bladdery, somewhat 3-sided, (4.5–)7–10(–12) × (2.2–)3–4.5 mm; seeds 2–10; plants from superficial or ± subterranean caudex; stems spreading or prostrate. . . . . 77. *Astragalus bodinii* (in part)
54. Legumes terete, subterete, obcompressed, dorsiventrally or laterally compressed, 3-sided, or bladdery-inflated, (5–)10–55(–60) × (2.7–)4.5–27(–35) mm, when less than 10 mm then bladdery-inflated or subterete, not 3-sided; seeds (6–)10–42; plants mostly from deeply subterranean caudex (superficial in *A. microcystis*, *A. miguelensis*, and *A. nuttallii*); stems erect to prostrate or sprawling.
55. Legumes 20–55 × (5–)6–10 mm, obcompressed; flowers (12–)13.5–18 mm; stems ± strongly flexuous; Inyo County, California, northward to Pershing and Washoe counties, Nevada, and in Nye County, Nevada. . . . . 246. *Astragalus casei* (in part)
55. Legumes 5–32(–60 in *A. nuttallii*) × 2.7–27(–35) mm, subterete, inflated, or laterally compressed; flowers 5.1–16(–21) mm; stems usually not flexuous, when flexuous then flowers less then 12 mm; n, w North America.
56. Legumes (3–)4–12 mm wide, stiffly cartilaginous to leathery; Oklahoma to Utah and Arizona.
57. Legumes cartilaginous, sometimes distinctly inflated, subsessile or stipitate, (3–)4–12 mm wide . . . . 26. *Astragalus hallii* (in part)
57. Legumes leathery, somewhat inflated, (not bladdery), ± sessile, (4.5–)5–9.5 mm wide . . . . 27. *Astragalus puniceus*
56. Legumes 2.7–27 mm wide, papery, papery-membranous, thin, or fleshy; n, w North America.
58. Legumes subterete or somewhat flattened, 2.7–9 mm wide.
59. Stems silky-canescent, hairs appressed, incurved-ascending, or curly . . . . 17. *Astragalus flexuosus* (in part)
59. Stems strigulose-villosulous or hirsutulous, hairs stiff, straight, spreading or subretrorse . . . . 21. *Astragalus subcinereus* (in part)
58. Legumes tumid or bladdery-inflated, (3.5–)9–27 mm wide.
60. Legumes 5–12(–14) × 4–7 mm; flowers 5.1–7.5(–8.3) mm; Montana to Washington into British Columbia . . . . 75. *Astragalus microcystis* (in part)
60. Legumes 12–55(–60) × (3.5–)9–27 mm; flowers 6.4–16 mm; Colorado and New Mexico west to California.
61. Legumes 16–55(–60) × (9–)13–27 mm; California.
62. Legumes 16–26 × (9–)13–23 mm; racemes 10–30-flowered; Anacapa, San Clemente, San Miguel, Santa Cruz, and Santa Rosa islands, California . . . . 249. *Astragalus miguelensis*
62. Legumes (20–)25–55(–60) × 15–27 mm; racemes (15–)20–90(–125)-flowered; coastal c California . . . . 250. *Astragalus nuttallii*
61. Legumes 12–32 × 3.5–20 mm; Colorado and New Mexico west to Arizona and Nevada.

[63. Shifted to left margin.—Ed.]

63. Stems, calyces, and legumes strigulose or strigose with appressed hairs; apex of keels triangular and beaklike; legumes ovoid, ellipsoid, or subglobose, 12–22 mm wide; plants of sandy desert shrublands . . . . 20. *Astragalus fucatus* (in part)
63. Stems, calyces, and legumes strigulose-villosulous or hirsutulous with spreading or subretrorse hairs; apex of keels broadly deltate; legumes ovoid to ellipsoid or cylindroid-ellipsoid, 3.5–13 mm wide; plants of ponderosa pine, pinyon-juniper, aspen, or oak woodlands, or mixed brush communities . . . . 21. *Astragalus subcinereus* (in part)

Key to Species of Group 7

1. Legumes on stipelike gynophores (joint between gynophore and legume base).
   2. Caudex deeply subterranean; leaflets (9 or)11–27, closely spaced on rachis; legumes 15–38 × 8–23 mm, unilocular; plants of Uinta Formation limestone, rim of Uinta Basin; Colorado, Utah . . . . 245. *Astragalus lutosus*
   2. Caudex superficial or aerial; leaflets 3–25(–33), either fewer or widely spaced along rachis; legumes (6–)13–70(–90) × (2.5–)3–13(–45) mm, mostly bilocular or subunilocular, sometimes unilocular; British Columbia south to Arizona, east to Florida, if of Uinta Basin then legumes larger and peduncles subradical.
      3. Plants acaulescent or subacaulescent, tuft-forming.
         4. Herbage usually villous to villous-tomentose, sometimes appearing white or grayish; legumes mostly shaggy-villous, sometimes tomentose or villous-hirsute (hairs often concealing surface), not mottled or spotted; British Columbia south to Utah . . . . 209. *Astragalus purshii* (in part)
         4. Herbage strigulose, appearing green or grayish; legumes sparsely strigulose, long silky-pilose, or hirsute (hairs not concealing surface), red-mottled or -spotted; Colorado Plateau.
            5. Legumes sparsely strigulose; wc, sw Colorado, nw New Mexico, extreme ne San Juan County, Utah . . . . 229. *Astragalus naturitensis* (in part)
            5. Legumes hirsute or long silky-pilose; Arizona, Colorado, New Mexico, Utah.
               6. Flowers 6–9 mm; n Arizona, wc Colorado, nw New Mexico, se Utah . . . . 226. *Astragalus desperatus* (in part)
               6. Flowers 12–16 mm; n Arizona, near Gateway, Mesa County, Colorado, e Utah.
                  7. Plants 1.5–5 cm; leaves 1.5–5 cm; racemes 2–8-flowered, axis 0.5–2.5 cm in fruit; Navajo County, Arizona, Garfield and Wayne counties, Utah . . . . 227. *Astragalus barnebyi*
                  7. Plants 5–18 cm; leaves 1.5–9 cm; racemes 4–13-flowered, axis 1.5–8 cm in fruit; Mesa County, Colorado, Uintah County, Utah . . . . 228. *Astragalus equisolensis* (in part)
      3. Plants usually caulescent (subacaulescent in *A. megacarpus*), mostly not tuft-forming, sometimes loosely so (densely so in *A. megacarpus*).
         8. Plants 70–150 cm, caudex trunklike; stems fistulose; legumes deflexed, 6.5–9 × (2.5–)3–4 mm, gynophores 0.5–0.7 mm; Los Angeles and Orange counties, California . . . . 340. *Astragalus brauntonii*
         8. Plants 2–50(–70) cm, caudex not trunklike; stems not fistulose; legumes usually spreading to erect (sometimes pendulous in *A. oophorus*, or declined or horizontal in *A. nutans* and *A. wetherillii*), 13–55(–90) × (2.5–)3.2–17 (–45) mm, gynophores 0.4–4(–11) mm; British Columbia south to Arizona, east to Georgia.

[9. Shifted to left margin.—Ed.]

9. Plants short-lived perennials; blooming throughout the growing season, often with flowers and mature fruit occurring simultaneously; seeds 9–13; on and below sandstone escarpments east of Grand Junction, Colorado . . . . 281. *Astragalus wetherillii*
9. Plants annuals, biennials, or perennials, rarely with flowers and mature fruit occurring simultaneously; seeds (7–)12–54; British Columbia south to Arizona, east to Georgia.
   10. Legumes bladdery-inflated, pale green becoming stramineous, not red or mottled; plants annual, biennial, or short-lived perennial; flowers 7.8–10.4 mm; deserts, s California . . . . 275. *Astragalus nutans* (in part)
   10. Legumes often 3-sided, dorsiventrally, or laterally compressed, when bladdery-inflated, then red- or reddish purple-mottled; plants long- or short-lived perennial; flowers (6.6–)8.5–24(–26) mm; various habitats, widespread, including s California.
      11. Legumes (20–)24–42 × 3.5–5.5 mm, 3-sided; flowers 7.1–15.7 mm.
         12. Peduncles 9–20 cm, arising from base or near middle of stem, together with racemes as long as or longer than stems; leaflets (17 or)19–25(or 27); flowers 12.6–15.7 mm; calyx tubes 4.1–5 mm . . . . 314. *Astragalus tricarinatus*
         12. Peduncles (1.5–)3–10 cm, arising from stem distally, together with racemes much shorter than stems; leaflets (7–)11–17(or 19); flowers 7.1–10.2 mm; calyx tubes 2.7–4.1 mm . . . . .315. *Astragalus bernardinus*
      11. Legumes 13–70(–90) × (2.8–)3.2–45 mm, dorsiventrally or laterally compressed, bluntly 3-sided, or bladdery-inflated; flowers (6.6–)8.2–24(–26) mm.
         13. Plants sometimes short-lived perennials; legumes green, not mottled; Great Plains and eastward.
            14. Herbage hirsute, hairs spreading, often spirally twisted, to 1.1–2 mm; legumes hirsute; leaflets (3–)7–15, thin-textured, larger ones with pinnate venation; corollas pale yellow to greenish ochroleucous; s, e Alabama, east to South Carolina, Georgia, and Florida . . . . 300. *Astragalus villosus* (in part)
            14. Herbage sparsely strigulose to hirsutulous, glabrous, or glabrate, hairs subappressed, to 0.7 mm; legumes glabrous; leaflets (9–)13–27, firm-textured, venation not apparent; corollas pink-purple, cream or whitish, sometimes with dark keel; Great Plains south to Oklahoma, east to Georgia.
               15. Legumes coarsely reticulate in age; flowers 8.5–11 mm; calyx lobes (1.8–)2.2–2.8 mm . . . . 299. *Astragalus obcordatus*
               15. Legumes not especially reticulate in age; flowers 8.2–17.4 mm; calyx lobes 1–4 mm.
                  16. Corollas pink-purple, purplish, or whitish; flowers 8.2–15.5 mm; calyx lobes 1–2 mm . . . . 297. *Astragalus distortus*
                  16. Corollas white to greenish white or cream; flowers 11.4–17.4 mm; calyx lobes (2–)2.4–4 mm. . . . . 298. *Astragalus soxmaniorum*
         13. Plants long-lived perennials; legumes red- or reddish purple-mottled; Rocky Mountains and westward.
            17. Plants loosely tuft-forming, 3–23 cm; flowers 6.6–8.6 mm; e Piute, s Sevier, and w Wayne counties, Utah . . . . 270. *Astragalus serpens* (in part)
            17. Plants densely or not tuft-forming, (3–)15–70 cm; flowers 11–24(–26) mm; British Columbia to California, east to Colorado.
               18. Legumes (15–)20–30 mm, dorsiventrally compressed, fleshy becoming leathery . . . . .244. *Astragalus beckwithii*
               18. Legumes (20–)25–70(–90) mm, bladdery-inflated, papery.
                  19. Plants subacaulescent or short caulescent; stems 1–7 cm, internodes mostly concealed by stipules; racemes among leaves, 1–7 (or 8)-flowered . . . . .242. *Astragalus megacarpus*
                  19. Plants caulescent; stems (2–)15–25 cm, some internodes elongated and longer than stipules; racemes often extending above leaves, 3–14-flowered. . . . . 243. *Astragalus oophorus*

1. Legumes on stipes (no joint between stipe and legume base).
  20. Legumes laterally compressed, mostly unilocular (sub-bilocular in *A. australis*).
    21. Wing petals bilobed; legumes appearing sub-bilocular . . . . 8. *Astragalus australis* (in part)
    21. Wing petals entire; legumes unilocular.
      22. Legumes usually incurved into a hook or sickle, or coiled into a ring or spiral (sometimes ± straight in *A. sclerocarpus*).
        23. Calyx tubes 2–2.5 mm, not marcescent; plants from deeply subterranean caudex; seeds 10–16 . . . . 55. *Astragalus alvordensis*
        23. Calyx tubes 4.7–11.9 mm, marcescent; plants from superficial or shallow subterranean caudex (sometimes rhizomatous); seeds 14–36.
          24. Plants with slender rhizomes; corollas pink-purple; Owyhee County, Idaho. . . . . 58. *Astragalus camptopus*
          24. Plants from superficial or shallow subterranean caudex; corollas ochroleucous, whitish, or lemon yellow; British Columbia and California east to Idaho and Nevada.
            25. Flowers nodding at anthesis; calyx tubes swollen, strongly oblique or saccate abaxially at base. . . . . 60. *Astragalus curvicarpus*
            25. Flowers ascending at anthesis; calyx tubes not swollen, scarcely oblique and never gibbous proximally.
              26. Calyces and leaflets mostly with straight, appressed hairs; leaflet blades linear, linear-oblanceolate, or narrowly oblong; legumes lunately or falcately ellipsoid, 6.5–9 mm wide, nearly straight to incurved through 0.5 spiral. . . . . 63. *Astragalus sclerocarpus*
              26. Calyces and leaflets with incumbent or curly hairs; leaflet blades oblong, obovate-cuneate, oblong-oblanceolate, cuneate-oblanceolate, or cuneate-obcordate; legumes linear-oblong or oblong, (2.7–)3.2–7 mm wide, lunate- or hamate-incurved, or coiled through 1.25–2.5 spirals.
                27. Peduncles 4.5–12 cm; pedicels 1.5–3.5 mm; legumes lunate- or hamate-incurved; s Chelan County, Washington . . . . 64. *Astragalus sinuatus*
                27. Peduncles (1–)2.5–5(–6.5) cm; pedicels 1–2.5 mm; legumes tightly coiled through 1.25–2.5 spirals, or elaborately and irregularly contorted; Benton, Kittitas, Klickitat, and Yakima counties, Washington . . . 65. *Astragalus speirocarpus*
      22. Legumes straight or gradually incurved or decurved (sometimes falcately decurved in *A. solitarius*).
        28. Calyces gibbous-saccate; corollas cream to pale lemon yellow; legumes 7–25 × 2.3–4.2 mm, stipes (3.5–)5–15 mm; s British Columbia south to ne Oregon, adjacent Idaho. . . . . 59. *Astragalus collinus*
        28. Calyces not gibbous; corollas whitish, lemon yellow, greenish white to cream, or pink-purple, sometimes tinged lilac or pinkish; legumes 8–40 (–45) × 2.4–18(–21) mm, stipes (1–)4–16(–19) mm; Oregon and California east to Wyoming and New Mexico.
          29. Legumes 8–11 × 2.4–2.8 mm, stipes 4–5 mm; flowers 6.5–7 mm; Klamath County, Oregon . . . . 57. *Astragalus applegatei*
          29. Legumes 12–40(–45) × 3–18(–21) mm, stipes (1–)6–16(–19) mm; flowers (6.3–)11.3–19 mm; Oregon and California east to Wyoming and New Mexico.
            30. Legumes erect-ascending, 22–30 × 6–9 mm, stipes 12–16(–19) mm, legumes inverted from twisting of pedicels; Towaoc, Montezuma County, Colorado. . . . . 47. *Astragalus tortipes*
            30. Legumes pendulous or declined, 12–40(–45) × (3–)3.5–18(–21) mm, stipes (1–)4–17 mm, legumes not inverted; Arizona, California, Colorado, New Mexico, Oregon, Utah, Wyoming.

31. Legumes (13–)15–40(–45) mm, stipes (6–)6.5–17 mm; corollas greenish white or cream; coastal or near coastal sw California . . . . .256. *Astragalus trichopodus*
31. Legumes 12–35 mm, stipes (1–)4–11 mm; corollas ochroleucous, pinkish white, or pink-purple; Arizona, Colorado, Nevada, New Mexico, Oregon, Utah, Wyoming.
    32. Calyx tubes 2.3–2.8 mm; leaflets 5–9. . . . . 56. *Astragalus solitarius*
    32. Calyx tubes 3.2–6.7 mm; leaflets (1 or)3–19.
        33. Corollas ochroleucous, tinged or veined with lilac, or pinkish white; flowers 7.3–8.5 mm; stipes 1–1.5 mm; nw Arizona south of Grand Canyon . . . . . . .33. *Astragalus titanophilus*
        33. Corollas pink-purple; flowers 12–19 mm; stipes 4–11 mm; sw Wyoming, south to e Utah, w Colorado, ne Arizona, nw New Mexico. . . . . 44. *Astragalus coltonii* (in part)

[20. Shifted to left margin.—Ed.]

20. Legumes usually 3-sided or dorsiventrally compressed, obcompressed, inflated, or subterete, rarely laterally compressed, unilocular to bilocular, when laterally compressed or appearing so, then fully bilocular (except unilocular in *A. tweedyi* where faces strongly convex).
    34. Legumes inflated, not bladdery, unilocular (or subunilocular in *A. praelongus*); plants selenophytes.
        35. Leaflets (1 or)3–13, blades 6–35(–50) mm, rhombic-oval, obovate, or elliptic; legumes sessile or subsessile, cylindroid or subcylindroid, 20–48 × 9–15 mm; corollas white or ochroleucous; Mancos Shale and Morrison formations; Grand and San Juan counties, Utah.
            36. Flowers 23–34 mm; nw of Moab (Morrison Formation) and Cisco (Mancos Shale) vicinities, Grand County, Utah . . . . 173. *Astragalus sabulosus* (in part)
            36. Flowers 17–19 mm; foothills of La Sal Mountains, Paradox and Morrison formations, Grand and San Juan counties, Utah. . . . . 174. *Astragalus iselyi* (in part)
        35. Leaflets (3 or)5–33, blades (1–)2–50 mm, linear, obovate, elliptic, oblong, lanceolate, oblanceolate, obcordate, or suborbiculate; legumes sessile, subsessile, or stipitate, if in Grand or San Juan counties, Utah, then stipes (1.5–)2–8 mm, ellipsoid, oblong- to lanceoloid-ellipsoid, ovoid, cylindroid, obovoid, or subglobose, 12–42 × 5–25 mm; corollas pink-purple, ochroleucous, or white; fine-textured substrates; California to Colorado south to Texas.
            37. Calyces green or yellowish; corollas ochroleucous or pale lemon yellow, keel often purplish-tipped; legumes fleshy becoming leathery-woody; Colorado and Texas west to Nevada and Arizona .171. *Astragalus praelongus* (in part)
            37. Calyces often purple, sometimes white; corollas pink-purple, pale greenish yellow, or white, then sometimes tinged purplish; legumes thinly cartilaginous or fleshy to leathery or papery; Colorado west to California.
                38. Corollas white or pale purple; plants short-lived and flowering first year, or long-lived and forming large clumps; wc Colorado and along San Juan River, San Juan County, Utah.
                    39. Corollas white or tinged purplish; calyces pale purple or whitish; stipes 3–3.5 mm; plants short-lived perennials, often flowering first year, not forming bushy clumps; along San Juan River, San Juan County, Utah . . . . 166. *Astragalus cutleri* (in part)
                    39. Corollas white; calyces usually greenish to stramineous, rarely white; stipes 2–2.5 mm; plants long-lived perennials, forming bushy clumps; De Beque, Mesa County, Colorado . . . . 168. *Astragalus debequaeus*
                38. Corollas pink-, magenta-, or reddish purple (often drying dark purple); plants often long-lived, forming small clumps; Colorado west to California.

40. Legumes erect or narrowly ascending; peduncles erect-ascending in fruit; stems erect or incurved-ascending; plants (10–)12–53 cm; nw, nc Arizona, disjunct in se California, wc Colorado, s Nevada, se Utah along Colorado and Green rivers. . . . . 165. *Astragalus preussii* (in part)
40. Legumes spreading, declined, or weakly ascending; peduncles weakly ascending or reclining in fruit; stems erect to ascending or decumbent; plants 8–20 or 15–50(–60) cm; Arizona, California, Colorado, Utah.
    41. Legumes usually glabrous, rarely minutely scabrid-pubescent; flowers 18–22 mm; plants relatively slender and diffuse, 8–20 cm; wc, sw Colorado, se Utah along Colorado River . . . . . 167. *Astragalus eastwoodiae*
    41. Legumes strigulose; flowers 21–28 mm; plants coarse, clump-forming, 15–50(–60) cm; Imperial, Riverside, and San Diego counties, California, sw Arizona .169. *Astragalus crotalariae*

[34. Shifted to left margin.—Ed.]

34. Legumes usually obcompressed, subterete, or 3-sided, dorsiventrally or laterally compressed, when legumes inflated or bladdery, then ± bilocular (± unilocular in *A. aequalis*, *A. ampullarioides*, and *A. praelongus*); plants selenophytes or not.
    42. Corollas ochroleucous or pale lemon yellow, keel petals often purple-tipped; legumes erect to spreading or declined, fleshy becoming leathery-woody; plants selenophytes . . . . .171. *Astragalus praelongus* (in part)
    42. Corollas pink-purple, whitish, yellow, keel petals maculate or immaculate; legumes pendulous, reflexed, spreading, ascending, or erect, if erect, then not fleshy; plants not selenophytes.
        43. Legumes bladdery-inflated, spreading or declined, 25–40 × 12–20 mm; flowers 11.5–12 mm; corollas ochroleucous, often lined or tinged purple; Spring (Charleston) Mountains, Clark County, Nevada . . . . .38. *Astragalus aequalis* (in part)
        43. Legumes not bladdery-inflated (except sometimes *A. lentiginosus*), mostly pendulous, sometimes spreading, erect, ascending, reflexed, or declined, (7–)10–40(–48) × 2.2–10(–19) mm; flowers 5–21.5 mm; corollas pink-purple, whitish, greenish white, yellow, or ochroleucous; Alaska south to Utah, east to Nova Scotia.
            44. Corollas ochroleucous; legumes (25–)30–40 mm, 3-sided, stipes 5–10(–12) mm; Mesa Verde, Montezuma County, Colorado . . . . .46. *Astragalus schmolliae*
            44. Corollas pink-purple, whitish, greenish white, yellow, or ochroleucous; legumes (7–)10–30(–48) mm, 3-sided or not, stipes (0–)1–20 mm; Alaska south to Utah, east to Nova Scotia.
                45. Legumes ascending, 15–21 × 2.8–3.8 mm, 3-sided compressed; flowers 12–14 mm; corollas reddish purple (drying bluish); nw Clark and sw Lincoln counties, Nevada . . . . 149. *Astragalus ackermanii*
                45. Legumes mostly pendulous to spreading, ascending, or erect, sometimes humistrate, declined, or reflexed; flowers 5–21.5 mm; corollas pink-purple, whitish, greenish white, yellow, or ochroleucous; Alaska south to Utah, east to Nova Scotia.
                    46. Legumes pendulous, obtusely 3-sided, papery-membranous, valves inflexed as hyaline septum, 0.2–2 mm wide; seeds 6–10; mesophytic habitats; Nevada and Colorado north to Arctic and n New England . . . . 7. *Astragalus robbinsii* (in part)
                    46. Legumes mostly pendulous to spreading, ascending, or erect, sometimes humistrate, declined, or reflexed, papery, membranous, leathery, woody, subligneous, or fleshy, valves inflexed or not, septum to 6 mm wide; seeds 6–42; xeric habitats; British Columbia south to Texas.

[47. Shifted to left margin.—Ed.]

47. Herbage softly villous-hirsute or shaggy-villous, hairs minutely dilated at base; flowers nodding; corollas whitish to ochroleucous, keel petals purple-tipped; legumes narrowly oblong to oblanceoloid, obscurely 3-sided compressed, glabrous, bilocular. . . . . 128. *Astragalus drummondii* (in part)
47. Herbage strigulose, villosulous, pilosulous, or tomentulose, not villous- or shaggy-hirsute, hairs not dilated at base; flowers nodding or not; corollas pink-purple, whitish, greenish white, yellow, or ochroleucous; legumes ellipsoid, oblong to lanceoloid, linear, ovoid, or cylindroid, subterete, compressed, or 3-sided, strigulose, villous, hirsutulous, tomentulose, or glabrous, unilocular to bilocular.
    48. Herbage villous-tomentulose or soft-villosulous, appearing gray or ashy; insular sw California.
        49. Leaflets 21–29; flowers 14.2–17.5 mm; keel petals 10.2–12.9 mm; legumes villous-tomentulose; Santa Barbara and San Nicolas islands . . . . 113. *Astragalus traskiae*
        49. Leaflets 11–25; flowers 10.6–12.7 mm; keel petals 9–10 mm; legumes glabrous; San Clemente Island . . . . 114. *Astragalus nevinii*
    48. Herbage strigulose, villosulous, pilosulous, or tomentulose, usually not appearing gray or ashy; British Columbia south to Texas.
        50. Stems with proximalmost internodes not or shortly elongated; peduncles sub-basal and appearing scapelike or, if plants caulescent and with axillary peduncles, then herbage villous with hairs 0.8–1.5 mm; Inyo and San Bernardino counties, California, Clark, Esmeralda, and Lincoln counties, Nevada . . . 132. *Astragalus minthorniae* (in part)
        50. Stems usually with elongated (well-spaced) internodes; peduncles axillary or, if sub-basal, then pubescence different, or not of Inyo and San Bernardino counties, California, Clark, Esmeralda, and Lincoln counties, Nevada.
            51. Legumes usually erect, rarely deflexed, not humistrate, 3-sided and 2.7–8 (–9) mm wide, or obcompressed to inflated and (4.5–)6.5–10(–12) mm wide.
                52. Plants from subterranean caudex; stems decumbent proximally, erect distally, often fistulose; legumes inflated (turgid), 8–10(–12) mm wide; Triassic Chinle Formation clays, Washington County, Utah. . . . . 163. *Astragalus ampullarioides* (in part)
                52. Plants from superficial caudex; stems erect-ascending (except sometimes decumbent in *A. scaphoides*), not fistulose; legumes usually not inflated (or moderately so in *A. scaphoides)*, 2.7–8(–10) mm wide; Arizona and New Mexico north to Washington and Montana.
                    53. Stipes 6–18 mm, incurved from spreading pedicels, racemes broad and loose.
                        54. Legumes cuneate basally, 3.5–8(–9) mm wide, grooved dorsally, keeled ventrally, septum 0.5–1.2 mm wide; New Mexico and Arizona north to Oregon and Idaho . . . . 147. *Astragalus eremiticus*
                        54. Legumes truncate basally, (4.5–)6.5–10 mm wide, both sutures grooved, septum 1.4–1.8 mm wide; Bitterroot Mountains, ec Idaho, w Montana . . . . 148. *Astragalus scaphoides*
                    53. Stipes 2.5–7 mm, fruits straight, erect in same plane as body and pedicels, legumes appressed or near to raceme axis and fruiting racemes strict and narrow, or if pedicels ascending at a slightly different angle and legumes slightly divergent (as in *A. arrectus*), then obcompressed.
                        55. Pedicels 0.5–1.2 mm at anthesis, clavately thickened in fruit, 1.5–4 mm; legumes 4.5–6.3 mm wide, obcompressed; ec, se Washington, adjacent Idaho . . . . 144. *Astragalus arrectus*
                        55. Pedicels 0.7–1.9 mm at anthesis, not or only somewhat thickened in fruit; legumes 2.7–4.5 mm wide, obtusely 3-sided or 3-sided compressed; Idaho, Montana, Nevada.

56. Legumes obtusely 3-sided, lateral face convex, abaxial face scarcely narrower, grooved or not; flowers nodding; leaflets (15–)19–27(or 29); c Idaho to sw Montana . . . . . 145. *Astragalus atropubescens*
56. Legumes 3-sided compressed, lateral face flat, abaxial face narrower and grooved; flowers ascending; leaflets 11–19 (or 21); Spring (Charleston) Mountains, Nevada . . . . . .146. *Astragalus remotus*

[51. Shifted to left margin.—Ed.]

51. Legumes either humistrately ascending from reclining peduncles, spreading-ascending, or pendulous from ascending pedicels, dorsiventrally, laterally, or 3-sided compressed or subterete, (2–)3.4–21 mm wide.
 57. Legumes laterally compressed, sutures forming prominent ridges.
 58. Legumes pendulous; flowers (6.5–)7–10 mm; keel petal apex triangular and subacute; plants from subterranean caudex; Mojave Desert, San Bernardino County, California . . . . 126. *Astragalus jaegerianus*
 58. Legumes spreading or ascending; flowers 15–22 mm; keel petal apex obtuse; plants from aerial caudex; Kern, Los Angeles, Riverside, San Benito, and Ventura counties, California . . . . .127. *Astragalus pachypus*
 57. Legumes not laterally compressed (except *A. tweedyi*, sometimes *A. accidens*), sutures not forming prominent ridges.
 59. Stipes (4–)5–20 mm.
 60. Legumes 3-sided compressed, or 3-sided and laterally compressed, bilocular; w Idaho, adjacent Oregon and Washington.
 61. Legumes (16–)20–30 × 3–4.5(–5) mm and 5–7-times longer than wide, lateral face flat, abaxial face grooved; herbage and legumes villosulous; leaflet surfaces pubescent; Wasco to Morrow counties, Oregon, and sw Washington . . . . .108. *Astragalus howellii*
 61. Legumes (25–)30–45 × 2.5–3.3 mm, mostly 10 times longer than wide, lateral face convex, abaxial face narrowly sulcate; herbage and legumes strigulose; leaflet surfaces pubescent abaxially, glabrous adaxially; near common boundary of Idaho, Oregon, and Washington, west to Umatilla County, Oregon. . . . . 109. *Astragalus arthurii*
 60. Legumes subterete or obcompressed (except laterally compressed in *A. tweedyi*, sometimes *A. accidens*), valves bilocular or not; California, Idaho, Nevada, Oregon, Washington.
 62. Calyces 8–10.5 mm; corollas ochroleucous; stipes pilosulous; Columbia and Deschutes valleys, nc Oregon and sc Washington . . . . 62. *Astragalus tweedyi*
 62. Calyces 5–9.4(–11) mm; corollas whitish, yellowish, or reddish purple; stipes glabrous; California to Washington, east to Nevada and Idaho.
 63. Legumes subterete and fleshy, becoming slightly laterally compressed and leathery or woody; sw Oregon, adjacent n California. . . . . 138. *Astragalus accidens*
 63. Legumes obcompressed and fleshy becoming woody, papery, leathery, or subligneous, or turgid and somewhat obcompressed and subligneous becoming transversely rugose; California to Washington, east to Nevada, Idaho, and Oklahoma.
 64. Legumes pendulous, somewhat obcompressed, transversely rugose in age . . . . .9. *Astragalus chinensis*
 64. Legumes spreading to ascending (humistrate), obcompressed, smooth in age.
 65. Leaves green; racemes 5–7-flowered, axis 1.5–2 cm in fruit . . . . 133. *Astragalus vallaris*
 65. Leaves glaucescent; racemes 10–25-flowered, axis 3–12 cm in fruit . . . . 134. *Astragalus cimae*
 59. Stipes (0–)1–4(–5) mm.

[66. Shifted to left margin.—Ed.]

66. Legumes usually decurved, adaxial suture convex in profile, or at least beak declined from body.
  67. Legumes 2.5–4.3 mm wide, unilocular or bilocular, septum (0 or)0.6–2.7 mm wide; se California, sw Idaho, nc, c Nevada, e Oregon . . . . 119. *Astragalus atratus* (in part)
  67. Legumes 4–6.5 mm wide, partially bilocular, septum incomplete to 0.7 mm wide; sw Idaho, n Nevada, se Oregon. . . . . 120. *Astragalus salmonis*
66. Legumes straight to deeply incurved, either adaxial suture appearing concave or beak curved.
  68. Legumes usually lunately or falcately curved (sometimes straight in *A. congdonii*), 10–35 × 2.3–4 mm; corollas yellowish, yellowish or greenish white, greenish ochroleucous, or white, rarely faintly tinged lilac or rose; flowers 6.5–14(–16.6) mm.
    69. Stipes 2.5–5 mm; corollas yellowish, yellowish white, or greenish ochroleucous, banner violet-veined; ne Oregon, adjacent Washington. . . . . 110. *Astragalus misellus*
    69. Stipes 0.8–2.5 mm; corollas white or whitish to greenish white, sometimes tinged lilac; California, Idaho, Oregon, Wyoming.
      70. Flowers 7–9 mm; corollas whitish, sometimes faintly tinged lilac; legumes 10–17 × 2.5–3.5 mm; nc Idaho, w Wyoming . . . . 106. *Astragalus paysonii*
      70. Flowers 10–16.6 mm; corollas white or greenish white; legumes 14–35 × 2.3–3.6 mm; California, Oregon.
        71. Legumes 15–35 × 2.3–3.2 mm, stipes 1–2.5 mm; leaflets (11–)17–35 (or 37); Sierra Nevada foothills, California . . . . 103. *Astragalus congdonii*
        71. Legumes 14–24 × 2.6–3.6 mm, stipes 0.8–1.9 mm; leaflets (11–)15–23; outer coast ranges of nw California, w, sw Oregon . . . . 105. *Astragalus umbraticus*
  68. Legumes straight to incurved, not falcately or lunately so, 7–40(–48) × 2–18(–19) mm; corollas ochroleucous, yellowish, cream, white, or pink-purple; flowers 5.5–23 mm.
    72. Stems usually shorter than longest inflorescence, with 3–7 developed internodes; corollas ochroleucous, white, or creamy white; legumes erect, unilocular or incompletely bilocular; se Washington, ne Oregon, adjacent Idaho . . . . . 140. *Astragalus sheldonii* (in part)
    72. Stems usually longer than longest inflorescence, if shorter then not with 3–7 developed internodes; corollas ochroleucous, yellowish, cream, white, pink-purple; legumes ascending, spreading, reflexed, declined, or pendulous (sometimes humistrate), unilocular to bilocular; Montana to Colorado, west to Washington and California.
      73. Legumes plumply ovoid, strongly inflated, leathery or stiffly papery, ± bilocular; Tooele County, Utah . . . . 285. *Astragalus lentiginosus* (in part)
      73. Legumes oblong, lanceoloid-ellipsoid, obliquely ovoid, or crescentic, obcompressed, 3-sided, or laterally compressed, fleshy, papery, membranous, leathery, or woody, when obcompressed, then often woody or leathery in age; Montana to Colorado, west to Washington and California.
        74. Legumes glabrous or strigose.
          75. Legumes 2.2–3 mm wide, green becoming stramineous; nw Arizona, se Nevada, sw Utah. . . . . 107. *Astragalus straturensis*
          75. Legumes 3–4.5 mm wide, mottled and glaucescent, becoming stramineous and faintly purple-tinged; n Nye County, Nevada . . . . . 112. *Astragalus toquimanus*
        74. Legumes strigulose, strigose, villosulous, hirsutulous, or hirsute.
          76. Flowers 5.3–6.8 mm; corollas whitish or ochroleucous; legumes 7–12 × 2–3.8 mm; n margin of Snake River Plains, Idaho . . . . 111. *Astragalus oniciformis*
          76. Flowers (8.6–)10–22 mm; corollas pink-purple, or whitish to ochroleucous, when less than 10 mm, then bright pink-purple and banner veined purple; legumes 12–40 × 3.6–10 mm; California and Oregon east to Colorado and Montana.
            77. Legumes shaggy-hirsute with lustrous spreading hairs, hairs 1–3 mm . . . . 135. *Astragalus malacus* (in part)
            77. Legumes strigose, hirsutulous, or villosulous, hairs appressed or incumbent, hairs to 1 mm.

[78. Shifted to left margin.—Ed.]

78. Legumes obcompressed or 3-sided obcompressed, 12–32 × 3.6–10 mm (wider than high in cross section), unilocular or incompletely bilocular, septum 0.6–1 mm wide.
   79. Legumes 12–16 × 3.6–5 mm, stipes 2–5 mm; Inyo County, California, Lincoln and Nye counties, Nevada . . . . 125. *Astragalus inyoensis*
   79. Legumes 17–32 × 7–10 mm, stipes to 2 mm; ne Nevada eastward to w Colorado, northward to Idaho and Montana . . . . 129. *Astragalus cibarius* (in part)
78. Legumes laterally or 3-sided compressed and biconvex, 20–45 × 5–8 mm (cross section at middle narrower or not wider than high), bilocular, septum 3.5–4.2 mm wide.
   80. Legumes: dorsal sutures prominent, body biconvex, cross section elliptic . . . . 131. *Astragalus malacoides* (in part)
   80. Legumes: dorsal sutures slightly grooved, body 3-sided, cross section deltoid . . . . 136. *Astragalus chamaemeniscus* (in part)

Key to Species of Group 8

1. Flowers 35–41 mm; corollas scarlet or crimson, banner and keel petals nearly equal length . . . . 206. *Astragalus coccineus*
1. Flowers 6–32 mm; corollas pink to pink-purple or lilac, white to ochroleucous, or yellowish, not scarlet or crimson, banners usually longer than keel petals.
   2. Legumes mostly bilocular (semibilocular in *A. eurylobus,* unilocular in *A. anserinus* and *A. purshii*).
      3. Plants from deeply subterranean caudex and slender rhizomes; stems single or few; Mojave Desert, Arizona, California, Nevada . . . . 233. *Astragalus layneae*
      3. Plants from superficial or shallow subterranean caudex, not rhizomatous; stems few to numerous, sometimes reduced to crowns, obsolete, or absent (sometimes single in *A. mollissimus*); w United States.
         4. Legumes 3-sided compressed; w Texas to c New Mexico.
            5. Flowers 18.5–23 mm; calyces 10–14 mm; herbage strigulose; legumes purple-mottled; se New Mexico, w Texas . . . . 196. *Astragalus waterfallii*
            5. Flowers 13–16 mm; calyces 5.2–8 mm; herbage villous or villosulous; legumes not mottled; c, nc New Mexico . . . . 197. *Astragalus feensis*
         4. Legumes terete, subterete, dorsiventrally or laterally compressed, or bladdery-inflated (3-sided in *A. cottamii, A. holmgreniorum,* and *A. obscurus*); w United States.
            6. Calyces 3–8 mm; flowers 7–17(–18) mm.
               7. Legumes bladdery-inflated, ovoid to subglobose, 15–33 × 10–22 mm; elevation 2400–3500 m, montane or subalpine . . . . .294. *Astragalus platytropis* (in part)
               7. Legumes subterete or 3-sided compressed, oblong to lanceoloid or linear, 10–27(–37) × 2–6 mm; elevation 900–2400 m, montane or lower.
                  8. Legumes erect or ascending, straight or slightly incurved, separating from receptacle well after maturity; ne California, n, sw Idaho, n, s Nevada, s, ec Oregon.
                     9. Racemes 7–35-flowered, axis 2.5–14(–25) cm in fruit; legumes 15–26(–30) × 4–6 mm; plants relatively coarse; se California, se to sw Nevada . . . . .132. *Astragalus minthorniae* (in part)
                     9. Racemes (3–)6–14-flowered, axis (1–)2–8 cm in fruit; legumes 10–25 × 2.4–3.3 mm; plants slender, delicate; n California, sw Idaho, n Nevada, Oregon . . . . 150. *Astragalus obscurus* (in part)
                  8. Legumes ascending or spreading-descending (humistrate), mostly incurved (crescentic), separating from receptacle at maturity; Four Corners region.

10. Flowers 7–10.5 mm; calyces 3.6–4.5 mm, tubes 3–3.5(–4.5) mm; Garfield and San Juan counties, Utah . . . . . . 230. *Astragalus monumentalis*
10. Flowers 11–17 mm; calyces 6.2–8 mm, tubes 4.8–6.7 mm; n Navajo County, Arizona, w, sw Montezuma County, Colorado, San Juan County, New Mexico, San Juan County, Utah . . . . 231. *Astragalus cottamii*

[6. Shifted to left margin.—Ed.]

6. Calyces 9.5–16(–19) mm; flowers 17–25(–26) mm.
11. Legumes mostly glabrous; leaflet blades glabrous abaxially or both surfaces hairy.
12. Leaflet blades loosely pilose abaxially, glabrous adaxially; plants acaulescent; Virgin River valley, Utah-Arizona border, s of St. George, Mohave County, Arizona, Washington County, Utah . . . . 137. *Astragalus holmgreniorum*
12. Leaflet blades hairy, sometimes densely so; plants acaulescent to subacaulescent or short caulescent; Idaho south to Texas . . . . 234. *Astragalus mollissimus* (in part)
11. Legumes hairy; leaflet blades hairy throughout.
13. Legumes shaggy-villous, hairs (2–)2.5–4(–5) mm, often concealing surfaces; California, sc, se Oregon, w Nevada. . . . . .209. *Astragalus purshii* (in part)
13. Legumes glabrous or variously pubescent (villous, pilose, strigulose, puberulent, villosulous, hispidulous, villous-hirsute, -tomentulose, or -tomentose), hairs not concealing surfaces; Idaho south to Texas.
14. Legumes sparsely villous, 9–12(–15) × 5–7 mm; flowers 9–11.2 mm; plants dwarf, tuft- or mat-forming, short caulescent; s Cassia County, Idaho, ne Elko County, Nevada, nw Box Elder County, Utah . . . . .210. *Astragalus anserinus* (in part)
14. Legumes glabrous, strigose, pilose or villous-tomentose, (6–)8–30(–40) × (3–)4–9(–16) mm; flowers 11.8–25 mm; plants usually not dwarf, tuft- or clump-forming, acaulescent, subacaulescent, or short caulescent; Idaho to Texas.
15. Legumes 8–10 × 6–8 mm, subterete to slightly obcompressed; Nutrioso, Apache County, Arizona, se of Red Hill, Catron County, New Mexico . . . . .235. *Astragalus nutriosensis*
15. Legumes (6–)9–30(–40) × (3–)4–9(–16) mm, inflated, terete, laterally or obcompressed; Nebraska and Texas west to Arizona and Idaho.
16. Legumes obliquely oblong- or lanceoloid-ellipsoid, 21–30(–40) × 7.5–9(–16) mm, length 3–4 times width, strigulose; nw Arizona, se Nevada . . . . 189. *Astragalus eurylobus*
16. Legumes oblong-ellipsoid, lanceoloid-ellipsoid, ovoid, or ovoid-ellipsoid, (6–)9–24 × (3–)4–13 mm, length 2 times width, glabrous, puberulent, villosulous, hispidulous, villous-hirsute, -tomentulose, or -tomentose; Nebraska to Texas, west to Nevada and Arizona . . . . 234. *Astragalus mollissimus* (in part)

[2. Shifted to left margin.—Ed.]

2. Legumes unilocular.
17. Leaflets (1 or)3 or 5.
18. Legumes strigulose, hirsutulous, or villous-hirsute, not tomentose.
19. Legumes strigulose (hairs appressed, 0.5–0.7 mm), thinly fleshy becoming leathery, valves much less than 1 mm thick; Bonneville Basin, c Nevada, w Utah . . . . 184. *Astragalus uncialis* (in part)
19. Legumes hirsutulous to villous-hirsute (hairs spreading, 0.6–2 mm), thickly succulent becoming alveolate-spongy (spongy-thickened cellular tissue 1.5–2 mm thick); w Colorado, c, sc Utah . . . . 204. *Astragalus musiniensis* (in part)
18. Legumes sparsely hirtellous to densely villous-tomentose or villous-hirsute.
20. Legumes pilose and tomentulose, hairs concealing surfaces . . . 199. *Astragalus newberryi* (in part)
20. Legumes villous-hirsute, hairs not concealing surfaces . . . . . . 201. *Astragalus eurekensis* (in part)
17. Leaflets of larger leaves 9–29.

[21. Shifted to left margin.—Ed.]

21. Herbage silvery-pilose-tomentose; plants subacaulescent, caudex branches obscured by persistent, white leaf bases; Ash Meadows, Nye County, Nevada . . . . 200. *Astragalus phoenix*
21. Herbage hirsute, strigose, villous, or pilose, if pilose-tomentose, then not giving a silvery appearance; plants acaulescent, subacaulescent, or short caulescent, caudex branches usually without persistent leaf bases, or if leaf bases persistent then not white; w North America.
    22. Legumes spreading and ascending in oblong or globose, headlike clusters, plumply ovoid or subglobose, 5–7 × 4–4.5 mm; Coconino Plateau and Mogollon Rim, Coconino County, Arizona . . . . 303. *Astragalus troglodytus*
    22. Legumes declined to deflexed, ascending to spreading (often humistrate), usually not in clusters, ovoid, ellipsoid, or lanceoloid- to oblong-ellipsoid, 6–50(–55) × 3–18 mm; w North America.
        23. Legumes papery-membranous, hirsute, hairs lustrous; rimrock habitats.
            24. Flowers 6–9 mm; n Arizona, wc Colorado, nw New Mexico, se Utah . . . . 226. *Astragalus desperatus* (in part)
            24. Flowers 12–16 mm; near Gateway, Mesa County, Colorado, Uintah County, Utah . . . . 228. *Astragalus equisolensis* (in part)
        23. Legumes leathery, woody, or stiffly papery, if papery, then without lustrous, hirsute hairs; various habitats, including rimrock.
            25. Legumes strigulose, strigulose-pilosulous, or silky-strigose, hairs appressed or incumbent, 0.4–1 mm.
                26. Calyx tubes 6.8–11.8 mm; stipules lanceolate, imbricate or not; legumes ovoid, lanceoloid-ellipsoid, oblong-ellipsoid, or ovoid-acuminate, pilosulous, or silky-strigose; not or seldom of rimrock habitats; nw Arizona, e California, nw Colorado, se Idaho, sw Montana, n Nevada, Utah, w Wyoming . . . . 182. *Astragalus argophyllus* (in part)
                26. Calyx tubes 4–6.2 mm; stipules broadly ovate (mostly broader than stem), imbricate; legumes obliquely ellipsoid, 13–22 × 4–6 mm, strigulose; rimrock habitats; wc, sw Colorado, McKinley and San Juan counties, New Mexico, San Juan County, Utah . . . . 229. *Astragalus naturitensis* (in part)
            25. Legumes hirsute, hirsutulous, tomentulose, villous-tomentulose, or tomentose, hairs 1–2.5 mm, or strigose, strigulose, pilosulous, villous, shaggy-villous, or glabrous.
                27. Plants acaulescent, caudex branches with thatch of persistent stipules and leaf bases.
                    28. Legumes strigose; corollas ochroleucous, sometimes tinged or veined purple, keel tip maculate, wing and keel petals purple-tipped; calyces 10.2–15 mm, cylindric, strigulose, tubes 8.2–11.5 mm, lobes 1.9–3.5 mm, subulate; Henry Mountains, Garfield County, Utah . . . . 183. *Astragalus henrimontanensis* (in part)
                    28. Legumes sparsely hirtellous to densely villous-tomentose or villous-hirsute; corollas pink-purple or ochroleucous and suffused with purple; calyces 7–20 mm, cylindric or campanulate, villous or pilose-villous, tubes 5–16 mm, lobes 1–5.7 mm, subulate to lanceolate; w United States.
                        29. Legumes sparsely hirtellous to densely villous-tomentose, hairs usually concealing surface. . . . . 199. *Astragalus newberryi* (in part)
                        29. Legumes villous-hirsute, surface visible between long, shining hairs . . . . 201. *Astragalus eurekensis* (in part)
                27. Plants acaulescent, subacaulescent, or caulescent to shortly so, caudex branches usually without thatch of persistent leaf bases and stipules, if leaf bases and stipules persistent then not acaulescent.

[30. Shifted to left margin.—Ed.]

30. Pubescence of leaflets softly villous or tomentose, of fine, cottony, sinuous or entangled hairs, sometimes hirsute-tomentose; legumes initially ascending, in fruit peduncles decumbent and legumes humistrate, villous-tomentose or -tomentulose, shaggy-villous, or hirsute.
   31. Leaves 1–4 cm; leaflets 5–15, blades 3.2–6.5 mm, obovate, surfaces villous; flowers 9–11.2 mm; corollas pink-purple; nw Utah, ne Nevada, and immediate adjacent Idaho. . . . . .210. *Astragalus anserinus* (in part)
   31. Leaves 1–12 cm; leaflets (3–)7–21, blades 2–15(–20) mm, elliptic, rhombic-elliptic, oblanceolate, obovate, oblong-obovate, or suborbiculate, surfaces villous to tomentose or hirsute; flowers (11–)11.5–29(–31) mm; corollas purple, pink-purple, cream, or white; British Columbia south to Utah and California.
      32. Legumes sparsely or densely villous-tomentulose, hairs to 1 mm; interior s California.
         33. Leaflets (7–)11–19; raceme axis (0.5–)2–8 cm in fruit; flowers 16–18.5 mm; legumes (13–)15–25 mm, grooved abaxially, bilocular; seeds 18–24; San Antonio, San Bernardino, and Santa Rosa mountains . . . . . .211. *Astragalus leucolobus* (in part)
         33. Leaflets 7–11(or 13); raceme axis 0.3–1.6 cm in fruit; flowers (11–)11.5–13.3 mm; legumes 8–15 mm, abaxially flattened proximally, groove slight, unilocular; seeds 11–14; Piute and Sierra Nevada mountains, Kern and Tulare counties . . . . .212. *Astragalus subvestitus* (in part)
      32. Legumes usually densely hirsute or shaggy-villous, sometimes tomentose or villous-hirsute, hairs 1–8 mm; British Columbia south to Utah.
         34. Flowers (22–)24–29 mm; legumes (25–)30–50 mm; Grapevine Mountains, Inyo County, California, Nye County, Nevada . . . . 213. *Astragalus funereus* (in part)
         34. Flowers 19–31 mm; legumes 7–30 mm; California to British Columbia, east to Colorado, South Dakota and Saskatchewan.
            35. Legumes lanceoloid-ellipsoid or narrowly ovoid-acuminate, 17–30 × 5.5–7.5 mm, length 3–4 times width, ± straight, shaggy-villous, hairs relatively long, obscuring surfaces; leaflet blades obovate to suborbiculate or ovate; corollas usually pink-purple, rarely white . . . . .208. *Astragalus utahensis* (in part)
            35. Legumes ovoid, ovoid-ellipsoid, or lanceoloid-ellipsoid, 7–26(–30) × 3.5–11(–13) mm, length 2 times width, incurved, shaggy-villous, villous-hirsute, or densely tomentose, hairs short or long, not always concealing surfaces; leaflet blades obovate, elliptic to oblanceolate, or rhombic-elliptic; corollas white, cream, purple, or pink-purple . . . . . .209. *Astragalus purshii* (in part)

30. Pubescence of leaflets straight, appressed or narrowly ascending, or of spreading-incurved and sometimes sinuous or contorted hairs, but not of extremely fine, entangled hairs, never entirely cottony-tomentose, sometimes glabrate; legumes ascending or spreading, strigulose, pilosulous, hirsutulous, hirsute, shaggy-hirsute, silky-strigose, or glabrous.
   36. Leaflets (7–)17–31 (21+ in at least some leaves).
      37. Legumes glabrous; calyces sparsely villous-villosulous; sw Colorado, nw New Mexico . . . . 191. *Astragalus iodopetalus* (in part)
      37. Legumes usually strigulose, hirsutulous, or pilosulous, rarely glabrous (if glabrous, then calyces strigulose and plants of Arizona and sw New Mexico); calyces hirsute, strigulose, pilosulous, or villous; Arizona, California east to New Mexico and Wyoming.
         38. Legumes densely hirsutulous, (20–)25–30 × 6–8 mm; corollas white, veins and keel tips pink; along axis of Rocky Mountains from se Wyoming south to s Colorado . . . . 215. *Astragalus parryi* (in part)
         38. Legumes usually strigulose or pilosulous, rarely glabrous, 13–50 × 5–13 mm; corollas usually pink-purple or dull lilac, rarely white; Arizona, Nevada, New Mexico.

39. Legumes 13–30(–34) × 5–10(–12) mm, thinly to thickly fleshy becoming thinly leathery, stiffly leathery, or subligneous, valves less than 1 mm thick; herbage strigulose, pilosulous, or villosulous . . . . 190. *Astragalus tephrodes* (in part)
39. Legumes 25–50 × 7–13 mm, thickly fleshy becoming woody, valves 1–2 mm thick; herbage strigulose. . . . . 193. *Astragalus cyaneus* (in part)

[36. Shifted to left margin.—Ed.]

36. Leaflets 7–21.
40. Legumes hirsute or shaggy-hirsute, longest hairs 2–3.5 mm; ec Nevada, c, w Utah.
41. Legumes hirsute, hairs relatively long, not concealing surfaces; sandy flats and dunes in valleys and low ranges; c Nevada, wc Utah. . . . . 186. *Astragalus callithrix*
41. Legumes densely hirsute or shaggy-hirsute, hairs concealing surfaces; montane or cool desert shrub communities; Nevada, Utah.
42. Leaflet blades strigose, hairs subappressed and silvery-silky; legumes spreading-ascending, humistrate; keel petals 17–19 mm (2 mm shorter than banners); e Nevada to c, sw Utah . . . . 187. *Astragalus piutensis*
42. Leaflet blades strigulose-villosulous, hairs ascending, dull; legumes ascending, not humistrate; keel petals 12–13.3 mm (4.5–9 mm shorter than banners); s Utah County, Utah . . . . .188. *Astragalus desereticus*
40. Legumes strigose, strigulose, villosulous, or strigulose-pilosulous, longest hairs less than 1.7 mm; Idaho south to Arizona.
43. Legumes laterally compressed at both ends, obcompressed at middle, ± dorsiventrally compressed, (15–)20–55 mm, incurved through 0.5+ spiral, not mottled; herbage villous-hirsute, sometimes also tomentose; Inyo and San Bernardino counties, California, s Clark County, Nevada. . . . . 195. *Astragalus tidestromii*
43. Legumes dorsiventrally compressed except for laterally compressed beak (if somewhat laterally compressed proximally then shorter and brightly mottled), 15–45 mm, straight or incurved, not spiraling; herbage strigulose, strigose, pilose, or villous-villosulous, not tomentose; Idaho south to Arizona, Nebraska, and Wyoming.
44. Legumes (20–)25–45 × (8–)9–18 mm; calyces villous, not silvery, herbage silvery-strigose . . . . .192. *Astragalus shortianus*
44. Legumes 15–35(–37) × 5–12(–13) mm; calyces and herbage hairs usually uniform in color.
45. Legumes green becoming brown or straw-colored, little or not grooved abaxially; plants mat-forming, caudex not or seldom with persistent leaf bases; Arizona to Idaho, east to Colorado . . . . 182. *Astragalus argophyllus* (in part)
45. Legumes brightly purple-mottled, grooved abaxially (proximally); plants mat- or tuft-forming, caudex branches sometimes with persistent leaf bases; n Arizona, se Nevada, nw New Mexico, s Utah. . . . . . 185. *Astragalus zionis* (in part)

Key to Species of Group 9

1. Legumes broadly ovoid, globose, oblong-ellipsoid or -cylindroid, ± obcompressed, terete, or dorsiventrally or laterally compressed, fleshy, often spongy or succulent, mesocarp 1.5+ mm thick, bilocular; stems usually sprawling or decumbent, sometimes ascending and radiating; sc Canada south to Arizona and Louisiana.
2. Legumes strigulose or pilosulous; stems single or few together from widely branching, subterranean, rhizomatous caudex . . . . .240. *Astragalus plattensis* (in part)
2. Legumes glabrous; stems usually several, clustered from subterranean caudex (not rhizomatous).
3. Legumes 15–40 × 12–27 mm (length less than 1.5 times width); stipules glabrous abaxially; leaflet blades glabrous or glabrescent adaxially; sc Canada south to Arizona and Louisiana . . . . 237. *Astragalus crassicarpus*
3. Legumes 25–45(–50 × (8–)10–21 mm (length 3–4 times width); stipules strigulose abaxially; leaflet blades cinereous-strigulose; se New Mexico, w Texas . . . .239. *Astragalus gypsodes*

1. Legumes linear-oblong and lanceoloid to cylindroid and oblong-ellipsoid, terete, inflated, or bladdery-inflated, obcompressed, 3-sided, dorsiventrally, or laterally compressed, thin to woody, if fleshy not succulent or spongy (initially succulent in *A. pattersonii*) and mesocarp less than 1.5 mm thick, unilocular to bilocular; stems erect to prostrate, usually not sprawling (sometimes sprawling in *A. ensiformis* and *A. iselyi*); widespread.
    4. Legumes hirsute, villosulous, villous, tomentose, or tomentulose, longer hairs mostly 1+ mm.
        5. Legumes bilocular.
            6. Legumes 11–38 mm.
                7. Legumes erect to ascending, subterete or somewhat laterally compressed, not grooved abaxially; s Nevada south and west to se California . . . . 132. *Astragalus minthorniae* (in part)
                7. Legumes reflexed or declined, 3-sided compressed, grooved abaxially; California, Idaho, Oregon, Nevada.
                    8. Legumes 11–15 × 3–3.4 mm; flowers 9.1–11 mm . . . . 104. *Astragalus agnicidus*
                    8. Legumes 18–38 × 4.5–6 mm; flowers 12–15 mm. . . . . . 135. *Astragalus malacus* (in part)
            6. Legumes (3.5–)4–8 mm.
                9. Calyx tubes narrowly campanulate or turbinate, 1.6–2.5 × 1.8–2.6 mm, not accrescent, covering less than 1/2 of mature legumes; Kittitas to Douglas and Franklin counties, Washington . . . . 333. *Astragalus lyallii*
                9. Calyx tubes broadly campanulate, (2.5–)3.1–4.5 × (2.4–)2.6–4.1 mm, somewhat accrescent, covering most or all of mature legume; Idaho, Oregon, Washington.
                    10. Corollas whitish, often tinged lavender, glabrous abaxially; leaflet blades villous or villous-pilose; wc Idaho, Blue Mountains, ne Oregon, c, se Washington, sc British Columbia . . . . 331. *Astragalus spaldingii*
                    10. Corollas pale yellow, pubescent abaxially; leaflet blades densely villous-tomentose; Wasco County, Oregon . . . . 332. *Astragalus tyghensis*
        5. Legumes unilocular.
            11. Flowers 8.3–11.4 mm; corollas pale or greenish yellow; legumes bladdery-inflated, 20–40 × 14–20 mm; leaflets (11–)17–27(or 29); racemes (8–)10–30(–35)-flowered; Inner Coast Ranges, San Benito and Monterey to San Luis Obispo and Santa Barbara counties, California . . . . 258. *Astragalus macrodon* (in part)
            11. Flowers (6.3–)8.2–25.5 mm; corollas pink-purple; legumes obcompressed, 13–40(–45) × (5–)7–13 mm; leaflets (7–)11–23(–27); racemes (2 or)3–18-flowered; Washington and Montana, south to Utah.
                12. Flowers (16.5–)19–25.5 mm; legumes fleshy becoming stiffly leathery.
                    13. Leaflets (7–)11–17; racemes (2–)4–8-flowered; legumes sparsely villous-hirsute, not tomentose; Owyhee Desert, sw Idaho, ec Oregon . . . . 207. *Astragalus nudisiliquus*
                    13. Leaflets (9–)17–23(–27); racemes (5–)8–18-flowered; legumes villous-hirsute or tomentose; w Montana, across n Idaho to sc Washington, ne Oregon . . . . 214. *Astragalus inflexus*
                12. Flowers 5.2–8.2 mm; legumes thin becoming papery or papery-membranous.
                    14. Legumes papery-membranous, hirsute, hairs lustrous; rimrock habitats.
                        15. Flowers 6–9 mm; n Arizona, wc Colorado, nw New Mexico, se Utah . . . . 226. *Astragalus desperatus* (in part)
                        15. Flowers 12–16 mm; near Gateway, Mesa County, Colorado, Uintah County, Utah. 228. *Astragalus equisolensis* (in part)
                    14. Legumes leathery, woody, or stiffly papery, if papery, then not hirsute with lustrous hairs; various habitats, including rimrock.

[16. Shifted to left margin.—Ed.]

16. Legumes strigulose, strigulose-pilosulous, or silky-strigose (hairs appressed or incumbent, 0.4–1 mm).
    17. Calyx tubes 6.8–11.8 mm; stipules lanceolate, imbricate or not; legumes ovoid, lanceoloid-ellipsoid, oblong-ellipsoid, or ovoid-acuminate, 15–32(–37) × 5–12 (–13) mm (often proportionately broader), strigulose, strigulose-pilosulous, or silky-strigose; seldom of rimrock habitats; nw Arizona, e California, nw Colorado, se Idaho, sw Montana, n Nevada, Utah, w Wyoming. 182. *Astragalus argophyllus* (in part)
    17. Calyx tubes 4–6.2 mm; stipules broadly ovate (mostly broader than stem), imbricate; legumes obliquely ellipsoid, 13–22 × 4–6 mm, strigulose; rimrock habitats; wc, sw Colorado, McKinley and San Juan counties, New Mexico, San Juan County, Utah . . . . 229. *Astragalus naturitensis* (in part)
16. Legumes hirsute, hirsutulous, tomentulose, villous-tomentulose, or tomentose (hairs 1–2.5 mm), or strigose, strigulose, pilosulous, villous, shaggy-villous, or glabrous.
    18. Plants acaulescent, caudex branches with thatch of persistent stipules and leaf bases.
        19. Legumes strigose; corollas ochroleucous, sometimes tinged or veined purple, keel tip maculate, wing and keel petals purple-tipped; calyces 10.2–15 mm, cylindric, strigulose, tubes 8.2–11.5 mm, lobes 1.9–3.5 mm, subulate; Henry Mountains, Garfield County, Utah . . . . 183. *Astragalus henrimontanensis* (in part)
        19. Legumes sparsely hirtellous to densely villous-tomentose or villous-hirsute; corollas pink-purple or ochroleucous and suffused with purple; calyces 7–20 mm, cylindric or campanulate, villous or pilose-villous, tubes 5–16 mm, lobes 1–5.7 mm, subulate to lanceolate; w United States.
            20. Legumes sparsely hirtellous to densely villous-tomentose, hairs usually concealing surfaces. . . . . 199. *Astragalus newberryi* (in part)
            20. Legumes villous-hirsute, surface visible between long, shining, hairs, hairs not concealing surfaces. . . . . 201. *Astragalus eurekensis* (in part)
    18. Plants acaulescent, subacaulescent, or caulescent to shortly so, caudex branches usually without thatch of persistent leaf bases and stipules, if leaf bases and stipules persistent then not acaulescent.
        21. Pubescence of leaflets softly villous or tomentose, of fine, cottony, sinuous or entangled hairs, sometimes hirsute-tomentose; legumes initially ascending, in fruit peduncles decumbent and legumes humistrate, villous-tomentose or -tomentulose, shaggy-villous, or hirsute.
            22. Leaves 1–4 cm; leaflets 5–15, blades 3.2–6.5 mm, obovate, surfaces villous; flowers 9–11.2 mm; corollas pink-purple; nw Utah, ne Nevada, and adjacent Idaho . . . . .210. *Astragalus anserinus* (in part)
            22. Leaves 1–12 cm; leaflets (3–)7–21, blades 2–15(–20) mm, elliptic, rhombic-elliptic, oblanceolate, obovate, oblong-obovate, or suborbiculate, surfaces villous to tomentose or hirsute; flowers (11–)11.5–29(–31) mm; corollas purple, pink-purple, cream, or white; British Columbia south to Utah.
                23. Legumes sparsely or densely villous-tomentulose, hairs to 1 mm; interior s California.
                    24. Leaflets (7–)11–19; raceme axis (0.5–)2–8 cm in fruit; flowers 16–18.5 mm; legumes (13–)15–25 mm, grooved abaxially, bilocular; seeds 18–24; San Antonio, San Bernardino, and Santa Rosa mountains. . . . . .211. *Astragalus leucolobus* (in part)
                    24. Leaflets 7–11(or 13); raceme axis 0.3–1.6 cm in fruit; flowers (11–)11.5–13.3 mm; legumes 8–15 mm, abaxially flattened proximally, groove slight, unilocular; seeds 11–14; Piute and Sierra Nevada mountains, Kern and Tulare counties . . . . .212. *Astragalus subvestitus* (in part)
                23. Legumes usually densely hirsute or shaggy-villous, sometimes tomentose or villous-hirsute, hairs 1–8 mm; British Columbia south to Utah.

25. Flowers (22–)24–29 mm; legumes (25–)30–50 mm; Grapevine Mountains, Inyo County, California, Nye County, Nevada . . . . 213. *Astragalus funereus* (in part)
25. Flowers 19–31 mm; legumes 7–30 mm; California to British Columbia, east to Colorado, South Dakota and Saskatchewan.
    26. Legumes lanceoloid-ellipsoid or narrowly ovoid-acuminate, 17–30 × 5.5–7.5 mm, length 3–4 times width, ± straight, shaggy-villous, hairs relatively long, obscuring surfaces; leaflet blades obovate, suborbiculate, or ovate; corollas usually pink-purple, rarely white. . . . . 208. *Astragalus utahensis* (in part)
    26. Legumes ovoid, ovoid-ellipsoid, or lanceoloid-ellipsoid, 7–26 (–30) × 3.5–11(–13) mm, length 2 times width, incurved, shaggy-villous, villous-hirsute, or densely tomentose hairs short or long, not always concealing surfaces; leaflet blades obovate, oblanceolate, elliptic, or rhombic-elliptic; corollas white, cream, purple, or pink-purple. . . . . 209. *Astragalus purshii* (in part)

21. Pubescence of leaflets straight, appressed or narrowly ascending, or of spreading-incurved and sometimes sinuous or contorted hairs, but not of extremely fine, entangled hairs, never entirely cottony-tomentose, sometimes glabrate; legumes ascending or spreading, strigulose, pilosulous, hirsutulous, hirsute, shaggy-hirsute, silky-strigose, or glabrous.
    27. Legumes glabrous; calyces sparsely villous-villosulous; sw Colorado, nw New Mexico . . . . 191. *Astragalus iodopetalus* (in part)
    27. Legumes usually strigulose, hirsutulous, or pilosulous, rarely glabrous (when legumes glabrous, then calyces strigulose and plants of Arizona and sw New Mexico); calyces hirsute, strigulose, pilosulous, or villous; California east to New Mexico and Wyoming.
        28. Legumes densely hirsutulous, (20–)25–30 × 6–8 mm; corollas white, veins and keel tips pink; along axis of Rocky Mountains from se Wyoming south to s Colorado. . . . . 215. *Astragalus parryi* (in part)
        28. Legumes usually strigulose or pilosulous, rarely glabrous, 13–50 × 5–13 mm; corollas usually pink-purple or dull lilac, rarely white; Arizona, Nevada, New Mexico.
            29. Legumes 13–30(–34) × 5–10(–12) mm, thinly to thickly fleshy becoming thinly leathery, stiffly leathery, or subligneous, valves less than 1 mm thick; herbage strigulose, pilosulous, or villosulous . . . . 190. *Astragalus tephrodes* (in part)
            29. Legumes 25–50 × 7–13 mm, thickly fleshy becoming woody, valves 1–2 mm thick; herbage strigulose . . . . 193. *Astragalus cyaneus* (in part)

[4. Shifted to left margin.—Ed.]

4. Legumes often glabrous, if pubescent then strigulose, strigose, pilose, villous, hirsutulous, or villosulous, hairs to 1 mm.
    30. Legumes deflexed, 4.5–12 × 1.3–2.3 mm, bilocular or sub-bilocular; flowers 4.2–6.2 mm.
        31. Legumes strigulose, 6–12 mm; sw New Mexico . . . . 329. *Astragalus vaccarum*
        31. Legumes glabrous, 4.5–7 mm; California inner coast ranges. . . . . .330. *Astragalus clevelandii*
    30. Legumes erect, spreading, ascending, declined, deflexed, or pendulous, (4–)8–48(–55) × (1.5–)3–20(–24) mm, unilocular to bilocular; flowers (4.6–)5–34 mm.

[32. Shifted to left margin.—Ed.]

32. Legumes mostly pendulous, sometimes ascending, spreading, or loosely declined, 2.3–5.5 mm wide, straight or slightly decurved (except incurved in *A. sparsiflorus*); plants from superficial caudex (sometimes slightly subterranean in *A. robbinsii*).
    33. Legumes obtusely 3-sided; seeds 6–10; plants mesophytic; n Utah north to Alaska, east to Newfoundland and New England . . . . 7. *Astragalus robbinsii* (in part)
    33. Legumes dorsiventrally, laterally, or ± 3-sided compressed; seeds (6–)10–29; plants xerophytic; California and Oregon east to Colorado and New Mexico.
        34. Legumes ± 3-sided compressed; racemes (1 or) 2–10-flowered; flowers 5.5–8 mm; upper Platte and Upper Arkansas drainages, montane Colorado . . . . 282. *Astragalus sparsiflorus* (in part)
        34. Legumes mostly dorsiventrally compressed (sometimes laterally compressed in *A. atratus*); racemes 1–18-flowered; flowers 4–13.4 mm; California and Oregon east to Colorado and New Mexico.
            35. Racemes all alike, (2–)5–18-flowered; keel petals 6–10 mm; Great Basin and Owyhee deserts . . . . 119. *Astragalus atratus* (in part)
            35. Racemes of 2 types: early ones subradical, shorter than leaves, 1(or 2)-flowered, later ones cauline, much surpassing leaves, 2–5(–7)-flowered; keel petals 3.5–4.5 mm; Arizona, Colorado, New Mexico, Utah . . . . 121. *Astragalus brandegeei* (in part)
32. Legumes erect, ascending, spreading, declined, deflexed or pendulous, (2–)4–32 mm wide, straight or slightly to strongly incurved (sometimes decurved in *A. panamintensis*); plants from superficial or subterranean caudex.
    36. Plants annual or biennial; legumes deflexed or declined, lunately incurved . . . . 283. *Astragalus diaphanus* (in part)
    36. Plants perennial, or sometimes annual or biennial; legumes erect, spreading, ascending, declined, deflexed, or pendulous, not lunately incurved (except *A. diaphanus*).
        37. Legumes erect, obliquely ovoid or ovoid-ellipsoid, 8–18 mm wide; flowers 11.6–15 mm; corollas whitish to pale yellow (drying ochroleucous); New York to Manitoba south to Ohio and South Dakota . . . . 175. *Astragalus neglectus*
        37. Legumes erect, spreading, ascending, declined, deflexed, or pendulous, if erect then not obliquely ovoid or ovoid-ellipsoid, (2–)4–32 mm wide; flowers (4.6–)5–34 mm; corollas white, ochroleucous, greenish yellow or pink-purple; widespread.
            38. Legumes erect to incurved-ascending.
                39. Banner petal crinkled apically, 10.5–14 mm, wings 12.8–17 mm (longer than banner); calyces (6.9–)7.6–10.6 mm, lobes (1.9–)2.2–5.2 mm; Nes Perce County, Idaho, Asotin, Columbia, and Whitman counties, Washington . . . . 143. *Astragalus riparius*
                39. Banner petal smooth apically, (13.5–)14–24(–25.3) mm, wings (12.4–)13.5–23.7 mm (usually shorter than banner); calyces (5.7–)6–14.8 mm, lobes 1–6.5 mm; w and se United States including Washington and Idaho.
                    40. Stipules herbaceous; legumes (20–)25–40 × (4–)5–7(–8) mm, 3-sided; c to se Washington, adjacent Oregon . . . . 327. *Astragalus succumbens*
                    40. Stipules mostly papery to membranous (herbaceous in *A. giganteus*, herbaceous distally in *A. michauxii*); legumes 13–31 × 4–13 mm, subterete, dorsiventrally, or obcompressed (sometimes turgid); w, se United States including Oregon and Washington.

41. Stems with 2–5(–7) developed internodes, shorter than combined length of peduncles and racemes (sometimes longer in *A. sheldonii*); legumes glabrous or strigulose; Idaho County, Idaho, to ne Oregon and adjacent Washington.
    42. Legumes glabrous, obliquely ovoid-acuminate to broadly lanceoloid- or oblong-ellipsoid, 7–10 mm wide, ± not grooved abaxially, ± unilocular, septum 0–0.9 mm wide; Blue Mountains in ne Oregon, adjacent se Washington, Ada County, Idaho . . . . 139. *Astragalus reventus*
    42. Legumes usually strigulose, rarely glabrous, narrowly oblong-ellipsoid, (4–)4.5–6.3 mm wide, grooved abaxially, semibilocular, septum 1–1.6 mm wide; Lewis and Nez Perce counties, Idaho, Wallowa County, Oregon, Asotin County Washington . . . . 140. *Astragalus sheldonii* (in part)
41. Stems with 5–10 well-developed internodes, longer than combined length of peduncles and racemes; legumes glabrous; sw, se United States.
    43. Herbage pilose and tomentulose; calyces (7.8–)10–14.7 mm; sc New Mexico, w Texas . . . . .236. *Astragalus giganteus*
    43. Herbage strigulose-pilosulous; calyces (5.7–)6–10.3 mm; se United States and Idaho.
        44. Legumes 13–18 mm, unilocular; racemes (4–)7–22-flowered; s Idaho, s from Boise and Custer counties. . . . . 141. *Astragalus adanus* (in part)
        44. Legumes 23–31 mm, sub-bilocular; racemes (12–)15–40-flowered; Atlantic Coastal Plain and Piedmont, se North Carolina south to se Georgia . . . . 151. *Astragalus michauxii*

[38. Shifted to left margin.—Ed.]

38. Legumes usually spreading, spreading-ascending (humistrate), or declined to pendulous, sometimes erect or erect-ascending.
    45. Stems prostrate; leaflet blades 2–11 mm, microphyllous; flowers 4.8–6.1 mm; legumes 4–7 mm; peduncles often 2 or 3 per node; seeds 2–8; California, Nevada, Oregon borders.
        46. Herbage gray-pilosulous; leaflets 7 or 9, blades folded, apex emarginate; legumes lunately ellipsoid-obovoid, somewhat depressed but not grooved abaxially, laterally compressed, lateral faces with shallow longitudinal groove, unilocular; seeds 2 or 3; arid ash deposits; c Washoe County, Nevada . . . . 291. *Astragalus tiehmii*
        46. Herbage villous-tomentose; leaflets (7 or)9–15, blades flat or loosely folded, apex obtuse to subacute; legumes ellipsoid or oblong-ellipsoid, 3-sided compressed, bilocular; seeds 4–8; stream banks and saline meadows; California, Nevada, Oregon . . . . .334. *Astragalus lemmonii*
    45. Stems erect, ascending, spreading, decumbent, reclining, or prostrate; leaflet blades 1–33(–50) mm, usually with at least some blades more than 11 mm; flowers 4.6–34 mm; legumes 6–55 mm; peduncles 1 per node; seeds 6–75(–84); widespread.
        47. Legumes mostly ± bilocular, septum usually 1+ mm wide (unilocular in *A. columbianus*, sometimes unilocular in *A. iodanthus*, *A. serenoi*, ± unilocular in *A. neomexicanus*, subunilocular in *A. praelongus*).
            48. Racemes 1–4(–6)-flowered; flowers ascending at anthesis; flowers 8.2–14 mm; legumes 8–18 × (2.3–)3.4–4.7 mm, bluntly 3-sided; plants tuft- or mat-forming; leaflet blades linear-elliptic or subulate; Inyo County, California. . . 302. *Astragalus panamintensis*
            48. Racemes (2–)5–35(–45)-flowered; flowers usually ascending, spreading, or declined, rarely deflexed; flowers 5.5–26(–27) mm; legumes (7–)9–45(–48) × (2–)2.4–12(–25) mm, inflated, subterete, obcompressed, 3-sided, laterally, or dorsiventrally compressed; plants not tuft- or mat-forming, sometimes clump-forming; leaflet blades usually linear to elliptic or broader, rarely filiform; w North America.

[49. Shifted to left margin.—Ed.]

49. Racemes subcapitate, loosely 2–10-flowered, flowers ascending, axis to 1 cm in fruit; flowers (17–)18.1–19.5(–20) mm; corollas whitish, keel petals maculate; legumes humistrate, 25–40 × 8.5–10.5 mm; Benton and Yakima counties, Washington . . . . 194. *Astragalus columbianus*
49. Racemes not subcapitate, (2 or)3–35(–48)-flowered, rarely loosely so, flowers straight, erect, or incurved-ascending, axis (0.3–)2–20(–26) cm in fruit; flowers 5.5–26(–27) mm; corollas usually pink-purple, ochroleucous, greenish purple, pale lemon yellow, or whitish, rarely cream, keel petals maculate or not; legumes humistrate or not, (7–)10–45(–48) × (2–)2.4–18(–19) mm; w North America.
    50. Racemes 5–12-flowered; flowers spreading to declined; legumes ascending to spreading, moderately inflated, ellipsoid or ovoid-ellipsoid, 15–17 × 7–8 mm; Butte and Custer counties, Idaho . . . . 295. *Astragalus amnis-amissi*
    50. Racemes (2 or)3–35(–48)-flowered; flowers erect, ascending, spreading, declined, or deflexed; legumes erect, ascending, descending, deflexed, declined, or pendulous, inflated, obcompressed, subterete, 3-sided, laterally, or dorsiventrally compressed, linear to subglobose or crescentic including ellipsoid and ovoid, 7–45(–48) × 2–25 mm; w North America.
        51. Flowers nodding, secund and retrorsely imbricate; corollas dull pinkish lavender, greenish purple, or bright magenta-purple; Lincoln and Otero counties, New Mexico . . . . 198. *Astragalus neomexicanus*
        51. Flowers ascending, spreading, erect, declined, or deflexed, when secund, retrorsely imbricate, then corolla not dull pinkish lavender, green-purple or magenta-purple; w North America.
            52. Legumes readily disjointing from receptacle.
                53. Legumes 7–9 × 2–2.5 mm, narrowly lanceoloid; flowers 7.5–8 mm; corollas pink-purple or bluish lavender; Cochise and Santa Cruz counties, Arizona . . . . 313. *Astragalus hypoxylus*
                53. Legumes 8–40(–48) × (2.5–)3–18(–19) mm, linear to subglobose (including lanceoloid); flowers 5.5–23 mm; corollas pink-purple, yellowish, or whitish; w North America.
                    54. Legumes inflated or swollen (ovoid to globose), ± bilocular . . . . 285. *Astragalus lentiginosus* (in part)
                    54. Legumes scarcely inflated or dorsiventrally or laterally compressed, unilocular to bilocular.
                        55. Legumes 3-sided or subterete, bilocular . . . . . . 285. *Astragalus lentiginosus* (in part)
                        55. Legumes 3-sided or dorsiventrally compressed, semibilocular or unilocular.
                            56. Plants from superficial caudex; herbage strigulose or glabrate, exceptionally villosulous, hairs to 0.3–0.7 mm; sagebrush or pinyon-juniper communities, not of dunes; California, Idaho, Nevada, Oregon, Utah . . . . 286. *Astragalus iodanthus*
                            56. Plants from shallow to deep subterranean caudex; herbage villosulous or villous, hairs to 0.7–1.2 mm; dunes and pumice sands; c, wc Nevada, adjacent California . . . . . . 287. *Astragalus pseudiodanthus*
            52. Legumes firmly attached to the receptacle, falling while still attached to pedicel.
                57. Leaflets (1–)5–13; w, nw Great Basin.
                    58. Legumes linear-oblong, straight, 2.4–3.3 mm wide, thinly fleshy becoming leathery; plants slender, wiry . . . . 150. *Astragalus obscurus* (in part)
                    58. Legumes plumply oblong, straight or slightly incurved, 5–12 mm wide, fleshy becoming woody; plants robust . . . . 152. *Astragalus serenoi* (in part)
                57. Leaflets (3–)11–33; w North America.

[59. Shifted to left margin.—Ed.]

59. Plants from subterranean caudex; stems usually ± decumbent, rarely ascending; legumes humistrate, 3-sided, subterete, or laterally compressed; plants not selenophytes.
   60. Legumes: abaxial suture slightly grooved, body 3-sided, cross section deltoid. . . . . 136. *Astragalus chamaemeniscus* (in part)
   60. Legumes: abaxial suture forming a prominent ridge, body sides biconvex, cross section elliptic.
      61. Leaflet blades usually strigose, sometimes glabrous adaxially; flowers (11–)13–17 mm; Mohave County, Arizona, Lincoln County, Nevada, Washington County, Utah . . . . 130. *Astragalus ensiformis*
      61. Leaflet blades hirtellous abaxially, glabrous adaxially; flowers 16–22 mm; Kane and Wayne counties, Utah . . . . 131. *Astragalus malacoides* (in part)
59. Plants from superficial caudex; stems erect to ascending; legumes erect-ascending or spreading, sometimes deflexed or declined, not humistrate, obcompressed, inflated, or subterete, sides not biconvex; when legumes declined or deflexed, then plants selenophytes.
   62. Legumes deflexed or declined; corollas purple, with white or pale wing tips; Cameron, Coconino County, Arizona . . . . .170. *Astragalus beathii*
   62. Legumes erect, spreading, ascending, or declined; corollas whitish, yellowish or pink-purple; w North America.
      63. Legumes ellipsoid, ovoid, cylindroid, obovoid, or subglobose, 5–25 mm wide, subunilocular (septum 0.8–2.3 mm wide); flowers deflexed; corollas usually ochroleucous, sometimes lemon yellow; plants selenophytes . . . . .171. *Astragalus praelongus* (in part)
      63. Legumes narrowly oblong or oblong-ellipsoid, 4–6.5 mm wide, ± bilocular; flowers ascending, spreading, or declined; corollas ochroleucous with dull purple keel tips or pink-purple with pale or white wing tips; plants not selenophytes.
         64. Legumes subsessile or substipitate (contracted at base into short neck, stipes to 1.5 mm), subterete (compressed laterally when pressed); Lincoln, Nye, and White Pine counties, Nevada . . . . .132. *Astragalus minthorniae* (in part)
         64. Legumes sessile (rounded or, sometimes, with short, thick neck at base), not or slightly inflated (slightly turgid); Mohave County, Arizona, Clark County, Nevada, Washington County, Utah . . . . .285. *Astragalus lentiginosus* (in part)

[47. Shifted to left margin.—Ed.]

47. Legumes ± unilocular, septum, when present, usually less than 1 mm wide (*A. serenoi* septum 2–4 mm).
   65. Legumes bladdery-inflated, (5–)6–45(–60) × (1.4–)5–20(–32) mm, terete, obcompressed, or dorsiventrally compressed (scarcely inflated in *A. sparsiflorus* and *A. diaphanus*).
      66. Plants from subterranean or superficial caudex; leaflets 9–15, or 25–41 and stems fistulose.
         67. Stems underground for (0–)1–4 cm, not fistulose; leaflets 9–15; Spring (Charleston) Mountains, Clark County, Nevada . . . . .38. *Astragalus aequalis* (in part)
         67. Stems aboveground, fistulose; leaflets 25–41; San Luis Obispo and Santa Barbara counties, California. . . . . .251. *Astragalus pomonensis*
      66. Plants from superficial caudex; leaflets (3–)7–29(–35), if stems fistulose, then leaflets (17 or)19–35.
         68. Legumes unilocular or subunilocular, partial septum 0.5–1 mm wide.
            69. Leaflets (19 or)21–29; racemes (13–)18–25-flowered; San Diego County, California . . . . 260. *Astragalus deanei* (in part)
            69. Leaflets (5 or)7–21; racemes (1 or)2–15-flowered; Colorado, New Mexico, Oregon, Washington.
               70. Herbage villosulous; seeds 18–22 . . . . 268. *Astragalus cerussatus* (in part)
               70. Herbage strigulose; seeds 6–15.
                  71. Legumes papery, not translucent; Colorado . . . 282. *Astragalus sparsiflorus* (in part)
                  71. Legumes papery-membranous, becoming translucent; e Oregon (formerly sc Washington) . . . . 283. *Astragalus diaphanus* (in part)
         68. Legumes unilocular, without any septum.

[72. Shifted to left margin.—Ed.]

72. Racemes (1 or)2–10(–15)-flowered.
  73. Calyces 6.7–7.8 mm, tube 3.7–3.9 mm; flowers 9.5–11 mm; corollas greenish white, often tinged or veined dull lilac; legumes 25–40 mm; lower Lemhi and upper Salmon rivers, Idaho . . . . 267. *Astragalus aquilonius*
  73. Calyces 3.4–6.4 mm, tube 1.7–3(–3.2) mm; flowers 4.6–7.5 mm; corollas pink-purple, pale lilac or whitish with lilac tips or tinged pink or lavender; legumes 10–37(–43) mm; Colorado and Texas west to California southward.
    74. Legumes strigulose with straight hairs . . . . 264. *Astragalus wootonii* (in part)
    74. Legumes loosely strigulose or strigulose-villosulous, hairs spreading, incumbent or curly.
      75. Leaflets 13–21; seeds 18–26 . . . . 268. *Astragalus cerussatus* (in part)
      75. Leaflets (7 or)9–15(or 17); seeds 10–14 . . . . 276. *Astragalus gilmanii* (in part)

72. Racemes (7–)10–60(–75)-flowered.
  76. Plants silvery- or satiny-strigulose; desert dunes . . . . 262. *Astragalus magdalenae*
  76. Plants villosulous, strigulose, glabrate, or glabrous, green, cinereous, or silvery, when silvery then not of desert dunes.
    77. Herbage and legumes villosulous or strigulose-villosulous; s Coast Ranges, California . . . . 258. *Astragalus macrodon* (in part)
    77. Herbage and legumes mostly strigulose, sometimes villosulous or glabrous; California to Texas.
      78. Legumes 6–13 × 6–10 mm, broadly and plumply ovoid- or obovoid-ellipsoid, obovoid, or subglobose, beak almost obsolete; s Arizona, sw New Mexico . . . . 265. *Astragalus thurberi*
      78. Legumes 9–40(–60) × (4–)5–20(–32) mm, when shorter than 15 mm then strongly beaked, ovoid to ellipsoid or subglobose; California to Texas.
        79. Racemes (15–)20–60(–75)-flowered; corollas ochroleucous, rarely tinged purple, drying brownish; leaflets (17 or)19–35; legumes stiffly papery; San Diego County, California. . . . . 259. *Astragalus oocarpus*
        79. Racemes 5–30(–40)-flowered; corollas whitish, yellowish, or pink-purple; leaflets (7–)11–29, when leaflets more than 21 then legumes thinly papery; California to Texas.
          80. Legumes subsymmetrically ovoid-ellipsoid or subglobose, beak poorly developed; plants winter annuals or biennials . . . . 264. *Astragalus wootonii* (in part)
          80. Legumes obliquely ovoid, ovoid-ellipsoid, ovoid-acuminate, or ellipsoid, beak strongly developed; plants usually perennials (*A. allochrous* sometimes biennial).
            81. Corollas pink-purple; Arizona, California, New Mexico, Texas.
              82. Legumes 9–23 mm . . . . 261. *Astragalus palmeri* (in part)
              82. Legumes (20–)25–40(–45) mm. . . . . 263. *Astragalus allochrous* (in part)
            81. Corollas ochroleucous, or greenish white, rarely tinged with purple; cismontane California south to edge of s Mojave and Colorado deserts.
              83. Legumes 25–60 mm; seeds 42–71; banners (6.4–)7.8–13 mm . . . . 257. *Astragalus douglasii*
              83. Legumes 9–28 mm; seeds (7–)12–40; banners 12–15 mm or 7–10.3 mm.
                84. Leaflets (19 or)21–29; banners 12–15 mm; keel petals 8–10.5 mm . . . . 260. *Astragalus deanei* (in part)
                84. Leaflets (9 or)11–21; banners 7–10.3 mm; keel petals 6.2–8.8 mm . . . . 261. *Astragalus palmeri* (in part)

[65. Shifted to left margin.—Ed.]

65. Legumes mostly not bladdery-inflated, (7–)9–55 × (2.8–)5–20(–24) mm, when bladdery, then 7–29 × 4.5–17(–18) mm, terete, subterete, obcompressed, 3-sided, or dorsiventrally compressed.
   85. Legumes pendulous, strongly incurved or coiled, fleshy becoming stiffly papery, sharply 4-angled; se Oregon to sw Utah and adjacent Arizona . . . . .247. *Astragalus tetrapterus* (in part)
   85. Legumes erect, ascending, spreading, horizontal, declined, deflexed, or pendulous, usually straight or slightly incurved, sometimes falcate, sigmoid-arcuate, or coiled, rarely decurved, fleshy, papery, leathery, or woody, inflated, terete, subterete, obcompressed, 3-sided, or dorsiventrally compressed; w United States.
      86. Leaflets (1 or)3–13, blades 6–35(–50) mm, apex mucronate or acute to mucronate; plants selenophytes; Grand and San Juan counties, Utah.
         87. Flowers 23–34 mm; calyx tubes 11–14 mm; Mancos Shale and Morrison formations, near Cisco and nw of Moab, Grand County, Utah . . . 173. *Astragalus sabulosus* (in part)
         87. Flowers 17–19 mm; calyx tubes 5.5–6.3 mm; Morrison and Paradox formations, foothills of La Sal Mountains, Grand and San Juan counties, Utah . . . . 174. *Astragalus iselyi* (in part)
      86. Leaflets (1–)5–27(–33), blades 1.5–30(–50) mm, apex acute to emarginate and mucronate; plants not selenophytes (except *A. pattersonii*, *A. praelongus*, and *A. preussii*); w United States including Utah.
         88. Plants 3–11 cm, humifusely mat-forming, densely gray-villous; tuffaceous sands; s Idaho, ne Nevada, nw Utah. .210. *Astragalus anserinus* (in part)
         88. Plants 1.5–60(–120) cm, not mat-forming, usually strigulose, villosulous, or pilosulous, rarely glabrous; canyon slopes, volcanic tuff, igneous, granite, or basaltic soils, grassland, sagebrush, and desert communities, pinyon-juniper communities, woodlands, rarely seleniferous soils; w United States.
            89. Legumes obliquely ovoid, ovoid-ellipsoid, or lanceoloid-ellipsoid, inflated or bladdery-inflated, deciduous from receptacle, papery or papery-membranous; axis of raceme 0.2–5 cm in fruit.
               90. Plants 1.5–13(–25) cm, not tuft- or clump-forming.
                  91. Leaflets (7 or)9–15(or 17), blades 5–12.5 mm; legumes 13–26 × 8–16 mm; se California, Lincoln County, Nevada . . .276. *Astragalus gilmanii* (in part)
                  91. Leaflets (3 or)5–9, blades 1.5–7 mm; legumes 7–14 × 4.5–7.5 mm; Pahute Mesa, sc Nye County, Nevada . . . . .277. *Astragalus beatleyae*
               90. Plants (3–)8–50 cm, mostly tuft- or clump-forming (except *A. wardii*).
                  92. Flowers 5–8 mm; plants tuft-forming or not; legumes bladdery-inflated, often purple-mottled; high plateaus of sc Utah, disjunct in e Great Basin.
                     93. Leaflets (11–)15–23, blades mostly glabrescent or glabrous; racemes loosely flowered, axis 1–5 cm in fruit; legumes glabrous . . . . .266. *Astragalus wardii*
                     93. Leaflets 9–15, blade surfaces strigose-pilosulous; racemes subumbellate, axis 0.2–1 cm in fruit; legumes strigose . . . . 270. *Astragalus serpens* (in part)
                  92. Flowers 8.8–12.2 mm and plants tuft-forming, or 6.3–8.2 mm and plants clump-forming; legumes inflated, not strongly bladdery, red- or purple-mottled or not mottled; Colorado, Utah, Wyoming.
                     94. Legumes strongly incurved, thin becoming papery, shaggy-pilose, hairs lustrous, 1–2 mm; seeds 9–18 . . . . . . 272. *Astragalus pubentissimus*
                     94. Legumes slightly incurved, firmly papery, villosulous, hairs incurved, to 0.7 mm; seeds 20–28 . . . . .273. *Astragalus pardalinus* (in part)
            89. Legumes either narrower than ovoid or persistent on receptacle, papery to woody, if fleshy then becoming leathery or woody, not bladdery-inflated or if swollen then racemes 6–20 cm.

[95. Shifted to left margin.—Ed.]

95. Plants from subterranean caudex; legumes pendulous, deflexed, or spreading-declined.
  96. Legumes fleshy, obcompressed, 20–55 × (5–)6–10 mm; nw, w Nevada, adjacent California . . . . 246. *Astragalus casei* (in part)
  96. Legumes papery, terete, dorsiventrally compressed, or 3-sided, 13–34 × 2.8–5 mm; Arizona, Colorado, Utah.
    97. Legumes 3-sided; stems prostrate to decumbent-ascending; Montezuma County, Colorado, San Juan County, Utah . . . . .35. *Astragalus cronquistii*
    97. Legumes terete or dorsiventrally compressed; stems erect; n Arizona . . . . 37. *Astragalus atwoodii* (in part)
95. Plants from superficial caudex (sometimes shallowly subterranean in *A. praelongus*); legumes ascending, spreading, declined, or erect.
  98. Stems decumbent to ascending (diffuse); peduncles spreading-ascending; legumes ascending and humistrate; ne Nevada eastward to w Colorado, northward to Idaho and Montana . . . . 129. *Astragalus cibarius* (in part)
  98. Stems mostly ascending to erect, sometimes decumbent or reclining; peduncles mostly erect or erect-ascending (*A. pinonis* divaricate or widely incurved-ascending); legumes erect, spreading, ascending, or declined, not humistrate; Arizona, California, Colorado, Idaho, Nevada, New Mexico, Texas, Utah.
    99. Leaflets (1–)5–11, blades linear, linear-oblanceolate, or filiform, surfaces silvery-canescent adaxially; c, w Nevada, adjacent California . . . . .152. *Astragalus serenoi* (in part)
    99. Leaflets (5–)9–33, blades linear, oblong, lanceolate, elliptic, oblanceolate, obovate, obcordate or suborbiculate, surfaces mostly glabrous adaxially, not silvery or canescent; Arizona, California, Colorado, Idaho, Nevada, New Mexico, Texas, Utah.
      100. Legumes 20–35 × 5.5–8 mm, terete or subterete; corollas greenish to ochroleucous, suffused with purple; usually growing upward through low sagebrush . . . . 36. *Astragalus pinonis*
      100. Legumes 12–42 × 4–25 mm, subterete, obcompressed, dorsiventrally compressed, or inflated; corollas ochroleucous, white to pale greenish yellow, pale lemon yellow, or pink-purple; seldom growing upward through low sagebrush.
        101. Legumes 13–18 × 4–6 mm, subligneous in age; plants not selenophytes . . . . 141. *Astragalus adanus* (in part)
        101. Legumes 12–42 × 5–25 mm, stiffly papery to leathery or leathery-woody in age; plants selenophytes.
          102. Corollas pink-purple; legumes stiffly papery to leathery, unilocular . . . . 165. *Astragalus preussii* (in part)
          102. Corollas ochroleucous, white, or pale lemon yellow, keel petals sometimes with purple tips; legumes fleshy becoming leathery-woody, or succulent becoming stiffly leathery, unilocular or subunilocular (septum 0–2.3 mm wide).
            103. Corollas ochroleucous or pale lemon yellow, keel petals with maculate (purple) or immaculate tips; calyx tubes campanulate, 4.4–7.5 mm, lobes erect-ascending . . .171. *Astragalus praelongus* (in part)
            103. Corollas white, keel petals rarely with faintly purplish tips; calyx tubes cylindric, 6–8.8 mm, lobes broadly spreading . . . . .172. *Astragalus pattersonii*

135a. Astragalus Linnaeus sect. Cenantrum Bunge, Mém. Acad. Imp. Sci. Saint Pétersbourg, Sér. 7, 11(16): 23. 1868

Phaca Linnaeus, Sp. Pl. 2: 755. 1753; *Astragalus* sect. *Phaca* (Linnaeus) Haláczy

Herbs perennial, caulescent; caudex subterranean or superficial, with creeping caudex branches. **Hairs** basifixed. **Stems** single or few to several. **Stipules** distinct or proximalmost connate. **Leaves** odd-pinnate, subsessile or short-petiolate; leaflets (5 or)7–15. **Racemes** usually loosely, sometimes compactly, flowered, flowers nodding. **Calyx tubes** campanulate or subcylindric. **Corollas** white, cream, or yellowish with whitish margins, banner recurved through 35–45°, keel slightly shorter than wings, apex blunt or round. **Legumes** ± persistent, pendulous, stipitate, obliquely ellipsoid or ovoid, ± inflated, usually bladdery, laterally compressed proximally, dorsiventrally compressed distally, unilocular. **Seeds** 6–10.

Species 42 (2 in the flora): w, c North America, Europe, Asia.

Section *Cenantrum* is mainly Asiatic.

1. **Astragalus umbellatus** Bunge, Mém. Acad. Imp. Sci. Saint Pétersbourg, Sér. 7, 11(16): 24. 1868 • Tundra milkvetch

Plants 5–30(–36) cm, villous; from rhizomelike or stoloniferous, branched caudex. **Stems** erect or ascending, (0–)1–12+ cm underground, villous. **Leaves** (2–)3–12 cm; stipules distinct, subterranean ones often fully amplexicaul but distinct, 7–15 mm, foliose at distal nodes; leaflets (5–)7–13(–15), blades elliptic, oblong or lanceolate-elliptic, 10–30(–35) mm, pinnately veined, apex obtuse to rounded, surfaces sparsely villosulous or villous abaxially, glabrous adaxially. **Peduncles** erect, 3–9.8 cm, usually longer than subtending leaf. **Racemes** appearing subumbellate, loosely 5–11-flowered; axis 1–5 cm in fruit; bracts (1.5–)2.5–3.8 mm; bracteoles 0. **Pedicels** 1.5–5 mm. **Flowers** 13–19 mm; calyx campanulate to subcylindric, 7.5–8.8 mm, villosulous, tube 6.3–8 mm, lobes broadly triangular, 0.6–0.8 mm; corolla yellowish with whitish margins, banner sometimes purple bordered white, keel 13.2–16 mm. **Legumes** green becoming brown, ± straight, ovoid, inflated, 15–21 × 5.5–8 mm, papery-membranous, black-pilose, hairs to 0.5 mm; stipe 5–7 mm, pubescent. **Seeds** 6–10. $2n$ = 16.

Flowering Jun–Aug. Arctic and alpine tundra, meadows, heath, woods, riparian areas; 10–2000 m; B.C., N.W.T., Nunavut, Yukon; Alaska; Asia (Russia).

2. **Astragalus americanus** (Hooker) M. E. Jones, Contr. W. Bot. 8: 8. 1898 • American milkvetch, astragale d'Amérique [E] [F]

Phaca frigida Linnaeus var. *americana* Hooker, Fl. Bor.-Amer. 1: 140. 1831; *Astragalus frigidus* (Linnaeus) A. Gray var. *gaspensis* (J. Rousseau) Fernald; *A. gaspensis* J. Rousseau

Plants robust, coarse, 25–90(–100) cm, villous; from stoloniferous, superficial or slightly subterranean caudex. **Stems** ascending to erect, villous. **Leaves** (6–)9–17 cm; stipules reflexed, connate-sheathing at proximal nodes, distinct at distal nodes, 10–22 mm, foliose becoming papery-membranous; leaflets (7 or) 9–15, blades broadly lanceolate- or ovate-oblong or elliptic, 15–60 mm, thin, pinnately veined, apex obtuse, surfaces sparsely villous abaxially, glabrous adaxially. **Peduncles** erect, (3.5–)5–14(–19) cm, equaling or shorter than subtending leaf, sometimes exceeding proximal ones, together with racemes usually not longer than distalmost leaves. **Racemes** 10–25(–30)-flowered; axis 2–5 cm in fruit; bracts 4–9 mm; bracteoles 0 or 2. **Pedicels** 3–9 mm. **Flowers** 8–13(–14.2) mm; calyx campanulate, (4.5–)4.9–5.8 mm, glabrous, tube (4.3–)4.9–5.8 mm, lobes deltate (often reduced to shallow crenulations), 0.2–0.7 mm, ciliate; corolla white or cream, keel 10.3–12.7 mm. **Legumes** stramineous, straight, obliquely ellipsoid, bladdery-inflated, 20–28 × 6.5–9.5 mm, papery, translucent, glabrous; stipe 4.5–7 mm. **Seeds** 6–9. $2n$ = 16.

Flowering late Jun–Aug. Gravelly or sandy soils in woods or thickets, glades, grasslands, stream banks, roadsides; 0–2200 m; Alta., B.C., Man., N.W.T., Ont., Que., Sask., Yukon; Alaska, Colo., Idaho, Mont., S.Dak., Wyo.

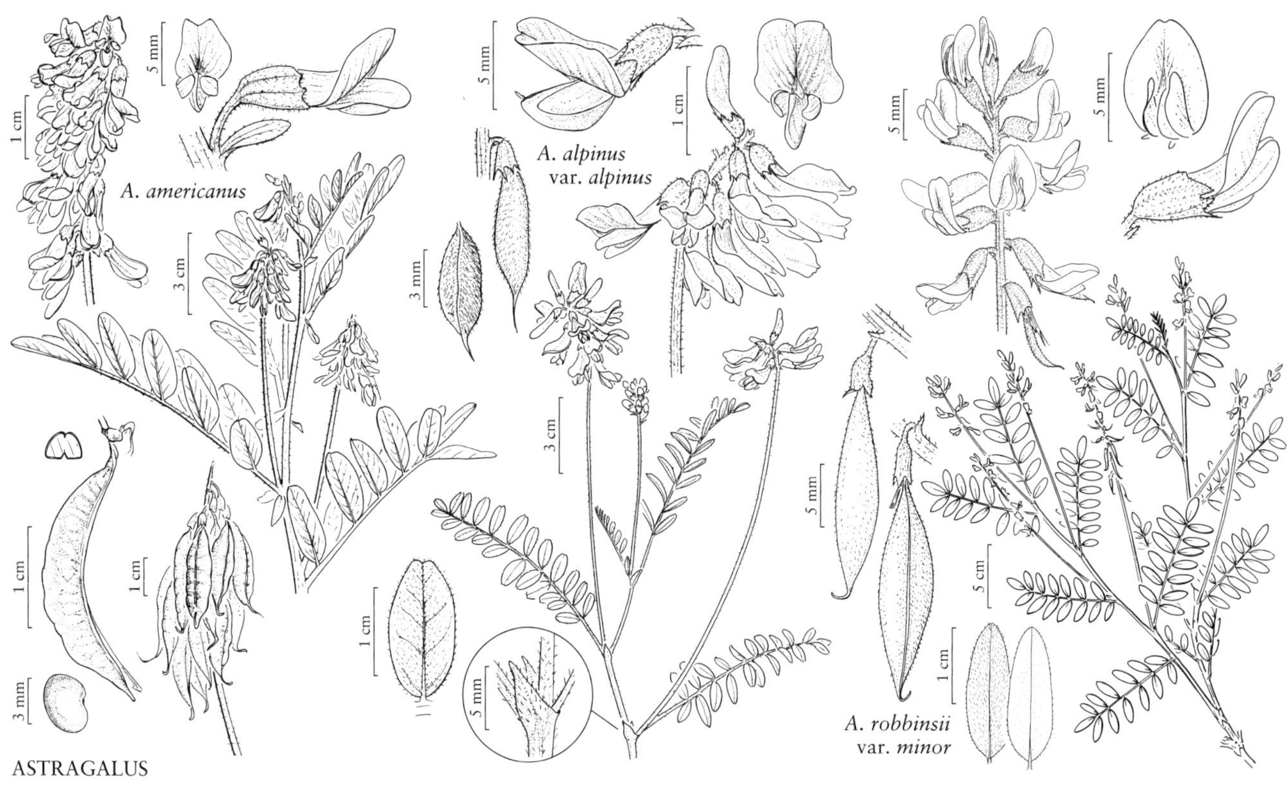

ASTRAGALUS

R. C. Barneby (1964) noted that the geographically isolated *Astragalus gaspensis* is connected to *A. americanus* along its main Cordilleran range through populations in central Canada and that the fruits and length of calyx lobes are not distinctive. D. Isely (1998) pointed out that *A. americanus* is sufficiently similar to the Eurasian *A. frigidus* (Linnaeus) A. Gray that the two might be united.

135b. ASTRAGALUS Linnaeus sect. ASTRAGALUS

Herbs perennial, caulescent; root-crown subterranean, with widely creeping rhizomatous or stoloniferous caudex branches. **Hairs** basifixed. **Stems** 1–several. **Stipules** connate at proximal or distal nodes, distinct at distal nodes. **Leaves** odd-pinnate, petiolate; leaflets (9 or)11–25(or 27). **Racemes** short or subumbellate, loosely or densely flowered, flowers erect to declined then nodding. **Calyx tubes** campanulate or subcylindric. **Corollas** bluish purple or lilac-purple, often pale or white with darker keel tip, banner recurved through 45° or abruptly incurved through 75–90°, keel apex obtuse or blunt. **Legumes** persistent, stipitate or subsessile, pendulous, oblong-lanceoloid to oblong-ellipsoid, obcompressed and bluntly 3-sided, unilocular or semiunilocular. **Seeds** 5–11.

Species ca. 52 (2 in the flora): North America, Europe, Asia.

Section *Astragalus* consists of somewhat fewer than 60 species of circumboreal arctic, montane, and alpine distribution. In a revision of Old World species, D. Podlech and S. Zarre (2013) designated *A. alpinus* as the type species of sect. *Komaroviella* Gontscharow, a section of 23 species that is Asian except for the circumboreal *A. alpinus*.

3. Astragalus alpinus Linnaeus, Sp. Pl. 2: 760. 1753 • Alpine milkvetch, astragale alpin [F]

Plants 1–30(–44) cm, strigulose to villosulous; from subterranean caudex, branches rhizomatous. **Stems** decumbent to ascending, 2–15+ cm underground, strigulose or villosulous. **Leaves** (2–)3–15 cm; stipules connate-sheating at proximal nodes, loosely amplexicaul at distal nodes, 1.5–8 mm, herbaceous becoming papery; leaflets (11–)15–25(or 27), blades ovate, elliptic, or oblong, (2–)6–20(–24) mm, apex retuse or rounded, surfaces strigulose. **Peduncles** erect or incurved-ascending, 3–15(–17) cm, longer or shorter than leaves, peduncle and raceme usually shorter than stem. **Racemes** densely 5–17(–23)-flowered; axis 0.5–5(–7) cm in fruit, elongating little after flowering; bracts 1–2.5 mm; bracteoles 0. **Pedicels** 0.5–2.3 mm. **Flowers** (6.2–)7.4–13.6 (–14.8) mm; calyx campanulate to subcylindric, 3.2–6.6 mm, strigulose, tube 2–4 mm, lobes subulate, 0.9–2.8(–3) mm; corolla pink-purple, blue-purple, or white; banner abruptly incurved through 75–90°; keel 0.5–2.2 mm, ± longer than wings and subequal to banner. **Legumes** green-stramineous, straight or slightly incurved, sulcate abaxially, oblong-lanceoloid, 3-sided compressed, (6–)7–14 × 2.5–4.2 mm, thin becoming papery-membranous, strigulose or villosulous, partial septum inflexed 0.2–0.8 mm, semibilocular; stipe 1.4–3 mm. **Seeds** 5–11.

Varieties 2 (2 in the flora): n North America, Eurasia.

Astragalus alpinus is possibly the most widely distributed species in the genus. Even with a broad geographic range and its occurrence in a wide variety of soils and climates, remarkably little geographically correlated variation is evident. R. C. Barneby (1964) noted that a variant from the highest latitudes around the pole, which he referred to as *A. arcticus* Bunge, an illegitimate name, is not consistently different from *A. alpinus* var. *alpinus* in the broad sense. He also noted that populations in the Rocky Mountains south of Wyoming have relatively smaller flowers. R. Spellenberg (1976) reported that diploids and polyploids occur in the species: the former from southern populations, the latter from northern ones.

1. Legume hairs loosely ascending, 0.4–0.8 mm; plants of northern and western North America . . . . 3a. *Astragalus alpinus* var. *alpinus*
1. Legume hairs usually appressed, rarely ascending, 0.2–0.4 mm; plants of se Canada and New England. . . . . 3b. *Astragalus alpinus* var. *brunetianus*

3a. Astragalus alpinus Linnaeus var. **alpinus** [F]

Stems usually 1–15(–25) cm. **Flowers** (6.2–)7.4–13.6(–14.8) mm; calyx 3.2–6.6 mm, tube 2.2–4 mm, lobes 0.9–2.8(–3) mm. **Legumes** straight or gently incurved, (6–)7–14 × 2.5–4.2 mm, usually villosulous, rarely glabrous, hairs loosely ascending, black or fuscous, often mixed with white, or all white, 0.4–0.8 mm; stipe 1.4–3 mm. $2n = 16, 32$.

Flowering mid Apr–Sep. Arctic and alpine tundra, heath, woods, stream banks, riverbeds, terraces, moraines, gravelly roadsides; 50–3900 m; Greenland; Alta., B.C., Man., Nfld. and Labr., N.W.T., Nunavut, Ont., Que., Sask., Yukon; Alaska, Colo., Idaho, Minn., Mont., Nev., N.Mex., Oreg., S.Dak., Utah, Wash., Wis., Wyo.; Eurasia.

3b. Astragalus alpinus Linnaeus var. **brunetianus** Fernald, Rhodora 10: 51. 1908 • Brunet's milkvetch, astragale de Brunet [E]

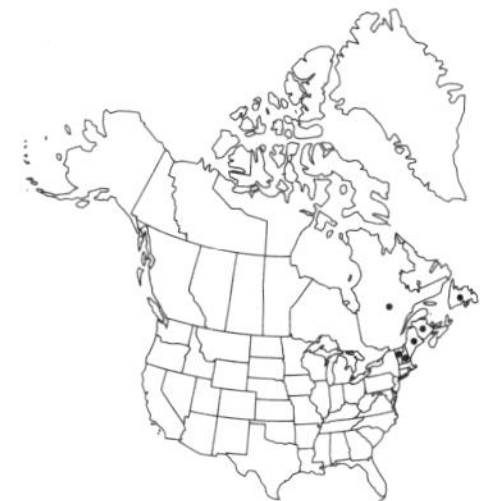

Stems 1.5–30(–44) cm (aboveground). **Flowers** 9.8–11.8 mm; calyx 3.2–4.4 mm, tube 2–2.9 mm, lobes 1–1.8 mm. **Legumes** straight or slightly incurved, 10–14 × 2.5–4 mm, strigulose, hairs usually appressed, rarely ascending, 0.2–0.4 mm; stipe 1.5–2.5 mm.

Flowering May–Aug. Rocky shores, ledges near high water, gravel bars, on schist, limestone, and sandstone; 0–200 m; N.B., Nfld. and Labr. (Nfld.), Que.; Maine, N.H., Vt.

4. Astragalus leptaleus A. Gray, Proc. Amer. Acad. Arts 6: 220. 1864 • Park milkvetch [E]

Plants loosely tuft-forming, 5–20(–30) cm, strigulose; from branched, subterranean caudex, underground for 6+ cm, and stout taproot. **Stems** sprawling, slender and delicate, forming entangled clumps, strigulose, green. **Leaves** 2.5–10 cm; stipules connate-sheathing at proximal nodes, distinct at distal nodes, 2–5 mm, thinly herbaceous or submembranous; leaflets (9–)15–23(–27), blades narrowly elliptic, lanceolate, or ovate, 3–15 mm, apex subacute or obtuse, surfaces sparsely strigulose abaxially, glabrate adaxially. **Peduncles** ascending, 2–2.5 cm, shorter than leaves. **Racemes** loosely (1 or)2 or 3(–5)-flowered; axis 0.2–1 cm in fruit; bracts 1.3–

3.3 mm; bracteoles 0–2. **Pedicels** 1.2–2.1 mm, 1.4–2.5 mm in fruit. **Flowers** 8.5–11.8 mm; calyx campanulate to subcylindric, 4–5.7 mm, densely to sparsely strigulose, tube 2.7–3.4 mm, lobes subulate or lanceolate-subulate, 1.1–2.5 mm; corollas white, keel apex maculate with dull bluish purple; banner recurved through 45°; keel 6–7.5 mm. **Legumes** stramineous, slightly decurved, oblong- or lanceoloid-ellipsoid, obcompressed and bluntly 3-sided, faces low-convex, 8–14 × 2.5–4 mm, papery, translucent, sparsely strigulose, hairs 1.8–2.1 mm, unilocular; stipe 0–1.5 mm. **Seeds** 6–10.

Flowering Jun–Aug. Moist sedge meadows and stream margins; 800–2700 m; Colo., Idaho, Mont., Wyo.

Astragalus leptaleus is a delicate species easily overlooked in floriferous meadows, which are often held privately and heavily utilized for livestock. These factors combine to suggest that it may be more common than records in collections would suggest.

135c. ASTRAGALUS Linnaeus sect. MINERALES Barneby, Mem. New York Bot. Gard. 13: 114. 1964 [E]

Herbs perennial, wide-spreading, mat-forming, shortly caulescent; caudex subterranean, extensively branched. **Hairs** basifixed. **Stems** several. **Stipules** connate. **Leaves** odd-pinnate, petiolate; leaflets 9–25. **Racemes** short or subumbellate, loosely flowered, flowers ascending. **Calyx tubes** campanulate. **Corollas** pink-purple, lilac, or whitish, banner recurved through 45–50°, keel apex bluntly triangular. **Legumes** persistent, discontinuous with receptacle, sessile or subsessile, ascending (humistrate), obliquely ovoid, lanceoloid-ovoid, or ovoid-ellipsoid, 3-sided compressed, flattened or depressed dorsally, unilocular. **Seeds** 6–9.

Species 1: w United States.

M. Lavin and H. Marriott (1997) placed sect. *Minerales* as a synonym of sect. *Polares*, a proposal with considerable merit. Nevertheless, sect. *Minerales* differs subtly, but significantly, in its fruits being sessile (or subsessile) and not at all inflated.

5. **Astragalus molybdenus** Barneby, Leafl. W. Bot. 6: 70. 1950 • Leadville milkvetch [E]

Astragalus plumbeus Barneby, Leafl. W. Bot. 5: 195. 1949, not (Nevski) Gontscharow 1946

Plants loosely mat-forming, dwarf, alpine, 0.5–6(–14) cm, strigulose-pilosulous; caudex branches rhizomatous, underground for 6+ cm, cinereous. **Stems:** aerial tips prostrate or ascending, nodes short, strigulose-pilosulous and ashy gray. **Leaves** 1.5–7(–8) cm; stipules connate-sheathing, 2–5 mm, submembranous; leaflets mostly crowded, blades folded or involute, ovate, ovate-oblong, or elliptic, 2–10 mm, apex obtuse to acute, surfaces pubescent, sometimes glabrescent adaxially. **Peduncles** procumbent (in fruit), 1–3(–6.5) cm. **Racemes** loosely (1–)3–6-flowered, (0–)1–10(–15) mm (in fruit); bracts 1.5–5 mm; bracteoles 0–2. **Pedicels** 0.5–1.5 mm, (1–2 mm in fruit). Flowers 10.7–12.5 mm; calyx 5–7 mm, strigulose, tube 3–4.2 mm, lobes subulate, 1.8–3 mm; corolla pink-purple, lilac, or whitish, keel apex maculate, banner veined and suffused with lilac; keel 9–10 mm. **Legumes** slightly incurved, 6.5–11.5 × 3–3.5 mm, thinly submembranous, strigulose. **Seeds** 6–9.

Varieties 3 (3 in the flora): w United States.

Astragalus molybdenus is one of the very few American astragali found in the tundra of the southern Rocky Mountains.

1. Leaflets 9–17 distally; racemes (1 or)2 (or 3)-flowered; legumes 8.5–11.5 mm; Salt River Range, Lincoln County, Wyoming . . . . 5c. *Astragalus molybdenus* var. *shultziorum*
1. Leaflets (13 or)15–25 distally; racemes (2 or) 3–6-flowered; legumes 6.5–11.2 mm; c Colorado, Teton County, Montana.
    2. Leaflet blade surfaces densely pubescent; legumes bluntly 3-sided compressed, 6.5–9 (–9.8) mm; c Colorado. . . . . 5a. *Astragalus molybdenus* var. *molybdenus*
    2. Leaflet blade surfaces sparsely pubescent; legumes 3-sided compressed, 8.5–11.2 mm; Teton County, Montana . . . . 5b. *Astragalus molybdenus* var. *lackschewitzii*

5a. Astragalus molybdenus Barneby var. **molybdenus** [E]

Leaflets 17–25 distally, blade surfaces densely pubescent. **Racemes** 3–6-flowered. **Legumes** bluntly 3-sided compressed, 6.5–9(–9.8) mm, abruptly contracted to a short beak.

Flowering Jul–Aug. Alpine tundra; 3500–4000 m; Colo.

5b. Astragalus molybdenus Barneby var. **lackschewitzii** (Lavin & Marriott) S. L. Welsh, N. Amer. Sp. Astragalus, 51. 2007 • Lackschewitz's milkvetch [C] [E]

Astragalus lackschewitzii Lavin & Marriott, Syst. Bot. 22: 214, fig. 1. 1997

Leaflets (13 or)15–23 distally, blade surfaces sparsely pubescent. **Racemes** (2 or)3–5-flowered. **Legumes** 3-sided compressed, 8.5–11.2 mm, gradually attenuated to a persistent style.

Flowering Jul–Aug. Alpine tundra; of conservation concern; 2200–2500 m; Mont.

Variety *lackschewitzii* is based on rather tenuous characteristics of leaflet pubescence and fruit compression, made significant by the geographic isolation of the populations from the other two varieties.

5c. Astragalus molybdenus Barneby var. **shultziorum** (Barneby) S. L. Welsh, Great Basin Naturalist 58: 46. 1998 • Shultzes' milkvetch [E]

Astragalus shultziorum Barneby, Brittonia 33: 156, fig. 1. 1981

Leaflets 9–17 distally. **Racemes** (1 or)2(or 3)-flowered. **Legumes** 3-sided compressed, 8.5–11.5 mm, attenuate apically, beak elongate.

Flowering Jul–Aug. Alpine tundra and krummholz, on talus; 2700–3500 m; Wyo.

D. Isely (1998) maintained this taxon at the specific level, although he pointed out that recent studies showed populations of *Astragalus molybdenus* of Colorado, Montana, and Wyoming (as treated here) to be closely related; populations of the former two states are more closely related than those of Wyoming.

135d. Astragalus Linnaeus sect. Oroboidei A. Gray, Proc. Amer. Acad. Arts 6: 203. 1864

Herbs perennial, caulescent; root-crown or caudex superficial or subterranean. **Hairs** basifixed. **Stems** few to several. **Stipules** connate at proximal nodes, distinct at distal nodes. **Leaves** odd-pinnate, subsessile or petiolate; leaflets (5 or)7–17. **Racemes** loosely or compactly flowered, flowers nodding. **Calyx tubes** campanulate. **Corollas** purple, pale pink, whitish, pink-purple, or blue-purple, banner recurved through 40°, wing apex rounded, keel apex usually round, rarely deltate. **Legumes** eventually deciduous, sessile or stipitate, spreading, reflexed, or pendulous, ellipsoid to ovoid-ellipsoid, laterally compressed or obtusely 3-sided, subunilocular, sub-bilocular, or semibilocular. **Seeds** 4–10.

Species ca. 47 (2 in the flora): North America, Europe, Asia.

Section *Oroboidei* occurs in northern and arctic Eurasia, montane central Asia, the Caucasus, and with two species in North America.

6. Astragalus eucosmus B. L. Robinson, Rhodora 10: 33. 1908 • Elegant milkvetch, astragale élégant

Phaca parviflora Nuttall in J. Torrey and A. Gray, Fl. N. Amer. 1: 348. 1838, not *Astragalus parviflorus* Lamarck 1783; *A. eucosmus* var. *facinorum* Fernald; *A. eucosmus* subsp. *sealei* (Lepage) Hultén

Plants slender, 10–75 cm, strigulose; from superficial or secondary subterranean caudex. **Stems** ascending to erect, strigulose. **Leaves** (2–)3–11 cm; stipules 3–9 mm, papery proximally, herbaceous distally; leaflets 9–15 (or 17), blades elliptic to lanceolate-elliptic or oblong, 1–22(–30) mm, apex obtuse, surfaces strigose abaxially, glabrous or glabrate adaxially. **Peduncles** erect or incurved-ascending, (3.5–)5–18 cm, surpassing subtending leaf. **Racemes** (5–)7–27-flowered; axis (1–)3.5–28 cm in fruit; bracts 1–3.5 mm; bracteoles 0(or 1). **Pedicels** 0.5–2 mm (0.8–3 mm in fruit). **Flowers** (4.1–)5.5–8 mm; calyx marcescent, 3.3–5.4 mm, strigulose to pilosulous, tube 2.5–3.5 mm, lobes narrowly lanceolate, 0.9–1.6 mm; corolla blue-purple, pale pink, or whitish; keel 4–5.7 mm. **Legumes** spreading or reflexed, dark when dry, usually somewhat decurved, subsymmetrically or obliquely ovoid-ellipsoid, laterally compressed, (4–)5–12(–13) × (2.3–)2.5–5.5 mm, subbilocular, firmly papery, base cuneate, apex shortly cuspidate, strigose-pilosulous; valves inflexed as hyaline septum (0.2–)0.4–1.2 mm wide; sessile or subsessile. **Seeds** 4–8. 2*n* = 16, 32.

Flowering late May–Aug. Arctic and alpine tundra, heathlands, thickets, woodlands, sandy or gravelly bars and terraces; 0–3300 m; Alta., B.C., Man., N.B., Nfld. and Labr., N.W.T., Nunavut, Ont., Que., Sask., Yukon; Alaska, Colo., Idaho, Maine, Mont., S.Dak., Wash., Wyo.; Asia (Russian Far East).

Astragalus eucosmus is decidedly closely related to *A. robbinsii*, and immature fruits are necessary for identification. It is also closely related to the Eurasian *A. norvegicus* Grauer and might be considered an element of that species (D. Isely 1998). Plants from the lowlands normally are erect and of moderate stature; at higher elevations and at northern latitudes, dwarfing occurs and racemes tend to be shorter and denser. A diploid chromosome number of 16 has been reported from the subsp. *sealei* variant of this species (G. F. Ledingham 1960).

7. Astragalus robbinsii (Oakes) A. Gray, Manual ed. 2, 98. 1856 • Robbins's milkvetch [E] [F]

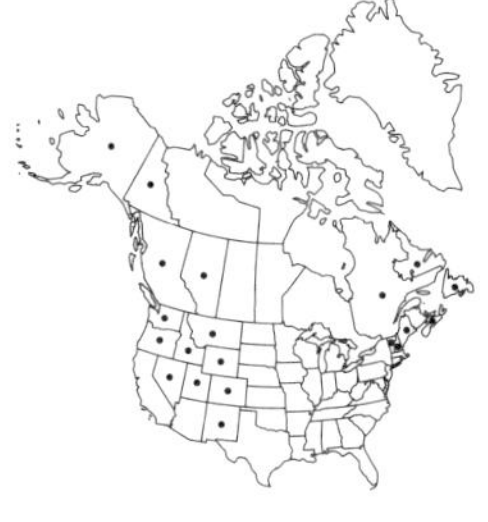

Phaca robbinsii Oakes, Mag. Hort. Bot. 7: 181. 1841

Plants clump-forming, slender to robust, 7–45(–60) cm, strigulose to pilose-villosulous; from superficial or somewhat subterranean caudex. **Stems** usually ascending, rarely decumbent, 0–2 cm underground, strigulose to pilose-villosulous. **Leaves** 2.5–12 cm; stipules 1.5–6 mm, papery at proximal nodes, herbaceous or submembranous at distal nodes; leaflets (5 or)7–17, blades lanceolate to oblong, (3–)5–30(–32) mm, apex obtuse or emarginate, surfaces usually strigulose, sometimes villous-pilosulous, cinereous, glabrate, or glabrous abaxially, glabrous, glabrescent, or sparsely strigose adaxially. **Peduncles** incurved-ascending or erect, 3.5–21(–23) cm, usually surpassing subtending leaf, together with racemes usually shorter than stems. **Racemes** (3–)5–25(–33)-flowered; axis 1–18 (–20) cm in fruit, elongating little after flowering, arising distal to middle of stem; bracts 1–3.5 mm; bracteoles usually 0. **Pedicels** 0.5–3 mm. **Flowers** (6–)7.2–11.5 mm; calyx 4–6.8 mm, strigulose, tube 3.2–4.5 mm, lobes subulate, 0.7–2.3 mm; corolla usually purple, pink-purple, pink, lilac, lavender, or whitish, sometimes whitish with maculate keel; wing apex obtuse; keel 5.4–7.9 mm, shorter than wings. **Legumes** pendulous, green or purplish, straight or slightly decurved, ellipsoid, obtusely 3-sided, faces slightly convex, flattened or depressed but not sulcate abaxially, 13–25 × 3.5–5.5 mm, subunilocular or semibilocular, papery-membranous, sparsely strigulose, hairs black or black and white; valves inflexed as hyaline septum 0.2–2 mm wide; stipe (0.5–)1.5–6.5 mm. **Seeds** 6–11.

Varieties 8 (8 in the flora): North America.

Astragalus robbinsii consists of a series of infraspecific taxa with two centers of dispersal in North America: Colorado to Alaska, and New England into eastern Canada. The distribution of three closely allied subordinate taxa within Vermont and New Hampshire is unmatched in the genus in North America. D. Isely (1998) questioned the taxonomic significance of the traditional varieties as recognized herein. The species is often confused in herbaria with *A. alpinus*, which has a keel longer than or as long as and wider than the wings (in *A. robbinsii* the keel is shorter than and little or no wider than the wings).

1. Leaflet blade surfaces abaxially densely gray or white villous-pilosulous, hairs 0.6–0.8 mm; legume stipes 1.2–3 mm, septae 1.2–2 mm wide; s coastal Alaska. . . . . 7g. *Astragalus robbinsii* var. *harringtonii*
1. Leaflet blade surfaces abaxially sparsely strigulose, cinereous, glabrous, or glabrate, hairs 0.2–0.6(–0.7) mm; legume stipes (0.5–)1.5–5(–6.5) mm, septae 0.2–1(–1.5) mm wide; not in s coastal Alaska.
   2. Legume stipes (1–)1.5–5(–6.5) mm; Alaska, New England, Nova Scotia, n Rocky Mountains.
      3. Stems 7–10 cm; racemes 5–11-flowered, axes 1–1.5 cm in fruit (barely elongated); legume stipes 5 mm; seeds 5 or 6; Mt. Roberts, near Juneau, Alaska . . . . 7h. *Astragalus robbinsii* var. *morganiae*
      3. Stems 10–40(–60) cm; racemes (5–)7–21-flowered, axes (1–)3–18(–20) cm in fruit; legume stipes (1–)1.5–5(–6.5) mm; seeds (6 or)7–11.
         4. Legumes 10–15 mm, sparsely strigulose, beaks to 1 mm; corollas whitish; Vermont historically . . . . 7a. *Astragalus robbinsii* var. *robbinsii*
         4. Legumes (10–)13–25 mm, sparsely or densely pubescent, beaks 0.8–3 mm; corollas pale purple, pink-purple, pink, or whitish and keel tip purple; widespread, including Vermont.
            5. Legumes sparsely strigose-pilosulous, beaks 0.8–1.5 mm; leaflet blade surfaces uniformly strigulose abaxially, or glabrate throughout; Alaska, Canada, w United States, Maine and Vermont . . . . 7b. *Astragalus robbinsii* var. *minor* (in part)
            5. Legumes sparsely strigulose, beaks 1.5–3 mm; leaflet blade surfaces cinereous abaxially, pubescent adaxially (margins sparsely pubescent); local along Connecticut River in Vermont and New Hampshire . . . . 7e. *Astragalus robbinsii* var. *jesupii*
   2. Legume stipes 0.5–3(–6.5) mm; coastal Labrador, adjoining Newfoundland, e Quebec to Alberta, northward to Northwest Territories, southward to New Mexico, including Maine and Vermont.
      6. Seeds 3–6; legumes 8–13 mm; Wallowa Mountains, ne Oregon . . . . 7d. *Astragalus robbinsii* var. *alpiniformis*
      6. Seeds (6 or)7–10; legumes (8–)10–25 mm; not Oregon.

[7. Shifted to left margin.—Ed.]

7. Raceme axis 1.2–6(–8) cm in fruit; leaflet blade surfaces sparsely pubescent along margins adaxially or strigulose throughout; s Labrador, adjoining Newfoundland, Quebec . . . . 7f. *Astragalus robbinsii* var. *fernaldii*
7. Raceme axis (2–)3–18(–20) cm in fruit; leaflet blade surfaces glabrous or glabrate adaxially; not s Labrador, adjoining Newfoundland, and Quebec.
   8. Legumes (10–)13–25 mm, stipes (1–)1.5–5(–6.5) mm; racemes (5–)7–25(–33)-flowered, axes (2–)3–18(–20) cm in fruit; proximal stipules distinct or obscurely connate; not ne Nevada . . . . 7b. *Astragalus robbinsii* var. *minor* (in part)
   8. Legumes (8–)10–15(–18) mm, stipes 0.5–1.4 mm; racemes remotely (3–)6–12-flowered, axes (2–)6–15 mm in fruit; proximal stipules connate 1/2 their length; East Humboldt and Ruby mountains, ne Nevada . . . . 7c. *Astragalus robbinsii* var. *occidentalis*

7a. Astragalus robbinsii (Oakes) A. Gray var. **robbinsii** E

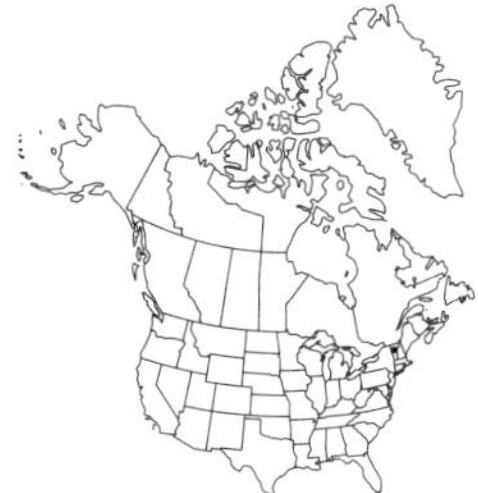

Stems ascending, (11–)15–27 cm. **Leaves** 3.5–8.5 cm; leaflets 7–13, blades 6–18 mm, surfaces strigulose abaxially, hairs scattered, to 0.3–0.4 mm. **Peduncles** (5–)7–15 cm. **Racemes** (6–)10–21-flowered; axis (1–)3–10(–14) cm in fruit. **Flowers** 8–8.5 mm; corolla whitish. **Legumes** flattened abaxially, compressed 3-sided, 10–15 × (3.5–)4–5 mm, beak to 1 mm, sparsely strigulose, hairs black; septum 0.3 mm wide; stipe (2–)3–3.5 mm. **Seeds** 7 or 8.

Flowering May–early Jun. Limestone ledges near and above water, with *Dasiphora fruticosa*; 150 m; Vt.

The only known location for var. *robbinsii*, the gorge of Winooski River near Burlington, was obliterated by a dam erected in 1894; the taxon is believed to be extinct. Variety *robbinsii* was once thought to be widely dispersed in New England, but such records are now understood to represent other varieties (R. C. Barneby 1964).

7b. Astragalus robbinsii (Oakes) A. Gray var. **minor** (Hooker) Barneby, Mem. New York Bot. Gard. 13: 125. 1964 • Lesser elegant milkvetch, astragale mineur [E] [F]

Phaca elegans Hooker var. *minor* Hooker, Fl. Bor.-Amer. 1: 144. 1831; *Astragalus blakei* Eggleston; *A. collieri* (Rydberg) A. E. Porsild; *A. macounii* Rydberg; *A. robbinsii* var. *blakei* (Eggleston) Barneby

Stems usually ascending, (10–) 15–40(–60) cm. **Leaves** 3–12 cm; proximal stipules distinct or obscurely connate; leaflets (7 or)9–13(or 15), blades (5–)7–25(–32) mm, surfaces uniformly strigulose abaxially or glabrate throughout, hairs subappressed or narrowly ascending-incumbent, to 0.2–0.6 mm. **Peduncles** (3.5–)4.5–16(–23) cm. **Racemes** (5–)7–25(–33)-flowered; axis (2–)3–18(–20) cm in fruit. **Flowers** (6–)7.2–11.5 mm; corolla pale purple, pink-purple, pink, or whitish (then keel apex purple). **Legumes** not remote, obtusely 3-sided, (10–)13–25 × 3.5–5.5 mm, beak 0.8–1.5 mm, sparsely strigulose-pilosulous, hairs black or black and white; septum 0.2–1(–1.5) mm wide; stipe (1–)1.5–5(–6.5) mm. **Seeds** (6 or)7–10.

Flowering Jun–Aug. Stream banks, meadows, thickets, moraines in humus or alluvial soils; 400–3700 m; Alta., B.C., Nfld. and Labr., N.S., Que., Yukon; Alaska, Colo., Idaho, Maine, Mont., N.Mex., Utah, Vt., Wash., Wyo.

R. C. Barneby (1964) considered var. *minor* of the Rocky Mountains and eastern Alaska and southern Yukon (but now with some collections known from northern British Columbia) to be central in the species, with the remaining varieties maintaining their identity through accidents of isolation. D. Isely (1998) suggested that the disrupted range of this variety resulted from fragmentation of a once more widely distributed complex, noting that similar patterns are shown by some other astragali (specifically *A. alpinus*).

7c. Astragalus robbinsii (Oakes) A. Gray var. **occidentalis** S. Watson, Botany (Fortieth Parallel), 70. 1871 • Western elegant milkvetch [E]

Stems usually ascending, (10–) 15–45 cm. **Leaves** 4–9.5 cm; proximal stipules connate ½ their length; leaflets (5 or)7–11, blades 8–30 mm, surfaces strigulose abaxially, hairs subappressed, to 0.2–0.5 mm. **Peduncles** (6–)8–21 cm. **Racemes** remotely (3–)6–12-flowered; axis (2–)6–15 cm in fruit. **Flowers** 7.5 mm; corolla lilac. **Legumes** flattened or obscurely depressed abaxially, (8–)10–15(–18) × (3–)4–5 mm, apex 0.8–1.2 mm, strigulose; septum 0.8–1.2 mm wide; stipe 0.5–1.4 mm. **Seeds** 8.

Flowering Jul–Aug. Banks of streams, moist soils of timbered creek beds; 1800–3100 m; Nev.

No single character distinguishes var. *occidentalis* from var. *minor*. In combination, the very slender growth-habit, few but ample leaflets, remotely few-flowered racemes, and usually small, short-stipitate or subsessile fruits distinguish the taxon. Variety *occidentalis* is a narrow endemic to the Humboldt and Ruby mountains of Elko County.

7d. Astragalus robbinsii (Oakes) A. Gray var. **alpiniformis** (Rydberg) Barneby in C. L. Hitchcock et al., Vasc. Pl. Pacif. N.W. 3: 258. 1961 • Wallowa elegant milkvetch [E]

Atelophragma alpiniforme Rydberg, Bull. Torrey Bot. Club 55: 129. 1928

Stems usually ascending, (10–) 15–45 cm. **Leaves** 4–9.5 cm; leaflets 9–17, blades (3–)5–12 mm, surfaces strigulose abaxially, hairs subappressed, to 0.2–0.5 mm. **Peduncles** (6–)8–21 cm. **Racemes** remotely (3–)6–12-flowered; axis (2–)6–15 cm in fruit. **Flowers** 7.5 mm; corolla lilac. **Legumes** flattened or obscurely depressed abaxially, 8–13 × 3.7–5 mm, cusp 0.7–2.2 mm, strigulose, hairs usually black, rarely all white; stipe 1.2–2 mm. **Seeds** 3–6.

Flowering Jun–Aug. Brushy stream banks, gravel bars, on granite; 1200–3500 m; Oreg.

7e. Astragalus robbinsii (Oakes) A. Gray var. **jesupii** Eggleston & E. Sheldon, Minnesota Bot. Stud. 1: 155. 1894 (as jesupi) • Jesup's milkvetch [C] [E]

Astragalus jesupii (Eggleston & E. Sheldon) Britton

Stems usually ascending, 10–30 cm. **Leaves** 3–8.5 cm; leaflets 9–15, blades (6–)8–20 (–25) mm, surfaces glabrous abaxially (sometimes with a few scattered hairs on margin and midrib), hairs to 0.4–0.6 mm. **Peduncles** (5–)7–16 cm. **Racemes** 8–21-flowered; axis (2.5–)4–13.5 cm in fruit. **Flowers** 9.7–11 mm; corolla pale purple. **Legumes** 14–21 × 3.5–5.5(–6) mm, beak cusplike, 1.5–3 mm, sparsely strigulose, hairs black; stipe 3.5–4.5(–5) mm. **Seeds** 9–11.

Flowering May–Jul. Moist crevices, just above high water, under shrubs; of conservation concern; 100–200 m; N.H., Vt.

D. Isely (1998) surmised the taxon to be extinct; it persists at three sites in a 25-kilometer stretch along the Connecticut River, with a total population of about 1000 plants.

Variety *jesupii* is in the Center for Plant Conservation's National Collection of Endangered Plants.

7f. Astragalus robbinsii (Oakes) A. Gray var. **fernaldii** (Rydberg) Barneby, Mem. New York Bot. Gard. 13: 131. 1964 • Fernald's elegant milkvetch, astragale de Fernald [C] [E]

Atelophragma fernaldii Rydberg, Bull. Torrey Bot. Club 55: 126. 1928; *Astragalus fernaldii* (Rydberg) H. F. Lewis

Stems decumbent or weakly ascending, 13–30 cm. **Leaves** 3.5–8 cm; leaflets 9–17, blades 7–22 mm, surfaces cinereous abaxially (sparsely pubescent along margins adaxially or strigulose), hairs subappressed to ascending, to 0.4–0.7 mm. **Peduncles** 4–10.5 cm. **Racemes** 7–20-flowered; axis 1.2–6(–8) cm in fruit. **Flowers** 9–10 mm; corolla purplish or grayish lilac. **Legumes** 10–18 × 4–5.5(–6) mm, densely or loosely strigose-pilosulous, hairs black, white, or mixed; septum 0.2–0.8 mm wide; stipe 1.2–3 mm. **Seeds** 8–10. $2n = 32$.

Flowering Jun–Aug. Limestone or calcareous sandstone terraces and bluffs, near coast; of conservation concern; 0–150 m; Nfld. and Labr., Que.

Morphological and molecular evidence indicates that this variety should be included within *Astragalus eucosmus* (P. C. Sokoloff 2010; Sokoloff and L. J. Gillespie 2012).

7g. Astragalus robbinsii (Oakes) A. Gray var. **harringtonii** (Rydberg) Barneby, Mem. New York Bot. Gard. 13: 132. 1964 • Harrington's milkvetch [E]

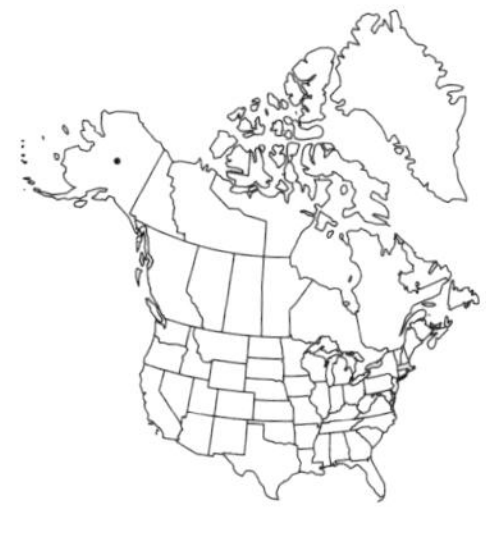

Atelophragma harringtonii Rydberg, Bull. Torrey Bot. Club 55: 126. 1928; *Astragalus harringtonii* (Rydberg) Hultén

Stems ascending, (10–)15–35 cm. **Leaves** 4–7.5(–10) cm; leaflets 9–15, blades 5–23 mm, surfaces densely gray or white villous-pilosulous abaxially, glabrous or sparsely strigulose adaxially, hairs fine, loosely spreading or ascending, 0.6–0.8 mm. **Peduncles** (3–)6.5–15 cm. **Racemes** densely 9–20-flowered; axis 1.5–5(–10) cm in fruit. **Flowers** 9.5–11.5 mm; corolla purplish or bluish lavender. **Legumes** 12–15 × 4–6 mm, densely villosulous, hairs black; septum 1.2–2 mm wide; stipe 1.2–3 mm. **Seeds** 6–8.

Flowering late May–Aug. Gravel bars and banks in alder, spruce, and birch woods; 10–400 m; Alaska.

Variety *harringtonii* occurs in southern coastal Alaska.

S. L. Welsh (1974) treated var. *harringtonii* at the specific level because of the degree of divergence expressed by this taxon relative to other variants within the species.

7h. Astragalus robbinsii (Oakes) A. Gray var. **morganiae** S. L. Welsh, N. Amer. Sp. Astragalus, 56, fig. 7h. 2007 • Maxine's milkvetch [E]

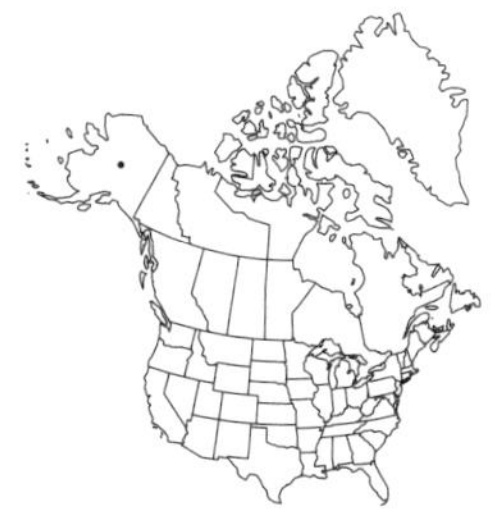

Stems ascending, 7–10 cm. **Leaves** 2.5–3.8 cm; leaflets 9 or 11, blades 8–11 mm, surfaces strigulose abaxially, hairs subappressed to ascending, to 0.6 mm. **Peduncles** 3.5–6 cm. **Racemes** barely elongating, 5–11-flowered; axis 1–1.5 cm in fruit. **Flowers** 7–9 mm; corolla pink-purple. **Legumes** 10–11 × 5–6 mm, densely villosulous, hairs black; septum 0.2–0.7 mm wide; stipe 5 mm. **Seeds** 5 or 6.

Flowering May–Aug. Alpine tundra; 1000–1100 m; Alaska.

The rationale for recognizing var. *morganiae*, which is found on Mt. Roberts near Gastineau Peak, Juneau, is to call attention to it, an entity at first considered a remote outlier of the distant var. *minor* that is more closely related to, but still distant from, var. *harringtonii*. Flowering measurements are based on scant material and are tentative.

135e. Astragalus Linnaeus sect. Hemiphragmium (W. D. J. Koch) Bunge, Mém. Acad. Imp. Sci. Saint Pétersbourg, Sér. 7, 11(16): 21. 1868

Phaca Linnaeus sect. *Hemiphragmium* W. D. J. Koch, Syn. Fl. Germ. Helv., 180. 1837

Herbs perennial, caulescent; caudex superficial or subterranean in talus. **Hairs** basifixed. **Stems** few to several. **Stipules** distinct or connate at proximal nodes. **Leaves** odd-pinnate, usually sessile, rarely petiolate; leaflets 5–19. **Racemes** loosely or subcompactly flowered, flowers ascending. **Calyx tubes** campanulate. **Corollas** whitish or cream, often suffused with lilac or purple-veined, keel apex maculate, banner recurved through 40–50°, wing apex unequally bilobed, keel apex blunt. **Legumes** persistent, stipitate, pendulous or spreading, asymmetrically ellipsoid, laterally compressed [inflated], usually bilocular or semibilocular. **Seeds** 8–16.

Species ca. 20 (1 in the flora): North America, Europe, Asia.

Section *Hemiphragmium* consists of about twenty species of alpine Europe, interior montane Asia, northward into arctic Siberia, and one species of arctic and temperate North America from Alaska to Quebec and southward into the western cordillera.

8. Astragalus australis (Linnaeus) Lamarck, Fl. Franç. 2: 637. 1779 • Subarctic milkvetch

Phaca australis Linnaeus, Mant. Pl. 1: 103. 1767

Plants (10–)20–40(–50) cm, from superficial caudex, silky-strigose, villous, or villous-tomentose, hairs basifixed. **Stems** ascending, decumbent, or sprawling, silky-strigose, villous, or villous-tomentose. **Leaves** (1–)2–7(–10) cm; stipules clasping with margins touching but distinct or shortly connate at proximal nodes, distinct at distal nodes, (1–)2–7(–11) mm, often veined, semileathery; leaflet blades linear, lanceolate, oblong, elliptic, or elliptic-oblanceolate, 3–33(–35) mm, apex acute, subacute, or obtuse, surfaces glabrous, glabrate, or pubescent. **Peduncles** usually erect, rarely humistrate in fruit, (2–)2.5–15 cm, equal to or longer than subtending leaf, together with racemes usually shorter than stems. **Racemes** densely or loosely 6–40-flowered; axis 1.5–15 cm in fruit, elongating little after flowering; bracts 1.2–5 mm; bracteoles 0. **Pedicels** 0.8–2.2 mm 1.2–3.5 mm in fruit. **Flowers** 7–13.8(–14.5) mm; calyx 3.7–6.4 mm, villous or strigulose, tube 2.4–5 mm, lobes subulate, (1–)1.1–4 mm; corolla white to purplish or creamy white; wing apex bidentate; keel (6.1–)6.7–9.6 mm, shorter than wings. **Legumes** green, often with red or purple, becoming stramineous, ± straight or slightly curved abaxially, convex adaxially, not sulcate, obliquely ellipsoid, semi-ellipsoid, or narrowly oblong, laterally compressed, 10–30 × 3–9(–11) mm, papery, translucent, usually glabrous, sometimes strigose, hyaline septum 0–0.6 mm wide; stipe 2.5–8[–10] mm. **Seeds** 8–16.

Varieties 5 (4 in the flora): w North America, Eurasia.

Astragalus australis is circumboreal and highly variable but with no intraspecific taxa recognized in a recent revision of Old World species (D. Podlech and S. Zarre 2013); Asiatic plants pass under several epithets (S. L. Welsh 2007). Differences among variants are in some instances part of a continuum; others are haphazard. The following key includes only the most conspicuous morphological variants and, even then, all specimens will not be included satisfactorily in one taxon or another.

1. Flowers (10.5–)11.5–13.8(–14.5) mm; calyces (4.7–)4.8–6.5 mm; wc, n Alaska, n Yukon . . . . 8b. *Astragalus australis* var. *lepagei*
1. Flowers 7.5–12.5 mm; calyces 4–8.4 mm; Yukon eastward to Quebec, southward to Nevada, New Mexico, and South Dakota.
    2. Leaves mostly petiolate, sometimes sessile distally; n, sw Yukon . . . . 8a. *Astragalus australis* var. *muriei*
    2. Leaves sessile or subsessile; British Columbia eastward to Quebec, southward to Nevada and New Mexico.
        3. Legumes 3–7(–9) mm wide, usually not, or not much, bladdery-inflated; peduncles (2–)6.5–15 cm; British Columbia eastward to Quebec, southward to Nevada and New Mexico . . . . 8c. *Astragalus australis* var. *glabriusculus*
        3. Legumes 7–9(–11) mm wide, bladdery-inflated; peduncles 3–6.5 cm; Olympic Mountains, Washington . . . . 8d. *Astragalus australis* var. *olympicus*

8a. Astragalus australis (Linnaeus) Lamarck var. **muriei** (Hultén) S. L. Welsh, Great Basin Naturalist 58: 47. 1998 • Yukon milkvetch [E]

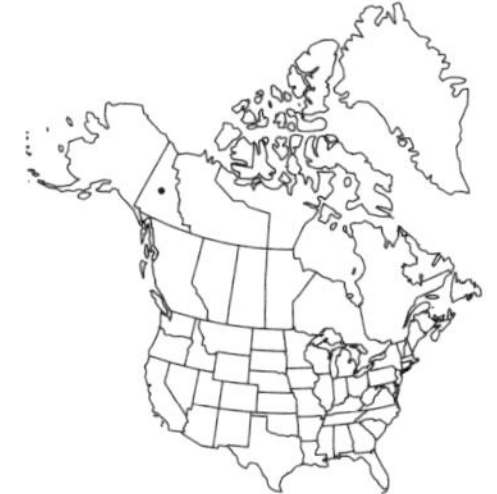

Astragalus aboriginorum Richardson var. *muriei* Hultén, Fl. Alaska Yukon 7: 1080. 1947; *A. linearis* (Rydberg) A. E. Porsild

Stems ascending, 7–35 cm. **Leaves** (2–)3–6.5 cm; mostly petiolate, sometimes sessile distally; leaflets (7 or)9–15, blades linear to narrowly elliptic, 6–15 mm, apex acute to obtuse, surfaces glabrous, strigulose-pilosulous, or villous. **Peduncles** 2.5–11 cm. **Racemes** densely to somewhat loosely (6–)8–21-flowered; axis 1.5–9.5 cm in fruit. **Flowers** 8.5–9.5 mm; calyx 4.2–5.5 mm, tube 2.4–2.7 mm, lobes 1.1–2.5 mm; corolla whitish to purplish. **Legumes** obliquely ellipsoid to narrowly oblong, 11–24 × 4–7 mm, glabrous or sometimes strigose; stipe 4–6 mm.

Flowering Jun–Jul. Mountain slopes, ridge crests, stream valleys, gravel bars, often with *Artemisia*; 600–1200 m; Yukon.

Absence of consistent diagnostic criteria appears to prohibit the complete distinction of var. *muriei* from var. *australis* of the southern Europe type locality for the species. Petiolate specimens occur throughout the range of var. *muriei*, with distal leaves less often sessile. The type of this variety has strigulose fruits, which are unusual in plants from the arctic but not of diagnostic value within the group.

8b. Astragalus australis (Linnaeus) Lamarck var. **lepagei** (Hultén) S. L. Welsh, Great Basin Naturalist 58: 47. 1998 • Lepage's milkvetch [E]

Astragalus lepagei Hultén, Fl. Alaska Yukon 10: 1761, fig. 4. 1950

Stems sprawling to ascending, (8–)24–40 cm. **Leaves** 3–9 cm; sessile or petiolate; leaflets (5–)9–15, blades elliptic to lanceolate, lanceolate-oblong, linear-lanceolate, or linear, 6–33 mm, apex acute to apiculate, surfaces glabrous, strigulose, pilosulous, or villous. **Peduncles** (4–)4.5–10 cm. **Racemes** densely to loosely 8–29(–32)-flowered; axis 3–14 cm in fruit. **Flowers** (10.5–)11.5–13.8(–14.5) mm; calyx (4.7–)4.8–6.5 mm, tube 2.8–5 mm, lobes (1–)1.4–2.4 mm. **Corollas** whitish to purplish. **Legumes** obliquely ellipsoid to narrowly oblong, (10–)15–30 × (3–)6–8.5 mm, glabrous; stipe (3–)5–7 mm.

Flowering Jun–Jul. Spits, gravel bars, slopes, ridge crests, in mixed tundra; 0–400 m; Yukon; Alaska.

8c. Astragalus australis (Linnaeus) Lamarck var. **glabriusculus** (Hooker) Isely, Iowa State J. Res. 59: 130. 1984 • Aboriginal milkvetch, astragale des aborigènes [E]

Phaca glabriuscula Hooker, Fl. Bor.-Amer. 1: 144. 1831; *Astragalus aboriginorum* Richardson; *A. forwoodii* S. Watson var. *wallowensis* (Rydberg) M. Peck; *A. richardsonii* E. Sheldon; *A. scrupulicola* Fernald & Weatherby

Stems ascending, 10–50 cm. **Leaves** 1–7(–10) cm; sessile; leaflets 5–19, blades linear to oblong, lanceolate, or elliptic, 3–27(–35) mm, apex acute to obtuse, surfaces glabrous, strigose, or villous. **Peduncles** (2–)6.5–15 cm. **Racemes** densely 6–40-flowered; axis 1.5–15 cm in fruit. **Flowers** 7–12.5 mm; calyx 4–7 mm, tube 3–4 mm, lobes 1.5–3 mm; corolla whitish to purplish. **Legumes** obliquely ellipsoid to narrowly oblong, seldom bladdery, 10–30 × 3–7(–9) mm, glabrous or sometimes strigose; stipe 2.5–8 mm. **Seeds** 8–16. 2*n* = 16.

Flowering May–Aug. Gravel bars, stony shores, talus, ridge crests, meadows; 20–3700 m; Alta., B.C., Man., N.W.T., Nunavut, Ont., Que., Sask., Yukon; Colo., Idaho, Mont., Nev., N.Mex., N.Dak., Oreg., S.Dak., Utah, Wyo.

R. C. Barneby (1964) provided an extensive and detailed overview of the variation within this variety (as *Astragalus aboriginorum*) and the taxonomy that was applied in an attempt to adequately classify the variation. To the north, distinction from var. *muriei* is debatable, but to the south, leaves are almost uniformly sessile. Still, along the cordillera are a great many morphological variants, some possibly worthy of taxonomic recognition.

8d. Astragalus australis (Linnaeus) Lamarck var. **olympicus** Isely, Syst. Bot. 8: 421. 1983 • Cotton's milkvetch [C] [E]

Astragalus olympicus J. S. Cotton, Bull. Torrey Bot. Club 29: 573. 1902, not Pallas 1800; *A. cottonii* M. E. Jones

Stems decumbent to ascending, 10–17 cm. **Leaves** (1.5–)2–5.5 cm; subsessile; leaflets 9–15 (or 17), blades linear-elliptic to elliptic-oblanceolate, 4–16 mm, apex acute to subacute, surfaces usually villosulous, sometimes glabrate adaxially. **Peduncles** 3–6.5 cm. **Racemes** densely 11–21-flowered; axis 2–6 cm in fruit. **Flowers** 10–12.2 mm; calyx 7–8.4 mm, tube 3.8–4.4 mm, lobes 3–4 mm; corolla creamy white. **Legumes**

semi-ellipsoid, bladdery-inflated, 20–25 × 7–9(–11) mm, glabrous; stipe 3–5 mm. **Seeds** 10–15. **2*n*** = 16.

Flowering Jun–Aug. Limestone ridge tops and talus; of conservation concern; 1300–1700 m; Wash.

Variety *olympicus* is geographically isolated in the Olympic Mountains in Clallam County and is the most distinctive variety within the *Astragalus australis* complex in North America, yet its inflated fruits approach those of populations of var. *lepagei*.

Astragalus australis var. *cottonii* (M. E. Jones) S. L. Welsh is a superfluous name that pertains here.

Variety *olympicus* is in the Center for Plant Conservation's National Collection of Endangered Plants.

135f. Astragalus Linnaeus sect. Nuculiella Gontscharow in V. L. Komarov, Fl. URSS 12: 876. 1946 [I]

Herbs perennial, caulescent; caudex subterranean. **Hairs** basifixed. **Stems** single or few to several. **Stipules** distinct. **Leaves** odd-pinnate, short-petiolate; leaflets 17–27. **Racemes** loosely flowered, flowers nodding. **Calyx tubes** campanulate. **Corollas** yellowish, banner abruptly recurved through 45°, keel much longer than wings and nearly equal to banner, keel apex obtuse to subacute. **Legumes** persistent, stipitate, pendulous, oblong-obovoid, turgid but not bladdery, obcompressed, bilocular. **Seeds** 12–14.

Species 1: introduced; Asia.

9. Astragalus chinensis Linnaeus f., Dec. Pl. Horti Upsal. 1: 5, plate 3. 1762 • Ma huang, China milkvetch [I]

Plants 30–60(–95) cm, coarse, strigulose. **Stems** erect or ascending, diffuse, strigulose. **Leaves** 7–15 cm; stipules 6–10 mm, herbaceous; leaflet blades oblong-elliptic to lanceolate, 14–30 mm, apex obtuse to apiculate, surfaces sparsely strigulose abaxially, glabrous adaxially. **Peduncles** erect, 2–6 cm. **Racemes** 7–15-flowered; axis 2–5 cm in fruit; bracts 2–4 mm; bracteoles 2. **Pedicels** 3–4 mm. **Flowers** 13–15 mm; calyx marcescent, 5–7 mm, glabrous, tube 3.5–5 mm, lobes broadly subulate, 1.5–2.5 mm; keel 13–15 mm. **Legumes** brownish, slightly convex, 10–15 × 6–10 mm, subligneous becoming transversely rugose, glabrous; stipe 6–8 mm.

Flowering Jun–Aug. Meadows, bottomlands, riverbanks; 1600–1700 m; introduced; Idaho, Okla.; Asia (China, Russian Far East).

Astragalus chinensis is locally naturalized in Idaho near Dubois, Clark County, and in Oklahoma in Payne County. A report from Saskatchewan was based on plants in cultivation.

The graduated cream-yellow petals and the long-stipitate, fleshy, but ultimately woody and rugulose, egg-shaped fruits distinguish *Astragalus chinensis* from all native astragali.

135g. Astragalus Linnaeus sect. Hemiphaca Karelin & Kirilov, Bull. Soc. Imp. Naturalistes Moscou 15: 329. 1842

Herbs perennial, caulescent; caudex superficial or shallowly buried. **Hairs** basifixed. **Stems** few to several. **Stipules** connate at proximal nodes, distinct at distal nodes. **Leaves** odd-pinnate, short-petiolate; leaflets 9–17. **Racemes** compactly flowered, flowers initially ascending then nodding. **Calyx tubes** campanulate. **Corollas** yellowish, keel purple-tipped, banner recurved through 30–45°, wing apex emarginate or bidentate, keel apex obtuse. **Legumes** deciduous, short gynophore present, erect-ascending, sessile, ovoid-ellipsoid, swollen but not bladdery, keeled ventrally, dorsally grooved, bilocular in proximal ½. **Seeds** 6–8.

Species 46 (1 in the flora): nw North America, Asia.

Plants mainly of montane, central Asia, and one in Alaska and upper Yukon River in Yukon.

Section *Hemiphaca* has been considered as synonymous with sect. *Oroboidei* (D. Podlech and S. Zarre 2013).

10. Astragalus williamsii Rydberg, Bull. New York Bot. Gard. 2: 175. 1901 • Williams's milkvetch [E]

Plants clump-forming, slender to robust, 40–70 cm, strigulose. **Stems** erect, with several elongated internodes, strigulose. **Leaves** 5–10 cm; stipules 7–11 mm, membranous or thinly herbaceous distally; leaflet blades linear, narrowly oblong, or elliptic, 18–34 mm, apex rounded to retuse, surfaces strigulose abaxially, glabrous adaxially. **Peduncles** stiffly erect, (3–)4–18(–20) cm, proximal peduncle and raceme much shorter than stem. **Racemes** (12–)16–30(–35)-flowered; axis 3–16 cm in fruit; bracts (1.5–)2.5–9 mm; bracteoles 0. **Pedicels** 1–2.4 mm, slightly longer in fruit. **Flowers** 12–15 mm; calyx 4.3–6.7 mm, black-strigose, tube 3.5–4.5(–4.8) mm, lobes linear-lanceolate, 1.5–2.5 mm; keel (7–)7.7–9.1 mm. **Legumes** brownish stramineous, (6–)9–15 × 3.5–6.5 mm, papery-membranous, minutely strigose; valves inflexed as hyaline septum 1.2–2.3 mm; gynophore 0.4–0.6 mm.

Flowering Jun–Jul. Gravelly or sandy soils with cottonwood and white spruce or aspen along stream courses, lakeshores, shale bluffs, woodlands; 500–1000 m; Yukon; Alaska.

Astragalus williamsii occurs in central and southern Alaska and southern Yukon Territory.

135h. Astragalus Linnaeus sect. Strigulosi M. E. Jones, Rev. N.-Amer. Astragalus, 184. 1923

Herbs perennial, caulescent; caudex superficial or shallowly buried. **Hairs** basifixed. **Stems** usually several to many. **Stipules** connate or distinct at distal nodes. **Leaves** odd-pinnate, subsessile to petiolate; leaflets (7 or)9–29[–41]. **Racemes** sometimes subumbellate, loosely or remotely flowered, flowers declined, sometimes initially ascending or spreading. **Calyx tubes** campanulate or turbinate-campanulate. **Corollas** whitish or ochroleucous, sometimes tinged lilac or lavender [purple], banner recurved through 45–100°, often equal to or shorter than wings, keel apex blunt, triangular, or slightly beaklike. **Legumes** persistent, stipitate or sessile, pendulous, broadly to narrowly oblong-ellipsoid or ellipsoid to clavate-ellipsoid, compressed dorsiventrally or ± 3-sided compressed, ± bilocular [unilocular]. **Seeds** 6–18.

Species 24 (5 in the flora): sw United States, Mexico, Central America.

Section *Strigulosi* includes two dozen species in temperate Mexico and extends into the southwestern United States, Guatemala, and Honduras. R. C. Barneby (1964) discussed putative relationships, noting that sect. *Strigulosi* seemed about equally close to sect. *Astragalus*, which is mostly Old World (but includes *A. alpinus* and *A. leptaleus* in the flora area), and is allied to other Old World groups with $x = 8$, and the New World sect. *Scytocarpi*, which has $x = 11$ or 12. At the time, no chromosome numbers in sect. *Strigulosi* were known. R. Spellenberg (1974) reported $2n = 22$ for some species in sect. *Strigulosi*, information that allies this section with the New World astragali.

11. Astragalus altus Wooton & Standley, Contr. U.S. Natl. Herb. 16: 136. 1913 • Tall milkvetch [C] [E]

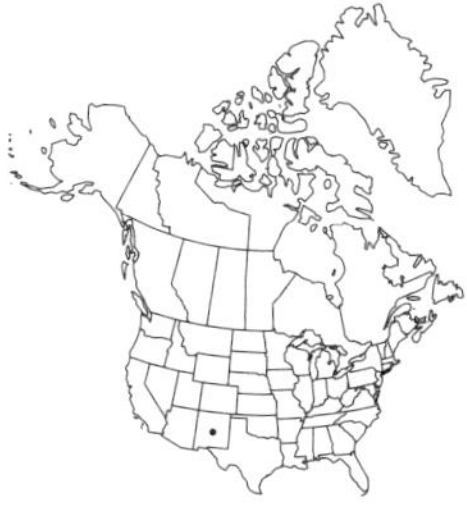

Plants slender, 30–60(–120) cm, strigulose; from superficial caudex or subterranean root-crown. **Stems** erect, stiffly ascending, or basally decumbent, 0–4 cm underground, strigulose. **Leaves** (2.5–)3.5–10(–12) cm; stipules connate at proximal nodes, distinct at distal nodes, 2.5–6 mm, submembranous becoming papery-scarious; leaflets (13 or)15–25, blades orbiculate, ovate, obovate, lanceolate-elliptic, or oblong-elliptic, (2–)3–12 mm, apex rounded to emarginate, surfaces pubescent abaxially, glabrous adaxially. **Peduncles** erect to ascending, 3.5–6(–10) cm, together with racemes usually shorter than stems. **Racemes** densely becoming loosely (15–)20–45-flowered; axis 2.5–6 cm in fruit; bracts 1.2–2.5 mm; bracteoles 0–2. **Pedicels** 1–1.3 mm, 1.2–1.5 mm in fruit. **Flowers** 9.6–10 mm; calyx marcescent, 4.5–5.1 mm, strigulose, hairs black, sometimes also white, tube 3.3–4 mm, lobes triangular-subulate, 0.8–1.3 mm; corolla ochroleucous, fading yellowish, keel immaculate; banner gently incurved through 45–50°; keel 6.4–7.6 mm. **Legumes** persisting and dehiscent on plant, slightly incurved, obliquely ellipsoid, laterally compressed and bluntly 3-sided, 10–15 × 4.5 mm, incompletely bilocular, thinly papery, strigulose; valves inflexed as hyaline septum 0.4 mm wide; stipe 5–6 mm. **Seeds** 6–10. **2*n*** = 22.

Flowering May–Sep. Openings on steep slopes and roadcuts, limestone soils, in ponderosa pine-oak, Douglas-fir, and spruce-fir-pinyon forests; of conservation concern; 1900–2700 m; N.Mex.

Most populations of *Astragalus altus* of the Sacramento Mountains seem to increase in disturbed areas, declining as succession proceeds.

12. Astragalus recurvus Greene, Bull. Calif. Acad. Sci. 1: 155. 1885 • Recurved milkvetch [E]

Plants slender, 10–28 cm, strigulose; from shallow, subterranean caudex. **Stems** decumbent, tips ascending, strigulose. **Leaves** (1.5–)3–7 cm; stipules connate at proximal nodes, connate to 1/2 their length at distal nodes, 1.5–4 mm, membranous becoming papery; leaflets 9–19, blades oblong-obovate, elliptic, or linear-oblong, 2–10 mm, apex obtuse or emarginate, surfaces pubescent abaxially, glabrate adaxially. **Peduncles** incurved-ascending, 3–10 cm. **Racemes** (5–)7–25-flowered; axis 1.5–9 cm in fruit; bracts 0.5–1.5 mm; bracteoles 0. **Pedicels** 0.5–1.5 mm. **Flowers** 5.2–7.7 mm; calyx marcescent, 3.5–4.7 mm, strigulose, hairs white, sometimes also black, tube 2–3.2 mm, lobes subulate, 1–1.6 mm; corolla whitish tinged with dull lilac; banner recurved through 65–90°; keel 5–6.5 mm. **Legumes** persisting and dehiscent on plant, green, sometimes also purple, becoming stramineous, strongly curved downward, linear-oblong or linear-ellipsoid, bluntly 3-sided compressed, 13–25 × 2.3–3 mm, incompletely bilocular, papery, finely strigulose; valves inflexed as nearly complete septum 0.7–1.5 mm wide; stipe 0–0.7 mm. **Seeds** 12–18. **2*n*** = 22.

Flowering Apr–early Jul. Open sites in ponderosa pine, mixed oak and pine or juniper communities, dry volcanic soils; 1400–2200 m; Ariz.

Without fruits, *Astragalus recurvus*, which is restricted to the Coconino Plateau, may be distinguished from *A. rusbyi*, also of basaltic soils of central Arizona, by the vigorous leaves with more numerous leaflets (9–19 versus 17–25) and later flowering period (April to early July versus mid June to September).

13. Astragalus rusbyi Greene, Bull. Calif. Acad. Sci. 1: 8. 1884 • Rusby's milkvetch [E]

Plants slender, 15–35(–40) cm, strigulose; from superficial caudex. **Stems** erect and incurved-ascending, strigulose. **Leaves** (2.5–)3–8 cm; stipules connate at proximal nodes, connate or distinct at distal nodes, 1.5–5.5 mm, papery-membranous; leaflets (11–)17–25, blades oval-oblong, oblanceolate, narrowly obovate, ovate, or narrowly oblong-elliptic, (3–)4–11 mm, apex obtuse, truncate, or retuse, surfaces strigulose abaxially, glabrous adaxially. **Peduncles** erect or incurved, (2–)4–11 cm, together with racemes usually shorter than stems. **Racemes** (10–)15–25(–30)-flowered; axis (2.5–)6–18 (–22) cm in fruit; bracts 1–2.5 mm; bracteoles 0. **Pedicels** 0.8–1.8 mm. **Flowers** 6.3–7.2 mm; calyx marcescent, 3.2–4.1 mm, strigulose, hairs white, black, or fuscous, tube 2.1–2.6 mm, lobes subulate or triangular-subulate, 1–1.6 mm; corolla whitish, sometimes tinged with lavender; banner abruptly incurved through 100°; keel 4.6–5.5 mm. **Legumes** stramineous, straight or nearly so, linear-oblong or ellipsoid, obscurely 3-sided compressed, 13–22 × 3.2–4.1 mm, incompletely bilocular, papery, black-strigulose; valves inflexed as nearly complete septum 0.8–1.5 mm wide; stipe 2.2–5 mm. **Seeds** 7–13. **2*n*** = 22.

Flowering mid Jun–Sep. Meadows in ponderosa pine forest, thickets or aspen groves, on basaltic substrates; 1600–2800 m; Ariz.

Astragalus rusbyi is restricted to the San Francisco Mountains and the vicinity of Oak Creek. It is similar to the geographically separate *A. egglestonii* and the northern Mexican *A. longissimus* (M. E. Jones) Barneby, to the point that D. Isely (1998) suggested that distinction at the species level is dubious. R. C. Barneby (1964) noted that intermediate populations do not exist.

An historical report of this species from New Mexico (E. O. Wooton and P. C. Standley 1915) may represent *Astragalus egglestonii.* The latter is a species that occurs in New Mexico but was not recognized as distinct until decades later.

14. Astragalus egglestonii (Rydberg) Kearney & Peebles, J. Wash. Acad. Sci. 29: 484. 1939 • Eggleston's milkvetch [E] [F]

Tium egglestonii Rydberg in N. L. Britton et al., N. Amer. Fl. 24: 396. 1929

Plants slender, stiff, (15–)20–55 cm, sparsely strigulose; from slightly subterranean caudex. **Stems** erect or ascending, sparsely strigulose. **Leaves** (3–)4–12 cm; stipules connate and scarious-papery at proximal nodes, distinct and herbaceous at distal nodes, 1.5–5 mm; leaflets (17–)21–29, blades flat or loosely folded, oblong-oblanceolate or elliptic, 3–13 mm, apex obtuse to subacute, surfaces sparsely strigulose abaxially, glabrate or glabrous adaxially. **Peduncles** (2–)4–11 cm. **Racemes** (5–)10–30-flowered; axis (1.5–) 3–19 cm in fruit; bracts 1–2 mm; bracteoles 2. **Pedicels** 0.6–1.5 mm. **Flowers** 5.8–8 mm; calyx marcescent, 3.4–4.3 mm, strigulose, hairs black and/or white, tube 2.1–2.7 mm, lobes subulate, 1–2 mm; corolla whitish or, sometimes, greenish ochroleucous, immaculate; banner abruptly incurved through 90°; keel 4.2–5.6 mm. **Legumes** stramineous, straight or slightly incurved or decurved, linear-oblong or linear-oblanceolate, 3-sided compressed, 15–30 × (2.5–)3–4 mm, bilocular, papery, glabrous; valves inflexed as complete septum 1.4–1.9 mm wide; stipe 1.5–2.5 mm. **Seeds** 12–16.

Flowering Jul–Sep(–Oct). Meadows and open pine woods, on basaltic or granitic soils; 1900–2700 m; Ariz., N.Mex.

Astragalus egglestonii is restricted to extreme east-central and northeastern Arizona and west-central New Mexico.

Astragalus egglestonii is the only late-flowering species of the genus in its region with declined, three-sided fruits (R. C. Barneby 1964).

15. Astragalus cobrensis A. Gray, Smithsonian Contr. Knowl. 5(6): 43. 1853 • Copper mine milkvetch

Plants slender, (4–)6–20(–25) cm, strigulose or pilosulous; from subterranean caudex. **Stems** decumbent to ascending, 1.5–10 (–18) cm underground, strigulose or pilosulous. **Leaves** 1.5–8(–11) cm; stipules connate at proximal nodes, sometimes connate to 1/2 their length at distal nodes, 1.5–5 mm, papery at proximal nodes to thinly herbaceous at distal nodes; leaflets (7–)11–19(–23), blades broadly obovate, obovate-cuneate, broadly oblong-elliptic, or suborbiculate, (1.5–)3–12(–17) mm, apex retuse, surfaces sparsely strigulose or pilosulous abaxially, glabrous, glabrate, or strigulose adaxially. **Peduncles** incurved-ascending, (1–)1.5–8.5 cm, equal to or shorter than subtending leaf. **Racemes** (4–)8–22 (–33)-flowered; axis (1–)2–6(–7.5) cm in fruit; bracts 1–2.2 mm; bracteoles 0. **Pedicels** 1–2 mm. **Flowers** 6.5–7.8 mm; calyx campanulate or turbinate-campanulate, 3.2–4.5 mm, strigulose, hairs black, white, or fuscous, tube 2.2–2.7 mm, lobes subulate, 1–1.8 mm; corolla whitish tinged with dull lilac; banner recurved through 85°; keel 4.4–6 mm. **Legumes** stramineous, straight or slightly arched downward, oblong or clavate-ellipsoid, obcompressed, (7–)9–15 × 3–6 mm, ± bilocular, papery, strigulose or villosulous; valves inflexed as partial or nearly complete septum 0.8–1.3 mm wide; stipe obscure. **Seeds** 10–13.

Varieties 2 (2 in the flora): sw United States, nw Mexico.

1. Herbage mostly sparsely strigulose, hairs appressed, fine, usually to 0.3–0.5(–0.6) mm, rarely a few longer; leaflet blades glabrous or glabrate adaxially; legumes strigulose; plants not of Chiricahua or Peloncillo mountains . . . . 15a. *Astragalus cobrensis* var. *cobrensis*
1. Herbage pilosulous, hairs spreading and incurved-ascending, somewhat stiff, to 0.6–0.8 mm; leaflet blades strigulose adaxially; legumes white-villosulous; plants of Chiricahua Mountains, Cochise County, Arizona, and Peloncillo Mountains, Hidalgo County, New Mexico. . . . . 15b. *Astragalus cobrensis* var. *maguirei*

15a. Astragalus cobrensis A. Gray var. **cobrensis** [E]

Herbage mostly sparsely strigulose, hairs appressed, fine, usually to 0.3–0.5(–0.6) mm, rarely a few longer. **Leaflets:** blade adaxial surface glabrous or glabrate. **Legumes** strigulose. $2n = 22$.

Flowering mid Mar–May. Dry sandy or gravelly hillsides, with walnut or oak in ponderosa pine forests; 1600–2400 m; Ariz., N.Mex.

Variety *cobrensis* occurs mainly within the drainage basin of the Gila River in southeastern Arizona and southwestern New Mexico, barely extending into the drainage of the Rio Grande in the Black Range.

15b. Astragalus cobrensis A. Gray var. **maguirei** Kearney, J. Wash. Acad. Sci. 30: 218. 1940 • Maguire's milkvetch [C]

Herbage pilosulous, hairs spreading and incurved-ascending, somewhat stiff, to 0.6–0.8 mm. **Leaflets:** blade adaxial surface strigulose. **Legumes** white-villosulous. **2*n*** = 22.

Flowering Apr–May. Sandy or gravelly, dry creekbeds, canyon sides, open slopes, pine-oak-juniper woodlands; of conservation concern; 1600–2200 m; Ariz., N.Mex.; Mexico (Sonora).

Of the two varieties, var. *maguirei* is the more southern, occurring in the Chiricahua Mountains of southeastern Arizona and the Peloncillo Mountains of southwestern New Mexico.

135i. Astragalus Linnaeus sect. Tiopsidei Barneby, Mem. New York Bot. Gard. 13: 196. 1964 [E]

Herbs perennial, caulescent; caudex subterranean. **Hairs** basifixed. **Stems** several to many. **Stipules** connate at proximal nodes. **Leaves** odd-pinnate, short-petiolate proximally, subsessile distally; leaflets (13 or)15–29(–35). **Racemes** densely flowered, flowers nodding and retrorsely imbricate. **Calyx tubes** subcylindric. **Corollas** ochroleucous, banner recurved through 45°, keel apex obtuse. **Legumes** persistent, stipitate, pendulous, oblong, narrowly elongate, 3-sided compressed, bilocular. **Seeds** 18–25.

Species 1: w United States.

Section *Tiopsidei* occurs in the mountains of Colorado, New Mexico, eastern Arizona, and eastern to north-central Utah.

16. Astragalus scopulorum Porter in T. C. Porter and J. M. Coulter, Syn. Fl. Colorado, 24. 1874 • Rocky Mountain milkvetch [E]

Plants 15–48 cm, strigulose. **Stems** decumbent to ascending, 3–13 cm underground, strigulose. **Leaves** 1.5–8.5 cm; stipules connate-sheathing and stiff-papery at proximal nodes, connate or distinct at distal nodes, 3–9 mm; leaflet blades oblong to elliptic or oblanceolate, some narrowly so, 2–19 mm, apex acute to obtuse or mucronate, surfaces sparsely strigose or glabrous abaxially, glabrous adaxially. **Peduncles** erect or incurved-ascending, 2–14 cm, shorter or much longer than leaves. **Racemes** 4–22-flowered; axis 1–7 cm in fruit; bracts 1.5–7 mm; bracteoles 0–2. **Pedicels** 1–4 mm. **Flowers** 18–24 mm; calyx 9–11.5(–14) mm, strigulose, tube 6.5–8.5 mm, lobes subulate, 1.5–4(–6) mm; corolla concolorous or keel faintly purplish; keel 13.6–15.4 mm. **Legumes** green, sometimes also purple, becoming brown, incurved to nearly straight, sulcate abaxially, 18–35 × 3–6.5 mm, papery, glabrous; valves inflexed as complete septum 2–4 mm wide; stipe 4–9 mm. **2*n*** = 22.

Flowering May–Aug. Mountain brush, sagebrush, ponderosa pine, pinyon-juniper, and aspen-white fir communities, roadsides, railroads; 1600–3300 m; Ariz., Colo., N.Mex., Utah.

In Utah, disturbance apparently has facilitated the spread of *Astragalus scopulorum* onto roadcuts, mid-elevation sheep-grazing areas, and along railroads.

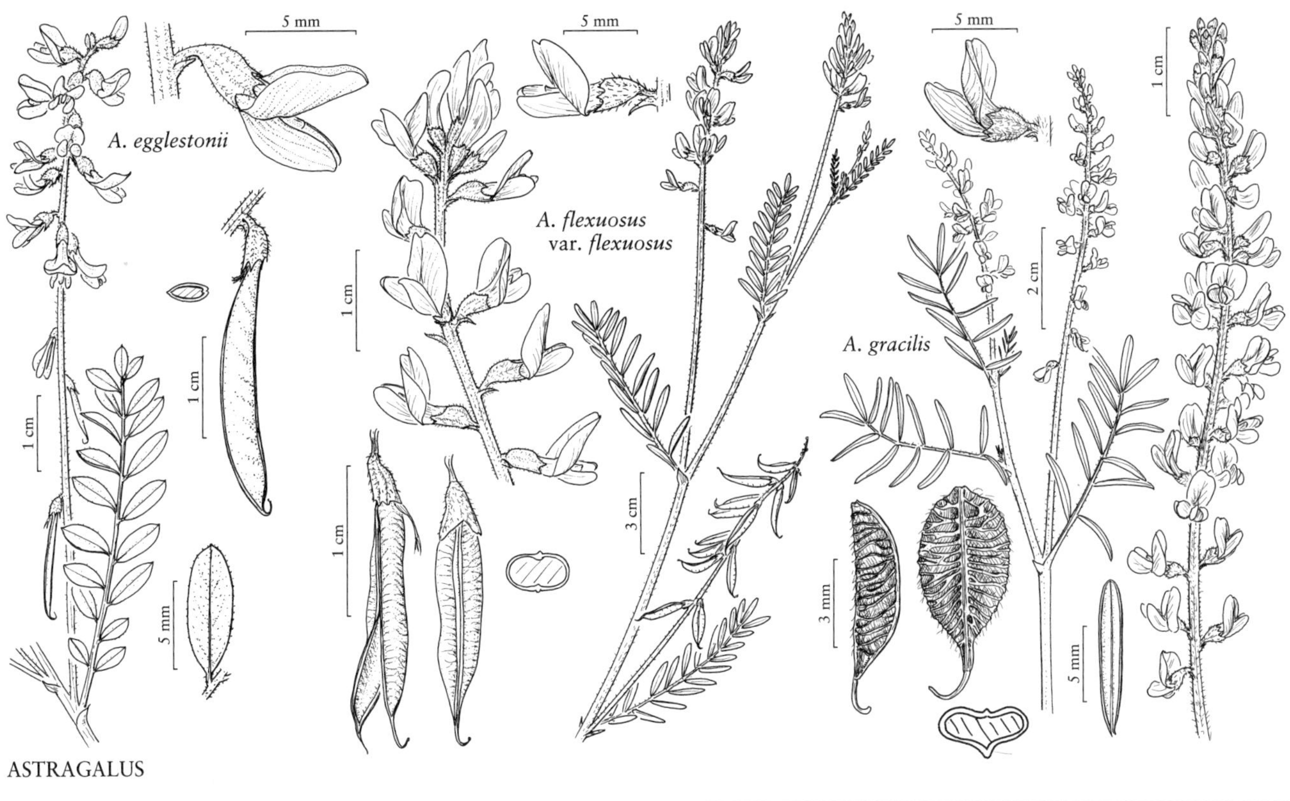

ASTRAGALUS

135j. Astragalus Linnaeus sect. Scytocarpi A. Gray, Proc. Amer. Acad. Arts 6: 222. 1864

Herbs perennial, caulescent; caudex subterranean. **Hairs** basifixed. **Stems** single or few to many. **Stipules** connate at proximal nodes, distinct ± distally. **Leaves** odd-pinnate, subsessile to petiolate; leaflets (3–)7–25(–31), sometimes decurrent. **Racemes** loosely flowered, flowers ascending, spreading, or declined. **Calyx tubes** shallowly to deeply campanulate or subcylindric. **Corollas** purple to pink or pink-purple, purplish, ochroleucous, yellowish, or whitish, banner recurved through 45–90°, keel apex obtuse or acute-triangular. **Legumes** persistent, sessile or subsessile to stipitate, spreading to declined, deflexed, or pendulous, oblong, ellipsoid, subglobose, or cylindroid, sometimes bladdery-inflated, 3-sided, subterete, or compression lateral or dorsiventral, unilocular. **Seeds** 4–36.

Species 14 (13 in the flora): c, w North America, Mexico.

In the flora area, sect. *Scytocarpi* consists of 13 species in six subsections found on the Great Plains, Rocky Mountains, and Colorado Basin, southward through Arizona, New Mexico, trans-Pecos Texas, and northeastern Mexico; one other subsection is found only in northeastern Mexico.

The subsections are: subsect. *Scytocarpi* (A. Gray) Barneby (*Astragalus flexuosus*, *A. fucatus*, *A. pictiformis*, *A. proximus*, and *A. subcinereus*); subsect. *Wingatani* Barneby (*A. cliffordii* and *A. wingatanus*); subsect. *Microlobi* (A. Gray) Barneby (*A. gracilis*); subsect. *Microcymbi* S. L. Welsh (*A. microcymbus*); subsect. *Halliani* (Rydberg) Barneby (*A. castetteri*, *A. hallii*, and *A. puniceus)*; subsect. *Shevockiani* Barneby (*A. shevockii*); and subsect. *Antonini* Barneby (*A. coriaceus* Hemsley), which is confined to Mexico.

17. Astragalus flexuosus (Hooker) Douglas ex G. Don, Gen. Hist. 2: 256. 1832 • Bent milkvetch [E] [F]

Phaca flexuosa Hooker, Fl. Bor.-Amer. 1: 141. 1831

Plants slender, 10–60 cm, strigulose to villosulous, canescent, or cinereous; from branched, subterranean caudex. **Stems** decumbent or ascending, 15–60 (–70) cm, 1–20+ cm underground, silky-canescent, hairs appressed, incurved-ascending or curly. **Leaves** 1.5–9 cm; stipules connate-sheathing and papery at proximal nodes, connate or distinct and herbaceous at distal nodes, 1–7 mm; leaflets (7 or)9–25(–29), blades linear, linear-oblong, oblong-oblanceolate, or obovate-cuneate, (2–)3–19 mm, apex obtuse to truncate or retuse, surfaces strigose to glabrate abaxially, usually glabrous adaxially. **Peduncles** incurved-ascending, divaricate, or erect, 1.5–19 cm, together with racemes usually shorter than stems. **Racemes** (7–)10–26(–30)-flowered, flowers spreading; axis (1–)2.5–13(–15) cm in fruit, elongating after flowering; bracts 0.6–4.5 mm; bracteoles 0–2. **Pedicels** 0.7–3.5 mm. **Flowers** 7–11 mm; calyx campanulate, 3.3–6 mm, strigose, tube 1.9–4.3 mm, lobes subulate, 0.5–2 mm; corolla pink-purple to dull purplish; keel 5–8.2 mm. **Legumes** descending to spreading, green or mottled becoming stramineous or brownish, straight or slightly incurved, linear-oblong, linear-oblanceoloid, oblong-ellipsoid, lanceoloid-ellipsoid, or ovoid-ellipsoid, subterete or ± flattened, (8–)11–24 × 2.7–9 mm, thinly to stiffly papery, usually strigulose or villosulous, rarely glabrous; stipe 0–1.3 mm. **Seeds** 12–25.

Varieties 3 (3 in the flora): North America.

D. Isely (1998) summarized the problems surrounding the epithet for *Astragalus flexuosus*, but it was retained by him, as it is herein, for nomenclatural consistency.

1. Calyces 3.3–4.1 mm; banners abruptly recurved through 90°; keel 5–5.5 mm, semiorbiculate, very strongly incurved through 120°; legumes 11–15 (–20) × 3–4(–4.5) mm; elevation 1300–2100 m . . . . 17c. *Astragalus flexuosus* var. *diehlii*
1. Calyces 3.5–6 mm; banners recurved through 45–50°; keel 5.3–8.2 mm, semiobovate, incurved through 90–100°; legumes (8–)12–24 × 2.7–9 mm; elevation 200–2900 m.
    2. Legume stipes 0.5–1.3 mm, body scarcely turgid, 2.7–4.8 mm wide, base usually cuneate-tapered. . . . . 17a. *Astragalus flexuosus* var. *flexuosus*
    2. Legume stipes 0–0.5 mm, body turgid or inflated, (4–)5–9 mm wide, base rounded (when less than 5 mm wide). . . . . 17b. *Astragalus flexuosus* var. *greenei*

17a. Astragalus flexuosus (Hooker) Douglas ex G. Don var. **flexuosus** [E] [F]

Astragalus flexuosus var. *elongatus* (Hooker) M. E. Jones

Herbage greenish or silky-canescent. **Stems** ± flexuous, 15–60(–70) cm. **Leaflets** 11–25 (–29), blades mostly linear or narrowly oblong-oblanceolate, 6–11 mm. **Peduncles** 4–19 cm. **Racemes** (7–)12–26(–30)-flowered; axis 3–13(–15) cm in fruit. **Flowers** 7.4–11 mm; calyx 3.5–5.8 mm, tube 2.7–4.3 mm, lobes 0.5–1.7 mm; corolla banner recurved through 45–50°; keel incurved through 90–100°, semiobovate, 5.3–7.5 mm. **Legumes** linear-oblong, linear-oblanceoloid, or narrowly oblong-elliptic in outline, scarcely turgid, (8–)12–24 × 2.7–4.8 mm, base usually cuneate-tapered, usually finely strigulose or villosulous, rarely glabrous; stipe 0.5–1.3 mm, concealed by marcescent calyx. **Seeds** 14–20. $2n = 22$.

Flowering May–Aug. Pinyon-juniper, sagebrush-oak, ponderosa pine, mountain brush, mesic prairies; 200–2900 m; Alta., B.C., Man., Ont., Sask.; Colo., Iowa, Minn., Mont., Nebr., N.Mex., N.Dak., S.Dak., Utah, Wyo.

17b. Astragalus flexuosus (Hooker) Douglas ex G. Don var. **greenei** (A. Gray) Barneby, Leafl. W. Bot. 9: 91. 1960 • Greene's milkvetch [E]

Astragalus greenei A. Gray, Proc. Amer. Acad. Arts 16: 105. 1881

Herbage greenish cinereous. **Stems** 15–40 cm. **Leaflets** (9–) 13–23, blades linear-oblong to obovate-cuneate. **Peduncles** 1.5–13.5 cm. **Racemes** (7–)10–30-flowered; axis (1–)2.5–10 cm in fruit. **Flowers** 9–10.8 mm; calyx 3.5–6 mm, tube 2.8–4.2 mm, lobes 0.8–2 mm; corolla banner recurved through 45–50°; keel incurved through 90–100°, semiobovate, 7–8.2 mm. **Legumes** lanceoloid-ellipsoid to plumply ellipsoid, oblong-ellipsoid, or ovoid-ellipsoid, turgid or inflated, (12–)14–23 × (4–)5–9 mm, base rounded when less than 5 mm wide, strigulose or villosulous; stipe 0–0.5 mm. **Seeds** 16–25. $2n = 22$.

Flowering Apr–Jun. Badlands, other semibarrens with pinyon-juniper or oak; 1300–2600 m; Ariz., N.Mex.

Variety *greenei* closely resembles var. *diehlii* and, except for a small geographical disjunction, they easily could be combined.

17c. Astragalus flexuosus (Hooker) Douglas ex G. Don var. **diehlii** (M. E. Jones) Barneby, Leafl. W. Bot. 4: 54. 1944 • Diehl's milkvetch [E]

Astragalus diehlii M. E. Jones, Rev. N.-Amer. Astragalus, 194. 1923

Herbage greenish cinereous. **Stems** usually obviously flexuous, 15–30(–40) cm. **Leaflets** (7–) 11–17, blades mostly linear or narrowly oblong-oblanceolate. **Peduncles** 2.5–7 cm. **Racemes** 12–26-flowered; axis 2.5–9.5 cm in fruit. **Flowers** 7–9 mm; calyx 3.3–4.1 mm, tube 1.9–2.3 mm, lobes 0.7–1.1(–1.4) mm; corolla banner abruptly recurved through 90°; keel very strongly incurved through 120°, semiorbiculate, 5–5.5 mm. **Legumes** oblong-ellipsoid, turgid or inflated, 11–15 (–20) × 3–4(–4.5) mm, strigulose; sessile. **Seeds** 12–18.

Flowering late Apr–Jun. Salt desert shrub and pinyon-juniper communities, on fine-textured substrates; 1300–2100 m; Ariz., Colo., N.Mex., Utah.

18. Astragalus pictiformis Barneby, Leafl. W. Bot. 8: 20. 1956 • Guadalupe milkvetch [E]

Plants slender, 10–60 cm, strigulose-villosulous; from shallow to deep subterranean caudex, branches rhizomatous. **Stems** (2–)3.5–40 cm underground, strigulose-villosulous. **Leaves** (1–)1.5–5.5 cm; stipules connate-sheathing and papery-membranous at proximal nodes, distinct and subherbaceous at distal nodes, 1.5–5 (–6.5) mm; leaflets 9–17, blades oblong-obovate to oblanceolate or orbiculate, 2–8(–10) mm, apex obtuse to retuse, surfaces strigulose-villosulous. **Peduncles** weakly ascending becoming declined, (1–)1.5–5(–6.5) cm. **Racemes** 4–14-flowered, flowers ascending; axis 0.5–2.5 cm in fruit; bracts 1.3–2.7 mm; bracteoles usually 2. **Pedicels** 0.8–1.4 mm. **Flowers** (8.5–)9–11 mm; calyx campanulate, 4–6.3 mm, strigulose-villosulous, tube 3–4 mm, lobes subulate, 1–2.5 mm; corolla flesh-pink; banner recurved through 50°; keel 7–8.9 mm. **Legumes** deflexed, green or purplish becoming brownish, straight or slightly decurved, cylindroid-ellipsoid, obscurely and obtusely 3-sided compressed, 9–17 × 4–6 mm, stiffly papery, strigulose; subsessile. **Seeds** (10–)14–18. $2n$ = 22, 44.

Flowering Apr–Jun. Sandy and gravelly soils on granite, sandstone, and limestone, with juniper, scrub-oak, and arid grasslands; 1400–2200 m; N.Mex., Tex.

The pale flowers and grayish foliage of *Astragalus pictiformis* make it inconspicuous in the arid grasslands and grayish soil of central and south-central New Mexico and western trans-Pecos Texas, where it is rather frequent. The species is reported to be tetraploid (x = 22) (R. Spellenberg 1976), a condition that apparently is rare in New World astragali. Two of the three known *Astragalus* tetraploids in the New World are rhizomatous (*A. pictiformis* and the unrelated *A. layneae*), a condition that is often associated with polyploidy in other plant groups (G. L. Stebbins 1971).

19. Astragalus proximus (Rydberg) Wooton & Standley, Contr. U.S. Natl. Herb. 19: 366. 1915 • Aztec milkvetch [E]

Homalobus proximus Rydberg, Bull. Torrey Bot. Club 32: 667. 1906

Plants slender, 15–45 cm, sparsely strigulose; from branched, subterranean caudex. **Stems** erect or ascending, 1–8 cm underground, often branched proximally, sparsely strigulose. **Leaves** 2–8 cm; stipules connate-sheathing and papery-membranous at proximal nodes, connate to 1/2 their length or distinct at distal nodes, 1.5–4.5 mm; leaflets 7–11, blades linear, linear-oblanceolate, or filiform to narrowly oblong, 6–22 mm, apex obtuse, surfaces strigulose abaxially, glabrous adaxially. **Peduncles** ascending, 3–11 cm, together with racemes usually shorter than stems. **Racemes** (7–)12–40-flowered, flowers spreading; axis 4–17 cm in fruit; bracts 0.6–1.5 mm; bracteoles 0. **Pedicels** 0.5–1.8 mm. **Flowers** 6–7 mm; calyx campanulate, 2.5–3.5 mm, strigulose, tube 1.8–2.5 mm, lobes subulate or deltate, 0.6–1.5 mm; corolla whitish, banner and keel apex lilac-tinged; banner recurved through 45–50°; keel 4.2–5.3 mm. **Legumes** pendulous, stramineous, ± straight, linear-ellipsoid, obcompressed, 10–15 × 2.3–3.2 mm, papery, glabrous; stipe (1–)1.2–2 mm. **Seeds** 6–10. $2n$ = 22.

Flowering late Apr–Jul. Sandy, often saline substrates derived from sandstone, among junipers or sagebrush; 1600–2300 m; Colo., N.Mex.

Astragalus proximus occurs only in northwestern New Mexico and barely into adjacent Colorado.

20. Astragalus fucatus Barneby, Leafl. W. Bot. 9: 89. 1960 • Hopi milkvetch [E]

Plants short-lived perennial, sometimes flowering first year, coarse, 7–45(–70) cm, strigulose; from subterranean or superficial caudex. **Stems** ascending to erect or sprawling, flexuous, (0–)1–8 cm underground, leafless, strigulose, hairs appressed. **Leaves** 2–13 cm; stipules connate-sheathing and papery at proximal nodes, distinct or obscurely connate subherbaceous or firmly papery at distal nodes, 1–5.5 mm; leaflets 9–17, blades oblanceolate to linear, 3–20(–25) mm, apex obtuse to retuse, surfaces strigose abaxially, glabrous adaxially. **Peduncles** 1–6.5 cm. **Racemes** 9–27-flowered, flowers ascending to declined; axis 2–11.5 cm in fruit; bracts 0.8–2 mm; bracteoles 0. **Pedicels** 0.7–3.5 mm. **Flowers** 6.4–8.7 mm; calyx campanulate, 3.3–5.4 mm, strigose, tube 2.3–3.3 mm, lobes broadly subulate or triangular, 0.8–2.2 mm; corolla pink-purple; banner recurved through 90°; keel 6–7.2 mm, apex triangular and beaklike. **Legumes** spreading to declined, purple-mottled, straight, ovoid, ellipsoid, or subglobose, bladdery-inflated, 17–32 × 12–22 mm, papery, strigose; sessile. **Seeds** 21–32. **2*n*** = 22.

Flowering May–Jul(–Sep). Mixed sandy desert shrub, resinbush, blackbrush, and juniper communities, usually on sand; 1300–1900 m; Ariz., Colo., N.Mex., Utah.

The inflated, purple-mottled legumes of *Astragalus fucatus* tend to be humistrate or, being pendulous, hang just above the ground like a string of small balloons. Burial of the caudex might be an artifact of the sandy habitats where this species grows. Occasional individuals have legumes greatly elongated and coiled into a complete circle.

21. Astragalus subcinereus A. Gray, Proc. Amer. Acad. Arts 13: 366. 1878 • Kaibab Plateau milkvetch [E]

Plants strongly caulescent, 14–90 cm, villosulous or hirsutulous; from deeply subterranean, branched caudex. **Stems** prostrate to weakly ascending, often flexuous, (1–)2–10(–15) cm underground, strigulose-villosulous or hirsutulous, hairs stiff, straight, spreading or subretrorse. **Leaves** 1.5–8.5 cm; stipules connate-sheathing and papery at proximal nodes, obscurely connate or distinct and herbaceous or foliaceous at distal nodes, 1.5–6.5 mm; leaflets 9–23, blades oblong to oblanceolate or obovate, 2–16 mm, apex obtuse, emarginate, or retuse, surfaces villosulous abaxially, villosulous or glabrate adaxially. **Peduncles** incurved-ascending or divaricate, 1.5–10 cm. **Racemes** 5–37-flowered, flowers ascending to declined; axis 1–7 cm in fruit; bracts 1–3 mm; bracteoles 0 or 1. **Pedicels** 0.5–2.5 mm. **Flowers** 6–11 mm; calyx campanulate, 3.4–6.3 mm, villosulous, tube 2.3–3.6 mm, lobes subulate, 0.9–2.9 mm; corolla ochroleucous, fading yellowish, and usually suffused with purple; banner recurved through 45°; keel (5.7–)6–7.7 mm, apex broadly deltate. **Legumes** spreading to declined, green or purplish, brightly red-mottled, straight, ovoid, ovoid-ellipsoid, ellipsoid, or cylindroid-ellipsoid, bladdery-inflated or turgid, subterete to dorsiventrally compressed, 12–27 × 3.5–13 mm, papery or papery-membranous, sparsely villosulous; stipe 0.3–1 mm. **Seeds** 10–20.

Varieties 3 (3 in the flora): w United States.

1. Legumes ellipsoid to cylindroid-ellipsoid, 3.5–6 (–7) mm wide; flowers 8.5–11 mm; stems 40–90 cm; plants of igneous gravel, c Utah . . . . 21c. *Astragalus subcinereus* var. *basalticus*
1. Legumes ovoid or ovoid-ellipsoid, (5–)6–13 mm wide; flowers 5–9 mm; stems 14–60 cm; plants of sedimentary gravel, shale, and clay, but sometimes from igneous substrates, n Arizona, se Nevada, s Utah.
   2. Legumes ovoid or ovoid-ellipsoid, bladdery-inflated, lengths less than 2 times widths; stems ascending or prostrate; nw Arizona, se Nevada, s Utah . . . . 21a. *Astragalus subcinereus* var. *subcinereus*
   2. Legumes ellipsoid, turgid (not bladdery-inflated), lengths more than 2 times widths; stems prostrate; se Nevada, s Utah. . . . . 21b. *Astragalus subcinereus* var. *sileranus*

21a. Astragalus subcinereus A. Gray var. **subcinereus** [E]

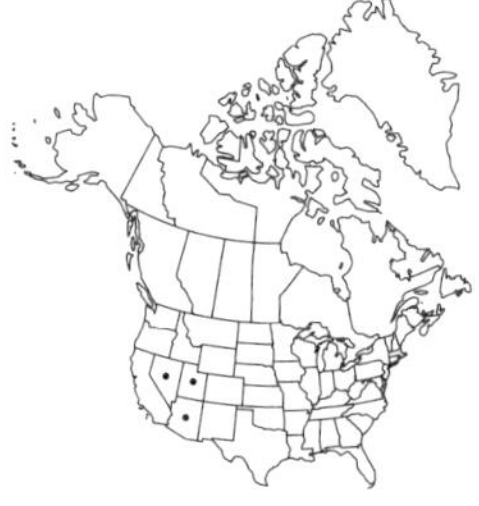

Astragalus sileranus M. E. Jones var. *cariacus* M. E. Jones

Stems ascending or prostrate, 14–50 cm. **Flowers** 5–9 mm. **Legumes** ovoid or ovoid-ellipsoid, bladdery-inflated, length less than 2 times width, relatively broad, usually 6–13 mm wide.

Flowering May–Sep. Ponderosa pine, white fir, pinyon-juniper, aspen, and sagebrush communities; 1600–2600 m; Ariz., Nev., Utah.

Variety *subcinereus* occurs in Coconino and Mohave counties in Arizona, Lincoln County in Nevada, and Garfield, Kane, and Washington counties in Utah.

Much of the material in southern Utah differs from plants in Mohave County, Arizona, in having broader leaflets, longer stems, and more firmly-walled fruits, and has been called *Astragalus sileranus* var. *cariacus*. The features are weak and overlapping at best.

21b. Astragalus subcinereus A. Gray var. **sileranus** (M. E. Jones) S. L. Welsh, Great Basin Naturalist 58: 49. 1998 • Siler's milkvetch [E]

Astragalus sileranus M. E. Jones, Zoë 2: 242. 1891; *Phaca sileriana* (M. E. Jones) Rydberg

Stems prostrate, 14–60 cm, often conspicuously flexuous. **Flowers** 5–9 mm. **Legumes** ellipsoid, turgid, not bladdery-inflated, length usually more than 2 times width, 5–8 mm wide (if shorter, less than 7 mm wide and texture leathery).

Flowering May–Aug. Ponderosa pine, aspen, oak, pinyon-juniper, and mixed mountain brush communities; 1700–2800 m; Nev., Utah.

Variety *sileranus* occurs in Lincoln County in Nevada, and Garfield, Iron, Kane, and eastern Washington counties in Utah.

The main overlap in distribution between vars. *subcinereus* and *sileranus* occurs in Lincoln County, Nevada, but still, this variety is most closely allied to the disjunct var. *basalticus* of central Utah.

21c. Astragalus subcinereus A. Gray var. **basalticus** S. L. Welsh, Great Basin Naturalist 38: 302. 1978 • Fremont Junction milkvetch [E]

Stems prostrate, 40–90 cm. **Flowers** 8.5–11 mm. **Legumes** ellipsoid to cylindroid-ellipsoid, inflated, length usually more than 2 times width, 3.5–6(–7) mm wide.

Flowering May–Jul. Pinyon-juniper and ponderosa pine communities; 1400–2400 m; Utah.

Variety *basalticus* is confined to western Emery and eastern Sevier counties.

Variety *basalticus* and *Astragalus flexuosus* var. *diehlii* are sympatric in the range of var. *basalticus*. Fruits of var. *basalticus* are usually wider and the flowers longer.

22. Astragalus wingatanus S. Watson, Proc. Amer. Acad. Arts 18: 192. 1883 • Fort Wingate milkvetch [E]

Plants clump-forming, (10–)15–45(–60) cm, strigulose; from branched, subterranean caudex, sometimes branches sub-rhizomatous. **Stems** spreading-ascending, forming diffuse clumps, often distinctly flexuous, (0–)1.5–15 cm underground, strigulose. **Leaves** 1.5–6.5 cm; stipules purplish or brownish, connate-sheathing and scarious at proximal nodes, connate or distinct and subherbaceous at distal nodes, 1.5–5 mm; leaflets (3–)7–15(or 17), blades linear to narrowly oblong, elliptic, or oblanceolate, 3–18 mm, apex acute, obtuse, or retuse, surfaces strigose or glabrous abaxially, glabrous adaxially, margins often ciliate; terminal leaflet sometimes decurrent distally, not jointed to rachis. **Peduncles** erect or incurved-ascending, stiff, 2–14 cm. **Racemes** very loosely 7–35-flowered, flowers ascending; axis 1 per leaf axil, 3–8 cm in fruit; bracts 0.5–2 mm; bracteoles 0–2. **Pedicels** 0.8–3 mm. **Flowers** 5.5–8 mm; calyx campanulate, 2.5–3.7 mm, black-strigose, tube 1.5–2.6 × 1.2–1.8(–2) mm, lobes triangular-subulate, 0.4–1.4 mm; corolla pink-purple, white, or white with banner and wing tips purple; banner recurved through 50°; keel 3.5–5.4 mm. **Legumes** deflexed, greenish and purple-speckled becoming stramineous, straight or slightly curved, ellipsoid to oblong, laterally compressed (2-sided), 9–15 × 3–4.5 mm, papery, glabrous; stipe 0–1.7 mm. **Seeds** 4–8. $2n = 22$.

Flowering mid Apr–Jul. Pinyon-juniper, mixed desert shrub, salt desert shrub, mountain brush communities; 1500–2400 m; Ariz., Colo., N.Mex., Utah.

Astragalus wingatanus resembles *A. multiflorus* in its relatively small flowers and laterally flattened fruits; the subterranean caudex and elongated fruiting racemes are diagnostic for *A. wingatanus* and indicate relationships with taxa such as *A. flexuosus* var. *diehlii*.

23. Astragalus cliffordii S. L. Welsh & N. D. Atwood in S. L. Welsh et al., Utah Fl. ed. 3, 839. 2003 • Clifford's milkvetch [E]

Plants forming diffuse clumps, 35–65 cm, strigulose; from shallowly subterranean caudex. **Stems** erect-ascending, 1–8 cm underground, strigulose. **Leaves** 3.5–6.5 cm; stipules connate-sheathing at proximal nodes, distinct at distal nodes, 1.5–4.5 mm; leaflets 5 or 7(or 9), blades linear, 8–28 mm, apex acute, surfaces strigose; terminal leaflet sometimes decurrent distally, not jointed to rachis. **Peduncles** 1.2–12 cm. **Racemes** 5–19-flowered, flowers ascending; axis 3–10.5(–13.5) cm in fruit; bracts 0.3–0.8 mm; bracteoles 0. **Pedicels** 2–2.5 mm. **Flowers** 4.3–6.1 mm; calyx campanulate, 1.8–3 mm, strigose, tube 1.2–1.8 mm, slightly expanding in fruit, lobes triangular, 0.6–1 mm; corolla whitish, faintly suffused with purple, keel maculate. **Legumes** declined, straight or slightly curved, ellipsoid to oblong, strongly laterally compressed, 9–12 × 2.5–3 mm, glabrous; stipe 0–0.2 mm. **Seeds** 4–5.

Flowering May–Jun. Rimrock ledges of the Mesaverde Group in pinyon-juniper, sagebrush, and galleta-blue grama communities; 1800–2200 m; N.Mex.

The relatively small, laterally flattened fruits of *Astragalus cliffordii* indicate alliance with *A. wingatanus*; however, it is rushlike in appearance with filiform peduncles and rachises, confluent terminal leaflets, and small, pale flowers.

24. Astragalus gracilis Nuttall, Gen. N. Amer. Pl. 2: 100. 1818 • Slender milkvetch [E] [F]

Dalea parviflora Pursh, Fl. Amer. Sept. 2: 474. 1813, not *A. parviflorus* Lamarck 1783; *Astragalus gracilis* var. *microlobus* (A. Gray) S. L. Welsh; *A. microlobus* A. Gray

Plants slender, forming diffuse clumps, 10–75(–110) cm, strigulose; from subterranean caudex. **Stems** ascending to erect, 1–9(–15) cm underground, strigulose. **Leaves** 2.5–9 cm; stipules connate-sheathing and papery-membranous at proximal nodes, distinct and herbaceous at distal nodes, (1–)1.5–4 mm; leaflets 7–17, blades linear, linear-oblong to narrowly oblong, oblanceolate, or cuneate-oblong, (3–)5–20(–25) mm, apex retuse, surfaces strigulose. **Peduncles** erect, ascending or incurved, or divaricate, 3–13 cm. **Racemes** loosely (6–)12–45(–55)-flowered, flowers ascending; axis (1.5–)3–13(–17) cm in fruit; bracts 0.7–1.5 mm; bracteoles 0–2. **Pedicels** 0.7–1.8 mm. **Flowers** 5.3–8.4 mm; calyx campanulate, 2.1–3.3 mm, strigose, tube 1–2.7 mm, lobes deltate to triangular-subulate, 0.4–0.9 mm; corolla pink-purple, banner purple-veined; banner recurved through 45°; keel 3.7–6.1 mm. **Legumes** declined or deflexed, brown or stramineous, obliquely subglobose, plumply ovoid, or ovoid-ellipsoid, obcompressed, (4–)4.3–8(–9) × 2.3–3.6 mm, fleshy becoming stiffly leathery, strigulose to villosulous; sessile. **Seeds** 5–9.

Flowering May–Jul. Prairies, among junipers; 500–2300 m; Sask.; Colo., Kans., Mont., Nebr., N.Mex., N.Dak., Okla., S.Dak., Tex., Wyo.

Justification exists for dividing *Astragalus gracilis* into two varieties, var. *gracilis* and var. *microlobus*. Even though they are largely sympatric, the differences seem to represent more than mere random variation. The former consists of taller, erect plants with long racemes and numerous flowers, shorter fruits, and mostly slender leaflets, while the latter consists of low, diffusely spreading plants, the stems often flexuous, with shorter, fewer-flowered racemes, longer fruits, and broader leaflets. Introgression with *A. flexuosus* might account for some features seen in var. *microlobus* (S. L. Welsh 1960).

25. Astragalus microcymbus Barneby, Amer. Midl. Naturalist 41: 499. 1949 • Skiff milkvetch [C] [E]

Plants slender, 25–60(–85) cm, strigulose to subvillosulous; from shallow subterranean caudex. **Stems** prostrate or weakly ascending, diffuse, modestly flexuous, 1–3 cm underground, strigulose to subvillosulous. **Leaves** (1.5–)2–4 cm; stipules connate and papery-scarious at proximal nodes, distinct and membranous at distal nodes, 1.5–3 mm; leaflets 9–15, blades oblong-ovate or oblong-cuneate, 3–9 mm, apex emarginate, surfaces densely strigulose to subvillosulous abaxially, glabrate adaxially. **Peduncles** divaricate and ascending, (0.8–)1.5–3.5 cm, together with racemes shorter than stems. **Racemes** (3–)7–14-flowered, flowers initially spreading, later declined; axis (1–)2–6.5 cm in fruit; bracts 0.8–1.4 mm; bracteoles 0. **Pedicels** 0.5 mm. **Flowers** 5.6–5.8 mm; calyx campanulate or obconic-campanulate, 2.2–2.6 mm, strigulose, hairs white and fuscous, sometimes also black, tube 1.4–1.9 mm, lobes subulate, 0.5–0.7 mm; corolla whitish tinged with lilac; banner recurved through 45°; keel 3.5–3.7 mm. **Legumes** pendulous, green with purple speckles becoming stramineous, slightly decurved, ellipsoid or lanceoloid-ellipsoid, obcompressed, dehiscent while attached, 6–9.5 × (2.5–)3–3.3 mm, papery, white-villosulous; valves inflexed, if at all, as hyaline septum 0–0.1 mm wide; stipe 0.4 mm. **Seeds** 4–6.

Flowering May–Aug. Dry, sandy and gravelly sites in sagebrush; of conservation concern; 2300–2600 m; Colo.

Astragalus microcymbus was discovered by R. C. Barneby in 1945 along a roadside about four miles west of Gunnison. For years the species was not known from elsewhere, and speculation existed that the population represented the introduction of an unknown foreign species. J. Barrell (1969) discovered the species in a relatively natural situation, and it now is presumed to be a native endemic. Its earlier placement in sect. *Strigulosi* (Barneby 1964) is questionable; it likely belongs within sect. *Scytocarpi* near *A. gracilis*.

Astragalus microcymbus is in the Center for Plant Conservation's National Collection of Endangered Plants.

26. Astragalus hallii A. Gray, Proc. Amer. Acad. Arts 6: 224. 1864 • Hall's milkvetch [E]

Plants 12–50(–55) cm, strigulose to villosulous; from subterranean caudex. **Stems** decumbent, ascending, prostrate, or diffuse, 1–13 cm underground, villosulous or loosely strigose. **Leaves** 2–9 cm; stipules connate-sheathing and scarious at proximal nodes, distinct or connate by a low collar and subherbaceous at distal nodes, 1–7 mm; leaflets (11 or)13–27(–31), blades obovate to oblanceolate or elliptic, (1.5–)3–14(–15) mm, apex retuse, truncate, or obtuse, surfaces strigulose abaxially, sparsely hairy or glabrous adaxially. **Peduncles** suberect, incurved-ascending, spreading, declined, or prostrate, 3–9.5(–11) cm. **Racemes** (7–)9–28-flowered, flowers spreading-declined; axis 1–7 cm in fruit; bracts 1.5–5 mm; bracteoles 0–2. **Pedicels** 1.2–4 mm. **Flowers** 12.4–15(–18.5) mm; calyx campanulate, (5–)6–7(–9) mm, strigulose or villosulous, tube 5–6.2 mm, lobes triangular-subulate, 0.5–2.3 mm; corolla purple or reddish violet, sometimes white-tipped or suffused with purple; banner recurved through 45°; keel 9–12 (–12.3) mm. **Legumes** spreading to declined, green or purplish becoming stramineous or brown, straight or slightly incurved, oblong, oblanceoloid-ellipsoid, ovoid, obovoid, or ellipsoid, slightly to distinctly inflated, (12–)13–27 × (3–)4–12 mm, cartilaginous becoming stiffly papery, somewhat fleshy opaque, glabrous, strigulose, or villosulous; stipe (0–)1–4.5 mm. **Seeds** 20–34.

Varieties 2 (2 in the flora): w United States.

1. Legumes glabrous or sparsely strigulose, not distinctly inflated, narrowly oblong-ellipsoid, oblanceoloid-ellipsoid, or subclavately ellipsoid, (3–)4–7(–8.5) mm wide; herbage usually green, rarely subcinereous, villosulous or loosely strigulose, hairs to 0.5–0.8(–1) mm; primarily in Rocky Mountains and San Juan basins of Colorado and New Mexico, also ne Arizona, w Oklahoma . . . . 26a. *Astragalus hallii* var. *hallii*
1. Legumes usually strigulose, rarely villosulous, usually distinctly inflated, obliquely ovoid or obovoid, rarely ellipsoid, 6–12 mm wide; herbage often (not consistently) cinereous, strigulose, hairs to 0.2–0.4(–0.6) mm; Arizona, w New Mexico, sc Utah . . . . 26b. *Astragalus hallii* var. *fallax*

26a. Astragalus hallii A. Gray var. **hallii** [E]

Herbage usually green, rarely subcinereous, villosulous or loosely strigulose, hairs to 0.5–0.8(–1) mm. **Stems** decumbent or prostrate with ascending tips. **Leaflets** (13–)19–27(–31). **Peduncles** usually ascending, spreading, or declined, rarely prostrate (in fruit). **Corollas** purple or reddish violet. **Legumes** humistrate, narrowly oblong-ellipsoid, oblanceoloid-ellipsoid, or subclavately ellipsoid, not distinctly inflated, (12–)13–24(–27) × (3–) 4–7(–8.5) mm, glabrous or sparsely strigulose; stipe 1–2 mm. **Seeds** 20–30. $2n = 22$.

Flowering Jun–Sep. Hillsides, meadows, sagebrush communities, mixed conifer-aspen communities; 2300–3100 m; Ariz., Colo., N.Mex., Okla.

Variety *hallii* occurs in central, south-central, and southwestern Colorado, north-central and northwestern New Mexico, and just into Arizona (Apache County), and is disjunct in Oklahoma (Cimarron County).

26b. Astragalus hallii A. Gray var. **fallax** (M. E. Jones) Barneby, Leafl. W. Bot. 9: 91. 1960 • Deceptive milkvetch [E]

Astragalus gracilentus (A. Gray) A. Gray var. *fallax* M. E. Jones, Contr. W. Bot. 8: 14. 1898, based on *A. fallax* S. Watson, Proc. Amer. Acad. Arts 20: 362. 1885, not Fischer 1853

Herbage often (not consistently) cinereous, strigulose, hairs to 0.2–0.4(–0.6) mm (when 0.4–0.6 mm, then legumes distinctly inflated). **Stems** diffuse or ascending. **Leaflets** (11 or)13–25. **Peduncles** incurved-ascending to suberect. **Corollas** bright or pale purple, or tipped with white, or suffused with purple. **Legumes** not or seldom humistrate, obliquely ovoid or obovoid, rarely broadly ellipsoid, usually distinctly inflated, 13–27 × 6–12 mm, usually strigulose, rarely villosulous; stipe 0–4.5 mm. **Seeds** (24–)28–34.

Flowering late May–Sep. Ponderosa pine, pinyon-juniper, oak, sagebrush, and mixed mountain brush communities; 1600–2300 m; Ariz., N.Mex., Utah.

Variety *fallax* is known from Arizona, western New Mexico, and Kane County in Utah.

27. **Astragalus puniceus** Osterhout, Muhlenbergia 1: 140. 1906 • Trinidad milkvetch [E]

Plants clump-forming, relatively robust, 15–50 cm, villous or villosulous; from subterranean caudex, branches subrhizomatous. **Stems** decumbent to ascending or erect, diffuse, 3–10(–17) cm underground, appressed-hairy or villosulous. **Leaves** (2–)3–11 cm; stipules connate-sheathing and papery at proximal nodes, ± distinct or connate to 1/2 their length and herbaceous becoming papery at distal nodes, 2–6 mm; leaflets 7–27, blades broadly to narrowly elliptic, oblong-lanceolate, obovate-cuneate, or linear-oblong, 3–16 mm, apex truncate-emarginate or obtuse, surfaces strigulose abaxially, sparsely hairy adaxially. **Peduncles** ascending, usually stout and ± straight, 2–8(–11.5) cm. **Racemes** 5–19(–27)-flowered, flowers ascending; axis (0.5–)1.5–6.5 cm in fruit; bracts 1.5–6 mm; bracteoles (0 or) 2. **Pedicels** 1–2.9 mm. **Flowers** 13.4–21 mm; calyx campanulate or cylindric-campanulate, 6–10.6 mm, villosulous, tube 4.9–8 mm, lobes subulate to triangular, 1.1–2.8 mm; corolla bright pink-purple or pale and lilac-tinged; banner recurved through 45°; keel 10.4–14 mm. **Legumes** spreading to declined, green, sometimes red-mottled, becoming brown or stramineous, straight or nearly so, oblong or ovoid-ellipsoid, turgid or somewhat inflated, not bladdery, 15–24 × (4.5–)5–9.5 mm, leathery, sparsely strigulose to villosulous; sessile or subsessile. **Seeds** 25–36.

Varieties 2 (2 in the flora): sw United States.

Astragalus puniceus forms sprawling clumps with almost cloverlike heads; it is similar to the contiguous *A. hallii* var. *hallii*, differing in its evident pubescent and heavier-walled fruits.

1. Corollas bright pink-purple; herbage and stems villosulous; legumes usually bright red-mottled; s Colorado, n New Mexico, w Oklahoma . . . . 27a. *Astragalus puniceus* var. *puniceus*
1. Corollas purple or whitish tinged dull lavender; herbage villous, stems appressed-hairy; legumes not red-mottled; n New Mexico . . . . 27b. *Astragalus puniceus* var. *gertrudis*

27a. **Astragalus puniceus** Osterhout var. **puniceus** [E]

Herbage villosulous. **Stems** villosulous. **Leaflets** (7–)17–27. **Bracts** herbaceous; bracteoles usually present. **Flowers** (13.5–)16–21 mm; corolla bright pink-purple. **Legumes** usually bright red-mottled, oblong-ellipsoid, (4.5–)5–8 mm wide.

Flowering May–Jul. Low bluffs, sandy mesas, fallow fields, stabilized dunes; 1400–2200 m; Colo., N.Mex., Okla.

R. C. Barneby (1964) provided a key, and discussion, detailing smaller-flowered plants from extreme western Oklahoma, noting that taxonomic recognition should await careful searches for intermediate populations.

Variety *puniceus* occurs in the Canadian River headwaters, northern New Mexico, southern Colorado, and western Oklahoma (Cimarron and Major counties). No voucher specimen has been located for a report from Texas (D. S. Correll and m. C. Johnston 1970).

27b. **Astragalus puniceus** Osterhout var. **gertrudis** (Greene) Barneby, Mem. New York Bot. Gard. 13: 229. 1964 • Gertrud's milkvetch [E]

Astragalus gertrudis Greene, Leafl. Bot. Observ. Crit. 2: 43. 1910

Herbage villous. **Stems** appressed-hairy. **Leaflets** 13–21. **Bracts** submembranous; bracteoles absent. **Flowers** 14.8–17.8 mm; corolla purple or whitish tinged dull lavender. **Legumes** not red-mottled, oblong or ovoid-ellipsoid, 6–9.5 mm wide.

Flowering May–Jun. Dry banks and gravelly benches with pinyon-juniper; 1800–2200 m; N.Mex.

Variety *gertrudis* is known from the upper Rio Grande Valley in Rio Arriba and Taos counties.

R. C. Barneby (1964) noted that distinguishing characteristics of var. *gertrudis* are not strong within the context of sect. *Scytocarpi*, and that distinction of the varieties may be largely geographical.

28. Astragalus castetteri Barneby, Mem. New York Bot. Gard. 13: 229. 1964 • Castetter's milkvetch [E]

Plants 20–40 cm, strigulose; from shallow subterranean caudex. **Stems** incurved-ascending, diffuse, 1–12 cm underground, strigulose. **Leaves** (3.5–)5–10 cm; stipules connate-sheathing at proximal nodes, distinct or shortly or obscurely connate distally, 2–7 mm, papery proximally, herbaceous distally; leaflets 11–25, blades oblong-elliptic or obovate, (2.5-)5–14 mm, apex emarginate, surfaces strigulose abaxially, sparsely hairy or glabrous adaxially. **Peduncles** 4.5–8 cm. **Racemes** 8–20-flowered, flowers spreading, later declined; axis 2–5 cm in fruit; bracts 2–4 mm; bracteoles 0. **Pedicels** 0.8–3.5 mm. **Flowers** 14–18.7 mm; calyx subcylindric, 7.9–10 mm, strigulose or villosulous, tube 5.8–7.2 mm, lobes subulate, 2–3.5 mm; corolla pale purple (drying dull lavender); banner recurved through 45°; keel 11–14.4 mm. **Legumes** humistrate, spreading, or declined, often red-mottled, subsymmetric, ovoid-acuminate or ovoid-ellipsoid, subterete, bladdery-inflated, 22–28 × 11–16 mm, papery-membranous, translucent, loosely strigulose to villosulous; stipe 1.5–3 mm. **Seeds** 22–26. $2n = 22$.

Flowering Apr–May. Dry, rocky slopes in pinyon forests, open juniper woodlands; 1500–1700 m; N.Mex.

Astragalus castetteri occurs in the Caballo and San Andres mountains of south-central New Mexico in Doña Ana and Sierra counties.

Astragalus castetteri is the only species in the group with thinly membranous inflated fruits, probably derived from *A. hallii* var. *fallax* (R. C. Barneby 1964). Barneby also noted that *A. castetteri* reverted to vernal flowering; recent collections indicate that about 20% of collections were from autumn-blooming plants.

29. Astragalus shevockii Barneby, Brittonia 29: 376, fig. 1. 1977 • Shevock's milkvetch [C] [E]

Plants slender, 10–35 cm, strigulose-pilose; from subterranean caudex. **Stems** prostrate, 1–9 cm underground, strigulose-pilose. **Leaves** 2.5–6(–6.5) cm; stipules connate-sheathing at proximal nodes, distinct or obscurely connate at distal nodes, 1–5 mm, membranous; leaflets (9 or)11–17, blades elliptic, oblong-elliptic, or obovate, 2–8.5 mm, apex emarginate or obtuse, surfaces strigulose. **Peduncles** ascending, (3–)4.5–13 cm. **Racemes** (2–)4–13-flowered, flowers ascending; axis (0.5–)1.5–9 cm in fruit; bracts 1–2 mm; bracteoles 0. **Pedicels** 1.2–2.6 mm. **Flowers** 9–9.8 mm; calyx campanulate, 5.4–7.6 mm, villosulous, tube 3.4–4.6 mm, lobes subulate, 1.9–2.3 mm; corolla yellowish, drying ochroleucous, immaculate; banner recurved through 75°; keel 9–9.8 mm. **Legumes** ascending, green and purple-mottled, incurved, lunately ellipsoid-oblanceoloid, 3-sided compressed, (13–)15–23 × 3.3–4 mm, papery, loosely strigulose-pilosulous; valves inflexed, septum 0–0.5 mm wide; obscurely stipitate, gynophore 1–1.5 mm. **Seeds** 10–12.

Flowering Jun–Jul. Open Jeffrey pine forests, in granitic sands and pine-needle duff; of conservation concern; 1800–2100 m; Calif.

Astragalus shevockii is known from the High Sierra Nevada of southeastern Tulare County.

The subterranean root-crown, connate proximal stipules, and substipitate fruits persistent on the receptacle of *Astragalus shevockii* indicate a relationship with sect. *Scytocarpi* (R. C. Barneby 1977), but the species differs from other members of that section, which have mostly terete or laterally compressed fruits that are neither three-sided nor septate.

135k. Astragalus Linnaeus sect. Genistoidei (Torrey & A. Gray) Barneby, Leafl. W. Bot. 5: 25. 1947 [E]

Homalobus Nuttall [unranked] *Genistoidei* Torrey & A. Gray, Fl. N. Amer. 1: 351. 1838 (as Genistoideae)

Herbs perennial, caulescent; caudex superficial or subterranean. **Hairs** basifixed or malpighian. **Stems** few or several to many. **Stipules** connate or distinct at distal nodes. **Leaves** odd-pinnate, petiolate to short-petiolate; leaflets (1 or)3–21, or reduced to phyllodium, sometimes terminal leaflet decurrent and not jointed to rachis. **Racemes** loosely flowered, flowers often ascending then declined. **Calyx tubes** campanulate. **Corollas** whitish, ochroleucous, lilac, or purple to pink-purple, banner recurved through 40–90°, keel apex obtuse, broadly triangular, or acute-triangular and beaklike. **Legumes** persistent, sessile or substipitate, declined-pendulous, spreading, or ascending, linear to linear-ellipsoid, oblanceoloid, or narrowly oblong, laterally compressed and 2-sided, unilocular. **Seeds** 6–26.

Species 3 (3 in the flora): w North America.

Section *Genistoidei* consists of three species that are widespread through the Rocky Mountains and intermontane United States, from British Columbia and Alberta southward to Washington, Arizona, and South Dakota.

30. Astragalus miser Douglas in W. J. Hooker, Fl. Bor.-Amer. 1: 153. 1831 • Weedy milkvetch [E] [F]

Plants clump-forming, caulescent or shortly caulescent, 1–35 cm, strigose, strigulose-pilosulous, pilosulous, strigulose, or villous, hairs basifixed or malpighian; from ± superficial, branched caudex. **Stems** decumbent to erect, sterile branches forming tuft of subbasal leaves, strigose, strigulose, or villous. **Leaves** 1.5–20 cm; stipules connate-sheathing (bidentate) at proximal nodes, shortly connate or distinct at distal nodes, 1.5–9 mm, papery-membranous throughout or, sometimes, herbaceous at distal nodes; leaflets 3–21, blades linear, oblong, elliptic, linear-elliptic, linear-oblanceolate, lanceolate, oblong-elliptic, elliptic-lanceolate, or, rarely, filiform-subulate (distally), 2–30(–42) × 0.5–7 mm, apex acute, obtuse, acuminate, apiculate, or, rarely, retuse, surfaces strigose, glabrescent, or glabrous abaxially, glabrous, glabrescent, or sparsely hairy adaxially; terminal leaflet sometimes decurrent distally, not jointed to rachis. **Peduncles** usually incurved-ascending, 2–14 cm. **Racemes** 3–19(–24)-flowered, flowers spreading-declined; axis 1–14 cm in fruit; bracts 0.6–4 mm; bracteoles usually 0. **Pedicels** 0.8–3 mm. **Flowers** 5.3–10.6 mm; calyx (2.3–)2.4–6 mm, strigose, tube 1.7–4.2 mm, lobes subulate, 0.5–2.6 mm; corolla lilac, pink-purple, ochroleucous, or whitish, often suffused, lined, or veined with purple; banner recurved through 40–90°; keel 5.9–10.7(–11.4) mm, apex beaklike. **Legumes** declined-pendulous; green, sometimes with purple speckles, becoming brown or stramineous, straight or nearly so, linear, linear-oblong, linear-ellipsoid, or oblanceoloid, laterally compressed, bicarinate by sutures, 11–25 × (1.2–)2–4 mm, papery, usually strigulose, villosulous, or glabrous, rarely with few hairs; stipe 0–1 mm. **Seeds** 6–19.

Varieties 8 (8 in the flora): w North America.

Astragalus miser, widespread in the American West, contains miserotoxin, a nitrogenous compound that is poisonous to cattle and sheep. In the key to varieties the presence of malpighian hairs is important. The point of attachment may be so near the base as to be almost indistinguishable from a basifixed trichome. The key is tentative and will not always reliably separate varieties; nevertheless, morphological trends exist and most plants are identifiable.

1. Herbage hairs obscurely malpighian; leaflet blades pubescent.
   2. Herbage villosulous or villous and pilosulous, hairs gray or silvery, mostly twisted and loose; legumes minutely villosulous, hairs twisted; ec Idaho, adjoining Montana . . . . 30h. *Astragalus miser* var. *crispatus*
   2. Herbage strigulose, hairs ± straight; legumes strigulose; Idaho, Montana, Wyoming.
      3. Leaflet blades linear to linear-elliptic or oblong-elliptic; corollas whitish, ochroleucous, or stramineous, sometimes brownish-veined, keel apex maculate; seeds 7–11; sw Montana, ec Idaho, nw Wyoming . . . . 30f. *Astragalus miser* var. *praeteritus*
      3. Leaflet blades narrowly elliptic to elliptic-lanceolate (leaves subtending racemes sometimes broadly elliptic or oblanceolate); corollas usually pink-purple, purplish, bluish, or dull purple, sometimes pallid or whitish, except maculate keel; seeds 12–18; Idaho and s Montana to c Wyoming . . . . 30g. *Astragalus miser* var. *decumbens*
1. Herbage hairs basifixed; leaflet blades abaxially pubescent, adaxially pubescent or glabrous.
   4. Leaflet blades with pubescent surfaces, hairs silvery or cinereous; calyces (4.2–)4.6–6 mm; corollas lilac or pink-purple, banners (9.5–)9.8–12 mm, keel (7.8–)8.6–10.7 mm; legumes densely strigulose; ne Washington to w Montana and adjacent Canada . . . . 30a. *Astragalus miser* var. *miser*
   4. Leaflet blades with surfaces pubescent or glabrous abaxially, usually glabrous or glabrate adaxially, sometimes pubescent; calyces 2.4–5.6 mm; corollas usually whitish, rarely ochroleucous, sometimes suffused or lined or veined with purple, banners (5.2–)6–13 mm, keel 5.9–10 mm; legumes strigulose or glabrous; British Columbia and Alberta southward to Washington, Arizona, New Mexico, and South Dakota.

[5. Shifted to left margin.—Ed.]

5. Leaflets (3–)7–11; stems 1–11(–15) cm; banners 6–8 mm; legumes linear (in profile), strigulose; seeds 8–12; se Idaho to sw Montana, ne Nevada, n Utah, and w Wyoming . . . . 30c. *Astragalus miser* var. *tenuifolius*
5. Leaflets (9 or)11–21; stems 1–35 cm; banners (5.2–)6.5–13 mm; legumes oblanceolate, linear, linear-oblong, -elliptic, or -oblanceolate (in profile), glabrous or strigulose; seeds (6 or)7–19; British Columbia and Alberta southward to Washington, Arizona, New Mexico, and South Dakota.
    6. Legumes strigulose; seeds 13–19; Montana to New Mexico, west to Nevada and Arizona . . . . 30b. *Astragalus miser* var. *oblongifolius*
    6. Legumes glabrous, strigulose, or few hairs present; seeds (6 or)7–11; South Dakota west to British Columbia and Washington.
        7. Stems 10–35 cm; banners 7–9.5 mm, keel 6–7.8(–8.4) mm; leaflet blades narrowly elliptic to linear or linear-oblanceolate; legumes glabrous or strigulose; Alberta and British Columbia southward to Montana, Idaho, and Washington . . . . 30d. *Astragalus miser* var. *serotinus*
        7. Stems 1–15 cm; banners (5.2–)6.5–13 mm, keel (7.1–)8–10(–11.4) mm; leaflet blades narrowly to broadly elliptic, lanceolate, or lanceolate-oblong; legumes usually glabrous, rarely with few, scattered hairs; w Wyoming and Montana, adjoining Idaho, and Black Hills of South Dakota . . . . 30e. *Astragalus miser* var. *hylophilus*

30a. Astragalus miser Douglas var. **miser** [E]

Astragalus strigosus J. M. Coulter & Fisher

Herbage strigulose-pilosulous, hairs basifixed, silvery or cinereous. **Stems** (5–)8–32 cm. **Leaves** 4–14(–17) cm; leaflets 9–19, blades linear-elliptic to narrowly linear, 3–26(–30) mm, apex acute, surfaces pubescent. **Racemes** loosely (5–)7–19-flowered; axis (2–)4–12 cm in fruit. **Flowers:** calyx (4.2–)4.6–6 mm, tube 2.6–4.2 mm, lobes (1.4–)1.8–2.6 mm; corolla lilac or pink-purple; banner (9.5–)9.8–12 mm; keel (7.8–)8.6–10.7 mm. **Legumes** linear-oblong or linear-ellipsoid, 15–22(–25) × (2.5–)3–4 mm, densely strigulose. **Seeds** 8–12(–17). $2n = 22$.

Flowering late Apr–early Aug. Ridges, flats, meadows, grasslands, shrublands, open forests; 300–1400 m; Alta., B.C.; Idaho, Mont., Wash.

Variety *miser* is known from southern British Columbia and extreme southwestern Alberta across northeastern Washington to western Montana.

30b. Astragalus miser Douglas var. **oblongifolius** (Rydberg) Cronquist, Leafl. W. Bot. 7: 18. 1953 • Baker's weedy milkvetch [E] [F] [W]

Homalobus oblongifolius Rydberg, Bull. Torrey Bot. Club 34: 50. 1907

Herbage strigulose-pilosulous, hairs basifixed. **Stems** (1–)2–20 (–24) cm. **Leaves** (2–)4–20 cm; leaflets (9 or)11–19(or 21), blades linear, narrowly oblong, or elliptic to broadly oblong or oval-elliptic, (3–)5–30(–42) mm, apex mostly acute, surfaces glabrous or glabrescent adaxially. **Racemes** 3–15(–20)-flowered; axis (1–)1.5—10 cm in fruit. **Flowers:** calyx (2.8–)3.4–5.2 mm, tube 2.2–2.9 mm, lobes (0.8–)1–1.2 mm; corolla whitish or suffused or lined with purple; banner (5.9–)6.5–9.5(–10.2) mm; keel 6.1–8.4 mm. **Legumes** oblanceoloid, (12–)15–25 × (1.2–)2.3–4 mm, strigulose. **Seeds** 13–19. $2n = 22$.

Flowering late May–Aug. Sagebrush, oak, aspen, and spruce-fir or pine communities; 1600–3500 m; Ariz., Colo., Idaho, Mont., Nev., N.Mex., Utah, Wyo.

Variety *oblongifolius* occurs in the southern Rocky Mountains of Colorado and Wyoming, westward across the Colorado Basin to eastern Nevada, montane Utah, central Arizona, and northwestern New Mexico.

Variety *oblongifolius* forms extensive carpets in the forests of Colorado and Utah, where it is the only representative of the species. The New Mexico record likely represents a recent introduction (K. D. Heil and S. L. O'Kane 2007).

30c. Astragalus miser Douglas var. **tenuifolius** (Nuttall) Barneby, Leafl. W. Bot. 7: 195. 1954 • Garrett's weedy milkvetch [E]

Homalobus tenuifolius Nuttall in J. Torrey and A. Gray, Fl. N. Amer. 1: 352. 1838

Herbage strigose, hairs basifixed. **Stems** 1–11(–15) cm. **Leaves** (1.5–)2.5–9(–10.5) cm; leaflets (3–)7–11, blades linear, narrowly linear-elliptic, or (distally) filiform-subulate, 2–10(–20) mm, apex sharply acute, surfaces pubescent or glabrescent. **Racemes** 3–6(–12)-flowered; axis 1–5(–7.5) cm in fruit. **Flowers:** calyx 2.4–3.5 mm, tube 1.9–2.5 mm, lobes 0.5–1.1 mm; corolla usually whitish or suffused, rarely ochroleucous; banner 6–8 mm; keel 5.9–7 mm. **Legumes** linear (in profile), 12–16 × 2–2.7 mm, strigulose. **Seeds** 8–12.

Flowering Jun–Aug. Hillsides, bluffs, mountain crests, in sagebrush; 1600–3200 m; Idaho, Mont., Nev., Utah, Wyo.

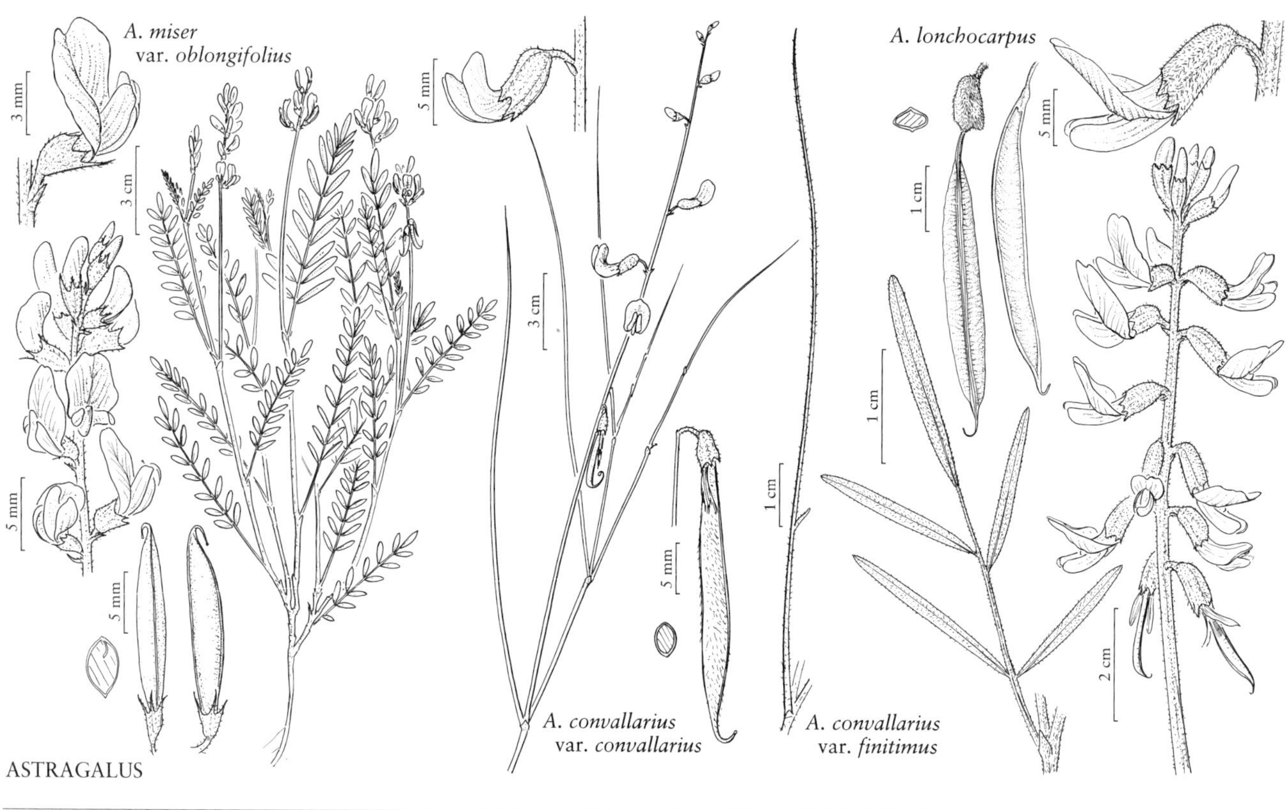

ASTRAGALUS

Variety *tenuifolius* is most abundant in eastern Idaho with a range that extends into southwestern Montana, western Wyoming, northeastern Nevada, and northern Utah.

30d. Astragalus miser Douglas var. **serotinus** (A. Gray) Barneby, Amer. Midl. Naturalist 55: 481. 1956 • Cooper's weedy milkvetch [E] [W]

Astragalus serotinus A. Gray in War Department [U.S.], Pacif. Railr. Rep. 12: 51, plate 5. 1860

Herbage strigulose, hairs basifixed. **Stems** 10–35 cm. **Leaves** 4–15(–17.5) cm; leaflets (9 or) 11–19(or 21), blades narrowly elliptic to linear or linear-oblanceolate, (2–)4–30(–40) mm, apex acute or obtuse, surfaces pubescent abaxially, glabrous adaxially. **Racemes** loosely (3–)6–16(–24)-flowered; axis (1.5–)2.5–14 cm in fruit. **Flowers:** calyx 3–4.2 mm, tube 2.3–3.1 mm, lobes 0.7–1.3 mm; corolla whitish or suffused or veined purple, keel pinkish lilac; banner 7–9.5 mm; keel 6–7.8(–8.4) mm. **Legumes** linear-oblong, 13–18(–21) × 2–2.8(–3.2) mm, glabrous or strigulose. **Seeds** 7–10. **2*n*** = 22.

Flowering May–Aug. Banks, flats, rocky or grassy slopes, glades in pine forests; 200–2000 m; Alta., B.C.; Idaho, Mont., Wash.

Variety *serotinus* is known from the Columbia Basin in Washington, northward into British Columbia and Rocky Mountains of Alberta, and southward into northwestern Montana.

D. Isely (1998) noted that var. *serotinus* is contiguous, and blends, with the purple-petaled var. *miser*. If origin is unknown, var. *serotinus* is often distinguished from var. *hylophilus* with difficulty.

30e. Astragalus miser Douglas var. **hylophilus** (Rydberg) Barneby, Amer. Midl. Naturalist 55: 482. 1956 • Woodlands weedy milkvetch [E] [W]

Homalobus hylophilus Rydberg, Mem. New York Bot. Gard. 1: 247. 1900

Herbage strigulose-pilosulous, hairs basifixed. **Stems** 1–15 cm. **Leaves** (3–)4.5–19 cm; leaflets (9 or)11–21, blades narrowly to broadly elliptic, lanceolate, or lanceolate-oblong, (3–)5–26 mm, apex acute, obtuse, obtuse and apiculate, or, rarely, retuse, surfaces glabrous or sparsely pubescent. **Racemes** (3–)6–16-flowered; axis (1–)1.5–7(–7.5) cm in fruit. **Flowers:** calyx (3.8–)4–5.6 mm, tube 2.6–3.5 mm, lobes (0.9–)1–2.3 mm; corolla whitish, sometimes purple-veined; banner (5.2–)6.5–13 mm; keel (7.1–)8–10(–11.4) mm. **Legumes** linear, linear-ellipsoid, or -oblanceoloid, (15–)18–25 × 2.5–4 mm, usually glabrous, rarely with few, scattered hairs. **Seeds** (6 or)7–11.

Flowering Jun–Aug. Meadows, banks, open parklands with lodgepole pine, Douglas-fir, and ponderosa pine; 900–2900 m; Idaho, Mont., S.Dak., Wyo.

Variety *hylophilus* occurs in the Rocky Mountains of western Wyoming and western Montana (and immediately adjoining Idaho), and the Black Hills of South Dakota.

Variety *hylophilus* is sympatric, in part, with vars. *crispatus*, *miser*, and *tenuifolius*. Its distinction may be preserved by ecological isolation; of the four varieties it is the most mesic, whereas the others are more xerophytic (D. Isely 1998).

30f. Astragalus miser Douglas var. **praeteritus** Barneby, Amer. Midl. Naturalist 55: 483. 1956 • Yellowstone milkvetch [E]

Herbage strigulose, hairs obscurely malpighian, silvery cinereous, ± straight. **Stems** (1.5–)2.5–20 cm. **Leaves** (1.5–)2.5–9.5 cm; leaflets 7–13(–17), blades linear to linear-elliptic or oblong-elliptic, 2–20 mm, apex attenuate to acute, surfaces pubescent; terminal leaflet confluent with rachis. **Racemes** loosely (3–)5–12-flowered; axis (1–)1.5–7.5 cm in fruit. **Flowers:** calyx (2.3–)2.8–3.9 mm, tube (1.7–)2.2–2.9 mm, lobes 0.6–1.4 mm; corolla whitish, ochroleucous, or stramineous, sometimes brownish-veined, keel apex maculate; banner 6.6–8.6 mm; keel 6.2–8.3(–8.8) mm. **Legumes** linear or linear-oblanceoloid, 11–20 × (2–)2.5–3.4 mm, strigulose. **Seeds** 7–11.

Flowering May–Aug. Banks, hillsides, gravelly ridges, in sagebrush upward into lodgepole pine forest; 2200–2900 m; Idaho, Mont., Wyo.

Variety *praeteritus* occurs in southwestern Montana on the upper forks of the Missouri River to adjoining east-central Idaho, to Yellowstone Park and Grand Tetons in northwestern Wyoming.

D. Isely (1998) stated that var. *praeteritus* represents the more northern aspects of an expanded var. *tenuifolius*, based on the presence of malpighian pubescence, and he synonymized the two under the latter name. He was unsuccessful in correlating pubescence with geography. It is probable that the two varieties are best combined, but there is a tendency for plants of var. *praeteritus* to have broader leaflets.

30g. Astragalus miser Douglas var. **decumbens** (Nuttall) Cronquist, Leafl. W. Bot. 7: 18. 1953 • Reclining weedy milkvetch [E]

Homalobus decumbens Nuttall in J. Torrey and A. Gray, Fl. N. Amer. 1: 352. 1838

Herbage strigulose, hairs obscurely malpighian, silvery-silky, ± straight. **Stems** 1–15 (–22) cm. **Leaves** 1.5–9(–12) cm; leaflets (7 or)9–15(or 17), blades narrowly elliptic to oval-lanceolate, leaflets subtending racemes more broadly elliptic or oblanceolate, (2–)4–16(–20) mm, apex acute to obtuse, surfaces pubescent; terminal leaflet decurrent or jointed. **Racemes** (4–)7–17-flowered; axis 1–3(–4) cm in fruit. **Flowers:** calyx 2.8–4.3 mm, tube 1.8–2.5 mm, lobes 0.9–1.9 mm; corolla usually pink-purple, purplish, bluish, or dull purple, sometimes pallid or whitish, except maculate keel; banner 6.9–9.6 mm; keel 6.2–7.8 mm. **Legumes** linear-oblong or -oblanceoloid, (12–)14–21 × 2.2–3.3 mm. **Seeds** 12–18.

Flowering May–Aug. Banks, hillsides, bluffs, ridge crests, with sagebrush, with limber pine and juniper; 1100–2600 m; Idaho, Mont., Wyo.

Variety *decumbens* occurs from southern Montana on the Yellowstone River, southward (mostly eastward of the Continental Divide except on upper Green River) to central Wyoming.

30h. Astragalus miser Douglas var. **crispatus** (M. E. Jones) Cronquist, Leafl. W. Bot. 7: 18. 1953 • Jones's weedy milkvetch [E]

Astragalus campestris (Nuttall) A. Gray [not Linnaeus] var. *crispatus* M. E. Jones, Rev. N.-Amer. Astragalus, 75. 1923

Herbage villosulous or villous and pilosulous, hairs obscurely malpighian, gray or silvery, mostly twisted and loose. **Stems** 2.5–15 cm. **Leaves** 1.5–8 cm; leaflets (9 or)11–17, blades narrowly elliptic or oblong-elliptic, 3–16(–20) mm, apex acute or shortly acuminate, surfaces pubescent; terminal leaflet decurrent or obscurely jointed. **Racemes** 9–17-flowered; axis 2–5.5 cm in fruit. **Flowers:** calyx 3.7–4.7 mm, tube 2.4–2.8 mm, lobes 1.1–2.4 mm; corolla whitish or ochroleucous, sometimes faintly lavender-tinged or -veined; banner 9.2–10.4 mm; keel 7.7–8.3 mm. **Legumes** linear-oblong, 14–17 × 2.5–3 mm, minutely villosulous, hairs twisted. **Seeds** 6–13.

Flowering Jun–Aug. Pine woodlands, sagebrush flats; 1200–1300 m; Idaho, Mont.

Variety *crispatus* is among the most restricted of the varieties in the species, occurring only in the Bitterroot Mountains, in east-central Idaho and adjoining Montana. It is geographically peripheral to var. *tenuifolius*, and some plants intergrade.

31. Astragalus convallarius Greene, Erythea 1: 207. 1893 • Lesser rushy milkvetch [E] [F]

Homalobus campestris Nuttall in J. Torrey and A. Gray, Fl. N. Amer. 1: 351. 1838, not *Astragalus campestris* Linnaeus 1753

Plants clump-forming, slender, wiry, (10–)20–50(–70) cm, strigulose, hairs basifixed; from deep, subterranean caudex. **Stems** erect or ascending, 1–9 (–17) cm underground, strigulose. **Leaves** sparse or nearly bladeless and rushlike, 2–11 cm; stipules connate-sheathing and papery-scarious at proximal nodes, mostly distinct and herbaceous at distal nodes, (1–)2–7 mm; leaflets 3–13 or distal leaves reduced to rachis (phyllodia), blades linear, linear-filiform, linear-elliptic, or elliptic, 5–30 × 0.5–4 mm, apex acute, surfaces strigulose; terminal leaflet sometimes decurrent and not jointed to rachis. **Peduncles** incurved-ascending, 1–14 cm. **Racemes** 3–25-flowered, flowers ascending to declined; axis 2–20(–23) cm in fruit; bracts 0.5–2.3 mm; bracteoles 0–2. **Pedicels** 1–8 mm. **Flowers** (6.6–)7.6–11.2 mm; calyx 4–6.3 mm, black-strigose and/or white-strigose, tube 3.4–5.4 mm, lobes triangular-subulate, 0.5–1.4 mm; corolla ochroleucous, sometimes tinged or veined with purple or pink; banner abruptly recurved through 90°; keel (6.2–)6.5–9.4 mm, apex broadly triangular. **Legumes** pendulous to spreading, green, purple, or mottled, becoming stramineous, straight, linear, narrowly oblong, or oblanceoloid, laterally compressed, bicarinate, 13–50(–53) × 2.3–5 mm, papery, strigose; sessile. **Seeds** 11–26.

Varieties 4 (4 in the flora): w United States.

Astragalus convallarius is known to contain nitrotoxins that are poisonous to livestock, especially sheep (L. F. James and S. L. Welsh 1992).

1. Legumes linear to narrowly oblong, gradually or abruptly contracted to ± symmetric apex; Montana south to Colorado west to Nevada and Arizona.
   2. Legumes linear or linear-lanceoloid, 25–50 (–53) × 2.5–3.3(–4.2) mm, lengths 8–18 times widths; Montana south to Colorado west to Nevada and Arizona . . . . 31a. *Astragalus convallarius* var. *convallarius*
   2. Legumes linear to narrowly oblong, 13–24(–30) × 3.4–4(–4.5) mm, lengths 4–8(–10) times widths; extreme sw Utah and adjoining Nevada . . . 31b. *Astragalus convallarius* var. *finitimus*
1. Legumes oblanceoloid, tapering downward into calyx from obliquely triangular apex; w Colorado or wc Nevada.
   3. Leaflets 7–11 throughout; wc Nevada . . . . 31c. *Astragalus convallarius* var. *margaretiae*
   3. Leaflets 3–13 proximally, some distal leaves reduced to naked rachis or with at most 1 pair of filiform leaflets; w Colorado . . . . 31d. *Astragalus convallarius* var. *scopulorum*

31a. Astragalus convallarius Greene var. **convallarius** [E] [F]

Stems (10–)20–50(–70) cm. **Leaflets** 0 or 3–11, blades 2–25 (–33) mm. **Bracteoles** 0. **Pedicels** 1–5 mm. **Flowers** 8–11 mm; calyx 4.2–6 mm, tube 3.4–4.8 mm, lobes 0.4–1.4 mm. **Legumes** linear, 25–50(–53) × 2.5–3.3(–4.2) mm, length 8–18 times width, gradually or abruptly contracted to ± symmetric apex. **Seeds** 13–20.

Flowering May–Aug. Mixed desert shrub, sagebrush, pinyon-juniper, mountain brush, ponderosa pine, and aspen communities; (1200–)1400–2900 m; Ariz., Colo., Idaho, Mont., Nev., Utah, Wyo.

Variety *convallarius* demonstrates considerable variability in presence or absence of leaflets, length of fruits, shape and length of calyx-lobes, pubescence coloration in the inflorescences, and degree of development of the stipelike bases of the fruits. Various combinations of these features in the past have resulted in recognition of several taxa. R. C. Barneby (1947c) detailed and summarized variation in the complex.

31b. Astragalus convallarius Greene var. **finitimus** Barneby, Leafl. W. Bot. 7: 192. 1954 • Enterprise milkvetch [E] [F]

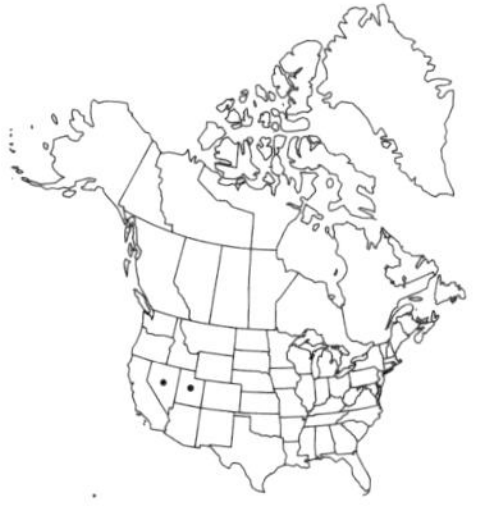

Stems (10–)20–50 cm. **Leaflets** 3–11, blades 2–25(–33) mm. **Bracteoles** 0. **Pedicels** 1–5 mm. **Flowers** 7.6–8.4 mm; calyx 4.2–6 mm, tube 3.4–4.8 mm, lobes 0.4–1.4 mm. **Legumes** linear to narrowly oblong, 13–24(–30) × 3.4–4(–4.5) mm, length 4–8 (–10) times width, gradually or abruptly contracted to ± symmetric apex. **Seeds** 18–26.

Flowering May–Jun. Pinyon-juniper and sagebrush communities; 1700–2300 m; Nev., Utah.

Variety *finitimus*, recognized by its relatively short, broad fruits, is restricted to extreme southwestern Utah and immediately adjacent Nevada.

31c. Astragalus convallarius Greene var. **margaretiae** Barneby, Brittonia 36: 167. 1984 (as margaretae) • Margaret's milkvetch [C] [E]

Stems (15–)18–30 cm. **Leaflets** 7–11 throughout, blades 3–13 mm. **Bracteoles** 0. **Pedicels** 0.5–1.5 mm. **Flowers** 9–10 mm; calyx 4.5–5 mm, tube 3–4 mm, lobes 0.8–1.2 mm. **Legumes** narrowly oblanceolate, 13–20 × 3.5–5 mm, tapering downward into calyx from obliquely triangular apex. **Seeds** 14–20.

Flowering May–Jun. Sagebrush and pinyon-juniper woodlands; of conservation concern; 1400–2800 m; Nev.

The disjunct var. *margaretiae* is restricted to the Pine Nut Mountains of west-central Nevada.

31d. Astragalus convallarius Greene var. **scopulorum** Barneby, Leafl. W. Bot. 5: 30. 1947 • Rocky Mountain milkvetch [E]

Stems 20–50 cm. **Leaflets** 3–13 proximally, some distal leaves reduced to naked rachis or with at most 1 pair of filiform leaflets, blades 2–25(–33) mm. **Bracteoles** 0–2. **Pedicels** 0.6–2.3 mm. **Flowers** (6.6–)8.1–11.2 mm; calyx 4–6.3 mm, tube (3.5–)3.8–5.4 mm, lobes 0.5–1.1 mm. **Legumes** oblanceoloid, 20–35 × 2.3–4 mm, tapering downward into calyx from obliquely triangular apex. **Seeds** 11–17.

Flowering May–Jul. Sagebrush, oak, and pinyon-juniper communities; 1700–2500 m; Colo.

Variety *scopulorum* is mostly from the valleys of the Grand and Gunnison rivers in west-central Colorado. It differs from var. *convallarius* primarily in the fruits that taper from obliquely triangular apices to the narrower bases at the calyces.

32. Astragalus diversifolius A. Gray, Proc. Amer. Acad. Arts 6: 230. 1864 • Mesic or meadow milkvetch [C] [E]

Homalobus orthocarpus Nuttall in J. Torrey and A. Gray, Fl. N. Amer. 1: 351. 1838, not *Astragalus orthocarpus* Boissier 1849

Plants 20–50 cm, strigulose, hairs basifixed; from shallow subterranean or superficial caudex and stout taproot. **Stems** prostrate to ascending or erect, strigulose. **Leaves:** distal leaves often unifoliolate, leaflets and rachis often expanded into flat, grasslike blade, 1.5–7 cm; stipules connate-sheathing and papery-scarious at proximal nodes, distinct or basally connate and herbaceous at distal nodes, 1–3 mm; petiole flattened or short and continuous with rachis; leaflets 1–7, blades narrowly elliptic, linear, oblanceolate, or lanceolate, 4–47(–67) × 1–5 mm, apex acute or acuminate, surfaces usually strigose, sometimes glabrous adaxially; terminal leaflet longer, sometimes decurrent distally, not jointed to rachis. **Peduncles** incurved-ascending, 2–15 cm. **Racemes** (1 or)2–8-flowered, flowers ascending; axis 0.5–3 cm in fruit; bracts 0.7–2.5 mm; bracteoles 0. **Pedicels** 1.8–4 mm. **Flowers** 8–13.5 mm; calyx (3.5–)4.4–6.7 mm, strigose, tube 3.2–4.7 mm, lobes broadly subulate, 1–2 mm; corolla greenish white, often tinged with purple; banner recurved through 50–80°; keel 7.8–11 mm, apex broadly triangular. **Legumes** ascending to declined, stramineous, straight or slightly decurved, narrowly oblong, strongly laterally compressed, bicarinate, 10–17 × 2.7–4 mm, papery, strigose; stipe 0.5–1.3 mm. **Seeds** 10–16.

Flowering May–Jul. Moist, often saline meadows, ditch banks, and swales, usually within the sagebrush community; of conservation concern; 1300–2000 m; Idaho, Nev., Utah, Wyo.

The rather widely scattered *Astragalus diversifolius* is not commonly collected and is presumed rare. It has long been confused with the common, more xerophytic, *A. convallarius.*

135l. Astragalus Linnaeus sect. Lonchocarpi A. Gray, Proc. Amer. Acad. Arts 6: 219. 1864 [E]

Herbs perennial, caulescent, sparsely leafy, often junceous or ephedroid; root-crown or caudex subterranean. **Hairs** basifixed. **Stems** single or few to several. **Stipules** distinct or connate (±) proximally. **Leaves** odd-pinnate, sessile or subsessile to petiolate; leaflets (0–)3–21, or lateral leaflets fewer and terminal leaflet continuous with rachis. **Racemes** loosely flowered, flowers ascending, spreading, declined, or nodding. **Calyx tubes** usually campanulate, rarely cylindric. **Corollas** whitish, ochroleucous, yellow, or pink-purple to dull lavender or purple, petals often strongly recurved, banner recurved through 30–130°, keel apex obtuse, acute, or triangular, sometimes beaklike. **Legumes** persistent or eventually deciduous, continuous with receptacle, sessile, subsessile, or stipitate, usually declined or pendulous, rarely spreading, ascending, or erect, linear-oblong to linear-oblanceoloid, ellipsoid, ovoid-ellipsoid and bladdery, compressed laterally or dorsiventrally, or 3-sided or 4-sided, usually unilocular, rarely semibilocular. **Seeds** 8–42.

Species 17 (17 in the flora): w United States.

Section *Lonchocarpi* consists of five subsections distributed in the Colorado Basin, southeastern Great Basin, and eastward and southeastward to Colorado and New Mexico.

The subsections are: subsect. *Pseudogenistoidei* Barneby (*Astragalus titanophilus*, *A. xiphoides*); subsect. *Pseudostrigulosi* Barneby (*A. cronquistii*); subsect. *Aequales* Barneby (*A. pinonis*, *A. atwoodii*, *A. aequalis*); subsect. *Lancearii* Barneby (*A. episcopus*, *A. lancearius*, *A. duchesnensis*, *A. nidularius*, *A. harrisonii*); and subsect. *Lonchocarpi* (A. Gray) Barneby (*A. coltonii*, *A. ripleyi*, *A. schmolliae*, *A. tortipes*, *A. lonchocarpus*, *A. hamiltonii*).

SELECTED REFERENCE Barneby, R. C. 1952. Pugillus *Astragalorum* XIV. Notes on sect. *Lonchocarpi*. Leafl. W. Bot. 6: 172–177.

33. Astragalus titanophilus Barneby, Amer. Midl. Naturalist 55: 477. 1956 • Limestone milkvetch [E]

Astragalus convallarius Greene var. *foliolatus* Barneby, Leafl. W. Bot. 5: 31. 1947

Plants slender, wiry, 15–30 cm, gray-strigulose, hairs sometimes flattened and scalelike; from shallow, subterranean caudex. **Stems** prostrate to ascending, 1–7 cm underground, gray-strigulose. **Leaves** 2.5–9 cm; stipules distinct, 2–8 mm, papery at proximal nodes, firm at distal nodes; leaflets 7–15, jointed to rachis throughout, blades narrowly linear to linear-oblong, 2–12(–16) mm, apex obtuse to emarginate, surfaces strigulose. **Peduncles** ascending or divaricate and incurved, 3.5–9.5 cm, surpassing leaves. **Racemes** (3–)7–20-flowered, flowers spreading or ± decurved; axis 2–14 cm in fruit; flowers declined or nodding; bracts 0.8–2 mm; bracteoles usually 0. **Pedicels** 2–6 mm. **Flowers** 7.3–8.5 mm; calyx campanulate, 4–5.9 mm, strigose, tube 3.2–4.5 mm, lobes subulate or triangular-subulate, 0.5–1.4 mm; corolla ochroleucous, tinged or veined with lilac, or pinkish white; banner strongly recurved through 100–130°; keel 7–8 mm, apex bluntly triangular. **Legumes** declined or pendulous, green or purplish becoming brown-stramineous, straight or gently incurved or decurved, narrowly oblong to ellipsoid, strongly laterally compressed, (18–)22–35 × 3.2–4.6(–5) mm, stiffly papery, strigulose; subsessile, base contracted into stout, stipelike neck 1–1.5 mm. **Seeds** (16–)20–24.

Flowering Apr–Jul. Sandy, gravelly, or fine-textured substrates in pinyon-juniper communities; 1300–1900 m; Ariz.

Astragalus titanophilus is known only from Coconino and Mohave counties.

Astragalus titanophilus was initially placed at the varietal level within *A. convallarius*, where it could still reside without serious damage to the taxonomy. Present placement of *A. titanophilus* and *A. xiphoides* within sect. *Lonchocarpi* is problematic and additional investigation is suggested.

34. Astragalus xiphoides (Barneby) Barneby, Amer. Midl. Naturalist 55: 477. 1956 • Gladiator milkvetch [E]

Astragalus convallarius Greene var. *xiphoides* Barneby, Leafl. W. Bot. 5: 30. 1947

Plants rushlike, 30–45 cm, strigulose-cinereous; from shallow, subterranean caudex. Stems prostrate to ascending, 2–7 cm underground, strigulose-cinereous. Leaves reduced to phyllodia or terminally expanded rachis, 2.5–13 cm; stipules distinct throughout, 2–7 mm, papery at proximal nodes, firm at distal nodes; leaflets (1 or)3–7, blades linear-filiform or linear-involute, continuous with rachis, 3–17 mm, apex acute, surfaces strigulose. Peduncles ascending, 3.5–7.5 cm. Racemes (3–)7–20(–35)-flowered, flowers declined or nodding; axis 2–18(–33) cm in fruit; bracts 1.2–2.6 mm; bracteoles 0 or 2. Pedicels 2–8 mm. Flowers 8–9 mm; calyx campanulate, 4.6–6 mm, strigulose, tube 3.8–4.1 mm, lobes subulate or triangular-subulate, 0.8–1.9 mm; corolla ochroleucous, immaculate; banner recurved through 100–130°; keel 8 mm, apex bluntly triangular. Legumes declined or pendulous, stramineous, straight or nearly so, narrowly lanceoloid-oblong, strongly laterally compressed, 25–40 × 4–5.5 mm, papery, strigulose; sessile. Seeds 14–18.

Flowering Apr–early Jun. Sandstone and clay bluffs; 1500–1600 m; Ariz.

Astragalus xiphoides is known from Apache, Coconino, and Navaho counties.

35. Astragalus cronquistii Barneby, Mem. New York Bot. Gard. 13: 257. 1964 • Cronquist's milkvetch [C] [E]

Plants 15–40(–50) cm, strigulose, some hairs flattened and scalelike; from subterranean caudex and stout taproot. **Stems** prostrate to decumbent-ascending, 5–14 cm underground, strigulose. **Leaves** 1.5–4.5 cm; stipules distinct throughout, 2–6 mm, papery at proximal nodes, herbaceous at distal nodes; leaflets 7–15, blades oblong to narrowly elliptic, 6–23 mm, apex retuse to truncate, surfaces strigose abaxially, glabrate adaxially. **Peduncles** divaricate and incurved-ascending, 2–6.5 cm. **Racemes** 6–20-flowered, flowers nodding; axis 1.5–8.5 cm in fruit; bracts 0.6–1.2 mm; bracteoles 1. **Pedicels** 1.5–2.5 mm. **Flowers** 8–9 mm; calyx campanulate, 3.8–5.3 mm, strigose, tube 3.3–4 mm, lobes triangular, 0.5–1.3 mm; corolla dull pink-purple, or lilac to vivid reddish purple; banner recurved through 90–100°; keel 8–8.5 mm, apex sharply deltate. **Legumes** declined or pendulous, green or faintly red-dotted becoming stramineous, usually straight or incurved, rarely decurved, narrowly ellipsoid, 3-sided compressed, 13–30 × 3–4.8 mm, semibilocular, papery, strigose; valves inflexed, septum 0.3–0.6 mm; stipe 0–0.8 mm. **Seeds** 16 or 17.

Flowering Apr–Jun. Blackbrush and salt desert shrub communities; of conservation concern; 1400–1800 m; Colo., Utah.

The principal distribution of *Astragalus cronquistii* is Montezuma County, Colorado, where it is confined to Cretaceous Mancos Shale, and two disjunct regions of San Juan County, Utah: Comb Wash area on the Permian Cutler Formation and near Aneth on the Jurassic Morrison Formation.

The propensity of *Astragalus cronquistii* for fine-textured, seleniferous substrates is evident in its distribution, but it does not have the characteristic garliclike odor of many selenophytes.

36. Astragalus pinonis M. E. Jones, Contr. W. Bot. 8: 14. 1898 • Pinyon milkvetch [E]

Plants slender, weak, 10–55 (–60) cm, gray-strigulose; from superficial caudex. **Stems** erect or reclining, gray-strigulose. **Leaves** sparse, 2–11 cm; stipules distinct throughout, 1.5–6 mm, papery at proximal nodes, herbaceous at distal nodes; leaflets (5–)9–19, blades linear or oblong, 2–19 mm, apex obtuse to retuse, surfaces strigose; terminal leaflet jointed to rachis. **Peduncles** divaricate or widely incurved-ascending, 1.5–8 cm. **Racemes** 5–20-flowered, flowers ascending-spreading; axis 2–7(–11) cm in fruit; bracts 1–2 mm; bracteoles 0 or 1. **Pedicels** 1–3 mm. **Flowers** 8.1–10.3 mm; calyx campanulate, 4.2–5.6(–7) mm, strigose, tube 2.3–3.8 (–4.5) mm, lobes subulate, (0.8–)1–2.4 mm; corolla greenish to ochroleucous, suffused with purple, or white and purple-veined; banner recurved through 90°; keel 7.5–9.7 mm, apex slightly beaked. **Legumes** spreading or declined, brownish- or purplish-tinged becoming brown-stramineous, straight to slightly curved, oblong-ellipsoid, ± terete, 20–35 × 5.5–8.5 mm, stiffly-papery, strigose; subsessile. **Seeds** 32–42.

Flowering May–Jul. With black sagebrush in juniper and pinyon-juniper woodlands, salt-grass meadows; 1500–2300 m; Nev., Utah.

Astragalus pinonis is found in Beaver and Juab counties in Utah, and Lincoln, Nye, and White Pine counties in Nevada.

Astragalus pinonis, a Great Basin endemic, commonly grows up through shrubs and is inconspicuous, possibly accounting for its rarity in collections.

37. Astragalus atwoodii S. L. Welsh & K. H. Thorne, Great Basin Naturalist 37: 103, fig. 1. 1977 • Atwood's milkvetch [C] [E]

Astragalus pinonis M. E. Jones var. *atwoodii* (S. L. Welsh & K. H. Thorne) Barneby & Isely

Plants 19–57 cm, gray-strigulose; from shallow, subterranean caudex. **Stems** erect, 2–6 cm underground, gray-strigulose. **Leaves** 0.6–9 cm; stipules distinct throughout, or amplexicaul and connate-sheathing at proximal nodes, 1.5–4 mm; leaflets (7 or)9–17, blades linear to narrowly oblong, 1.5–12.5 mm, apex obtuse to rounded, surfaces strigose; terminal leaflet often continuous with rachis. **Peduncles** 4–7.5 cm. **Racemes** 2–15-flowered, flowers ascending-spreading; axis 2–11 cm in fruit; bracts 1–2 mm; bracteoles 0 or 1. **Pedicels** 1–2.5 mm. **Flowers**

8–11 mm; calyx campanulate, 5–6.5 mm, strigose, tube 3.5–4 mm, lobes subulate, 1.1–2.6 mm; corolla ochroleucous, suffused with purple, faintly lilac-tinged; banner recurved through 90°; keel 7.5–9.7 mm, apex slightly beaked. **Legumes** spreading or declined, stramineous, straight to slightly curved, oblong-ellipsoid, terete or dorsiventrally compressed, slightly inflated, 21–34 × 2.8–5 mm, papery, strigose; stipe to 1 mm. **Seeds** 18–22.

Flowering Apr–Jun. Pinyon-juniper, cliffrose, sagebrush communities; of conservation concern; 1800–2100 m; Ariz.

Astragalus atwoodii, known from the Kaibab Plateau and House Rock Valley in Coconino County, is similar to, but geographically disjunct from, *A. pinonis*. It grows in shrubs, displaying leaves and flowers above the shrubs.

38. Astragalus aequalis Clokey, Madroño 6: 215, plate 27, figs. a–j. 1942 • Clokey's milkvetch C E

Plants slender, 20–50(–65) cm, gray-strigulose; from shallow, subterranean, thickened and woody caudex. **Stems** diffuse or ascending, (0–)1–4 cm underground, gray-strigulose. **Leaves** sparse, 2.5–9 cm; stipules distinct throughout, 1.5–4.5 mm, papery-membranous at proximal nodes, herbaceous at distal nodes; leaflets 9–15, blades linear-lanceolate or -oblanceolate, 5–20(–27) mm, apex rounded to retuse, surfaces strigose; terminal leaflet usually longer than adjacent pair. **Peduncles** incurved-ascending, 3–9 cm. **Racemes** 3–12-flowered, flowers ascending-spreading; axis 1–6 cm in fruit; bracts 1–1.5 mm; bracteoles 0–2. **Pedicels** 1–3 mm. **Flowers** 11.5–12 mm; calyx campanulate, 5.5–6.8 mm, strigose, tube 3.5–4.5 mm, lobes subulate or triangular, 2–2.7 mm; corolla ochroleucous, often tinged or lined with purple; banner recurved through 90°; keel 9.2–10.4 mm, apex slightly beaked. **Legumes** spreading or declined, stramineous or brownish with purple spots, straight, broadly and subsymmetrically ellipsoid, ovoid, or obovoid-ellipsoid, terete or somewhat dorsiventrally compressed, bladdery-inflated, 25–40 × 12–20 mm, papery, strigose; stipe 0.7–1.5 mm. **Seeds** 26–33.

Flowering Apr–Jun. Sagebrush and pinyon-juniper communities upward to ponderosa pine forests; of conservation concern; 1800–2500 m; Nev.

Astragalus aequalis is known only from the Spring (Charleston) Mountains in Clark County. The impressive bladdery-inflated fruits easily distinguish it from its relatives in subsect. *Aequales* (*A. atwoodii*, *A. pinonis*).

39. Astragalus episcopus S. Watson, Proc. Amer. Acad. Arts 10: 346. 1875 • Bishop's milkvetch E

Plants rushlike, 20–45 cm, strigose; from subterranean caudex. **Stems** erect or ascending; strigose. **Leaves** most reduced to phyllodia, continuous with rachis, 2–10 cm; stipules distinct throughout, 2–13 mm, papery at proximal nodes, herbaceous at distal nodes; leaflets 0–(1–13), blades linear, elliptic, or oblong, 1–15 mm, apex acute to obtuse or emarginate, surfaces strigose; terminal leaflet decurrent distally, not jointed to rachis. **Peduncles** erect or incurved-ascending, 6–23 cm. **Racemes** 6–30-flowered, flowers ascending; axis 3–30 cm in fruit; bracts 1.3–3 mm; bracteoles 0–2. **Pedicels** 1.5–3.5 mm. **Flowers** 10–15.5 mm; calyx suffused with purple or very pale, shortly cylindric, 4.1–8(–8.5) mm, white-strigose, tube 3.4–5.2(–6) × 1.9–2.9(–3.4) mm, lobes triangular to subulate, 0.6–2.2 mm; corolla pale pink or whitish to pink-purple; banner recurved through 40–45°; keel 9–12.3 mm, apex obtuse to subacute, not beaklike. **Legumes** pendulous, stramineous or suffused with purple or mottled, slightly curved or straight, oblong to lanceoloid-ellipsoid, laterally compressed, 14–32 × 4–8 mm, stiffly papery, glabrous or strigose; stipe 0–0.6 mm. **Seeds** 16–26. $2n = 22$.

Flowering May–Jun. Mixed desert shrub and pinyon-juniper communities, in clay or silty soils; 1200–2000 m; Ariz., N.Mex., Utah.

Astragalus episcopus occurs largely on fine-textured substrates, including Carmel, Chinle, Entrada, and Moenkopi formations in Emery, Garfield, Grand, Kane, San Juan, and Wayne counties in Utah, northeastern Mohave and northern Coconino counties in Arizona, and San Juan County in New Mexico.

Interpretations and misinterpretations of *Astragalus episcopus* were reviewed by R. C. Barneby (1947c, 1964).

40. Astragalus lancearius A. Gray, Proc. Amer. Acad. Arts 13: 370. 1878 • Lancer milkvetch E

Astragalus episcopus S. Watson var. *lancearius* (A. Gray) Isely

Plants rushlike, 15–55 cm, strigose; from subterranean caudex. **Stems** erect or ascending, 2.5–10 cm underground, strigose. **Leaves** some or most reduced to phyllodia and continuous with rachis, 1.5–10.5 cm; stipules distinct throughout, 2–7 mm, papery at proximal nodes, herbaceous at distal nodes; leaflets 0(or 3–7), blades linear to oblong, 2–14 mm, apex acute to obtuse, surfaces strigose; terminal leaflet decurrent distally, not jointed to rachis. **Peduncles** 4–23 cm. **Racemes** 6–25-flowered, flowers ascending; axis 3–19(–26) cm in fruit; bracts 1–1.5 mm; bracteoles 0–2. **Pedicels** 1–3 mm. **Flowers** 8.8–11.5 mm; calyx campanulate, 3.5–5.2 mm, black-strigose, tube 2.8–4.2 × 2.2–2.6 mm, lobes triangular, 0.5–1.2 mm; corolla pink-purple or tinged purplish or pinkish; banner recurved through 45°; keel 7.7–8.4 mm, apex obtuse to subacute, not beaklike. **Legumes** deflexed, brown or stramineous, slightly curved or straight, lanceoloid-oblong to oblong or lanceoloid-ellipsoid, laterally compressed, 20–35 × 5–9 mm, papery, glabrous or strigose; sessile or subsessile. **Seeds** 8–14.

Flowering Apr–Jun. Sagebrush, *Eriogonum*, service-berry, blackbrush, and pinyon-juniper communities; 1200–1800 m; Ariz., Utah.

Astragalus lancearius has been included as a variety within the geographically contiguous *A. episcopus*, but the differences are as distinct as those of other relatives within sect. *Lonchocarpi* and subsect. *Lancearii*.

41. Astragalus duchesnensis M. E. Jones, Contr. W. Bot. 13: 9. 1910 • Duchesne milkvetch [E]

Plants rushlike, 15–40(–45) cm, strigulose; from subterranean caudex or rhizomes. **Stems** straggling to ascending or erect, mostly branched near base, 1.5–8+ cm underground, strigulose. **Leaves** 2–10 cm; stipules distinct throughout, 3–8 mm, papery-membranous at proximal nodes, firm at distal nodes; leaflets 5–15, blades linear, oblong, or narrowly oblanceolate, 3–20 mm, apex obtuse to retuse, surfaces strigose or, sometimes, glabrate adaxially; terminal leaflet decurrent distally, not jointed to rachis. **Peduncles** erect or incurved-ascending, 3–10.5 cm. **Racemes** 5–22-flowered, flowers ascending, finally nodding; axis 2.5–13 cm in fruit; bracts 0.7–2 mm; bracteoles 0. **Pedicels** 0.8–2.2 mm. **Flowers** 8.5–12.5 mm; calyx usually dull purple, campanulate, 3.5–5.5 mm, strigulose, tube 3–4.3 mm, lobes triangular, 0.4–1.5 mm; corolla pink-purple, wing tips white; banner recurved through 90–95°; keel 8–9.8 mm, apex obtuse to subacute, not beaklike. **Legumes** declined, pale green or purplish becoming stramineous, straight or gently decurved, oblong to narrowly oblanceoloid, dorsiventrally compressed in proximal 1/2, laterally compressed distally, 20–35 × 3.3–6 mm, stiffly papery, strigose; sessile. **Seeds** 21–31.

Flowering Apr–Jun. Sandy or gravelly to fine-textured clay soils, in mixed desert shrub and pinyon-juniper communities; 1400–2000 m; Colo., Utah.

Astragalus duchesnensis, a sparsely foliose plant, is known from northeastern Utah and adjacent Colorado and is locally common on the floor of the Uinta Basin. It is unusual among xerophytic astragali in being rhizomatous. Plants occur in colonies and, in favorable years, form bold clumps; in dry years the same colony may produce only a few straggling stems, sterile or nearly so.

42. Astragalus nidularius Barneby, Leafl. W. Bot. 8: 16. 1956 • Bird's-nest milkvetch [E]

Plants clump-forming, 15–51 cm, strigose; from elongated, subterranean caudex, taproot deeply set. **Stems** forming rounded, birds-nestlike clumps, ascending to erect, many-branched, 3–14+ cm underground, strigose. **Leaves** 1.5–7 cm; stipules sometimes connate-sheathing at proximal nodes, mostly distinct, 1–6 mm, papery-membranous at proximal nodes, herbaceous at distal nodes; leaflets 5–11(or 13), blades linear or oblong, 2–20(–25) mm, apex obtuse to emarginate or acute, surfaces pubescent or adaxially glabrous; terminal leaflet of distal leaves decurrent and not jointed to rachis. **Peduncles** erect or incurved-ascending, 4–16(–28) cm. **Racemes** (3–)8–33-flowered, flowers ascending to declined; axis 1.5–28 cm in fruit; bracts 1.2–2.2 mm; bracteoles 0–2. **Pedicels** 1.2–3 mm. **Flowers** (9–)10–15 mm; calyx campanulate, (3.5–)3.8–7 mm, black-strigose, tube (3–)3.3–5.5 mm, lobes subulate, (0.5–)1–2.2 mm; corolla pink-purple; banner recurved through 30–45°; keel (7.5–)8.4–10.3 mm, apex obtuse to subacute, not beaklike. **Legumes** pendulous, green or purple-tinged becoming brownish stramineous, straight or gently decurved, narrowly oblong, dorsiventrally compressed, 20–32 × 3.5–4.5 mm, thinly fleshy becoming stiffly papery, strigose; stipe (2.5–)3.5–6 mm. **Seeds** (16–)20–26.

Flowering May–Jun. Pinyon-juniper and mixed desert shrub communities, on sandstone soils; 1300–1900 m; Utah.

Astragalus nidularius is known only from south-eastern Utah. It resembles an untidy bird's nest; the entangled, interlocking branches form rounded clumps overtopped by the racemes.

43. Astragalus harrisonii Barneby, Mem. New York Bot. Gard. 13: 270. 1964 • Harrison's milkvetch [E]

Plants clump-forming, rushlike, 40–70 cm, strigulose; from subterranean caudex. **Stems** ascending to erect, flexuous, diffusely interbranched, 6–16 cm underground, proximalmost epigeous internodes the shortest, clumps to 1+ m wide, strigulose. **Leaves** 1.5–6.5 cm, unifoliolate throughout or distally, terminal leaflet slightly expanded and confluent with filiform rachis; stipules distinct throughout, 1–5 mm, membranous becoming papery at proximal nodes, herbaceous at distal nodes; leaflets (1 or)3–9, blades linear-oblong to linear-elliptic or linear, 2–11 mm, apex acute, surfaces strigose; terminal leaflet decurrent distally, not jointed to rachis. **Peduncles** incurved-ascending, 6–19 cm. **Racemes** 3–17-flowered, flowers ascending; axis 5–40(–42) cm in fruit; bracts 0.5–1.1 mm; bracteoles 0. **Pedicels** 1.5–5.5 mm. **Flowers** 8–10.5 mm; calyx campanulate, 2.5–4.6 mm, strigose, tube 1.5–3.7 mm, lobes triangular, 0.5–1.9 mm; corolla pink-purple; banner recurved through 50°; keel 7.4 mm, apex obtuse to subacute, not beaklike. **Legumes** pendulous, stramineous, straight or decurved, narrowly ellipsoid, dorsiventrally or laterally compressed or subterete, 17–28 × 3.8 mm, papery, strigose or glabrous; stipe 2.5–5 mm. **Seeds** 10–12.

Flowering Apr–Jun. Pinyon-juniper communities; 1500–1900 m; Utah.

Astragalus harrisonii is known from Capitol Reef and southward to the Water Pocket Fold. It is a delicate, wispy plant with stems and racemes that greatly surpass the leaves. Flowers may be widely spaced (to 3 cm) along racemes.

44. Astragalus coltonii M. E. Jones, Zoë 2: 237. 1891 (as coltoni) • Colton's or coal-cliffs milkvetch [E]

Plants clump-forming, 10–75 cm, strigulose, canescent, cinereous, or greenish cinereous; from subterranean or branched, superficial caudex. **Stems** erect or ascending, strigulose, canescent, cinereous, or greenish cinereous. **Leaves** dimorphic, some unifoliolate distally and reduced to phyllodia, continuous with rachis, 2–10 cm; stipules distinct throughout, 1–7 mm, papery at proximal nodes, herbaceous at distal nodes; leaflets (1 or)3–19, blades linear, oblong, cuneate-oblong, or ovate, (3–) 4–20 mm, apex acute, obtuse, truncate or retuse, surfaces strigose; terminal leaflet decurrent distally, not jointed to rachis. **Peduncles** erect or incurved-ascending, (4–)6.5–30 cm. **Racemes** (2–)5–30-flowered, flowers spreading-declined; axis 3–20 cm in fruit; bracts 0.5–3.2 mm; bracteoles 0. **Pedicels** 0.8–2.5 mm. **Flowers** 12–19 mm; calyx purplish, cylindric, 4.5–8 mm, strigose, tube 4–6.7 mm, lobes broadly subulate, 0.6–2.3 mm; corolla pink-purple; banner recurved through 35–50°; keel 9–13 mm, apex bluntly or sharply deltate. **Legumes** pendulous, green or reddish becoming stramineous, straight or gently decurved, oblong to oblanceoloid, strongly compressed, flattened laterally, 19–35 × (3–) 3.5–6 mm, stiffly papery, glabrous; stipe 4–11 mm. **Seeds** 14–20.

Varieties 2 (2 in the flora): w United States.

R. C. Barneby (1964) aligned *Astragalus coltonii* with *A. filipes* in *Homalobus* or the equivalent sect. *Homalobi*. Although *A. filipes* is similar with its compressed and stipitate fruit, the stipules are fundamentally different. P. A. Rydberg (1929) and M. E. Jones (1923) described the stipules of *A. coltonii* as connate; proximal stipules do form a bidentate, more or less amplexicaul sheath, but the interpretation is not strictly correct. The stipules are united by adherence to a vestigial petiole and are consistent with all genuine sect. *Lonchocarpi* and not like those in *A. filipes*, which are united by their contrapetiolar margins.

1. Leaves odd-pinnate or distalmost unifoliolate; leaflets (1 or)3–11, terminal leaflet each confluent with rachis . . . . 44a. *Astragalus coltonii* var. *coltonii*
1. Leaves odd-pinnate; leaflets (5–)9–17(–19), jointed or joint obscure distally. . . . . 44b. *Astragalus coltonii* var. *moabensis*

44a. Astragalus coltonii M. E. Jones var. **coltonii** [E]

Stems strigulose; from subterranean or superficial caudex. **Leaves** odd-pinnate or distalmost unifoliolate, 2–10 cm; leaflets (1 or)3–11, blades usually linear, rarely linear-oblong, 4–14 mm, apex obtuse or acute, surfaces brighter green and, usually, less densely pubescent abaxially; terminal leaflet confluent with rachis. **Peduncles** 10–30 cm. **Racemes** (2–)5–20-flowered. **Legumes** 25–32 × (3–)3.5–5.2 mm; stipe 4–9 mm.

Flowering Apr–Jun. Bunchgrass, salt desert shrub, pinyon-juniper, and mountain brush communities; 1400–2300 m; Colo., Utah.

Variety *coltonii* occurs almost exclusively below the coal measures of the Mesaverde Group sandstone. However, the type specimen was collected on another substrate near Richfield, Sevier County, Utah. The primary range of var. *coltonii* is in Carbon, Emery, Garfield, Grand, Kane, Millard, Sevier, and Wayne counties in Utah, and a disjunct population occurs in Montezuma County in Colorado.

44b. Astragalus coltonii M. E. Jones var. **moabensis** M. E. Jones, Contr. W. Bot. 8: 11. 1898 (as coltoni) • Moab milkvetch [E]

Stems strigulose, cinereous, greenish cinereous, or canescent; from subterranean caudex. **Leaves** odd-pinnate, (2–)3–9 cm; leaflets (5–)9–17(or 19), blades oblong, cuneate-oblong, or ovate, (3–)5–20 mm, apex obtuse, truncate, or retuse, surfaces brighter green and, usually, less densely pubescent abaxially; leaflets jointed or joint obscure in distal ones. **Peduncles** (4–)6.5–21 cm. **Racemes** (6–)10–30-flowered. **Legumes** 19–35 × (3–)3.5–6 mm; stipe 5–11 mm.

Flowering Apr–Jun. Pinyon-juniper and mountain brush communities; 1400–2600 m; Ariz., Colo., N.Mex., Utah, Wyo.

Variety *moabensis* is primarily in the Four Corners region of Apache and Navajo counties in northeastern Arizona, Dolores, Mesa, Montezuma, and Montrose counties in southwestern Colorado, San Juan County in northwestern New Mexico, and Grand and San Juan counties in southeastern Utah. The populations in Sweetwater and Uinta counties in southwestern Wyoming may represent recent introductions due to livestock transport.

45. Astragalus ripleyi Barneby, Leafl. W. Bot. 6: 175. 1952 • Ripley's milkvetch [E]

Plants robust, 40–70 cm, strigulose; from subterranean branched caudex. **Stems** erect or ascending, 2–10 cm underground, strigulose. **Leaves** 4–9(–11) cm; stipules distinct throughout, 1–5 mm, papery-scarious at proximal nodes, herbaceous at distal nodes; leaflets 11–21, blades linear or linear-elliptic to subfiliform, 8–30 mm, apex acute, obtuse, or truncate, surfaces strigulose abaxially, glabrate adaxially; terminal leaflet usually continuous with rachis. **Peduncles** arcuate-erect, (3.5–)6–12(–15) cm. **Racemes** (5–)15–45-flowered, flowers declined and secund; axis 2–16 cm in fruit; bracts 1–2 mm; bracteoles 0. **Pedicels** 2.3–7 mm. **Flowers** 13–17 mm; calyx purplish or whitish, cylindric, 5.5–7 mm, strigose, tube 5–6.6 mm, lobes triangular-subulate, 0.5–1.1 mm; corolla pale lemon yellow, concolorous; banner recurved through 35°; keel (9.5–)10–11.3 mm, apex bluntly or sharply deltate. **Legumes** pendulous, green or reddish becoming stramineous, straight or slightly curved, linear-oblong to lanceoloid or narrowly ellipsoid, strongly compressed, flattened laterally, (14–)20–33 × (3.5–)4–6 mm, papery, ± translucent in age, strigulose; stipe 8–15 mm. **Seeds** 11–17.

Flowering Jun–Jul. Sagebrush, rabbitbrush, pinyon-juniper, ponderosa pine, Douglas-fir, Gambel oak, and aspen communities; 2100–2800 m; Colo., N.Mex.

Astragalus ripleyi has a restricted range in Archuleta and Conejos counties in Colorado, and Rio Arriba and Taos counties in New Mexico.

The glabrous leaflets and the continuity of the terminal leaflet with the rachis on most leaves, in conjunction with the laterally compressed fruits and elongate fruiting pedicels, distinguish *Astragalus ripleyi* from *A. schmolliae*, its close ally. The smaller, lemon yellow petals and laterally flattened fruits distinguish *A. ripleyi* from the coarser, larger-flowered *A. lonchocarpus*.

Astragalus ripleyi is in the Center for Plant Conservation's National Collection of Endangered Plants.

46. Astragalus schmolliae Ced. Porter, Madroño 8: 100, plate 9, figs. 4–7. 1945 (as schmollae) • Schmoll's milkvetch [C] [E]

Plants robust, 30–70 cm, strigulose; from shallow, subterranean branched caudex. **Stems** erect or ascending, 2–10 cm underground, strigulose. **Leaves** 4–10(–11) cm; stipules distinct throughout, 2–7 mm, papery at proximal nodes, herbaceous at distal nodes; leaflets (7–)11–21, blades linear or linear-oblong to -elliptic, 6–20 × mm, apex obtuse to retuse, surfaces strigulose. **Peduncles** erect, 9–21 cm. **Racemes** (7–)10–28-flowered, flowers declined and secund; axis (2.5–)4.5–20 cm in fruit; bracts 1.5–3 mm; bracteoles 0–2. **Pedicels** 1–2.5 mm. **Flowers** 14.5–18 mm; calyx cylindric, 6–7.5 mm, strigose, tube (5–)5.5–6 mm, lobes triangular-subulate, 1–1.7 mm; corolla ochroleucous, concolorous; banner recurved through 45°; keel 9.5–11.5 mm, apex bluntly or sharply deltate. **Legumes** pendulous, stramineous, straight or evenly to hamately curved, linear-oblanceoloid, 3-sided, abaxially compressed, (25–)30–40 × 3.5–5 mm, stiffly papery, strigulose; stipe 5–10 (–12) mm. **Seeds** 18–20.

Flowering May–Jun. Pinyon-juniper communities; of conservation concern; 1800–2300 m; Colo.

Astragalus schmolliae is locally common on Chapin Mesa, Montezuma County, near Mesa Verde National Park, on Cliff House Sandstone of the Mesaverde Group. It is in the Center for Plant Conservation's National Collection of Endangered Plants.

47. Astragalus tortipes J. L. Anderson & J. M. Porter, Syst. Bot. 19: 116, fig. 1. 1994 • Towaoc milkvetch [C] [E]

Plants robust, 30–80 cm, strigulose; from shallow, subterranean caudex. **Stems** erect or ascending, 0.5–2.2 cm underground, strigulose. **Leaves** (6–) 8–14(–18) cm; stipules distinct throughout, 3–12 mm, white-papery at proximal nodes; leaflets 7–15, blades linear, 10–43 mm, apex acute, surfaces strigulose; terminal leaflet jointed to rachis. **Peduncles** 8–15 cm. **Racemes** 10–25(–30)-flowered, flowers becoming twisted through 180°; axis 7–12 cm in fruit; bracts 1.5–2 mm; bracteoles 1 or 2. **Pedicels** 1–5 mm. **Flowers** (12–)14–18 mm; calyx campanulate, (4–)7–9 mm, strigose, tube 3.5–7 mm, lobes lanceolate-subulate, (0.5–)1.2–2.5 mm; corolla lemon yellow, concolorous; banner recurved through 80–110°; keel apex bluntly or sharply deltate. **Legumes** inverted from flexion of pedicels, ascending to erect, green becoming maroon-mottled, oblong-ellipsoid, moderately laterally compressed, 22–30 × 6–9 mm, glabrous; stipe 12–16(–19) mm. **Seeds** 17–27.

Flowering Apr–Jun. Mixed salt desert shrub (shadscale, rabbitbrush, and *Eriogonum*) communities, on Cretaceous Mancos Shale knolls and ridges with pedimental gravel; of conservation concern; 1700–1800 m; Colo.

Astragalus tortipes is the most unusual member of sect. *Lonchocarpi*, known only from the vicinity of Towaoc, Montezuma County; the plants grow on Mancos shale with another rare species, *A. cronquistii.*

Astragalus tortipes is in the Center for Plant Conservation's National Collection of Endangered Plants.

48. Astragalus lonchocarpus Torrey in War Department [U.S.], Pacif. Railr. Rep. 4(5): 80. 1857 • Great rushy milkvetch [E] [F]

Phaca macrocarpa A. Gray, Mem. Amer. Acad. Arts, n. s. 4: 36. 1849, not *Astragalus macrocarpus* de Candolle 1802

Plants often densely clump-forming, slender, (22–)30–85 (–90) cm, strigulose; from shallow, subterranean caudex. **Stems** erect, 1–8 cm underground, strigulose. **Leaves** 2–13 cm; stipules distinct throughout, 1–9(–10) mm, stiff-papery at proximal nodes, herbaceous becoming papery at distal nodes; leaflets (1 or)3–9(or 11), blades linear to narrowly oblanceolate, 2–36 × 0.5–4 mm, apex obtuse to acute, surfaces usually strigose, sometimes glabrous adaxially; terminal leaflet decurrent distally, not jointed to rachis. **Peduncles** erect or incurved-ascending, 6–24 cm. **Racemes** 7–40+-flowered, flowers spreading-declined; axis 3.5–45 cm in fruit; bracts 0.8–2.5 mm; bracteoles 0. **Pedicels** 1.3–4.5 mm. **Flowers** 13–20 mm; calyx brown, cylindric-gibbous, 5.8–10.3 mm, strigose, tube 5–8 mm, lobes subulate, 0.6–2.5 mm; corolla ochroleucous to nearly white, concolorous; banner recurved through 50°; keel 10.5–14 mm, apex bluntly or sharply deltate. **Legumes** pendulous, often brownish, straight or slightly curved, ellipsoid to oblong, dorsiventrally compressed, convex, 22–50 × 3.3–6.2(–7.5) mm, stiffly papery, faces smooth or cross-reticulate, strigose or glabrous; stipe 3–15 mm. **Seeds** 12–26. $2n = 22$.

Flowering May–Jul. Salt desert shrub, blackbrush, and pinyon-juniper communities, often on low-quality substrates such as saline shale and clay; 1100–2600 m; Ariz., Colo., Nev., N.Mex., Utah.

The main center of distribution of *Astragalus lonchocarpus*, a relatively tall, handsome, pale-flowered species, is in the Colorado Plateau. The species is sporadic and widely dispersed in the Great Basin as if recently introduced, perhaps by livestock. G. W. Smith et al. (1992) reported the indolizidine alkaloid swainsonine in this species, but there is little evidence that the plant is grazed by livestock. J. D. Karron (1989) reported the species to be self-compatible, and no inbreeding depression was detected in seedling produced by self-fertilization.

49. Astragalus hamiltonii Ced. Porter, Rhodora 54: 159. 1952 (as hamiltoni) • Hamilton's milkvetch [C] [E]

Astragalus lonchocarpus Torrey var. *hamiltonii* (Ced. Porter) Isely

Plants clump-forming, robust, 25–60 cm, densely strigulose; from shallow, subterranean caudex. **Stems** erect and ascending; densely strigulose. **Leaves:** distalmost unifoliolate, sometimes also proximalmost, 3–8 cm; stipules usually distinct throughout, rarely shortly connate-sheathing at proximal nodes, 1.5–9.5 mm, firm, early becoming papery; leaflets (1 or) 3–7, blades elliptic to narrowly oblanceolate, 10–47 × 2–9(–13) mm, apex obtuse to retuse, surfaces strigose; terminal leaflet decurrent, not jointed to rachis. **Peduncles** erect and incurved-ascending, 2.5–15.5 cm. **Racemes** 7–30-flowered, flowers spreading-declined; axis 2–11 cm in fruit; bracts 1–2.5 mm; bracteoles 0–2. **Pedicels** 1.2–3 mm. **Flowers** (16–) 20–24 mm; calyx light brown, cylindric-gibbous, (7–) 8.2–11(–12) mm, strigose, tube (5.5–)6.5–9.2 mm, lobes subulate, 1.7–2.6(–4) mm; corolla ochroleucous, concolorous; banner recurved through 45°; keel 13.7–16.6 mm, apex bluntly or sharply deltate. **Legumes** pendulous, brown, straight, ellipsoid, dorsiventrally compressed, sometimes becoming subterete, 25–35 × 4–7.5 mm, papery, strigose; stipe 8–12 mm. **Seeds** 16–22.

Flowering May–Jun. Tertiary Duchesne River and Wasatch, and less commonly on Cretaceous Mowry Shale, and Dakota, or other formations, pinyon-juniper and desert shrub communities; of conservation concern; 1600–1900 m; Colo., Utah.

Astragalus hamiltonii is a specialized inhabitant of peculiar geological strata north and west of Vernal, Utah, especially the Tertiary Duchesne River and Cretaceous Mowry Shale formations. It also occurs in Dinosaur National Monument, Moffat County, Colorado.

135m. ASTRAGALUS Linnaeus sect. DRABELLA (Torrey & A. Gray) Barneby, Leafl. W. Bot. 5: 3. 1947 (as Drabellae) [E]

Homalobus Nuttall [unranked] *Drabella* Torrey & A. Gray, Fl. N. Amer. 1: 352. 1838 (as Drabellae)

Herbs perennial, tufted, diminutive, mat-forming, or pulvinate, usually acaulescent, rarely subacaulescent; caudex superficial. **Hairs** malpighian, herbage usually silvery. **Stems** mostly reduced to crowns, usually obscured by marcescent leaf bases or stipules. **Stipules** connate. **Leaves** dimorphic, most proximal ones reduced to phyllodia, sessile; leaflets 0(or 3–7), jointed. **Racemes** sometimes subumbellate, loosely or compactly flowered, flowers ascending. **Calyx tubes** campanulate or turbinate-campanulate. **Corollas** pink to purple, ochroleucous, or whitish, banner recurved through 45–90°, keel apex obtuse. **Legumes** eventually deciduous or nearly persistent, sessile, erect or ascending (humistrate), ellipsoid to linear, oblong, or lanceoloid, usually laterally compressed, with sutures protruding, sometimes bluntly 3-sided and sulcate abaxially, unilocular. **Seeds** 4–24.

Species 5 (5 in the flora): w North America.

SELECTED REFERENCE Barneby, R. C. 1947. Pugillus *Astragalorum* VI. Notes on section *Drabellae*. Leafl. W. Bot. 5: 1–9.

50. Astragalus spatulatus E. Sheldon, Minnesota Bot. Stud. 1: 22. 1894 • Draba milkvetch [E] [F]

Homalobus caespitosus Nuttall in J. Torrey and A. Gray, Fl. N. Amer. 1: 352. 1838, not *Astragalus caespitosus* Pallas 1800–1803

Plants tuft- or mat-forming, 1.5–9(–12) cm, densely strigulose; from branched caudex. **Stems** obscured by marcescent leaf bases and stipules. **Leaves** mostly reduced to phyllodia, few with leaflets, 0.8–10 cm; stipules connate-sheathing throughout, 2–7 mm, papery-scarious; leaflets 0(or 3–5), blades (phyllodia) oblanceolate to linear, 4–30 mm, apex acute, mucronate, or spinulose, surfaces strigose; terminal leaflet often confluent with rachis. **Peduncles** erect or ascending, outer ones often prostrate in fruit, 0.4–9 cm. **Racemes** densely 1–11-flowered; axis 0.2–3.5 cm in fruit; bracts 0.5–4 mm; bracteoles 0. **Pedicels** 0.3–1.7 mm. **Flowers** 5.7–9.5 mm; calyx 2.6–5 mm, strigose, tube 1.9–3.4 mm, lobes subulate, 0.5–2.5 mm; corolla pink purplish to ochroleucous or whitish; banner recurved through 45°; keel 4–6 mm. **Legumes** erect, pale green tinged purple, with red-mottle, becoming brown or stramineous, straight or slightly curved, lanceoloid to lanceoloid-oblong, 2-sided, laterally compressed, 4–13 × 1.5–3.3 mm, papery, usually strigose, rarely glabrous; sessile. **Seeds** 4–12. $2n = 24$.

Flowering May–Jul. Pinyon-juniper, sagebrush, and mountain brush communities, exposed ridges; 600–2700 m; Alta., Sask.; Colo., Idaho, Kans., Mont., Nebr., N.Dak., S.Dak., Utah, Wyo.

The nomenclature of *Astragalus spatulatus* was confused from the start with three epithets proposed by T. Nuttall in J. Torrey and A. Gray (1838–1843) within *Homalobus* that were previously used in *Astragalus* and, as a result, not available. The habit of *A. spatulatus* varies from a low cushion, with flowers borne barely above the very short leaves, to taller plants with elongate leaves and flowers borne well above the ground. The extremes are distinctive but are connected by a series of intermediates.

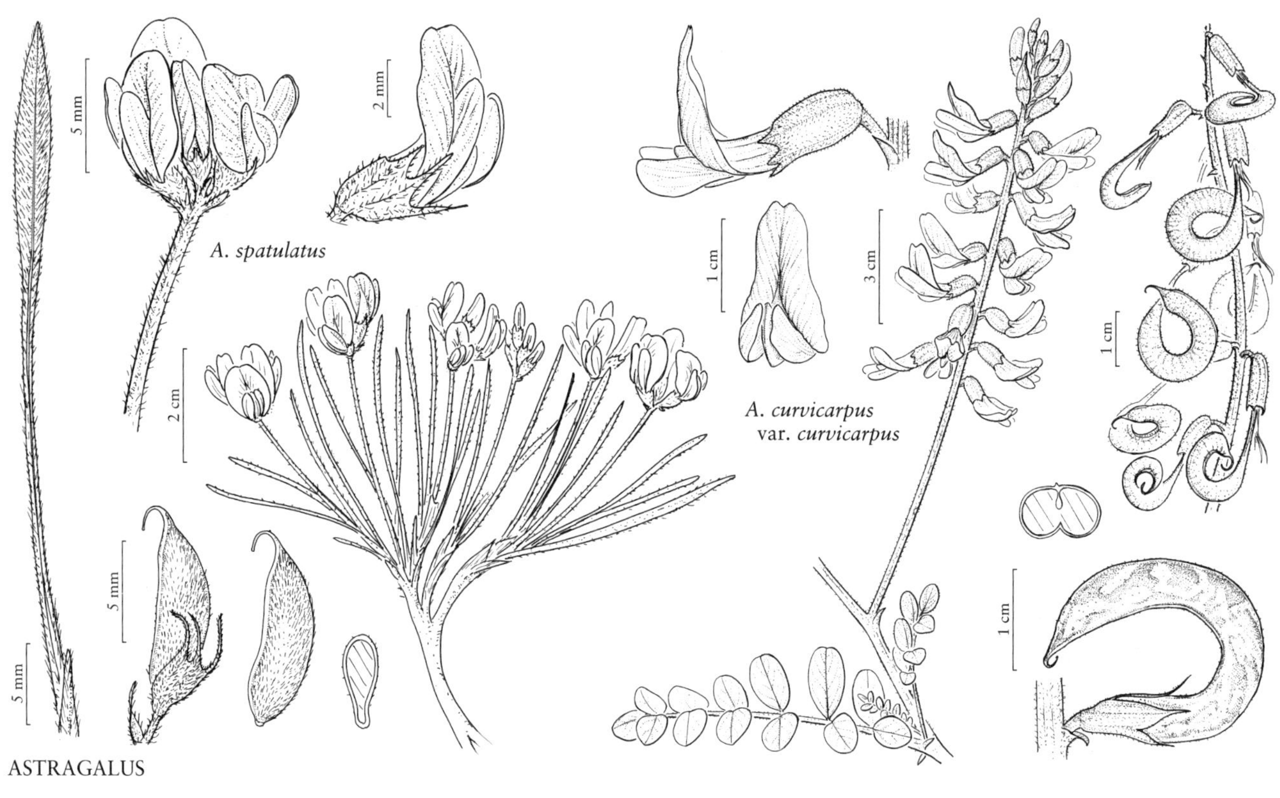

ASTRAGALUS

51. Astragalus chloödes Barneby, Leafl. W. Bot. 5: 6. 1947 • Grass milkvetch E

Plants tuft-forming, resembling grass bunch, acaulescent or subacaulescent, 5–28 cm, silvery- or gray-strigulose; from branched caudex. **Stems** obscured by stipules. **Leaves** reduced to phyllodia, 1–13(–17) cm; stipules conspicuous, usually connate-sheathing, 2–8 mm, white-membranous; phyllodia linear-oblanceolate proximally, narrowly linear distally, 1–3 mm wide, apex very acute and subspinulose distally, surfaces strigose. **Peduncles** erect, slender, wiry, 2–9(–11) cm. **Racemes** loosely 7–23-flowered, in bud resembling grass spikelets; axis 4.5–24 cm in fruit; bracts 2–4.5 mm; bracteoles 0. **Pedicels** 1–2.5 mm. **Flowers** 6.2–8.5 mm; calyx 4.5–8.5 mm, strigose, tube 2–3.5 mm, lobes rigid-spreading and subulate-aristiform, 2.5–5.2 mm; corolla pink-purple, banner striate; banner recurved through 90°; keel 6–6.6 mm. **Legumes** erect or ascending, green, often with purple or red spots, becoming stramineous, curved, obliquely lanceoloid or oblong, laterally compressed, 7–12 × 1.7–3 mm, stiffly papery, glabrous or strigose; sessile. **Seeds** 4–8.

Flowering May–Jul. Sandstone hogbacks and cuestas in pinyon-juniper and mixed desert shrub communities; 1400–1900 m; Utah.

The foliage of *Astragalus chloödes* is initially grass-like but matures to resemble a cluster of pine needles; the flower buds resemble grass spikelets. This narrow Uintah County endemic is locally common atop weathered sandstone formations.

52. Astragalus drabelliformis Barneby, Mem. New York Bot. Gard. 13: 287. 1964 • Big Piney milkvetch E

Plants tuft- or mat-forming, 1–3 cm, densely strigose-strigulose; from branched caudex. **Stems** obscured by marcescent leaf bases and stipules. **Leaves** mostly reduced to phyllodia, 1–2.5 cm; stipules connate-sheathing throughout, 1.5–5 mm, membranous; phyllodia oblanceolate or spatulate proximally, linear-oblanceolate distally, 10–25 mm, apex acute or subacute, surfaces strigose. **Peduncles** ascending, prostrate in fruit, 1–2.5 cm. **Racemes** densely 1–4-flowered; axis 0–0.5 cm in fruit; bracts 0.6–1 mm; bracteoles 0. **Pedicels** 0.6–1 mm. **Flowers** 5.2–7 mm; calyx turbinate-campanulate, 2.5–3.3 mm, strigose, tube 1.7–2.1 mm, lobes subulate, 0.8–1.2 mm; corolla pink purplish; banner recurved through 50–70°; keel 3.7–4.3 mm. **Legumes** ascending, green, often red-mottled, becoming stramineous, straight or slightly curved, narrowly and obliquely lanceoloid to lanceoloid-ellipsoid, 3-sided compressed,

5.5–8.5 × 1.8–2.5 mm, papery, usually strigose, rarely glabrous; sessile. **Seeds** 7–11.

Flowering late May–early Jul. Sagebrush or cushion plant communities of windswept summits and gullied slopes of low sandy or stony clay bluffs; 2100–2200 m; Wyo.

Astragalus drabelliformis is restricted to the upper Green River Valley between Big Piney and Daniel in Sublette County.

53. Astragalus simplicifolius (Nuttall) A. Gray, Proc. Amer. Acad. Arts 6: 231. 1864 • Bun milkvetch [E]

Phaca simplicifolia Nuttall in J. Torrey and A. Gray, Fl. N. Amer. 1: 350. 1838

Plants tuft- or mat-forming, 10–35 cm, densely strigulose; from branched caudex. **Stems** obscured by marcescent leaf bases and stipules. **Leaves** reduced to phyllodia, 0.4–2.5 cm; stipules connate-sheathing, 3–6 mm, membranous; phyllodia oblanceolate or spatulate, 4–25 mm, apex acute or apiculate, surfaces strigose. **Peduncles** erect or ascending, (0.5–)1–3 cm. **Racemes** 1–4-flowered; axis 0–0.5 cm in fruit; bracts 0.4–1.8 mm. **Pedicels** 0.5–1.8 mm. **Flowers** 10.6–12 mm; calyx 4.5–7 mm, prominently veined in fruit, strigose, tube 3–4.1 mm, lobes broadly subulate, 1.3–3 mm; corolla pink-purple; banner recurved through 45°; keel 7–9.6 mm. **Legumes** ascending, green or red-mottled becoming stramineous or brown, slightly curved, narrowly ovoid-ellipsoid to lanceoloid-ellipsoid, laterally compressed, 6–13(–15) × 2–5 mm, papery, glabrous or glabrate; sessile. **Seeds** 11–14.

Flowering May–Aug. Hilltops, barren ridges, on gullied bluffs, on shale or sandstone, on limestone pavement; 1600–2300 m; Wyo.

Astragalus simplicifolius, restricted to valleys of the upper Platte and Wind rivers, is completely included within the range of *A. spatulatus*, from which it is distinguished by its relatively larger flowers and laterally ridged fruits.

54. Astragalus detritalis M. E. Jones, Contr. W. Bot. 13: 9. 1910 • Debris milkvetch [E]

Plants dwarf, tuft-forming, 0.5–8 cm, densely silver-strigulose or -strigose; from branched caudex, branches with thatch of persistent stipules and leaf-bases. **Stems** very short or ± absent, forming depressed tufts. **Leaves** reduced to phyllodia or palmately trifoliolate or odd-pinnate distally, 0.5–8 cm; stipules mostly connate-sheathing, 3–10 mm, scarious; leaflets 0(or 3–7), blades narrowly oblanceolate to linear, 3–30 mm, apex spinulose, surfaces strigose; phyllodia not differentiated into petiole and blade. **Peduncles** erect or incurved-ascending, ascending or decumbent in fruit, 1–9 cm. **Racemes** densely 2–8-flowered; axis 0.9–3.8 cm in fruit; bracts 2.5–7 mm; bracteoles 0–2. **Pedicels** 0.5–2.5 mm. **Flowers** 12–20 mm; calyx 5–9.6 mm, strigose, tube 3.1–5.4 mm, lobes subulate, 1.6–4.7 mm; corolla pink-purple; banner recurved through 45°; keel (8.4–)9.4–12.8(–13.4) mm. **Legumes** erect, green, usually also red-mottled, becoming stramineous, straight or curved, linear-oblong, laterally compressed, 15–38 × 2–3.5 mm, papery, strigose; sessile. **Seeds** 15–24.

Flowering late Apr–Jun. Pinyon-juniper and shadscale, greasebush, black sagebrush, galleta, wildrye, *Ephedra* and other mixed desert shrub communities, on Duchesne, Green, and Uinta river formations, on pedimental Quaternary gravel; 1500–2800 m; Colo., Utah.

Astragalus detritalis is restricted to the Uinta Basin in northeastern Utah and adjacent Colorado. It is in the Center for Plant Conservation's National Collection of Endangered Plants.

135n. Astragalus Linnaeus sect. Solitarii Barneby, Mem. New York Bot. Gard. 13: 293. 1964 [E]

Herbs perennial, caulescent, slender; caudex subterranean. **Hairs** basifixed. **Stems** single or few. **Stipules** distinct. **Leaves** odd-pinnate, petiolate to short-petiolate; leaflets 5–21. **Racemes** loosely flowered, flowers ascending or spreading then declined. **Calyx tubes** campanulate. **Corollas** ochroleucous, pale lilac, or whitish-tinged or lilac-veined, banner abruptly recurved through 85–90°, wings somewhat shorter than keel or longer than banner, keel apex obtuse or subacute. **Legumes** eventually deciduous, stipitate, usually declined or pendulous, sometimes spreading, narrowly oblong, lanceoloid-oblong, or oblong-ellipsoid, strongly laterally flattened, unilocular. **Seeds** (6–)8–16.

Species 3 (3 in the flora): w United States.

55. Astragalus alvordensis M. E. Jones, Contr. W. Bot. 10: 67. 1902 • Alvord milkvetch E

Plants 15–30 cm, cinereous, hairs twisted; from deeply, subterranean caudex. **Stems** erect, 3–10 cm underground, cinereous. **Leaves** (1–)1.5–5 cm; stipules 0.5–2.5 mm, papery-scarious at proximal nodes, herbaceous at distal nodes; leaflets (7–)11–21, blades narrowly or broadly obovate, 1–7 mm, apex retuse or obcordate, surfaces strigose, sometimes adaxially glabrescent. **Peduncles** divaricate, often hanging below subtending leaf, 1–3.5 cm. **Racemes** 5–14+-flowered; axis 1–5 cm in fruit; bracts 0.5–1 mm; bracteoles 0. **Pedicels** 1–2 mm. **Flowers** 7–8.2 mm; calyx 2.5–3 mm, villosulous, tube 2–2.5 mm, not marcescent, lobes triangular, 0.5–0.7 mm; corolla pale lilac, or whitish to yellowish and veined and suffused with lilac, keel tip maculate; keel 4.6–5.3 mm. **Legumes** pendulous, stramineous, strongly curved or coiled through (1–)1.5–2 spirals, narrowly oblong, 3–4 mm wide, papery, villosulous; stipe 2–9 mm. **Seeds** 10–16.

Flowering May–Jul. Knolls, bluffs, xeric hillsides, loose volcanic sands, with sagebrush, shadscale, and rabbitbrush; 1000–1400 m; Nev., Oreg.

Astragalus alvordensis occurs in Baker, Harney, and Malheur counties, Oregon, and in northern Humboldt County, Nevada.

56. Astragalus solitarius M. Peck, Leafl. W. Bot. 4: 181. 1945 • Lonesome milkvetch E

Plants 20–45 cm, strigulose-cinereous; from shallow, subterranean caudex. **Stems** erect, strigulose-cinereous. **Leaves** 2–7 cm; stipules 1–3 mm, papery at proximal nodes, herbaceous at distal nodes; leaflets 5–9, blades linear to linear-oblong, 3–15 mm, apex obtuse to subacute, surfaces strigose, sometimes glabrescent adaxially. **Peduncles** divaricate and incurved-ascending, (3–)5–15 cm. **Racemes** (3–)7–30-flowered; axis (1.5–)4–25 cm in fruit; bracts 0.6–1.5 mm; bracteoles 0. **Pedicels** 1–2 mm. **Flowers** 6.3–8 mm; calyx 2.6–3.2 mm, strigose, tube 2.3–2.8 mm, lobes deltate or subulate, 0.3–0.8 mm; corolla ochroleucous, concolorous; keel 6.3–7.4 mm. **Legumes** pendulous, pale green, often faintly purple-mottled, becoming stramineous, straight or falcately decurved, narrowly oblong or lanceoloid-oblong, 12–25 × 3–4(–5) mm, papery, strigulose; stipe 4–8 mm. **Seeds** (6–)8–14.

Flowering May–early Jul. Sandy clay soils, almost always under low sagebrush; 900–1500 m; Nev., Oreg.

Astragalus solitarius is a narrow endemic of southern Harney and Malheur counties, Oregon, and adjacent Nevada. Plants are usually intertangled with low sagebrush and may establish only with protection (R. C. Barneby 1964). It is closely related to *A. alvordensis*, and the ranges of the two overlap along the Owyhee River, near Rome, Oregon, but there they are ecologically separate. *Astragalus solitarius* occurs on stiff clays of valley floors and mesas, whereas *A. alvordensis* grows on bluffs and knolls where the soil is deep, soft, and porous, and plants often form colonies in the open.

57. Astragalus applegatei M. Peck, Proc. Biol. Soc. Wash. 49: 111. 1936 (as applegatii) • Applegate's milkvetch C E

Plants 30–40 cm, sparsely strigulose; root and base of stems not known. **Stems** diffuse, sparsely strigulose. **Leaves** 3.5–7 cm; stipules 1.5–3 mm, papery at proximal nodes, herbaceous at distal nodes; leaflets 7–11, blades linear to linear-elliptic, (5–)8–20 mm, apex obtuse and apiculate, surfaces strigulose abaxially, glabrous adaxially. **Peduncles** incurved-ascending, 3–6 cm. **Racemes** 10–18-flowered; axis 3–7 cm in fruit; bracts 1–1.5 mm; bracteoles 0. **Pedicels** 1.3 mm. **Flowers** 6.5–7 mm; calyx 3–3.3 mm, strigose, tube 2.3–2.5 mm, lobes triangular, 0.7–0.9 mm; corolla whitish, tinged with lilac; keel 5.5–5.9 mm. **Legumes** spreading or declined, green or purple-mottled becoming stramineous, ± straight, narrowly and subsymmetrically oblong-ellipsoid, 8–11 × 2.4–2.8 mm, papery, strigulose; stipe 4–5 mm. **Seeds** 8–10.

Flowering Jun–early Aug. Seasonally wet meadows, moist ground along wayside ditches in moderately saline substrates; of conservation concern; 1200–1300 m; Oreg.

Astragalus applegatei occurs in the vicinity of the Klamath River, south of Klamath Falls in Klamath County.

As noted by L. Abrams (1944b), *Astragalus applegatei* most closely resembles *A. filipes*, but the fruits split at the apex initially, as in *A. trichopodus* var. *antisellii*.

Astragalus applegatei is in the Center for Plant Conservation's National Collection of Endangered Plants.

135o. ASTRAGALUS Linnaeus sect. CAMPTOPODES Barneby, Mem. New York Bot. Gard. 13: 298. 1964 [E]

Herbs perennial, caulescent; caudex deeply subterranean, with horizontally creeping rhizomes. **Hairs** basifixed. **Stems** single or few. **Stipules** distinct. **Leaves** odd-pinnate, petiolate; leaflets (9–)13–21. **Racemes** loosely flowered, flowers ascending-spreading. **Calyx tubes** campanulate. **Corollas** bright pink-purple, banner recurved through ca. 45°, keel apex blunt. **Legumes** eventually deciduous, stipitate, spreading to ascending, oblong, coiled into a ring, strongly laterally flattened, unilocular. **Seeds** 20 or 21.

Species 1: Idaho.

58. **Astragalus camptopus** Barneby, Leafl. W. Bot. 4: 228. 1946 • Bruneau milkvetch [E]

Plants colonial, 20–30 cm, strigulose or villosulous; from caudex and slender rhizomes. **Stems** erect or ascending, current season stems 3–10 cm underground, strigulose or villosulous. **Leaves** 3–8 cm; stipules 1–3 mm, scarious at proximal nodes, herbaceous at distal nodes; leaflet blades obovate-cuneate, 4–12 mm, apex obtuse, retuse, or obcordate, surfaces strigulose or villosulous abaxially, strigose to glabrescent adaxially. **Peduncles** erect or divaricate-ascending, 1–6.5 cm. **Racemes** 9–15-flowered; axis 3–8 cm in fruit; bracts 1 mm; bracteoles 0. **Pedicels** 1–1.5 mm. **Flowers** 14–17 mm; calyx 5–6.5 mm, strigose, tube 5–6 mm, marcescent, lobes triangular, 0.5–0.9 mm; corolla keel 12–13 mm. **Legumes** pale green sometimes mottled becoming stramineous, coiled through 1.5–2 spirals into a closed ring, 3.5–4 mm wide, scarcely fleshy becoming stiffly papery, sparsely villous; stipe 10–15 mm.

Flowering May–Jun. Barren knolls, gulches, sagebrush scablands, dune and dunelike hillsides in loose sandy substrates of basaltic or rhyolitic origins; 700–1100 m; Idaho.

Astragalus camptopus is restricted to the Bruneau Valley and vicinity, Owyhee County. Among species with coiled fruits, the colonial rhizomatous growth (often not seen on specimens) is not shared with *A. curvicarpus* and *A. speirocarpus*, and flowers are much larger than those of *A. alvordensis*.

135p. ASTRAGALUS Linnaeus sect. COLLINI M. E. Jones, Rev. N.-Amer. Astragalus, 139. 1923 [E]

Herbs perennial, caulescent; caudex superficial or subterranean. **Hairs** basifixed. **Stems** several to many. **Stipules** distinct or connate at proximal nodes. **Leaves** odd-pinnate, short-petiolate or subsessile; leaflets (7 or)9–21(–25), jointed. **Racemes** densely flowered initially, sometimes loose, flowers nodding, often retrorsely imbricate. **Calyx tubes** broadly campanulate or cylindric, usually somewhat swollen, strongly oblique, either gibbous-saccate behind pedicel or truncate at base and pedicel attached at proximal corner. **Corollas** white, ochroleucous, or pale yellow, banner recurved through 45–90(–100)°, keel apex obtuse. **Legumes** eventually deciduous, stipitate, pendulous or horizontally spreading, linear-, ovoid-, or lunate-oblong, or coiled, laterally compressed, with protruding sutures, unilocular. **Seeds** (7 or)8–30.

Species 3 (3 in the flora): w North America.

59. Astragalus collinus (Hooker) Douglas ex G. Don, Gen. Hist. 2: 256. 1832 • Hill milkvetch [E]

Phaca collina Hooker, Fl. Bor.-Amer. 1: 141. 1831

Plants clump-forming, robust or slender, 15–40(–50) cm, villosulous; from superficial or shallow subterranean caudex. **Stems** decumbent to ascending or erect, villosulous. **Leaves** 3–9(–10.5) cm; stipules distinct, 2–5(–7) mm, papery at proximal nodes, herbaceous at distal nodes; leaflets (9 or)11–21(–25), blades oblong-oblanceolate, narrowly obovate-cuneate, or linear-elliptic, 4–20(–22) mm, apex truncate-retuse to obtuse or retuse, surfaces villosulous abaxially, strigose to glabrescent or glabrous adaxially. **Peduncles** erect or incurved-ascending, (4–)5–16 cm. **Racemes** (10–)15–40(–55)-flowered; axis (3–)4–12(–18) cm in fruit; bracts 1.5–3.5 mm; bracteoles 2. **Pedicels** 0.8–2.8 mm. **Flowers** (10.5–)12–17.2 mm; calyx campanulate to broadly cylindric, gibbous-saccate, 7–12.3 mm, strigose, tube 5.8–9.4 mm, lobes lanceolate to triangular-subulate or triangular, (0.8–)1–2.7(–3.5) mm; corolla cream to pale lemon yellow; banner usually sigmoidally arched and apex very abruptly and strongly folded over calyx to more than 100°, sometimes recurved through 50°; keel 8.7–13.2 mm. **Legumes** pendulous, stramineous, straight or gently incurved, linear-oblong or obliquely ovoid-oblong, laterally compressed, 7–25 × 2.3–4.2 mm, somewhat fleshy becoming leathery, usually villosulous or strigulose, rarely glabrous; stipe (3.5–)5–15 mm. **Seeds** (7 or)8–18.

Varieties 2 (2 in the flora): w North America.

D. Isely (1998) remarked that the so-called stubby appearance of the flowers of *Astragalus collinus* (and of *A. curvicarpus* var. *subglaber*, *A. gibbsii*, and somewhat of *A. tweedyi*) is compounded by the pouchlike calyx, brief exsertion of the petals, and the sigmoid shape of the shortened banner. Except for *A. tweedyi*, these taxa could perhaps be considered geographical elements of one species.

1. Legumes linear-oblong, 7–25 × 2.5–3.4(–4) mm, usually straight, rarely slightly incurved, villosulous or loosely strigulose, hairs to 0.3–0.5 mm; seeds (10–)12–18; British Columbia, Idaho, Oregon, Washington . . . . 59a. *Astragalus collinus* var. *collinus*
1. Legumes obliquely ovate-oblong, gently incurved, 8–15 × 3.3–4.2 mm, usually villosulous, rarely glabrous, hairs to 0.5–1 mm; seeds (7 or)8–12; Gilliam, Morrow, and Umatilla counties, Oregon . . . . 59b. *Astragalus collinus* var. *laurentii*

59a. Astragalus collinus (Hooker) Douglas ex G. Don var. **collinus** [E]

Legumes usually straight, rarely slightly incurved, linear-oblong, 7–25 × 2.5–3.4(–4) mm, villosulous or loosely strigulose, hairs to 0.3–0.5 mm; stipe (5)6–15 mm. **Seeds** (10–)12–18.

Flowering May–Jul. Bunchgrass prairies and sagebrush communities on substrates overlying basalt, pine forests; 200–1000 m; B.C.; Idaho, Oreg., Wash.

59b. Astragalus collinus (Hooker) Douglas ex G. Don var. **laurentii** (Rydberg) Barneby, Amer. Midl. Naturalist 55: 487. 1956 • Lawrence's milkvetch [C] [E]

Homalobus laurentii Rydberg, Bull. Torrey Bot. Club 51: 15. 1924; *Astragalus laurentii* (Rydberg) M. Peck

Legumes gently incurved, obliquely ovoid-oblong, 8–15 × 3.3–4.2 mm, usually villosulous, rarely glabrous, hairs to 0.5–1 mm; stipe (3.5–)5–10 mm. **Seeds** (7 or)8–12.

Flowering May–Jul. Dry grassy sites, on sandy or clay soils derived from basalt; of conservation concern; 800–1100 m; Oreg.

In the southwestern corner of Morrow County and adjoining Gilliam County, Oregon, there are extensive and uniform populations of *Astragalus collinus* with glabrous fruits a little longer than the villosulous fruits of var. *laurentii* that may have resulted from introgression with *A. curvicarpus* var. *subglaber*. The indumentum of the herbage and impressed reticulation of the fruit are characteristic of *A. collinus* (R. C. Barneby 1964).

60. Astragalus curvicarpus (A. Heller) J. F. Macbride, Contr. Gray Herb. 65: 38. 1922 • Sickle milkvetch [E] [F]

Homalobus curvicarpus A. Heller, Muhlenbergia 2: 86. 1905; *Astragalus gibbsii* Kellogg var. *falciformis* (A. Gray) M. E. Jones; *A. speirocarpus* A. Gray var. *falciformis* A. Gray

Plants robust or slender, 10–40 cm, strigulose, villosulous, glabrous, or with few scattered hairs; from superficial or slightly subterranean caudex. **Stems** decumbent to ascending, strigulose, villosulous, glabrous, or with few scattered hairs. **Leaves** 2.5–9 cm; stipules distinct, (1–)1.5–5 mm, scarious at proximal nodes, herbaceous at distal nodes; leaflets (9 or)11–21 (–25), blades obovate-cuneate, oblong-obovate, or elliptic to broadly oblanceolate, (7–)9–19(–21) mm, apex retuse or truncate to obtuse, surfaces strigulose or villosulous abaxially, strigose to glabrescent or glabrous adaxially. **Peduncles** erect or arcuate-erect, 4–15 cm. **Racemes** (5–)10–25(–35)-flowered, flowers retrorsely imbricate, ascending then nodding; axis 2–10(–13) cm in fruit; bracts 0.7–2.5 mm; bracteoles 0. **Pedicels** 1–3.5 mm. **Flowers** 13.5–21 mm; calyx broadly campanulate to broadly cylindric (gibbous-saccate or gibbous-truncate), 6.1–13.6 mm, strigulose or villosulous, marcescent, tube 5.4–11.9 mm, marcescent, lobes triangular, 0.4–2.3 mm; corolla ochroleucous, white, or lemon yellow; banner recurved through 45°; keel 9.4–15.2 mm. **Legumes** pendulous, green or purple-spotted becoming brown-stramineous, hamately or lunately incurved or, rarely, coiled through 1.5 spirals, narrowly oblong, laterally compressed, 14–35 × (2.7)3–4.5(–5.5) mm, stiffly papery or thinly leathery, usually glabrous, villosulous, or strigulose, rarely glabrate; stipe 6–20 mm. **Seeds** 14–25(–28).

Varieties 3 (3 in the flora): w United States.

Astragalus curvicarpus and its immediate relatives (*A. collinus* to the north, *A. gibbsii* to the south) are geographically exclusive. Formal classification of these three species is speculative because relationships seem reticulate and the origin of the group polyphyletic (D. Isely 1998). R. C. Barneby (1964) discussed the evolutionary irrationalities of sect. *Collini*.

Astragalus gibbsii var. *curvicarpus* (E. Sheldon) M. E. Jones and *A. speirocarpus* var. *curvicarpus* E. Sheldon are illegitimate names that pertain here.

1. Legumes usually villosulous or strigulose, rarely glabrate or glabrous; flowers (15–)16.4–21 mm; leaflet blades sparsely pubescent adaxially; California, Idaho, Nevada, Oregon. .60a. *Astragalus curvicarpus* var. *curvicarpus*
1. Legumes glabrous; flowers 13.6–19.5 mm; leaflet blades pubescent or glabrous adaxially; nw transmontane Oregon, in drainage of Deschutes and John Day rivers.
    2. Flowers 13.6–15(–16.8) mm; calyces 6.1–8.5 (–9.3) mm; leaflet blade adaxial surface pubescent. . . . . 60b. *Astragalus curvicarpus* var. *brachycodon*
    2. Flowers 13.5–19.5 mm; calyces (8–)9–13.6 mm; leaflet blade adaxial surface glabrous, sparsely ciliate . . . . 60c. *Astragalus curvicarpus* var. *subglaber*

60a. Astragalus curvicarpus (A. Heller) J. F. Macbride var. **curvicarpus** E F

Plants loosely strigulose to villosulous. **Stems** 10–40 cm. **Leaflets:** adaxial blade surface pubescent, sometimes sparsely so. **Flowers** (15–)16.4–21 mm; calyx (7.9–)9.1–11.2 mm, tube (6.9–)7.5–9.7 mm, lobes (0.5–) 1–2.3 mm. **Legumes** hamately incurved or coiled into a ring, 20–35 × (2.7–)3–4.1(–5.5) mm, usually villosulous or strigulose, rarely glabrate or glabrous; stipe (9–)11–20 mm. **Seeds** 18–25(–28).

Flowering mid Apr–Jul. Plains and foothills with sagebrush on sandy or gravelly soils overlying igneous formations, on dunes, with sagebrush; 800–2800 m; Calif., Idaho, Nev., Oreg.

Specimens of var. *curvicarpus* with fruits coiled in a ring have sometimes been mistaken for *Astragalus speirocarpus*, which has flowers ascending and the calyx gibbous abaxially. Plants of this variety with fruits tightly coiled were named *A. whitedii* Piper forma *speirocarpoides* Barneby.

60b. Astragalus curvicarpus (A. Heller) J. F. Macbride var. **brachycodon** (Barneby) Barneby, Amer. Midl. Naturalist 55: 487. 1956 • Deschutes milkvetch E

Astragalus whitedii Piper var. *brachycodon* Barneby, Amer. Midl. Naturalist 41: 496. 1949

Plants strigulose. **Stems** 20–40 cm. **Leaflets:** adaxial blade surface pubescent. **Flowers** 13.6–15(–16.8) mm; calyx 6.1–8.5 (–9.3) mm, tube 5.4–7.6(–8.6) mm, deeply campanulate or cylindric, lobes 0.4–1 mm. **Legumes** lunately incurved or hamate, 14–22 × 3.4–4.5 mm, glabrous; stipe 6–12 (–15) mm. **Seeds** 15–21.

Flowering May–Jul. Plains and hillsides on rough basaltic gravel or pumice sand; 800–1200 m; Oreg.

Variety *brachycodon* is known from the upper Deschutes River drainage in Crook, Deschutes, and Jefferson counties.

In some plants of var. *brachycodon*, the calyx is usually obscurely saccate, sometimes merely truncate; the pedicel then is attached at a right angle to the lower corner.

60c. Astragalus curvicarpus (A. Heller) J. F. Macbride var. **subglaber** (Rydberg) Barneby, Amer. Midl. Naturalist 55: 487. 1956 • John Day milkvetch [E]

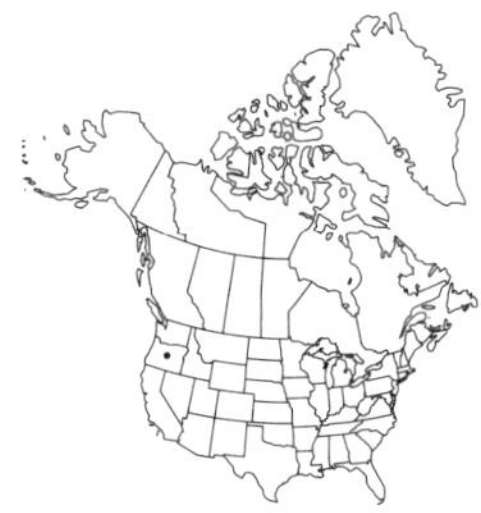

Homalobus subglaber Rydberg, Bull. Torrey Bot. Club 51: 17. 1924; *Astragalus subglaber* (Rydberg) M. Peck

Plants glabrous or herbage with a few scattered hairs. **Stems** 10–40 cm. **Leaflets:** adaxial blade surface glabrous, sparsely ciliate. **Flowers** 13.5–19.5 mm; calyx (8–)9–13.6 mm, tube (7.5–)8–11.9 mm, lobes 0.5–2.3 mm. **Legumes** gently incurved or, sometimes, hamate, 16–23 × 3–4 mm, glabrous; stipe 10–15 mm. **Seeds** 14–20.

Flowering late Apr–early Jul. Dry rocky hillsides, rough prairies, gravelly sagebrush slopes and flats on basalt; 500–1200 m; Oreg.

Variety *subglaber* is known from the lower Deschutes and John Day valleys in Gilliam, Grant, Sherman, Wasco, and Wheeler counties.

Attention was drawn by R. C. Barneby (1964) to the succulent nature of the banner and the auricles of the wings and keel.

61. Astragalus gibbsii Kellogg, Proc. Calif. Acad. Sci. 2: 161, fig. 50. 1863 • Gibbs's milkvetch [E]

Plants stout, 15–35 cm, villosulous; from slightly subterranean caudex. **Stems** decumbent to prostrate, 5–8 cm underground, villosulous. **Leaves** (1.5–)3–9.5 cm; stipules connate-sheathing and scarious at proximal nodes, distinct and herbaceous at distal nodes, 1.5–5 mm; leaflets (7–)11–19, blades broadly or narrowly cuneate, obovate-cuneate, or oblanceolate, 4–20 mm, apex retuse, surfaces villosulous abaxially, strigose to glabrescent adaxially. **Peduncles** incurved-ascending, 3–10(–12.5) cm. **Racemes** 10–30-flowered; axis 2.5–10 cm in fruit; bracts 1–3(–4.5) mm; bracteoles 2. **Pedicels** 1.5–4.3 mm. **Flowers** 14–17(–18) mm; calyx ovoid-campanulate to subcylindric, gibbous behind pedicel, 9.5–12.3 mm, villosulous or villous-tomentulose, tube 7.6–9.8 mm, lobes triangular, 2.3–3.7 mm; corolla dull yellow; banner strongly recurved or recurved through 90°; keel 12–15 mm. **Legumes** pendulous (or humistrate, apparently ascending), green or purple-mottled becoming stramineous, incurved through 0.5 spiral, lunately or falcately oblong, narrowly oblong-ellipsoid, or linear-oblong, laterally compressed, bicarinate by sutures, 22–30 × (4–)4.5–8 mm, fleshy becoming woody, villosulous or glabrous; stipe (7–)10–22 mm. **Seeds** 18–30.

Flowering May–Jul. Sagebrush valleys, silty meadows, openings in ponderosa pine forest, on dry sandy or clay substrates mostly of volcanic origin; 1200–1900 m; Calif., Nev.

The strongly and abruptly recurved banner, evident even in pressed material, is diagnostic for flowering material of *Astragalus gibbsii* and distinguishes it from *A. curvicarpus*, with which it had been once combined. The connate stipules distinguish *A. gibbsii* from all other species of sect. *Collini*. It occurs in the eastern Sierra Nevada region.

135q. Astragalus Linnaeus sect. Tweedyani Barneby, Mem. New York Bot. Gard. 13: 309. 1964 [E]

Herbs perennial, caulescent; caudex shallowly subterranean. **Hairs** basifixed. **Stems** few. **Stipules** distinct. **Leaves** odd-pinnate, short-petiolate or subsessile; leaflets (7–)11–23. **Racemes** compactly flowered early, flowers nodding. **Calyx tubes** broadly cylindric or deeply campanulate. **Corollas** ochroleucous, banner recurved through 45°, keel apex obtuse. **Legumes** persistent, stipitate, erect or incurved-ascending, oblong-ellipsoid, somewhat laterally compressed, with protruding sutures, unilocular. **Seeds** 6–8.

Species 1: nw United States.

Section *Tweedyani* is distributed in the lower Columbia Valley in northern Oregon and adjacent Washington.

62. Astragalus tweedyi Canby, Bot. Gaz. 15: 150. 1890 • Tweedy's milkvetch [E]

Plants robust, (25–)35–80 cm, loosely strigulose to villosulous. **Stems** erect or ascending, loosely strigulose to villosulous. **Leaves** 3–10(–13) cm; stipules (1–)2–7 mm, papery at proximal nodes, herbaceous at distal nodes; leaflet blades narrowly oblong-oblanceolate to linear-oblong, 5–18(–25) mm, apex retuse, surfaces strigulose to villosulous. **Peduncles** erect, (5–)7–15 cm. **Racemes** 12–35(–40)-flowered; axis 2.5–10 cm in fruit; bracts 1.5–6 mm; bracteoles 0. **Pedicels** 0.8–2 mm. **Flowers** 15–18.6 mm; calyx gibbous-convex behind pedicel, 8–10.5 mm, villosulous or villous-tomentulose, tube 7.5–9 mm, lobes triangular, 1–2.1 mm; corolla keel 11.5–14.3 mm. **Legumes** green becoming stramineous, 12–15 × (3–)3.4–4(–5.4) mm, stiffly leathery, glabrous or sparsely pilosulous; stipe 6–10 mm, pilosulous.

Flowering late May–Jul. Dry hillsides, grassy banks, stony meadows or ridges, on basaltic substrates, among sagebrush; 100–800 m; Oreg., Wash.

Astragalus tweedyi is a relatively tall, graceful plant from the lower Columbia and Deschutes valleys and is unusual in its tumid, pallid, basally pouched calyces and stipitate, unilocular fruits that remain attached to the raceme axis long after seeds are shed.

135r. Astragalus Linnaeus sect. Podosclerocarpi A. Gray, Proc. Amer. Acad. Arts 6: 225. 1864 [E]

Herbs perennial, caulescent; caudex superficial or shallowly subterranean. **Hairs** basifixed. **Stems** clustered or several to many. **Stipules** distinct. **Leaves** odd-pinnate, sessile or subsessile to short-petiolate; leaflets (5 or)7–17(–21). **Racemes** loosely flowered, sometimes initially densely flowered, flowers ascending. **Calyx tubes** campanulate to subcylindric. **Corollas** whitish or lilac-tinged, banner recurved through 40–45°, keel apex obtuse. **Legumes** eventually deciduous, stipitate, pendulous or horizontally spreading, lunately to falcately ellipsoid or oblong, incurved or coiled, laterally compressed, with protruding sutures, or subterete, unilocular. **Seeds** (14–)20–36.

Species 3 (3 in the flora): w North America.

Section *Podosclerocarpi* consists of species from the Columbia Basin in interior Washington, extreme northeastern Oregon, and southern British Columbia.

63. Astragalus sclerocarpus A. Gray, Proc. Amer. Acad. Arts 6: 225. 1864 • Dallas or woody-legumes milkvetch [E]

Phaca podocarpa Hooker, Fl. Bor.-Amer. 1: 142. 1831, not *Astragalus podocarpus* C. A. Meyer 1849

Plants clump-forming, 20–50 cm, strigulose; from superficial or shallow subterranean caudex. **Stems** clustered, decumbent to ascending or straggling, often conspicuously flexuous, diffuse, strigulose. **Leaves** (3–)5–13 cm; stipules 1.5–5 mm, papery at proximal nodes, subherbaceous at distal nodes; leaflets (5 or)7–17, blades linear, linear-oblanceolate, or narrowly oblong, 3–23 mm, apex obtuse or retuse, surfaces strigulose or, sometimes, glabrescent or glabrous adaxially. **Peduncles** 4–9.5 cm. **Racemes** (3–)7–21-flowered; axis (1–)2.5–6.5 cm in fruit; bracts 1–2 mm; bracteoles 2. **Pedicels** 1–2.5 mm. **Flowers** 13–16.3 mm; calyx 5.9–8 mm, strigulose, hairs white, black, and brown, tube 5.3–7 mm, not swollen or gibbous proximally, marcescent, lobes triangular, 0.5–1.3 mm; corolla whitish, banner and wing tips tinged with lilac, keel maculate; keel 10–12.1 mm. **Legumes** pendulous, brown-stramineous, ± straight to sigmoidally incurved through 0.5 spiral, lunately or falcately ellipsoid, subterete becoming laterally compressed, 20–35 × (5.5–)6.5–9 mm, stiffly leathery or subligneous, strigulose; stipe 12–20 mm, arched downward from calyx, distally sigmoidal-incurved. **Seeds** 30–36.

Flowering Apr–Jul. Dunes, sandy cutbacks, terraces, and barrens, with sagebrush; 60–500 m; B.C.; Oreg., Wash.

Astragalus sclerocarpus is known from the banks of the Columbia and lower Snake and Yakima rivers, from The Dalles upstream to Kettle Falls and northward through central and northeastern Washington to southern British Columbia.

The long-stipitate, scimitar-shaped, bicarinate fruits tapering at both ends are characteristic of this rather handsome, clump-forming, sparsely leafy xerophyte. The body tapers so gently into the stipe that it is sometimes difficult to differentiate the two.

A similar species, 356. *Astragalus asotinensis*, keys here. That species differs from *A. sclerocarpus* in having sparse pubescence, trichomes shorter than 0.5 mm, 15–23 oblong to narrowly oblong leaflets, and a pod 3–3.5 mm and incurved 70–110°.

64. Astragalus sinuatus Piper, Bull. Torrey Bot. Club 28: 40. 1901 • Whited's milkvetch C E

Astragalus whitedii Piper

Plants robust, 20–45 cm, villosulous; from superficial caudex. **Stems** decumbent to ascending, villosulous. **Leaves** 2–7 cm; stipules 2–4.5 mm, papery at proximal nodes, herbaceous at distal nodes; leaflets (9 or)11–17(or 19), blades obovate-cuneate or oblong-oblanceolate, (4–)6–16 mm, apex truncate-retuse to obtuse, surfaces villosulous. **Peduncles** erect or incurved-ascending, 4.5–12 cm. **Racemes** 8–16-flowered; axis 1.5–4.5 cm in fruit; bracts 2–3 mm; bracteoles usually 2. **Pedicels** 1.5–3.5 mm. **Flowers** 16.6–20 mm; calyx 9–11.5 mm, densely villosulous, tube 6.9–8.5 mm, not swollen or gibbous proximally, marcescent, lobes triangular, 1.4–3 mm; corolla whitish, keel tip faintly maculate; keel 12–13.4 mm. **Legumes** spreading or pendulous, stramineous, lunate- or hamate-incurved, laterally falcately oblong, laterally compressed, 18–30 × (4–)5–7 mm, fleshy becoming leathery, densely villosulous; stipe 5–8 mm. **Seeds** 24–30. **2*n*** = 22.

Flowering mid Apr–Jun. Dry hillsides, among sagebrush; of conservation concern; 600 m; Wash.

A similar species, 356. *Astragalus asotinensis*, differs from *A. sinuatus* by its straight, appressed calyx pubescence and oblong to narrowly oblong leaflets.

Astragalus sinuatus is restricted to Colockum Creek, Chelan County. It is in the Center for Plant Conservation's National Collection of Endangered Plants.

65. Astragalus speirocarpus A. Gray, Proc. Amer. Acad. Arts 6: 225. 1864 • Medick milkvetch E

Plants somewhat slender, 20–45 cm, strigulose; from superficial caudex. **Stems** ascending or diffuse, strigulose. **Leaves** 1.5–7.5 cm; stipules (1–)1.5–4(–5), papery at proximal nodes; leaflets 7–17(–21), blades cuneate-oblanceolate, oblong, or cuneate-obcordate, 2–10(–12) mm, apex truncate to deeply retuse, surfaces strigulose, sometimes adaxially glabrescent. **Peduncles** erect or incurved-ascending, (1–)2.5–5(–6.5) cm. **Racemes** (3–)7–17(–20)-flowered; axis 1–3.5(–5) cm in fruit; bracts 1–2.5 mm; bracteoles 2. **Pedicels** 1–2.5 mm. **Flowers** 14.7–20 mm; calyx 5.2–8(–9.1) mm, villosulous, tube 4.7–7.3 mm, not swollen or gibbous proximally, marcescent, lobes triangular, 0.5–1.2 mm; corolla whitish or tinted lilac, keel tip maculate; keel 10.6–13(–14.5) mm. **Legumes** pendulous, green or slightly mottled, becoming brown or stramineous, coiled through flat 1.25–2.5 spirals, or elaborately and irregularly contorted, linear-oblong, laterally compressed, 9–14 × (2.7–)3.2–5(–6) mm, stiffly leathery or subligneous, strigulose; stipe (4–)5–11 mm. **Seeds** (14–)20–28(–30). **2*n*** = 22.

Flowering May–Jul. Dry hillsides and valleys, stony or sandy substrates over basalt, in sagebrush scabland; 200–800 m; Wash.

Astragalus speirocarpus is locally abundant along the Columbia and Yakima river valleys in Kittitas and Yakima counties, southward to eastern Klickitat and western Benton counties.

The coiled or contorted fruits, diagnostic for the medick milkvetch, suggest the common name by their gross resemblance to the much smaller fruits of *Medicago*.

135s. Astragalus Linnaeus sect. Cusickiani (Rydberg) Barneby, Mem. New York Bot. Gard. 13: 326. 1964

Phaca Linnaeus sect. *Cusickiani* Rydberg in N. L. Britton et al., N. Amer. Fl. 24: 338. 1929 (as Cusickianae)

Herbs perennial, caulescent; caudex superficial or subterranean (branches rhizomelike in *A. ceramicus*). **Hairs** usually basifixed, sometimes malpighian (*A. ceramicus*). **Stems** usually several to many, rarely single or few clustered (*A. ceramicus*). **Stipules** connate or distinct at distal nodes. **Leaves** odd-pinnate, subsessile to short-petiolate or petiolate; leaflets (0 or 1–)5–23, distally reduced to phyllodia; terminal leaflet often decurrent. **Racemes** loosely flowered, flowers ascending, spreading, or declined, eventually all declined. **Calyx tubes** subcylindric or campanulate. **Corollas** white, pinkish white to pinkish red, yellowish, ochroleucous, or purplish, banner recurved through 35–90°, keel apex triangular or deltate, obtuse, or subacute, sometimes beaklike. **Legumes** eventually deciduous, usually stipitate, rarely sessile (*A. ceramicus*), pendulous, narrowly oblong and strongly compressed, or bladdery-inflated and obovoid-ellipsoid, unilocular. **Seeds** 10–30(–37).

Species 6 (6 in the flora): w North America, nw Mexico.

Section *Cusickiani* consists of three subsections distributed in the Columbia and Great basins, and Colorado Plateau, from southern British Columbia (although less commonly so), southward to Baja California, eastward to New Mexico, and northward to North Dakota.

The subsections are: subsect. *Inversi* (M. E. Jones) Barneby (*Astragalus californicus*, *A. filipes*, *A. inversus*); subsect. *Hookeriani* M. E. Jones (*A. cusickii*, *A. whitneyi*); and subsect. *Picti* (M. E. Jones) Barneby (*A. ceramicus*).

66. Astragalus filipes Torrey ex A. Gray, Proc. Amer. Acad. Arts 6: 226. 1864 • Basalt milkvetch F

Astragalus filipes var. *residuus* Jepson; *A. macgregorii* (Rydberg) Tidestrom

Plants large clump-forming, 20–90 cm, glabrate to densely strigulose; from superficial caudex. **Stems** erect or ascending, glabrate to densely strigulose. **Leaves** 2.5–12 cm; stipules connate-sheathing and papery-membranous at proximal nodes, distinct and herbaceous at distal nodes, 2–5 mm; leaflets (5–)9–23, blades linear to narrowly elliptic or oblong, 3–25(–30) mm, apex obtuse to truncate, retuse, or subacute, surfaces usually glabrous, sometimes strigose. **Peduncles** erect or ascending, 4.5–22 cm. **Racemes** (4–)6–30-flowered, 1 per leaf axil; axis 4–22 cm in fruit; bracts 1–3.5 mm; bracteoles 0. **Pedicels** 1.5–6 mm. **Flowers** 10–14.3(–15) mm; calyx subcylindric to campanulate, 4–7.7 mm, strigulose, hairs black and white, tube 3.3–6.4 × 2.4–3.5(–4.4) mm, lobes triangular, 0.5–1.5 mm; corolla whitish to ochroleucous, keel immaculate or bright yellow; banner recurved through 50–85°; keel abruptly incurved through 95–120°, blades about as long as claws, (6.7–)7.6–10(–12) mm, apex deltate or triangular. **Legumes** pale green, not mottled, not stramineous, straight, oblong to ellipsoid, strongly laterally compressed, 17–30(–35) × (3–)3.5–6.5 mm, papery, glabrous or strigulose; stipe 6–16 mm. **Seeds** 11–22. $2n = 22, 24$.

Flowering May–Jul. On sandy, loamy, or gravelly soils derived from igneous or sedimentary (often limestone) bedrock, with various plant communities, mostly with sagebrush; 70–2500 m; B.C.; Calif., Idaho, Nev., Oreg., Utah, Wash.; Mexico (Baja California).

Astragalus filipes is often so dense as to color hillsides with a wash of creamy, fragrant blossoms; it is unmistakable throughout most of its range. Except in northeastern California, where its range overlaps those of two closely related species, *A. californicus* and *A. inversus*, *A. filipes* is the only *Astragalus* combining connate stipules with stipitate, laterally compressed, unilocular fruits (except for *A. multiflorus*, with much smaller flowers and fruits).

Astragalus stenophyllus Torrey & A. Gray 1838 was historically used for *A. filipes*, but its type specimen lacks the features necessary for species-level identification (R. C. Barneby 1964).

67. Astragalus inversus M. E. Jones, Zoë 4: 276. 1893 • Susanville or Lava Beds milkvetch E

Plants slender, 20–50 cm, sparsely strigulose; from superficial caudex. **Stems** indistinctly flexuous (if at all), spreading to prostrate, sparsely strigulose. **Leaves** (3–)5–12 cm; stipules connate-sheathing and papery-membranous at proximal nodes, distinct and herbaceous at distal nodes, 1.5–5 mm; leaflets 5–11, blades linear, linear-oblanceolate, -elliptic, or filiform, (2–)5–25 mm, apex acute to subacute, surfaces strigulose; terminal leaflet sometimes decurrent distally, not jointed to rachis. **Peduncles** divaricate and incurved, (2–)4–20 cm. **Racemes** (3–)5–15(–22)-flowered, 1 per leaf axil; axis (1.5–)2–10 cm in fruit; bracts 1–2.5 mm; bracteoles 0–2. **Pedicels** 0.6–1.5 mm. **Flowers** 9.4–12.2 mm; calyx subcylindric to campanulate, 3.5–5 mm, strigulose, hairs black and white, tube 3–4 × 2.3–2.8(–3.1) mm, lobes triangular, 0.6–1 mm; corolla pinkish red, with

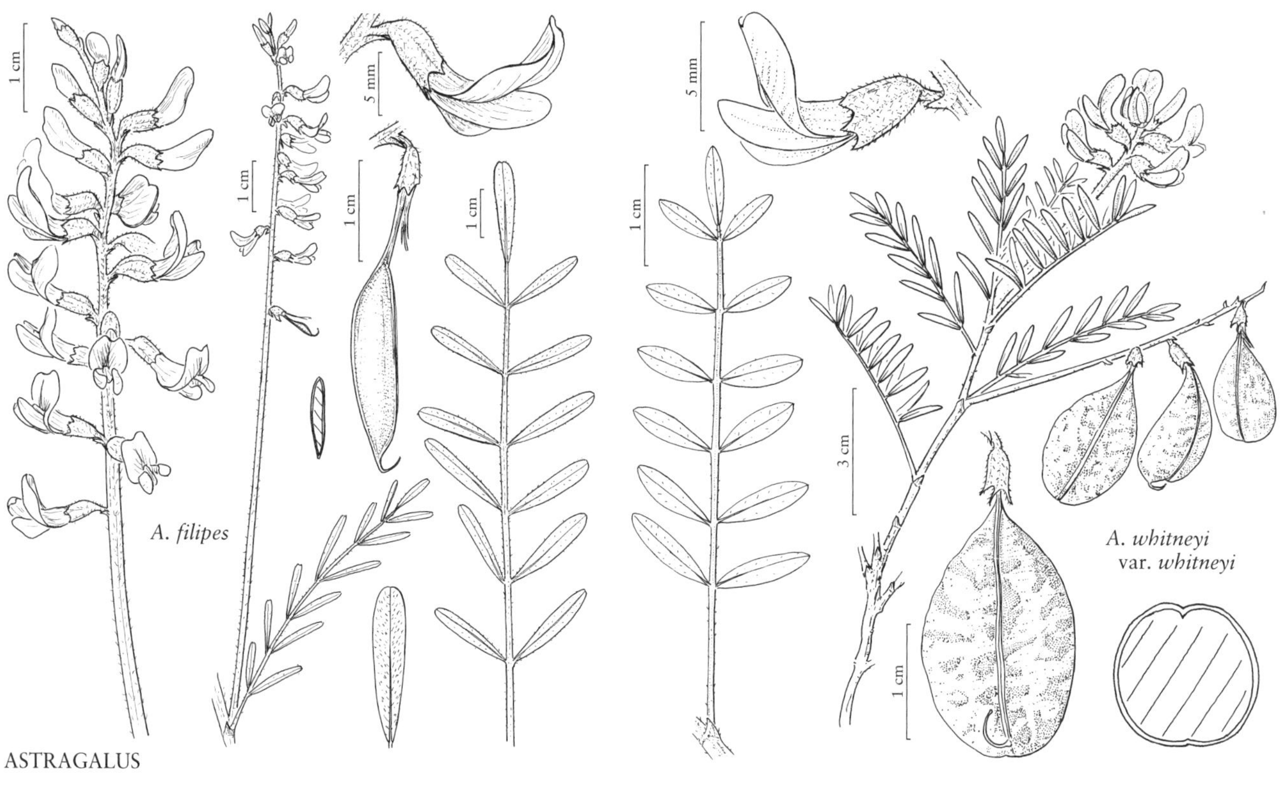

darker red veins, keel and wings buff-yellow, banner white-tipped; banner recurved through 35–45°; keel incurved through 40–85°, blades longer than claws, 8.2–10 mm, apex obtuse and beaklike. **Legumes** brown or stramineous, sometimes initially mottled, straight or slightly curved, linear-oblong or linear-lanceoloid, strongly laterally compressed, 15–35 x 3–4 mm, thinly fleshy becoming leathery, strigulose or if glabrous then mottled; stipe (4–)6–14 mm. **Seeds** 13–17.

Flowering Jun–Aug. Among sagebrush, xeric pine forests, dry basaltic or pumice soils; 1200–1900 m; Calif.

Astragalus inversus, a relatively tall, rushlike plant restricted to northeastern California, is readily distinguished from *A. filipes* by its few, remote leaflets, rather bicolored flowers, and mottled fruit.

68. Astragalus californicus (A. Gray) Greene, Bull. Calif. Acad. Sci. 1: 157. 1885 • Klamath milkvetch [E]

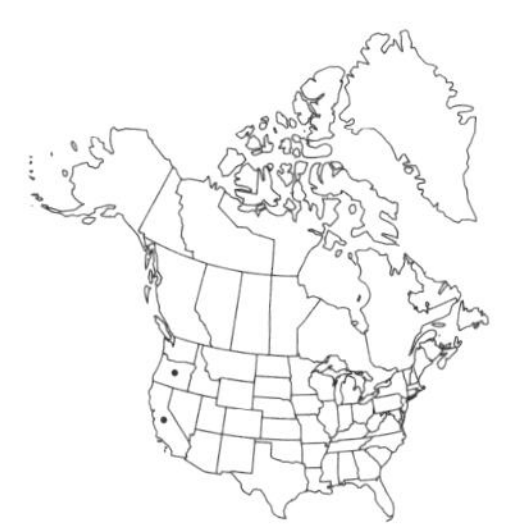

Astragalus collinus (Hooker) Douglas ex G. Don var. *californicus* A. Gray, Proc. Amer. Acad. Arts 12: 54. 1876

Plants robust, 15–50 cm, villous-villosulous; from superficial or slightly subterranean caudex. **Stems** decumbent to ascending, villous-villosulous. **Leaves** 3–8.5 cm; stipules connate-sheathing and papery-scarious at proximal nodes, submembranous at distal nodes, (1.5–)2–6.5 mm; leaflets 13–21, blades narrowly oblong- or cuneate-oblanceolate, (4–)6–20(–23) mm, apex truncate-retuse to obtuse, surfaces usually villosulous, sometimes glabrescent or glabrous adaxially. **Peduncles** erect or incurved-ascending, (3–)6–14 cm. **Racemes** (10–)15–25(–30)-flowered, 1 per leaf axil; axis 3–10.5 cm in fruit; bracts (1.5–)2–5 mm; bracteoles 0–2. **Pedicels** 1.3–3.5 mm, densely villous. **Flowers** (11.5–)13–17.4 mm; calyx campanulate, obliquely cuneate, 6.4–9.7 mm, silky-villous, hairs white, sometimes also black, tube 5.2–7 x 3.5–4.5 mm, lobes triangular, 0.9–3 mm; corolla ochroleucous or yellowish, immaculate; banner recurved through 45°; keel (9.5–)10.1–12.4 mm, apex sharply deltate. **Legumes** green and purple-mottled becoming brown or stramineous, straight or slightly curved, linear-oblong, strongly laterally compressed, 27–43 x 3.4–5, thinly fleshy becoming papery, strigulose or glabrous; stipe 8–14 mm. **Seeds** (15–)19–25(–27).

Flowering Apr–early Jul. Sagebrush, oak, and coniferous forest communities, on metamorphic or basaltic bedrock; 900–1400 m; Calif., Oreg.

Astragalus californicus is known from the Shasta and Siskiyou region of northeastern California and southern Jackson County in Oregon.

Within its range, *Astragalus californicus* is distinguished by its exserted-stipitate, narrowly oblong, flat fruits, villosulous foliage, and ochroleucous flowers.

69. Astragalus cusickii A. Gray, Proc. Amer. Acad. Arts 13: 370. 1878 • Cusick's milkvetch E

Plants clump-forming, slender, 30–70 cm, strigulose; from subterranean or superficial caudex. **Stems** erect to ascending, strigulose. **Leaves** 4–10(–13) cm; stipules connate-sheathing and papery-membranous at proximal nodes, connate or distinct and herbaceous at distal nodes, 0.5–4.5 mm; leaflets 13–21, blades linear to linear-filiform, (5–)7–15(–17) mm, apex acute to obtuse, surfaces strigulose or adaxially glabrous; terminal leaflet sometimes decurrent distally, not jointed to rachis. **Peduncles** erect or incurved-ascending, 5–15(–22) cm. **Racemes** becoming loosely (3–)4–14(–18)-flowered; axis 1–8.5 cm in fruit; bracts 0.8–1.5 mm; bracteoles 0. **Pedicels** ascending, 1.2–3.5 mm. **Flowers** 12.5–15.5 mm; calyx campanulate, obliquely cuneate, 4–6.7 mm, silky-villous, hairs white, sometimes also black, tube 3.2–5.8 mm, lobes triangular, 0.5–1 mm; corolla white, creamy white, or purplish, banner recurved through 40°; keel 8–11 mm, apex bluntly deltate or triangular, often slightly beaklike. **Legumes** pale green, sometimes also red-mottled, becoming stramineous, straight or slightly curved, obliquely obovoid, semi-obovoid, or semi-ellipsoid, bladdery-inflated, 20–48 x 5–16(–22) mm, papery-membranous, translucent, apex differentiated into broad, low-deltoid beak, glabrous; stipe (5–)8–12 mm. **Seeds** 10–20.

Varieties 4 (4 in the flora): nw United States.

Astragalus cusickii is known from the great canyons of the Snake and lower Salmon rivers and their tributaries; it is peripheral to the closely related, variable *A. whitneyi*, from which it differs conspicuously in its reduced foliage. The varieties of *A. cusickii* seem to have resulted from its geographical isolation and ability to adapt in various habitats.

Recent phylogenetic analysis indicates that three monophyletic entities exist within traditional *Astragalus cusickii* and justification exists to recognize each as a distinct species (J. F. Smith and J. C. Zimmers 2017; Zimmers et al. 2017). Two of the present varieties, vars. *packardiae* and *sterilis*, would become *A. packardiae* (Barneby) J. F. Smith & Zimmers and *A. sterilis* Barneby, respectively, with var. *flexilipes* maintained within *A. cusickii*.

SELECTED REFERENCE Zimmers, J. C. et al. 2017. Species boundaries in the *Astragalus cusickii* complex delimited using molecular phylogenetic techniques. Molec. Phylogen. Evol. 114: 93–110.

1. Leaflets 9–15(or 17), blade surfaces glabrous adaxially; calyces 3.2–4.4 mm; legumes semi-obovoid or semi-ellipsoid, 6–12 mm wide when pressed; lower Salmon and Little Salmon rivers, Idaho and Adams counties, Idaho, Asotin County, Washington . . . . . 69b. *Astragalus cusickii* var. *flexilipes*
1. Leaflets (5 or)7–11(or 13), blade surfaces usually strigulose (often densely so); calyces 3–5.8 mm; legumes usually broadly obovoid or obovoid-ellipsoid, rarely semi-ellipsoid, (1–)1.2–2.2 mm wide when pressed; Snake River canyon and streams affluent from the west, ne Oregon, immediately adjacent Idaho, and extreme se corner of Washington.
   2. Leaflets to 2–5 mm, terminal leaflet not jointed with rachis to slightly dilated; plants from subterranean caudex, sometimes with stolonlike branches; legumes purple-mottled; Owyhee County, Idaho, and Malheur County, Oregon . . . . 69d. *Astragalus cusickii* var. *sterilis*
   2. Leaflets to 5–18(–27) mm, terminal leaflet jointed or continuous with rachises; plants from shallow subterranean or superficial caudex; legumes not or faintly mottled; wc Idaho, e Oregon (including Malheur County), and se Washington.
      3. Leaves foliose distally; calyces 4.4–5.8 mm; corollas white or creamy white, concolorous, banners 14–15.5 mm; legumes much inflated, 1–2 cm wide when pressed; Malheur County, Oregon, n on both sides of the Snake River to Asotin County, Washington . . . . 69a. *Astragalus cusickii* var. *cusickii*
      3. Leaves reduced to naked rachis distally; calyces 3.7–4.3 mm; corollas purplish, banners 8.5–10.5 mm; legumes narrowly ellipsoid, 7–10 mm wide; Payette County, Idaho . . . 69c. *Astragalus cusickii* var. *packardiae*

69a. Astragalus cusickii A. Gray var. **cusickii** [E]

Plants from shallow subterranean or superficial caudex; distal leaves foliose. **Leaves:** stipules connate-sheathing at proximal nodes, distinct at distal nodes; leaflets (5 or)7–11(or 13), blades to 5–18(–27) mm, surfaces strigulose adaxially (often densely so); terminal leaflet continuous with rachis. **Flowers:** calyx 4.4–5.8 × 3–4 mm; corolla white or creamy white, concolorous; banner 14–15.5 mm. **Legumes** not mottled, turning stramineous, much inflated, usually broadly obovoid or obovoid-ellipsoid, rarely semi-ellipsoid, 20–48 mm, (1–)1.2–2.2 mm wide when pressed; stipe 3–5(–6) mm. **Seeds** 10–20. **2*n*** = 22.

Flowering May–Jul. Rocky and gravelly slopes, canyon terraces, ledges of basalt; 400–1000 m; Idaho, Oreg., Wash.

Variety *cusickii* is known from Malheur County in Oregon, northward on both sides of the Snake River to Asotin County in Washington.

The enclosed ovules or seeds of var. *cusickii* are partially visible through the walls of the balloonlike, transparent fruits.

69b. Astragalus cusickii A. Gray var. **flexilipes** Barneby, Amer. Midl. Naturalist 55: 485. 1956 • Little Salmon milkvetch [E]

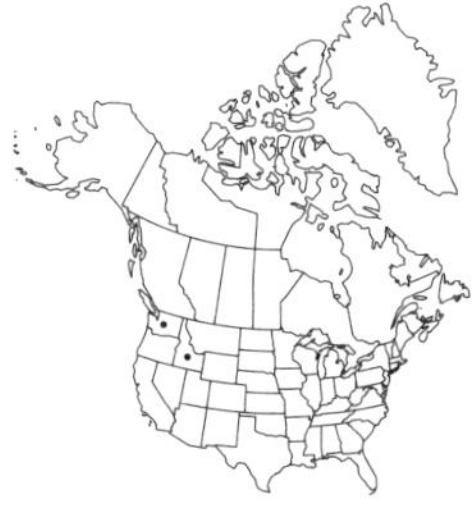

Plants from shallow subterranean or superficial caudex; distal leaves foliose. **Leaves:** stipules connate at proximal nodes, usually distinct at distal nodes; leaflets 9–15(or 17), blade surfaces glabrous adaxially; terminal leaflet jointed or continuous with rachis. **Flowers:** calyx 3.2–4.4 × 2.3–2.8 mm; corolla usually pale purple, tinged purplish, or with maculate keel tip, rarely all concolorous; banner 12–15.5 mm. **Legumes** faintly mottled, semi-ovoid or semi-ellipsoid, 20–35 mm, 6–12 mm wide when pressed; stipe (4–)5–8 mm. **Seeds** 10–16.

Flowering May–Jul. Rocky and gravelly slopes, canyon terraces, ledges of basalt; 300–600 m; Idaho, Wash.

Variety *flexilipes* is known from the lower Salmon and Little Salmon rivers, Adams and Idaho counties in Idaho, and Asotin County in Washington.

69c. Astragalus cusickii A. Gray var. **packardiae** Barneby in A. Cronquist et al., Intermount. Fl. 3(B): 78, plate [p. 79], fig. s.n. [upper right]. 1989 • Packard's milkvetch [C] [E]

Plants from shallow subterranean or superficial caudex; distal leaves foliose, reduced to naked rachis distally. **Leaves:** stipules connate-sheathing at proximal nodes, distinct at distal nodes; leaflets (5 or)7–11(or 13), blades to 5–18(–27) mm, surfaces strigulose adaxially (often densely so); terminal leaflet continuous with rachis. **Flowers:** calyx 3.7–4.3 × 3–5 mm; corolla purplish; banner 8.5–10.5 mm. **Legumes** not or faintly mottled, becoming stramineous, narrowly ellipsoid, 20–45 mm, 7–10 mm wide when pressed; stipe 3–5 mm. **Seeds** 10–20. **2*n*** = 22.

Flowering May–Jun. Bare clay hillsides; of conservation concern; 800–1000 m; Idaho.

Variety *packardiae* is known from Dry Creek in Payette County.

69d. Astragalus cusickii A. Gray var. **sterilis** (Barneby) Barneby in A. Cronquist et al., Intermount. Fl. 3(B): 78. 1989 • Barren milkvetch [C] [E]

Astragalus sterilis Barneby, Leafl. W. Bot. 5: 193. 1949

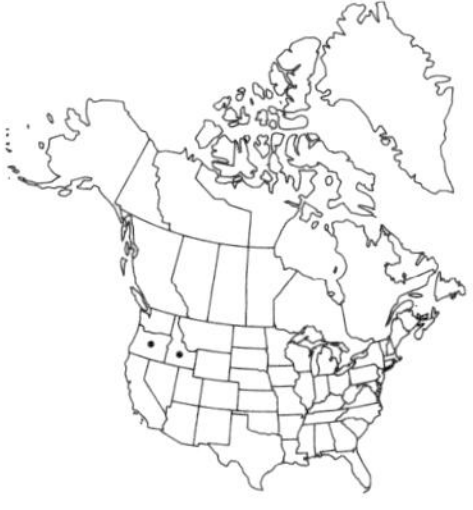

Plants from subterranean caudex, sometimes with stolonlike branches, 2–8 cm underground; distal leaves mostly foliose. **Leaves:** stipules connate-sheathing at proximal nodes, distinct at distal nodes; leaflets 7–11, blades to 2–5 mm, surfaces strigulose adaxially (often densely so); terminal leaflet not jointed to slightly dilated rachis. **Flowers:** calyx 3–3.6 × 2.2–2.5 mm; corolla ochroleucous, fading yellowish; banner 9–10 mm. **Legumes** purple-mottled, obliquely ovoid, bladdery-inflated, 20–25 mm, (1–)1.2–2.2 mm wide when pressed; stipe 3 mm. **Seeds** 17–20.

Flowering Jun–Jul. Barren clay and white or brown ash soils, bluffs, talus slopes, open hilltops; of conservation concern; 1400–1500 m; Idaho, Oreg.

D. Isely (1998) maintained var. *sterilis*, a rare and local endemic from Owyhee County, Idaho, and Malheur County, Oregon, at the specific level, suggesting that it was derived from *Astragalus cusickii*.

70. Astragalus whitneyi A. Gray, Proc. Amer. Acad. Arts 6: 526. 1865 • Balloon milkvetch [E] [F]

Plants 2–30(–40) cm, strigulose, hirsutulous, or villosulous; from shallow subterranean caudex. **Stems** ascending, erect, decumbent, or prostrate, sometimes diffuse, 2–6 cm underground, strigulose. **Leaves** (1–)1.5–10 (–11) cm; stipules connate-sheathing and papery at proximal nodes, connate or distinct and subherbaceous at distal nodes, 1–5 mm; leaflets (5–)9–21, blades oblong-oblanceolate, elliptic, narrowly obovate, or linear-elliptic, 2–21 mm, apex obtuse to acute, surfaces usually strigulose, sometimes glabrescent or glabrous adaxially. **Peduncles** incurved-ascending or erect, 1–9.5(–12) cm. **Racemes** (3 or)4–16-flowered; axis 0.5–7 cm in fruit; bracts 1–3 mm; bracteoles 0. **Pedicels** 0.5–2.5 mm. **Flowers** (8.3–)9–17.2 mm; calyx campanulate, 4.5–9.3 mm, strigulose, hairs white, sometimes also black, tube 3.5–5.9 mm, lobes triangular, 0.5–3.6 mm; corolla ochroleucous, pinkish white, lilac, or pink-purple, wing tips often paler than banner; banner recurved through 50–80°; keel 7.3–13.8, apex narrowly triangular, acute or subacute, often slightly beaked. **Legumes** green, usually red- or purple-mottled, becoming stramineous, balloon-shaped, bladdery-inflated, 15–60(–75) × (8–) 10–25(–35) mm, apex broad, round, beak obsolete, papery-membranous, translucent, glabrous or strigulose; stipe 2–9 mm. **Seeds** (13–)15–30(–37).

Varieties 5 (5 in the flora): w United States.

Astragalus whitneyi has a wide, discontinuous distribution and has adapted to a variety of environments. The beakless fruit contrasts with that of *A. cusickii*, which has a laterally compressed beak. The races of *A. whitneyi* are often difficult to define in contrasting terms. *Astragalus whitneyi* contains nitrotoxins that are poisonous to livestock (L. F. James and S. L. Welsh 1992).

1. Legumes strigulose.
   2. Raceme rachises 0.5–2(–2.5) cm in fruit; calyces 4–6 mm; banners 9–12.8 mm; stems slender, prostrate to weakly descending, 2–12(–17) cm; leaves 1–4 cm; wc Idaho, ne, ec Oregon, Washington . . . . 70d. *Astragalus whitneyi* var. *sonneanus*
   2. Raceme rachises (1–)1.5–4 cm in fruit; calyces (5.8–)6.1–9.3 mm; banners (12.8–)13.5–17.2 mm; stems robust, decumbent, ascending, or erect, (5–)10–30 cm; leaves (2–)3–10 cm; ne California, adjoining Oregon, to ne Nevada and sw, sc Idaho . . . . 70e. *Astragalus whitneyi* var. *confusus*
1. Legumes glabrous.
   3. Raceme rachises (2–)3–7 cm in fruit; corollas ochroleucous; legumes (15–)25–60(–75) mm; n Coastal Ranges, California, sw Oregon . . . . 70c. *Astragalus whitneyi* var. *siskiyouensis*
   3. Raceme rachises 0.5–4(–4.5) cm in fruit; corollas often lilac or pink-purple; legumes 15–35(–40) mm; Sierra Nevada, California (not north of Nevada County), n Nevada.
      4. Herbage strigulose, hairs appressed or narrowly ascending, straight or subsinuous, (0.3–)0.4–0.6 mm; leaves (1.5–)3–8.5 (–11) cm; California Sierra Nevada southward from Alpine County, n Nevada . . . . 70a. *Astragalus whitneyi* var. *whitneyi*
      4. Herbage hirsutulous, hairs spreading or ascending, stiff, ± straight, 0.5–0.7 mm; leaves (1.5–)2–4 cm; Sierra Nevada in Nevada and Placer counties, California. . . . . 70b. *Astragalus whitneyi* var. *lenophyllus*

70a. Astragalus whitneyi A. Gray var. **whitneyi** [E] [F]

Herbage strigulose, hairs appressed or narrowly ascending, straight or subsinuous, (0.3–)0.4–0.6 mm. **Stems** low and diffuse or erect (when supported by sagebrush), 5–25 cm. **Leaves** (1.5–)3–11 cm; leaflets 9–17(or 19), blades 2–13(–15) mm. **Racemes** (3–)5–15-flowered; axis 1–4(–4.5) cm in fruit. **Flowers:** calyx 4.5–6.4 mm, tube (3.5–)3.7–4.2(–4.7) mm, lobes 0.8–1.5(–1.8) mm; corolla lilac or pink-purple, wing tips pale or white; banner (8.3–)10–14.2(–16.5) mm. **Legumes** 15–30(–40) × 10–18(–22) mm, glabrous; stipe 2–4.5 mm. **Seeds** 18–30. $2n = 22$.

Flowering May–Sep. Slopes and ridges at or above timberline, sagebrush valleys and foothills; 2000–3700 m; Calif., Nev.

Ranging from the mountains of southern California through the Sierra Nevada to northwestern Nevada, the widespread var. *whitneyi* can usually be distinguished by its red-purple or pink-purple petals and the fruits of relatively medium size. Morphological characters overlap, and some specimens of vars. *siskiyouensis* and *whitneyi* can be distinguished only by origin.

70b. Astragalus whitneyi A. Gray var. **lenophyllus** (Rydberg) Barneby, Aliso 2: 205. 1950 • Placer County milkvetch [E]

Phaca lenophylla Rydberg in N. L. Britton et al., N. Amer. Fl. 24: 341. 1929

Herbage densely hirsutulous, hairs ascending or spreading, stiff, ± straight, 0.5–0.7 mm. **Stems** low, diffuse, 4–15(–20) cm. **Leaves** (1.5–)2–4 cm; leaflets 9–17, blades 3–13 mm. **Racemes** 5–9-flowered; axis 0.5–2 cm in fruit. **Flowers:** calyx 5.8–9 mm, tube 4.4–5.6 mm, lobes 1.2–1.8 mm, hirsutulous, hairs white or mixed black and white; corolla ochroleucous; banner (8.3–)10–14.2(–16.5) mm. **Legumes** obovoid, tapering to base, 15–35(–42) × 10–20(–25) mm, glabrous; stipe 3–5(–7) mm. **Seeds** 13–25.

Flowering Jul–Aug. Treeless summits and open, stony places in timber belt; 2600–3100 m; Calif.

Variety *lenophyllus* is most common in open places along the crest of the Sierra Nevada in Placer and Nevada counties.

70c. Astragalus whitneyi A. Gray var. **siskiyouensis** (Rydberg) Barneby, Aliso 2: 205. 1950 • Siskiyou milkvetch [E]

Phaca siskiyouensis Rydberg in N. L. Britton et al., N. Amer. Fl. 24: 340. 1929; *Astragalus whitneyi* subsp. *siskiyouensis* (Rydberg) Abrams

Herbage usually loosely strigulose in variable amounts, hairs appressed or narrowly ascending, straight or subsinuous, 0.4–0.6(–0.7) mm. **Stems** low, diffuse, 10–30 (–40) cm. **Leaves** 3–9 cm; leaflets 9–17(or 19), blades 4–18(–21) mm. **Racemes** 4–16-flowered; axis (2–)3–7 cm in fruit. **Flowers:** calyx 4.6–5.6(–6) mm, tube 3.8–4.7 mm, lobes 0.5–1.5(–1.7) mm; corolla ochroleucous, immaculate; banner 9.5–13.5 mm. **Legumes** (15–)25–60(–75) × 10–25(–35) mm, glabrous; stipe 3–6 mm. **Seeds** (13–)15–22.

Flowering Jun–Aug. Rocky slopes, ridge crests, usually in pine forests but ascending into fir forests, on igneous or metamorphic bedrock, common on serpentine; (700–)1200–2700 m; Calif., Oreg.

The transparent fruits of var. *siskiyouensis*, with ovules readily apparent through the walls, are the largest for the species. Variety *siskiyouensis* occurs in northern Coastal Ranges in California and southwestern Oregon, passing in the Klamath Basin into var. *confusus*.

70d. Astragalus whitneyi A. Gray var. **sonneanus** (Greene) Jepson, Fl. Calif. 2: 347. 1936 • Sonne's milkvetch [E]

Astragalus sonneanus Greene, Pittonia 3: 186. 1897, based on *Phaca hookeriana* Torrey & A. Gray, Fl. N. Amer. 1: 693. 1840, not *A. hookerianus* D. Dietrich 1847; *A. whitneyi* subsp. *hookerianus* (Torrey & A. Gray) Abrams

Herbage loosely strigulose or villosulous, hairs subappressed, spreading-incurved, or incurved-ascending, often sinuous, 0.3–0.7 mm. **Stems** low, prostrate to weakly ascending, slender, 2–12 (–17) cm. **Leaves** 1–4 cm; leaflets (5–)11–17, blades 2–10(–12) mm. **Racemes** 4–9(–11)-flowered; axis 0.5–2 (–2.5) cm in fruit. **Flowers:** calyx 4.8–6 mm, tube 3.5–4.3 mm, lobes 1–1.7 mm; corolla whitish or cream, sometimes lilac-tinged; banner 9–12.8 mm. **Legumes** (15–)20–40(–55) × (8–)10–22(–26) mm, loosely and sparsely strigulose; stipe 2.5–5.5(–6) mm. **Seeds** 21–27.

Flowering Jun–Aug. Ridges near timberline and lower into timberbelt, on igneous and metamorphic bedrock, especially abundant on serpentine bedrock; 1300–2800 m; Idaho, Oreg., Wash.

Variety *sonneanus* is found in the Blue and Cascade mountains of Washington, southward through northeastern and east-central Oregon to Steens Mountain in Harney County, and eastward to Valley County in west-central Idaho.

70e. Astragalus whitneyi A. Gray var. **confusus** Barneby, Aliso 2: 206. 1950 • Alturas milkvetch [E]

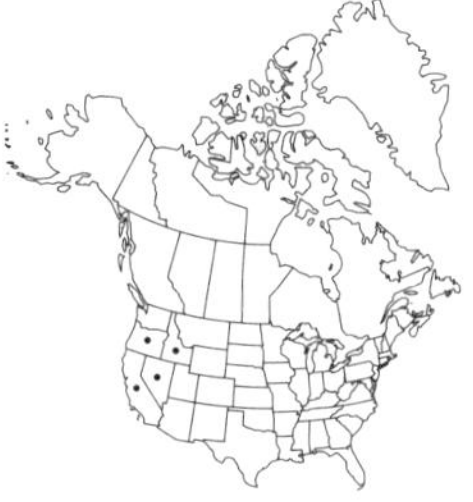

Herbage gray- or silvery-villosulous, hairs incurved-ascending or straight, 0.5–0.8 mm. **Stems** robust to low, decumbent, ascending, or erect, (5–)10–30 cm. **Leaves** (2–)3–10 cm; leaflets (7–)13–21, blades (3–)5–20 mm. **Racemes** (5–)8–16-flowered; axis (1–)1.5–4 cm in fruit. **Flowers:** calyx (5.8–)6.1–9.3 mm, tube (4–)4.5–5.9 mm, lobes (1.5–)1.8–3.6 mm; corolla whitish tinged with pale pink or lavender, sometimes drying ochroleucous; banner (12.8–)13.5–17.2 mm. **Legumes** (17–)20–60 × (10–)13–25(–28) mm, strigulose; stipe 4–9 mm. **Seeds** 22–30(–37).

Flowering Apr–Jul. Sandy or gravelly, basaltic or granitic substrates, usually with sagebrush; 1300–2600 m; Calif., Idaho, Nev., Oreg.

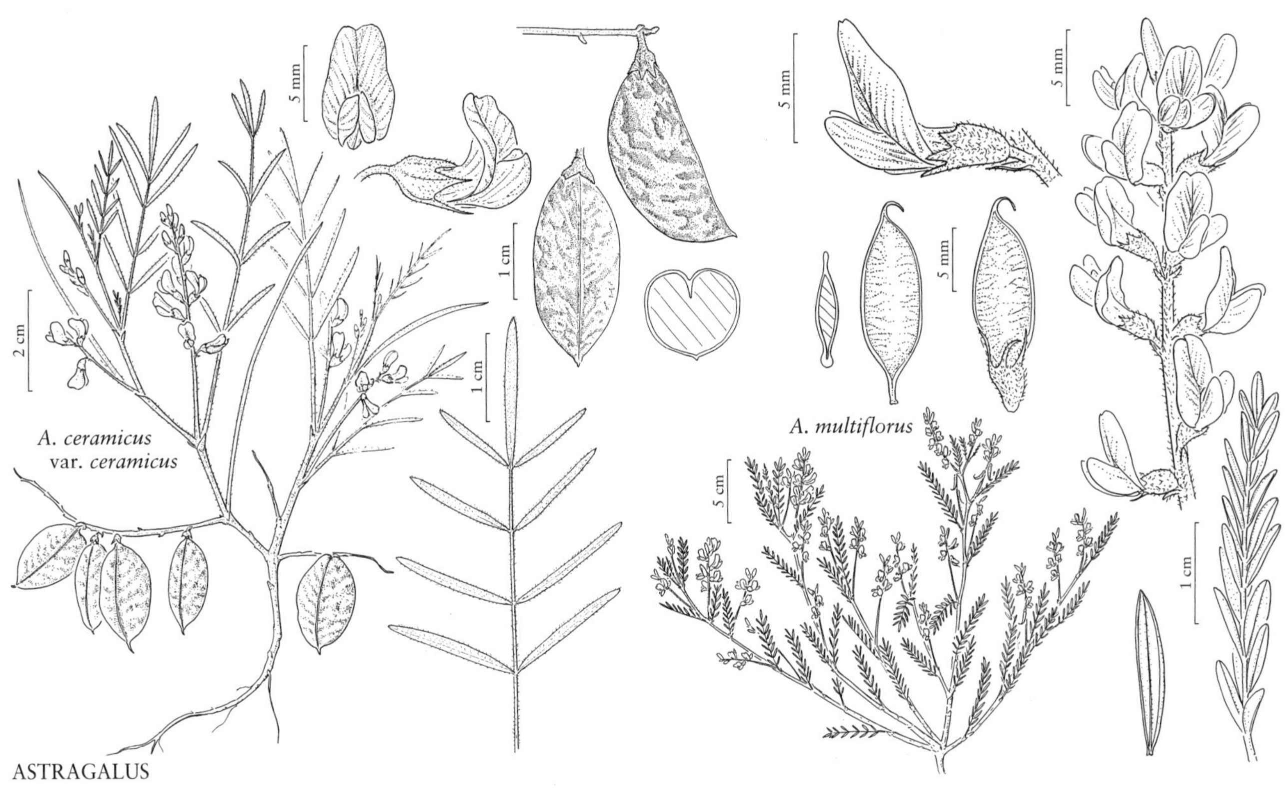

ASTRAGALUS

The range of var. *confusus* is from northeastern California and adjoining Oregon to northeastern Nevada, and southwestern and south-central Idaho.

D. Isely (1998) expressed concern over maintaining var. *confusus* as distinct from the more northern var. *sonneanus*. It seems to have about equal integrity as other varieties; nevertheless, southward it forms intermediates with var. *siskiyouensis*.

71. Astragalus ceramicus E. Sheldon, Minnesota Bot. Stud. 1: 19. 1894 • Painted milkvetch E F

Phaca picta A. Gray, Mem. Amer. Acad. Arts, n. s. 4: 37. 1849, not *Astragalus pictus* Boissier & Gaillardot 1859

Plants slender, 3–40(–45) cm, densely strigulose, hairs malpighian or basifixed; from deep subterranean branched caudex, branches slender, elongate, rhizomelike. **Stems** single or few and clustered, sprawling to erect, 3–40+ cm underground, densely strigulose or ashen or silvery-canescent. **Leaves** sometimes reduced to phyllodia distally, 2–17 cm; stipules connate-sheathing and subscarious at proximal nodes, mostly connate and herbaceous at distal nodes, 1.5–9 mm; leaflets (0 or 1)3–13, blades narrowly oblong to filiform, 3–50(–80) mm, apex obtuse to retuse or acute, surfaces strigulose, hairs very slightly spreading; terminal leaflet continuous with rachis distally, reduced to phyllodia. **Peduncles** divaricate and incurved, 0.7–7.5 cm. **Racemes** 2–15(–25)-flowered; axis 1–8(–15) cm in fruit; bracts 1–2.5 mm; bracteoles 0. **Pedicels** 0.7–3.1 mm. **Flowers** 6.3–10.8 mm; calyx campanulate, 3.1–6 mm, strigose, tube 2.1–3.5 mm, lobes subulate, 1–3 mm; corolla usually dull purplish to pink, rarely whitish; banner abruptly recurved through 85–90°; keel 6.4–9.1 mm, apex narrowly triangular, subacute, sometimes beaklike. **Legumes** purple-mottled becoming purplish brown, straight or slightly curved, ellipsoid, bladdery-inflated, (10–)15–50 × 5–26 mm, papery, glabrous; stipe 0–3.3 mm. **Seeds** 12–29.

Varieties 3 (3 in the flora): nw, w, c United States.

Junceous or sparsely foliolose, *Astragalus ceramicus* is inconspicuous in flower but showy in fruit; it is marked by its rhizomatous habit and red-mottled, bladdery fruits. The caudex, in sandy sites, is often extensively branched and pervasive.

1. Stipes 0 mm; se Idaho, sw Montana . . . . 71c. *Astragalus ceramicus* var. *apus*
1. Stipes (1–)1.5–3.3 mm; not Idaho or Montana.
   2. Plants with mostly malpighian hairs on stems and herbage; calyces mostly 3.1–4.2 mm; legumes (10–)15–30 × 5–15(–22) mm; seeds 12–16(–26); n Ariz., w Colorado, nw New Mexico to Utah . . . . 71a. *Astragalus ceramicus* var. *ceramicus*
   2. Plants with mostly basifixed hairs on stems and herbage; calyces (3.7–)4–6 mm; legumes (20–)30–50 × 14–26 mm; seeds (17–)20–29; eastern slope of Rocky Mountains and Great Plains. . . . . . 71b. *Astragalus ceramicus* var. *filifolius*

71a. Astragalus ceramicus E. Sheldon var. ceramicus [E] [F]

Plants with mostly malpighian hairs on stems and herbage. **Leaves** 2–12 cm; usually 1–6 pairs of lateral leaflets proximally or throughout, distalmost often reduced to naked rachis. **Racemes** 6–15(–25)-flowered; axis (1–)1.5–8(–15) cm in fruit. **Flowers** 6.3–8.3(–9.5) mm; calyx 3.1–4.2 mm, tube 2.1–2.6(–3.3) mm, lobes 1–1.8 mm. **Legumes** (10–)15–30 × 5–15(–22) mm; stipe (1–)1.5–3.3 mm. **Seeds** 12–16(–26). **2*n*** = 22.

Flowering late Apr–Jul. Dunes, sandy sites in pinyon-juniper, sagebrush, stream banks, grasslands, mixed desert shrub communities; 1200–2500 m; Ariz., Colo., N.Mex., Utah.

71b. Astragalus ceramicus E. Sheldon var. filifolius (A. Gray) F. J. Hermann, J. Wash. Acad. Sci. 38: 237. 1948 • Bradbury's milkvetch [E]

Astragalus pictus (A. Gray) A. Gray [not Steudel] var. *filifolius* A. Gray, Proc. Amer. Acad. Arts 6: 215. 1864, based on *Psoralea longifolia* Pursh, Fl. Amer. Sept. 2: 741. 1813; *A. angustus* (M. E. Jones) M. E. Jones var. *longifolius* (Pursh) M. E. Jones; *A. ceramicus* var. *longifolius* (Pursh) Rydberg; *A. mitophyllus* Kearney; *Orobus longifolius* (Pursh) Nuttall; *Phaca longifolia* (Pursh) Nuttall ex Torrey & A. Gray; *Physondra longifolia* (Pursh) Rafinesque

Plants with mostly basifixed hairs on stems and herbage. **Leaves** 2.5–17 cm; sometimes 1 or 2 (or 3) pairs of lateral leaflets proximally, mostly reduced to filiform rachis throughout. **Racemes** 2–7-flowered; axis 1–4.5(–5.5) cm in fruit. **Flowers** 7.4–10.8 mm; calyx (3.7–)4–6 mm, tube (2.3–)2.5–3.5 mm, lobes (1.4–)1.6–3 mm. **Legumes** (20–)30–50 × 14–26 mm. **Seeds** (17–)20–29; stipe 1.5–3 mm. **2*n*** = 22.

Flowering late Apr–Jul. Dunes, sandy hollows in rolling plains, sandy fields, sand bars of intermittent streams; 900–2200(–2600) m; Colo., Kans., Mont., Nebr., N.Mex., N.Dak., Okla., S.Dak., Wyo.

Variety *filifolius* is known from the Great Plains and eastern slope of the Rocky Mountains.

Astragalus angustus var. *imperfectus* (Sheldon) M. E. Jones, *A. ceramicus* var. *imperfectus* E. Sheldon, *A. filifolius* A. Gray (not *A. filifolius* Clos 1847), and *A. longifolius* (Pursh) Rydberg are illegitimate names that pertain here.

71c. Astragalus ceramicus E. Sheldon var. apus Barneby, Mem. New York Bot. Gard. 13: 341. 1964 • Bonneville County milkvetch [E]

Plants with mostly basifixed hairs on stems and herbage. **Leaves** 2.5–17 cm, mostly reduced to filiform rachis; leaflets 0(–5). **Racemes** 2–7-flowered; axis 1–4.5(–5.5) cm in fruit. **Flowers** 7.4–10.8 mm; calyx (3.7–)4–6 mm, tube (2.3–)2.5–3.5 mm, lobes (1.4–)1.6–3 mm. **Legumes** 2–40 × 15–24 mm; stipe 0 m m. **Seeds** (17–)20–29. **2*n*** = 22.

Flowering May–Jul. Dunes, sandy flats; 1300–1500 m; Idaho, Mont.

Variety *apus* occurs on the eastern end of the Snake River Plains eastward to Bonneville and Madison counties, Idaho, and Beaverhead County, Montana.

135t. Astragalus Linnaeus sect. Ervoidei (Torrey & A. Gray) Barneby, Mem. New York Bot. Gard. 13: 344. 1964 [E]

Homalobus Nuttall [unranked] *Ervoidei* Torrey & A. Gray, Fl. N. Amer. 1: 350. 1838 (as Ervoideae)

Herbs perennial, caulescent; caudex superficial. **Hairs** usually basifixed, rarely malpighian (in some varieties of *A. kentrophyta*). **Stems** several to many. **Stipules** connate or distinct at distal nodes. **Leaves** odd-pinnate, sessile or subsessile to petiolate; leaflets (3–)5–21, jointed or decurrent. **Racemes** sometimes paired, loosely or remotely flowered, flowers ascending, spreading, or declined. **Calyx tubes** usually campanulate, sometimes turbinate-campanulate. **Corollas** pink-purple, whitish, or ochroleucous, banner recurved through 40–90°, keel apex obtuse. **Legumes** eventually deciduous or persistent, sessile or stipitate, deflexed, declined, or pendulous, linear, oblong, ellipsoid, lenticular, or ovoid- or obovoid-subglobose, compressed laterally or bladdery-inflated, unilocular. **Seeds** 2–9(–11).

Species 5 (5 in the flora): w North America.

Section *Ervoidei* consists of three subsections, widely distributed from Yukon southward to California, New Mexico, Hudson Bay, Minnesota, and Nebraska.

The subsections are: subsect. *Ervoidei* (Torrey & A. Gray) Barneby (*Astragalus bourgovii*, *A. multiflorus*, *A. vexilliflexus*); subsect. *Microcystei* (A. Gray) Barneby (*A. microcystis*); and subsect. *Submonospermi* (A. Gray) Barneby (*A. kentrophyta*).

72. Astragalus multiflorus (Pursh) A. Gray, Proc. Amer. Acad. Arts 6: 226. 1864 • Pulse milkvetch [E] [F]

Ervum multiflorum Pursh, Fl. Amer. Sept. 2: 739. 1813; *Astragalus tenellus* Pursh var. *strigulosus* (Rydberg) F. J. Hermann

Plants clump-forming, 10–70(–75) cm, usually sparsely strigulose, sometimes pilosulous; from branched, superficial caudex. **Stems** usually erect or ascending, sometimes decumbent, rarely prostrate, usually sparsely strigulose, sometimes pilosulous. **Leaves** 2–9 cm; stipules connate-sheathing and papery at proximal nodes, connate or distinct and herbaceous or submembranous at distal nodes, usually black or blackish when dry, 1.5–7 mm; leaflets 11–21, blades narrowly oblong to elliptic, linear, oblanceolate, or obovate, 3–24 mm, apex acute to obtuse, mucronate, or emarginate, surfaces sparsely strigose abaxially, glabrous adaxially. **Peduncles** narrowly ascending or incurved, 0.2–4 cm. **Racemes** (1–)3–23-flowered, often paired in leaf axils, flowers ascending; axis 0.5–11 cm in fruit; bracts 0.5–2.7 mm; bracteoles 0–2. **Pedicels** 0.7–3.2 mm. **Flowers** 6–9(–11) mm; calyx 2.6–5.2 mm, strigose, tube 2–2.7 mm, lobes subulate, 0.7–2.5 mm; corolla usually white to ochroleucous, sometimes pink-purple; banner recurved through 40°; keel 4.3–5.7(–6.5) mm. **Legumes** pendulous, green, often brown- or red-mottled, becoming brown or black, straight or curved, ellipsoid to oblong, laterally flattened, 7–16 × 2.5–4.5 mm, papery, usually glabrous, sometimes strigose; stipe 0.6–6 mm. **Seeds** 3–9. **2*n*** = 16, 24.

Flowering May–Aug. Grasslands, shrublands, open forests; 300–3200 m; Alta., B.C., Man., N.W.T., Sask., Yukon; Colo., Idaho, Minn., Mont., Nebr., Nev., N.Mex., N.Dak., Oreg., S.Dak., Utah, Wash., Wyo.

The stipitate, laterally flattened fruits disposed in very loose, sometimes paired, always very shortly pedunculate racemes are characteristic of *Astragalus multiflorus*.

The name *Astragalus tenellus* Pursh, widely used for this species, is not valid (J. L. Reveal et al. 2004).

73. Astragalus vexilliflexus E. Sheldon, Minnesota Bot. Stud. 1: 21. 1894 • Bent-flowered milkvetch [E]

Astragalus pauciflorus Hooker, Fl. Bor.-Amer. 1: 149. 1831, not Pallas 1800–1803

Plants mat- or tuft-forming, 3–25(–30) cm, usually sparsely to densely strigulose or strigose-pilosulous, rarely silky-villosulous; from branched, superficial caudex. **Stems** incurved-ascending, decumbent, or prostrate, usually sparsely to densely strigulose or strigose-pilosulous, rarely silky-villosulous. **Leaves** 1–5.5 cm; stipules connate-sheathing and papery at proximal nodes, mostly connate and herbaceous at distal nodes, turning black in drying, 2–5 mm; leaflets (5 or)7–13, blades elliptic, linear-elliptic, lanceolate, oblanceolate, or narrowly obovate, 2–12 mm, apex usually acute, sometimes obtuse or retuse and apiculate, surfaces strigose abaxially, silky-strigulose, villosulous, glabrescent, or glabrous adaxially. **Peduncles** 0.2–4 cm. **Racemes** 3–7(–11)-flowered, flowers spreading; axis 0.5–3 cm in fruit; bracts 0.5–2.7 mm; bracteoles 0–1. **Pedicels** 1.5–3.5(–4.2) mm. **Flowers** (4.3–)5.2–9.3 mm; calyx turbinate-campanulate to campanulate, 2.4–4.5 mm, strigose, tube 1.4–2.2 mm, lobes setaceous, (0.8–) 1.3–2.5 mm; corolla pink-purple, lilac, or whitish, sometimes lilac-tipped or -tinged, banner sometimes purple-veined, keel maculate; banner abruptly recurved through 90°; keel (2.9–)3.4–5.6 mm. **Legumes** deflexed or declined, stramineous, straight, ellipsoid, obovoid-ellipsoid, oblong-ellipsoid, or linear, laterally flattened, 3.5–12 × 1.8–3.5 mm, bicarinate, papery, strigose; stipe 0–0.3 mm. **Seeds** (4 or)5–8(–11).

Varieties 2 (2 in the flora): w North America.

Astragalus vexilliflexus is a multiracial, ecologically diverse complex with an interrupted range; the races differ in plant size and stem development, nature of pubescence, and flower color. Plants from middle Montana to Alberta, and populations from higher elevations, tend to be short and purple-petaled, whereas southern populations have longer-stemmed and white-petaled plants. Plants from the Dakotas are similar to southern populations.

1. Plants loosely matted to diffusely tufted, hairs appressed or subappressed; stems prostrate, decumbent, or ascending; leaflet blades glabrous or glabrescent adaxially; corollas often pink-purple or lilac, sometimes lilac-tinged or -tipped, rarely whitish and keel apices maculate, banners (4.3–) 5.2–9.3 mm; legumes (5–)6–12 mm; widespread . . . . 73a. *Astragalus vexilliflexus* var. *vexilliflexus*
1. Plants densely matted; stems prostrate; leaflet blades silky-strigulose or villosulous adaxially; corollas whitish, keel maculate, banners faintly purple-veined, banners 5.2–6.2 mm; legumes 3.5–5 mm; alpine in c Idaho . . . . .73b. *Astragalus vexilliflexus* var. *nubilus*

73a. Astragalus vexilliflexus E. Sheldon var. **vexilliflexus** E

Plants loosely matted to diffusely tufted, hairs appressed or subappressed. **Stems** prostrate, decumbent with ascending tips, or ascending. **Leaflets:** blade surfaces glabrous or glabrescent adaxially. **Corollas** often pink-purple or lilac, drying bluish, sometimes lilac-tipped or -tinged, rarely whitish, keel apex maculate; banner (4.3–)5.2–9.3 mm. **Legumes** symmetric or oblique, (5–)6–12 mm.

Flowering late May–Aug. Barrens, rocky knolls, outcrops and scree of shale or sandstone; 800–2500 m; Alta., B.C., Sask.; Idaho, Mont., N.Dak., S.Dak., Wyo.

73b. Astragalus vexilliflexus E. Sheldon var. **nubilus** Barneby, Amer. Midl. Naturalist 55: 484. 1956 • Cloud Range milkvetch C E

Plants densely matted. **Stems** prostrate. **Leaflets:** blade surfaces silky-strigulose or villosulous adaxially. **Corollas** whitish, keel maculate, banner faintly purple-veined; banner 5.2–6.2 mm. **Legumes** subsymmetrically lenticular, 3.5–5 mm.

Flowering Aug–Sep. Stony ridgecrests above timberline; of conservation concern; 3000–3400 m; Idaho.

The ashy canescence results in the grayish hue to the tufts or mats of var. *nubilus*, which is endemic to Custer and Valley counties. D. Isely (1998) questioned whether this variety is any more significant than other local phases.

74. Astragalus bourgovii A. Gray, Proc. Amer. Acad. Arts 6: 227. 1864 • Bourgeau's milkvetch E

Plants slender, (1–)4–15(–25) cm, sparsely to densely strigulose; from superficial or barely subterranean branched, suffruticose caudex. **Stems** decumbent and incurved-ascending or erect, sparsely to densely strigulose or glabrate. **Leaves** 1.5–9.5 cm; stipules connate-sheathing and papery-scarious at proximal nodes, connate or distinct and submembranous at distal nodes, 1–4 mm, not blackened when dry; leaflets 11–19, blades elliptic to oblong, lanceolate, or broadly oval, 3–17(–19) mm, apex acute to obtuse and apiculate, surfaces strigose abaxially, strigose or glabrous adaxially. **Peduncles** decumbent or humistrate (in fruit), 3–10(–14) cm. **Racemes** (1–)3–13-flowered, flowers ascending to spreading; axis (1–)2–8 cm in fruit; bracts 0.7–1.7 mm; bracteoles 0. **Pedicels** 1.5–4(–4.5) mm. **Flowers** 8–10.5 mm; calyx (3.4–)4.5–6.7 mm, strigose, tube (2.6–)3–4.3 mm, lobes subulate, (0.8–)1.2–2.9 mm; corolla pink-purple, or whitish and purple-tipped; banner recurved through 50°; keel 6.7–8.8 mm. **Legumes** pendulous, brown, straight or nearly so, ellipsoid or oblong-ellipsoid, laterally flattened, (7–)9–15 × 3–4.2 mm, thinly papery, strigose; stipe 1–1.5(–2) mm. **Seeds** 2–6.

Flowering Jul–Sep. Ridges, talus slopes, cliffs, rocky hillsides, gravel bars, near or above timberline; 1200–2600 m; Alta., B.C.; Idaho, Mont.

Astragalus bourgovii is known from southwestern Alberta, southeastern British Columbia, northern Idaho (exclusive of Custer County), and western Montana.

The elongate peduncles of *Astragalus bourgovii* help distinguish it from *A. multiflorus*, which in some areas of its range also has pink-purple flowers.

75. Astragalus microcystis A. Gray, Proc. Amer. Acad. Arts 6: 220. 1864 • Least bladdery milkvetch [E]

Plants slender, 5–40(–50) cm, densely gray-villosulous; from superficial branched, suffruticose caudex. **Stems** decumbent and ascending, strigulose. **Leaves** 1.5–6.5 cm; stipules connate-sheathing and papery at proximal nodes, connate or distinct and herbaceous at distal nodes, 1–5(–6) mm, often drying blackish; leaflets 9–15, blades narrowly to broadly elliptic to oblong, oblanceolate, or obovate-cuneate, 3–14(–18) mm, apex acute to obtuse, surfaces strigose abaxially, strigose or glabrous adaxially. **Peduncles** 1–3 per leaf axil, 1.5–6.5(–8.5) cm. **Racemes** 4–20-flowered, flowers declined; axis 1.5–4.5(–6) cm in fruit; bracts 1–2.5 mm; bracteoles 0. **Pedicels** 0.7–2.5 mm. **Flowers** 5.1–7.8(–8.3) mm; calyx 2.7–3.8(–4.3) mm, strigulose-pilosulous, tube 1.5–2.2 mm, lobes subulate, 1–2(–2.3) mm; corolla pink-purple, or whitish and purple-veined or -tipped, wing tips often pale or white; banner recurved through 90°; keel 3.7–4.8 mm. **Legumes** spreading or declined, brown or stramineous, straight, plumply ellipsoid, obovoid-ellipsoid, or subglobose, bladdery-inflated, 5–12(–14) × 4–7 mm, slightly fleshy becoming papery-membranous, densely pilosulous; sessile. **Seeds** 6–8 (or 9).

Flowering Apr–Aug. Rocky scree slopes, grassy slopes, lakeshores, gravelly flats and bars; 300–1900 m; B.C.; Idaho, Mont., Wash.

Astragalus microcystis is known along the Columbia River and tributaries near the mouth of the Spokane River, from northeastern Washington and adjacent British Columbia, eastward to west-central Montana, and is disjunct on Mt. Tyler in Clallam County, Washington.

At least partially developed fruits are required to distinguish *Astragalus microcystis* from *A. vexilliflexus*. With flowering material only, distinction is difficult or impossible, leading to confusion regarding the geographic ranges of the species. Both species are partially sympatric; *A. microcystis* is the more western in Montana.

76. Astragalus kentrophyta A. Gray, Proc. Acad. Nat. Sci. Philadelphia 15: 60. 1863 • Nuttall's kentrophyta [E] [F]

Kentrophyta montana Nuttall in J. Torrey and A. Gray, Fl. N. Amer. 1: 353. 1838, not *Astragalus montanus* Linnaeus 1753

Plants often mat- or cushion-forming, sometimes suffruticose basally, 15–45 cm, usually strigulose, sometimes villosulous or villous, hairs basifixed or malpighian; from caudex bearing stolonlike, creeping stems. **Stems** prostrate, decumbent, spreading, or erect, compact to elongate, usually strigulose, sometimes villosulous or villous. **Leaves** (0.2–)0.4–2.6 cm; stipules connate-sheathing, sometimes distinct at distal nodes, 1–12 mm, scarious throughout, or herbaceous becoming papery, or stiff and spiny, apex acuminate, spinulose, or callous-mucronate; leaflets (3 or)5–9, blades decurrent, continuous with rachis, linear to narrowly elliptic or lanceolate, (1–)3–15(–17) mm, apex spinulose, surfaces usually strigose, rarely glabrous adaxially. **Peduncles** subobsolete or 0.1–0.6(–3) cm. **Racemes** 1–3-flowered, flowers declined; axis to 0.5 cm in fruit; bracts 0.8–3.5 mm; bracteoles 0. **Pedicels** 0.5–2 mm. **Flowers** (3.9–)4–10 mm; calyx (2–)2.4–8.3 mm, strigose, tube 1.2–2.8(–3.3) mm, lobes subulate, setaceous, or spinulose, (0.5–)1.4–5 mm; corolla usually pink-purple or whitish, sometimes pink-, lilac-, or purple-tinged; banner recurved through 45°; keel 3–6 mm. **Legumes** declined or spreading, stramineous, straight or slightly curved, ellipsoid to oblong-ellipsoid, lenticular, ovoid, ovoid-lenticular, lanceoloid-ellipsoid, or lanceoloid-acuminate, laterally compressed, 3–10 × (0.6–)1.4–4 mm, papery, strigose; sessile. **Seeds** 2–8.

Varieties 9 (9 in the flora): w North America.

The varieties of *Astragalus kentrophyta* are distinguished from other astragali by the few leaflets continuous with the leafstalk while blades are simultaneously apically mucronate or spinulose, and by their racemes, usually subsessile in leaf axils, bearing one to three small flowers. There are two major groups: alpine or upper elevation, prostrate-matted to pulvinate-depressed plants, usually with bright purple flowers and basifixed hairs, with five to eight seeds; and lower elevation forms that range from prostrate to bushy and ascending, with white or lavender flowers, hairs sometimes malpighian, and two to five ovules. With the exception of the widespread var. *tegetarius*, the varieties are largely allopatric.

1. Hairs basifixed; seeds (3–)5–8; corollas purple, purplish, or whitish and keel purple or pink- or purplish-tipped.
   2. Leaflets (3–)5–9, blades 1–9 mm; plants forming cushions 5–40(–50) cm wide; widespread, extending into California only to Inyo and White mountains and c High Sierra Nevada ....76b. *Astragalus kentrophyta* var. *tegetarius*
   2. Leaflets 3(–7), blades 3–7 mm; plants forming cushions to 15 cm wide; sc Sierra Nevada, California ..76c. *Astragalus kentrophyta* var. *danaus*
1. Hairs malpighian or basifixed; seeds 2–4(–8); corollas whitish, keel apices sometimes pink or lilac-tinged or purplish (except pink-purple in var. *coloradoensis*, rarely in var. *elatus*).
   3. Calyces 6–8.3 mm, lobes 3.4–5 mm; legumes (5–)7–10 × 2.8–4 mm; seeds 4–8; canyons of Colorado River in nc Arizona and sc Utah .....76i. *Astragalus kentrophyta* var. *coloradoensis*
   3. Calyces 2.4–5.2 mm, lobes 0.7–3 mm; legumes 3–7(–7.5) × 1.4–3.8 mm; seeds 2–4; California to Alberta, eastward to New Mexico and South Dakota.
      4. Legumes ovoid-lenticular, ovoid, or lenticular.
         5. Stipules uniform, connate to 1/2 their lengths, spinulose; calyx lobes 0.7–1.5 mm; n New Mexico.............................76g. *Astragalus kentrophyta* var. *neomexicanus*
         5. Stipules dimorphic, those at most proximal nodes connate into short, bidentate sheath, those at distal nodes longer, connate at base only, lanceolate or lanceolate-acuminate, often without spines; calyx lobes 1.4–3 mm; North Dakota west to Alberta, southward to Colorado and Oregon.
            6. Leaflet blades glabrous or glabrescent adaxially, pubescent abaxially, hairs basifixed or obscurely malpighian; legumes (3.5–)4–7 × 2.4–3.8 mm; s Wyoming east of Continental Divide to Alberta and Saskatchewan, southward to Colorado, South Dakota, and w Nebraska ... .76a. *Astragalus kentrophyta* var. *kentrophyta*
            6. Leaflet blades pubescent, hairs malpighian; legumes 3–4.5 × 1.4–2 mm; sw Wyoming, ne Utah to se Oregon ....76e. *Astragalus kentrophyta* var. *jessiae*
      4. Legumes ovoid-acuminate, lanceoloid, or lanceoloid-acuminate.

[7. Shifted to left margin.—Ed.]

7. Plants usually erect or assurgent, rarely trailing, often bushy, sometimes mat-forming; Arizona, California, Colorado, Nevada, New Mexico, Utah, Wyoming.................................... 76h. *Astragalus kentrophyta* var. *elatus*
7. Plants prostrate, mat- or cushion-forming; California, e, c Nevada, Oregon, se Washington.
   8. Hairs basifixed; calyx lobes 2.3–3 mm; Oregon, se Washington ....76d. *Astragalus kentrophyta* var. *douglasii*
   8. Hairs malpighian; calyx lobes 1.8–2.6 mm; California, Nevada ....76f. *Astragalus kentrophyta* var. *ungulatus*

76a. Astragalus kentrophyta A. Gray var. **kentrophyta** [E]

Plants decumbent, loosely mat-forming. **Stems** and herbage strigulose, hairs basifixed or obscurely malpighian. **Leaves** (0.7–)1–2.5 cm; stipules dimorphic, those at proximal nodes connate into short, bidentate sheath, those at distal nodes longer, connate at base only, lanceolate or lanceolate-acuminate, often without spines, 2–7 mm; leaflets 5 or 7, blades 7–12 mm, surfaces pubescent abaxially, glabrous or glabrescent adaxially. **Peduncles** subobsolete to 0.2 cm. **Flowers** 4–5.5 mm; calyx 3.4–4 mm, tube 1.9–2.4 mm, lobes subulate to setaceous, 1.4–2 mm; corolla whitish. **Legumes** subsymmetrically ovoid-lenticular, (3.5–)4–7 × 2.4–3.8 mm. **Seeds** 2 or 3(or 4). $2n = 24$.

Flowering Jun–Sep. Bluffs, dunes, gullied ridges in badlands; 1200–1600 m; Alta., Sask.; Colo., Mont., Nebr., N.Dak., S.Dak., Wyo.

Variety *kentrophyta* is a taxon of the High Plains from southeastern Alberta and southwestern Saskatchewan through eastern Montana, Wyoming and Colorado, the western Dakotas, and western Nebraska.

76b. Astragalus kentrophyta A. Gray var. **tegetarius** (S. Watson) Dorn, Vasc. Pl. Wyoming, 297. 1988 • Mountain kentrophyta [E] [F]

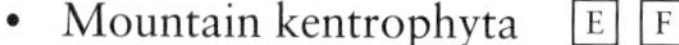

Astragalus tegetarius S. Watson, Botany (Fortieth Parallel), 76, plate 13, figs. 7–10. 1871; *A. aculeatus* A. Nelson; *A. kentrophyta* subsp. *implexus* (Canby ex Porter & J. M. Coulter) W. A. Weber; *A. kentrophyta* var. *implexus* (Canby ex Porter & J. M. Coulter) Barneby; *A. kentrophyta* var. *rotundus* (M. E. Jones) M. E. Jones; *A. montanus* (Nuttall) M. E. Jones var. *rotundus* (M. E. Jones) M. E. Jones;

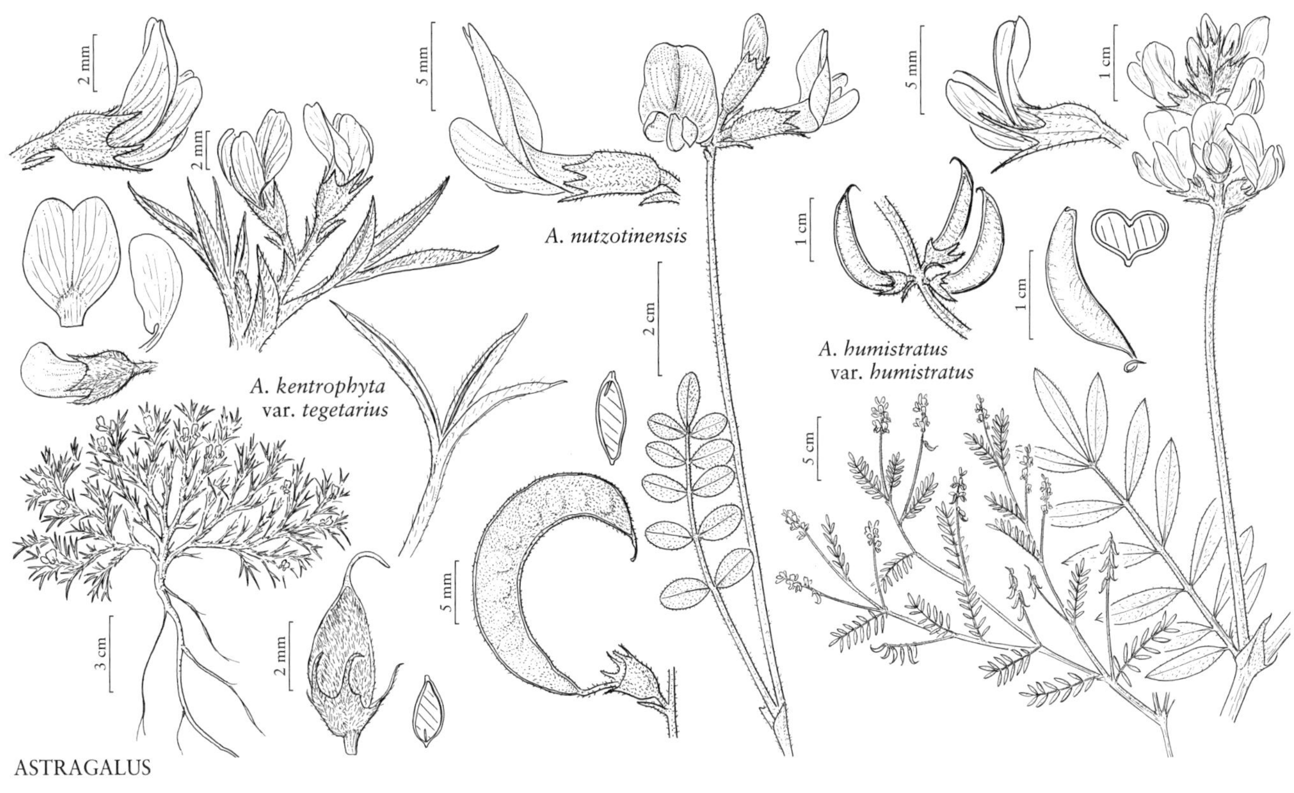

ASTRAGALUS

A. montanus var. *tegetarius* (S. Watson) M. E. Jones; *A. tegetarius* var. *implexus* Canby ex Porter & J. M. Coulter; *A. tegetarius* var. *rotundus* M. E. Jones; *Homalobus aculeatus* (A. Nelson) Rydberg; *H. tegetarius* (S. Watson) Rydberg; *H. wolfii* Rydberg; *Kentrophyta aculeata* (A. Nelson) Rydberg; *K. minima* Rydberg; *K. rotunda* (M. E. Jones) Rydberg; *K. tegetaria* (S. Watson) Rydberg; *K. wolfii* (Rydberg) Rydberg; *Tragacantha tegetaria* (S. Watson) Kuntze

Plants prostrate, cushion-forming, 5–40(–50) cm wide. **Stems** and herbage densely to sparsely strigulose, villosulous, or villous, hairs basifixed. **Leaves** (0.2–)0.4–1.5(–2) cm; stipules 2–7 mm; leaflets (3 or)5–9, blades 1–9 mm, surfaces pubescent or adaxially glabrous or medially glabrescent. **Peduncles** 0–1.5(–3) cm. **Flowers** (3.9–)4.5–8(–9.2) mm; calyx (2–)2.4–5.7(–7) mm, tube 1.2–2.6(–2.8) mm, lobes subulate to setaceous, (0.5–)1.9–2.6(–4.2) mm; corolla usually purple or purplish, sometimes white and keel tip pink or purplish. **Legumes** ellipsoid or oblong-ellipsoid, (3–)4–8(–9) × (0.6–)2–2.5 mm. **Seeds** (3–)5–8. **2*n*** = 24.

Flowering Jun–Sep. Ridgetops, breaks, alpine shrub and tundra with *Phlox*, *Geum rossii*, other forbs, grasses, less commonly with shrubs and trees, often in barrens; 2000–3700 m; Calif., Colo., Idaho, Mont., Nev., N.Mex., Oreg., Utah, Wyo.

The moderately large, usually purplish flowers borne just above the mat of foliage set var. *tegetarius* apart and make it one of the showiest phases of the species.

76c. Astragalus kentrophyta A. Gray var. **danaus** (Barneby) Barneby, Leafl. W. Bot. 6: 154. 1951 • Mount Dana kentrophyta E

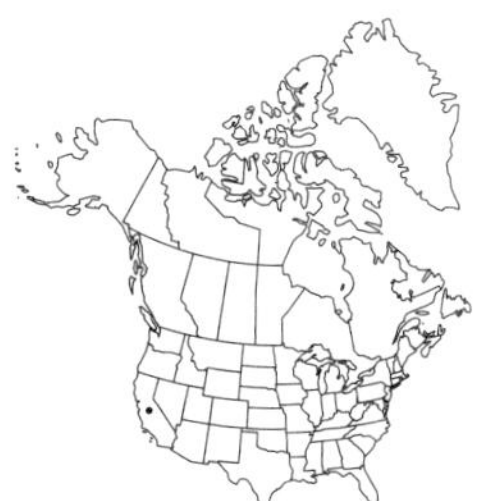

Astragalus tegetarius S. Watson var. *danaus* Barneby, Leafl. W. Bot. 6: 95. 1951

Plants prostrate, mat- or cushion-forming, to 15 cm wide. **Stems** and herbage strigulose, hairs basifixed. **Leaves** 0.4–1.5(–2) cm; stipules somewhat dimorphic, 2–7 mm; leaflets 3(–7), blades 3–7 mm. **Peduncles** 0.2–0.6 cm. **Flowers** 4–5.6 mm; calyx 2.4–3.2 mm, tube 1.6–1.9 mm, lobes subulate to setaceous, 0.8–1.3 mm; corolla purple or whitish and keel purple. **Legumes** subsymmetrically lenticular, 3.5–5 × 2–2.5 mm. **Seeds** 5–8. **2*n*** = 24.

Flowering Jul–Sep. Gravelly slopes and talus upward from timberline, or in bristle-cone pine forest; 3000–4000 m; Calif.

Variety *danaus* is restricted to high elevations in the southern Sierra Nevada.

76d. Astragalus kentrophyta A. Gray var. **douglasii** Barneby, Mem. New York Bot. Gard. 13: 364. 1964 • Douglas kentrophyta E

Plants prostrate, densely mat-forming, becoming suffruticose. **Stems** and herbage strigulose, hairs basifixed. **Leaves** 1–1.7 cm; stipules dimorphic, 2–5 mm; leaflets 5(or 7), blades 5–12 mm, surfaces pubescent. **Peduncles** subobsolete. **Flowers** 5.8 mm; calyx 4.7–5.2 mm, tube 2.2–2.4 mm, lobes subulate, spinulose, 2.3–3 mm; corolla whitish. **Legumes** lanceoloid, 5–5.5 × 2 mm. **Seeds** 2. $2n = 24$.

Flowering Jun. Sandy substrates; 150–400 m; Oreg., Wash.

Variety *douglasii* is known from only a few, vague historical records, probably taken near the present city of Walla Walla near the Great Bend of the Columbia River, and appears to be extinct.

76e. Astragalus kentrophyta A. Gray var. **jessiae** (M. Peck) Barneby, Leafl. W. Bot. 6: 154. 1951 • Jessie's kentrophyta E

Astragalus jessiae M. Peck, Leafl. W. Bot. 4: 180. 1945

Plants spreading or prostrate, loosely mat-forming, 5–35 cm wide. **Stems** and herbage strigulose, hairs malpighian. **Leaves** 1–1.7 cm; stipules dimorphic, those at proximal nodes connate into short, bidentate sheath, those at distal nodes longer, connate at base only, lanceolate or lanceolate-acuminate, often without spines, 1.5–7(–8) mm; leaflets 5, blades 4–10 mm, surfaces pubescent. **Peduncles** 0.1–0.6 cm. **Flowers** 5.2–6.5 mm; calyx 3.6–5.1 mm, tube 1.6–2.5 mm, lobes subulate, spinulose, 1.9–3 mm; corolla whitish, banner and keel tips sometimes faintly tinged pink or lilac. **Legumes** lenticular or ovoid-lenticular, 3–4.5 × 1.4–2 mm. **Seeds** 2(or 3). $2n = 24$.

Flowering Jun–Aug. Bluffs, ridges, dunes, sandy sites; 700–2400 m; Idaho, Oreg., Utah, Wyo.

The distribution of var. *jessiae* is bicentric: southwestern Idaho and southeastern Oregon, and northeastern Utah and southwestern Wyoming.

76f. Astragalus kentrophyta A. Gray var. **ungulatus** M. E. Jones, Proc. Calif. Acad. Sci., ser. 2, 5: 650. 1895 • Talon kentrophyta E

Plants prostrate, mat- or cushion-forming, 8–20 cm wide. **Stems** and herbage strigulose, hairs malpighian. **Leaves** 0.5–1.3 cm; stipules dimorphic, those at proximal nodes connate, those at distal nodes free and ± spine-tipped, 1.5–4 mm; leaflets (3 or)5, blades 3–9 mm. **Peduncles** 0.1–0.4 cm. **Flowers** 5.2–6.5 mm; calyx 3.6–4.7 mm, tube 1.8–2.1 mm, lobes subulate, spinulose, 1.8–2.6 mm; corolla whitish, keel tip purplish. **Legumes** obliquely lanceoloid-acuminate, 5–7.5 × 1.6–2 mm. **Seeds** 2 or 3(or 4). $2n = 24$.

Flowering May–Jul. Calcareous gravel or gravelly clay knolls and hillsides with sagebrush; 1500–2200 (–3000) m; Calif., Nev.

Variety *ungulatus* contributes to the peculiar pseudo-alpine, mound- and cushion-forming vegetation on the knolls and valley floors and foothills in the high valleys of central and northeastern Nevada and Mono County, California.

76g. Astragalus kentrophyta A. Gray var. **neomexicanus** (Barneby) Barneby, Leafl. W. Bot. 6: 154. 1951 • New Mexican kentrophyta E

Astragalus tegetarius S. Watson var. *neomexicanus* Barneby, Leafl. W. Bot. 6: 99. 1951

Plants decumbent and mat- or cushion-forming, or erect and bushy-branched basally, 4–30 (–40) cm. **Stems** and herbage strigulose, hairs malpighian. **Leaves** 0.8–2.2 cm; stipules uniform, connate to 1/2 their length, 1–1.5(–2.5) mm; leaflets usually 5, blades 3–13 mm. **Peduncles** 0.1–0.3 cm. **Flowers** 4.8–5.2 mm; calyx 2.4–3.3 mm, tube 1.8–2.1 mm, lobes subulate, spinulose, 0.7–1.5 mm; corolla whitish. **Legumes** obliquely ovoid, 3–4 × 1.8–2.4 mm. **Seeds** 2 or 3. $2n = 24$.

Flowering Jun–Sep. Bluffs, badlands, dunes, mixed desert shrub and pinyon-juniper communities; 1600–2200 m; N.Mex.

Variety *neomexicanus* is predominantly of the northwestern quarter of New Mexico, with outlying populations along the drainage of the Pecos River in De Baca and Chaves counties. Plants from the latter area have somewhat the habit of var. *kentrophyta* but the pungent leaflets and short calyx lobes of var. *neomexicanus*.

76h. Astragalus kentrophyta A. Gray var. **elatus** S. Watson, Botany (Fortieth Parallel), 77. 1871 • Tall kentrophyta [E]

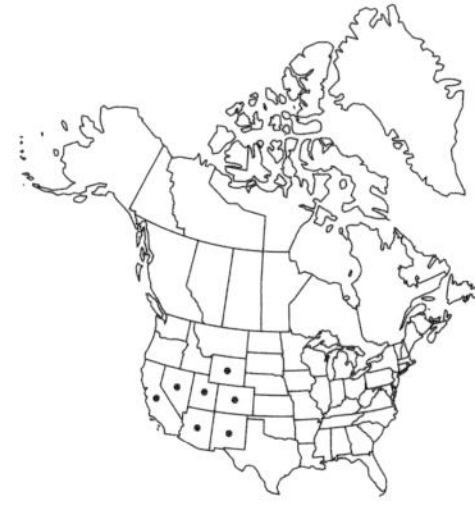

Astragalus impensus Wooton & Standley

Plants usually erect or assurgent, rarely trailing, suffruticose and often bushy-branched basally, forming low, prickly bushes, 10–45(–65) cm, sometimes mat-forming. **Stems** and herbage strigulose, hairs malpighian. **Leaves** (0.8–)1–2.6 cm; stipules dimorphic, those at proximal nodes connate with bidentate tip, those at distal nodes connate near base with spiny tips, 1–12 mm; leaflets (3 or)5 or 7, blades (2–)5–15(–17) mm, surfaces usually pubescent, sometimes glabrous adaxially. **Peduncles** 0.1–0.6 cm. **Flowers** 4.8–6.2 mm; calyx 3.4–4.4 mm, tube 1.8–2.3 mm, lobes subulate, spinulose, 1.5–2.4 mm; corolla usually whitish or faintly veined or tinged purple, fading ochroleucous, rarely pink-purple. **Legumes** narrowly ovoid-acuminate, (3.5–)4–7 × 1.5–2 mm. **Seeds** 2–4. **2*n*** = 24.

Flowering Jun–Sep. Mixed desert and salt desert shrub, juniper-pinyon, ponderosa pine, bristlecone pine, and pine-spruce communities, floodplains; 1500–2900 (–3200) m; Ariz., Calif., Colo., Nev., N.Mex., Utah, Wyo.

Both erect and prostrate phases are known, which at maturity form ascending or sprawling tangles of untidy, branched stems with prickly leaves, hence an alternative common name of barb-wire kentrophyta. The prostrate phases, typically from upper-middle elevations, simulate var. *tegetarius*, which has basifixed hairs.

76i. Astragalus kentrophyta A. Gray var. **coloradoensis** M. E. Jones, Contr. W. Bot. 10: 63. 1902 • Canyonlands kentrophyta [E]

Plants loosely mat- or clump-forming, low, to 12 cm. **Stems** and herbage strigulose, hairs malpighian. **Leaves** 0.9–2.4 cm; stipules 1–12 mm; leaflets (3 or) 5(or 7), blades 4–15 mm, surfaces pubescent. **Peduncles** 0.2–0.6 cm. **Flowers** 7.3–10 mm; calyx 6–8.3 mm, tube 2.4–3.3 mm, lobes subulate, spinulose, 3.4–5 mm; corolla pink-purple. **Legumes** subsymmetrically ellipsoid, lanceoloid- or oblong-ellipsoid, (5–)7–10 × 2.8–4 mm. **Seeds** 4–8. **2*n*** = 24.

Flowering Apr–Jun. Sandy wash bottoms, sandy pockets on sandstone rimrock, in mixed desert shrub communities; 900–1700 m; Ariz., Utah.

Variety *coloradoensis* is known from north-central Arizona and south-central Utah.

135u. Astragalus Linnaeus sect. Polares (Rydberg) Barneby, Mem. New York Bot. Gard. 13: 370. 1964

Phaca Linnaeus sect. *Polares* Rydberg in N. L. Britton et al., N. Amer. Fl. 24: 349. 1929

Herbs perennial, caulescent; caudex superficial or subterranean. **Hairs** basifixed. **Stems** few or several to many. **Stipules** connate or distinct at distal nodes. **Leaves** odd-pinnate, petiolate or subsessile; leaflets 7–17(or 19). **Racemes** sometimes subumbellate, compactly or loosely flowered, flowers ascending or spreading. **Calyx tubes** campanulate. **Corollas** usually pink-purple, rarely white, banner recurved through 40–45°, keel apex obtuse. **Legumes** deciduous, sessile on a slightly elevated receptacle, spreading or ascending and humistrate, obliquely ovoid, moderately to greatly inflated, ± laterally compressed or 3-sided, unilocular. **Seeds** 2–17.

Species 2 (2 in the flora): North America, Asia (Siberia).

Section *Polares* consists of mesophytic species distributed from Alaska to Newfoundland, southward to Utah, New Mexico, and Nebraska. M. Lavin and H. Marriott (1997) realigned *Astragalus molybdenus* of the monospecific sect. *Minerales*, placing it within sect. *Polares*, a proposal with considerable merit, but not followed here (see discussions under 5. *A. molybdenus*).

77. **Astragalus bodinii** E. Sheldon, Minnesota Bot. Stud. 1: 122. 1894 (as bodini) • Bodin's milkvetch [E]

Astragalus stragalus Fernald; *A. yukonis* M. E. Jones

Plants slender, 15–80(–100) cm, sparsely strigulose; from superficial or subterranean caudex; taproot stout. **Stems** spreading or prostrate, sparsely strigulose. **Leaves** (1–)2.5–8.5 cm; stipules connate-clasping and membranous becoming papery-scarious at proximal nodes, connate or distinct and subherbaceous at distal nodes, 1–7 mm; leaflets 7–17(or 19), blades oblanceolate to obovate, ovate, or elliptic, 2–15(–17) mm, apex rounded to emarginate or acute, surfaces strigose abaxially, glabrous adaxially. **Peduncles** 1.5–12.5 (–18.5) cm. **Racemes** compactly or loosely 3–16-flowered; axis 0.5–10 cm in fruit; bracts 0.5–2.5 mm; bracteoles 0. **Pedicels** 0.7–2.2 mm. **Flowers** (7–)8–12 mm; calyx 3.8–6.1(–7.2) mm, black-strigose, tube 2.4–3.8 mm, lobes subulate, 1.2–2.4 mm; corolla pink-purple suffused with purple or partly white; banner recurved through 40–45°; keel (5.3–)5.5–8.9 mm. **Legumes** ascending to spreading, stramineous, straight or slightly curved, obliquely ovoid, somewhat 3-sided compressed, swollen, slightly bladdery, (4.5–)7–10(–12) × (2.2–)3–4.5 mm, papery-membranous, translucent, strigose; gynophore 0.3–1 mm. **Seeds** 2–10. $2n$ = 24, 32.

Flowering Jun–Sep. Wet meadows, gravel bars, stream banks, less often on dunes, willow-alder-spruce-birch and meadow communities; 200–2300 m; Alta., Man., Nfld. and Labr. (Nfld.), N.W.T., Sask., Yukon; Alaska, Colo., Idaho, Nebr., N.Mex., Utah, Wyo.

Of the great number of species of *Astragalus* in North America, only a handful are mesophytic: *A. agrestis*, *A. argophyllus* var. *argophyllus*, *A. bodinii*, *A. canadensis*, and *A. diversifolius*. In Utah, *A. bodinii* has persisted, even flourished, in heavily grazed meadows. It appears to be avoided by livestock.

78. **Astragalus polaris** Bentham, Trans. Linn. Soc. London 23: 323. 1861 • Polar milkvetch

Plants 5–20 cm, sparsely strigulose; from rhizomatous, subterranean branched caudex. **Stems** prostrate or weakly ascending, 1.5–9+ cm underground, sparsely strigulose. **Leaves** 1–7 cm; stipules connate-sheathing and papery-membranous throughout, (1.3–)2–5 mm; leaflets (7 or)9–17, blades elliptic to oblong, 1.5–6 mm, apex emarginate, retuse, or obtuse, surfaces strigulose abaxially, glabrous adaxially. **Peduncles** decumbent (in fruit), (1.5–)2–7 cm. **Racemes** loosely 1–3(–6)-flowered; axis 3–13 mm; bracts 0.7–2 mm; bracteoles 0. **Pedicels** 1–2 mm. **Flowers** 10–16 mm; calyx 4.6–7, black-strigulose, tube 3.4–6 mm, lobes triangular to lanceolate, 1–2.5 mm; corolla usually pink-purple, rarely white; banner recurved through 45°; keel 9–9.7 mm. **Legumes** loosely ascending, green, often red-tinged, straight or slightly curved, ovoid, strongly turgid or bladdery, (15–)18–43 × 4.5–12(–15) mm, papery-membranous, black-strigose; gynophore 0–1 mm. **Seeds** 8–17. $2n$ = 24.

Flowering Jun–Aug. Beaches, glacial moraines, gravelly fans, slopes, spits; 0–1600 m; Alaska; Asia (Siberia).

Astragalus polaris is distinctive among arctic species of the genus with its ultimately inflated fruits; it occurs throughout much of the state except the southeast. In habit and stature, it resembles *A. alpinus*, but the deeply retuse leaflets, strongly graduated petals, and sessile fruits provide differential characters.

135v. Astragalus Linnaeus sect. Gynophoraria (Rydberg) Barneby, Mem. New York Bot. Gard. 13: 375. 1964 (as Astragaluus) [E]

Gynophoraria Rydberg in N. L. Britton et al., N. Amer. Fl. 24: 280. 1929

Herbs perennial, caulescent; caudex subterranean. **Hairs** basifixed. **Stems** few to several. **Stipules** connate. **Leaves** odd-pinnate, petiolate; leaflets (7 or)9–15(or 17). **Racemes** loosely flowered, flowers spreading-ascending. **Calyx tubes** campanulate. **Corollas** usually pink or purplish, rarely white, banner recurved through 30–45°, keel apex obtuse, length nearly equal to wings. **Legumes** deciduous, sessile, gynophore present, ascending and humistrate, linear-oblong, lunately to annulately incurved, strongly compressed laterally, with protruding sutures, unilocular. **Seeds** 8–16.

Species 1: nw North America.

79. Astragalus nutzotinensis J. Rousseau, Contr. Lab. Bot. Univ. Montréal 24: 14. 1933 • Nutzotin milkvetch [E] [F]

Gynophoraria falcata Rydberg in N. L. Britton et al., N. Amer. Fl. 24: 280. 1929, not *Astragalus falcatus* Lamarck 1783

Plants slender, weak, 10–40 (–50) cm, minutely strigulose; from shallow to deep subterranean caudex. **Stems** prostrate or diffuse, 1–6+ cm underground, minutely strigulose. **Leaves** 1–6.5 cm; stipules connate-sheathing at least at proximal nodes, often becoming anthocyanic and somewhat enlarged at distal nodes, 3–6 mm, thinly herbaceous becoming papery; leaflet blades elliptic to oblong, 1.5–8 mm, apex obtuse to retuse, surfaces strigulose, sometimes glabrous or glabrate adaxially. **Peduncles** ascending, (2.5–)3–10 cm. **Racemes** 1–5-flowered; axis 1–3 cm in fruit; bracts 1.5–4.5 mm; bracteoles 0. **Pedicels** 1.8–4 mm. **Flowers** 12–20 mm; calyx 6–6.7 mm, black-strigose to glabrate, tube 3–4.7 mm, lobes triangular-acuminate to linear, 1–2.5 mm; corolla keel 11.2–13.7 mm. **Legumes** pale green with purple dots, curved in 0.5–1 spiral, laterally compressed, 30–50 × 50–75 mm, papery-membranous, semitransparent, minutely strigose; gynophore 4–10 mm. $2n = 22$.

Flowering Jun–Aug. Gravel bars, rock outcrops, gravelly ridgecrests, scree and talus with *Dryas* and other pioneering species, often at foot of melting glaciers; 200–1800 m; B.C., Yukon; Alaska.

The pink or purple flowers and the great sickle-shaped, purple-suffused fruits, which recline on the ground, make this one of the most attractive of subarctic species.

135w. Astragalus Linnaeus sect. Jejuni (M. E. Jones) Barneby, Mem. New York Bot. Gard. 13: 379. 1964 [E]

Astragalus subsect. *Jejuni* M. E. Jones, Rev. N.-Amer. Astragalus, 95. 1923

Herbs perennial, dwarf, subacaulescent or acaulescent; caudex superficial or subterranean. **Hairs** basifixed. **Stems** obsolete or clustered. **Stipules** connate. **Leaves** odd-pinnate, petiolate; leaflets 5–15(or 17), terminal leaflet confluent or jointed. **Racemes** loosely flowered, flowers ascending, spreading, or declined. **Calyx tubes** campanulate. **Corollas** pink-purple, ochroleucous, or white, banner recurved through 50–70°, keel apex strongly incurved, obtuse. **Legumes** deciduous, sessile, spreading, obovoid or subglobose, bladdery-inflated, unilocular. **Seeds** 10–14.

Species 3 (3 in the flora): w United States.

Section *Jejuni* comprises species distributed in Idaho, Colorado, east-central Nevada to south-central Utah, and southwestern Wyoming.

80. Astragalus jejunus S. Watson, Botany (Fortieth Parallel), 73, plate 13, figs. 1–6. 1871 • Starveling milkvetch [E]

Astragalus jejunus var. *articulatus* Dorn

Plants densely clump-, cushion-, or tuft-forming, 1–5 cm, strigulose; from superficial much-branched caudex, branches covered with thatch of marcescent leaf rachises. **Stems** obscured by stipules and leaf bases. **Leaves** erect, 1–4 cm; stipules 1.5–3 mm, membranous becoming papery; leaflets 9–15(or 17), blades linear to narrowly elliptic, 1–5 mm, apex obtuse to acute, surfaces strigose; terminal leaflet often decurrent distally, not jointed to rachis. **Peduncles** erect, 0.5–3.5 cm, together with racemes subequal to or ± surpassing leaves. **Racemes** 3–7-flowered, flowers spreading; axis 0.2–1 cm in fruit; bracts 1–1.5 mm; bracteoles 0. **Pedicels** 1–2.5 mm. **Flowers** 5–6.5 mm; calyx 2.3–3 mm, strigose, tube 1.5–2 mm, lobes subulate, 0.5–1 mm; corolla pink-purple or white; keel 3.7–4.4 mm. **Legumes** green with purple mottling, slightly curved, subglobose, 10–17 × 7–11 mm, papery-membranous, strigose. **Seeds** 10–14.

Flowering May–Jul. Sagebrush and sagebrush-juniper or pinyon-juniper communities, windswept ridgetops; 1700–2400 m; Colo., Idaho, Nev., Utah, Wyo.

Astragalus jejunus is a tufted plant that produces masses of small, inflated fruits, usually gaily mottled with reddish purple, nestled amid broomlike clusters of leaf rachises.

Plants with articulated terminal leaflets and pale flowers from Big Horn County, Wyoming, form the basis of var. *articulatus*. Whether such plants constitute a distinct taxon or merely recurrent expression of variable phenotypes requires additional research. Both of the critical differences are encountered occasionally in other populations.

81. Astragalus limnocharis Barneby, Leafl. W. Bot. 4: 236. 1946 • Navajo Lake milkvetch [C] [E]

Plants tuft-forming, 1–5 cm, strigose; from superficial or subterranean branched caudex, soboliferous or not, branches with persistent petioles; taproot stout. **Stems** prostrate to erect, (0.5–)2–20+ cm underground, strigose, glabrate, or glabrous. **Leaves** 1.5–7 cm; stipules 2–4 mm, herbaceous becoming papery; leaflets (5 or)7–13, blades lanceolate to elliptic or oblong, 2–9 mm, margins involute and long-ciliate, apex obtuse, surfaces strigose abaxially, glabrous adaxially. **Peduncles** erect and ascending, reclined in fruit, 2–5 cm. **Racemes** 2–10-flowered, flowers spreading to declined; axis 0.2–0.5 cm in fruit; bracts 1–3 mm; bracteoles 0. **Pedicels** 0.8–1.5 mm. **Flowers** 6.2–7.5 mm; calyx 2.8–3.6 mm, strigose, tube 2–2.5 mm, lobes subulate, 0.7–1.6 mm; corolla ochroleucous or pink-purple, then wing tips same color; keel 3.9–4.8 mm. **Legumes** pale green, red-mottled, becoming stramineous, ovoid, 9–18(–22) × 7–13(–15) mm, papery-membranous, opaque, strigose. **Seeds** 10–12.

Varieties 2 (2 in the flora): Utah.

1. Corollas ochroleucous; plants usually not soboliferous; Navajo Lake vicinity, Iron and Kane counties, Utah . . . . 81a. *Astragalus limnocharis* var. *limnocharis*
1. Corollas pink-purple; plants usually soboliferous; Table Cliff Plateau, Garfield County, Utah . . . . 81b. *Astragalus limnocharis* var. *tabulaeus*

81a. Astragalus limnocharis Barneby var. **limnocharis** [C] [E]

Plants usually not soboliferous. **Corollas** ochroleucous.

Flowering Jul–Sep. Lakeshores, limestone breaks, ridge crests and slopes with western bristlecone pine; of conservation concern; 2700–3100 m; Utah.

The specific epithet refers to lake beauty, alluding to the habitat of var. *limnocharis* on the shore of Navajo Lake in Iron County; it is known also from limestone breaks only a few kilometers southeast in Kane County.

81b. Astragalus limnocharis Barneby var. **tabulaeus** S. L. Welsh, Great Basin Naturalist 46: 261. 1986 • Table Cliff milkvetch [C] [E]

Plants usually soboliferous. **Corollas** pink-purple.

Flowering Jun–Aug. Western bristlecone pine-Douglas-fir communities; of conservation concern; 2900–3200 m; Utah.

Variety *tabulaeus* is restricted to the Table Cliff Plateau, Horse Creek Top vicinity in Garfield County. R. C. Barneby (1989) placed it in synonymy with *Astragalus limnocharis* var. *montii* (treated here as *A. montii*), but it differs in having smaller, concolorous flowers.

82. Astragalus montii S. L. Welsh, Great Basin Naturalist 38: 11. 1978 • Heliotrope milkvetch [C] [E]

Astragalus limnocharis Barneby var. *montii* (S. L. Welsh) Isely

Plants 1–5 cm, strigose; from superficial or slightly subterranean branched caudex. **Stems** clustered, ascending to erect, strigose. **Leaves** 1.3–4.8 cm; stipules 2–4 mm; leaflets 5–13, blades lanceolate to oblong or elliptic, 2–8 mm, margins involute and not ciliate, surfaces strigose abaxially, glabrous adaxially. **Peduncles** reclined in fruit, 0.8–4.5 cm. **Racemes** 2–8-flowered, flowers ascending to spreading; axis 0.2–0.5 cm in fruit; bracts 1–3 mm; bracteoles 0. **Pedicels** 0.8–1.5 mm. **Flowers** 7.2–8 mm; calyx 3.3–4 mm, strigose, tube 2.2–2.5 mm, lobes triangular-subulate, 0.6–1.5 mm; corolla pink-purple, wing tips white. **Legumes** mottled, straight or nearly so, ovoid, 11–18 × 8–12 mm, membranous, opaque, strigose. **Seeds** 10.

Flowering Jul–Aug. Openings in spruce-fir forests, plateau margins; of conservation concern; 3300–3500 m; Utah.

Astragalus montii is a near, though disjunct, congener of *A. limnocharis* from Sanpete and Sevier counties. It is in the Center for Plant Conservation's National Collection of Endangered Plants.

135x. Astragalus Linnaeus sect. Humistrati (M. E. Jones) Barneby, Mem. New York Bot. Gard. 13: 383. 1964

Astragalus subsect. *Humistrati* M. E. Jones, Rev. N.-Amer. Astragalus, 68. 1923

Herbs perennial, mat-, clump-, or cushion-forming, stems prostrate, caulescent; caudex superficial or subterranean. **Hairs** basifixed or malpighian. **Stems** several to many. **Stipules** connate or distally distinct. **Leaves** odd-pinnate, usually petiolate, sometimes subsessile to short-petiolate; leaflets (3 or)5–17(or 19). **Racemes** compactly flowered, flowers ascending or spreading. **Calyx tubes** campanulate, sometimes obconic-campanulate. **Corollas** whitish, ochroleucous, greenish, pink-purple, or purple, banner recurved through 40–85°, keel apex obtuse or acuminate and beaked. **Legumes** deciduous, sessile, ascending or spreading, sometimes, usually humistrate, ovoid, oblong, or oblong-ellipsoid, compressed dorsiventrally proximally or 3-sided, unilocular. **Seeds** 4–26.

Species 4 (4 in the flora): w, sc United States, nw Mexico.

Section *Humistrati* consists of two subsections distributed in Arizona, New Mexico, Nevada, eastern Oregon, southern Utah, southwestern Colorado, and trans-Pecos Texas.

The subsections are: subsect. *Humistrati* (*Astragalus humistratus*, *A. sesquiflorus*); and subsect. *Micromerii* Barneby (*A. chuskanus*, *A. micromerius*).

83. Astragalus humistratus A. Gray, Smithsonian Contr. Knowl. 5(6): 43. 1853 • Groundcover milkvetch [F]

Plants mat- or clump-forming, (4–)7–80 cm, pubescent, hairs malpighian (shorter ones) or basifixed (longer ones), herbage green or grayish; from superficial or slightly subterranean caudex. **Stems** mostly prostrate with upturned tips, strigose, strigulose, pilose, pilosulous, villous, or subtomentose. **Leaves** 1–6(–7.5) cm; stipules 1.5–10(–11) mm, submembranous becoming scarious; leaflets (5–)9–17(or 19), blades elliptic to oblong or oblanceolate to obovate, (2–)3–17(–19) mm, apex acute or obtuse, surfaces strigose, sometimes glabrate or glabrous adaxially. **Peduncles** divaricate or incurved-ascending, 1–9 cm. **Racemes** 3–30-flowered, flowers ascending; axis 1–9(–13) cm in fruit; bracts 1.5–7 mm; bracteoles 0–2. **Pedicels** 0.4–2.2 mm. **Flowers** 5.9–11.8 mm; calyx 3.2–7.6(–8.8) mm, strigose, tube 2.1–4(–4.1) mm, lobes lanceolate-acuminate, filiform-setaceous, or subulate, (1–)1.2–4.5(–5) mm; corolla greenish to ochroleucous or purple, banner often suffused, margined, or veined purplish, pink, or lilac-purple, sometimes wing tips whitish; banner recurved through 50–85°; keel 5.1–10 mm. **Legumes** ascending to spreading, stramineous or brown, incurved, obliquely oblong-ellipsoid, lanceoloid-ellipsoid, ovoid, obovoid, linear-oblong, oblanceoloid, semi-ovoid, or semi-ellipsoid, compressed, 6–20 × 3.5–6.5 mm, thickly fleshy becoming leathery or papery, strigulose or villosulous. **Seeds** 6–26.

Varieties 6 (6 in the flora): sw United States, nw Mexico.

The forms of *Astragalus humistratus* constitute two main categories: a southwestern branch characterized by fruits that are relatively long, narrow, and pluriovulate; and a northwestern branch characterized by fruits that are short, plumper in profile, and relatively few-ovulate. Varieties are spring- or autumn-flowering or, with rains, blooming both times.

1. Legumes (10–)13–20 × 3.1–6.5 mm; seeds (16–)18–26; sw Colorado to se Arizona, New Mexico, extreme w Texas.
    2. Herbage sparsely pubescent, green or greenish cinereous; leaflet blades glabrous or glabrate adaxially .... 83a. *Astragalus humistratus* var. *humistratus*
    2. Herbage cinereous or silvery-canescent; leaflet blades pubescent adaxially............... .... 83b. *Astragalus humistratus* var. *sonorae*
1. Legumes 6–14 × 2.5–5.7 mm; seeds 6–16; e, w Arizona, New Mexico to Nevada and s Utah.
    3. Plants with extremely fine, weak, sinuous or curly hairs; banner (3–)4–5 mm wide; legumes 2.5–3 mm wide; seeds 6–9; leaflet blades pubescent adaxially; White Mountains, Arizona, San Francisco Mountains, New Mexico ... 83f. *Astragalus humistratus* var. *crispulus*
    3. Plants with ± straight hairs, sometimes shorter ones crispate or sinuous; banner 5–8.4(–9) mm wide; legumes 3–5.7 mm wide; seeds (7 or) 8–16; leaflet blades pubescent, glabrous, or glabrescent adaxially; Arizona, Nevada, New Mexico, Utah.

[4. Shifted to left margin.—Ed.]

4. Racemes 3–6(–8)-flowered; leaflet blades 2–6.5 mm; Kaibab Plateau, n Arizona . . . . 83e. *Astragalus humistratus* var. *tenerrimus*
4. Racemes (3–)7–22-flowered; leaflet blades (2–) 3–17(–19) mm; Arizona, Nevada, New Mexico, Utah.
   5. Herbage cinereous or silvery-canescent; leaflet blades pubescent adaxially; w New Mexico to s Nevada and s Utah . . . 83c. *Astragalus humistratus* var. *humivagans*
   5. Herbage green or greenish cinereous; leaflet blades glabrous adaxially; c Arizona, wc New Mexico . . . . 83d. *Astragalus humistratus* var. *hosackiae*

83a. Astragalus humistratus A. Gray var. **humistratus** [F]

Plants sparsely pilose-pilosulous, herbage green or greenish cinereous, sparsely pubescent. **Stems** (15–)20–60 cm. **Stipules** 2–9(–11) mm. **Leaves** (1–)1.5–5.5 cm; leaflets 11–17, blades 4–14 mm, surfaces glabrous or glabrate adaxially. **Peduncles** 2–8(–9.5) cm. **Racemes** (5–)7–30-flowered; axis 1–6 cm in fruit. **Flowers:** calyx 5.8–7.6 mm, tube 3–3.8 mm, lobes lanceolate-acuminate or filiform-setaceous, 2.5–4.5 mm; corolla greenish white to ochroleucous, often suffused or veined with purple; banner 9.5–11.8 × 6–8 mm. **Legumes** obliquely oblong-ellipsoid or lanceoloid-ellipsoid, ± incurved, 14–18 × 4–6.5 mm, strigulose. **Seeds** (16–)18–26. **2*n*** = 24.

Flowering May–Sep. Pine forests, pinyon-juniper, mesquite-juniper-saltbush, and blue-grama grassland communities, less commonly in spruce-fir forests; 1300–2700 m; Ariz., Colo., N.Mex., Tex.; Mexico (Chihuahua).

Variety *humistratus* intergrades with var. *sonorae* in southwestern New Mexico.

83b. Astragalus humistratus A. Gray var. **sonorae** (A. Gray) M. E. Jones, Contr. W. Bot. 10: 58. 1902 • Sonoran groundcover milkvetch

Astragalus sonorae A. Gray, Smithsonian Contr. Knowl. 5(6): 44. 1853

Plants densely strigose-pilose and strigulose, herbage cinereous or silvery-canescent. **Stems** (5–)10–35 cm. **Stipules** 3.5–10 mm. **Leaves** (1.5–)2.5–5 cm; leaflets (5–)9–17, blades 3–13 (–15) mm, surfaces pubescent adaxially. **Peduncles** 3–8 cm. **Racemes** 10–26-flowered; axis 1.5–5.5 cm in fruit. **Flowers:** calyx 4.6–6.8(–8) mm, tube 2.5–3.5 mm, lobes lanceolate-acuminate or filiform-setaceous, 2–4 (–4.5) mm; corolla dull purplish, purple, or banner purple margined or veined; banner 8.3–10.3(–11.4) × 6–9 mm. **Legumes** lunately linear-oblong or narrowly oblanceoloid, (10–)13–20 × 3.2–4.1 mm, densely strigulose. **Seeds** (16–)18–26.

Flowering late Mar–Sep. Dry substrates, among junipers, in ponderosa pine forests, grasslands; 1400–2100 m; Ariz., N.Mex.; Mexico (Sonora).

Variety *sonorae* is similar to var. *humistratus* except for the more densely ashen or silky-pubescent foliage. It is usually found at lower elevations and is primarily spring-flowering.

83c. Astragalus humistratus A. Gray var. **humivagans** (Rydberg) Barneby, Amer. Midl. Naturalist 55: 478. 1956 • Spreading milkvetch [E]

Batidophaca humivagans Rydberg in N. L. Britton et al., N. Amer. Fl. 24: 316. 1929

Plants densely strigose-pilose or pilosulous, hairs ± straight, sometimes shorter ones crispate or sinuous, herbage cinereous or silvery-canescent. **Stems** (6–) 10–60(–80) cm, radiating from root-crown. **Stipules** 1.5–9 mm. **Leaves** 1–6(–7.5) cm; leaflets (7–)11–17(or 19), blades (2–)5–17(–19) mm, apex usually acute, surfaces pubescent adaxially. **Peduncles** 2–9 cm. **Racemes** (3–)7–22-flowered; axis 1–9(–13) cm in fruit. **Flowers:** calyx (4.5–)5–7.4(–8.8) mm, tube (2.4–)2.7–3.7(–4.1) mm, lobes lanceolate-acuminate or filiform-setaceous, (1.4–)1.9–3.6(–5) mm; corolla greenish white or ochroleucous, lined or suffused or margined with dull purple, sometimes all purple; banner 7.2–10.2(–11.6) × 5.5–8.4(–9) mm. **Legumes** obliquely ovoid, obovoid, semi-ovoid, or oblong-ellipsoid, (6–) 8–14 × 3.5–5.7 mm, densely strigulose. **Seeds** 10–16. **2*n*** = 24.

Flowering May–Sep. Mountain brush, desert shrub, galleta grassland, sagebrush, pinyon-juniper, ponderosa pine, oak, manzanita, and aspen communities in gravelly, sandy, or clay substrates; 1300–3300 m; Ariz., Nev., N.Mex., Utah.

Variety *humivagans* is closely allied to var. *humistratus* and intergrades with it in northwestern New Mexico.

83d. Astragalus humistratus A. Gray var. **hosackiae** (Greene) M. E. Jones, Contr. W. Bot. 10: 58. 1902 • Lotus milkvetch [E]

Astragalus hosackiae Greene, Bull. Calif. Acad. Sci. 1: 157. 1885

Plants sparsely strigulose or pilose-pilosulous, hairs ± straight, sometimes shorter one crispate or sinuous, herbage green or greenish cinereous. **Stems** (4–) 7–36 cm. **Stipules** (1.5–)2.5–8 mm. **Leaves** 1–5 cm; leaflets 9–15, blades 3–9(–12) mm, surfaces glabrous adaxially. **Peduncles** 2–6 cm. **Racemes** 8–20-flowered; axis (0.8–) 1.2–3.5 cm in fruit. **Flowers:** calyx (3.8–)4–5.5 mm, tube 2.5–3.2 mm, lobes lanceolate-acuminate or filiform-setaceous, (1–)1.4–2.5 mm; corolla greenish white or lined or suffused or margined with dull purple, sometimes all purple or wing tips whitish; banner 6.4–8 × 5–7 mm. **Legumes** plumply semi-ovoid or obliquely ovoid, 7–10 × (3.6–)4–5.5 mm, finely strigulose. **Seeds** (7 or)8–14. **2*n*** = 24.

Flowering May–Sep. Ponderosa pine, mixed pine-oak, oak-chaparral, and pinyon-juniper communities, on igneous bedrock; 1300–1700 m; Ariz., N.Mex.

Variety *hosackiae* is the smallest-flowered variety and is easily recognized by the small, nearly inflated fruits. It is locally sympatric with var. *humivagans*.

83e. Astragalus humistratus A. Gray var. **tenerrimus** M. E. Jones, Proc. Calif. Acad. Sci., ser. 2, 5: 649. 1895 • Delicate milkvetch [E]

Plants forming loose mats, to 8+ dm wide, strigulose, hairs ± straight, sometimes shorter ones crispate or sinuous, herbage greenish cinereous or silvery. **Stems** 10–30 cm, sometimes 1–3 cm underground. **Stipules** 1.5–4.5(–5.5) mm. **Leaves** 1–3 (–4) cm; leaflets (9 or)11–15, blades 2–6.5 mm, surfaces pubescent or glabrescent adaxially. **Peduncles** 1–3(–4) cm. **Racemes** 3–6(–8)-flowered; axis 0.5–2 cm in fruit. **Flowers:** calyx 3.2–4.7 mm, tube 2.1–2.7 mm, lobes subulate, 1–1.2 mm; corolla whitish, veined or suffused with lilac-purple; banner 5.9–7.2 × 5.2–6.6 mm. **Legumes** lunately semi-ovoid-ellipsoid, 6–9 × 3–4.5 mm, loosely strigulose. **Seeds** 9–14.

Flowering Jul–Sep. Meadows, ponderosa pine, white fir, and spruce forests, margins of aspen stands; 2400–2800 m; Ariz.

Variety *tenerrimus*, a diminutive Kaibab Plateau endemic, may deserve specific status as proposed by P. A. Rydberg (1929) in the segregate genus *Batidophaca* Rydberg. R. C. Barneby (1964) considered it closely allied to var. *humivagans*.

83f. Astragalus humistratus A. Gray var. **crispulus** Barneby, Leafl. W. Bot. 4: 53, figs. 24–26. 1944 • Curly-hair milkvetch [E]

Plants gray-villous, often also subtomentose, hairs extremely fine, weak, sinuous or curly, herbage cinereous. **Stems** (5–) 15–55 cm. **Stipules** 2.5–8 mm. **Leaves** 1–4.5(–5) cm; leaflets 11–15, blades (2–)3–14 mm, surfaces pubescent adaxially. **Peduncles** (1–)1.5–3.5(–4) cm. **Racemes** (3–)5–12-flowered; axis (0.5–)1–3 cm in fruit. **Flowers:** calyx 4.6–5.5 mm, tube 2.9–4 mm, lobes subulate, 1.2–2.4 mm; corolla whitish, faintly tinged with pink; banner 7–9.2 × (3–)4–5 mm. **Legumes** lunately semi-ellipsoid, incurved, 8–10 × 2.5–3 mm, villosulous. **Seeds** 6–9.

Flowering Aug–Sep. Xeric pine forests, on sandy soils of volcanic origin on slopes, benches, ledges; 2100–2500 m; Ariz., N.Mex.

Variety *crispulus*, endemic to the White Mountains of southeastern Arizona and the San Francisco Mountains of adjacent New Mexico, is sometimes sympatric with var. *humistratus*, and the two are remarkably different in appearance. The link between them is var. *humivagans*, which extends eastward into their range, but generally, and perhaps exclusively, at lower elevations.

84. Astragalus sesquiflorus S. Watson, Proc. Amer. Acad. Arts 10: 346. 1875 • Sandstone milkvetch [E]

Plants densely mat- or cushion-forming, suffruticose, 5–28(–37+) cm, strigulose, hairs malpighian, sometimes crinkly, especially on stems; from branched, superficial caudex, ± with thatch of persistent leaf bases. **Stems** strigulose-canescent. **Leaves** 1–4 (–6) cm; stipules 1.5–4.5 mm, subherbaceous becoming papery; leaflets 7–11(–17), blades elliptic to obovate, 1.5–10 mm, apex acute to obtuse, surfaces strigose. **Peduncles** divaricate or incurved-ascending, 0.8–4.5 cm. **Racemes** 1–4-flowered, flowers ascending; axis 0–8 mm in fruit; bracts 1.2–3 mm; bracteoles 0–2. **Pedicels** 0.7–4 mm. **Flowers** 6–8 mm; calyx 3.7–5.5 mm, strigulose, tube 1.5–2.8 mm, lobes subulate, 1.9–3 mm; corolla pink-purple; banner recurved through 80°; keel 6–7.4 mm. **Legumes**

spreading-ascending, purple-mottled becoming stramineous, incurved, obliquely oblong, 3-sided and laterally compressed, 8–10 × 3–4 mm, papery, strigulose, hairs often contorted; gynophore 0–0.8 mm. **Seeds** 7–10.

Flowering Apr–Aug. Mixed desert shrub, pinyon-juniper, and ponderosa pine or aspen to spruce-fir communities, on sandstone or sandy substrates; 1100–3100 m; Ariz., Colo., Utah.

Astragalus sesquiflorus forms distinctive mats or so-called powder-puff cushions on sand below escarpments in northeastern Arizona, southwestern Colorado, and southeastern Utah.

85. Astragalus chuskanus Barneby & Spellenberg, Brittonia 39: 188, fig. 1. 1987 • Chuska milkvetch [E]

Plants long-lived, mat- or cushion-forming, 10–35(–40+) cm, strigulose, hairs basifixed; from branched caudex. **Stems** strigulose. **Leaves** (1–)1.5–5.5 cm; stipules 2–5.5 mm, subherbaceous becoming papery; leaflets (7 or)9–15, not crowded, blades obovate- or oblong-elliptic, 0.7–10 mm, apex abruptly acuminate, surfaces pilosulous. **Peduncles** erect, 1.5–3.5(–4) cm, shorter than leaves. **Racemes** 4–10-flowered, flowers ascending-spreading; axis 3–15 mm in fruit; bracts 2–3.5 mm; bracteoles 0. **Pedicels** 0.9–1.5 mm. **Flowers** 7.3–10 mm; calyx 4.5–6.9 mm, pilosulous, tube 2.5–3.8 mm, lobes subulate, 1.5–3.1 mm; corolla whitish, fading ochroleucous; banner recurved through 40°. **Legumes** ascending, humistrate, obliquely semi-ovoid, compressed, 6 × 3 mm, papery, strigulose. **Seeds** 4–6.

Varieties 2 (2 in the flora): sw United States.

Astragalus chuskanus is restricted to the Chuska Mountains and vicinity in northeastern Arizona and northwestern New Mexico.

1. Leaflet blades convex, keeled, surfaces conspicuously gray-hairy; calyces 4.5–5.3 mm, tubes 2.5–3.2 mm, lobes 1.5–2.6 mm; banners 7.3–8 mm ...... 85a. *Astragalus chuskanus* var. *chuskanus*
1. Leaflet blades flat, not keeled, surfaces inconspicuously gray-hairy; calyces 5.5–6.9 mm, tubes 3–3.8, lobes 2–3.1 mm; banners 8–10 mm .... 85b. *Astragalus chuskanus* var. *spellenbergii*

85a. Astragalus chuskanus Barneby & Spellenberg var. **chuskanus** [E]

Plants compact. **Leaflet blades** convex, keeled, surfaces conspicuously gray-hairy. **Flowers:** calyx 4.5–5.3 mm, tube 2.5–3.2 mm, lobes 1.5–2.6 mm; corolla banner 7.3–8 mm. $2n = 24$.

Flowering late May–Jul. Slopes of degraded Pliocene Chuska Sandstone, with ponderosa pine, Douglas-fir, and Rocky Mountain juniper; 2200–2800 m; Ariz., N.Mex.

85b. Astragalus chuskanus Barneby & Spellenberg var. **spellenbergii** S. L. Welsh & N. D. Atwood in S. L. Welsh, N. Amer. Sp. Astragalus, 128. 2007 • Spellenberg's milkvetch [E]

Plants robust. **Leaflet blades** flat, not keeled, surfaces inconspicuously gray-hairy. **Flowers:** calyx 5.5–6.9 mm, tube 3–3.8, lobes 2–3.1 mm; corolla banner 8–10 mm. $2n = 24$.

Flowering Jun–Jul. Slopes of degraded Pliocene Chuska Sandstone, with ponderosa pine, Douglas-fir, and oak; 2200–2800 m; Ariz., N.Mex.

86. Astragalus micromerius Barneby, Leafl. W. Bot. 5: 85. 1948 • Chaco milkvetch [E] [F]

Plants mat- or cushion-forming, suffruticose, 5–30+ cm, villous-hirtellous, hairs basifixed; radiating from branched caudex. **Stems:** older ones to 30 cm underground, densely villous-hirtellous, hairs silvery. **Leaves** 0.4–1(–2) cm; stipules 1–3 mm, herbaceous becoming papery; leaflets subpalmate, crowded, (3 or)5–9, blades oblong-elliptic to obovate, 1–3.5(–6) mm, apex obtuse, surfaces pubescent. **Peduncles** 0.3–1 cm. **Racemes** 1–3(–5)-flowered, flowers spreading; axis 0.5 cm in fruit; bracts 1–2 mm; bracteoles 0. **Pedicels** to 1 mm. **Flowers** 5.5–6.5 mm; calyx obconic-campanulate, 2.5–3.5 mm, hirsutulous, tube 1.5–2.5 mm, lobes subulate, 1–1.3 mm; corolla greenish white, with pale purple veins or tips; banner recurved through 45°; keel 4–4.5 mm. **Legumes** spreading, stramineous, straight or curved (apically), obliquely ovoid, obcompressed, flattened abaxially, 4–5 × 2.5–3 mm, papery, hirsutulous. **Seeds** 4.

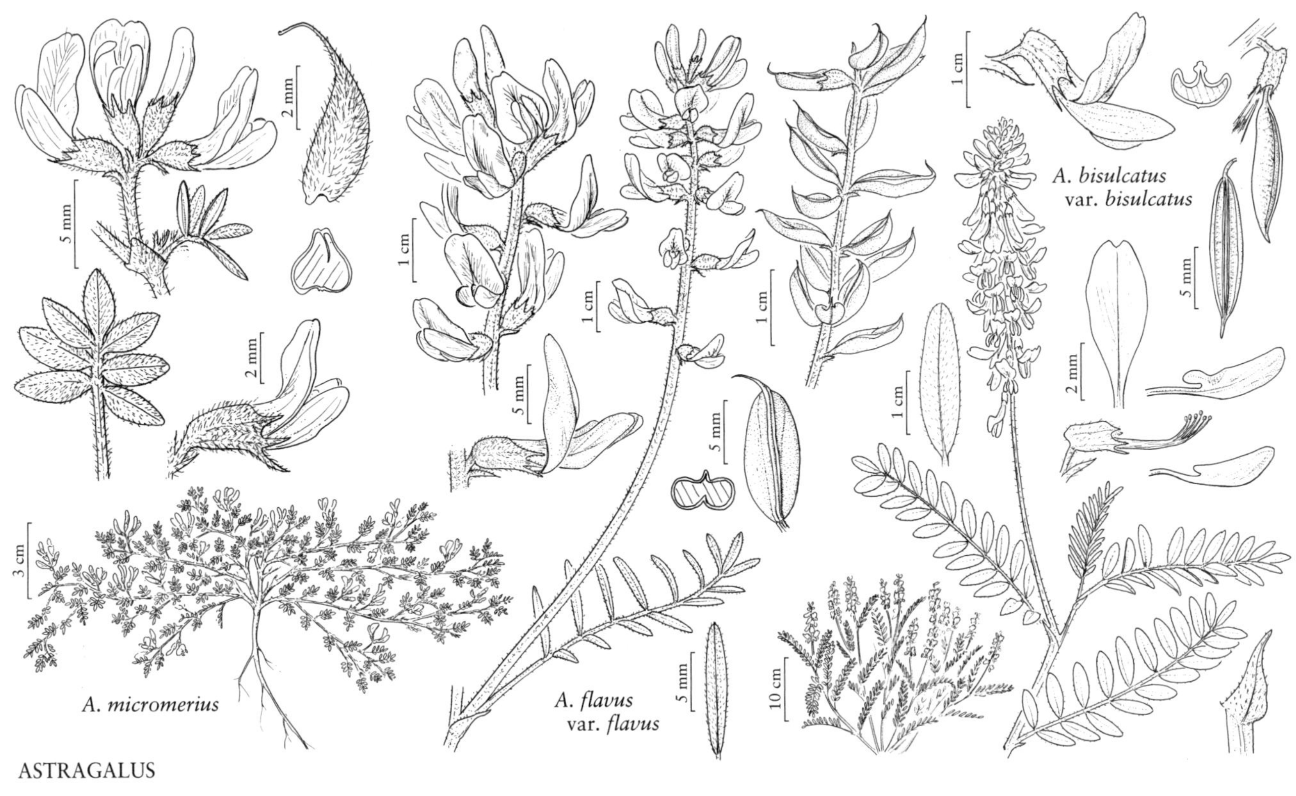

ASTRAGALUS

Flowering Jul–Aug. Gypseous or limey sandstone in pinyon-juniper woodland or Great Basin desert scrub, sometimes partly submerged in drifting sand; 2000–2300 m; N.Mex.

As noted by D. Isely (1998), the miniature *Astragalus micromerius*, with subpalmate leaves, so resembles a starved *Syrmatium-Lotus* that it was first described as *Hosackia nana* S. Watson; the epithet is blocked in *Astragalus* by *A. nanus* de Candolle. It is restricted to northwestern New Mexico.

135y. Astragalus Linnaeus sect. Ocreati A. Gray, Proc. Amer. Acad. Arts 6: 201. 1864

E

Herbs perennial, selenophytes, loosely tufted, ill-scented, caulescent; caudex usually superficial. **Hairs** basifixed or malpighian. **Stems** several to many. **Stipules** connate or distinct at distal nodes. **Leaves** odd-pinnate, petiolate; leaflets (5 or)7–21, terminal leaflet usually jointed, rarely confluent. **Racemes** densely or loosely flowered, flowers ascending. **Calyx tubes** campanulate or turbinate-campanulate. **Corollas** whitish to cream, lemon yellow, ochroleucous, reddish to lilac, or pink-purple, banner recurved through 45(–90)°, keel apex obtuse. **Legumes** eventually deciduous, sessile, erect, ascending, or spreading, ovoid or oblong to ellipsoid, compressed dorsiventrally, laterally, or obcompressed, unilocular. **Seeds** 4–17.

Species 3 (3 in the flora): w United States.

Section *Ocreati* consists of two subsections distributed from southern Nevada eastward and northward to northern New Mexico, Colorado, and Wyoming. The subsections are: subsect. *Ocreati* (A. Gray) Barneby (*Astragalus flavus*, *A. sophoroides*); and subsect. *Moencoppenses* Barneby (*A. moencoppensis*).

87. Astragalus flavus Nuttall in J. Torrey and A. Gray, Fl. N. Amer. 1: 335. 1838 • Yellow milkvetch [E] [F]

Plants tuft- or clump-forming, 5–30(–40) cm, strigulose, hairs malpighian; from branched, superficial caudex. **Stems** decumbent to ascending or erect, usually strigulose, rarely pilose-pilosulous, usually cinereous or canescent, rarely greenish. **Leaves** 3–15(–18) cm; stipules connate, 2–10 mm, papery-scarious; leaflets (5–)9–21, blades linear, narrowly oblong, or oblanceolate to ovate, 3–31 mm, apex obtuse to acute, surfaces silvery-strigose, rarely greenish, or glabrate or glabrous adaxially. **Peduncles** erect or ascending, (3–)5–23 cm, surpassing subtending leaves. **Racemes** 6–30-flowered; axis 2–15 cm in fruit; bracts 1.5–5 mm; bracteoles 0. **Pedicels** 0.7–1.2 mm. **Flowers** 9–17.8 mm; calyx campanulate, 4–10 mm, pilosulous, strigulose, or hirsute, tube 3–5.2 mm, lobes broadly subulate to narrowly triangular, 2–6 mm; corolla usually cream, lemon yellow, white, stramineous, reddish lilac, reddish purple, blue, rarely pink-purple or suffused with pale pink or purple; banner recurved through 45(–90)°; keel 6.5–10 mm. **Legumes** erect, stramineous, straight, oblong, dorsiventrally compressed, 7–13 × 3.5–5.5 mm, somewhat fleshy becoming leathery or stiffly papery, strigose. **Seeds** (6–)8–17.

Varieties 3 (3 in the flora): w United States.

Astragalus flavus occupies usually fine-textured, seleniferous clay, mud, and silt. The characters used to distinguish varieties are not absolute; varieties intergrade, and populations within varieties often have different features.

In this treatment, plants previously known as var. *candicans* A. Gray from the vicinity of Richfield, Sevier County, Utah, (the type locality) are included in var. *flavus*. Plants known as var. *candicans* A. Gray from southern Nevada across southern Utah and northern Arizona to southwestern Colorado and northwestern New Mexico here are placed in var. *higginsii*.

1. Calyces hirsute; corollas usually reddish lilac, reddish purple, or blue, rarely white; Emery, Garfield, Grand, and Wayne counties, Utah . . . . .87c. *Astragalus flavus* var. *argillosus*
1. Calyces strigose to short-villous; corollas usually cream, lemon yellow, white, or stramineous, rarely pink-purple or suffused with pale pink or purple; Arizona, Colorado, Nevada, New Mexico, Utah, Wyoming.

[2. Shifted to left margin.—Ed.]

2. Peduncles usually to 12 cm; racemes slightly to much surpassing leaves; corollas usually cream to lemon yellow, rarely suffused with pale pink or purple; ne Arizona, Colorado, nw New Mexico, Utah, Wyoming. . . . . . .87a. *Astragalus flavus* var. *flavus*
2. Peduncles usually 12–23 cm; racemes surpassing leaves; corollas usually white to cream or stramineous, rarely pink-purple; s Nevada, Washington County, Utah, eastward through n Arizona to sw Colorado, nw New Mexico . . . . 87b. *Astragalus flavus* var. *higginsii*

87a. Astragalus flavus Nuttall var. **flavus** [E] [F]

Plants forming tufts. **Peduncles** usually to 12 cm. **Racemes** slightly to much surpassing leaves. **Flowers** 11–17.8 mm; calyx 4–7.5 mm, strigose to short-villous, tube 3.2–5.2 mm; corolla usually cream to lemon yellow, rarely suffused with pale pink or purple. **Seeds** 8–17. $2n$ = 24, 26.

Flowering Apr–Jul(–Sep). Seleniferous substrates composed of saline silts and clays derived from Triassic Chinle and Moenkopi, Jurassic Arapien Shale, Entrada, Curtis, Summerville, Morrison, and Cedar Mountain formations, and from Cretaceous Mancos Shale and Tropic Shale formations, and other similarly fine-textured Tertiary formations, in salt desert shrub, pinyon-juniper communities; 800–2300 m; Ariz., Colo., N.Mex., Utah, Wyo.

Sheep poisoning attributable to var. flavus, possibly due to ingestion of selenium, is known from lower elevations of the Uinta Basin in northeastern Utah.

87b. Astragalus flavus Nuttall var. **higginsii** S. L. Welsh in S. L. Welsh et al., Utah Fl. ed. 3, 373. 2003 • Larry's stinking milkvetch [E]

Plants forming small clumps, sometimes flowering first season. **Peduncles** usually 12–23 cm. **Racemes** surpassing leaves. **Flowers:** calyx 4–6.7 mm, strigose to short-villous, tube 3.7–5.2 mm; corolla usually white to cream or stramineous, rarely pink-purple. **Seeds** (6–) 8–14.

Flowering Apr–Jun. Triassic Chinle, Moenkopi, and other similar, fine-textured, seleniferous formations; 800–1900 m; Ariz., Colo., Nev., N.Mex., Utah.

There is considerable variation within var. *higginsii*, particularly with regard to relative peduncle length and overall height of plants, and not all specimens from within its geographic range fit comfortably within its description. Short-pedunculate phases simulate purple-flowered *Astragalus sophoroides* of the Painted Desert of Coconino County, Arizona, but these peculiar short-pedunculate specimens from beyond the range of that species have the pale flowers of var. *higginsii*.

87c. **Astragalus flavus** Nuttall var. **argillosus** (M. E. Jones) Barneby, Mem. New York Bot. Gard. 13: 401. 1964 • Clay milkvetch [E]

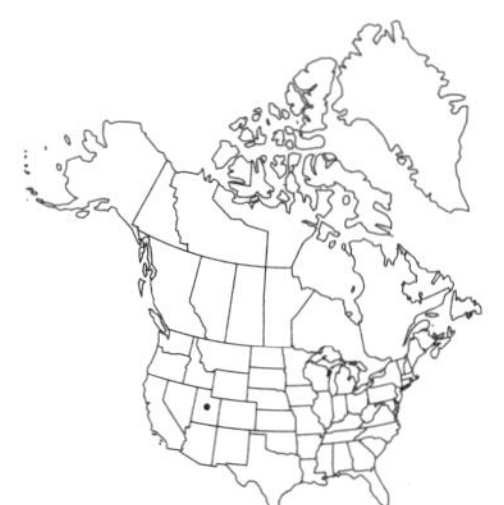

Astragalus argillosus M. E. Jones, Zoë 2: 241. 1891

Plants forming loose tufts. **Peduncles** 5–10 cm. **Flowers** 9–10.5 mm; calyx 6–10 mm, hirsute, tube 3–4.5 mm; corolla usually reddish lilac, reddish purple, or blue, rarely white. **Seeds** 8–11.

Flowering Apr–Jul. Cretaceous Mancos Shale and Jurassic Summerville, Cedar Mountain, and Morrison formations, on saline clays and silts with salt desert shrubs; 1200–1800 m; Utah.

Variety *argillosus* is common in east-central Utah.

88. **Astragalus sophoroides** M. E. Jones, Zoë 2: 12. 1891 • Painted Desert milkvetch [C] [E]

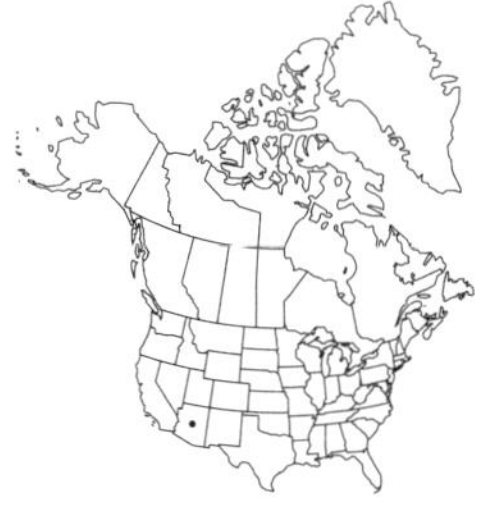

Plants clump- or tuft-forming, 2.5–20(–35) cm, densely strigose-strigulose, hairs malpighian; from shortly forked caudex; taproot tough, woody. **Stems** decumbent to ascending, densely strigose-strigulose, canescent. **Leaves** 3–8(–12) cm; stipules connate, 2–10 mm, scarious; leaflets 7–13, blades narrowly oblong or linear-elliptic, 3–12(–21) mm, apex subacute to obtuse, surfaces pubescent. **Peduncles** narrowly ascending, (0.7–)1–3 (–4) cm, together with racemes slightly surpassing leaves. **Racemes** 7–17-flowered; axis (0.7–)1–4 cm in fruit; bracts 1.5–5 mm; bracteoles 0. **Pedicels** 0.5–1 mm. **Flowers** 8.5–10 mm; calyx campanulate to turbinate-campanulate, 5–6.3 mm, densely white-strigulose, tube 3–3.6 mm, lobes lanceolate-subulate, 2–3 mm; corolla usually reddish lilac, rarely white tinged with pink, banner with pallid eye-spot; banner recurved through 45°; keel 5.7–6.8 mm. **Legumes** erect or ascending, stramineous, straight, oblong-ellipsoid, laterally compressed, 6.5–8 × 3–4 mm, thinly fleshy becoming papery, canescent-strigulose. **Seeds** 4–6.

Flowering May–Jun. Sandy flats and knolls, on red sandstone and silts of the seleniferous Triassic Chinle Formation; of conservation concern; 1200–1500 m; Ariz.

Astragalus sophoroides is restricted to eastern Coconino County. It is distinguished from the more widespread *A. flavus* var. *higginsii* by having slightly accrescent calyces, marcescent petals, few ovules, and usually relatively short peduncles, combined with typically reddish lilac flowers.

89. **Astragalus moencoppensis** M. E. Jones, Zoë 2: 12. 1891 • Moenkopi milkvetch [E]

Plants slender, clump-forming, 9–60 cm, strigulose, hairs basifixed; from superficial or slightly subterranean branched caudex. **Stems** erect or ascending, usually shorter than longest peduncles, sparsely strigulose. **Leaves** 4–17 cm; stipules connate-sheathing at proximal nodes, connate or distinct at distal nodes, 1.5–7 mm, scarious; leaflets 5–15, blades filiform to linear or narrowly elliptic, 2–23 mm, apex acute to obtuse, surfaces strigose abaxially, glabrous adaxially; terminal leaflet sometimes decurrent distally, not jointed to rachis. **Peduncles** erect, 4–25 cm, together with racemes longer than stems, much surpassing subtending leaves. **Racemes** 6–34-flowered; axis 3–25 cm in fruit; bracts 1.5–3.5 mm; bracteoles 0 or 1. **Pedicels** 0.3–2 mm. **Flowers** 7–11 mm; calyx campanulate, 5–7.5 mm, white-pilose, tube 3–4 mm, lobes lanceolate-subulate, 1.8–3.5 mm; corolla marcescent, pink-purple; banner recurved through 45°; keel 5.7–7 mm. **Legumes** ascending-spreading, stramineous, slightly incurved, ovoid to ellipsoid, obcompressed, 5.5–8 × 2.3–3.4 mm, thinly fleshy becoming papery, strigulose. **Seeds** 4–6.

Flowering May–Jul. Salt desert shrub, mixed desert shrub, pinyon-juniper communities, usually in saline, silty or clay, seleniferous soils; 1300–2200 m; Ariz., Utah.

Astragalus moencoppensis is marked by its greenish, semijunceous appearance and slender racemes bearing small flowers with villous calyces that, along with the marcescent petals, largely enclose the small fruits. It is a selenium indicator restricted to southeastern Utah and northeastern Arizona.

135z. ASTRAGALUS Linnaeus sect. ALBULI Barneby, Mem. New York Bot. Gard. 13: 404. 1964 [E]

Herbs perennial, selenophytes, caulescent; caudex superficial. **Hairs** malpighian. **Stems** several to many. **Stipules** connate. **Leaves** odd-pinnate, subsessile; leaflets (7–)11–23, jointed to rachis. **Racemes** densely becoming loosely flowered, flowers ascending. **Calyx tubes** short-cylindric. **Corollas** whitish, keel tip faintly maculate, banner recurved through 45°, keel obtuse. **Legumes** ultimately deciduous, short-stipitate or subsessile, declined or pendulous, narrowly ellipsoid or lanceoloid-ellipsoid, compressed dorsiventrally, slightly 3-sided, unilocular. **Seeds** 5–11.

Species 1: sw United States.

90. Astragalus albulus Wooton & Standley, Contr. U.S. Natl. Herb. 16: 136. 1913 • Cibola milkvetch [E]

Plants forming bushy clumps, robust, 15–85(–120) cm, strigulose to pilose; from branched caudex bearing thick, woody, shortly forked taproot, becoming suffruticose. **Stems** erect or ascending, strigulose to pilose, cinereous or canescent. **Leaves** 3–10(–14) cm; stipules 2.5–10 mm, scarious; leaflet blades linear, linear-oblanceolate, or narrowly elliptic, (2–)4–27(–45) mm, apex acute to subobtuse, surfaces strigose abaxially, glabrous adaxially. **Peduncles** erect, 1–4(–5.5) cm, much shorter than subtending leaves. **Racemes** 9–47-flowered; axis (2–)3–15(–20) cm in fruit; bracts (2–)3–7 mm; bracteoles 0–2. **Pedicels** 0.3–1.2 mm. **Flowers** 13–17.2 mm; calyx (7.2–)7.5–11 mm, strigulose to pilose, tube (5.4–)5.7–7.4 mm, lobes lanceolate-subulate, (1.5–)1.8–3.6 mm; corolla banner recurved through 45°; keel 10.4–12.8 mm. **Legumes** brown-stramineous, gently incurved, dorsiventrally compressed or 3-sided at dehiscence, carinate by ventral suture, beak laterally compressed, 9–12 × 3.3–5 mm, papery, strigose or glabrous; stipe 0.7–2.5 mm. **2*n*** = 22.

Flowering Jul–Oct. Gullied badlands, sandy clay talus under cliffs, on seleniferous substrates, with juniper, rabbitbrush, *Eriogonum*, and saltbush, in salt-seep communities; 1600–2600 m; Ariz., Colo., N.Mex., Tex.

Astragalus albulus is mainly a New Mexico plant. At first sight, it resembles a somewhat taller, more robust *A. flavus* but is easily distinguished by declined or pendulous, stipitate, obcompressed and three-sided legumes (except for the laterally compressed, cuspidate beak). It is the only milkvetch within its region (northeastern Arizona, southwestern Colorado, northwestern New Mexico) that flowers and fruits from mid summer to autumn on a regular basis. Racemes sometimes are borne from below the middle of the stem, with the portion bearing racemes much exceeding the non-flowering lower portion of the plant. It has been reported also from Culbertson County in Texas (D. K. Northington and T. L. Burgess 1979).

135aa. ASTRAGALUS Linnaeus sect. BISULCATI A. Gray, Proc. Amer. Acad. Arts 6: 220. 1864

Herbs perennial, selenophytes, clump-forming, caulescent; branched caudex superficial. **Hairs** usually basifixed, rarely incipiently malpighian. **Stems** several to many. **Stipules** connate or distinct at distal nodes. **Leaves** odd-pinnate, short-petiolate or subsessile; leaflets (7–)11–35. **Racemes** initially densely flowered, flowers declined or nodding, often retrorsely imbricate. **Calyx tubes** short cylindric or oblique-campanulate, gibbous at base. **Corollas** pink-purple, ochroleucous, or white, banner recurved through 45(–90)°, keel longer or shorter than banner, apex rounded. **Legumes** ultimately deciduous, stipitate, pendulous, linear-ellipsoid to oblong-ovoid, compressed dorsiventrally with 2 adaxial grooves or 3-sided, unilocular. **Seeds** 5–22.

Species 2 (2 in the flora): w North America, n Mexico.

Section *Bisulcati* is distributed from Alberta to Manitoba, in southern to western Oklahoma, western Texas, northern Arizona, and southwestern Utah, westward to east-central Nevada, southeastern Idaho, and western Montana, and disjunctly in central Mexico.

91. Astragalus bisulcatus (Hooker) A. Gray in War Department [U.S.], Pacif. Railr. Rep. 12: 42. 1860 • Two-grooved milkvetch [E] [F] [W]

Phaca bisulcata Hooker, Fl. Bor.-Amer. 1: 145. 1831

Plants 15–75 cm, mostly strigulose. **Stems** often erect or ascending, sometimes decumbent, diffuse, or spreading, strigulose or glabrous. **Leaves** 3–13.5 cm; stipules connate-sheathing at proximal nodes, connate or distinct at distal nodes, 2.5–10(–12) mm, submembranous becoming scarious, pallid; leaflets (7–)11–35, blades lanceolate-oblong to oblong, elliptic, or oblanceolate, 5–27(–32) mm, apex usually acute or obtuse, rarely emarginate, surfaces strigulose abaxially, glabrous or glabrate adaxially. **Peduncles** erect, ascending, or incurved, 2.5–13 cm. **Racemes** (15–)25–80-flowered; axis 3–25 cm in fruit; bracts (1–)2.5–7 mm; bracteoles 0–2. **Pedicels** 1–3.5 mm. **Flowers** (6.7–)8–17.5 mm; calyx obliquely campanulate, gibbous-saccate, 3.5–9.6 mm, sparsely strigose, tube 2.8–5.7(–7) mm, lobes subulate, (0.7–)1–4.5(–6) mm; corolla ochroleucous, white, whitish, or pink-purple, keel tip often maculate, sometimes purple; banner recurved through 45° (except 90° in var. *nevadensis*); keel 7–13 mm. **Legumes** stramineous, straight or slightly curved, linear, ellipsoid, or oblong-ellipsoid, dorsiventrally compressed, abaxial face with suture forming prominent ridge flanked by depressed grooves, adaxial face convexly rounded, (5–)6.5–17(–20) × 2–4.5 mm, fleshy becoming thinly leathery or papery, strigulose or glabrous; stipe 1.4–5.2(–6) mm. **Seeds** 5–15.

Varieties 4 (4 in the flora): w North America.

Astragalus bisulcatus is an ill-scented primary indicator of selenium in most areas. In the Missouri drainage, it is easily recognized by its two-grooved fruits, and is relatively nonvariable and presents no taxonomic problems. West of the Front Ranges it is multivariate, the many forms difficult to classify.

1. Flowers 6.7–9.2 mm; corollas ochroleucous, banner shorter than keel; raceme bracts 1–2.5 mm; ec Nevada . . . 91d. *Astragalus bisulcatus* var. *nevadensis*
1. Flowers 8–17.5 mm; corollas white, whitish, ochroleucous, or pink-purple, banner longer than keel; raceme bracts (2–)2.5–7 mm; widespread, not in Nevada.
   2. Legumes transversely rugose-reticulate, (5–)6.5–9.5 mm; flowers 8–11 mm; nw New Mexico, adjoining Arizona and Utah, northward through w Colorado to ne Utah and sw Wyoming . . . . 91c. *Astragalus bisulcatus* var. *haydenianus*

[2. Shifted to left margin.—Ed.]

2. Legumes smooth or faintly reticulate, 8–17(–20) mm; flowers 11–17.5 mm; Alberta to Manitoba, southward and westward to Arizona and Oklahoma.
   3. Flowers 13–17.5 mm; corollas usually pink-purple, rarely white; calyces usually red-purple; Alberta to Manitoba, southward and westward to Utah, New Mexico, and Oklahoma . . . . 91a. *Astragalus bisulcatus* var. *bisulcatus*
   3. Flowers 11–15 mm; corollas white or ochroleucous, less commonly with purple center and purple lines, or suffused with pale purple throughout; calyces usually white; nw Colorado, sw Wyoming southward to c Utah and to n Arizona, disjunct in Fremont County, Idaho . . . . 91b. *Astragalus bisulcatus* var. *major*

91a. Astragalus bisulcatus (Hooker) A. Gray var. **bisulcatus** [E] [F]

Plants stout, usually erect, herbage sparsely hairy or stems glabrous. **Leaflets** 17–29, (5–)10–25(–32) mm. **Racemes** 25–75-flowered; axis 5–18 cm in fruit; bracts (2–)2.5–7 mm. **Flowers** 13–17.5 mm; calyx usually red-purple, tube 3.3–5.7 mm, lobes 1.5–4.5(–6) mm; corolla pink-purple, or pallid and purple- or lilac-tipped or suffused, or white or whitish and keel tip maculate; banner longer than keel. **Legumes** linear- or narrowly oblong-ellipsoid, (8–)10–17(–20) × 2–4.5 mm, smooth or faintly reticulate, glabrous or strigulose; stipe 3–5(–6) mm. **Seeds** 10–14(or 15). $2n$ = 22, 24.

Flowering May–Aug. On fine-textured, saline or seleniferous substrates, short-grass prairies, plains, badlands, in steppes, with sagebrush-grass, shadscale, less commonly with pinyon-juniper and mountain brush communities; 400–2500 m; Alta., Man., Sask.; Colo., Idaho, Kans., Mont., Nebr., N.Mex., N.Dak., Okla., S.Dak., Utah, Wyo.

Variety *bisulcatus* has been confused with *Astragalus racemosus*, with which it sometimes intermingles. The gibbous calyx of *A. bisulcatus* and two-grooved versus ± three-sided fruit serve to distinguish them. Where they are sympatric, *A. bisulcatus* is usually purple-flowered. The vars. *bisulcatus* and *haydenianus* are known to contain selenium and swainsonine, both poisonous to livestock (S. F. Trelease and O. A. Beath 1949; J. M. Kingsbury 1964).

91b. Astragalus bisulcatus (Hooker) A. Gray var. **major** (M. E. Jones) S. L. Welsh, Great Basin Naturalist 38: 266. 1978 • Johnson Canyon milkvetch [E]

Astragalus haydenianus A. Gray var. *major* M. E. Jones, Zoë 2: 241. 1891

Plants stout, usually erect, herbage sparsely hairy or stems glabrous. **Leaflets** 15–19, (5–) 10–25 mm. **Racemes** 20–34-flowered; axis 3–9 cm in fruit; bracts 2.5–4 mm. **Flowers** 11–15 mm; calyx usually white, tube 3.5–5.5(–7) mm, lobes narrowly subulate, (1.5–)1.8–3.8 mm; corolla white or whitish and keel tip maculate, banner sometimes with purple center and purple lines, or suffused with pale purple throughout; banner longer than keel. **Legumes** linear- or narrowly oblong-ellipsoid, 8–13.5 × 2.2–3.7 mm, smooth, glabrous or strigulose; stipe 4–5.2 mm. **Seeds** 4–10. 2*n* = 24.

Flowering Apr–Jul. Pinyon-juniper, sagebrush, mountain brush communities, salt desert scrub; 1500–2500 m; Ariz., Colo., Idaho, Utah, Wyo.

The concept of var. *major* is here expanded to include the so-called basin variants of R. C. Barneby (1964), which occur from southern Wyoming through western Colorado and eastern and southern Utah. These are a diverse lot of pale-flowered populations, each of which varies toward smaller flowers and fruits than are present in var. *bisulcatus*.

91c. Astragalus bisulcatus (Hooker) A. Gray var. **haydenianus** (A. Gray) Barneby, Mem. New York Bot. Gard. 13: 413. 1964 • Hayden's milkvetch [E]

Astragalus haydenianus A. Gray, Bull. U.S. Geol. Geogr. Surv. Territ. 2: 235. 1876; *A. bisulcatus* subsp. *haydenianus* (A. Gray) W. A. Weber; *A. grallator* S. Watson; *Diholcos haydenianus* (A. Gray) Rydberg; *Tragacantha haydeniana* (A. Gray) Kuntze

Plants stout, erect or diffuse and spreading, herbage usually pubescent. **Leaflets** (13–)21–35, 5–27 mm. **Racemes** 35–80-flowered; axis (4–)5.5–25 cm in fruit; bracts (2.5–)3–5 mm. **Flowers** 8–11 mm; calyx usually pallid, tube 3.1–4 mm, lobes 1–2.7 mm; corolla white or whitish to ochroleucous; banner longer than keel. **Legumes** ellipsoid or oblong-ellipsoid, (5–) 6.5–9.5 × 2–4 mm, transversely rugose-reticulate, strigulose; stipe 1.4–3 mm. **Seeds** 5–8. 2*n* = 24.

Flowering May–Jul. Sagebrush-mountain brush, pinyon-juniper, ponderosa pine, and spruce-fir communities, on fine-textured, often saline, seleniferous substrates; 1900–3300 m; Ariz., Colo., N.Mex., Utah, Wyo.

Variety *haydenianus* from the Wasatch Plateau in Utah has been confused by some workers with the similarly pale-flowered var. *major*, but the flowers are consistently smaller, much more numerous, and the fruits smaller than in var. *major*.

91d. Astragalus bisulcatus (Hooker) A. Gray var. **nevadensis** (M. E. Jones) Barneby, Leafl. W. Bot. 7: 195. 1954 • Nevada two-grooved milkvetch [E]

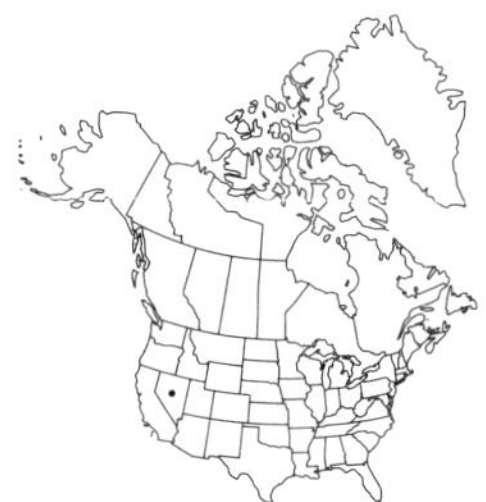

Astragalus haydenianus A. Gray var. *nevadensis* M. E. Jones, Zoë 2: 241. 1891

Plants decumbent or incurved-ascending, herbage usually pubescent. **Leaflets** (7–)11–19, 5–27 mm. **Racemes** (15–)25–45-flowered; axis (3–)6–20 cm in fruit; bracts 1–2.5 mm. **Flowers** 6.7–9.2 mm; calyx usually pallid, tube 2.8–3.2 mm, lobes 0.7–1.6 mm; corolla ochroleucous, keel tip maculate; banner shorter than keel. **Legumes** narrowly ellipsoid, 8–12 × 2.5–4 mm, delicately reticulate, white-strigulose; stipe 3–3.7 mm. **Seeds** 6–8.

Flowering May–Jul. Knolls, hillsides, desert pans, on fine-textured white or red substrates, in pinyon, juniper, or sagebrush communities; 1500–2000 m; Nev.

Variety *nevadensis* is restricted to the northeastern quadrant of Nevada.

92. Astragalus racemosus Pursh, Fl. Amer. Sept. 2: 740. 1813 • Alkali milkvetch

Plants coarse, 20–60 cm, strigulose. **Stems** erect or ascending, strigulose. **Leaves** 4–15 cm; stipules connate-sheathing at proximal nodes, connate or distinct at distal nodes, 3–8 (–12) mm, scarious; leaflets (9 or)11–31, blades lanceolate-elliptic to linear-lanceolate, 3–35 mm, apex acute to acuminate, surfaces glabrous or glabrate, sometimes ciliate. **Peduncles** erect, 3–13 cm. **Racemes** 9–45(–70)-flowered; axis (3–)5–20(–25) cm in fruit; bracts 1.5–7.5(–9) mm; bracteoles 0–2. **Pedicels** 2–8 mm. **Flowers** 12–19(–21) mm; calyx pallid or pinkish, short-cylindric, strongly gibbous, (7.3–)8.6–12(–19) mm, glabrous or sparsely strigose, tube (4.7–) 5–6(–9) mm, lobes subulate or subulate-setaceous, (1.5–)3.3–6(–10) mm; corolla usually white or ochroleucous, concolorous, rarely lightly suffused with purple or with purple veins, sometimes keel tip lilac; banner recurved through 45°; keel 10.8–15.2 mm. **Legumes** stramineous, straight or slightly curved, linear-oblong, oblong-ellipsoid, or oblong-ovoid, sharply 3-sided compressed, faces of subequal width, nearly flat, 10–30 × 3–8 mm, papery, glabrous or sparsely strigose; stipe (3.5–)4–6(–7) mm. **Seeds** 12–22.

Varieties 2 (2 in the flora): w, c North America, n Mexico.

1. Legumes linear-oblong to narrowly oblong-ellipsoid, (15–)20–30 × 3–5.7 mm; leaflets (11–)17–31; flowers 16–19(–21) mm; e of Continental Divide, Saskatchewan southward . . . . 92a. *Astragalus racemosus* var. *racemosus*
1. Legumes plump, oblong-ellipsoid or -ovoid, 10–20 × (4–)5–8 mm; leaflets (9 or)11–19; flowers 12–16 mm; Green River and Uinta basins, sw Wyoming, ne Utah, extreme nw Colorado. . . . . 92b. *Astragalus racemosus* var. *treleasei*

92a. Astragalus racemosus Pursh var. **racemosus**

Astragalus racemosus var. *longisetus* M. E. Jones

Leaflets (11–)17–31, blades 3–12 mm wide. **Flowers** 16–19(–21) mm; corolla whitish, concolorous, or keel tip lilac, wings and banner sometimes lightly suffused with purple or purple-veined. **Legumes** linear-oblong to narrowly oblong-ellipsoid, (15–)20–30 × 3–5.7 mm. $2n$ = 24.

Flowering May–Jul. Seleniferous bluffs, knolls, alluvial bottoms and roadsides on clay, shale, or gypsum; 500–1400 m; Sask.; Colo., Kans., Minn., Mont., Nebr., N.Mex., N.Dak., Okla., S.Dak., Tex., Wyo.; Mexico (San Luis Potosí).

T. Nuttall (1818) noted the disagreeable garlic odor associated with selenium in his description of *Astragalus galegoides* Nuttall (an illegitimate name pertaining to *A. racemosus*). The species often grows intermixed with *A. bisulcatus*; both are poisonous to livestock, producing so-called alkali disease or the blind-staggers. Variety *racemosus* does not occur west of the Continental Divide.

92b. Astragalus racemosus Pursh var. **treleasei** Ced. Porter, Madroño 8: 99, plate 9, figs. 1–3. 1945 • Trelease's alkali milkvetch [C] [E]

Leaflets (9 or)11–19, blades 1.5–9(–12) mm wide. **Flowers** 12–16 mm; corolla ochroleucous, keel tip maculate or immaculate. **Legumes** plump, oblong-ellipsoid or -ovoid, 10–20 × (4–)5–8 mm.

Flowering May–Jul. Sparsely vegetated, seleniferous saline clay and silty soils; of conservation concern; 1500–2300(–2500) m; Colo., Utah, Wyo.

The disjunct western var. *treleasei* has two geographical races in Utah. Plants with the keel immaculate occur exclusively in the southern portion of the Uinta Basin. Elsewhere, keels are maculate.

Variety *treleasei* is primarily associated with the Tertiary Uinta and Duchesne River formations in Utah and on equivalent formations in Wyoming. It occurs in Moffat County in Colorado, Duchesne and Uintah counties in Utah, and Lincoln, Sublette, and Uinta counties in Wyoming.

135bb. Astragalus Linnaeus sect. Oocalyces Barneby, Mem. New York Bot. Gard. 13: 419. 1964 [E]

Herbs perennial, selenophytes, caulescent; caudex superficial or shallowly subterranean. **Hairs** basifixed. **Stems** several to many. **Stipules** connate at proximal nodes, distinct at distal nodes. **Leaves** odd-pinnate, short-petiolate or subsessile; leaflets (9–)19–27. **Racemes** densely flowered, flowers nodding. **Calyx tubes** deciduous, obliquely ovoid, accrescent and inflated, enclosing small pod. **Corollas** ochroleucous, banner recurved through 45°, keel apex round. **Legumes** deciduous, sessile, gynophore present, curved, declined, oblong-ellipsoid, strongly obcompressed with 2 adaxial grooves, unilocular. **Seeds** 6–8.

Species 1: sw United States.

93. Astragalus oocalycis M. E. Jones, Contr. W. Bot. 8: 10. 1898 • Arbole's milkvetch [E]

Plants coarse, forming bushy clumps, (15–)25–40 cm, strigulose; from branched caudex. **Stems** erect or ascending, strigulose. **Leaves** 5–15(–17) cm; stipules connate-sheathing and bidentate at proximal nodes, distinct at distal nodes, 2.5–6 mm, scarious; leaflet blades linear- or linear-oblong, 3–35 mm, apex acute or obtuse and mucronate, surfaces glabrous abaxially, glabrous or glabrate adaxially; terminal leaflet sometimes decurrent distally, not jointed to rachis. **Peduncles** erect, 9–17 (–22) cm. **Racemes** 35–60-flowered; axis 4–8(–14) cm in fruit; bracts 3–8 mm; bracteoles 0–2. **Pedicels** 2–5 mm. **Flowers** 14–17 mm; calyx contracted apically, 10–11 mm, hirsute, hairs long, straight, tube to 14 mm, enclosing fruit, lobes subulate, 2–3 mm; corolla keel 11.2–13 mm. **Legumes** deciduous within accrescent calyx, straight or slightly incurved, 6–7.5 × 3.5–4 mm, thinly fleshy becoming leathery, glabrous; gynophore 1 mm. 2*n* = 24.

Flowering May–Jul. Seleniferous clay on knolls, hillsides, and plains in sagebrush and pinyon-juniper communities, disturbed sites; 1700–2200 m; Colo., N.Mex.

Astragalus oocalycis is known from Archuleta and adjacent La Plata counties in Colorado, and northeastern San Juan and Rio Arriba counties in New Mexico.

The greatly inflated, accrescent calyces enclosing the small, few-seeded fruits of *Astragalus oocalycis* are unmatched in North American *Astragalus*. The mature inflorescences are massive, cylindroid-spiciform heads.

135cc. ASTRAGALUS Linnaeus sect. PECTINATI A. Gray, Proc. Amer. Acad. Arts 6: 221. 1864 [E]

Herbs perennial, selenophytes, clump-forming, caulescent; caudex subterranean or superficial. **Hairs** basifixed. **Stems** several to many. **Stipules** connate or distinct at distal nodes. **Leaves** odd-pinnate, sessile, subsessile, or petiolate; leaflets (0 or 1–)5–15(–21), confluent with rachis or reduced to phyllodia. **Racemes** densely or loosely flowered, flowers ascending to declined or nodding. **Calyx tubes** cylindric. **Corollas** white, cream, ochroleucous, or pink-purple, banner recurved through 40–50°, keel apex obtuse. **Legumes** persistent, usually sessile, rarely stipitate, erect, deflexed, or pendulous, linear-ellipsoid, narrowly oblong, oblong-ellipsoid, or ellipsoid, compressed dorsiventrally or laterally, sutures protruding, unilocular. **Seeds** 12–32.

Species 8 (8 in the flora): w North America.

Section *Pectinati* consists of two subsections: subsect. *Osterhoutiani* Barneby (*Astragalus osterhoutii*) and subsect. *Pectinati* (A. Gray) M. E. Jones (the other seven species).

94. Astragalus pectinatus (Hooker) Douglas ex G. Don, Gen. Hist. 2: 257. 1832 • Tine-leaved milkvetch [E] [F] [W]

Phaca pectinata Hooker, Fl. Bor.-Amer. 1: 141, plate 54. 1831; *Cnemidophacos pectinatus* (Hooker) Rydberg; *Ctenophyllum pectinatum* (Hooker) Rydberg; *Tragacantha pectinata* (Hooker) Kuntze

Plants relatively coarse, forming bushy clumps, 10–60 cm, strigulose; from branched caudex. **Stems** usually decumbent or ascending, sometimes erect, strigulose. **Leaves** 4–11 cm; stipules connate-sheathing and papery at proximal nodes, connate or distinct and herbaceous at distal nodes, 1.5–10 mm; leaflets (5–)9–15(–21), blades linear, filiform, or linear-oblanceolate, 15–70 mm, margins involute, apex acuminate, surfaces strigulose abaxially, glabrous adaxially; terminal leaflet decurrent, not jointed to rachis. **Peduncles** incurved-ascending, (2–) 3.5–8(–10.5) cm. **Racemes** (7–)12–30-flowered, flowers nodding; axis 3–13(–17) cm in fruit; bracts 2–7 mm; bracteoles 0. **Pedicels** 2–3(–3.5) mm. **Flowers** (16–)21–24(–27) mm; calyx 8–12 mm, strigulose, tube 6.5–9 × 2.8–4.3 mm, lobes subulate, 1.5–3 mm; corolla white or ochroleucous, drying yellowish; keel 13.8–16 mm. **Legumes** declined or deflexed, stramineous or brown, straight or slightly decurved, ellipsoid or oblong-ellipsoid to clavate-ellipsoid, ± obcompressed, (10–)15–25 × (4.5–)5–8 mm, woody, glabrous; sessile. **Seeds** (23–)26–32. 2*n* = 22.

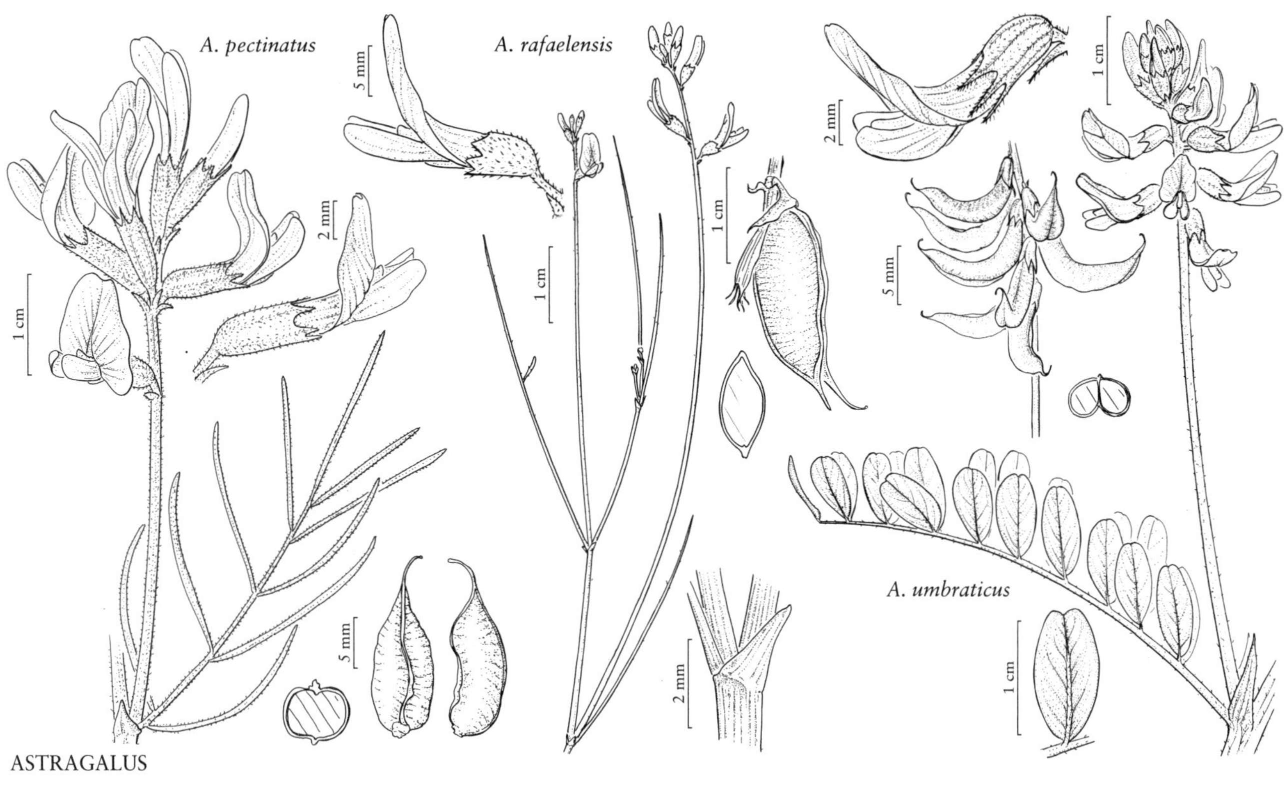

ASTRAGALUS

Flowering May–Jul. Saline flats, bluffs, hilltops, on seleniferous substrates derived from shale; 400–2400 m; Alta., Man., Sask.; Colo., Kans., Mont., Nebr., N.Dak., S.Dak., Wyo.

Astragalus pectinatus is an elevationally and geographically widely distributed selenophyte of the western Great Plains showing no sign of racial differentiation. Its leaves, with extremely long, narrow, stiffly incurved leaflets, have no exact counterpart in the genus. J. D. Karron (1989) reported it to be essentially self-incompatible, and Karron et al. (1988) found it to have higher genetic polymorphism than the geographically restricted *A. linifolius* and *A. osterhoutii*, and also the widespread *A. pattersonii*.

95. **Astragalus nelsonianus** Barneby, Mem. New York Bot. Gard. 13: 426. 1964 • Nelson's milkvetch [E]

Astragalus pectinatus (Hooker) Douglas ex G. Don var. *platyphyllus* M. E. Jones, Contr. W. Bot. 10: 87, plate 4, fig. s.n. [lower left]. 1902

Plants stout, clump-forming, 10–30 cm, sparsely strigulose; from subterranean caudex. **Stems** decumbent to ascending or erect, sparsely strigulose. **Leaves** 2.5–9 cm; stipules connate-sheathing and papery at proximal nodes, connate or distinct and herbaceous at distal nodes, 4–13 mm; leaflets 5–13, blades linear-oblong, 10–45 (–60) mm, margins flat, elevated, apex obtuse to apiculate, surfaces strigose; terminal leaflet decurrent, not jointed to rachis. **Peduncles** erect and incurved-ascending, 3–12 cm. **Racemes** 6–20-flowered, flowers ascending; axis 2–12 cm in fruit; bracts 2.5–7 mm; bracteoles 1 or 2. **Pedicels** 1.5–4 mm. **Flowers** 24–30 mm; calyx 10–14.5 mm, strigose, tube 7–10.2 × 4.5–6.2 mm, lobes subulate, 2–4.5 mm; corolla white, concolorous; keel 13.6–20.2 mm. **Legumes** deflexed, brown or stramineous, straight, oblong-ellipsoid, subterete becoming laterally compressed, 13–33 × 6–12 mm, fleshy becoming woody, glabrous or minutely puberulent; sessile. **Seeds** 20–28.

Flowering late May–Aug. Saline, seleniferous soil in desert shrub and juniper-sagebrush communities; 1800–2200 m; Colo., Utah, Wyo.

Astragalus nelsonianus is known from Moffat County in Colorado, Daggett County in Utah, and Fremont, Natrona, Sweetwater, and Uinta counties in Wyoming.

The selenophyte *Astragalus nelsonianus* is essentially a broad-leaved, larger-flowered phase of *A. pectinatus* and might best be placed as a variety of that species as was proposed by M. E. Jones.

96. Astragalus grayi Parry ex S. Watson, Amer. Naturalist 8: 212. 1874 • Gray's milkvetch [E]

Plants stout, clump-forming, 15–35 cm, sparsely strigulose; from subterranean caudex. **Stems** ascending to erect, sparsely strigulose. **Leaves** (2.5–)4–10 cm; stipules connate-sheathing and papery at proximal nodes, connate or distinct and herbaceous at distal nodes, 2.5–10 mm; leaflets 3–11, blades linear-oblong or oblanceolate, (6–)15–50 mm, margins flat, elevated, apex obtuse to subacute, surfaces strigulose abaxially, glabrous or strigulose adaxially; terminal leaflet decurrent, not jointed to rachis. **Peduncles** erect and strict, 3–10 cm. **Racemes** (5–)9–27-flowered, flowers ascending; axis 1–7 cm in fruit; bracts 2.5–7 mm; bracteoles 2. **Pedicels** 2–7 mm. **Flowers** 15–22.5 mm; calyx 6.5–10.3 mm, strigose, tube 5.2–8 × 2.9–4.2 mm, lobes subulate, 1.2–2.5 mm; corolla cream; keel (11.5–)12.7–15.2 mm. **Legumes** erect or ascending, brown or stramineous, ± straight, narrowly oblong or oblong-ellipsoid, terete or somewhat laterally compressed, 9–18 × 2.7–3.5 mm, fleshy becoming stiffly leathery, usually glabrous, rarely strigulose; sessile. **Seeds** (14–)16–21(–23). $2n = 44$.

Flowering May–Jul. Clay flats, hills, badlands, with sagebrush, along valley bottoms, in saline meadows; 1100–2100 m; Mont., Wyo.

Astragalus grayi is known from western Wyoming and eastward to Carbon County in Montana.

97. Astragalus toanus M. E. Jones, Zoë 3: 296. 1893 • Toano milkvetch [E]

Plants stout, rushlike, forming bushy clumps, 15–50 cm, strigulose; from shallow, subterranean or superficial caudex. **Stems** erect or ascending, usually strigulose, rarely glabrous. **Leaves** distally unifoliolate or reduced to phyllodia, 2–10 cm; stipules connate-sheathing and papery-scarious at proximal nodes, distinct and herbaceous at distal nodes, 1.5–6.5 mm; leaflets (0 or 1–)3–13, blades linear-filiform to oblong, 3–30 mm, margins involute, apex obtuse to acute, surfaces strigose abaxially, strigose or glabrous adaxially; terminal leaflet of compound leaves sometimes decurrent distally, not jointed to rachis. **Peduncles** strict, 6–25 cm. **Racemes** 7–35-flowered, flowers ascending; axis 3–30 cm in fruit; bracts 1–3 mm; bracteoles 0–2. **Pedicels** 0.8–3.5 mm. **Flowers** (13–)14–20 mm; calyx 4.6–8 mm, strigose, tube 4.1–6.4 × (2.6–)3–3.9 mm, lobes subulate, 0.5–2 mm; corolla pink-purple and wing tips white, or greenish yellow or whitish; keel (9.5–)10.5–13.5 mm. **Legumes** erect, green sometimes purple-mottled becoming stramineous, straight or slightly incurved, oblong, slightly compressed laterally, bicarinate, 13–25 × 3.7–9 mm, stiffly leathery to somewhat woody, glabrous or strigose; sessile. **Seeds** 14–26.

Varieties 2 (2 in the flora): w United States.

Astragalus toanus forms broomlike, apparently leafless tufts of stiffly clustered stems, the fruits remaining into late summer, the valves bent outward in a widely gaping dehiscence. The species is attractive in flower, bearing loose spikes of relatively large, brightly colored flowers.

1. Flowers (13–)15–20 mm; corollas pink-purple; legumes 3.5–5.5(–7) mm wide; sw Idaho, Nevada, se Oregon, w Utah . . .97a. *Astragalus toanus* var. *toanus*
1. Flowers 14–16.5 mm; corollas greenish yellow or whitish; legumes 8–9 mm wide; Mohave County, Arizona. . . . . 97b. *Astragalus toanus* var. *scidulus*

97a. Astragalus toanus M. E. Jones var. **toanus** [E]

Leaflets (0 or 1–)3–9. **Flowers** (13–)15–20 mm; corolla pink-purple. **Legumes** 3.5–5.5(–7) mm wide. $2n = 22$.

Flowering May–Jul. Seleniferous, saline clay and silty soils, desert shrub communities, often with shadscale, bursage, greasewood, and matchweed; 1400–1900 m; Idaho, Nev., Oreg., Utah.

Variety *toanus* resembles the distantly disjunct *Astragalus saurinus* of the Uinta Basin and *A. rafaelensis* of the San Rafael Swell, Utah.

97b. Astragalus toanus M. E. Jones var. **scidulus** S. L. Welsh & N. D. Atwood, Rhodora 95: 403, fig. 11. 1993 • Arizona Strip milkvetch [C] [E]

Leaflets (0 or 1 or)11 or 13. **Flowers** 14–16.5 mm; corolla greenish yellow or whitish. **Legumes** 8–9 mm wide. A $2n = 22$.

Flowering Apr–May. Mixed desert shrub and grass communities; of conservation concern; 1600 m; Ariz.

Variety *scidulus* is distantly isolated from var. *toanus* in the Arizona Strip, Mohave County.

98. Astragalus linifolius Osterhout, Bull. Torrey Bot. Club 55: 75. 1928 • Grand Junction milkvetch [E]

Plants stout, rushlike, forming bushy clumps, 35–50 cm; from shallow, subterranean or superficial caudex. **Stems** erect or ascending, sparsely strigulose. **Leaves** distally (rarely all) unifoliolate or reduced to phyllodia, 3–12 cm; stipules connate-sheathing and papery-membranous at proximal nodes, distinct and herbaceous at distal nodes, 3.5–5 mm; leaflets (0 or 1–)3–9, blades obovate or linear, 2–12 mm, apex obtuse to acute, surfaces sparsely strigulose; terminal leaflet of compound leaves decurrent, not jointed to rachis. **Peduncles** erect or incurved-ascending, 10–25 cm. **Racemes** loosely 3–10-flowered, flowers ascending; axis 1.5–9(–12) cm; bracts 2–3 mm; bracteoles 1 or 2. **Pedicels** 0.5–3.5 mm. **Flowers** 14.6–18(–22) mm; calyx 5.0–7.8 mm, strigose, tube 3.8–5.3 × 3.7–3.8 mm, lobes subulate, 1.1–2.8 mm; corolla white, keel tip pink-purple fading dark purple; keel 11.3–12.3 mm. **Legumes** erect, stramineous, ± straight, narrowly oblong-ellipsoid, slightly compressed laterally, (10–)12–17(–20) × 4.4–6 mm, fleshy becoming woody, glabrous or strigose; sessile. **Seeds** 18–20.

Flowering May–Jun. Pinyon-juniper woodlands and sagebrush communities on seleniferous substrates; 1400–1800 m; Colo.

Astragalus linifolius has erect fruits and white flowers that distinguish this handsome clump-former from the morphologically similar but disjunct *A. rafaelensis*, with which it was synonymized by P. A. Rydberg (1929). J. D. Karron (1989) reported this species to be self-compatible and moderately autogamous, but to exhibit inbreeding depression when self-pollinated. Karron et al. (1988) reported the species to have restricted genetic polymorphism, but to still exhibit a moderate level of isozyme variation.

Astragalus linifolius is restricted to Delta and Montrose counties. It is in the Center for Plant Conservation's National Collection of Endangered Plants.

99. Astragalus rafaelensis M. E. Jones, Rev. N.-Amer. Astragalus, 146. 1923 • San Rafael milkvetch [E] [F]

Plants stout, rushlike, forming bushy clumps, 32–65 cm, sparsely hairy; from a usually branched, superficial caudex. **Stems** usually erect or ascending, sometimes diffuse, glabrous or sparsely hairy. **Leaves** compound, unifoliolate, or reduced to phyllodia, 2.5–14.8 cm; stipules connate-sheathing at proximal nodes, connate or distinct at distal nodes, 1–5 mm, papery-scarious; leaflets (0 or 1–)3–5, lateral blades linear to oblong, 3–20 mm, apex acute, surfaces glabrate abaxially, glabrous adaxially; terminal leaflet longer, decurrent, not jointed to rachis. **Peduncles** erect, 11–27(–29) cm. **Racemes** loosely 5–12(–14)-flowered, flowers ascending to declined; axis 2–5 cm in fruit; bracts 1.2–3.5 mm; bracteoles 2. **Pedicels** 2–5.5 mm. **Flowers** 19–26 mm; calyx 6–9.6 mm, sparsely strigose to glabrate, tube 5.2–7.5 × 3.6 mm, lobes triangular, (0.8–)1.1–2.1 mm; corolla pale pink-purple, wing tips paler or white, keel maculate; keel 12.2–13 mm. **Legumes** deflexed (through curvature of pedicel), stramineous, straight (and subsymmetric) or slightly decurved, oblong-ellipsoid, laterally compressed, 12–25 × 5–7.5 mm, leathery-woody, terminal cusp 2.5–4 mm), glabrous; sessile. **Seeds** 18–20. $2n = 22$.

Flowering late Apr–Jun. Seleniferous clay and silty soil, salt desert shrub communities of the Jurassic Buckhorn Conglomerate, Cedar Mountain, Morrison, Summerville, and Triassic Chinle and Moenkopi formations; 1300–2100 m; Colo., Utah.

Astragalus rafaelensis is restricted to Emery and Grand counties in Utah, and near Gateway in Montrose County, Colorado. It is most abundant in the eastern portion of the San Rafael Swell in Emery County.

100. Astragalus saurinus Barneby, Leafl. W. Bot. 8: 17. 1956 • Dinosaur milkvetch [E]

Plants robust, rushlike, clump-forming, 25–45 cm, finely strigulose; from shallow, subterranean caudex. **Stems** erect or ascending, finely strigulose. **Leaves** compound proximally, unifoliolate or reduced to phyllodia distally, sometimes unifoliolate throughout, 2.5–9 cm; stipules connate-sheathing and papery-scarious at proximal nodes, connate or distinct and herbaceous with scarious margins becoming papery at distal nodes, 1.2–7 mm; leaflets (0 or 1–)3–9, blades linear to linear-elliptic, 10–28 mm, apex obtuse to acute, surfaces strigose; terminal leaflet decurrent, not jointed to rachis. **Peduncles** erect, 7–21 cm. **Racemes** 3–15-flowered, flowers ascending-spreading; axis 0.5–6 cm in fruit; bracts 1.2–2 mm; bracteoles 1 or 2. **Pedicels** 1.5–3 mm. **Flowers** 18–22 mm; calyx 6.4–9.6 mm, strigulose, tube 5.6–6.7 × 2.8–5.2 mm, lobes triangular-subulate, 0.9–2.9 mm; corolla usually pink-purple with white wing tips, rarely white throughout; keel 12–16 mm. **Legumes** deflexed or declined, stramineous, straight or slightly incurved, narrowly oblong, laterally compressed, bicarinate by sutures, (15–)20–35 × 4.4–6(–7) mm, thinly fleshy becoming stiffly papery, terminal cusp 0.5–1 mm, strigose to glabrate; sessile or subsessile. **Seeds** 19–29. $2n = 22$.

Flowering late Apr–Jul. Salt desert shrub and pinyon-juniper communities; 1400–1800 m; Utah.

Astragalus saurinus, with its bicolored flowers, is restricted to Uintah County. As is the case with other selenophytes, it is largely avoided by grazing ungulates, lagomorphs, and rodents.

101. Astragalus osterhoutii M. E. Jones, Rev. N.-Amer. Astragalus, 251. 1923 (as osterhouti) • Osterhout's milkvetch [C] [E]

Plants stout, clump-forming, 25–45 cm, very sparsely strigulose; from shallow, subterranean caudex. **Stems** erect or ascending, very sparsely strigulose. **Leaves** sometimes unifoliolate distally, 3–8.5 cm; stipules shortly connate-sheathing and scarious at proximal nodes, connate or distinct and herbaceous at distal nodes, 2–8 mm; leaflets (1 or)5–15, blades linear-oblong, oblanceolate, or filiform, 6–40 mm, apex obtuse to acute, surfaces glabrous or sparsely strigulose abaxially, glabrous adaxially; terminal leaflet decurrent, not jointed to rachis. **Peduncles** erect, (6–)8–14 cm. **Racemes** 12–25-flowered, flowers spreading-declined; axis 2.5–10 cm in fruit; bracts 1–3.5 mm; bracteoles 1 or 2. **Pedicels** 2–6 mm. **Flowers** 17–23 mm; calyx 8.5–12 mm, strigulose, tube 7–10 × 3.5–4.7 mm, lobes triangular-subulate, 0.8–2 mm; corolla white; keel 12.3–14.8 mm. **Legumes** pendulous, green-stramineous, straight or slightly incurved, linear-ellipsoid, strongly laterally compressed, 25–45 × 3–4 mm, fleshy becoming stiffly papery, glabrous; stipe 2–6.5 mm. **Seeds** 12–17.

Flowering Jun–Aug. Seleniferous clay hills, barren knolls, bluffs on openings in sagebrush-grass communities, under sagebrush; of conservation concern; 2200–2400 m; Colo.

Astragalus osterhoutii, with the combination of white flowers and stipitate, laterally compressed, ultimately deflexed and proportionally very long fruits, is unique in sect. *Pectinati*. This selenophyte, restricted to Grand County, was estimated to have a geographic range of approximately 120 km^2 in soils derived from shales of the Niobrara, Pierre, and Troublesome formations (S. Spackman et al. 1997b). J. D. Karron (1989) reported this species as self-compatible, but not particularly autogamous. It was reported to have restricted genetic polymorphism, but still to exhibit a moderate level of isozyme variation (Karron et al. 1988).

Astragalus osterhoutii is in the Center for Plant Conservation's National Collection of Endangered Plants.

135dd. Astragalus Linnaeus sect. Woodruffiani Barneby, Mem. New York Bot. Gard. 13: 436. 1964 [E]

Herbs perennial, selenophyte, forming broomlike clumps, caulescent; caudex subterranean. **Hairs** basifixed or incipiently malpighian. **Stems** several to many. **Stipules** sheathing and amplexicaul at proximal nodes, distinct throughout. **Leaves** odd-pinnate, short-petiolate or petiole subobsolete; leaflets (0 or 1 or)3–9. **Racemes** initially densely flowered, flowers ascending. **Calyx tubes** short-cylindric. **Corollas** pink to red-purple, wing apices pale or white, banner recurved through 35–45°, keel apex obtuse. **Legumes** ultimately deciduous, sessile, erect, narrowly oblong, straight or incurved, compressed laterally, unilocular. **Seeds** 18–20.

Species 1: Utah.

102. Astragalus woodruffii M. E. Jones, Rev. N.-Amer. Astragalus, 77. 1923 (as woodruffi) • Woodruff's milkvetch [E]

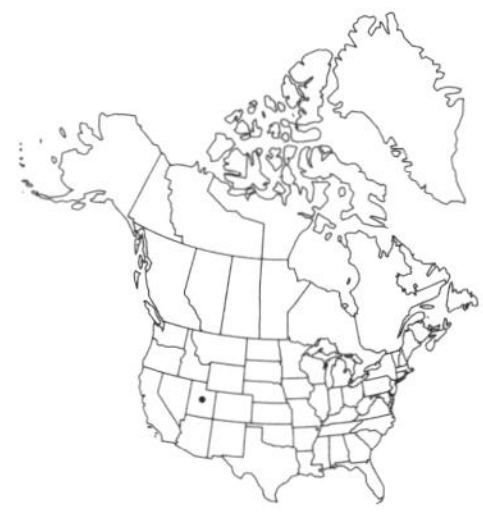

Plants stout, rushlike, coarse, 25–55(–65) cm, strigulose-pilose; from deep, subterranean caudex. **Stems** erect or ascending, 4–24 cm underground and cream to stramineous, strigulose-pilose. **Leaves** unifoliolate distally, reduced to phyllodia, 1.5–6.5(–8) cm; stipules 10–25 mm, firm, papery at proximal nodes, foliaceous at distal nodes; leaflet blades (when present), decurrent, closely folded, linear to narrowly oblong, 2–17 mm, apex acute to obtuse, surfaces silvery-strigose; terminal leaflet decurrent, not jointed to rachis. **Peduncles** ascending or erect, 3.5–18 cm. **Racemes** 8–45-flowered; axis 2–28 cm in fruit; bracts 2.5–7 mm; bracteoles 0–2. **Pedicels** 1–5 mm. **Flowers** 12–19 mm; calyx 7.2–10.9 mm, pilosulous, tube 4.2–6.6 mm, lobes lanceolate-subulate, 2.7–6 mm; corolla pink to red-purple with pale or white wing tips; keel 9.4–14.3 mm. **Legumes** dehiscent on plant, stramineous, straight to hamately incurved, 14–24 × 2.5–4.8 mm, stiffly papery, strigulose.

Flowering May–Jul. Seleniferous, sandy or sandy-silty soils, with purple or sand sage, *Amsonia*, and *Ephedra*, mainly on the Jurassic Entrada Formation or sand derived from it; 1300–1700 m; Utah.

Jones described *Astragalus woodruffii* as the most beautiful species of the genus when the whole mass is ablaze with pink-purple bloom. The species is restricted to east-central Utah in Emery, Garfield, and Wayne counties.

135ee. Astragalus Linnaeus sect. Miselli (Rydberg) Barneby, Mem. New York Bot. Gard. 13: 438. 1964

Tium Medikus [unranked] *Misella* Rydberg in N. L. Britton et al., N. Amer. Fl. 24: 388. 1929

Herbs perennial, caulescent; caudex superficial or subterranean. **Hairs** basifixed. **Stems** several to many. **Stipules** distinct. **Leaves** odd-pinnate, usually subsessile to petiolate, rarely sessile; leaflets (3–)9–27(–37). **Racemes** loosely or densely flowered, flowers usually declined, sometimes ascending. **Calyx tubes** campanulate. **Corollas** white, greenish white, ochroleucous, yellowish, or pink-purple, banner recurved through 45–90°, keel apex obtuse to sharply acute. **Legumes** ultimately deciduous, stipitate or subsessile, usually pendulous, sometimes declined or spreading, straight or incurved, linear, lanceoloid, oblong, or narrowly oblong-ellipsoid, 3-sided, ± bilocular. **Seeds** (6–)8–30.

Species 13 (10 in the flora): w United States, Mexico.

Section *Miselli* comprises 13 species distributed in the western United States from the Sierra Nevada and Cascade and Coast ranges eastward to the Rocky Mountains, and in Coahuila and the Sierra Madre Occidental, Mexico.

103. Astragalus congdonii S. Watson, Proc. Amer. Acad. Arts 20: 360. 1885 (as congdoni) • Congdon's milkvetch [E]

Plants coarse to slender, (10–)15–75(–90) cm, villous-villosulous; from superficial caudex. **Stems** decumbent to ascending, villous-villosulous or white-villous-tomentulose. **Leaves** (3–)4–14(–17) cm; stipules 2–8 mm, papery at proximal nodes, thinly herbaceous at distal nodes; leaflets (11–)17–35(–37), blades oblong-elliptic, ovate, obovate, or suborbiculate, 3–15 mm, apex truncate, retuse, apiculate, or subacute, surfaces villous-villosulous or sparsely so adaxially. **Peduncles** (5–)7–18(–20) cm. **Racemes** 8–35-flowered; axis 3.5–20 cm in fruit; bracts 1.2–3.4 mm; bracteoles 0–2. **Pedicels** 0.3–3 mm. **Flowers** 10.4–16.6 mm; calyx 5.3–7.5(–8) mm, villosulous, tube 3.8–5.3 mm, lobes subulate, 1.1–3 mm; corolla white or whitish, immaculate, drying ochroleucous; banner recurved through 45°; keel 7.4–12.7 mm. **Legumes** declined, green or purple-tinged becoming stramineous, straight to falcately incurved, linear, 3-sided compressed, 15–35 × 2.3–3.2 mm, thinly fleshy becoming stiffly papery, densely to sparsely strigulose-villous; septum 1–2 mm wide; stipe 1–2.5 mm, concealed within calyx. **Seeds** (17–)23–29. **2*n*** = 26.

Flowering Mar–May. Brushy banks, canyon slopes, roadcuts, substrates derived from metamorphic or serpentine parent materials, within and slightly below digger pine zone; 100–700 m; Calif.

Astragalus congdonii, a so-called ungainly, homely species (D. Isely 1998), is restricted to the western foothills of the southern half of the Sierra Nevada. The species seems not particularly closely related to its closest relatives from the outer Coast Ranges, *A. agnicidus* and *A. umbraticus*.

104. Astragalus agnicidus Barneby, Madroño 14: 39. 1957 • Lambkill milkvetch [C] [E]

Plants robust, clump-forming, (30–)40–90 cm, glabrous or sparsely villous; from superficial caudex. **Stems** erect, glabrous or sparsely villous. **Leaves** (3.5–)5–12(–16) cm; stipules 4–15 mm, submembranous; leaflets (13–)19–27(–37), blades ovate, lanceolate-oblong, or oblong-obovate, (3–)5–22 mm, midrib prominent, pubescent abaxially, apex truncate and apiculate, retuse, obtuse, or subacute, surfaces glabrous or sparsely villous abaxially, glabrous adaxially. **Peduncles** erect, 5–13 cm. **Racemes** (10–)15–40-flowered; axis (1–)2–4.5 cm in fruit; bracts 2–6 mm; bracteoles 0–2. **Pedicels** 0.6–1.8 mm. **Flowers** 9.1–11 mm; calyx 6.6–9 mm, sparsely villous-villosulous, tube 3.2–4.3 × 2.4–3 mm, lobes linear to lanceolate-acuminate, 3.3–4.9 mm; corolla white, immaculate; banner recurved through 45°; keel 7–7.4 mm. **Legumes** declined, stramineous or brown, slightly incurved, obliquely lanceoloid, 3-sided compressed, grooved dorsally, 11–15 × 3–3.4 mm, papery, villosulous, hairs 1+ mm; septum 1.5–2.2 mm wide; stipe 0.3–0.4 mm. **Seeds** 8 or 9.

Flowering late May–Aug. Openings on brushy ridges in partially timbered forests; of conservation concern; 800 m; Calif.

For more than four decades, *Astragalus agnicidus* was known only from the type locality in Humboldt County and reputedly was responsible for the loss of lambs where it grew abundantly in partially timbered forest land; it has recently been discovered to occur in disturbed areas in logged forest in western Mendocino County.

Astragalus agnicidus is in the Center for Plant Conservation's National Collection of Endangered Plants.

105. Astragalus umbraticus E. Sheldon, Minnesota Bot. Stud. 1: 23. 1894 • Sylvan milkvetch [E] [F]

Astragalus sylvaticus Howell ex S. Watson, Proc. Amer. Acad. Arts 23: 262. 1888, not (Pallas) Willdenow 1802

Plants slender, (20–)25–50 cm, glabrous or sparsely villous; from superficial caudex. **Stems** spreading to ascending, glabrous or glabrate. **Leaves** 4–12 cm; stipules 3.5–9.5 mm, papery at proximal nodes, submembranous at distal nodes; leaflets (11–)15–23, blades broadly oblong, ovate, or obovate to suborbiculate, (4–)6–16(–20) mm, apex retuse or abruptly short-acuminate, surfaces glabrous, sparsely ciliate, abaxially with few hairs on midrib. **Peduncles** erect or incurved-ascending, 5–12 cm. **Racemes** 10–25-flowered; axis (1.5–)2–5 cm in fruit; bracts 1.7–4 mm; bracteoles 0. **Pedicels** 0.6–1.2 mm. **Flowers** 10–14 mm; calyx 5.2–7 mm, sparsely strigulose, tube 3.1–4 mm, lobes subulate, 2.1–3.2 mm; corolla greenish white, immaculate, often drying cream; banner recurved through 40–60°; keel 7.7–10 mm. **Legumes** spreading or declined, stramineous or blackish, incurved to 0.5 spiral, lunately or falcately linear-lanceoloid or linear, 3-sided, 14–24 × 2.6–3.6 mm, firmly papery, glabrous; septum 1.5–2.3 mm wide; stipe 0.8–1.9 mm. **Seeds** 10–15.

Flowering May–Jul. Oak and pine woodlands; 100–1300 m; Calif., Oreg.

The wide morphological gap between *Astragalus umbraticus*, restricted to the Cascade Range of Oregon and Coast Ranges of northwestern California, and its closest relatives is suggestive of age and a long period of isolation (R. C. Barneby 1964).

106. Astragalus paysonii (Rydberg) Barneby, Leafl. W. Bot. 4: 60. 1944 • Payson's milkvetch [E]

Hamosa paysonii Rydberg, Bull. Torrey Bot. Club 54: 22. 1927

Plants somewhat slender, 20–45(–65) cm, glabrous or sparsely strigulose; from superficial or slightly subterranean caudex. **Stems** decumbent to ascending, glabrous or sparsely strigulose. **Leaves** 4–9.5 cm; stipules 2–5 mm, submembranous becoming papery; leaflets 7–15(or 17), blades ovate, ovate-oblong, or obovate-cuneate, 5–20 mm, apex retuse, surfaces sparsely strigulose abaxially, glabrous adaxially. **Peduncles** incurved-ascending, 3–9 cm. **Racemes** 5–20-flowered; axis 1–4.5 cm in fruit; bracts 0.8–2 mm; bracteoles

0. **Pedicels** 0.5–1.2 mm. **Flowers** 7–9 mm; calyx 3.2–4.6 mm, strigulose, tube 2–2.9 mm, lobes subulate, 1–1.7 mm; corolla whitish, sometimes faintly tinged lilac; banner recurved through 45°; keel 4.8–5.5 mm. **Legumes** pendulous, stramineous or brown, lunate, linear-ellipsoid, 3-sided compressed, 10–17 × 2.5–3.5 mm, papery, glabrous; septum 1.3–2 mm wide; stipe 1–1.5 mm. **Seeds** 8–10.

Flowering Jun–Oct. Open aspen, lodgepole pine, and Douglas-fir timber forests, burned-over or clear-cut forests, roadcuts, on decomposed granite; 1700–3000 m; Idaho, Wyo.

Despite the disjunction of *Astragalus paysonii* in north-central Idaho and western Wyoming, plants from the two areas are essentially the same morphologically.

107. Astragalus straturensis M. E. Jones, Contr. W. Bot. 8: 19. 1898 • Silver Reef milkvetch [E]

Plants slender, forming bushy clumps, 13–36(–48) cm, strigulose; from superficial or shallow, subterranean caudex. **Stems** decumbent to ascending or erect, strigulose. **Leaves** 3.5–10 cm; stipules 1–2.5 mm, thinly herbaceous becoming papery; leaflets (3–)9–19, blades oblong to linear or oval, 3–13 mm, apex obtuse to retuse, surfaces strigose abaxially, glabrous adaxially. **Peduncles** ascending, 1.5–7.5 cm. **Racemes** 9–25-flowered, flowers ascending to declined; axis 1.5–14(–17) cm in fruit; bracts 0.8–1.5 mm; bracteoles 0. **Pedicels** 0.8–1.5 mm. **Flowers** 6.5–8.5 mm; calyx 3.5–4.2 mm, strigose, tube 2.5–3.5 mm, lobes triangular, 0.7–1.1 mm; corolla pink-purple with white wing tips; banner recurved through 50–90°; keel 5–6 mm. **Legumes** pendulous, stramineous, incurved or straight, oblong, 3-sided compressed, 10–15(–17) × 2.2–3 mm, thinly fleshy becoming papery, strigose; septum 0.8–1 mm wide; stipe 1.4–2.5 mm. **Seeds** 10–13. $2n = 22$.

Flowering late Apr–Jun. Sagebrush, pinyon-juniper, ponderosa pine, and mountain brush communities; 1500–2500 m; Ariz., Nev., Utah.

Astragalus straturensis is known from Mt. Trumbull, Mohave County in Arizona, Needle Mountains and Highland Range, Lincoln County in Nevada, and Beaver, Iron, Millard, and Washington counties in Utah.

The relationships of *Astragalus straturensis* lie with species in sect. *Miselli* with distributions southward into the Sierra Madre Occidental, Mexico. It is the only *Astragalus* in its region that is perennial, with pendulous, stipitate, dorsally-grooved fruits, and purple flowers.

108. Astragalus howellii A. Gray, Proc. Amer. Acad. Arts 15: 46. 1879 (as howelli) • Howell's milkvetch [E]

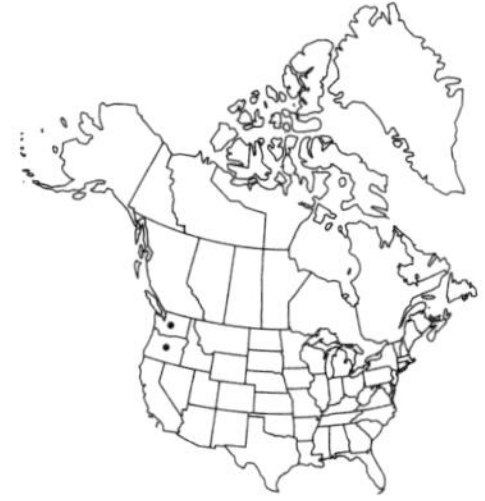

Plants slender, forming bushy clumps, (5–)8–41 cm, villosulous; from superficial or shallow, subterranean caudex. **Stems** erect or ascending, villosulous. **Leaves** (4–)5–14 cm; stipules 3–5 mm, papery; leaflets (17–)21–27(–33), blades oblong, obovate-cuneate, or oblanceolate, 4–14 mm, apex obtuse to truncate-retuse, surfaces villosulous, sometimes sparsely so adaxially. **Peduncles** erect, 5.5–18 cm. **Racemes** 10–25-flowered; axis 5–12.5 cm in fruit; bracts 1–2.5 mm; bracteoles 0. **Pedicels** 1–4.5 mm. **Flowers** 6.5–8.5 mm; calyx 5–7.5 mm, strigose, tube 2.5–3.5 mm, lobes triangular, 0.7–1.1 mm; corolla ochroleucous, immaculate; banner recurved through 50–85°; keel 8.2–12 mm. **Legumes** pendulous, stramineous, lunate, lanceoloid, 3-sided compressed, lateral face flat, dorsal face grooved, (16–)20–30 × 3–4.5(–5) mm, length 5–7 times width, stiffly papery, villosulous; septum 2–3 mm wide; stipe (4–)7–12 (–14) mm. **Seeds** (11–)13–21.

Flowering May–Jun. Dry grassy hills, sandy or stony substrates overlying basalt, under low brush; 500–1100 m; Oreg., Wash.

Astragalus howellii occurs in north-central and northeastern Oregon with historical collections from Columbia, Franklin, Walla Walla, and Whitman counties in southwestern Washington.

The varieties in *Astragalus howellii* recognized by C. L. Hitchcock (1961b) and D. Isely (1998) are herein included in *A. misellus*, following the treatment by R. C. Barneby (1964).

109. Astragalus arthurii M. E. Jones, Contr. W. Bot. 8: 20. 1898 (as arthuri) • Waha milkvetch [E]

Plants slender, forming bushy clumps, 2–16(–26) cm, strigulose; from superficial caudex. **Stems** erect or ascending, strigulose. **Leaves** (4–)5–14 cm; stipules 2–6(–7) mm, thinly herbaceous becoming papery; leaflets (15–)19–25(or 27), blades elliptic, linear-elliptic, or oblanceolate, 2–14 mm, apex obtuse to subacute, truncate-apiculate, or shallowly retuse, surfaces strigulose abaxially, glabrous adaxially. **Peduncles** ascending, often incurved, (7–)10–18(–20) cm. **Racemes** (5–)8–20-flowered; axis (2.5–)5–15 cm in fruit; bracts 1.5–3.5 mm; bracteoles 0. **Pedicels** 1–4 mm. **Flowers** 11.7–15.2 mm; calyx 6.6–8.8 mm, strigose, tube 4.5–6 mm, lobes lanceolate-subulate, 1.8–3.5 mm; corolla ochroleucous, immaculate; banner recurved through 50–85°; keel (9.5–)10–11.7 mm. **Legumes** pendulous, stramineous, straight or gently incurved, linear-ellipsoid, 3-sided and laterally compressed, lateral face flat, dorsal face grooved, (25–)30–45 × 2.5–3.3 mm, length mostly 10 times width, papery, finely strigulose; septum 1.6–2.3 mm wide; stipe 6–15 mm. **Seeds** (16–)18–30. $2n$ = 24.

Flowering mid Apr–Jun. Grassy hills, meadows, basaltic soils; 200–900 m; Idaho, Oreg., Wash.

The main area of dispersal of *Astragalus arthurii* does not exceed 80 km; it is restricted to the Snake River and its tributaries in extreme southeastern Washington and contiguous Idaho and northeastern Oregon.

110. Astragalus misellus S. Watson, Proc. Amer. Acad. Arts 21: 449. 1886 • Pauper milkvetch [E]

Plants somewhat slender, 2.5–25 cm, finely strigulose; from superficial caudex. **Stems** ascending or prostrate, finely strigulose. **Leaves** 2.5–7 cm; stipules 1.5–3 mm, herbaceous becoming papery at proximal nodes, herbaceous at distal nodes; leaflets (7 or)9–21, blades oblong-obovate to linear-oblong or -elliptic, 2–10 mm, apex obtuse to subacute or retuse, surfaces strigulose abaxially, strigulose, glabrous, or glabrate adaxially. **Peduncles** ascending, 1.5–8(–10) cm. **Racemes** 5–15-flowered; axis 1–8 cm in fruit; bracts 1–1.5 mm; bracteoles 0. **Pedicels** 0.8–1.7 mm. **Flowers** 6.5–10 mm; calyx 3.4–4.8 mm, strigose, tube 2.2–2.8 mm, lobes lanceolate-subulate, 0.9–2.2 mm; corolla yellowish, yellowish white and lightly tinged rose, or greenish ochroleucous, banner violet-veined; banner recurved through 45–85°; keel 4.6–6.4 mm. **Legumes** pendulous, brown or stramineous, lunate, lanceoloid-ellipsoid, 3-sided compressed, 12–25 × 2.6–4 mm, papery, strigulose-villosulous; septum 1.3–2.4 mm wide; stipe 2.5–5 mm. **Seeds** 11–16.

Varieties 2 (2 in the flora): nw United States.

D. Isely (1983) redefined *Astragalus howellii* by expanding it to include the geographically contiguous *A. misellus* and its varieties as recognized here, noting that these might be viewed as representatives of a single complex with some quantitative regional differentiation. The proposal has merit and is worthy of study; however, this treatment follows that of R. C. Barneby (1964).

1. Plants 10–25 cm; leaflets (9–)13–21, blade surfaces glabrous or glabrate adaxially .... 110a. *Astragalus misellus* var. *misellus*
1. Plants 2.5–15 cm; leaflets (7–)11 or 13, blade surfaces strigulose adaxially.................. .... 110b. *Astragalus misellus* var. *pauper*

110a. Astragalus misellus S. Watson var. **misellus** [E]

Astragalus howellii A. Gray var. *aberrans* (M. E. Jones) C. L. Hitchcock

Plants 10–25 cm. **Leaves** 2.5–6.5 cm; leaflets comparatively crowded, (9–)13–21, blade surfaces glabrous or glabrate adaxially.

Flowering May–Jul. Stony pastures, gravelly clay banks, on basaltic bedrock; 300–1200 m; Oreg.

Variety *misellus* is restricted to the upper forks of the Deschutes and John Day rivers in central Oregon.

110b. Astragalus misellus S. Watson var. **pauper** Barneby, Mem. New York Bot. Gard. 13: 458. 1964 • Ellensburg milkvetch [E]

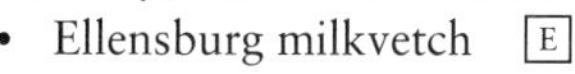

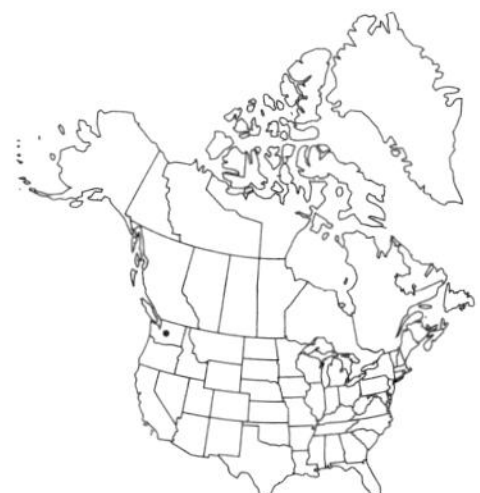

Plants 2.5–15 cm. **Leaves** 2.5–7 cm; leaflets relatively distant and scattered, (7–)11 or 13, blade surfaces strigulose adaxially.

Flowering Apr–early Jun. Mostly ridges and upper slopes, sometimes middle and lower slopes, sagebrush scablands; 150–1400 m; Wash.

Long known from only one or two collections, var. *pauper* occurs primarily along the western margin of the Columbia Basin province from Douglas to Klickitat counties.

111. Astragalus oniciformis Barneby, Leafl. W. Bot. 8: 122. 1957 • Picabo milkvetch [E]

Plants somewhat slender, clump-forming, 5–25(–40) cm, strigulose to villosulous; from superficial, usually much-branched caudex. **Stems** decumbent or prostrate, strigulose to villosulous. **Leaves** 2.5–7.5(–9) cm; stipules 1.5–4 mm, papery-membranous; leaflets (13–)17–25(or 27), blades broadly elliptic, oval, or oblong, 1–6.5 mm, apex obtuse or retuse, surfaces strigulose to villosulous, sometimes glabrous or glabrescent adaxially. **Peduncles** 0.5–5.5 cm. together with racemes shorter than leaves. **Racemes** loosely (4–)6–12-flowered; axis 1–7 cm in fruit; bracts 0.5–1.8 mm; bracteoles 0. **Pedicels** 1–1.6 mm. **Flowers** 5.3–6.8 mm; calyx 2.9–3.8 mm, strigose, tube 2.1–2.3 mm, lobes subulate, 0.8–1.5 mm; corolla whitish or ochroleucous, banner veined purplish; banner recurved through 45–85°; keel 4–5 mm.

Legumes pendulous, stramineous, slightly incurved, nearly lanceoloid-ellipsoid or oblong-ellipsoid, 3-sided compressed, 7–12 × 2–3.8 mm, papery, strigulose; septum 0.7–1.2 mm wide; stipe 1.5–4 mm. **Seeds** 6–12.

Flowering May–early Jul. Sandy substrates, among boulders, open spaces in tall sagebrush, basaltic soils; 1300–1600 m; Idaho.

Astragalus oniciformis, a delicate endemic to south-central Idaho, was placed by R. C. Barneby (1964) in sect. *Miselli* because of its technical similarity to *A. misellus*, but he compared it to the somewhat contiguous and similar *A. mulfordiae* (sect. *Neonix*).

112. Astragalus toquimanus Barneby, Leafl. W. Bot. 3: 111, plate 1, fig. D. 1942 • Toquima milkvetch [C] [E]

Plants slender, 7–30 cm, strigulose; from superficial caudex. **Stems** ascending, strigulose. **Leaves** 2.5–11 cm; stipules 1.5–3 mm, papery at proximal nodes, firm at distal nodes; leaflets 9–17, blades oblong-oblanceolate, linear-oblong, or obovate, 3–15 mm, apex obtuse or retuse, surfaces strigulose, sometimes glabrescent adaxially. **Peduncles** incurved-ascending or divaricate, 2.5–6(–10) cm. **Racemes** loosely 9–20-flowered; axis 4.5–13 cm in fruit; bracts 1–1.5 mm; bracteoles 2. **Pedicels** 0.8–2 mm. **Flowers** 6.9–7.6 mm; calyx 3.5–4 mm, strigose, tube 2.5–2.8 mm, lobes subulate, 1–1.5 mm; corolla ochroleucous, banner veined or suffused with purple; banner recurved through 90°; keel 6.8–7.7 mm. **Legumes** pendulous, mottled (and glaucescent) becoming stramineous and faintly purple-tinged, slightly incurved, oblong-lanceoloid, distinctly 3-sided compressed, 18–25 × 3–4.5 mm, papery, glabrous; septum 2.4–2.7 mm wide; stipe 3–4 mm. **Seeds** 11–16.

Flowering late Apr–early Jul. Gravelly, calcareous substrates in pinyon-juniper and sagebrush communities, under low sagebrush; of conservation concern; 2000–2300 m; Nev.

Astragalus toquimanus is restricted to the eastern slope of the Toquima Range, Nye County.

135ff. Astragalus Linnaeus sect. Neviniani Barneby, Mem. New York Bot. Gard. 13: 461. 1964 [C] [E]

Herbs perennial, caulescent; caudex superficial. **Hairs** basifixed. **Stems** several. **Stipules** distinct. **Leaves** odd-pinnate, petiolate; leaflets 11–29. **Racemes** loosely or densely flowered, flowers declined. **Calyx tubes** short-cylindric or campanulate. **Corollas** ochroleucous or pale yellow, drying yellowish, banner recurved through 30–40°, keel apex obtuse. **Legumes** eventually deciduous or persistent, stipitate, pendulous, incurved, lanceoloid-oblong, semi-ellipsoid, or narrowly ellipsoid, 3-sided, grooved dorsally, ± bilocular. **Seeds** 12–20.

Species 2 (2 in the flora): California.

Section *Neviniani* comprises maritime species of the seaward islands off the coast of southern California.

113. Astragalus traskiae Eastwood, Proc. Calif. Acad. Sci., ser. 3, 1: 102, plate 8, fig. 6. 1898 • Trask's milkvetch [C] [E]

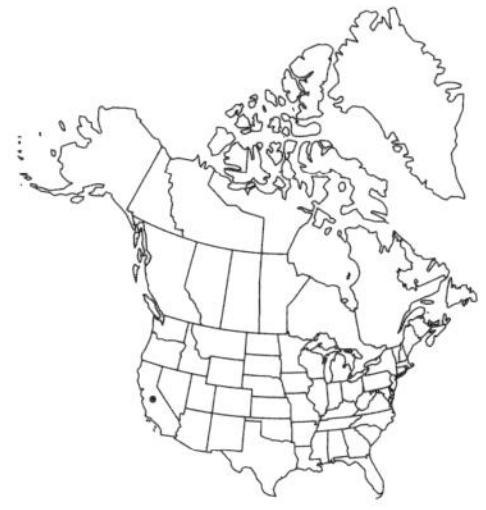

Plants 8–25(–45) cm, villous-tomentulose, appearing gray or ashy. **Stems** decumbent to ascending or spreading, villous-tomentulose or white-pannose. **Leaves** 4–10 cm; stipules 1.5–4 mm; leaflets 21–29, blades ovate, obovate, oval, or oblong-elliptic, 2.5–15 mm, apex obtuse or emarginate, surfaces villous-tomentulose. **Peduncles** ascending, drooping or humistrate in fruit, 4–14 cm. **Racemes** loosely 12–30-flowered; axis 2.5–8 cm in fruit; bracts 1.5–2 mm; bracteoles 2. **Pedicels** 1–1.5 mm. **Flowers** 14.2–17.5 mm; calyx short-cylindric, 7.5–9 mm, villous, tube 5.2–6.2 mm, lobes broadly subulate, 2.2–3.5 mm; corolla ochroleucous, concolorous, banner veined or suffused with purple; keel 10.2–12.9 mm. **Legumes** pendulous but appearing otherwise when humistrate, green-stramineous, straight or slightly incurved, lanceoloid-oblong, semi-ellipsoid, distinctly 3-sided compressed, 8–16 × 3.2–5.5 mm, leathery, villous-tomentulose; septum 1.1–1.8 mm wide; stipe 4–8.5 mm, pubescent. **Seeds** 12–16.

Flowering Mar–Jul. Sandy, windswept ocean bluffs, banks, coastal dunes; of conservation concern; 0–300 m; Calif.

The close relationship of *Astragalus traskiae* to *A. nevinii* is clearly evident and the two have sometimes been considered conspecific. *Astragalus traskiae* is endemic to, and the only perennial *Astragalus* on, San Nicolas and Santa Barbara islands.

114. Astragalus nevinii A. Gray, Proc. Amer. Acad. Arts 21: 412. 1886 • Nevin's milkvetch [C] [E]

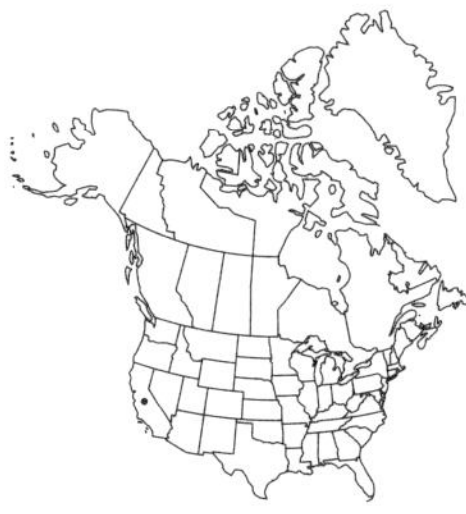

Plants 8–30+ cm, soft-villosulous, appearing gray or ashy. **Stems** spreading to ascending, erect when young, canescent-tomentulose, distinctly woody when over-wintering. **Leaves** 2–8 cm; stipules 2–5 mm, papery at proximal nodes; leaflets 11–25, blades oblong-obovate, -elliptic, or -oblanceolate, (1.5–)3–12 mm, apex obtuse or retuse, surfaces villosulous. **Peduncles** ascending, sometimes humistrate in fruit, 6–12 cm. **Racemes** densely (15–)20–30-flowered; axis 2–4 cm in fruit; bracts 1.5–3 mm; bracteoles 0–2. **Pedicels** 0.5–2 mm. **Flowers** 10.6–12.7 mm; calyx campanulate, 5.7–6.4 mm, villosulous, tube 3.8–4.5 mm, lobes broadly subulate, 1.4–2.4 mm; corolla pale yellow, concolorous; keel 9–10 mm. **Legumes** brown-stramineous, lunate, obliquely narrow-ellipsoid, 3-sided compressed, 14–20 × 3–5 mm, thinly fleshy becoming stiffly papery, glabrous; septum 1–1.3 mm wide; stipe 4.5–9.5 mm. **Seeds** 16–20.

Flowering Feb–Jul. Sandy flats, dunes, sandy bluffs, on or near shore; of conservation concern; 0–300 m; Calif.

Astragalus nevinii is restricted to San Clemente Island.

135gg. Astragalus Linnaeus sect. Neonix Barneby, Mem. New York Bot. Gard. 13: 464. 1964 [E]

Herbs perennial, slender, caulescent; caudex superficial, ultimately suffruticose. **Hairs** basifixed. **Stems** few or several to many. **Stipules** connate or distinct at distal nodes. **Leaves** odd-pinnate, petiolate or short-petiolate; leaflets (6–)8–25, terminal leaflet jointed or confluent. **Racemes** loosely flowered, flowers declined or nodding. **Calyx tubes** campanulate. **Corollas** whitish or ochroleucous, sometimes lilac-veined, banner recurved through (50–)85–100°, keel apex deltate. **Legumes** ultimately deciduous, stipitate or subsessile, pendulous or deflexed, symmetrically or lunately oblong-ellipsoid or semi-ellipsoid, 3-sided, ± bilocular. **Seeds** 6–16.

Species 4 (4 in the flora): w United States.

Section *Neonix* is distributed from central California to interior Oregon, western Nevada, and southwestern Idaho.

115. Astragalus mulfordiae M. E. Jones, Contr. W. Bot. 8: 18. 1898 (as mulfordae) • Mulford's milkvetch [C] [E]

Plants 10–30 cm, sparsely strigulose; caudex without thatch of persistent leaf bases. **Stems** spreading to ascending and diffuse, with well-developed internodes, sparsely strigulose. **Leaves** (2.5–)4.5–10.5 cm; stipules connate-sheathing at proximal nodes, distinct at distal nodes, 1.5–6 mm, papery-scarious; leaflets (7–)15–25, blades linear-oblong, -oblanceolate, or filiform, 1–11 mm, apex obtuse or subacute, surfaces strigulose abaxially, glabrous adaxially; terminal leaflet sometimes decurrent distally, not jointed to rachis. **Peduncles** (0.5–)1.5–7 cm. **Racemes** (5–)8–20-flowered; axis (2–)3–10 cm in fruit; bracts 0.7–2 mm; bracteoles 0–2. **Pedicels** 0.7–2 mm. **Flowers** 6–8.2 mm; calyx 2.5–5 mm, strigulose, tube (1.5–)1.8–3 mm, lobes subulate, 0.8–2 mm; corolla usually white or whitish, rarely yellow, drying yellowish, banner sometimes brownish-striate; banner abruptly recurved through (50–)85–100°; keel 4.7–5.7 mm. **Legumes** pendulous, stramineous, slightly incurved, lunately semi-ellipsoid, 3-sided compressed, 9–16 × 3–4.5 mm, papery, finely strigulose; septum 1.3–2 mm wide; stipe 3–5 mm. **Seeds** 11–16.

Flowering May–Jun. Sandy bluffs and dunelike talus, foothills, with rabbitbrush, western wheatgrass, and bitterbrush; of conservation concern; 600–900 (–1000) m; Idaho, Oreg.

Astragalus mulfordiae occurs near the Boise and Snake rivers and tributaries, near the western end of the Snake River Plains in Ada, Owyhee, and Washington counties in southwestern Idaho, and eastern Malheur County in Oregon.

Despite the distinct stipules and pubescence of *Astragalus oniciformis*, *A. mulfordiae* seems more appropriately aligned with that species. R. C. Barneby (1957) discounted any relationship of *A. mulfordiae* with the Old World, monospecific *Onix* Medikus and concluded that the similarity in fruits is to be attributed to convergence. He erected sect. *Neonix* to accommodate this attractive, small plant and its two presumed closest relatives.

Astragalus mulfordiae is in the Center for Plant Conservation's National Collection of Endangered Plants.

116. Astragalus johannis-howellii Barneby, Leafl. W. Bot. 8: 124. 1957 • Long Valley milkvetch [C] [E]

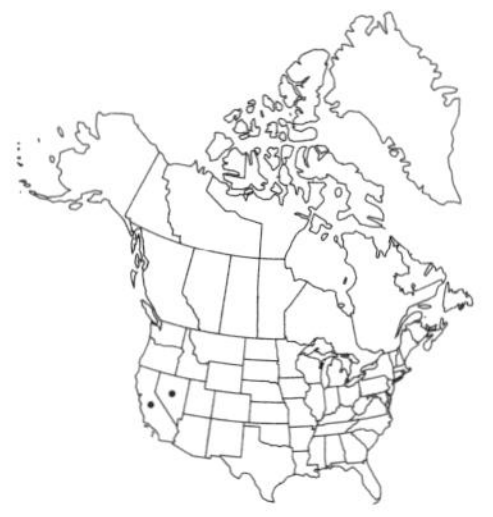

Plants 3–20 cm, sparsely strigulose-villosulous; caudex without thatch of persistent leaf bases. **Stems** prostrate to ascending, internodes well developed, sparsely strigulose-villosulous. **Leaves** 4–6 cm; stipules connate and scarious, 1.5–4 mm; leaflets (9 or)11–23, blades oblong-oblanceolate, -elliptic, or narrowly obovate, 1–6 mm, apex obtuse, surfaces strigulose-villosulous abaxially, glabrous adaxially. **Peduncles** ascending, 0.5–2.5 cm. **Racemes** 5–12-flowered; axis 1.5–4 cm in fruit; bracts 0.6–1.5 mm; bracteoles 0. **Pedicels** 0.8–1.3 mm. **Flowers** 4.5–5.5 mm; calyx 2.8–4 mm, strigulose, tube 1.5–2 mm, lobes subulate, 1–1.8 mm; corolla whitish, immaculate; banner recurved through 90°; keel 3.3–3.9 mm. **Legumes** pendulous, stramineous, lunate, oblong-ellipsoid, 3-sided compressed, 6–10.5 × 2–3 mm, thin becoming papery-membranous, finely strigulose; septum 1 mm wide; stipe 0.5–2.5 mm. **Seeds** 6–11.

Flowering Jul–Aug. Dry sandy substrates among sagebrush; of conservation concern; 2100–2700 m; Calif., Nev.

Astragalus johannis-howellii originally was thought to be endemic to Mono County, California, where the type locality and much of the population was inundated by the formation of Crowley Lake; it has subsequently been discovered to occur in adjacent Mineral County, Nevada.

117. Astragalus peckii Piper, Proc. Biol. Soc. Wash. 37: 92. 1924 • Peck's milkvetch [E]

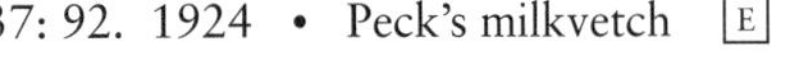

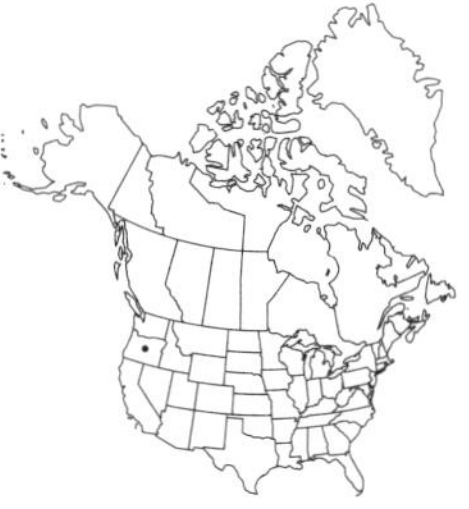

Plants (1–)5–20 cm, strigose-pilosulous; caudex with persistent petioles. **Stems** prostrate, strigose-pilosulous. **Leaves** 1–3.5 cm; stipules connate, 1–3 mm, submembranous becoming scarious at proximal nodes; leaflets 7–13, blades lanceolate, oblanceolate, or linear-elliptic, 1–6 mm, apex acute or subacute, surfaces strigose-pilosulous, sometimes glabrescent adaxially; terminal leaflets decurrent distally, not jointed to rachis, often recurved. **Peduncles** straight, 0.7–2 cm. **Racemes** 5–9-flowered; axis 1–2 cm in fruit; bracts 1–1.5 mm; bracteoles 0. **Pedicels** 1–2.5 mm. **Flowers** 5–7.5 mm; calyx 3.3–4.4 mm, strigulose, tube 1.8–2.1 mm, lobes subulate, 1.4–2.4 mm; corolla ochroleucous, banner

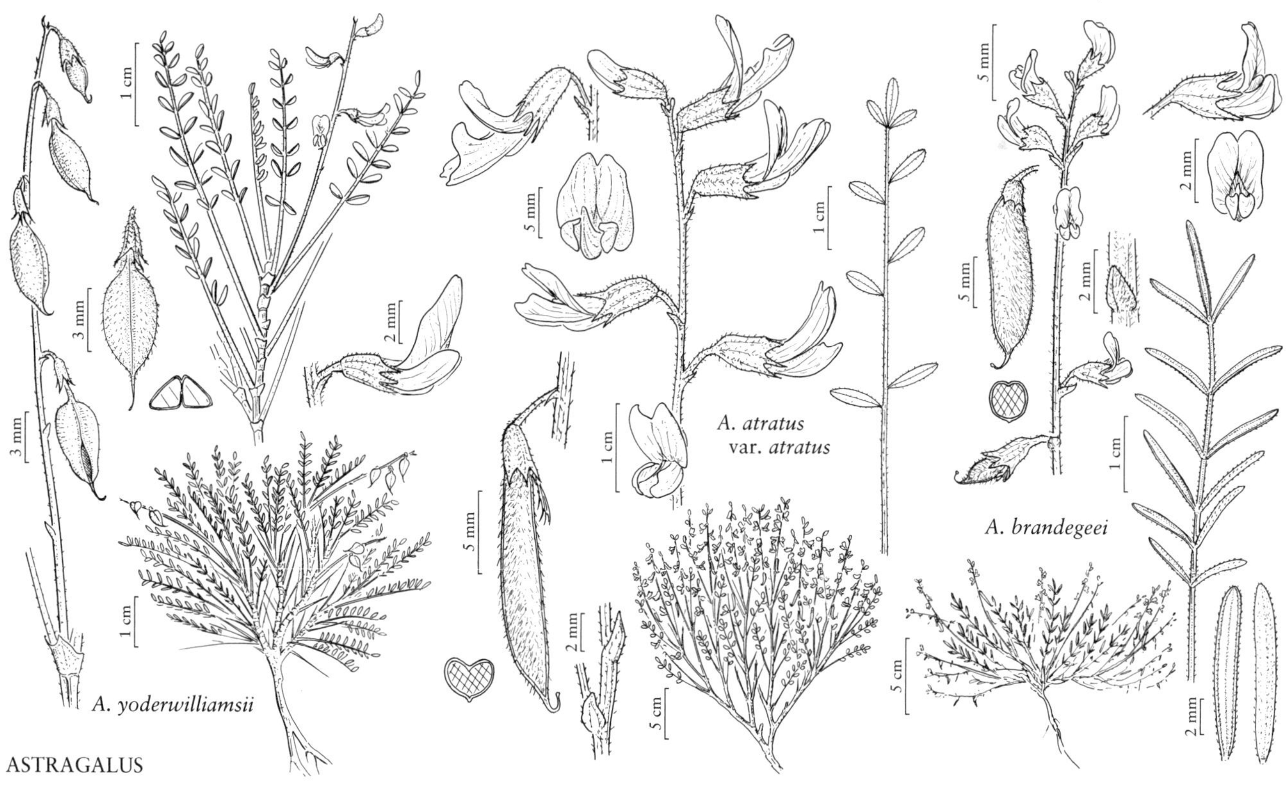

ASTRAGALUS

veined purple; banner recurved through 90–100°; keel 4–4.5 mm. **Legumes** deflexed, stramineous, incurved, subsymmetrically oblong-ellipsoid, 3-sided compressed, 5–8 × 1.9–3(–3.3) mm, papery, white-pilose; septum 0.8–1.7 mm wide; stipe 0.1–0.5 mm. **Seeds** 6–9.

Flowering Jun–early Aug. Flats, slopes, under sagebrush, in pumice sand or fine volcanic grit; 700–1000 m; Oreg.

Astragalus peckii occurs along the eastern base of the Cascade Range in Crook, Deschutes, and Klamath counties.

118. Astragalus yoderwilliamsii Barneby, Brittonia 32: 30, fig. 1. 1980 • Osgood Mountains milkvetch [E] [F]

Plants densely tuft-forming, diminutive, 1–3(–7) cm, sparsely strigulose; short caudex with thatch of persistent leaf bases. **Stems** erect or ascending, sparsely strigulose. **Leaves** 2.5–5.5 cm; stipules connate-sheathing and papery-membranous at proximal nodes, 1–2 mm; leaflets (7 or)9–17(or 19), blades obovate or narrowly elliptic, 1–3 mm, apex obtuse, surfaces sparsely strigulose; terminal leaflet smallest, jointed or continuous with rachis. **Peduncles** erect, 0–0.5 cm. **Racemes** 2–8-flowered; axis 1–3.5 cm in fruit. **Flowers** 5–7 mm; calyx 2.3–3.3 mm, strigulose, tube 1.5–2 mm, lobes subulate to triangular, 0.5–1 mm; corolla whitish, faintly veined pink; banner abruptly recurved; keel 4–4.5 mm. **Legumes** persistent, pendulous, stramineous, incurved, ellipsoid, sharply 3-sided compressed, 4–7 × 2–3 mm, thin becoming papery; valves inflexed, septum 1–2 mm wide; stipe 1–3 mm. **Seeds** 6–8.

Flowering Jun–Jul. Sagebrush-rabbitbrush communities, on decomposed granitic gravel; 1500–2200 m; Idaho, Nev.

Astragalus yoderwilliamsii, once thought to be restricted to the northern Osgood Mountains in Humboldt County, Nevada, precipitated the first emergency ruling under the Endangered Species Act because the species occurs within a region of mining activity. It is now also known from Elko County, Nevada, and Owyhee County, Idaho.

135hh. Astragalus Linnaeus sect. Atrati M. E. Jones, Rev. N.-Amer. Astragalus, 179. 1923 [E]

Herbs perennial, caulescent or subacaulescent; caudex superficial or aerial. **Hairs** basifixed. **Stems** several to many. **Stipules** distinct or connate. **Leaves** odd-pinnate, petiolate; leaflets 7–15(–19), terminal leaflet jointed to or confluent with rachis. **Racemes** loosely flowered, flowers nodding or horizontal. **Calyx tubes** campanulate. **Corollas** whitish or lilac-tinged, or lurid, banner recurved through 90°, keel apex rounded or sharply deltate. **Legumes** ultimately deciduous, subsessile or stipitate, pendulous (sometimes humistrate), linear-oblong or oblong-ellipsoid, decurved or straight, compressed dorsiventrally or laterally, unilocular or bilocular. **Seeds** 10–29.

Species 2 (2 in the flora): w United States.

Section *Atrati* is known from the Columbia and Great basins, from northeastern Oregon to southwestern Idaho, central Nevada, and southeastern California.

119. Astragalus atratus S. Watson, Botany (Fortieth Parallel), 69, plate 11. 1871 • Mourning milkvetch [E] [F]

Plants caulescent, (1–)3–24(–30) cm, strigulose. **Stems** prostrate to ascending, strigulose. **Leaves** (1.5–)3–14(–14.5) cm; stipules distinct, 1–5 mm, papery-scarious at proximal nodes, subherbaceous at distal nodes; leaflets 7–15, blades oblong-oblanceolate, elliptic, oval-oblong, linear-oblong, linear-elliptic, or linear-setaceous, 1.5–16 mm, apex obtuse, retuse, subacute, or emarginate, surfaces strigulose abaxially, strigulose or glabrous adaxially; terminal leaflet sometimes decurrent distally, jointed to or continuous with rachis. **Peduncles** incurved-ascending, (1.5–)3–16.5 cm. **Racemes** (2–)5–18-flowered, flowers nodding; axis (1.5–)3–17 cm in fruit; bracts (0.8–)1–2.5 mm; bracteoles usually 0. **Pedicels** (1.5–)2–6.5 mm. **Flowers** 6.3–13.4 mm; calyx 3–7.6 mm, strigulose, tube 2.3–5.6 mm, lobes subulate, 0.7–2.6 mm; corolla whitish or dirty white, sometimes veined, tipped, margined, or suffused with purple, or faintly tinged lavender; keel 6–10 mm. **Legumes** pendulous, green, purplish, or mottled, decurved or straight, linear-oblong, linear-oblanceoloid, or narrowly ellipsoid, compressed, ventral suture convex in profile or at least beak declined from body, 10–22 × 2.3–4.3 mm, unilocular or bilocular, thinly fleshy becoming papery or leathery, strigulose; septum (0 or)0.6–2.7 mm wide; stipe 0–2 mm, concealed within calyx when present. **Seeds** 10–29.

Varieties 4 (4 in the flora): w United States.

R. C. Barneby (1964) related that the main pattern underlying the complex racial differentiation in *Astragalus atratus* is one of northern and southern branches relating to the Snake-Humboldt divide in northeastern Nevada. Populations there and northward have subentire wing petals and unilocular fruits. Southward, the wings are toothed or lobed, and the fruit is nearly bilocular.

1. Legumes laterally compressed, bilocular, stipes 0–0.7 mm; Death Valley, Inyo County, California .... 119b. *Astragalus atratus* var. *mensanus*
1. Legumes ± dorsiventrally compressed, unilocular or bilocular, stipes 0.3–2 mm; c Nevada to e Oregon and sw Idaho.
   2. Legumes sub-bilocular, leathery, septae 0.6–1.3 mm wide; terminal leaflets jointed to rachises; c, nc Nevada .... 119a. *Astragalus atratus* var. *atratus*
   2. Legumes unilocular, leathery or papery, septae obsolete or to 0.2 mm wide; terminal leaflets jointed to or continuous with rachises; Idaho, Oregon, extreme ne Nevada.
      3. Leaflet blades narrowly oblong-oblanceolate to linear-oblong or oval, 3–13 mm, terminal leaflets jointed to rachises; legumes leathery; n side of Snake River Plains in Blaine, Camas, and Lincoln counties, Idaho .... 119c. *Astragalus atratus* var. *inseptus*
      3. Leaflet blades linear-elliptic, 1.5–7(–10) mm, terminal leaflets continuous with rachises or reduced to slight dilation of rachis tips; legumes papery; e Oregon, extreme sw Idaho (Owyhee to Washington counties), ne Nevada .... 119d. *Astragalus atratus* var. *owyheensis*

119a. Astragalus atratus S. Watson var. **atratus** [E] [F]

Stems 3–17(–25) cm. **Leaves** (1.5–)3–11.5(–14.5) cm; stipules 1.5–4 mm; leaflets (7 or)9–13(or 15), blades linear-setaceous or oval-oblong, 2.5–14 mm, apex obtuse or subacute, surfaces glabrous or pubescent adaxially; terminal leaflet jointed to rachis. **Peduncles** (3.5–)5–16.5 cm. **Racemes** (4–)6–15-flowered; axis (1.5–)3–14 cm in fruit. **Flowers** (8–)9–12.2 mm; calyx (4.9–)5.2–7.2 mm, tube (3.4–)3.6–4.6 mm, lobes 1.3–2(–2.6) mm; corolla sometimes dirty white, veined or suffused with purple. **Legumes** ± dorsiventrally compressed, 10–22 × 2.3–4 mm, sub-bilocular, leathery; septum 0.6–1.3 mm wide; stipe 0.5–2 mm. **Seeds** 17–24.

Flowering May–Jul. Gravelly clay basaltic or granitic substrates, openings in pinyon-juniper woodlands, with sagebrush; 1400–2800 m; Nev.

Variety *atratus* is known from the valleys of the Humboldt and Reese rivers, Elko to Pershing counties southward to northern Churchill and northern Nye counties, and on limestone in the White Pine Mountains of White Pine County.

Variety *atratus* is transitional to var. *owyheensis*. R. C. Barneby (1964) called attention to the peculiar architecture of the corolla.

119b. Astragalus atratus S. Watson var. **mensanus** M. E. Jones, Proc. Calif. Acad. Sci., ser. 2, 5: 665. 1895 • Darwin milkvetch [E]

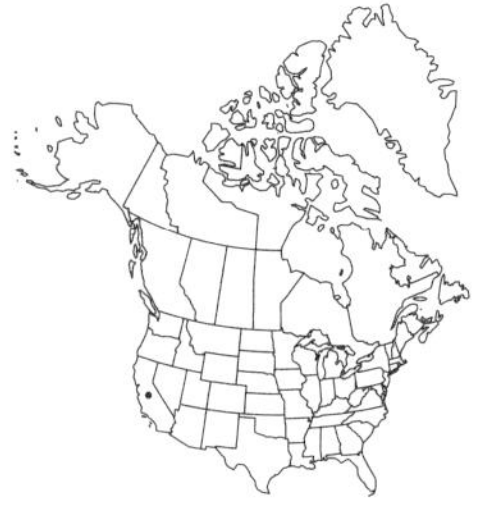

Astragalus mensanus (M. E. Jones) Abrams

Stems 10–24(–30) cm. **Leaves** (3.5–)5–13.5 cm; stipules 2.5–5 mm; leaflets (7 or)9–15, blades oblong-oblanceolate or oblong-elliptic to oval, 3–16 mm, apex obtuse or retuse, surfaces glabrous or pubescent adaxially; terminal leaflet jointed to rachis. **Peduncles** (3–)4.5–13 cm. **Racemes** (5–)7–18-flowered; axis (3–)4–10.5 cm in fruit. **Flowers** 9.8–13.4 mm; calyx 5–7.6 mm, tube 4.5–5.6 mm, lobes 0.8–2.6 mm; corolla broadly margined or tipped with purple. **Legumes** laterally compressed, 16–22 × 3.5–4.3 mm, bilocular; septum 1–2.7 mm wide; stipe 0–0.7 mm. **Seeds** 18–29.

Flowering late Apr–Jun. Volcanic clay and gravel, with pinyon and sagebrush, often sheltered by sagebrush or *Salvia dorrii*; 1400–2700 m; Calif.

R. C. Barneby (1964) noted that it would be impossible to distinguish specimens of var. *mensanus* and var. *atratus* that do not have fruit or locality data. The few specimens of var. *mensanus* apparently come from two local populations approximately 50 km apart in Death Valley in Inyo County (D. Isely 1998).

119c. Astragalus atratus S. Watson var. **inseptus** Barneby in C. L. Hitchcock et al., Vasc. Pl. Pacif. N.W. 3: 220, plate [p. 221], fig. s.n. [lower left center]. 1961 • Camas milkvetch [E]

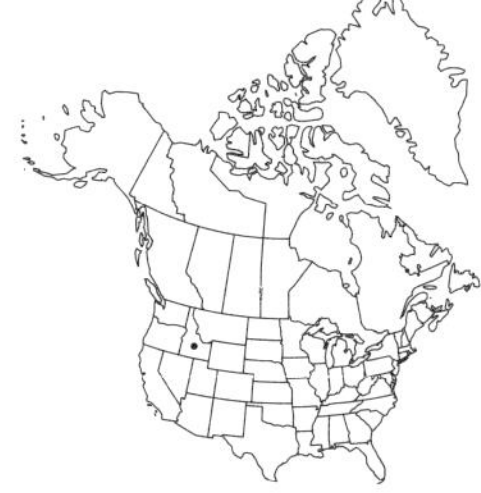

Stems 3–20 cm. **Leaves** 3–13 cm; stipules 2.5–5 mm; leaflets 9–15, blades narrowly oblong-oblanceolate to linear-oblong or oval, 3–13 mm, apex obtuse or emarginate, surfaces glabrous adaxially; terminal leaflet jointed to rachis. **Peduncles** 5–15 cm. **Racemes** 5–15-flowered; axis 3–13 cm in fruit. **Flowers** 8–11.3 mm; calyx 4.7–6.4 mm, tube 3.3–4.2 mm, lobes 1.5–2.2 mm; corolla banner and keel tip tinged purple. **Legumes** ± dorsiventrally compressed, 12–18 × 3–4.2 mm, unilocular, leathery; septum obsolete; stipe 0.3–1.1 mm. **Seeds** (14–)16–21.

Flowering May–Jun. Stony flats, stiff soils moist in spring; ca. 1500 m; Idaho.

D. Isely (1998) placed var. *inseptus* in synonymy with var. *owyheensis*, noting the alleged differences to be hazy. Variety *inseptus* is known only from the northern edge of the Snake River Plains in northern Blaine, southern Camas, northern Lincoln, and Twin Falls counties in south-central Idaho.

119d. Astragalus atratus S. Watson var. **owyheensis** (A. Nelson & J. F. Macbride) M. E. Jones, Rev. N.-Amer. Astragalus, 182. 1923 • Owyhee milkvetch [E]

Astragalus owyheensis A. Nelson & J. F. Macbride, Bot. Gaz. 55: 375. 1913

Stems 1–15(–20) cm. **Leaves** (2–)4–14 cm; stipules 1–3.5 mm; leaflets 7–11(or 13), blades linear-elliptic, 1.5–7(–10) mm, surfaces glabrous adaxially; terminal leaflet continuous with rachis or reduced to slight dilation of rachis tip. **Peduncles** (1.5–)3.5–12.5. **Racemes** (2–)5–12-flowered; axis (2–)5–17 cm in fruit. **Flowers** 6.3–9.9 mm; calyx 3–5.8 mm, tube 2.3–4 mm, lobes 0.7–2.1 mm; corolla faintly tinged lavender. **Legumes** ± dorsiventrally compressed, 14–20 × 3–4 mm, unilocular, papery; septum to 0.2 mm wide; stipe 1–2 mm. **Seeds** 10–17.

Flowering May–Jul. Dry gravelly substrates, under sagebrush; 1000–1900 m; Idaho, Nev., Oreg.

Variety *owyheensis* occurs from the Burnt and Powder rivers, Baker and northern Malheur counties in Oregon, to Washington County, Idaho, and along the Bruneau River, Owyhee County, Idaho, and southward and eastward to southern Twin Falls County and the headwaters of the Humboldt River in Elko County, Nevada.

120. Astragalus salmonis M. E. Jones, Contr. W. Bot. 8: 9. 1898 • Trout Creek milkvetch [E]

Plants tuft-forming, shortly caulescent or subacaulescent, 1–5 cm, strigulose. **Stems** ascending-erect, strigulose. **Leaves** mostly clustered at stem base, 2.5–10 cm; stipules mostly all connate, 2–4.5 mm, submembranous; leaflets (9 or)11–15(–19), blades narrowly oblong-elliptic, linear-oblong, or oblong-obovate, (1–)2–8 mm, apex obtuse to subacute, surfaces strigulose abaxially, glabrous adaxially; terminal leaflet jointed to rachis. **Peduncles** incurved-ascending, 3–12(–15) cm. **Racemes** 2–8-flowered, flowers horizontal or nodding; axis (0.5–)1–8(–11) cm in fruit; bracts 1–1.5(–2) mm; bracteoles 0. **Pedicels** 1–4 mm. **Flowers** 9.5–13.2 mm; calyx 5–8.9 mm, strigulose, tube 3.6–6 mm, lobes subulate, 1.4–2.9 mm; corolla whitish or tinged with lavender, keel tip maculate; keel 7.3–10.2 mm. **Legumes** pendulous, often humistrate, brightly red-mottled, decurved, obliquely oblong-ellipsoid, inversely boat-shaped, ± 3-sided compressed, ventral suture convex in profile or at least beak declined from body, 13–22 × 4–6.5 mm, partly bilocular, fleshy becoming leathery, strigulose; septum incomplete, to 0.7 mm wide; stipe 1.5–3.5 mm. **Seeds** (14–)17–29.

Flowering Apr–Jun. Dry sites, clay substrates, overlying basalt, under sagebrush; 1000–1300 m; Idaho, Nev., Oreg.

Astragalus salmonis is known from Baker, Harney, Lake, and Malheur counties in Oregon, southward to Washoe, Elko, and Humboldt counties in Nevada and Owyhee County in Idaho.

Astragalus salmonis is closely related to *A. atratus*, consistently differing from that species only in its slightly broader fruit (D. Isely 1998).

135ii. ASTRAGALUS Linnaeus sect. QUINQUEFLORI Barneby, Mem. New York Bot. Gard. 13: 478. 1964

Herbs perennial or (precocious) annual, caulescent, very slender, inconspicuous; caudex superficial. **Hairs** basifixed. **Stems** few to several. **Stipules** distinct or ± connate at proximal nodes. **Leaves** odd-pinnate, often shorter than distal racemes, petiolate; leaflets 5–15. **Racemes** dimorphic, proximal ones subradical and often reduced to a single flower, more distal ones loosely 2–7-flowered, flowers ascending. **Calyx tubes** campanulate. **Corollas** ochroleucous or violet-tinged, banner recurved through 90°, keel apex strongly incurved, obtuse. **Legumes** persistent or eventually deciduous, sessile or subsessile, humistrate, obovoid to oblong-ellipsoid, straight or ± decurved, slightly compressed dorsiventrally, semibilocular. **Seeds** 14–18.

Species 2 (1 in the flora): sw United States, Mexico.

Section *Quinqueflori* comprises a solitary species in the southwestern United States and *Astragalus quinqueflorus* S. Watson in Mexico.

121. Astragalus brandegeei Porter in T. C. Porter and J. M. Coulter, Syn. Fl. Colorado, 24. 1874 (as brandegei) • Brandegee's milkvetch [E] [F]

Plants delicate, 5–35(–40) cm, strigulose; caudex branched. **Stems** very slender, prostrate-spreading, strigulose. **Leaves** (1–)2–11.5(–15) cm; stipules connate-sheathing and papery at proximal nodes, connate or distinct and herbaceous at distal nodes, 1.5–5 mm; leaflet blades linear-filiform to narrowly oblong, involute or conduplicate, 5–27 mm, apex acute to obtuse, surfaces strigose abaxially, glabrous adaxially. **Peduncles** pendulous or ascending, humistrate in fruit, 2.5–14(–17) cm (early subradical, shorter than leaves, later much surpassing leaves). **Racemes** of subradical inflorescences 1(or 2)-flowered, others 2–5(–7)-flowered; axis filiform, 0.5–6(–8) cm in fruit; bracts 1–2 mm; bracteoles 2. **Pedicels** 1.2–4 mm. **Flowers** 4–6(–7) mm; calyx 2.7–4 mm, black-strigose, tube 1.8–2.5 mm, lobes subulate, 0.9–2 mm; corolla keel 3.5–4.5 mm. **Legumes** greenish or purple-dotted becoming brownish stramineous, 10–18 × 3.5–5 mm, thin becoming papery, strigose; septum 1.2–2 mm wide; stipe 0–1 mm. $2n = 22$.

Flowering Apr–Sep. Gravelly substrates in mixed shrublands, pinyon-juniper, or oak brush; 1600–2800 m; Ariz., Colo., N.Mex., Utah.

Astragalus brandegeei is a cryptic plant that is seldom collected, probably because of its inconspicuous small flowers, filiform peduncles, and slender stems.

135jj. Astragalus Linnaeus sect. Knightiani S. L. Welsh, N. Amer. Sp. Astragalus, 154. 2007 [C] [E]

Herbs perennial, low, tuft-forming, shortly caulescent or subacaulescent; caudex superficial. **Hairs** malpighian, incipiently malpighian, or basifixed. **Stems** few to many. **Stipules** connate or distinct at distal nodes. **Leaves** odd-pinnate, often shorter than distal racemes, petiolate; leaflets 7–15. **Racemes** not especially dimorphic, proximal ones subradical, often 1-flowered, distal ones loosely 2–10(–14)-flowered, flowers ascending then declined. **Calyx tubes** campanulate. **Corollas** whitish or violet-tinged, banner recurved through 45–80°, keel apex incurved, obtuse. **Legumes** persistent or ultimately deciduous, gynophore present, 0.3–1 mm, pendulous, spreading, or humistrate, narrowly ellipsoid or obovoid-ellipsoid, straight, unilocular. **Seeds** 8–18.

Species 3 (3 in the flora): New Mexico.

Section *Knightiani* consists of New Mexico endemics that are distinguished by small but tangible differences.

122. Astragalus knightii Barneby, Brittonia 35: 109, fig. 1. 1983 • Knight's milkvetch [C] [E]

Plants delicate, 10–15 cm, strigulose, hairs gray, malpighian, slight so, or basifixed; caudex branched. **Stems** slender, decumbent to incurved-ascending, strigulose. **Leaves** (2–)2.5–8.5 cm; stipules: proximals connate-sheathing, bidentate scarious at proximal nodes, distinct or connate at base and subherbaceous at distal nodes, 2–5 mm; leaflets 9–15, blades elliptic to ovate-elliptic, 2–8 mm, apex obtuse or subapiculate, surfaces strigulose. **Peduncles** ascending to declined, 2–5.5 cm. **Racemes** 5–10(–14)-flowered; axis (1–)1.5–4 cm in fruit; bracts 0.7–1.2 mm; bracteoles 0. **Flowers** 5–6 mm; calyx 3.3–4 mm, strigose, hairs white or black, tube 2.1–2.7 mm, lobes subulate, 1–1.4 mm. **Legumes** pendulous (or humistrate), red-mottled, narrowly obovoid-ellipsoid, slightly dorsiventrally compressed, 8–14 × 4–6 mm, thin becoming papery-membranous, strigulose; gynophore 0.5–1 mm. **Seeds** 12–14(–16).

Flowering May–Jun. Ledges and sand-pockets of cliff terraces and rimrock in juniper savannas and grasslands; of conservation concern; 1700–1800 m; N.Mex.

Astragalus knightii is restricted to Sandoval County.

123. Astragalus kerrii P. J. Knight & Cully, SouthW. Naturalist 36: 198, fig. 1. 1991 • Kerr's milkvetch [C] [E]

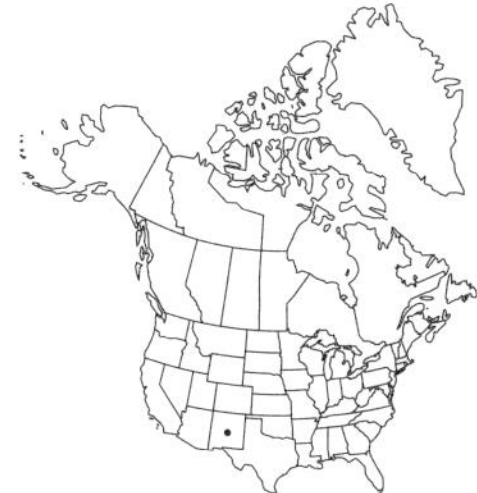

Plants 5–9 cm, strigulose, hairs basifixed or obscurely malpighian; caudex branched. **Stems** slender, ascending, strigulose. **Leaves** 2–4 cm; stipules connate, bidentate, 2.5–5 mm, membranous; leaflets 9–15, blades ovate-elliptic, 2.5–8 mm, apex obtuse or acute, surfaces strigulose. **Peduncles** erect, very slender, 1.5–8 cm. **Racemes** (1 or)2–4-flowered; axis (1–)1.5–4 cm in fruit. **Flowers** 5–6.2 mm; calyx 2–3.5 mm, strigose, hairs white or black, tube 1.2–2.5 mm, lobes linear-subulate, 0.7–1.2 mm. **Legumes** spreading or pendulous, red-mottled, ellipsoid, subinflated, slightly dorsiventrally compressed, 8–14 × 4–6 mm, thin becoming papery, strigulose or glabrous; gynophore 0.5–0.8 mm. **Seeds** 16–18.

Flowering May–Jun. Upper pinyon-juniper and ponderosa pine communities, gravelly bars, benches of granitic alluvium, disturbed or compacted sandy soils; of conservation concern; 1600–2300 m; N.Mex.

Astragalus kerrii is restricted to the eastern area of the Capitan Mountains in Lincoln County.

124. Astragalus heilii S. L. Welsh & N. D. Atwood in S. L. Welsh et al., Utah Fl. ed. 3, 839. 2003 • Heil's milkvetch [C] [E]

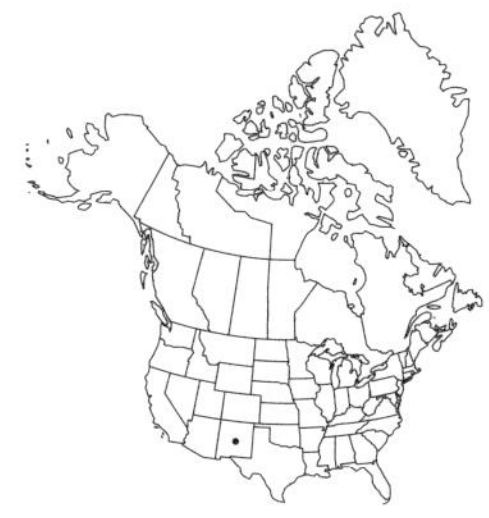

Plants subacaulescent, 2–4(–6) cm, strigulose, hairs basifixed; caudex branched, branches with marcescent leaf bases and peduncles. **Stems** obscured by stipules and leaf bases. **Leaves** 1–2.5(–5.8) cm; stipules connate-sheathing at proximal nodes, amplexicaul at distal nodes, 2–3 mm; leaflets 7–13, blades oval-ovate to narrowly oblanceolate or elliptic, 1.8–5.5 mm, apex obtuse, surfaces strigulose. **Peduncles** ascending, 1–7 cm. **Racemes** (1 or)2–4-flowered; axis 0.5–1 cm in fruit. **Flowers** 4–5 mm; calyx 2.3–3 mm, strigose, hairs white or black, tube 1.6–1.9 mm, lobes subulate, 0.7–0.9(–1.1) mm. **Legumes** spreading or pendulous, red-mottled, ellipsoid, subinflated, slightly dorsiventrally compressed, 9–9.8 × 4.5–4.6 mm, thin becoming papery, strigulose; gynophore 0.3–0.6 mm. **Seeds** 8–10.

Flowering May. Sandstone ledges in pinyon-juniper woodlands; of conservation concern; ca. 2200 m; N.Mex.

Astragalus heilii is restricted to McKinley County and is closely similar to the disjunct *A. kerrii*, differing in subtle ways, among them the truly basifixed hairs.

135kk. ASTRAGALUS Linnaeus sect. INYOENSES Barneby, Mem. New York Bot. Gard. 13: 482. 1964 [E]

Herbs perennial, caulescent; caudex superficial. **Hairs** basifixed. **Stems** several to many. **Stipules** distinct. **Leaves** odd-pinnate, short-petiolate or subsessile; leaflets (9 or)11–19(or 21). **Racemes** loosely flowered, flowers spreading. **Calyx tubes** campanulate. **Corollas** pink-purple, banner striate with purple veins, banner recurved through 30–40°, keel apex obtuse. **Legumes** ultimately deciduous, stipitate, declined, obliquely ovoid, strongly incurved, 3-sided obcompressed, long-cuspidate apically, grooved dorsally, semibilocular. **Seeds** 17–21.

Species 1: sw United States.

125. Astragalus inyoensis E. Sheldon, Contr. U.S. Natl. Herb. 4: 86. 1893 • Inyo milkvetch [E]

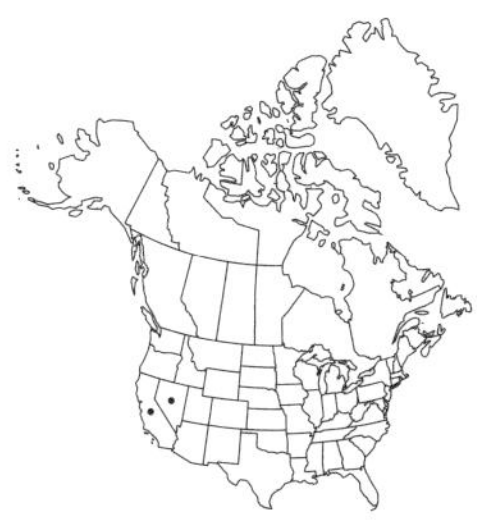

Plants slender, 10–60 cm, strigulose; caudex branched. **Stems** prostrate to ascending, strigulose. **Leaves** 1.5–4.5 cm; stipules 1.5–4.5 mm, papery-membranous at proximal nodes, herbaceous at distal nodes; leaflet blades obovate, oblanceolate, or oblong-obovate, (2–)3–10 mm, apex obtuse to retuse, surfaces strigulose abaxially, glabrous adaxially. **Peduncles** divaricate and spreading-incurved, 2.5–7 cm. **Racemes** 6–15-flowered; axis (1.5–)2.5–7 cm in fruit; bracts 0.8–1.8 mm; bracteoles 0–2. **Pedicels** 0.8–2.5 mm. **Flowers** 8.6–10.8 mm; calyx 3.7–5.8 mm, strigose, tube 2.4–3.7 mm, lobes subulate, 1.1–2.4 mm; corolla keel 8.2–9.6 mm. **Legumes** purplish, gently to strongly incurved to 0.5 spiral, 12–16 × 3.6–5 mm, incompletely bilocular, wider than high in cross section, fleshy becoming stiffly leathery, strigose, hairs ± 1 mm; septum 0.6–1 mm wide; stipe 2–5 mm.

Flowering May–Jul. Gravelly and sandy or clay substrates, among sagebrush and pinyon pines, on igneous bedrock; 1500–2400 m; Calif., Nev.

Astragalus inyoensis, notable for its prostrate, zigzag stems that radiate in all directions from the root crown, is restricted to desert mountains east of Owens Valley in Inyo County in California, and Lincoln and Nye counties in Nevada.

135ll. ASTRAGALUS Linnaeus sect. JAEGERIANI Barneby, Mem. New York Bot. Gard. 13: 484. 1964 [C] [E]

Herbs perennial, caulescent; caudex subterranean. **Hairs** basifixed. **Stems** few. **Stipules** distinct. **Leaves** odd-pinnate, short-petiolate or subsessile; leaflets (7 or)9–15. **Racemes** loosely flowered, flowers declined, later secund. **Calyx tubes** campanulate or obconic-campanulate. **Corollas** pink-purple, banner veined purple, banner recurved through 50–75°, keel apex triangular or subacute. **Legumes** persistent, stipitate, pendulous, straight or slightly decurved, linear-oblong, compressed laterally, sutures keeled, bilocular. **Seeds** 16–20.

Species 1: California.

126. Astragalus jaegerianus Munz, Leafl. W. Bot. 3: 49. 1941 • Jaeger's milkvetch [C] [E]

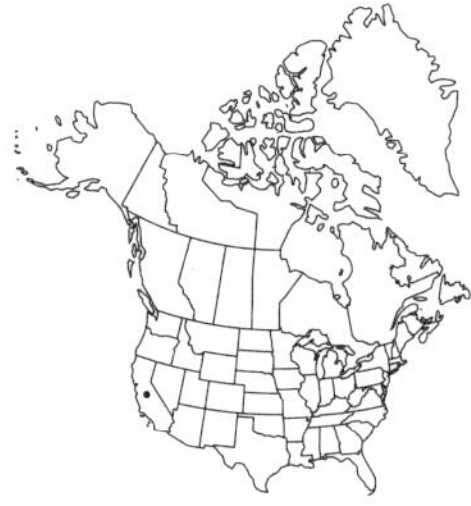

Plants 30–70 cm, strigulose; caudex branched. **Stems** weak, reclining or scrambling through low shrubs, 1–4 cm underground, strigulose. **Leaves** 2.5–5 cm; stipules 2–3.5(–5) mm, papery at proximal nodes, herbaceous at distal nodes; leaflet blades linear, linear-oblong, or lanceolate to subfiliform, 3–15(–20) mm, apex acute to obtuse, surfaces strigulose. **Peduncles** divaricate and incurved-ascending, 3–8 cm. **Racemes** 5–15-flowered; axis 1.5–7 cm in fruit; bracts 1.3–2 mm; bracteoles 1 or 2. **Pedicels** 0.7–2.2 mm. **Flowers** (6.5–)7–10 mm; calyx (3.6–)4–5.6 mm, strigose, tube 2.5–3.8 mm, lobes subulate, (1.1–)1.7–2.2 mm; corolla keel 6.4–8.5 mm. **Legumes** reddish or green and red-mottled, becoming brown, 16–23 × 3.5–5 mm, leathery or stiffly papery, glabrous; septum 3–4.5 mm wide; stipe 3–5 mm.

Flowering Apr–Jun. Rocky places, on granitic sand and gravel, with Joshua trees, under or growing through low shrubs; of conservation concern; 900–1200 m; Calif.

Astragalus jaegerianus is a straggling plant often tangled in desert shrubs and has a range of approximately 15 km in the middle of the Mojave Desert between Barstow and Goldstone, San Bernardino County.

135mm. ASTRAGALUS Linnaeus sect. PACHYPODES (M. E. Jones) Barneby, Mem. New York Bot. Gard. 13: 487. 1964 [E]

Astragalus subsect. *Pachypodes* M. E. Jones, Rev. N.-Amer. Astragalus, 144. 1923

Herbs perennial, clump-forming, caulescent; caudex aerial. **Hairs** basifixed. **Stems** several to many. **Stipules** distinct. **Leaves** odd-pinnate, short-petiolate or subsessile; leaflets 11–25(or 27). **Racemes** loosely flowered, flowers ascending. **Calyx tubes** broadly campanulate. **Corollas** white, faintly lavender, or lemon yellow, banner recurved through 45°, keel apex obtuse. **Legumes** persistent, stipitate, spreading or incurved-ascending, lunate or falcate, oblong-cylindroid, compressed laterally, sutures keeled, bilocular. **Seeds** 20–36.

Species 1: California.

Section *Pachypodes* occurs in the South Coast Ranges, western Mohave Desert, and interior southern California.

127. Astragalus pachypus Greene, Bull. Calif. Acad. Sci. 1: 157. 1885 • Bush milkvetch [E]

Plants robust, 15–55(–80) cm, strigulose; caudex branched. **Stems** erect or ascending, densely silvery white-strigulose. **Leaves** (2.5–)5–15(–16.5) cm; stipules 1.5–5 mm, papery; leaflet blades linear or linear-oblong, (3–)5–25(–34) mm, apex truncate-emarginate or sub-acute, surfaces sparsely strigulose abaxially, densely silvery white-strigulose adaxially. **Peduncles** erect, (5–)7–20 cm. **Racemes** (4 or)5–20(–28)-flowered; axis (2–)3–13 cm in fruit; bracts 0.7–2.5 mm; bracteoles 2. **Pedicels** 0.9–3 mm. **Flowers** 15–22 mm; calyx 5.5–9.5 mm, strigose, tube 3.6–5 mm, lobes subulate, (1.5–)1.8–4.3 mm; corolla keel 10.7–15.3 mm. **Legumes** brownish or stramineous, strongly laterally compressed, 12–28 × 4–7.5 mm, fleshy becoming leathery or sub-ligneous, glabrous; septum 3.5–6 mm wide; stipitate (stipe 4–8 mm).

Varieties 2 (2 in the flora): California.

1. Calyx tubes 4.5–5 mm wide, lobes (1.5–)2.7–4.3 mm; corollas white or faintly lavender, rarely suffused with pink or lilac, banners 17–22 mm, keel 12.3–15.3 mm; leaflets 11–19(or 21); Kern and Ventura counties and northward . . . . 127a. *Astragalus pachypus* var. *pachypus*
1. Calyx tubes 3.7–4 mm wide, lobes 1.8–2.9 mm; corollas clear lemon yellow, banners 15–17 mm, keel 10.7–12.6 mm; leaflets (15 or)17–25(or 27); Riverside County . . . . 127b. *Astragalus pachypus* var. *jaegeri*

127a. Astragalus pachypus Greene var. **pachypus** [E]

Leaflets 11–19(or 21). **Pedicels** (1–)1.5–3 mm, (1.5–)2–5.5 mm in fruit. **Flowers:** calyx tube 4.3–5 mm wide, lobes (1.5–)2.7–4.3 mm; corolla usually white or faintly lavender, rarely suffused with pink or lilac, drying yellowish; banner 17–22 × 9–14.5 mm; keel 12.3–15.3 mm; wings 14.3–18 mm, claws 5.4–7 mm, blades 7.7–10.3 × 3.4–4.2 mm. $2n = 22$.

Flowering Mar–Jul. Gravely clay, shale, sandstone, or granitic substrates; 500–2000 m; Calif.

Around the head of the San Joaquin Valley, fruits of var. *pachypus* are relatively broad, approximately 5–7.5 mm diam.; northward, in San Benito County, fruits are 4–5 mm diam. Plants do not seem to differ significantly in other ways.

127b. Astragalus pachypus Greene var. **jaegeri** Munz & McBurney, Bull. S. Calif. Acad. Sci. 31: 67. 1932 • Jaeger's bush milkvetch [C] [E]

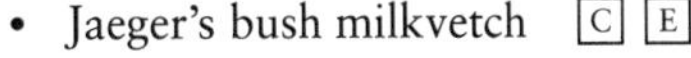

Leaflets (15 or)17–25(or 27). **Pedicels** 0.9–1.7 mm, 1.5–2.7 mm in fruit. **Flowers:** calyx tube 3.6–4 mm wide, lobes 1.8–2.9 mm; corolla clear lemon yellow, drying ochroleucous; banner 15–27 × 7.2–9 mm; keel 10.7–12.6 mm; wings 14–15 mm, claws 5–6.5 mm, blades 9–9.7 × 2.7–3.1 mm.

Flowering Dec–Jun. Grasslands, oak-chaparral; of conservation concern; 500–1100 m; Calif.

Variety *jaegeri* is narrowly restricted to arid valleys of the northwestern foothills of the San Jacinto Mountains in western Riverside County.

135nn. Astragalus Linnaeus sect. Drummondiani Barneby, Mem. New York Bot. Gard. 13: 489. 1964 [E]

Herbs perennial, forming bushy clumps, caulescent; caudex superficial to shallowly subterranean. **Hairs** basifixed. **Stems** several to many. **Stipules** distinct or connate at proximal nodes. **Leaves** odd-pinnate, usually subsessile; leaflets (13–)17–33. **Racemes** loosely flowered, flowers nodding. **Calyx tubes** deeply campanulate, often slightly swollen, oblique proximally. **Corollas** white to ochroleucous, keel apex purple, banner recurved through 45°, keel apex deltate. **Legumes** persistent or ultimately deciduous, continuous with receptacle, stipitate, pendulous, narrowly oblong to oblanceoloid, straight or incurved or decurved, obscurely 3-sided compressed, with convex lateral and grooved dorsal faces, ± bilocular. **Seeds** 14–30.

Species 1: w North America.

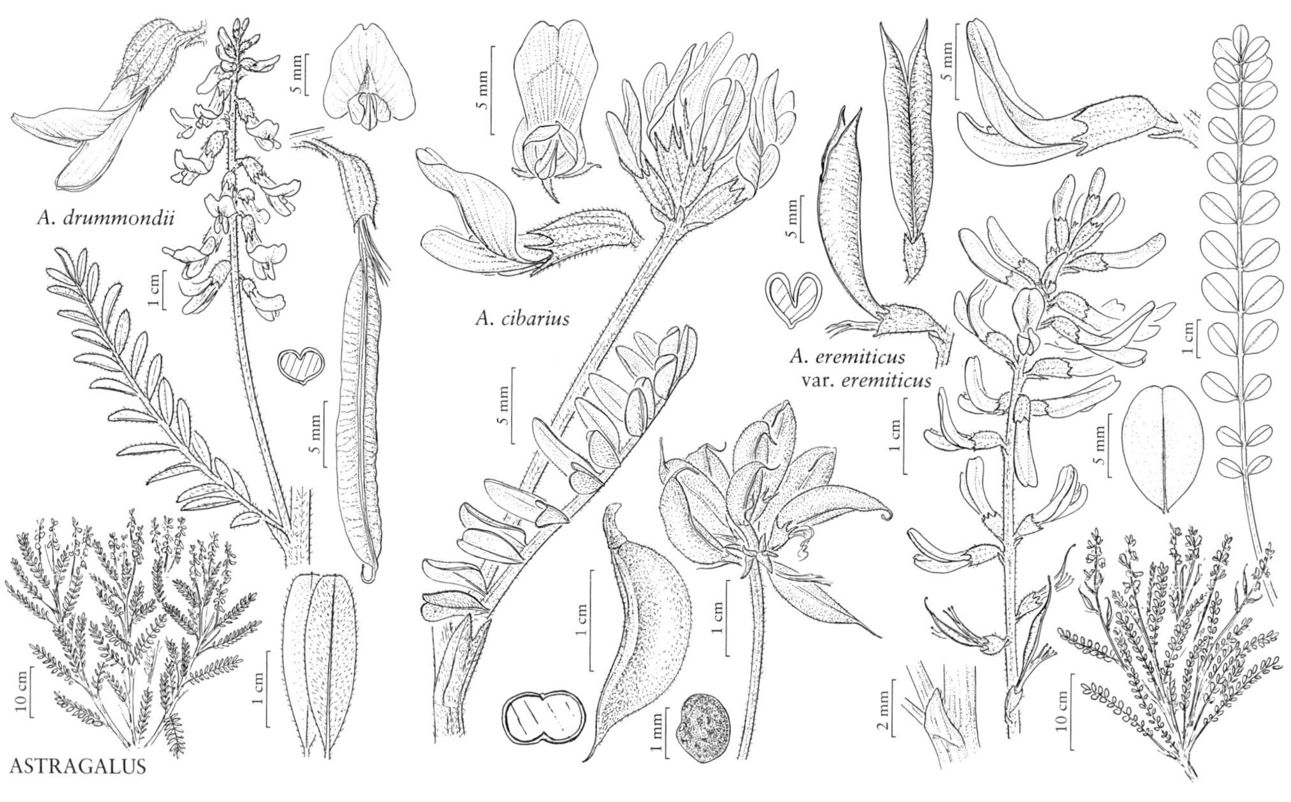

Section *Drummondiani* is distributed from southeastern British Columbia to Saskatchewan southward through Montana, western North Dakota, western South Dakota, eastern Idaho, Wyoming, western Nebraska, and Colorado to northern New Mexico and disjunctly westward to Utah.

128. Astragalus drummondii Douglas in W. J. Hooker, Fl. Bor.-Amer. 1: 153, plate 57. 1831 • Drummond's milkvetch [E] [F]

Plants robust, stout, 25–60(–65) cm, softly villous-hirsute or shaggy-villous, hairs minutely dilated at base; caudex branched. **Stems** erect or ascending, softly villous-hirsute or shaggy-villous. **Leaves** 4–13 cm; stipules connate-sheathing or distinct at proximal nodes, distinct at distal nodes, (2–)3–12 mm, submembranous becoming papery-scarious; leaflet blades oblong to oblanceolate or obovate, 4–33 mm, apex obtuse to truncate or emarginate, surfaces villous-pilose abaxially, glabrous adaxially. **Peduncles** erect, 4–12(–15) cm. **Racemes** 14–30-flowered; axis 3–22 cm in fruit; bracts 2–5 mm; bracteoles 0–2. **Pedicels** 1.5–5 mm. **Flowers** (16–)18–25 mm; calyx 7–12.5 mm, sparsely villous, tube 4.7–8 mm, lobes subulate, 1.7–4.5 mm; corolla keel 12–15 mm. **Legumes** stramineous, 17–32 × 3.5–5.5 mm, fleshy becoming stiffly papery or leathery, glabrous; septum 0.6–1.5 mm wide; stipe 5–11 mm. **2*n*** = 22.

Flowering May–Aug. Prairies, plains, grasslands, montane, or steppe sites in oak brush, sagebrush, pinyon-juniper and ponderosa pine communities; 500–2700 m; Alta., B.C., Sask.; Colo., Idaho, Mont., Nebr., N.Mex., N.Dak., S.Dak., Utah, Wyo.

Astragalus drummondii is easily recognized by a combination of the ochroleucous or white, nodding flowers, the shaggy pubescence, and the pendulous, glabrous fruits; it contains swainsonine and is therefore potentially poisonous to livestock (W. E. Fox et al. 1998).

Two historic collections from Oregon appear to have been isolated introductions.

135oo. ASTRAGALUS Linnaeus sect. MALACI M. E. Jones, Rev. N.-Amer. Astragalus, 225. 1923 [E]

Herbs perennial, caulescent; caudex superficial or shallowly subterranean. **Hairs** basifixed. **Stems** single or few to many. **Stipules** distinct. **Leaves** odd-pinnate, usually petiolate, sometimes short-petiolate or subsessile; leaflets (5–)9–29. **Racemes** sometimes subcapitate, usually loosely flowered, flowers ascending or spreading to declined. **Calyx tubes** cylindric or campanulate-cylindric. **Corollas** usually reddish violet, reddish purple, pink-purple, purplish, ochroleucous, or whitish, sometimes suffused with purple, banner recurved through 30–45°, keel apex obtuse. **Legumes** deciduous or persistent, stipitate or subsessile, recurved, humistrate and ascending or descending or reclining, or erect, narrowly oblong, oblong-ellipsoid, or cylindric, incurved or ± straight, compressed laterally or dorsiventrally or 3-sided, ± bilocular or subunilocular. **Seeds** 16–36.

Species 9 (9 in the flora): w United States.

Section *Malaci* consists of four subsections: subsect. *Cibarii* Barneby (*Astragalus cibarius*); subsect. *Ensiformes* Barneby (*A. ensiformis*, *A. malacoides*, *A. minthorniae*); subsect. *Vallares* (M. E. Jones) Barneby (*A. cimae*, *A. vallaris*); and subsect. *Malaci* (M. E. Jones) Barneby (*A. chamaemeniscus*, *A. holmgreniorum*, *A. malacus*).

129. Astragalus cibarius E. Sheldon, Minnesota Bot. Stud. 1: 149. 1894 • Browse milkvetch [E] [F]

Plants 6–30(–35) cm, strigulose; from branched, superficial caudex. **Stems** several, decumbent to ascending, diffuse, strigulose. **Leaves** 3.5–10 cm; stipules 3–8 mm, mostly membranous; leaflets 11–19, blades obovate, oblong, or oblanceolate, 4–17 mm, apex obtuse or retuse, surfaces strigose abaxially, glabrous adaxially. **Peduncles** incurved-ascending, reclined in fruit, 3–8 cm. **Racemes** subcapitate at early anthesis, 4–14-flowered, flowers spreading-ascending; axis 0.5–2.7 cm in fruit; bracts 2–4 mm; bracteoles 0–2. **Pedicels** 1–2.5 mm. **Flowers** 15–19 mm; calyx cylindric, 6.4–9.2 mm, strigose, tube 5–7 mm, lobes subulate, 1.4–2.5 mm; corolla pink-purple with white wing tips, or whitish to ochroleucous and tinged; keel 9.8–12.7 mm. **Legumes** ascending (humistrate), stramineous, incurved to ± straight, ellipsoid to oblong, obcompressed, 17–32 × 7–10 mm, subunilocular, wider than high in cross section, woody or stiffly leathery, strigose, hairs ± 1 mm; stipe to 2 mm. **Seeds** 27–32. $2n = 22$.

Flowering Apr–early Aug. Mountain brush, sagebrush, juniper-pinyon, mixed desert shrub communities; 1000–2900 m; Colo., Idaho, Mont., Nev., Utah, Wyo.

Astragalus cibarius is a low-growing plant with stems radiating from the superficial or almost superficial root-crown, with rather compact racemes of pale to dark purple flowers and closely clustered legumes, obcompressed except for the beak. It resembles in habit several of the larger-flowered forms of *A. lentiginosus* and has a distributional pattern unmatched among western American species of *Astragalus*. The primary centers of occurrence are along the Wasatch Mountains of Utah and southeastern Idaho, but *A. cibarius* extends to northeastern Nevada, southern Utah, western Colorado, northeastern Wyoming, and western Montana.

130. Astragalus ensiformis M. E. Jones, Proc. Calif. Acad. Sci., ser. 2, 5: 658. 1895 • Pagumpa milkvetch [E]

Astragalus ensiformis var. *gracilior* Barneby; *A. minthorniae* (Rydberg) Jepson var. *gracilior* (Barneby) Barneby

Plants 8–45 cm, strigulose; from shallow, subterranean caudex. **Stems** several, decumbent or sprawling to erect, (1–)2–6(–8) cm underground, strigulose. **Leaves** 4–16 cm; stipules strongly decurrent, 3–11 mm, papery at proximal nodes, subherbaceous at distal nodes; leaflets (5–)11–23, blades ovate to oblong, obovate, or oblanceolate, 6–24 mm, apex obtuse to retuse, surfaces strigose to sparsely so abaxially, strigose or glabrous adaxially. **Peduncles** incurved-ascending, subhorizontal in fruit, 2.5–13(–24) cm. **Racemes** 10–30-flowered, flowers ascending to declined; axis 3–14 cm in fruit; bracts 2–6 mm; bracteoles 0–2. **Pedicels** 1–3.5 mm. **Flowers** (11–)13–17 mm; calyx short-cylindric, 5.2–7.8 mm, black-pilosulous, tube 4.5–6.5 mm, lobes subulate, 1.2–2.5 mm; corolla purplish to pink-purple, wing tips pale to white; keel 10.5–10.8 mm. **Legumes** firmly attached to receptacle, falling while still attached to pedicel, ascending to descending (sometimes humistrate), green and red-tinged becoming brownish, incurved 0.5 spiral, narrowly oblong, subterete, laterally compressed when pressed, sides convex, elliptic in cross section, dorsal suture forming a prominent ridge, 15–32 × 4–7 (–8) mm, bilocular, thick becoming leathery, strigose to strigulose; stipe 0.5–2 mm. **Seeds** 24–36.

Flowering Apr–May. Pinyon-juniper, sagebrush, salt desert shrub, and blackbrush communities on various substrates; 1200–2400 m; Ariz., Nev., Utah.

Astragalus ensiformis is known from Mohave County in Arizona, Lincoln County in Nevada, and Washington County in Utah.

Astragalus ensiformis is distinguishable from *A. minthorniae* by its superficial root crown, closely clustered, conspicuous, basal stipules, and legumes that are ± straight.

131. Astragalus malacoides Barneby, Mem. New York Bot. Gard. 13: 500. 1964 • Kaiparowits milkvetch [E]

Plants clump-forming, shortly caulescent, 7–26 cm, hirsutulous; from slightly to deeply subterranean caudex; taproot stout. **Stems** few, decumbent or prostrate to ascending, (0–)1.5–13 cm underground, hirsutulous. **Leaves** 4.5–14 cm; stipules 2–7 mm, stramineous or whitish-papery at proximal nodes, submembranous at distal nodes; leaflets 15–29, blades obovate to oblong or elliptic, 3–25 mm, apex obtuse to emarginate, surfaces hirtellous abaxially, glabrous adaxially. **Peduncles** incurved-ascending, procumbent in fruit, 4–12 mm. **Racemes** 10–24-flowered, flowers ascending-spreading; axis 1.2–10 cm in fruit; bracts 3–5 mm; bracteoles 0–2. **Pedicels** 1–2.5 mm. **Flowers** 16–22 mm; calyx cylindric, 10–15 mm, hirsutulous, tube 7–12 mm, lobes linear-subulate, 2–6.2 mm; corolla dull pink-purple; keel 16–17 mm. **Legumes** firmly attached to receptacle, falling while still attached to pedicel, declined to ascending (sometimes humistrate), brown or purple-dotted, incurved through 0.25–0.5 spiral, oblong, laterally compressed, sides convex, elliptic in cross section, dorsal suture forming a prominent ridge, 25–40 × 5–8 mm, bilocular, middle narrower or not wider than high in cross section, ± fleshy becoming papery, hirsutulous, hairs 0.3–0.5 mm; stipe 2–3 mm. **Seeds** 24–30.

Flowering Apr–May. Clay or silty or sandy silty substrates, in juniper-pinyon, sagebrush, *Ephedra*, shadscale, and blackbrush communities; 1600–2400 m; Utah.

Astragalus malacoides is restricted to Kane and Wayne counties in south-central Utah; it combines features of three related species: *A. chamaemeniscus* (habit), *A. ensiformis* (bilocular, bicarinate fruit), and *A. malacus* (vestiture, long calyx lobes).

132. Astragalus minthorniae (Rydberg) Jepson, Fl. Calif. 2: 374. 1936 • Minthorn's milkvetch [E]

Hamosa minthorniae Rydberg, Bull. Torrey Bot. Club 54: 15. 1927

Plants 8–40 cm, strigulose or villosulous; from superficial caudex. **Stems** few or several, ascending to erect, proximalmost internodes very short, strigulose or villosulous. **Leaves** (4–)6–17 cm; stipules obscuring proximal internodes, 3–11 mm, papery-membranous at proximal nodes, subherbaceous at distal nodes; leaflets (7 or)9–17, blades obovate, lanceolate, or broadly elliptic to suborbiculate, 8–20(–26) mm, apex obtuse to emarginate, surfaces strigose or sparsely so abaxially, strigose, glabrous, or glabrescent adaxially. **Peduncles** erect, 6–16 cm, together with racemes usually longer than leaves, often sub-basal and appearing scapelike. **Racemes** 7–35-flowered, flowers ascending to declined; axis 2.5–14 (–25) cm in fruit; bracts 2–6 mm; bracteoles 0–2. **Pedicels** 1–3.5 mm. **Flowers** 12–17(–18) mm; calyx short-cylindric, 6–7.8 mm, black-pilosulous, tube 4.5–5.2 mm, lobes subulate, 1.2–2.7 mm; corolla ochroleucous with keel tip dull purple, banner sometimes suffused with lavender, or pink-purple and wing tips pale or white; keel 9.5–13 mm. **Legumes** persisting on receptacle until well after maturity, falling while still attached to pedicel, erect to ascending, straight or slightly incurved, narrowly oblong, subterete, laterally compressed when pressed, not grooved ventrally, 15–26(–30) × 4–6 mm, ± bilocular, fleshy becoming leathery, silky-pilose or villous, hairs 1+ mm; septum 2.5–3.5(–4) mm wide; stipe 0.5–1.5 mm. **Seeds** 24–36.

Varieties 2 (2 in the flora): w United States.

The closest relative of *Astragalus minthorniae* is apparently the south-central Utah endemic *A. malacoides*, which has similar but strongly curved and stipitate fruits, and larger flowers.

1. Herbage sparsely strigulose, hairs appressed or subappressed, to 0.7(–1) mm; basal internodes and stipules sparsely pubescent, not conspicuously more so than stem distally; s Calcareous and e Tonopah mountains in n Clarke, Lincoln, nw Nye, and s White Pine counties, Nevada ....132a. *Astragalus minthorniae* var. *minthorniae*
1. Herbage villosulous, hairs spreading, to 0.8–1.5 mm; basal internodes and stipules densely and canescently villous-pilose, usually more densely so than stems distally; e, c Mojave Desert and Death Valley regions, se California and adjoining Nevada .... 132b. *Astragalus minthorniae* var. *villosus*

132a. Astragalus minthorniae (Rydberg) Jepson var. **minthorniae** [E]

Herbage sparsely strigulose, greenish to cinereous, hairs appressed or subappressed, to 0.7(–1) mm; basal internodes and stipules sparsely pubescent, not conspicuously more densely so than stem distally. **Stems:** internodes short or ± absent. **Leaflets** 7–11(–17), blades usually broadly elliptic to ± suborbiculate, sometimes lanceolate. **Corollas** ochroleucous, keel tip dull purple, banner sometimes suffused with lavender. **Legumes** silky-pilose, hairs mostly white.

Flowering Apr–early Jun. Sagebrush and pinyon-juniper communities; 1700–2200 m; Nev.

Variety *minthorniae* is restricted to east-central Nevada.

The leaflets of var. *minthorniae* are generally broader than those of var. *villosus*.

132b. Astragalus minthorniae (Rydberg) Jepson var. **villosus** Barneby, Aliso 2: 208. 1950 [E]

Herbage villosulous, hairs spreading (sometimes curly), to 0.8–1.5 mm; basal internodes and stipules densely, canescently villous-pilose, usually more densely so than stems distally. **Stems:** internodes often clearly present. **Leaflets** 17–25, blades obovate. **Corollas** ochroleucous, keel tip maculate, or pink-purple and wing tips pale or white. **Legumes** often shaggy-villous, hairs white or black.

Flowering late Mar–Jun. Pinyon-juniper forests; 1300–2400 m; Calif., Nev.

Variety *villosus* is a taxon of the eastern and central Mojave Desert.

133. Astragalus vallaris M. E. Jones, Contr. W. Bot. 10: 59, plate 13. 1902 • Snake Canyon milkvetch [E]

Plants coarse, 8–30 cm, glabrous or sparsely strigose; from superficial caudex. **Stems** many, decumbent, glabrous or sparsely strigose. **Leaves** 3–7 cm; stipules 2.5–5 mm, membranous or membranous-margined; leaflets 13–25(–29), blades oblanceolate or obovate-cuneate, 6–16 mm, apex retuse or apiculate, surfaces glabrous (except midrib sparsely strigose) abaxially, glabrous adaxially. **Peduncles** reclined in fruit, 2–6 cm. **Racemes** 5–7-flowered, flowers ascending; axis 1.5–2 cm in fruit; bracts 2–4 mm; bracteoles 2. **Pedicels** 1.5–5 mm. **Flowers** 16–23 mm; calyx short-cylindric, 9.5–11 mm, strigulose, tube 5.5–6.5 mm, lobes linear-subulate, 3.5–4.5 mm; corolla whitish; keel 12–13 mm. **Legumes** ascending (humistrate), stramineous, slightly incurved, obliquely oblong-ovoid, obcompressed, 20–40 × (9–)11–19 mm, bilocular, fleshy becoming woody, glabrous; septum 3–4 mm wide; stipe 5–20 mm. **Seeds** 26–28.

Flowering late Apr–Jun. Sagebrush and bunchgrass communities; 700–1000 m; Idaho, Oreg.

Astragalus vallaris occurs in the Snake River Canyon and its tributaries in northeastern Oregon and adjacent Idaho.

134. Astragalus cimae M. E. Jones, Rev. N.-Amer. Astragalus, 163. 1923 • Cima milkvetch [C] [E]

Plants somewhat coarse, 3.5–24 cm, glabrous or sparsely strigose; from superficial or shallow, subterranean caudex. **Stems** single or few, decumbent-ascending, glabrous or sparsely strigose. **Leaves** 4.5–11 cm; stipules 5–10 mm, papery at proximal nodes; leaflets 11–21(or 23), blades obovate-cuneate, ovate, broadly oblong-elliptic, or suborbiculate, 5–20 mm, apex obtuse or emarginate, surfaces glabrous or glabrate and glaucescent. **Peduncles** incurved-ascending, 3–8.5 cm. **Racemes** 10–25-flowered, flowers declined; axis 3–12 cm in fruit; bracts 3–6 mm; bracteoles 2. **Pedicels** 0.6–2 mm. **Flowers** 12–15 mm; calyx short-cylindric, 5.9–7.6 mm, strigulose, tube 4.5–5.6 mm, lobes subulate, 1.3–2.5 mm; corolla reddish purple with white or lilac wing tips; keel 9.5–10.6 mm. **Legumes** spreading-ascending (humistrate), green suffused or dotted red becoming stramineous, straight to incurved, oblong or broadly oblong-ovoid, obcompressed, 15–37 × 8–21 mm, ± bilocular, fleshy becoming papery, stiffly leathery, or subligneous, glabrous; septum to 3.5 mm wide; stipe 5–8 mm. **Seeds** (27–)30–36.

Varieties 2 (2 in the flora): w United States.

Varieties *cimae* and *sufflatus*, separated by approximately 240 km, are nearly identical except for the fruits.

1. Legumes 15–25 × 8–12 mm, not or slightly inflated, fleshy becoming stiffly leathery or subligneous; septae to 1.8 mm wide; New York Mountains and vicinity, e Mojave Desert . . . . .134a. *Astragalus cimae* var. *cimae*
1. Legumes 30–37 × 13–21 mm, much inflated, fleshy becoming papery; septae 2–3.5 mm wide; Inyo Mountains, e Mojave Desert. . . . . .134b. *Astragalus cimae* var. *sufflatus*

134a. Astragalus cimae M. E. Jones var. **cimae** C E

Legumes usually strongly incurved, not or slightly inflated, 15–25 × 8–12 mm, fleshy becoming stiffly leathery or subligneous; septum to 1.8 mm wide; stipe 6–8 mm.

Flowering Apr–May. Sagebrush communities; of conservation concern; 1400–1900 (–2100) m; Calif., Nev.

Variety *cimae* is restricted to the New York Mountains and immediate vicinity in eastern San Bernardino County in California, and Mineral and Nye counties in Nevada.

134b. Astragalus cimae M. E. Jones var. **sufflatus** Barneby, Aliso 2: 209. 1950 • Darwin milkvetch C E

Legumes straight to moderately incurved, much inflated, 30–37 × 13–21 mm, fleshy becoming papery; septum 2–3.5 mm wide; stipe 5–8 mm.

Flowering late Apr–early Jun. Sagebrush and pinyon-juniper communities; of conservation concern; 1500–2100 m; Calif.

Variety *sufflatus* occurs on the eastern slope of the Inyo Mountains, near the southern end of Saline Valley, Inyo County.

135. Astragalus malacus A. Gray, Proc. Amer. Acad. Arts 7: 336. 1868 • Shaggy milkvetch E

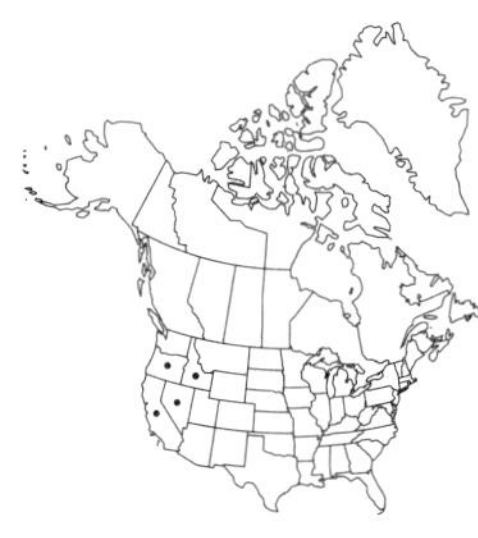

Plants somewhat coarse, 2.5–25 (–30) cm, hirsute-villosulous; from superficial caudex. **Stems** several, erect or ascending, proximalmost internodes very short, hirsute-villosulous. **Leaves** 4–15 cm; stipules obscuring proximal internodes, 7–17 mm, whitish-papery at proximal nodes, thinly herbaceous at distal nodes; leaflets (7–)11–19(or 21), blades obovate, obovate-cuneate, or elliptic, 5–20 mm, apex obtuse, retuse, or subacute, surfaces hirsute-villosulous, sometimes glabrescent adaxially. **Peduncles** erect or incurved-ascending, sometimes reclined in fruit, 4–11 cm. **Racemes** 9–35-flowered, flowers declined; axis 2–10(–15) cm in fruit; bracts 4–9 mm; bracteoles 2. **Pedicels** 0.7–3 mm. **Flowers** 12–15 mm; calyx cylindric, 8.6–13(–14) mm, hirtellous, tube 7–9 mm, lobes subulate, 1.6–4(–5) mm; corolla reddish purple; keel 12.3–14.5(–16) mm. **Legumes** reflexed, green and suffused or dotted red, becoming stramineous, shallowly to deeply incurved, narrowly oblong or oblong-ellipsoid, 3-sided compressed, grooved dorsally, 18–38 × 4.5–6 mm, bilocular, fleshy becoming stiffly papery, shaggy-hirsute, hairs lustrous, spreading, 1–3 mm; stipe 1–3 mm. **Seeds** 16–24.

Flowering later Apr–early Jun. Sagebrush or pinyon communities, various substrates; 1200–2300 m; Calif., Idaho, Nev., Oreg.

Astragalus malacus, although completely allopatric, is reminiscent of a coarse *A. minthorniae*, especially var. *villosus*, which it resembles in the greatly shortened proximalmost internodes obscured by stipules, similar though shorter vestiture, and in the general conformation of the plant. It differs, however, in many features, such as the deflexed or declined, three-sided compressed, dorsally grooved legumes.

D. Isely (1998) noted that the conspicuous characters of *Astragalus malacus* include its shaggy pilosity, long stipules, narrow, red-purple, deflexed flowers, and pilose, sulcate, bilocular, deflexed, upcurved legumes.

136. Astragalus chamaemeniscus Barneby, Leafl. W. Bot. 3: 105, plate 1, fig. A. 1942 • Ground-crescent milkvetch [E]

Plants shortly caulescent, 3–13 cm, villous-hirsutulous; from shallow, subterranean woody caudex. **Stems** several, reclining or ascending, proximal few nodes 0.5–5 cm underground, villous-hirsutulous. **Leaves** 2–8 cm; stipules 3–7 mm, membranous; leaflets 9–21, blades obovate to oblanceolate, 3–11 mm, apex obtuse or emarginate, surfaces loosely pilose abaxially, glabrous adaxially. **Peduncles** incurved-ascending, reclined in fruit, 1.5–5 cm. **Racemes** 3–10-flowered, flowers ascending; axis 0.5–2 cm in fruit, not much elongating; bracts 2.5–4.5 mm; bracteoles 2. **Pedicels** 1.5–3 mm. **Flowers** 14–19 mm; calyx campanulate-cylindric, 5.8–10 mm, villosulous, tube 4.7–7 mm, lobes subulate, 1.1–3 mm; corolla reddish violet to pink-purple; keel 10.2–11.5(–15) mm. **Legumes** firmly attached to receptacle, falling while still attached to pedicel, ascending to declined (humistrate), stramineous, incurved through 0.3 spiral, crescentic, 3-sided compressed, deltoid in cross section, dorsal suture slightly grooved, 20–45 × 5–8 mm, bilocular, scarcely fleshy becoming leathery, faces prominently reticulate, sparsely villosulous, hairs to 1 mm; septum 3.5–4.2 mm wide; stipe 1–2.5 mm.

Flowering mid Apr–early Jul. Rabbitbrush, greasewood, sagebrush, horsebrush, ricegrass, and galleta communities; 1500–1700 m; Nev., Utah.

Astragalus chamaemeniscus is known from Lincoln, Nye, and White Pine counties in Nevada, and Beaver and Iron counties in Utah.

As the long crescent-shaped fruits of *Astragalus chamaemeniscus* mature, the rather slender peduncles are quickly weighed down, the fruits lying in a ring upon the ground, often largely concealed by leaves. Fruits tend to fall at random angles to the raceme axis, making it is difficult to determine whether the fruits are by nature ascending or declined (R. C. Barneby 1964).

137. Astragalus holmgreniorum Barneby, Brittonia 32: 24, fig. 1. 1980 • Holmgrens' or paradox milkvetch [C] [E]

Plants acaulescent, 4–12 cm, loosely pilosulous; from thickened, superficial root-crown. **Stems** essentially absent. **Leaves** 4–21.5 cm; stipules 2.5–8 mm, papery; leaflets (5–)9–15(or 17), blades broadly obovate to obcordate, 6–16 mm, apex emarginate, surfaces loosely pilose abaxially, glabrous adaxially. **Peduncles** procumbent, 2–9 cm, shorter than leaves. **Racemes** 4–16-flowered, flowers ascending to spreading; axis 0.4–6.5 cm in fruit; bracts 4+ mm. **Pedicels** 1–2 mm. **Flowers** 18–23.5 mm; calyx cylindric, 10.5–12.5 mm, sparsely white-pilose, tube 8–9.5 mm, lobes subulate, 2–3.5 mm; corolla pink-purple; keel 16.5–18.5 mm. **Legumes** reclined (humistrate), green or purplish becoming stramineous or brownish, lunately incurved, ellipsoid, 3-sided compressed, 2.5–5.5 × 6–9 mm, bilocular, leathery, glabrous. **Seeds** 30–34. $2n = 22$.

Flowering Apr–Jun. Warm desert shrub (*Larrea*) community; of conservation concern; 800–900 m; Ariz., Utah.

Astragalus holmgreniorum has a narrow distribution along the Virgin River in St. George County in Utah and adjacent Mohave County in Arizona.

Long known from collections, *Astragalus holmgreniorum* was only recently described. It is apparently the historical basis of reports of *A. tephrodes* from Utah (R. C. Barneby 1989). At the time of description, Barneby placed *A. holmgreniorum* within sect. *Argophylli*, but its curved, three-sided, bilocular fruits are similar in fundamental details to those within sect. *Malaci*, where it is here allied.

Astragalus holmgreniorum is in the Center for Plant Conservation's National Collection of Endangered Plants.

135pp. Astragalus Linnaeus sect. Pruniformes (M. E. Jones) Barneby, Mem. New York Bot. Gard. 13: 513. 1964 [E]

Astragalus subsect. *Pruniformes* M. E. Jones, Rev. N.-Amer. Astragalus, 159. 1923

Herbs perennial, caulescent; caudex superficial. **Hairs** basifixed. **Stems** several to many. **Stipules** distinct. **Leaves** odd-pinnate, petiolate proximally, subsessile distally; leaflets (15–)19–29. **Racemes** loosely flowered, flowers horizontal or declined. **Calyx tubes** campanulate. **Corollas** whitish, banner recurved through 45°, keel apex obtuse. **Legumes** deciduous, stipitate, loosely pendulous or humistrate, plumply semi-ovoid or oblong-ovoid, solid, terete, becoming subligneous and somewhat laterally compressed, bilocular. **Seeds** 11–24.

Species 1: w United States.

138. Astragalus accidens S. Watson, Proc. Amer. Acad. Arts 22: 471. 1887 • Rogue River milkvetch E

Plants 30–55 cm, villosulous. **Stems** decumbent to ascending, proximal internodes greatly shortened, villosulous. **Leaves** (3–)5–12 cm; stipules obscuring proximal internodes, 3–6 mm, papery-membranous at proximal nodes; leaflet blades lanceolate-oblong, oblong, or oblong-elliptic, 6–22 mm, apex emarginate or retuse, surfaces villosulous, sometimes glabrous adaxially. **Peduncles** incurved-ascending, 4.5–15 cm. **Racemes** 7–15-flowered; axis 1.5–7.5 cm in fruit; bracts 1.5–3.3 mm; bracteoles (0–)2. **Pedicels** ascending, 1.5–3.3 mm. **Flowers** 13.8–19.3 mm; calyx 6–9.4 mm, villosulous, tube 4.2–5.5 mm, lobes subulate, 1.7–4 mm; corolla whitish, drying ochroleucous or yellowish; keel 9.5–12.3 mm. **Legumes** pendulous (humistrate), brownish stramineous, oblong-ovoid or semi-ovoid, 10–25 × (4–)4.5–12 mm, fleshy becoming leathery or woody, glabrous or loosely strigulose; stipe 5–12 mm.

Varieties 2 (2 in the flora): w United States.

1. Legumes 10–16 × (4–)4.5–7 mm, loosely strigulose; Douglas and Josephine counties, Oregon .... 138a. *Astragalus accidens* var. *accidens*
1. Legumes 16–25 × 8–12 mm, glabrous; Jackson County, Oregon, to n California............. .... 138b. *Astragalus accidens* var. *hendersonii*

138a. Astragalus accidens S. Watson var. **accidens** E

Leaflets 23–29, blade surfaces glabrous adaxially. **Peduncles** 4.5–10.5 cm, often equaling leaf. **Legumes** 10–16 × (4–)4.5–7 mm, loosely strigulose; stipe slender, 5–8 mm.

Flowering late Apr–Jul. Dry sites with oaks, soils derived from litter; 100–800 m; Oreg.

Variety *accidens* is restricted to southern Douglas and eastern Josephine counties.

138b. Astragalus accidens S. Watson var. **hendersonii** M. E. Jones, Rev. N.-Amer. Astragalus, 164. 1923 (as hendersoni) • Henderson's milkvetch E

Astragalus hendersonii S. Watson, Proc. Amer. Acad. Arts 22: 471. 1887, not Baker 1876; *A. cymatodes* Greene; *A. pruniformis* M. E. Jones; *A. watsonii* E. Sheldon; *Hesperonix watsonii* (Sheldon) Rydberg

Leaflets (15–)19–27, blade surfaces glabrous or sparsely pubescent adaxially. **Peduncles** 7–15 cm, usually slightly longer than leaves. **Legumes** 16–25 × 8–12 mm, glabrous; stipe ± stout, 6–12 mm. 2*n* = 26.

Flowering late Apr–Jul. Grassy or brushy slopes, open woods, and oak thickets on igneous bedrock; 200–1300 m; Calif., Oreg.

R. C. Barneby (1964) proposed that var. *hendersonii*, a northwestern California and southwestern Oregon endemic, is ancestral to the typical variety because of the wide dispersion and fragmented distribution of var. *hendersonii*. *Astragalus pacificus* E. Sheldon is an illegitimate name that pertains here.

135qq. Astragalus Linnaeus sect. Reventi-arrecti M. E. Jones, Rev. N.-Amer. Astragalus, 158. 1923

Herbs perennial, caulescent, stems shorter or longer than combined length of peduncles and racemes; caudex usually superficial, rarely slightly subterranean. **Hairs** basifixed or malpighian. **Stems** several to many. **Stipules** distinct. **Leaves** odd-pinnate, usually petiolate, rarely short-petiolate or subsessile; leaflets (5 or)7–41. **Racemes** loosely flowered, sometimes initially densely flowered, flowers usually ascending, spreading, or nodding, rarely declined; length of peduncle and raceme combined usually exceeding stem length, sometimes shorter. **Calyx tubes** short-cylindric or campanulate. **Corollas** whitish, greenish white, cream, ochroleucous, pink, or purple with pale wing apices, banner 40–90°, keel apex usually round or narrowly triangular, sometimes sharply deltate or beaklike. **Legumes** persistent, sessile or stipitate, usually erect or incurved-ascending, rarely deflexed, ovoid, oblong-ovoid to ellipsoid, or linear-oblong or -oblanceoloid, obcompressed or dorsiventrally or 3-sided compressed or subterete, unilocular or ± bilocular. **Seeds** 14–36.

Species 14 (12 in the flora): w United States, Mexico.

Section *Reventi-arrecti* consists of six subsections with distribution in the Columbia and Great basins, eastward to southwestern Montana and northwestern Wyoming, southward to southern Nevada, Arizona, and western New Mexico, and in Baja California.

The subsections are: subsect. *Reventi* M. E. Jones (*Astragalus adanus*, *A. reventus*, *A. sheldonii*); subsect. *Terminales* Barneby (*A. terminalis*); subsect. *Arrecti* M. E. Jones (*A. arrectus*, *A. riparius*); subsect. *Eremitici* Barneby (*A. atropubescens*, *A. eremiticus*, *A. remotus*, *A. scaphoides*); subsect. *Orcuttiani* (Rydberg) Barneby (*A. ackermanii*); and subsect. *Obscuri* Barneby (*A. obscurus*).

139. Astragalus reventus A. Gray, Proc. Amer. Acad. Arts 15: 40. 1879 • Blue Mountains milkvetch [E]

Plants somewhat coarse, 15–40 cm, strigulose to villosulous, hairs basifixed; from superficial caudex. **Stems** erect to ascending, with 2–5(–7) well-developed internodes, strigulose to villosulous. **Leaves** (6–)8–18(–21) cm; stipules 3.5–9 mm, membranous becoming papery; leaflets (17–)23–41, blades lanceolate-oblong, lanceolate-ovate, oblanceolate, or narrowly elliptic to linear, 5–21 mm, apex obtuse, retuse, or acute, surfaces glabrous, or glabrate adaxially. **Peduncles** erect, 10–20 cm, together with racemes longer than stems. **Racemes** 8–21-flowered, flowers spreading to nodding; axis (2.5–)4–10 cm in fruit; bracts 2.7–5.5 mm; bracteoles (0 or)2. **Pedicels** 1.4–5.4 mm. **Flowers** (15.2–)16.2–24(–25.3) mm; calyx short-cylindric, (8.9–)10.7–14.8 mm, strigulose to villosulous, tube (6.2–)6.8–9.8 mm, lobes subulate, (2.2–)3–5 mm; corolla white or creamy white, immaculate; banner recurved through 90°; keel (12.1–)13–16.3 mm. **Legumes** erect, stramineous or brownish, straight or slightly incurved, obliquely ovoid-acuminate to broadly lanceoloid-ellipsoid or oblong-ellipsoid, subterete, somewhat obcompressed, (15–)17–30 × 7–10 mm, unilocular or incompletely bilocular, fleshy becoming stiffly leathery or woody, glabrous; septum 0–0.9 mm wide; sessile. **Seeds** 25–36.

Flowering Apr–Jul. Ponderosa pine forests, often where dry; 900–1600 m; Idaho, Oreg., Wash.

Astragalus reventus is restricted to the Blue Mountains of northeastern Oregon and southeastern Washington, as well as Ada County, Idaho.

140. Astragalus sheldonii (Rydberg) Barneby, Amer. Midl. Naturalist 55: 489. 1955 (as sheldoni) • Sheldon's milkvetch [E]

Tium sheldonii Rydberg in N. L. Britton et al., N. Amer. Fl. 24: 393. 1929 (as sheldoni); *Astragalus reventus* A. Gray var. *sheldonii* (Rydberg) C. L. Hitchcock

Plants somewhat coarse, 20–50 cm, strigulose-pilosulous, hairs basifixed; from superficial caudex. **Stems** erect to ascending, with 3–7 well-developed internodes, strigulose-pilosulous. **Leaves** 7–19 cm; stipules 3–10 mm, papery-scarious at proximal nodes, subherbaceous at distal nodes; leaflets (17–)23–35(–39), blades oblong-obovate, elliptic, or nearly oblanceolate, 5–22 mm, apex retuse, obtuse, or subacute, surfaces strigulose-pilosulous abaxially, glabrous adaxially. **Peduncles** erect, (11–)16–30 cm, together with racemes usually longer than stems. **Racemes** 10–30(–35)-flowered, flowers nodding; axis (3–)6–16 cm in fruit; bracts 2.5–9 mm; bracteoles 0–2. **Pedicels** 1.3–6 mm. **Flowers** 15.5–21.5 mm; calyx short-cylindric, 8.5–12.6 mm, strigulose-pilosulous, tube 5.6–7.5 mm, lobes subulate, 2–5.2(–6) mm; corolla ochroleucous, white, or creamy white, immaculate; banner recurved through 45°; keel 11.5–14.4 mm. **Legumes** erect, stramineous, straight or slightly incurved, narrowly oblong-ellipsoid, obcompressed, grooved dorsally, (15–)17–23 × (4–)4.5–6.3 mm, semibilocular, fleshy becoming leathery, usually strigulose, rarely glabrous; septum 1–1.6 mm wide; stipe 0–1.5 mm. **Seeds** (20–)24–31. $2n$ = 24.

Flowering May–Jul. Meadows, bunchgrass prairies, with sagebrush, on basaltic substrates; 500–1300 m; Idaho, Oreg., Wash.

Astragalus sheldonii is found near the lower Salmon and Snake rivers in Lewis and Nez Perce counties in Idaho, the Wallowa Mountains, Wallowa County in Oregon, and Asotin County in Washington.

Astragalus sheldonii is one of a group of Columbia Basin species, essentially vicarious, that share a suite of somewhat similar characteristics. These were compared in key form by D. Isely (1998) under *A. reventus*, and their shifting classification was reviewed by R. C. Barneby (1964) in the introduction to sect. *Reventi-arrecti*.

141. Astragalus adanus A. Nelson, Bot. Gaz. 53: 222. 1912 • Boise or Ada milkvetch [E]

Plants robust, 20–45 cm, strigulose-pilosulous, hairs basifixed; from superficial caudex. **Stems** erect to ascending, with 5–10 well-developed internodes, strigulose-pilosulous. **Leaves** 7–13(–16) cm; stipules 4–9 mm, papery at proximal nodes, membranous at distal nodes; leaflets (13–)17–27, blades obovate, oblong, lanceolate-oblong, or broadly elliptic, 6–26 mm, apex retuse or obtuse, surfaces strigulose-pilosulous abaxially, glabrous adaxially. **Peduncles** erect, (4–)10–18 cm, together with racemes shorter than stems. **Racemes** (4–)7–22-flowered, flowers ascending-spreading; axis (2–)3–8 cm in fruit; bracts 1.5–3.5 mm; bracteoles 2. **Pedicels** 1–5 mm. **Flowers** 15.5–22 mm; calyx short-cylindric, 6.9–10.3 mm, pilosulous, tube 5.2–8 mm, lobes subulate, 1.6–2.8 mm; corolla ochroleucous, keel immaculate; banner recurved through 45°; keel 11–13.1 mm. **Legumes** erect, brown-stramineous, straight or slightly incurved, obliquely ovoid or oblong-ovoid, somewhat dorsiventrally compressed, 13–18 × 4–6 mm, unilocular, fleshy becoming leathery or subligneous, glabrous; sessile. **Seeds** 14–18.

Flowering May–Jul. With sagebrush, on various substrates derived from basalt and other igneous sources; 800–1900 m; Idaho.

Astragalus adanus is restricted to southern Idaho.

142. Astragalus terminalis S. Watson, Proc. Amer. Acad. Arts 17: 370. 1882 • Railhead milkvetch [E]

Plants loosely tuft- or mat-forming, 20–40 cm, strigulose, hairs malpighian; from superficial caudex. **Stems** erect, decumbent, or incurved-ascending, with 2–4 much-elongated internodes, strigulose. **Leaves** (3–)5–17 cm; stipules 4–7 mm, papery-scarious at proximal nodes, submembranous at distal nodes; leaflets (11 or)13–21, blades oblong-obovate, ovate, linear-oblong, or linear-elliptic, 3–17 mm, apex truncate to deeply retuse or obtuse to subacute, surfaces strigulose. **Peduncles** incurved-ascending, 6–20(–24) cm. **Racemes** 7–25(–30)-flowered, flowers nodding; axis 1.5–12(–16) cm in fruit; bracts 1–2.5 mm; bracteoles 0–2. **Pedicels** 0.7–5 mm. **Flowers** (11.2–)12.5–16.6 mm; calyx campanulate, 4.5–7 mm, strigulose, tube 3.8–5.5 mm, lobes subulate, 0.7–1.2(–1.5) mm; corolla white, keel tip maculate; banner recurved through 90°; keel 8.8–10.7 mm. **Legumes** erect, stramineous, ± straight or slightly incurved, narrowly oblong or ovoid-oblong, obcompressed, 12–17 × 3.3–6.3 mm, ± bilocular, fleshy becoming leathery, glabrous; septum 0.7–1.1 mm wide; sessile. **Seeds** 24–36.

Flowering Jun–Aug. Sagebrush or coniferous forest communities, rocky substrates; 1600–3200 m; Idaho, Mont., Wyo.

Astragalus terminalis ranges from southwestern Montana into the adjacent mountains of eastern Idaho and Teton County, Wyoming.

Astragalus terminalis is commonly called the railhead milkvetch because its type was collected from the then terminus of the Utah and Northern Railroad. It has the typical erect fruits and distinct stipules of *A. reventus* and allies but differs in its malpighian hairs.

143. Astragalus riparius Barneby, Amer. Midl. Naturalist 55: 490. 1956 • Piper's milkvetch [C] [E]

Plants clump-forming, slender, 25–50 cm, strigulose, hairs basifixed; from superficial caudex. **Stems** erect to ascending, with 2–5(or 6) developed internodes, strigulose. **Leaves** (5–)10–21 cm; stipules 2.5–7 mm, membranous becoming papery-scarious; leaflets 21–33, blades linear-oblong, linear-oblanceolate, or narrowly lanceolate-oblong, 2–21 mm, apex obtuse or truncate-emarginate to subacute, surfaces strigulose abaxially, glabrous adaxially. **Peduncles** erect, 14–30 cm, together with racemes much longer than stems. **Racemes** (8–)12–21-flowered, flowers spreading; axis 4–12(–18) cm in fruit; bracts 1.2–7.5 mm; bracteoles 2. **Pedicels** 0.7–5 mm. **Flowers** 11.2–14.1(–17) mm; calyx short-cylindric, (6.9–)7.6–10.6 mm, strigulose, tube 4.6–5.8 mm, lobes lanceolate-subulate, (1.9–)2.2–5.2 mm; corolla greenish white, drying yellowish, immaculate; banner recurved through 45°, apex crinkled, 10.5–14 mm; wings 12.8–17 mm, longer than banner; keel (9.4–)10.2–12.8 mm. **Legumes** erect, brown or stramineous, straight or slightly incurved, obliquely oblong-ellipsoid or narrowly ovoid-ellipsoid, obcompressed, 15–25 × (5.5–)6.5–10 mm, unilocular, fleshy becoming leathery, glabrous; septum to 0.6 mm wide; sessile. **Seeds** 23–28. **2*n*** = 24.

Flowering Apr–Jun. Dry bluffs, canyon banks; of conservation concern; 200–600 m; Idaho, Wash.

Astragalus riparius occurs along the lower Snake River tributaries from the mouth of the Clear Water to the Tucannon rivers, Nez Perce County, Idaho, and historically in Latah County as well as in the southeastern Washington counties of Asotin, Columbia, Garfield, and Whitman.

The combination of the sessile, unilocular, glabrous fruits of *Astragalus reventus* with the uniquely modified flowers of *A. arrectus* led R. C. Barneby (1964) to suggest hybrid origin for *A. riparius*. Despite the unique backward-folded margin of the banner, giving the illusion of a foreshortened flower, the plant closely simulates in all other aspects *A. sheldonii* and its close relatives, and may be more properly allied there.

144. Astragalus arrectus A. Gray, Proc. Amer. Acad. Arts 8: 289. 1870 • Palouse milkvetch [E]

Astragalus palousensis Piper

Plants clump-forming, slender, 28–52 cm, strigulose, hairs basifixed; from superficial caudex. **Stems** erect to ascending, strigulose. **Leaves** (6–)9–22 cm; stipules 4–8 mm, membranous becoming papery-scarious; leaflets (17–)21–31, blades linear-oblong, narrowly oblong-elliptic, lanceolate, or oval, (3–)8–22 mm, apex obtuse or truncate-emarginate, surfaces strigulose abaxially, glabrous adaxially. **Peduncles** erect, 10–25(–30) cm. **Racemes** 15–30-flowered, flowers ascending; axis 8–22 cm in fruit; bracts 1.7–2.5 mm; bracteoles 2. **Pedicels** 0.5–4 mm, clavately thickened in fruit. **Flowers** 10–10.7 mm; calyx campanulate, 5–6.3 mm, strigulose-pilosulous, tube 3.7–4.7 mm, lobes lanceolate-subulate, (1.9–)2.2–5.2 mm; corolla ochroleucous, drying yellowish, immaculate; banner recurved through 45°; keel 10.1–10.6 mm. **Legumes** erect, brownish stramineous, straight or slightly incurved or decurved, narrowly oblong-ellipsoid, obcompressed, 15–23 × 4.5–6.3 mm, ± bilocular, ± fleshy becoming stiffly leathery, strigulose; septum 0.5–0.9 mm wide; stipe (2.5–)3–6 mm. **Seeds** 18–26. **2*n*** = 24.

Flowering mid Apr–Jul. Grassy hillsides, sagebrush slopes, ponderosa pine forests; 300–800 m; Idaho, Wash.

Astragalus arrectus is restricted to southeastern Washington and immediately adjacent Idaho. D. Isely (1998) presented a key to distinguish this from *A. atropubescens* and *A. leibergii*, which are similar in fruit.

145. Astragalus atropubescens J. M. Coulter & Fisher, Bot. Gaz. 18: 300. 1893 • Kelsey's milkvetch [E]

Plants clump-forming, slender, 30–60 cm, strigulose, hairs basifixed; from superficial caudex. **Stems** erect to ascending, strigulose. **Leaves** 5–21 cm; stipules 2.5–6 mm, papery at proximal nodes, subherbaceous at distal nodes; leaflets (15–)19–27 (or 29), blades oblong, oblong-oblanceolate, or linear-oblong to linear, 5–25 mm, apex truncate to retuse or apiculate, surfaces strigulose abaxially, glabrous adaxially. **Peduncles** erect, 8–20(–25) cm. **Racemes** 10–20(–25)-flowered, flowers nodding; axis (3–)5–27 cm in fruit; bracts 1–3.5 mm; bracteoles 0–2. **Pedicels** 0.7–4 mm, little, if any, clavate thickening in fruit. **Flowers** 13–15.5 mm; calyx campanulate, 5.1–6.6 mm, strigulose-pilosulous, tube 3.8–4.9 mm, lobes subulate, 1–1.9 mm; corolla white or cream, drying ochroleucous, immaculate; banner recurved through 45–90°; keel 10.2–11.8(–12.5) mm. **Legumes** erect, greenish stramineous, straight, linear-oblong or narrowly oblong-ellipsoid, obtusely 3-sided, lateral face convex, dorsal face scarcely narrower, grooved or not, 14–24(–28) × 2.7–4.5 mm, ± bilocular, firm and scarcely fleshy becoming leathery, glabrous or strigulose; septum 0.8–1.7 mm wide; stipe (2.5–)3–6 mm. **Seeds** 20–29. **2*n*** = 22.

Flowering May–Jul. Grass and sagebrush-grass communities; 300–2500 m; Idaho, Mont.

Astragalus atropubescens occurs in Custer, Idaho, and Lemhi counties in Idaho, and adjacent Beaverhead, Lewis and Clark, and Silver Bow counties in western Montana.

The combination of typically widely spaced, moderately sized, white (drying ochroleucous) flowers with immaculate keel followed by erect or erect-ascending, stipitate, subcylindrical (obtusely three-sided) legumes is diagnostic for *Astragalus atropubescens*. The legume bodies and shorter stipes borne in the same plane (or nearly so) distinguish this species from the closely geographically adjacent *A. scaphoides*.

146. Astragalus remotus (M. E. Jones) Barneby, Leafl. W. Bot. 4: 59. 1944 • Spring Mountain milkvetch [C] [E]

Astragalus arrectus A. Gray var. *remotus* M. E. Jones, Rev. N.-Amer. Astragalus, 162. 1923

Plants clump-forming, slender, 28–60 cm, strigulose, hairs basifixed; from superficial caudex. **Stems** erect to ascending, strigulose. **Leaves** 4–15(–18) cm; stipules 2–4(–6) mm, papery-scarious at proximal nodes, subherbaceous at distal nodes; leaflets 11–19(or 21), blades linear-oblong, narrowly oblong-oblanceolate, or obovate, 2–13 mm, apex obtuse, subtruncate, or shallowly retuse, surfaces strigose, sometimes glabrous adaxially. **Peduncles** erect, 6–21(–24) cm. **Racemes** (5–)8–15-flowered, flowers ascending; axis (3–)5–18(–20) cm in fruit; bracts 1.5–2.3 mm; bracteoles 0. **Pedicels** 1–2.8 mm, little or no clavate thickening in fruit. **Flowers** 10.5–13.8 mm; calyx campanulate, 4.8–6.3 mm, strigulose-pilosulous, tube 3.1–4.2 mm, lobes subulate, 1.2–2.1 mm; corolla ochroleucous, keel tip tinged lilac; banner recurved through 40°; keel 8.5–9.6 mm. **Legumes** erect, pale green or purplish becoming stramineous, straight, linear-oblong, 3-sided compressed, lateral face flat, dorsal face narrower and grooved, 15–30 × 2.7–4 mm, ± bilocular, thin becoming papery, glabrous; septum 1–2 mm wide; stipe 3.5–7 mm. **Seeds** 16–18.

Flowering Apr–early Jun. Pinyon-juniper, oak, and less commonly creosote bush communities; of conservation concern; 1000–2100 m; Nev.

Astragalus remotus is restricted to southern Nevada, in the Spring (Charleston) Mountains. It is a southern member of a small group, several of which occur as far north as the Columbia Basin.

147. Astragalus eremiticus E. Sheldon, Minnesota Bot. Stud. 1: 161. 1894 • Hermit milkvetch [E] [F]

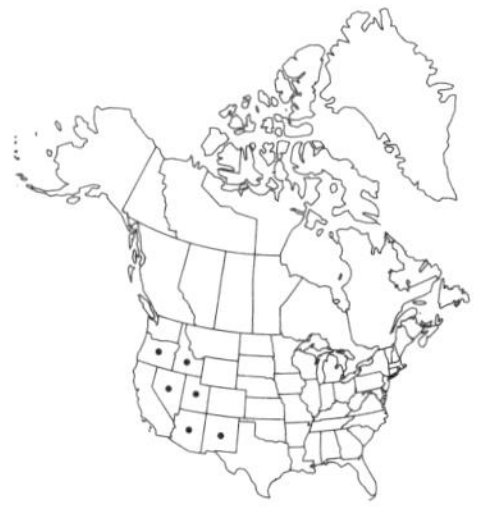

Plants 20–55(–63) cm, sparsely to densely strigulose, hairs basifixed; from branched, superficial caudex. **Stems** erect or ascending, sparsely to densely strigulose. **Leaves** (3–)4.5–18 cm; stipules 3–11 mm, papery-scarious at proximal nodes, subherbaceous at distal nodes; leaflets 11–25, blades ovate, oblong, elliptic, or narrowly oblong to linear, 5–26 mm, apex obtuse to retuse, surfaces strigose abaxially, usually glabrous adaxially, sometimes glabrate. **Peduncles** erect, (1.5–)2.5–17 (–35) cm. **Racemes** (7–)10–26(–30)-flowered, flowers ascending to declined; axis 4–10(–15) cm in fruit; bracts 1.5–4 mm; bracteoles 0–2. **Pedicels** spreading in fruit, 0.7–3.5 mm. **Flowers** 12–20 mm; calyx short-cylindric, 5.4–9.5 mm, strigose, tube 4.4–8 mm, lobes triangular to subulate, 0.7–2.6 mm; corolla ochroleucous, tinged pink, purplish, pink-purple, or red-violet, keel maculate or immaculate; banner recurved through 45°; keel 9.4–14.4 mm. **Legumes** usually erect, rarely deflexed, green or suffused or speckled with purple becoming brownish stramineous, oblong to ellipsoid, 3-sided compressed, grooved dorsally, keeled ventrally, 12–27(–30) × 3.5–8(–9) mm, base cuneate, ± bilocular, fleshy becoming thinly or stiffly leathery, glabrous; septum 0.5–1.2 mm wide; stipe 6–15(–17) mm. **Seeds** 17–32. $2n = 22, 24$.

Varieties 2 (2 in the flora): w United States.

Astragalus eremiticus displays extensive variation. R. C. Barneby (1964) discussed five unnamed morphological and ecological races in place of fewer varieties that he earlier recognized (1944, 1949). D. Isely (1998) recognized two varieties, as presented here. He considered var. *ampullarioides* Welsh a vigorous form of the species but did not place it into synonymy in either of the varieties (by his map it would be in var. *eremiticus*). That entity is here considered a species (as 163. *A. ampullarioides*).

1. Calyces basally symmetric; pedicels medially attached to calyces, ascending; racemes lax, axes 5–10(–15) cm in fruit; nw Arizona, se Nevada, disjunct in sw New Mexico, sw Utah . . . . 147a. *Astragalus eremiticus* var. *eremiticus*
1. Calyces basally asymmetric; pedicels attached to calyces on one side, spreading to descending; racemes compact, axes 4–6(–15) cm in fruit; sw Idaho, ec to n Nevada, e, se Oregon . . . . 147b. *Astragalus eremiticus* var. *spencianus*

147a. Astragalus eremiticus E. Sheldon var. **eremiticus** [E] [F]

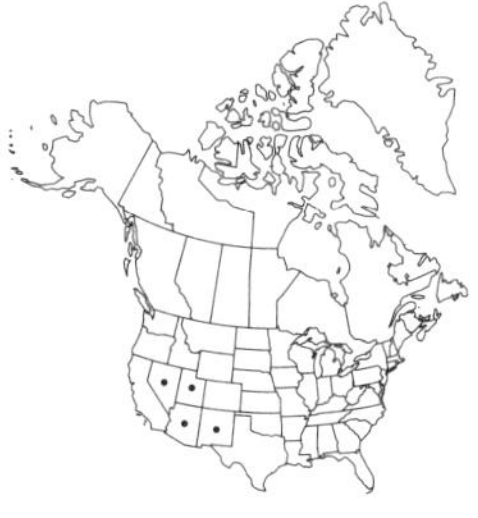

Racemes lax, axis 5–10(–15) cm in fruit. **Pedicels** medially attached to calyx, ascending. **Calyces** basally symmetric.

Flowering Apr–Jul. Creosote bush, blackbrush, *Ephedra*, juniper-pinyon, live oak, and sagebrush communities; (600–) 900–1900(–2000) m; Ariz., Nev., N.Mex. Utah.

Most plants of var. *eremiticus* from northern Arizona, and from eastern Kane County and some from Washington County, Utah, have blue, purple, or pink petals, or petals suffused with those colors. They seem not to differ otherwise from the typically pale yellowish-(ochroleucous) or whitish-flowered specimens that form the bulk of the variety away from those areas. Legumes vary from thin and almost papery to thick and leathery-woody, and from oblong to linear-oblong, and not at all or not much inflated to definitely though slightly inflated. Legume variation appears to be haphazard in the vicinity of the Pine Valley Mountains in Washington County, Utah.

147b. Astragalus eremiticus E. Sheldon var. **spencianus** M. E. Jones, Contr. W. Bot. 10: 60. 1902 E

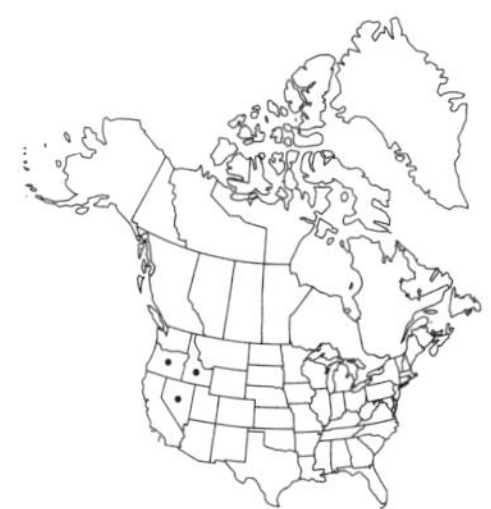

Astragalus eremiticus var. *malheurensis* (A. Heller) Barneby; *A. malheurensis* A. Heller

Racemes compact; axis 4–6 (–15) cm in fruit. **Pedicels** attached to calyx on one side, spreading to descending. **Calyces** basally asymmetric.

Flowering May–Jul. Sagebrush, rabbitbrush, and juniper communities, various substrates; 600–1900 m; Idaho, Nev., Oreg.

Plants recognized as *Astragalus malheurensis* or *A. eremiticus* var. *malheurensis*, which occur in Owyhee County, Idaho, and adjacent Malheur County, Oregon, have purple petals or at least suffused distally with purple. They may be sufficiently distinct to warrant taxonomic recognition.

148. Astragalus scaphoides (M. E. Jones) Rydberg, Mem. New York Bot. Gard. 1: 241. 1900 (as scophioides) • Bitterroot milkvetch E

Astragalus arrectus A. Gray var. *scaphoides* M. E. Jones, Proc. Calif. Acad. Sci., ser. 2, 5: 664. 1895

Plants 15–40 cm, strigulose, hairs basifixed; from subterranean branched caudex. **Stems** decumbent to erect, strigulose. **Leaves** (6–)8–20(–24) cm; stipules 3–8 mm, submembranous early becoming papery; leaflets (9–)17–25, blades oblong, elliptic, rhombic-ovate, or rhombic-lanceolate to linear-elliptic, (7–)10–20(–28) mm, apex obtuse to subacute, surfaces strigulose abaxially, glabrous adaxially. **Peduncles** erect, 8–16 cm. **Racemes** (9–)15–30-flowered, flowers spreading to nodding; axis (3–)5–17 cm in fruit; bracts 2–4.5 mm; bracteoles 2. **Pedicels** 1.5–5 mm. **Flowers** 18.5–20.5 mm; calyx short-cylindric, 9.6–12.2 mm, strigulose, tube 7–9 mm, lobes triangular to subulate, (1–)2–3.2 mm; corolla ochroleucous, immaculate; banner recurved through 50°; keel 13–15 mm. **Legumes** erect, green, sometimes suffused or speckled with purple, becoming stramineous, straight or nearly so, subsymmetrically oblong- or ovoid-ellipsoid, moderately inflated, obcompressed, both sutures grooved, 11–22 × (4.5–)6.5–10 mm, base truncate, ± bilocular, fleshy becoming leathery, glabrous; septum 1.4–1.8 mm wide; stipe 12–18 mm. **Seeds** 21–32.

Flowering Jun–early Aug. With sagebrush, on limestone or basalt soils; 1000–1900 m; Idaho, Mont.

Astragalus scaphoides, found in the Bitterroot Mountains, Beaverhead County, Montana, and adjacent valleys of the upper Salmon and Lemhi rivers, Lemhi County, Idaho, appears much like a rather coarse version of *A. eremiticus* at anthesis. The thick fruit, truncate at the base, is diagnostic.

149. Astragalus ackermanii Barneby, Brittonia 32: 26, fig. 2. 1980 • Ackerman's milkvetch C E

Plants tuft-forming, suffrutescent, caulescent, 15–25 cm, strigulose, hairs basifixed; from branched, superficial caudex. **Stems** erect or ascending, strigulose. **Leaves** (3.5–)5–12 cm; stipules 0.8–2 mm; leaflets 9–15, blades obovate, oblong-obovate, or oblong-elliptic, 2.5–7 mm, apex obtuse or emarginate, surfaces glabrous. **Peduncles** (3.5–)5–11 cm. **Racemes** 2–5-flowered, flowers ascending; axis 2–4 cm in fruit; bracts 1.1–2.2 mm; bracteoles 0–2. **Pedicels** 2.4–6 mm. **Flowers** 12–14 mm; calyx campanulate, 6.3–7.5 mm, strigulose, tube 4–4.5 mm, lobes lanceolate-subulate, 1.8–3 mm; corolla reddish purple, drying bluish; banner recurved through 45°; keel 9.4–14.4 mm, apex sharply deltate. **Legumes** persistent and dehiscent by gaping beak, ascending, green, or suffused or speckled with purple, becoming brownish stramineous, lunate, linear-oblanceoloid, 3-sided compressed, 15–21 × 2.8–3.8 mm, ± bilocular, fleshy becoming thinly or stiffly leathery, sparsely strigulose; septum 1–1.3 mm wide; stipe 1–1.5 mm. **Seeds** 16–19.

Flowering Apr–Jun. Ledges and crevices of limestone cliffs in mixed shrub, sagebrush, and juniper woodland communities; of conservation concern; (1200–)1500–1900 m; Nev.

Astragalus ackermanii is restricted to northwestern Clark and southwestern Lincoln counties.

150. Astragalus obscurus S. Watson, Botany (Fortieth Parallel), 69. 1871 • Arcane milkvetch E

Plants slender, delicate, wiry, caulescent, 15–40 cm, strigulose, hairs basifixed; from superficial to slightly subterranean branched caudex. **Stems** decumbent to ascending, strigulose. **Leaves** (2.5–)4–10 cm; stipules 1.5–2.5 mm, papery at proximal nodes, herbaceous or with herbaceous tips at distal nodes; leaflets (5 or)7–13, blades broadly oblong-elliptic to lanceolate-oblong or linear-elliptic, 2–10(–15) mm, apex obtuse to truncate, shallowly retuse, or subacute, surfaces strigulose abaxially, sparsely strigulose or glabrous adaxially. **Peduncles** straight, sometimes incurved-ascending, 3–15 cm. **Racemes** (3–)6–14-flowered, flowers ascending; axis (1–)2–8 cm in fruit; bracts 0.8–2.5 mm; bracteoles 0–2. **Pedicels** 0.5–2.2 mm. **Flowers** 7–10.5 mm; calyx short-cylindric, (3.1–)3.6–5.5 mm, strigulose, tube (2.3–)2.8–4 mm, lobes triangular to subulate, 0.4–1.6 mm; corolla ochroleucous or whitish suffused with lilac; banner recurved through 45°; keel (6.3–)7–10 mm, apex triangular and beaklike. **Legumes** persistent on receptacle until well after maturity, falling while still attached to pedicel, erect, stramineous, straight, linear-oblong, obtusely 3-sided compressed, 10–25 × 2.4–3.3 mm, ± bilocular, thinly fleshy becoming leathery, strigulose; septum 1–1.4 mm wide; sessile or subsessile. **Seeds** 14–23.

Flowering May–Jul. Sandy to fine-textured substrates or gravelly slopes, with juniper, sagebrush, bitterbrush, or rabbitbrush; 900–2300 m; Calif., Idaho, Nev., Oreg.

Astragalus obscurus occurs in northern and north-central California, southwestern Idaho, northern and western Nevada, and southeastern Oregon.

R. C. Barneby (1964) discussed variation in *Astragalus obscurus*, including one morphologically differentiated outlier from the northern foothills of Mount Shasta in Siskiyou County, which may represent a distinct variety.

135rr. Astragalus Linnaeus sect. Michauxiani Barneby, Mem. New York Bot. Gard. 13: 542. 1964 [E]

Herbs perennial, caulescent; caudex slightly subterranean, branched. **Hairs** basifixed. **Stems** usually single. **Stipules** distinct. **Leaves** odd-pinnate, usually sessile or subsessile, rarely short-petiolate proximally; leaflets (15–)21–33(or 35). **Racemes** loosely flowered, flowers ascending. **Calyx tubes** short-cylindric. **Corollas** pink-purple or whitish tinged with lilac, banner recurved through 40°, keel apex sharply deltate-triangular. **Legumes** persistent, subsessile, incurved-ascending or suberect, narrowly oblong-ellipsoid, dorsiventrally compressed, keeled ventrally, grooved dorsally, semibilocular. **Seeds** 30–40.

Species 1: se United States.

151. Astragalus michauxii (Kuntze) F. J. Hermann, J. Wash. Acad. Sci. 38: 237. 1948 • Michaux's milkvetch [E]

Tragacantha michauxii Kuntze, Revis. Gen. Pl. 2: 941. 1891, based on *Astragalus glaber* Michaux, Fl. Bor.-Amer. 2: 66. 1803, not de Candolle 1802; *Tium michauxii* (Kuntze) Rydberg

Plants slender, 35–90(–95) cm, strigulose-pilosulous. **Stems** erect or ascending, with 5–10 well-developed internodes, glabrous or glabrate. **Leaves** (4.5–)7–17 cm; stipules 0.5–2.5 mm, papery-membranous at proximal nodes, herbaceous and membranous-margined at distal nodes; leaflet blades narrowly oblong, lanceolate-elliptic, narrowly oval, or sublinear, (3–)6–26 mm, apex retuse to obtuse, surfaces sparsely strigulose-pilosulous or, sometimes, glabrous adaxially or ciliate. **Peduncles** erect or incurved-ascending, 6–15 cm, together with racemes shorter than stems. **Racemes** (12–)15–40-flowered; axis 5–15(–18) cm in fruit; bracts 1–3 mm; bracteoles 0. **Pedicels** 0.6–3 mm. **Flowers** (13.5–)14.4–18.8 mm; calyx (5.7–)6–8.3 mm, strigulose, tube (4.7–)5–6.3 mm, lobes triangular to subulate, 1–2.3 mm; corolla banner recurved through 40°; keel 12.5–15 mm. **Legumes** brownish stramineous, strongly incurved, 23–31 × 4.5–6 mm, fleshy becoming stiffly leathery or subligneous, glabrous; septum 0.8–1 mm wide.

Flowering Mar–Jun. Dry, sandy scrub-oak and pine woods; ca. 200 m; Ga., N.C., S.C.

Astragalus michauxii is known from the Atlantic Coastal Plain and Piedmont of southeastern Georgia to southeastern North Carolina. A report from central Florida should be disregarded since it is based on a Schallert specimen that probably came from North Carolina (D. Isely 1998). This is the only tall *Astragalus* from the southeastern United States, except for *A. canadensis* from the North Carolina mountains, that has connate stipules and much smaller fruits.

135ss. Astragalus Linnaeus sect. Nudi (Rydberg) Barneby, Mem. New York Bot. Gard. 13: 545. 1964 [E]

Brachyphragma Rydberg [unranked] *Nuda* Rydberg in N. L. Britton et al., N. Amer. Fl. 24: 399. 1929

Herbs perennial, forming bushy clumps, caulescent; caudex superficial, branched. **Hairs** basifixed. **Stems** several to many. **Stipules** distinct. **Leaves** odd-pinnate, short-petiolate; leaflets (1–)5–11. **Racemes** loosely flowered, flowers ascending. **Calyx tubes** short-cylindric or narrowly cylindric. **Corollas** purple, or ochroleucous and margined or tinged lavender, banner recurved through 35–45°, keel apex obtuse. **Legumes** persistent, sessile, erect, ovoid or oblong-ovoid, subterete, unilocular to semibilocular. **Seeds** 29–42.

Species 1: w United States.

152. Astragalus serenoi (Kuntze) E. Sheldon, Minnesota Bot. Stud. 1: 130. 1894 • Naked milkvetch [E]

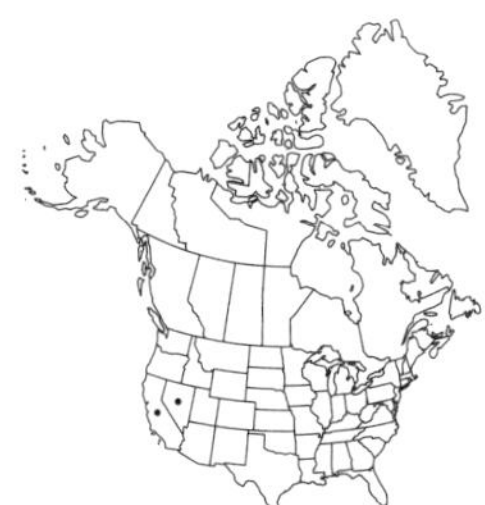

Tragacantha serenoi Kuntze, Revis. Gen. Pl. 2: 941. 1891, based on *Astragalus nudus* S. Watson, Botany (Fortieth Parallel), 74. 1871, not Clos 1847

Plants robust, 15–45(–53) cm, strigulose. **Stems** erect or ascending, sparsely strigulose. **Leaves** 2–15 cm; stipules 1.5–5 mm, papery-scarious at proximal nodes, subherbaceous at distal nodes; leaflet blades linear, linear-oblanceolate, or filiform, 5–30 mm, apex acute, subacute, or, often, mucronate, surfaces silvery-canescent, more densely so adaxially; terminal leaflet sometimes decurrent distally, not jointed to rachis. **Peduncles** erect, 3–25 cm. **Racemes** (3–)5–25-flowered; axis 2–20 cm in fruit; bracts 1.5–4 mm; bracteoles 2. **Pedicels** 0.7–4 mm. **Flowers** 14.5–26 mm; calyx 7.9–13.7 mm, strigulose, tube 6.5–10 mm, lobes lanceolate-subulate, 1.5–4.3 mm; corolla keel 12.8–18.5 mm. **Legumes** firmly attached to receptacle, falling while still attached to pedicel, stramineous, straight or slightly incurved, obliquely ovoid or plumply oblong, 15–31 × 5–12 mm, fleshy becoming woody, glabrous; septum (0–)1–2.5(–4) mm wide.

Varieties 3 (3 in the flora): w United States.

The vernacular name for *Astragalus serenoi*, naked milkvetch, refers to the persistent fruits borne naked because of the fragile calyx that is soon deciduous by a circumscissile fracture (R. C. Barneby 1964). The plant is coarse, scarcely leafy, with nearly zigzag stems.

1. Corollas ochroleucous and margined or tinged lavender, petals not especially graduated, banners 14.5–16 mm; legumes unilocular or subunilocular, septae 0–1 mm wide; Esmeralda and Nye counties, Nevada .... 152c. *Astragalus serenoi* var. *sordescens*
1. Corollas purple, petals strongly graduated, banners 17–24(–26) mm; legumes unilocular or semibilocular, septae 2–4 mm wide; California, Nevada.
    2. Legumes unilocular, septae 0 mm; nc Humboldt County southward to Churchill and adjacent Lander and nw Nye counties, Nevada ....152a. *Astragalus serenoi* var. *serenoi*
    2. Legumes semibilocular, septae 2–4 mm wide; Lyon and Mineral counties, southward through Esmeralda County, Nevada, to Inyo and Mono counties, California .... 152b. *Astragalus serenoi* var. *shockleyi*

152a. Astragalus serenoi (Kuntze) E. Sheldon var. **serenoi** [E]

Stems 20–45 cm. **Leaves** 5–15 cm. **Peduncles** (7–)10–25 cm. **Racemes** (3–)7–25-flowered; axis (2–)5–20 cm in fruit. **Corollas** purple, petals strongly graduated; banner 17–26 mm. **Legumes** plumply oblong, straight or slightly incurved, 17–31 × 7–10.5(–12) mm, unilocular. $2n = 22$.

Flowering May–Jul. Sagebrush and pinyon-juniper communities; 1100–2300 m; Nev.

Variety *serenoi* occurs from northcentral Humboldt County southward to Churchill and adjacent Lander and northwestern Nye counties.

152b. Astragalus serenoi (Kuntze) E. Sheldon var. **shockleyi** (M. E. Jones) Barneby, Brittonia 36: 168. 1984 • Shockley's milkvetch [E]

Astragalus shockleyi M. E. Jones, Proc. Calif. Acad. Sci., ser. 2, 5: 659. 1895

Stems 20–45(–53) cm. **Leaves** 5–11(–15) cm. **Peduncles** 9–18 cm. **Racemes** (3–)9–16-flowered; axis (2–)5–15 cm in fruit. **Corollas** purple, petals strongly graduated; banner 17–20 mm. **Legumes** plumply oblong, straight or slightly incurved 17–31 × 5–12 mm, semibilocular, septum 2–4 mm wide.

Flowering May–Jun. Tuff and gravel to clay washes; 1400–2000 m; Calif., Nev.

Variety *shockleyi* is known from Lyon and Mineral counties, western Nevada, to Inyo and Mono counties in eastern California.

152c. Astragalus serenoi (Kuntze) E. Sheldon var. **sordescens** Barneby, Leafl. W. Bot. 7: 195. 1954 • Dirtyish milkvetch [C] [E]

Stems 15–30 cm. **Leaves** 2–10 cm. **Peduncles** 3–10 cm. **Racemes** 5–15-flowered; axis 2–7(–10) cm in fruit. **Corollas** ochroleucous and margined or tinged lavender, petals not especially graduated; banner 14.5–16 mm. **Legumes** obliquely ovoid, slightly incurved, 15–22 × 5–7 mm, unilocular or subunilocular, septum 0–1 mm wide.

Flowering May–Jul. Gentle slopes and flats among, and often sheltering under or scrambling up through, low sagebrush; of conservation concern; 1500–2100 m; Nev.

Variety *sordescens* is known from Esmeralda and Nye counties.

135tt. Astragalus Linnaeus sect. Conjuncti Barneby, Mem. New York Bot. Gard. 13: 549. 1964 [E]

Herbs perennial, subacaulescent or shortly caulescent, sometimes caulescent (in *A. reventiformis*); caudex superficial, branched. **Hairs** basifixed. **Stems** several to many, usually shorter than longest peduncles. **Stipules** connate or distinct at distal nodes. **Leaves** odd-pinnate, petiolate, rarely subsessile distally; leaflets (9–)13–37, terminal leaflet sometimes confluent. **Racemes** loosely flowered, flowers ascending, spreading, or nodding. **Calyx tubes** cylindric or campanulate. **Corollas** whitish, cream, or purple, banner recurved through 30–90°, keel apex obtuse. **Legumes** persistent, sessile or stipitate, erect, oblong-ellipsoid or ovoid-acuminate, ± obcompressed, unilocular or sub-bilocular. **Seeds** 15–35.

Species 4 (4 in the flora): nw United States.

Section *Conjuncti* occurs in interior Oregon and Washington and southwestern Idaho.

153. Astragalus conjunctus S. Watson, Proc. Amer. Acad. Arts 17: 371. 1882 • John Day Valley milkvetch [E]

Astragalus reventus A. Gray var. *conjunctus* (S. Watson) M. E. Jones

Plants forming bushy clumps, subacaulescent or shortly caulescent, 15–65 cm, strigulose. **Stems** erect or ascending, strigulose. **Leaves** mostly in subbasal cluster, (6–)10–30 cm; stipules connate-sheathing at proximal nodes, mostly connate at distal nodes, 3–10(–11) mm, scarious throughout; leaflets (9–)13–25(–31), blades linear-oblong, linear-elliptic, lanceolate, or subfiliform, 3–23 mm, apex obtuse, acute, or retuse, surfaces sparsely strigulose abaxially, usually glabrous adaxially; terminal leaflet sometimes continuous with rachis. **Peduncles** erect, sometimes divergent in fruit, 5–33 cm, together with racemes longer than stems. **Racemes** 7–20-flowered, flowers ascending to spreading; axis (3–)4–13(–15) cm in fruit; bracts 2–4.5 mm; bracteoles 2. **Pedicels** 1–4.5 mm. **Flowers** 15–25.5 mm; calyx campanulate, cylindric, or subcylindric, 7–12 mm, strigulose-pilosulous, tube 4.9–9.2 mm, lobes subulate, 1.3–3(–4) mm; corolla whitish with keel tip purple, sometimes banner and wings also purple-tipped, sometimes purple throughout; banner recurved through 30–45°, oblanceolate or broadly rhombic-oblanceolate, 16–25.5 mm, apex emarginate; keel 11.6–17.5 mm. **Legumes** stramineous, straight or slightly incurved, oblong-ellipsoid to narrowly oblong-ovoid, obcompressed, 12–25 × 4.3–8 mm, sub-bilocular, fleshy becoming leathery or subligneous, glabrous or strigulose; septum to 1.4 mm wide; sessile. **Seeds** 15–30.

Varieties 2 (2 in the flora): nw United States.

1. Calyces cylindric or subcylindric, tubes (5.7–)6–9.2 mm; legumes glabrous, 5–8 mm wide; pedicels 1–4.5 mm; Yakima County, Washington, nc to se Oregon, and sw Idaho . . . . 153a. *Astragalus conjunctus* var. *conjunctus*
1. Calyces campanulate, tubes 4.9–6.2 mm; legumes strigulose, 4.3–5 mm wide; pedicels 1–2.5 mm; Wasco County, Oregon, Benton County, Washington. . . . . 153b. *Astragalus conjunctus* var. *rickardii*

153a. Astragalus conjunctus S. Watson var. **conjunctus** E

Peduncles 10–33 cm. **Racemes** 7–17(–20)-flowered; axis (3–)4–12(–15) cm in fruit. **Pedicels** 1–4.5 mm. **Flowers** 16–25.5 mm; calyx cylindric or subcylindric, (7–)8.5–12 mm, tube (5.7–)6–9.2 mm, lobes 1.3–3(–4) mm. **Legumes** 12–25 × 5–8 mm, glabrous. **Seeds** 23–30. **2*n*** = 24.

Flowering mid Apr–Jun. Meadows, brushy slopes, grasslands, sagebrush desert, pine forests, on basaltic bedrock; 400–1600 m; Idaho, Oreg., Wash.

Variety *conjunctus* is most easily recognized in bloom, the long, narrow flowers, with their cylindric calyces and, usually, lilac- or purple-tinged petals being diagnostic. When in fruit, it is easily confused with the narrow-fruited form of *Astragalus reventiformis*, a species of the inner slope of the Cascade Range in Washington.

153b. Astragalus conjunctus S. Watson var. **rickardii** S. L. Welsh, K. A. Beck & Caplow, Great Basin Naturalist 57: 354. 1997 • Rickard's milkvetch E

Peduncles 5–26 cm. **Racemes** 10–19-flowered; axis 4–13 cm in fruit. **Pedicels** 1–2.5 mm. **Flowers** 15–18.5 mm; calyx campanulate, 7–9 mm, tube 4.9–6.2 mm, lobes 1.5–3 mm. **Legumes** 13–20 × 4.3–5 mm, strigulose. **Seeds** 15–20.

Flowering May–Jun. Bunchgrass-sagebrush communities; 400–1100 m; Oreg., Wash.

Variety *rickardii* was once thought to be confined to the Hanford Atomic Energy Site, Benton County, Washington, but has more recently been documented in Wasco County, Oregon. Although plants of var. *rickardii* contrast in features relative to other members of the complex, it appears to be most closely related to var. *conjunctus* despite its strigulose fruits, shorter fruiting pedicels, and smaller floral parts.

154. Astragalus hoodianus Howell, Erythea 1: 111. 1893 • Hood River milkvetch E

Astragalus conjunctus S. Watson var. *oxytropidoides* M. E. Jones; *A. reventus* A. Gray var. *oxytropidoides* (M. E. Jones) C. L. Hitchcock; *Cnemidophacos knowlesianus* Rydberg

Plants somewhat coarse, forming bushy clumps, subacaulescent or shortly caulescent, 15–45 cm, pilosulous. **Stems** erect or ascending, pilosulous. **Leaves** both cauline and in sub-basal cluster, (5–)7–20 cm; stipules connate-sheathing at proximal nodes, (3–)5–11 mm, fragile, submembranous early becoming papery-scarious; leaflets 25–37, blades linear-elliptic, linear-oblong, oblanceolate, or ovate-oblong, 5–27 mm, apex obtuse, acute, or retuse, surfaces pilosulous, sometimes glabrous adaxially; terminal leaflet often continuous with rachis. **Peduncles** erect, 12–30 cm, together with racemes longer than stems. **Racemes** (6–)10–30-flowered, flowers ascending to spreading; axis (3–)5–18 cm in fruit; bracts 2–9.5 mm; bracteoles 2. **Pedicels** 1–3.7 mm. **Flowers** 18–23 mm; calyx short-cylindric, (10–)11–15 mm, strigulose-pilosulous, tube (5.7–)6–7.9 × 3.6–4.8 mm, lobes lanceolate or lanceolate-caudate, (2.6–)4.6–6.7(–7.5) mm; corolla cream, immaculate; banner recurved through 45°; keel 13.4–15.6 mm. **Legumes** brownish stramineous, ± straight, broadly oblong-ovoid to narrowly oblong-ellipsoid, obcompressed, 11–22 × 4.5–7.2 mm, unilocular or sub-bilocular, fleshy becoming stiffly leathery or subligneous, usually villous-pilose or glabrescent, rarely glabrous; septum to 1 mm wide; sessile.

Flowering late Mar–Jun. Dry, gravelly or grassy hillsides, canyon benches; 100–150 m; Oreg., Wash.

Astragalus hoodianus is known from Hood River and Wasco counties in Oregon, and Klickitat County in Washington.

Astragalus hoodianus could easily be treated as a variety of *A. conjunctus*, as was done by C. L. Hitchcock (1961b). The long peduncles and pale flowers are reminiscent of some species of *Oxytropis*, such as *O. sericea*. The first and second peduncles displace the stem primordium laterally, giving the appearance that the first leaves are opposite the leaf subtending the peduncle.

155. Astragalus reventiformis (Rydberg) Barneby, Amer. Midl. Naturalist 55: 492. 1956 • Yakima milkvetch [E]

Cnemidophacos reventiformis Rydberg in N. L. Britton et al., N. Amer. Fl. 24: 284. 1929; *Astragalus reventus* A. Gray var. *canbyi* M. E. Jones

Plants robust, stout, caulescent to subacaulescent, 15–45 cm, strigulose-pilose. **Stems** erect or ascending, distalmost internode longer than others combined, strigulose-pilose. **Leaves** (6.5–)8–22(–30) cm; stipules connate-sheathing at proximal nodes, mostly connate at distal nodes, 2.5–7 mm, papery-membranous; leaflets (13–)17–27(–33), blades linear-oblong, lanceolate, lanceolate-elliptic, or oval-oblong, 4–21(–25) mm, apex obtuse, truncate-emarginate, apiculate, or acute, surfaces strigulose-pilose abaxially, usually glabrous or glabrescent adaxially. **Peduncles** stiffly erect, (7–)10–30 cm, together with racemes longer than stems. **Racemes** (7–)10–19-flowered, flowers ascending initially; axis (2.5–)4–12 cm in fruit; bracts 1.5–4.5(–6) mm; bracteoles 2. **Pedicels** 2.7–6 mm. **Flowers** (13.2–)14–20.7 mm; calyx campanulate, (7.8–)8–12.2 mm, pilosulous, tube (4.7–)5.3–7.5 mm, lobes lanceolate-subulate, (2.4–)2.7–5.1 mm; corolla white or whitish, drying yellowish, immaculate or keel tip purplish; banner recurved through 90°, oblong-oblanceolate, rhombic-oblanceolate, elliptic, oblong-ovate, or somewhat quadrately ovate-cuneate, (13.2–)14–20.7 mm, apex usually deeply notched; keel 10–13(–13.7) mm. **Legumes** brownish, straight or slightly incurved, ovoid-acuminate to oblong-ellipsoid, somewhat obcompressed, (10–)15–22 × (5–)6–11 mm, sub-bilocular, thick and fleshy becoming stiffly leathery or woody, glabrous; septum 0.6–2 mm wide; sessile. **Seeds** (20–)22–35.

Flowering late Apr–Jun. With sagebrush on basalt bedrock or alluvium; 300–1600 m; Wash.

Astragalus reventiformis and its immediate relatives have connate stipules and erect, persistent, leathery fruits. They form a pattern of geographic replacement mostly east of the Cascade Range: *A. conjunctus*, with a cylindric calyx tube, is from south-central Washington, north-central and eastern Oregon, and southwestern Idaho; *A. hoodianus*, from low elevations along the Columbia River in north-central Oregon and adjacent Washington, has long, commonly divergent calyx lobes; *A. reventiformis* lies to the north in Washington, immediately southward of *A. leibergii*, which has shortly stipitate fruits (D. Isely 1998).

156. Astragalus leibergii M. E. Jones, Proc. Calif. Acad. Sci., ser. 2, 5: 663. 1895 (as leibergi) • Leiberg's milkvetch [E]

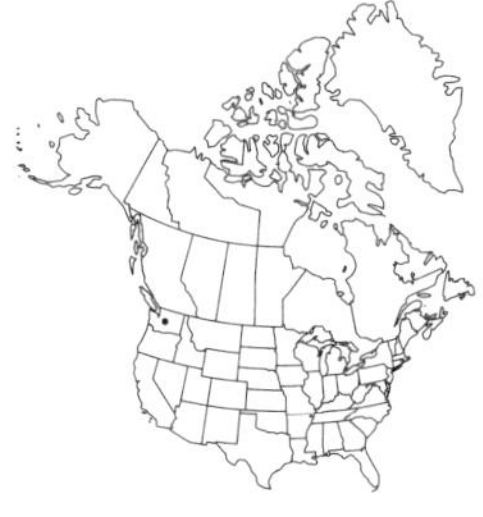

Astragalus arrectus A. Gray var. *leibergii* (M. E. Jones) M. E. Jones

Plants forming bushy clumps, subacaulescent or shortly caulescent, 15–45 cm, strigulose. **Stems** erect or ascending, strigulose. **Leaves** mostly in subbasal cluster, (5–)8–20(–28) cm; stipules connate-sheathing at proximal nodes, sometimes also at distal nodes, often connate at distal nodes, distalmost sometimes distinct, 3–10 mm, scarious becoming fragile; leaflets (11–)15–27(–31), blades linear to narrowly lanceolate-elliptic or lanceolate-oblong to oblong, 2–25(–38) mm, apex obtuse to acute, surfaces usually strigulose, sometimes glabrescent adaxially. **Peduncles** erect, 10–33 cm, together with racemes equaling or longer than stems. **Racemes** (6–)10–28-flowered, flowers nodding; axis 4–17 cm in fruit; bracts 2–4.5 mm; bracteoles 2. **Pedicels** 0.8–4.5 mm. **Flowers** (10.8–)11.6–16.4 mm; calyx campanulate, 5.3–8.6 mm, strigulose-pilosulous, tube 3.2–4.9(–5.8) mm, lobes subulate, 1.6–3.8 mm; corolla whitish, immaculate; banner recurved through 90°; keel (8.9–)9.3–12.6 mm. **Legumes** brownish, straight or slightly incurved, oblong-ellipsoid, 3-sided obcompressed, 16–27 × 4–7.5 mm, sub-bilocular, fleshy becoming stiffly leathery or woody, glabrous or strigulose; valves inflexed, septum 0.4–1.3 mm wide; stipe 3–5(–8) mm. **Seeds** 23–32. $2n = 22$.

Flowering mid Apr–Jun. Low hills, plains, in sagebrush scablands on basaltic bedrock, open pine forests on granitic or serpentine soils; 300–900 m; Wash.

Astragalus leibergii is restricted to the Columbia River Valley in Chelan, Douglas, Grant, and Kittitas counties.

135uu. Astragalus Linnaeus sect. Hesperonix (Rydberg) Barneby, Mem. New York Bot. Gard. 13: 558. 1964 [E]

Hesperonix Rydberg in N. L. Britton et al., N. Amer. Fl. 24: 438. 1929

Herbs perennial, forming bushy clumps, caulescent; caudex superficial or shallowly subterranean. **Hairs** basifixed. **Stems** several to many. **Stipules** connate or distinct at distal nodes. **Leaves** odd-pinnate, short-petiolate proximally, sessile or subsessile distally; leaflets (13–)17–25(or 27). **Racemes** loosely flowered, flowers ascending or spreading. **Calyx tubes** campanulate or short-cylindric. **Corollas** whitish or lilac-tinged, banner recurved through 40°, keel apex obtuse. **Legumes** eventually deciduous, continuous with receptacle, stipitate, ascending, spreading, or declined, obliquely ovoid or ovoid-acuminate, inflated, ± obcompressed, bilocular. **Seeds** 12–21.

Species 1: w United States.

157. Astragalus bolanderi A. Gray, Proc. Amer. Acad. Arts 7: 337. 1868 • Bolander's milkvetch [E]

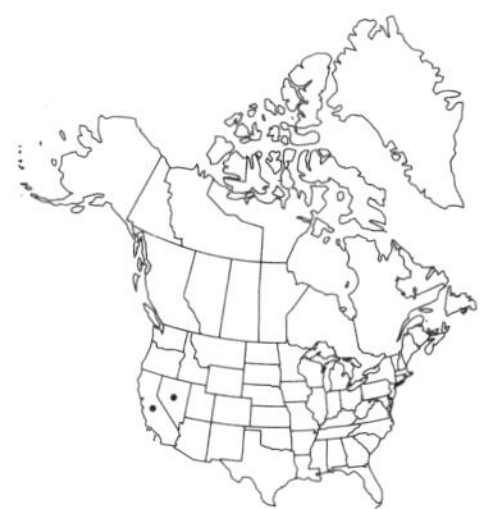

Plants robust to slender, (10–)15–45 cm, villosulous. **Stems** erect or ascending, 0–2.5 cm underground, sparsely villosulous or glabrous proximally. **Leaves** (3–)4–12 cm; stipules connate-sheathing at proximal nodes, connate or distinct at distal nodes, (1.5–)2–6 mm, scarious; leaflet blades narrowly oblong-elliptic, oblanceolate, linear-oblong, or oblong-obovate, (3–)5–20(–23) mm, apex acute to subobtuse or retuse, surfaces villosulous. **Peduncles** erect or narrowly ascending, (4.5–)6–15 cm. **Racemes** 6–12(–14)-flowered; axis 2.5–10 cm in fruit; bracts 1.3–4.5 mm; bracteoles 0–2. **Pedicels** 1–3.5 mm. **Flowers** 15.4–18.8 mm; calyx 8.8–11.8 mm, strigulose, tube 6.3–7.5 mm, lobes lanceolate-subulate, 2.5–4.3 mm; corolla white or lilac-tinged, drying ochroleucous; keel (9.8–)10–12.4 mm. **Legumes** ascending to divaricately spreading or somewhat declined, set at angle to stipe, stramineous or brownish, straight or slightly incurved, inflated, scarcely bladdery, (10–)13–24(–32) × 6–12 mm, thinly fleshy, glabrous; stipe (4–)5–12 mm. $2n = 22$.

Flowering Jun–Sep. Dry, sandy or stony margins of meadows, mountain flats, lakeshores, openings in coniferous forests, on granitic soils; 1500–3100 m; Calif., Nev.

Astragalus bolanderi, restricted to the Sierra Nevada, California, and Mount Rose, Washoe County, Nevada, is the only *Astragalus* found along the western slope of the Sierra Nevada at 2000–3100 m.

135vv. Astragalus Linnaeus sect. Bicristati Barneby, Mem. New York Bot. Gard. 13: 560. 1964 [E]

Herbs perennial, caulescent; caudex shallowly or deeply subterranean. **Hairs** basifixed. **Stems** several to many. **Stipules** proximally connate, distally distinct. **Leaves** odd-pinnate, subsessile to short-petiolate; leaflets 13–21(–25), terminal leaflet sometimes continuous with rachis. **Racemes** densely or loosely flowered, flowers ascending or spreading. **Calyx tubes** campanulate or short-cylindric. **Corollas** ochroleucous or greenish white, banner recurved through 45–75°, keel apex deltate. **Legumes** ultimately deciduous, sessile or stipitate, ascending or pendulous, obliquely oblong to ellipsoid or oblanceoloid-ellipsoid, slightly incurved to 0.5 to 1 full spiral, ± dorsiventrally compressed or 3-sided or obcompressed, unilocular or sub-bilocular. **Seeds** 18–33.

Species 3 (3 in the flora): California.

Section *Bicristati* consists of two subsections: subsect. *Webberani* Barneby (*Astragalus webberi*), and subsect. *Bicristati* Barneby (*A. bicristatus*, *A. ertterae*).

158. Astragalus webberi A. Gray in W. H. Brewer et al., Bot. California 1: 154. 1876 • Webber's milkvetch C E

Plants somewhat robust, 15–50 cm, strigulose; from shallow, subterranean caudex. **Stems** decumbent to ascending, (0–)1–5 cm underground, strigulose. **Leaves** (2.5–)4–13(–15) cm; stipules (1.5–)2–7 mm, papery-scarious at proximal nodes, herbaceous at distal nodes; leaflets (9–)15–21(–25), blades broadly to narrowly oblanceolate or elliptic-oblanceolate, (5–)10–25(–35) mm, apex obtuse, retuse, or truncate and apiculate or subacute, surfaces strigulose. **Peduncles** incurved-ascending, reclined in fruit, (3–)4–8 cm. **Racemes** (5–)8–18-flowered, flowers spreading; axis (0.5–)1–3(–5) cm in fruit; bracts 1.2–3 mm; bracteoles 0–2. **Pedicels** (0.8–)1–2.5(–3.5) mm. **Flowers** 13–17.6 mm; calyx campanulate to short-cylindric, (6.4–)7–12(–13) mm, villosulous, tube (4.5–)4.8–6.3(–6.8) mm, lobes subulate, (1.8–)2.5–5.3(–6.2) mm; corolla ochroleucous, immaculate; banner strongly recurved through 50–75°; keel 11.4–13.7 mm. **Legumes** ascending (humistrate), green or red-spotted becoming brownish stramineous, slightly incurved, obliquely oblong-ellipsoid, slightly obcompressed, (20–)25–35 × (7–)8–12 mm, unilocular or sub-bilocular, fleshy becoming stiffly leathery or woody, glabrous; valves inflexed, septum 0–1.5 mm wide; sessile. **Seeds** 20–26.

Flowering May–Jul. Open, brushy slopes and flats in xeric pine or mixed pine-oak forests; of conservation concern; 800–1600 m; Calif.

Astragalus webberi occurs in the headwaters of the Feather River in Plumas and Sierra counties.

159. Astragalus bicristatus A. Gray, Proc. Amer. Acad. Arts 19: 75. 1883 • Two-keeled or crested milkvetch E

Plants 20–50 cm, strigulose; from shallow, subterranean caudex. **Stems** decumbent to ascending, strigulose. **Leaves** 3–11(–13.5) cm; stipules 1.5–4 mm, papery-scarious at proximal nodes, herbaceous at distal nodes; leaflets (11 or)13–21(or 23), blades rarely flat, linear, linear-elliptic, narrowly oblong to oblong-elliptic, or oblanceolate, (2–)4–25(–27) mm, apex obtuse, retuse, or subacute, surfaces strigulose abaxially, strigulose, densely cinereous, or glabrous adaxially; terminal leaflet sometimes decurrent distally, not jointed to rachis. **Peduncles** incurved-ascending, 5–12(–15) cm. **Racemes** loosely 5–15(–20)-flowered, flowers ascending; axis 1–6(–9) cm in fruit; bracts 1.5–2.5 mm; bracteoles 2. **Pedicels** 0.8–2.5 mm. **Flowers** 15–19 mm; calyx deeply campanulate, 8.1–10.1 mm, loosely strigulose, tube 5.8–7.6 mm, lobes subulate, 1.8–3.3 mm; corolla greenish white, drying ochroleucous, immaculate; banner recurved through 45–50°; keel 12–13 mm. **Legumes** pendulous, not set at angle to stipe, brownish, shallowly to deeply incurved or hamate, to 0.5 or 1 spiral, obliquely oblong or clavate-ellipsoid, subterete to somewhat obcompressed becoming dorsiventrally compressed, 20–40(–43) × 5–8.5(–9) mm, unilocular, thick becoming stiffly leathery or subligneous, glabrous; stipe (6–)8–12 mm. **Seeds** 26–33.

Flowering May–Aug. Ridges, sagebrush flats, lakeshores, canyon benches, pine forests; 1700–2500 m; Calif.

Astragalus bicristatus is restricted to the mountains of Los Angeles, western Riverside, and western San Bernardino counties.

160. Astragalus ertterae Barneby & Shevock, Aliso 11: 585, fig. 1. 1987 • Ertter's milkvetch C E

Plants dwarf, 3–9 cm, pilose; from deep, subterranean caudex. **Stems** procumbent to ascending, 2–8 cm underground, pilose. **Leaves** 3–6.5 cm; stipules 2–3 mm, papery-scarious; leaflets 9–13, blades elliptic-oblanceolate or narrowly obovate-cuneate, (6–)8–13 mm, apex obtuse to subemarginate, surfaces pilose. **Peduncles** erect or slightly spreading, 2–5 cm. **Racemes** densely 7–17-flowered, flowers ascending-spreading; axis 1–4 cm in fruit; bracts 1.5–2 mm; bracteoles 0. **Pedicels** 1–1.5 mm. **Flowers** 10–11.5 mm; calyx campanulate, 5.5–6 mm, loosely strigulose, tube 3.5–4.2 mm, lobes subulate, 1.6–2 mm; corolla ochroleucous, immaculate; banner recurved through 45°. **Legumes** pendulous (humistrate), brown, sometimes purple-mottled, gently incurved, obliquely ellipsoid to oblanceoloid-ellipsoid, 3-sided compressed, 16–22 × 7–9 mm, unilocular, leathery, glabrous; stipe 1–2 mm. **Seeds** 18–21.

Flowering Apr–early May (fruiting by early Jun). Sandy-loamy granitic soils, pinyon woodlands with canyon live oak; of conservation concern; 1700–1900 m; Calif.

Astragalus ertterae is a rare and local species known from the vicinity of Walker Pass in the southern Sierra Nevada, Kern County.

135ww. ASTRAGALUS Linnaeus sect. PORRECTI (Rydberg) Barneby, Mem. New York Bot. Gard. 13: 565. 1964 [E]

Homalobus Nuttall sect. *Porrecti* Rydberg, Bull. Torrey Bot. Club 51: 19. 1924

Herbs perennial, forming bushy clumps, caulescent; caudex superficial or slightly subterranean. **Hairs** basifixed. **Stems** several. **Stipules** connate at proximal nodes, distinct at distal nodes. **Leaves** odd-pinnate, short-petiolate or subsessile; leaflets 9–13. **Racemes** loosely flowered, flowers ascending. **Calyx tubes** campanulate. **Corollas** white, banner recurved through 60–80°, keel apex obtuse. **Legumes** persistent, continuous with receptacle, stipitate, incurved-ascending, lunately oblong-ellipsoid, laterally compressed, both sutures keeled, incurved, unilocular. **Seeds** 7–10.

Species 1: Nevada.

161. Astragalus porrectus S. Watson, Botany (Fortieth Parallel), 75. 1871 • Lahontan milkvetch [E]

Plants stiff, 25–50(–60) cm, strigulose. **Stems** erect, strigulose or glabrous, or glabrate proximally. **Leaves** 3.5–11 cm; stipules 2–9 mm, scarious; leaflet blades broadly obovate-cuneate or obovate-flabellate, 7–15(–18) mm, apex obtuse to retuse, surfaces glabrous. **Peduncles** erect, 3.5–15 cm. **Racemes** (7–)12–33-flowered; axis 4–20(–28) cm in fruit; bracts 1–3.4 mm; bracteoles 0. **Pedicels** 0.5–2 mm. **Flowers** 8–11 mm; calyx 4.7–5.5 mm, strigulose, tube 3–3.5 mm, lobes subulate, 1.7–2 mm; corolla white, drying ochroleucous; banner recurved through 60–80°; keel 6.8–7.7 mm. **Legumes** incurved-ascending, green, sometimes purple-tinged or -mottled, becoming stramineous, sometimes suffused with purplish brown, incurved through 0.25 spiral, 8–15 × 3–5 mm, fleshy becoming leathery, glabrous; stipe (2.5–)3–5 mm.

Flowering May–Jun. Washes, alluvial fans, on igneous sand and detritus; 1200–1600 m; Nev.

Astragalus porrectus is a rare and local species known only from northwestern Churchill, Humboldt, Lyon, Pershing, and Washoe counties.

135xx. ASTRAGALUS Linnaeus sect. AMPULLARII Barneby, Mem. New York Bot. Gard. 13: 567. 1964 [C] [E]

Herbs perennial, caulescent; caudex deeply subterranean. **Hairs** basifixed. **Stems** single or few. **Stipules** connate or distally distinct. **Leaves** odd-pinnate, petiolate; leaflets 7–21. **Racemes** loosely flowered, flowers ascending. **Calyx tubes** short-cylindric. **Corollas** ochroleucous or pink-purple, banner recurved through 25–30°, keel apex obtuse. **Legumes** persistent, stipitate, erect or ascending, ellipsoid, ovoid, or subglobose, inflated, ± unilocular. **Seeds** 17–25.

Species 2 (2 in the flora): sw United States.

Section *Ampullarii* is considered here to contain two distinctive species held together by their subterranean caudices, connate proximalmost stipules, and inflated pods; distributions on Triassic Chinle muds are as noted below.

162. Astragalus ampullarius S. Watson, Amer. Naturalist 7: 300. 1873 • Gumbo milkvetch [C] [E]

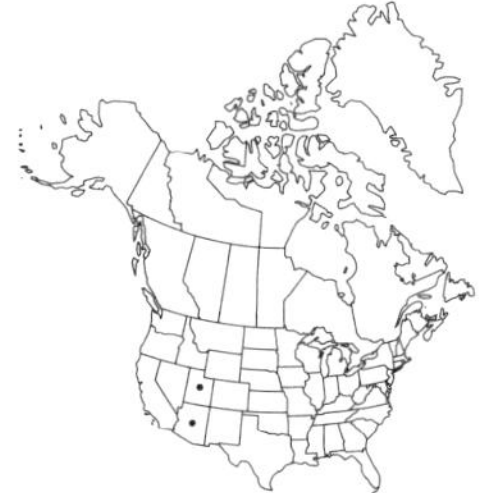

Plants shortly caulescent, 2–28 cm, strigulose. **Stems** single or few, prostrate-ascending, 3.5–14 cm underground, strigulose. **Leaves** 3–14 cm; stipules connate-sheathing at proximal nodes, connate or distinct at distal nodes, 2–6 mm, membranous; leaflets 7–15(–19), blades obovate, 4–15 mm, apex round to emarginate, surfaces strigose, sometimes glabrous adaxially. **Peduncles** erect, 0.5–9.5 cm. **Racemes** 5–20-flowered; axis 1.2–13 cm in fruit; bracts 1.5–3 mm; bracteoles 2. **Pedicels** 1–3 mm. **Flowers** 13.5–22 mm; calyx 4.8–7.5 mm, black-strigose, tube 4.2–6 mm, lobes broadly triangular, 0.5–1.5 mm; corolla ochroleucous, or pink-purple with white wing tips; banner recurved through 30°; keel 9–12.2 mm. **Legumes** ascending-erect, green and purple-dotted becoming purple-stramineous, straight or slightly decurved, ovoid to subglobose, terete, inflated, 12–20 × 8–11 mm, thin becoming papery, glabrous or glabrate; stipe 9–19 mm.

Flowering late Apr–Jun. Clay soils, on knolls in pinyon-juniper communities; of conservation concern; 900–1700 m; Ariz., Utah.

Astragalus ampullarius is restricted to outcrops of the Triassic Chinle Formation in western Kane and eastern Washington counties, Utah, and immediately adjacent Arizona. It is often the most prevalent plant among several endemics on this formation. The marcescent stems and fruits of the previous year, circular-reclining, bleached and skeletonlike, are quite unlike those of any other species. After its discovery, it remained obscure for nearly seven decades until rediscovered by Alice Eastwood and J. T. Howell in 1941, not that it is so rare, but because it is restricted to such a narrowly exposed geological formation, much of which is remote.

163. Astragalus ampullarioides (S. L. Welsh) S. L. Welsh, Great Basin Naturalist 58: 51. 1998 • Shivwits milkvetch [C] [E]

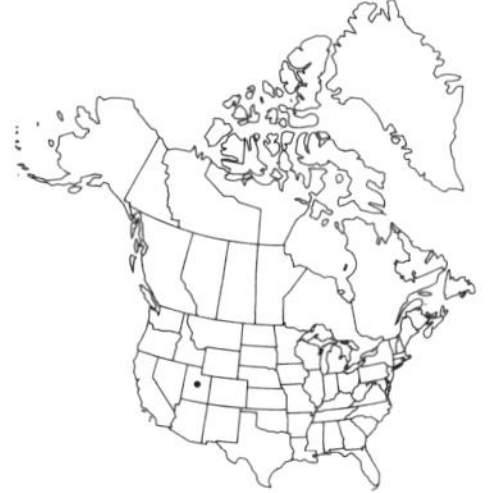

Astragalus eremiticus E. Sheldon var. *ampularioides* S. L. Welsh, Great Basin Naturalist 46: 262. 1986

Plants caulescent, 20–63 cm, sparsely strigulose; from subterranean branched caudex. **Stems** decumbent proximally, erect distally, 2–10 cm underground, often fistulose, sparsely strigulose. **Leaves** 5–22 cm; stipules connate-sheathing at proximal nodes, distinct at distal nodes, 3–9 mm; leaflets 13–21, blades ovate to obovate, lanceolate, or elliptic, 4–24 mm, apex obtuse to retuse, surfaces strigose along veins abaxially, glabrous adaxially. **Peduncles** (4–)9–23 cm. **Racemes** (15–)20–40-flowered; axis (4–)10–16 cm in fruit; bracts 1.5–4 mm; bracteoles 0–2. **Pedicels** 0.7–3.5 mm. **Flowers** (11–)14–18 mm; calyx 5–6 mm, strigose, tube 4–5 mm, lobes triangular to subulate, 0.5–0.9(–1.2) mm; corolla ochroleucous; banner recurved through 25°. **Legumes** erect, ovoid to ellipsoid, obcompressed, inflated (turgid), 12–18 × 8–10(–12) mm, papery, glabrous; septum to 0.2 mm wide; stipe slender, 7–15 mm.

Flowering Apr–May. Gypsiferous substrates, in boils on the Triassic Chinle Formation, with creosote bush, warm desert shrubs, juniper communities; of conservation concern; 900–1200 m; Utah.

Astragalus ampullarioides was dismissed as taxonomically inconsequential by R. C. Barneby (1989) and D. Isely (1998), yet the combination of characteristics that distinguish this species from its closest relative is as strong as similar comparisons elsewhere in the genus. It is restricted to Washington County.

Astragalus ampullarioides is in the Center for Plant Conservation's National Collection of Endangered Plants.

135yy. Astragalus Linnaeus sect. Pachyphylla M. E. Jones, Zoë 2: 239. 1891 [E]

Herbs perennial, caulescent; caudex superficial or shallowly subterranean. **Hairs** basifixed. **Stems** single or few to many. **Stipules** distinct. **Leaves** unifoliolate, subsessile, petiole ± clasping. **Racemes** densely flowered, flowers ascending. **Calyx tubes** cylindric. **Corollas** greenish yellow or purplish, suffused with purple or almost ochroleucous, banner recurved through 30°, keel apex obtuse. **Legumes** persistent, stipitate, erect-ascending, ovoid or ovoid-ellipsoid, inflated, unilocular. **Seeds** 40–62.

Species 1: w United States.

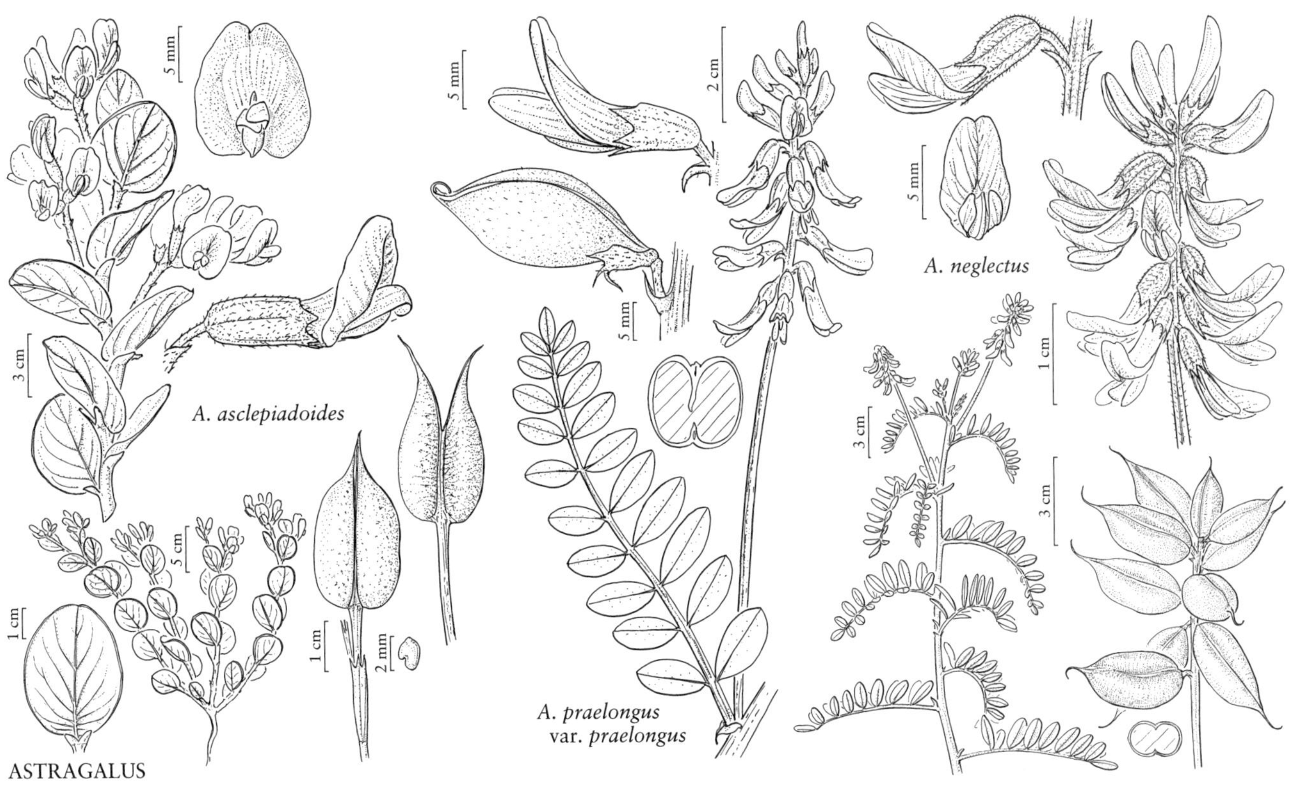

ASTRAGALUS

164. Astragalus asclepiadoides M. E. Jones, Zoë 2: 238. 1891 • Milkweed milkvetch E F

Plants stout, 7–62 cm, glabrous or glabrate. **Stems** erect, 0–7 cm underground, glabrous. **Leaves** crowded, loosely imbricate, 1.5–6.5 cm; stipules 2–15 mm, membranous; leaflet blade ovate, orbiculate, or cordate, 15–65 mm, apex obtuse to rounded or retuse, surfaces glabrous. **Peduncles** erect, 0.5–4.5 cm. **Racemes** 2–12-flowered; axis 0.4–2.5 cm in fruit; bracts 1–5 mm; bracteoles 2. **Pedicels** 1–5 mm. **Flowers** 17–27 mm; calyx 10–17 mm, black-strigose, tube 8.3–13 mm, lobes linear to subulate, 1.5–3.8 mm; corolla keel 14.2–18.5 mm. **Legumes** pale green and purple-speckled becoming stramineous, straight, 25–35 × 11–16 mm, fleshy becoming leathery or stiffly papery, glabrous; stipe 10–23 mm. $2n = 24$.

Flowering May–Jun. Saline desert shrub communities on fine-textured, seleniferous, Arapien, Cretaceous Mancos, and Tropic shales, Jurassic Carmel, Tertiary Duchesne River, and Triassic Moenkopi formations; 1200–2400 m; Colo., Utah.

Astragalus asclepiadoides is known from western Colorado and northeastern and north-central Utah.

Astragalus asclepiadoides is unique for the genus in the flora area, with broad, leathery, unifoliolate leaves. The blade apparently represents the terminal leaflet of an ancestral imparipinnate leaf; a few Eurasian taxa show somewhat parallel modification (R. C. Barneby 1964). The leaves, though alternate, bear an uncanny resemblance to those of the milkweed *Asclepias cryptoceras*.

135zz. Astragalus Linnaeus sect. Preussiani M. E. Jones, Rev. N.-Amer. Astragalus, 152. 1923

Herbs perennial (sometimes flowering as annual), course, selenophytes, clump-forming, caulescent; caudex usually superficial (sometimes subterranean in *A. praelongus*). **Hairs** basifixed. **Stems** few or several to many. **Stipules** usually distinct, rarely connate-sheathing at proximal nodes (in *A. praelongus*). **Leaves** odd-pinnate, shortly subsessile to petiolate; leaflets

(1 or)3–33, jointed (terminal leaflet sometimes decurrent in *A. preussii*). **Racemes** loosely flowered, sometimes initially densely flowered, flowers ascending to deflexed, declined, or nodding. **Calyx tubes** cylindric, sometimes base oblique or gibbous. **Corollas** pink to purple, magenta-purple, reddish purple, ochroleucous, white, or yellowish, banner recurved through 30–90°, keel apex round, obtuse, blunt, bluntly triangular, or bluntly rectangular. **Legumes** persistent, sessile or subsessile to stipitate, erect, spreading, or declined, narrowly ellipsoid to broadly ovoid, oblong-ellipsoid, obovoid, or subglobose, scarcely swollen to strongly inflated, unilocular or subunilocular. **Seeds** 20–75(–84).

Species 10 (10 in the flora): sw United States, nw Mexico.

Section *Preussiani* consists of three subsections: subsect. *Preussiani* (M. E. Jones) Barneby (*Astragalus beathii*, *A. crotalariae*, *A. cutleri*, *A. eastwoodiae*, *A. debequaeus*, *A. preussii*); subsect. *Pattersoniani* M. E. Jones (*A. pattersonii*, *A. praelongus*); and subsect. *Sabulosi* Barneby (*A. iselyi*, *A. sabulosus*). Taxa in sect. *Preussiani* are distributed on seleniferous substrates.

165. Astragalus preussii A. Gray, Proc. Amer. Acad. Arts 6: 222. 1864 • Preuss's milkvetch [E]

Plants sometimes flowering first year, moderate to robust, forming bushy clumps, (10–) 12–53 cm, appressed-hairy; from superficial woody caudex. **Stems** erect or incurved-ascending, diffuse, glabrous or glabrate. **Leaves** 3.5–15 cm; stipules 2–7 mm, papery at proximal nodes, herbaceous at distal nodes; leaflets (7 or)9–25, blades obovate, suborbiculate, obcordate to oblong, narrowly elliptic, lanceolate, or linear, 6–28 mm, apex retuse-emarginate to rounded, obtuse, acute, or truncate, sometimes apiculate, surfaces glabrous, hairs sometimes on margins or midrib. **Peduncles** erect-ascending, 2–15 cm. **Racemes** 3–24-flowered, flowers ascending; axis 1–20 cm in fruit; bracts 1.5–4 mm; bracteoles 2. **Pedicels** 1–5.5 mm. **Flowers** 14–24 mm; calyx purple, 6.4–12.3 mm, sparsely strigose, tube 5.1–9.7 mm, lobes subulate, 1.3–2.6 mm; corolla pink-purple, bicolored, or white to pale greenish yellow and, sometimes, modestly suffused with purple; banner recurved through 40–45°; keel (11.1–)11.5–19 mm, apex blunt. **Legumes** dehiscent on plant, erect to ascending, green or red-dotted becoming stramineous, straight or slightly incurved, cylindroid, ellipsoid, ovoid, or oblong-ellipsoid, inflated, 12–34 × 6–13 mm, unilocular, stiffly papery to leathery, glabrous or puberulent; stipe 0–7 mm. **Seeds** 20–44.

Varieties 3 (3 in the flora): sw United States.

Astragalus preussii was named for Charles Preuss, the topographer with J. C. Frémont on his second expedition in 1843–44, when the type was collected.

1. Legumes sessile or subsessile; raceme axes 9–19.5 cm in fruit; calyces 6.4–8.5(–9.4) mm; nw Arizona, s Nevada, and sw Utah .... 165b. *Astragalus preussii* var. *laxiflorus*
1. Legumes stipitate (stipes 2–7 mm); raceme axes (1–)4–20 cm in fruit; calyces (6.4–)8.5–12.3 mm; n Arizona, se California, s Nevada, and se Utah.
   2. Leaflets usually (7–)11–17, blades (2–)5–10 mm wide; nw Arizona, se California, and s Nevada ..... 165a. *Astragalus preussii* var. *preussii*
   2. Leaflets 17–25, blades 1–6 mm wide; nc Arizona, sw Colorado, and se Utah..... .... 165c. *Astragalus preussii* var. *latus*

165a. Astragalus preussii A. Gray var. **preussii** [E]

Plants 20–35(–40) cm. **Leaves** 4–8 cm; leaflets usually (7–) 11–17, blades broadly obovate, 3–14 × (2–)5–10 mm, apex retuse-emarginate to truncate, sometimes apiculate. **Peduncles** (4.5–)8–11.5 cm. **Racemes** (8–) 10–19-flowered; axis 4–9.5 cm, slightly elongated in fruit. **Flowers:** calyx 8.5–11 mm, tube purplish and not strongly contrasting with corolla, 8–9 mm, lobes 1.5–1.9 mm; corolla usually purple or suffused with purple; banner 17.4–24 mm. **Legumes** cylindroid to narrowly ellipsoid, length often 3+ times width, 24–33 × 6–10 mm, tapering at base; stipe 2–5+ mm. $2n = 24$.

Flowering late Mar–May. Blackbrush, mixed desert shrub communities, on seleniferous clay or silt, valley floors; 1100–1600 m; Ariz., Calif., Nev.

Variety *preussii* occurs from Clark and Nye counties in the southern tip of Nevada into adjacent San Bernardino County in California, and Mohave County in Arizona. D. Isely (1998) provided a key to eastern and western phases of this variety.

165b. Astragalus preussii A. Gray var. **laxiflorus** A. Gray, Proc. Amer. Acad. Arts 13: 369. 1878 • Littlefield milkvetch [C] [E]

Astragalus crotalariae (Bentham) A. Gray var. *davidsonii* (Rydberg) Munz & McBurney

Plants sometimes flowering first year, (10–)30–53 cm. **Leaves** 4–15 cm; leaflets (7 or)9–15 (or 17), blades broadly obovate to suborbiculate, 6–18(–23) × 3–11(–13) mm, apex obtuse or truncate and apiculate. **Peduncles** (6–)8–15 cm. **Racemes** lax, (8–)15–24-flowered; axis 9–19.5 cm, slightly elongated in fruit. **Flowers:** calyx 6.4–8.5(–9.4) mm, tube color strongly contrasting with corolla, 5.5–7 mm, lobes 1.5–1.9 mm; corolla usually pale greenish yellow, less commonly suffused with pale purple; banner 14–17.5 mm. **Legumes** ovoid to ellipsoid, length usually less than 3 times width, 17–20(–25) × 7–10(–11) mm, abruptly contracted at base; sessile or subsessile. $2n = 24$.

Flowering late Feb–May. Creosote bush and desert-holly communities, on gypsum soils; of conservation concern; 600–2500 m; Ariz., Calif., Nev., Utah.

Variety *laxiflorus* is restricted to the vicinity of the juncture of Mohave County in Arizona, Clark County in Nevada, and Washington County in Utah; it is not known from modern Utah collections. R. C. Barneby (1964) suggested that in the widely disjunct station on the western edge of the Mojave Desert at Lancaster, the plants recognized as *Astragalus crotalariae* var. *davidsonii*, though similar in habit and fruit, may represent an independent origin because of the small flowers and fewer ovules. There are no recent collections, and that population is likely extinct.

165c. Astragalus preussii A. Gray var. **latus** M. E. Jones, Zoë 4: 36. 1893 • Green River stinking milkvetch [E]

Plants sometimes flowering first year, 12–45(–50) cm. **Leaves** 3.5–13 cm; leaflets 17–25, blades obovate, obcordate to oblong, narrowly elliptic, lanceolate, or linear, 6–28 × 1–6 mm, apex emarginate to rounded, obtuse, or acute. **Peduncles** 2–15 cm. **Racemes** 3–22-flowered; axis 1–20 cm in fruit. **Flowers:** calyx 6.4–12.3 mm, tube color not contrasting with corolla, 5.1–9.7 mm, lobes 1.3–2.6 mm; corolla usually pink-purple or bicolored, rarely white; banner 17–24 mm. **Legumes** oblong-ellipsoid to ovoid, length usually less than 3 times width, sutures becoming moderately salient, 12–34 × 6–13 mm; stipe 2–7 mm. $2n = 24$.

Flowering late Mar–early Jun. Blackbrush, mixed desert shrub on seleniferous clay or silt; 1100–1600 m; Ariz., Colo., Utah.

Variety *latus* is the common phase of the species in southeastern Utah and north-central Arizona and is the only one to reach Colorado. The petals are ordinarily a dark purple that does not contrast greatly with the vivid purple calyx, and the fruits are typically much less than three times longer than broad.

166. Astragalus cutleri (Barneby) S. L. Welsh, Great Basin Naturalist 58: 51. 1998 • Cutler's milkvetch [C] [E]

Astragalus preussii A. Gray var. *cutleri* Barneby, Great Basin Naturalist 46: 256. 1986

Plants sometimes flowering first year, forming large, bushy clumps, 10–30(–35) cm, sparsely strigulose to glabrate; from superficial caudex. **Stems** ascending to erect, sparsely strigulose to glabrate. **Leaves** 3–13 cm; stipules 2–6.5 mm; leaflets 5–17(or 19), blades elliptic to lanceolate, oblanceolate, or obovate, 3–17(–20) mm, apex acute to obtuse or apiculate, surfaces strigulose or glabrous abaxially, glabrous adaxially. **Peduncles** 2.5–10 cm. **Racemes** 5–9-flowered; bracts 1.5–2.5 mm; bracteoles 2. **Pedicels** 1.5–2.5 mm. **Flowers** 15–16 mm; calyx pale purple or whitish, cylindric, (7.3–)7.5–8.5(–9) mm, sparsely black-strigose, tube 5.9–6.7 mm, lobes subulate, 1.3–1.7(–2.3) mm; corolla white or tinged purplish (or drying purplish); banner recurved through 40–45°. **Legumes** ascending to erect, greenish sometimes suffused with purple, oblong-ellipsoid, inflated, 14–18 × 9–11 mm, thinly cartilaginous, glabrous; unilocular; stipe 3–3.5 mm. **Seeds** 20–38.

Flowering Apr–May. Saltbush and blackbrush communities, on Permian Formations; of conservation concern; 1100–1300 m; Utah.

Astragalus cutleri, restricted to San Juan County, was earlier thought to be an annual, but more recent collections demonstrated that it is at least a short-lived perennial.

167. Astragalus eastwoodiae M. E. Jones, Zoë 4: 368. 1894 (as eastwoodae) • Eastwood's milkvetch [E]

Astragalus preussii A. Gray var. *sulcatus* M. E. Jones, Zoë 4: 37. 1893, not *A. sulcatus* Linnaeus 1753; *A. preussii* var. *eastwoodiae* (M. E. Jones) M. E. Jones

Plants slender, diffuse, forming small, bushy clumps, shortly caulescent, 8–20 cm, mostly glabrous; from superficial caudex. **Stems** decumbent to ascending, glabrous. **Leaves** 3–13 cm; stipules 2–6.5 mm, submembranous becoming papery-scarious; leaflets 13–25, blades elliptic to lanceolate-elliptic, oblanceolate, or obovate, 1–15 mm, apex obtuse to truncate-emarginate, surfaces glabrous. **Peduncles** erect or ascending, 2–10.5 cm. **Racemes** 3–7-flowered, flowers ascending; axis 0.5–3.5(–4) cm in fruit; bracts 1.5–4.5 mm; bracteoles 2. **Pedicels** 1.5–3.5 mm. **Flowers** 18–22 mm; calyx purple, 10–12.2 mm, sparsely black-strigose, tube 8–9.5 mm, lobes subulate, 1.3–2.7 mm; corolla pink-purple; banner recurved through 45°; keel 15.4–17.7 mm, apex round. **Legumes** spreading to declined, pale green or red-tinged becoming stramineous, straight, oblong-ellipsoid, inflated, 14–26 × 7–14.5 mm, thinly fleshy becoming papery, usually glabrous, rarely minutely scabrid-pubescent; unilocular; stipe 1.5–4.5 mm. **Seeds** 20–38. $2n$ = 24, 26.

Flowering late Apr–Jun. Seleniferous, often fine-textured soils, mixed desert shrub and pinyon-juniper communities; 1300–2100 m; Colo., Utah.

Astragalus eastwoodiae is very closely related to *A. preussii*, and possibly derived from the narrow-leaved form of that species from the Colorado Basin (R. C. Barneby 1964). M. E. Jones noted this from the start and ultimately considered it as *A. preussii* var. *eastwoodiae*. The taxon is found in west-central and southwestern Colorado and southeastern Utah.

168. Astragalus debequaeus S. L. Welsh, Great Basin Naturalist 45: 31, fig. 1. 1985 • Debeque milkvetch [C] [E]

Astragalus eastwoodiae M. E. Jones var. *debequaeus* (S. L. Welsh) Isely

Plants forming prostrate to bushy clumps, 14–30 cm, mostly glabrous; from superficial caudex. **Stems** decumbent or curved-ascending, glabrous. **Leaves** 2–10 cm; stipules 3–6 mm, membranous becoming papery-scarious; leaflets 13–21, blades elliptic to oblong, oblanceolate, or obovate, 2–12 mm, apex obtuse to truncate, surfaces glabrous. **Peduncles** erect or ascending, 4.5–8.8 cm. **Racemes** (5 or)6–9-flowered, flowers spreading to ascending; axis 3–5.5 cm in fruit; bracts 2.2–2.5 mm; bracteoles 1 or 2. **Pedicels** 2–3.5 mm. **Flowers** 17–21 mm; calyx greenish to stramineous, 6.3–8 mm, sparsely black-strigose, tube 5–6 mm, lobes subulate, 1.3–2 mm; corolla white; banner recurved through 30°; keel 13–15 mm, apex obtuse. **Legumes** ascending, stramineous, straight, oblong-ellipsoid to lanceoloid-ellipsoid, inflated, 15–23 × 6–11 mm, thinly leathery, scabrid-pubescent; unilocular; stipe 2–2.5 mm. **Seeds** 20–38.

Flowering May–Jun. Varicolored, fine-textured seleniferous and saline substrates, in pinyon-juniper and mixed shrub communities; of conservation concern; 1600–2000 m; Colo.

Astragalus debequaeus occurs on the Atwell Gulch Member of the Tertiary Wasatch and Jurassic Morrison formations in Mesa County. It is a broadly spreading to prostrate clump-former, quite unlike its close relatives. The range of *A. debequaeus* lies to the east of, and elevationally above, the allied and similar *A. eastwoodiae*. D. Isely (1998) considered it worthy of recognition at the varietal level; W. A. Weber (1987) considered it to be a color form of *A. eastwoodiae*, but later Weber and R. C. Wittmann (1992) restored it to specific rank.

Astragalus debequaeus is in the Center for Plant Conservation's National Collection of Endangered Plants.

169. Astragalus crotalariae (Bentham) A. Gray, Proc. Amer. Acad. Arts 6: 216. 1864 • Rattlebox milkvetch

Phaca crotalariae Bentham, Pl. Hartw., 307. 1849

Plants coarse, forming small, bushy clumps, 15–50(–60) cm, strigulose to pilose; from superficial caudex. **Stems** erect to ascending, strigulose to pilose. **Leaves** 5–14(–16.5) cm; stipules 4–12 mm, thinly herbaceous becoming papery; leaflets (3–)9–17(or 19), blades obovate-cuneate, broadly oblong-obovate, or oblong-elliptic to suborbiculate-obcordate, (5–)7–30(–35) mm, apex retuse or emarginate, surfaces glabrous or, sometimes, sparsely pubescent adaxially. **Peduncles** erect becoming weakly ascending, (5–)7–17 cm. **Racemes** 10–25-flowered, flowers ascending; axis (2–)3–10 cm in fruit; bracts 1.5–4 mm; bracteoles 0–2. **Pedicels** 1.2–4.5 mm. **Flowers** 21–28 mm; calyx purple, (7.6–)8–12.3 mm, strigulose to pilosulous, tube (6.3–)6.7–9.7 mm, lobes subulate, (1.3–)1.8–2.7 mm; corolla usually magenta-purple, reddish purple, or pink-purple, rarely white; banner recurved through 40°; keel 17.4–

21 mm, apex round. **Legumes** ascending to spreading, light green, sometimes suffused with red, becoming stramineous, straight, oblong-, ovoid-, or broadly ellipsoid, inflated, hardly bladdery, 20–30 × 10–14 mm, papery, strigulose; unilocular; stipe 1–1.5 mm. **Seeds** 24–38. **2*n*** = 24.

Flowering Jan–Apr. With creosote bush in Colorado Desert; 60–300 m; Ariz., Calif.; Mexico (Baja California).

Astragalus crotalariae is a close relative of *A. preussii* and occurs around the Salton Sea in California eastward to the Yuma Desert in southwestern Arizona and northern Baja California.

170. Astragalus beathii Ced. Porter, Madroño 6: 18, plate 3. 1941 • Beath's milkvetch C E

Plants coarse, forming bushy clumps, 25–60 cm, strigulose; from superficial caudex. **Stems** erect to ascending, becoming stout, fistulose, strigulose, sometimes glabrate proximally. **Leaves** 6–12(–15) cm; stipules 3–9.5 mm, submembranous becoming papery-scarious, pallid; leaflets 11–21(or 23), blades narrowly elliptic-oblanceolate to broadly obovate or oblong-obovate, 5–25 mm, apex obtuse to retuse, surfaces proximally glabrous, distally pubescent abaxially, glabrous adaxially. **Peduncles** incurved-ascending, (2.5–)4–10 cm. **Racemes** 10–27-flowered, flowers spreading-ascending; axis 3.5–10 cm in fruit; bracts 2–4.2 mm; bracteoles 0–2. **Pedicels** 0.9–3 mm. **Flowers** (17–)20–25(–27) mm; calyx (7.7–)8.2–10.5 mm, sparsely to densely strigulose, tube (5.3–)5.7–7.8 mm, lobes subulate, 1.8–3.1 mm; corolla purple, wing tips pale or white; banner recurved through 40°; keel (9.6–)11.2–16.4 mm, apex bluntly triangular. **Legumes** firmly attached to receptacle, falling while attached to pedicel, deflexed or declined, green or purplish green becoming stramineous, straight or slightly incurved, narrowly to plumply oblong-ellipsoid, somewhat obcompressed, 20–39 × 7–11 mm, sub-bilocular, thick, fleshy becoming leathery, glabrous or minutely puberulent; septum 1.3–2.3 mm wide; stipe 0–0.6 mm. **Seeds** 29–52. **2*n*** = 24.

Flowering late Mar–May. Sandy flats, red clay knolls, and gullied washes in badlands, *Atriplex*, *Ephedra*, matchweed, *Yucca*, and galleta communities, seleniferous substrates of Moenkopi Formation; of conservation concern; 1200–1500 m; Ariz.

Astragalus beathii is a locally abundant, narrow endemic, found near Cameron, in Coconino County.

171. Astragalus praelongus E. Sheldon, Minnesota Bot. Stud. 1: 23. 1894 • Stinking milkvetch E F

Astragalus procerus A. Gray, Proc. Amer. Acad. Arts 13: 369. 1878, not Boissier & Haussknecht 1872

Plants robust to very robust, forming moderate to very large, bushy clumps, 10–120 cm, strigulose; from superficial or subterranean branched caudex. **Stems** erect or ascending, glabrate, sometimes sparsely strigose distally. **Leaves** 3–22 cm; stipules usually distinct throughout, rarely connate-sheathing at proximal nodes (var. *avonensis*), 2–7(–9) mm, thinly herbaceous becoming papery-scarious; leaflets 7–33, blades obovate, elliptic, oblong, lanceolate, or oblanceolate, 3–50 mm, apex obtuse or retuse to acute, surfaces sparsely strigose or glabrescent abaxially, glabrous adaxially. **Peduncles** erect, 4–26 cm. **Racemes** 8–33-flowered, flowers deflexed; axis 3–16 cm in fruit; bracts 1–7 mm; bracteoles 2. **Pedicels** 1–7 mm. **Flowers** (11–)15–24 mm; calyx green or yellowish, gibbous, 5.8–14 mm, glabrous or sparsely strigose, tube 4.4–7.5 mm, lobes erect-ascending, subulate, deltate, lanceolate-subulate, lanceolate-attenuate, or triangular-subulate, 0.3–6 mm; corolla ochroleucous or pale lemon yellow, keel often faintly to definitely maculate (purplish-tipped) or immaculate; banner recurved through 45°; keel 11.5–17 mm, apex bluntly rectangular. **Legumes** firmly attached to receptacle, falling while attached to pedicel, erect to spreading or declined, green or purplish-speckled becoming brown or stramineous, usually straight, ellipsoid, ovoid, cylindroid, obovoid, or subglobose, inflated, 18–42 × 5–25 mm, subunilocular, fleshy becoming leathery-woody, glabrous or puberulent; septum 0.8–2.3 mm wide; stipe 0–8 mm. **Seeds** 40–75(–84).

Varieties 4 (4 in the flora): sw United States.

Astragalus praelongus is malodorous and smells so strongly that some find the odor nauseating.

1. Flowers 11–14(–16) mm; corollas pale lemon yellow, keel immaculate; stipules connate at proximal nodes (or completely amplexicaul) or distinct; Escalante Desert, Beaver, w Iron, and barely n into Millard counties, Utah .... 171d. *Astragalus praelongus* var. *avonensis*
1. Flowers 15–24 mm; corollas ochroleucous, keel often faintly to definitely maculate; stipules distinct; not of Escalante Desert of Utah.

[2. Shifted to left margin.—Ed.]

2. Legumes ellipsoid, oblong-ellipsoid, ellipsoid-cylindroid, or narrowly clavate-ellipsoid; stipes 4.5–8 mm; San Juan County, Utah, adjacent ne Arizona, sw Colorado, and nw New Mexico . . . . 171c. *Astragalus praelongus* var. *lonchopus*
2. Legumes oblong, ellipsoid, oblong-ellipsoid, or narrowly clavate-ellipsoid; stipes 0–2.5 mm; Arizona, Colorado, Nevada, New Mexico, Texas, Utah.
   3. Legumes broadly oblong to ellipsoid, (9–)10–15(–25) mm wide; n Arizona, sw Colorado, se Nevada, w New Mexico, and c, ec Utah . . . . .71a. *Astragalus praelongus* var. *praelongus*
   3. Legumes ellipsoid, oblong-ellipsoid, or narrowly clavate-ellipsoid, (5–)6–10(–11) mm wide; wc Colorado, much of New Mexico and w Texas, ec Utah . . . . 171b. *Astragalus praelongus* var. *ellisiae*

171a. Astragalus praelongus E. Sheldon var. **praelongus** [E] [F]

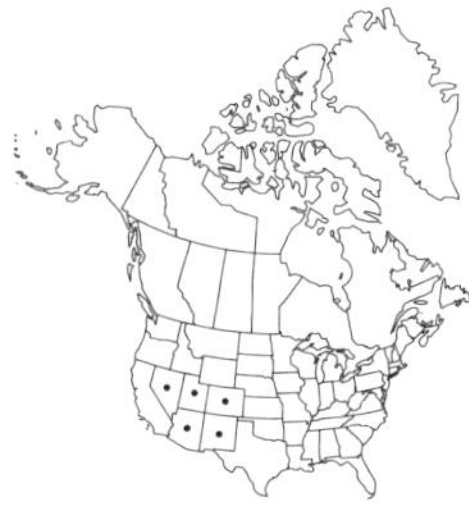

Stipules distinct throughout. **Flowers** 15–24 mm; calyx lobes deltate to lanceolate-subulate, 0.3–4.7 mm; corolla ochroleucous, keel often faintly to definitely maculate. **Legumes** broadly oblong to ellipsoid, 20–38(–42) × (9–)10–15(–25) mm, glabrous or puberulent; stipe obconic when present, 0–2.5 mm. **2*n*** = 22, 24.

Flowering Apr–Jul. Clay and silt of the Cretaceous Mancos and Tropic shales, Triassic Moenkopi, and Chinle formations, other seleniferous soils, in salt desert shrub and pinyon-juniper communities; 700–2600 m; Ariz., Colo., Nev., N.Mex., Utah.

An extreme phase of var. *praelongus* is present in Zion Canyon and vicinity, growing tall and with fistulous stems.

Variety *praelongus* is highly toxic but is seldom grazed by healthy animals except during drought. W. E. Fox et al. (1998) reported that plants also contained swainsonine. The Hopi reportedly used the plant, under the name siskinga, in treatment of bladder problems.

171b. Astragalus praelongus E. Sheldon var. **ellisiae** (Rydberg) Barneby, Mem. New York Bot. Gard. 13: 588. 1964 • Ellis's stinking milkvetch [E]

Jonesiella ellisiae Rydberg in N. L. Britton et al., N. Amer. Fl. 24: 403. 1929

Stipules distinct throughout. **Flowers** 15–24 mm; calyx lobes subulate or lanceolate-attenuate, 2–5.5 mm; corolla ochroleucous, keel often faintly to definitely maculate. **Legumes** ellipsoid, oblong-ellipsoid, or narrowly clavate-ellipsoid, 1.8–34 × (5–)6–10(–11) mm, strigulose, glabrous, or puberulent along sutures; stipe 1–2.5 mm. **2*n*** = 24.

Flowering Apr–Jul. Clay soils, on Cretaceous Mancos Shale and Triassic Moenkopi and Chinle formations, on alluvial substrates containing selenium, in warm and salt desert shrub and pinyon-juniper communities; 1300–2000 m; Colo., N.Mex., Tex., Utah.

Variation in var. *praelongus*, primarily of fruit shape and texture, and its interpretation by past authors, was reviewed by R. C. Barneby (1964). The broadest, almost subspheroid fruits of the more western var. *praelongus* appear very different from the oblong ones of the more eastern var. *ellisiae*, but their form is regionally clinal. Therefore, D. Isely (1998) placed the latter into var. *praelongus*, which is not an illogical disposition.

171c. Astragalus praelongus E. Sheldon var. **lonchopus** Barneby, Leafl. W. Bot. 9: 90. 1960 • Longstipe stinking milkvetch [E]

Stipules distinct throughout. **Flowers** 15–24 mm; calyx lobes subulate or lanceolate-attenuate, 3–6.5 mm; corolla ochroleucous, keel often faintly to definitely maculate. **Legumes** ellipsoid, oblong-ellipsoid, ellipsoid-cylindroid, or narrowly clavate-ellipsoid, 20–30 × 6–9 mm, strigulose; stipe 4.5–8 mm.

Flowering late Apr–Jul. Seleniferous fine-textured, less commonly sandy, substrates in blackbrush, mixed desert shrub, sagebrush, and pinyon-juniper communities; 1200–2100 m; Ariz., Colo., N.Mex., Utah.

Variety *lonchopus* ranges from the Four Corners region to approximately 160 km to the west.

171d. Astragalus praelongus E. Sheldon var. **avonensis** (S. L. Welsh & N. D. Atwood) S. L. Welsh, N. Amer. Sp. Astragalus, 190. 2007 • Avon milkvetch [C] [E]

Astragalus avonensis S. L. Welsh & N. D. Atwood in S. L. Welsh et al., Utah Fl. ed. 3, 363. 2003

Stipules connate at proximal nodes (or completely amplexicaul) or distinct throughout. **Flowers** 11–14(–16) mm; calyx lobes triangular-subulate, (0.8–) 1–1.9(–2.8) mm; corolla pale lemon yellow, keel immaculate. **Legumes** ellipsoid, 18–33 × 9–11 mm, puberulent; stipe thick, to 1.5 mm.

Flowering May. Stabilized dunes and silty-sandy wind-blown hummocks in playa and saline lake bottoms, greasewood, sagebrush-rabbitbrush, mixed desert shrub communities; of conservation concern; 1400–1600 m; Utah.

Variety *avonensis* is apparently a smaller version of var. *praelongus*, more or less isolated along the floor of the Escalante Valley in Beaver, Iron, and Millard counties, which was submerged until a few thousand years ago by a shallow arm of Pleistocene Lake Bonneville.

172. Astragalus pattersonii A. Gray, Bull. U.S. Geol. Geogr. Surv. Territ. 2: 235. 1876 (as pattersoni) • Patterson's milkvetch [E]

Plants clump-forming, 20–45 (–50) cm, glabrous or strigulose; from branched, superficial caudex. **Stems** decumbent to ascending or erect, glabrous proximally, sparsely strigulose distally. **Leaves** 5–13 cm; stipules 3–8 mm, firm becoming papery, sometimes membranous at distal nodes or throughout; leaflets 7–15+, blades elliptic to lanceolate, oblanceolate, or obovate, 6–38 mm, apex obtuse to acute, retuse, or mucronate, surfaces strigose or glabrous. **Peduncles** erect, 3–18 cm. **Racemes** 6–24-flowered, flowers declined-nodding; axis 2–15 cm in fruit; bracts 2–8 mm; bracteoles 2. **Pedicels** 1–4.5 mm. **Flowers** 14–22(–25) mm; calyx tan or whitish, gibbous or base strongly oblique, 8.8–14.2 mm, sparsely pale-strigulose, tube 6–8.8 mm, lobes broadly spreading, subulate, 2.3–6.5 mm; corolla usually white, concolorous, rarely keel tip faintly purplish; banner recurved through 50–90°; keel 12.4–15 mm, apex sharply triangular. **Legumes** erect, green or reddish brown becoming brown or stramineous, straight or slightly incurved, cylindroid to ellipsoid or ovoid, subterete to strongly obcompressed, 17–35 × 6–10 mm, unilocular, succulent becoming stiffly leathery, glabrous or puberulent; sessile. **Seeds** 22–38. $2n = 24$.

Flowering May–Jul. Pinyon-juniper and mixed desert shrub communities, often on fine textured, seleniferous substrates; 1400–2700 m; Ariz., Colo., N.Mex., Utah, Wyo.

Astragalus pattersonii fruits are extremely variable, helping to confuse it with *A. praelongus*, as occurred even in the original description (R. C. Barneby 1964). Floral characters such as ovule number, form of calyx, flower color, and shape of the keel provide the distinctions. J. D. Karron et al. (1988) reported that genetic polymorphism in this species was comparable to that of two geographically restricted species, *A. linifolius* and *A. osterhoutii*, and less than that of the also widespread *A. pectinatus*.

173. Astragalus sabulosus M. E. Jones, Zoë 2: 239. 1891 • Cisco milkvetch [C] [E]

Plants robust, clump-forming, 13–38 cm, strigulose; from superficial, woody caudex. **Stems** decumbent to ascending or erect, strigulose. **Leaves** 3–10.5 cm; stipules 4–9 mm; leaflets 5–11, blades flat, rhombic-oval to obovate or elliptic, 6–35(–50) mm, apex mucronate, surfaces strigose or glabrous. **Peduncles** incurved, 3.5–7 cm. **Racemes** 4–10-flowered, flowers ascending-spreading; axis 0.5–2 cm in fruit; bracts 2–6 mm; bracteoles 0–2. **Pedicels** 2–5 mm. **Flowers** 23–34 mm; calyx 12–17.5 mm, strigulose, tube 11–14 mm, lobes subulate, 2–4 mm; corolla ochroleucous (fading yellowish), or white (fading off-white); banner recurved through 40°; keel 22–23 mm, apex blunt. **Legumes** spreading to declined, pallid-stramineous or brownish, straight or slightly incurved, cylindroid, inflated, 20–48 × 9–15 mm, moderately fleshy-thickened, becoming stiffly papery to leathery, strigose; unilocular; subsessile or substipitate. **Seeds** 55–59.

Varieties 2 (2 in the flora): Utah.

Astragalus sabulosus is a primary selenium indicator.

1. Corollas ochroleucous, fading yellowish, banners 27–34 mm; Cisco-Thompson vicinity, Grand County, Utah ....173a. *Astragalus sabulosus* var. *sabulosus*
1. Corollas white or pink, fading off-white, banners 23–27 mm; northwest of Moab, Grand County, Utah ....173b. *Astragalus sabulosus* var. *vehiculus*

173a. Astragalus sabulosus M. E. Jones var. **sabulosus** [C] [E]

Flowers: calyx 15–17.5 mm, tube 11.5–14 mm, lobes 3–4 mm; corolla ochroleucous, fading yellowish; banner 27–34 mm. **Legumes** 20–48 × 10–15 mm, stiffly papery to leathery. $2n = 26$.

Flowering late Mar–May. Mat-*Atriplex*-shadscale communities; of conservation concern; 1300–1600 m; Utah.

Variety *sabulosus* is restricted to the clayey soils in the vicinities of Cisco and Thompson, Grand County.

173b. Astragalus sabulosus M. E. Jones var. **vehiculus** S. L. Welsh, Great Basin Naturalist 58: 53. 1998 • Stage milkvetch [C] [E]

Flowers: calyx 12–16 mm, hairs black, tube 11–13 mm, lobes 2–3.5 mm; corolla white or pink, fading off-white; banner 23–27 mm. **Legumes** 28–45 × 9–13 mm, stiffly leathery. $2n = 26$.

Flowering (late Mar–)Apr–May. Shadscale, woody-aster, galleta communities, on seleniferous Jurassic Morrison Formation; of conservation concern; 1300–1500 m; Utah.

Variety *vehiculus* is restricted to near the head of Courthouse Wash, Grand County; the type locality is near a spring that evidently was a watering place for horses along a historical stage line. It is more or less intermediate between var. *sabulosus* and *A. iselyi* in floral characteristics and is approximately 35 km disjunct from either taxon.

Variety *vehiculus* has been considered at the rank of species, as *Astragalus vehiculus* (S. L. Welsh) S. L. Welsh (S. L. Welsh et al. 2015), but this combination has not been validly published.

174. Astragalus iselyi S. L. Welsh, Great Basin Naturalist 34: 305, fig. 1. 1974 • Isely's milkvetch [C] [E]

Plants clump-forming, 8–25(–38+) cm, strigulose; from branched, superficial caudex. **Stems** ascending (and somewhat sprawling from the root-crown) to erect, strigulose. **Leaves** 3.2–22 cm; stipules 3–9 mm, membranous; leaflets (1 or)3–13, blades elliptic to rhombic, 7–23(–45) mm, apex acute to mucronate, surfaces sparsely strigose or glabrous. **Peduncles** incurved, 1.4–10 cm. **Racemes** 7–20-flowered, flowers spreading; axis 1–3 cm in fruit; bracts 2–4.5 mm; bracteoles 0. **Pedicels** 0.8–2.5 mm. **Flowers** 17–19 mm; calyx 6.7–10 mm, strigulose, tube 5.5–6.3 mm, lobes subulate, 1.8–3.1 mm; corolla white, concolorous, drying white or ochroleucous; banner recurved through 40–50°; keel 13 mm, apex blunt. **Legumes** spreading-declined, pallid-stramineous or brownish, straight or slightly incurved subcylindroid, inflated, 25–32(–38) × 10–15 mm, leathery, strigose; unilocular; sessile or subsessile. **Seeds** 38–44.

Flowering Mar–Apr(–May). Seleniferous Jurassic Morrison and Permian Paradox formations in pinyon-juniper and salt desert shrub communities; of conservation concern; 1500–2000 m; Utah.

Astragalus iselyi is a Navajo Basin endemic that occurs in the western foothills of the La Sal Mountains in Grand and San Juan counties. This early-flowering selenophyte was earlier confused with *A. sabulosus* because specimens were taken only in fruit. Seeds germinate readily after long periods in the soil, when conditions are favorable. Populations persist while moisture conditions are favorable, the cycle interrupted in years of drought.

135aaa. Astragalus Linnaeus sect. Neglecti (Rydberg) Barneby, Mem. New York Bot. Gard. 13: 593. 1964 [E]

Phaca Linnaeus [unranked] *Neglectae* Rydberg in N. L. Britton et al., N. Amer. Fl. 24: 364. 1929

Herbs perennial, clump-forming, caulescent; caudex superficial. **Hairs** basifixed. **Stems** several. **Stipules** distinct. **Leaves** odd-pinnate, short-petiolate or subsessile; leaflets 11–23(or 25). **Racemes** loosely flowered, flowers nodding. **Calyx tubes** cylindric. **Corollas** whitish to pale yellow, banner recurved through 45°, keel apex obtuse, sometimes obscurely beaklike. **Legumes**

persistent, sessile, erect, obliquely ovoid or ovoid-ellipsoid, strongly inflated, unilocular or subunilocular. **Seeds** 12–20.

Species 1: c, e North America.

175. Astragalus neglectus (Torrey & A. Gray) E. Sheldon, Minnesota Bot. Stud. 1: 59. 1894 • Cooper's milkvetch [E] [F]

Phaca neglecta Torrey & A. Gray, Fl. N. Amer. 1: 344. 1838

Plants robust, 25–90 cm, strigulose; from branched, superficial caudex. **Stems** erect, hollow, glabrous or glabrate. **Leaves** 4–12 cm; stipules (1.5–)2–6 mm, membranous or thinly herbaceous; leaflet blades oblong-elliptic, oblong, or oblong-obovate to linear-oblong, (4–)7–23(–25) mm, apex obtuse to retuse-emarginate, surfaces sparsely strigulose abaxially, glabrous adaxially. **Peduncles** erect, (2.5–)3–7.5 cm. **Racemes** (6–)10–20-flowered; axis 1–4.5 cm in fruit; bracts 1–2.2 mm; bracteoles 0–2. **Pedicels** 1–5 mm. **Flowers** 11.6–15 mm; calyx 5.6–8 mm, strigulose, tube 3.7–5 mm, lobes subulate, 1.8–3 mm; corolla drying ochroleucous; keel 10.1–12.4 mm. **Legumes** stramineous to brownish, turning dark brown to nearly black, ± straight, 14–30 × 8–18 mm, stiffly papery, glabrous; septum to 1.5 mm wide, seed-bearing flange 0.8–1.3 mm wide. 2*n* = 22.

Flowering Jun–Sep. Lakeshores, riverbanks, cool ravines, in shade or on limestone ledges, moist roadsides, barrens, overlying limestone pavement, dry, gravelly calcareous soils, often at edge of aspen groves; 150–300 m; Man., Ont.; Mich., Minn., N.Y., N.Dak., Ohio, S.Dak., Wis.

Astragalus neglectus may be confused with, and sometimes grows with, *A. canadensis*, from which it can be distinguished by several features, among them the basifixed hairs.

Astragalus cooperi A. Gray is an illegitimate name that applies here.

135bbb. Astragalus Linnaeus sect. Uliginosi A. Gray, Proc. Amer. Acad. Arts 6: 196. 1864

Herbs perennial, caulescent; from rootstock or creeping rhizomes. **Hairs** malpighian. **Stems** single or few. **Stipules** connate. **Leaves** odd-pinnate, short-petiolate or subsessile; leaflets (7 or)9–35. **Racemes** usually densely, rarely loosely flowered, flowers spreading-declined or nodding. **Calyx tubes** short-cylindric or deeply campanulate. **Corollas** ochroleucous, greenish white, or stramineous, banner recurved through 40–90°, keel apex obtuse. **Legumes** persistent, sessile or subsessile, erect or narrowly ascending, cylindroid or oblong, terete or slightly obcompressed, straight or incurved, bilocular. **Seeds** (16–)18–28.

Species 10 (2 in the flora): North America, e Asia.

Section *Uliginosi* consists of eight species from eastern Asia and two from North America.

176. Astragalus canadensis Linnaeus, Sp. Pl. 2: 757. 1753 • Canada milkvetch [E] [W]

Plants usually robust, rarely quite slender, (10–)15–120(–160) cm, strigose; from oblique or horizontal rhizomes. **Stems** usually erect, sometimes decumbent and ascending, green or purplish, fistulose when stout, 1–7+ cm underground, strigose. **Leaves** (3–)5–25(–35) cm; stipules 3–18 mm, membranous early becoming scarious; leaflets (7–)13–35, blades lanceolate, lanceolate-oblong, or elliptic, (5–)6–45(–52) mm, apex obtuse, apiculate, or truncate-emarginate, surfaces strigose, sometimes glabrous adaxially. **Peduncles** erect or incurved-ascending, (2.5–)4–22 cm. **Racemes** 20–100+-flowered, flowers spreading-declined; axis 2.5–16 cm in fruit; bracts 1.5–10 mm; bracteoles 0–2. **Pedicels** 1.2–3.5 (–4) mm. **Flowers** 11.3–17(–17.5) mm; calyx short-cylindric, (4.6–)5.5–10.5(–11) mm, strigose or pilosulous, tube 4–8.5 mm, lobes subulate or triangular, 1.2–4.4(–5) mm; corolla ochroleucous, greenish white, or stramineous; keel (9.5–)10.2–13.6 mm. **Legumes** brown then blackish, straight or incurved, cylindroid, terete, (9–)10–20 × 2.9–5.2 mm, somewhat fleshy becoming stiffly papery or leathery, usually strigose, strigulose, glabrate, or glabrous, rarely puberulent; sessile or subsessile. **Seeds** (16–)18–26(–28).

Varieties 3 (3 in the flora): North America.

The chromosome number of $2n = 16$ is in harmony with the view that the alliance of *Astragalus canadensis*, along with its near relative *A. oreganus*, is with the Asiatic *A. uliginosus* Linnaeus. The relationship is sufficiently close that R. C. Barneby (1964) said of the Canada milkvetch, the New World's most widely dispersed *Astragalus*, that taxonomy would most closely reflect biological realities if the New World forms were reduced to varietal status under a bicentrically dispersed *A. uliginosus*.

1. Legumes not grooved dorsally, usually glabrous, rarely puberulent or strigulose; distribution primarily eastern, extending westward to New Mexico, Utah, Idaho, British Columbia, and Northwest Territories .... 176a. *Astragalus canadensis* var. *canadensis*
1. Legumes grooved dorsally, strigose or glabrate; distribution largely intermontane, extending eastward to Black Hills of South Dakota.
   2. Stems (25–)30–70(–90) cm; calyx lobes (1.5–) 2–4.4 mm, adaxial pair usually not much broader (though sometimes shorter) than the rest; legume beaks (3–)3.5–5 mm; forest belt of n Rocky Mountains (British Columbia southward to Oregon, eastward to Montana) .... 176b. *Astragalus canadensis* var. *mortonii*
   2. Stems (10–)15–55(–75) cm; calyx lobes 1–2.5 (–3) mm, adaxial pair nearly always broadly triangular or deltate (and mostly shorter) than the rest; legume beaks 1.5–3 mm; sagebrush valleys, less commonly in meadows, and xeric pine forests (British Columbia southward to California, eastward to Colorado and Montana). .... 176c. *Astragalus canadensis* var. *brevidens*

176a. Astragalus canadensis Linnaeus var. **canadensis** • Astragale du Canada [E]

Astragalus canadensis var. *carolinianus* (Linnaeus) M. E. Jones; *A. canadensis* var. *longilobus* Fassett; *A. carolinianus* Linnaeus; *A. halei* Rydberg

Stems usually branched or with spur branches 1 or several nodes preceding first peduncle, sometimes unbranched, robust, slender and almost solid, or stout and hollow, (35–)40–120(–160) cm. **Stipules** 3–18 mm, proximalmost usually ruptured becoming irregularly circumscissile. **Leaves** (3.5–)5–25(–35) cm; leaflets (9–)15–35, blades 6–45(–52) mm, apex obtuse, apiculate, or truncate-emarginate. **Peduncles** slender or stout, (2.5–)4–12(–13) cm. **Racemes** rarely loose, 3–16 × (2–)2.5–3 cm, flowers 11.3–16.3 mm. **Pedicels** 1.2–2.5 mm. **Flowers:** calyx (4.6–)5.5–9.6(–10.3) mm, lobes 1.5–5.5 mm; corolla greenish white or dull stramineous. **Legumes** terete or subterete, carinate by ventral suture, not grooved dorsally, (9–)10–15 × 4–5.2 mm, beak 2–6 mm, usually glabrous, rarely puberulent or strigulose. **Seeds** (18–)20–26(or 27). $2n = 16$.

Flowering May–Sep. Low, moist prairies or meadows, river banks, lakeshores, open deciduous forests, open coniferous forests, sandy soils, sometimes rocky soils, often disturbed areas (post-logging, trails), roadside ditches, on rich soils moist in spring; 0–2200 m; Alta., B.C., Man., N.W.T., Ont., Que., Sask.; Ala., Ark., Colo., D.C., Ga., Idaho, Ill., Ind., Iowa, Kans., Ky., La., Md., Mich., Minn., Miss., Mo., Mont., Nebr., N.J., N.Mex., N.Y., N.C., N.Dak., Ohio, Okla., Pa., S.C., S.Dak., Tenn., Tex., Utah, Vt., Va., W.Va., Wis., Wyo.

R. C. Barneby (1964) circumscribed var. *canadensis* rather broadly to include multiracial variation. As reviewed by D. Isely (1998), several regional manuals (such as M. L. Fernald 1950) have recognized var. *carolinianus* and var. *longilobus* in the eastern states. The rationale, largely derived by N. C. Fassett (1939b), was extensively counter-argued by Barneby.

176b. Astragalus canadensis Linnaeus var. **mortonii** (Nuttall) S. Watson, Botany (Fortieth Parallel), 68. 1871 (as mortoni) • Morton's milkvetch [E]

Astragalus mortonii Nuttall, J. Acad. Nat. Sci. Philadelphia 7: 19. 1834 (as mortoni)

Stems unbranched, relatively slender, (25–)30–70(–90) cm. **Stipules** 3.5–11(–14) mm, proximalmost persistent, not ruptured. **Leaves** (3–)6–19(–22.5) cm; leaflets (9–)13–19(or 21), blades 10–45(–50) mm, thin. **Peduncles** rather slender, 6–22 cm. **Racemes** sometimes interrupted proximally, 2.5–12 × 2.7–3.5 cm, flowers (12.6–)13.2–16.5 mm. **Pedicels** 1.4–2 mm. **Flowers:** calyx (6.5–)7.4–10.5(–11) mm, lobes (1.5–)2–4.4 mm, adaxial pair usually not much broader (though sometimes shorter) than the rest; corolla greenish white or ochroleucous. **Legumes** grooved dorsally, (9–)11–20 × 3–5 mm, beak (3–)3.5–5 mm, thinly strigose or glabrate; septum (2–)2.5–3.4 mm wide. **Seeds** (16–)18–26. $2n = 16$.

Flowering Jun–Sep. Coniferous forests; (400–)900–2100 m; B.C.; Idaho, Mont., Oreg., Wash.

A. Gray (1864), under the discussion of *Astragalus mortonii*, cited both *A. spicatus* Nuttall ex Torrey & A. Gray (an illegitimate name, not Pallas 1773), and *A. tristis* Nuttall ex Torrey & A. Gray (see synonymy of var. *brevidens*), but considered ovary and legume pubescence as the primary distinguishing feature. This is commonly an elongate, slender plant with thin-textured foliage of forested regions within its range. The flowers vary in color from greenish white to cream, sometimes suffused with purple, but dry to cream or brownish. Flowers are ascending in bud but soon become spreading to declined, until in fruit they are erect-ascending.

176c. Astragalus canadensis Linnaeus var. **brevidens** (Gandoger) Barneby, Leafl. W. Bot. 4: 238. 1946 • Pasture milkvetch [E]

Astragalus mortonii Nuttall forma *brevidens* Gandoger, Bull. Soc. Bot. France 48: xvi. 1902 (as mortoni); *A. brevidens* Rydberg

Stems branched, slender, sometimes decumbent and ascending, (10–)15–55(–75) cm. **Stipules** (3–)4–14 mm, proximalmost ruptured in some very robust specimens. **Leaves** 5–15(–23) cm; leaflets (7–)15–23(or 25), blades (5–)7–30(–40) mm, apex usually apiculate. **Peduncles** stout, (4–)5–15(–20) cm, longer or shorter than leaves. **Racemes** (2.5–)4–9.5(–15) × 2.5–3.5 cm, flowers (11.7–)12.5–17(–17.5) mm. **Pedicels** 1.2–3.5 (–4) mm. **Flowers:** calyx (6.8–)7.1–10.5(–11) mm, lobes 1–2.5(–3) mm, adaxial pair nearly always broadly triangular or deltate (and mostly shorter) than the rest; corolla ochroleucous, stramineous, or greenish white. **Legumes** grooved dorsally, (9–)10–15 × 2.9–4 (–4.5) mm, beak 1.5–3 mm, mostly at least moderately strigulose; septum 1.5–3 mm wide. **Seeds** (17 or)18–25(–28). **2*n*** = 16.

Flowering Jun–Sep. Moist but often summer-dry bottomlands, ditches, creek banks with willows, lakeshores, sagebrush hillsides, near springs and seeps, alkaline meadows, depressions on rolling plains, rarely on dry sandy or gravelly soils of brushy hills or lava flows, on stiff, often alkaline, alluvial soils of diverse origin, with sagebrush but ascending along water courses into xeric pine forests; 400–2500 m; B.C.; Calif., Colo., Idaho, Mont., Nev., Oreg., Utah, Wash., Wyo.

Variety *brevidens* is the more xeric form of *Astragalus canadensis*. It is partly sympatric with var. *mortonii*, but var. *mortonii* is usually of higher, more mesic, wooded habitats. No single feature distinguishes vars. *brevidens* and *mortonii*. In Utah, var. *brevidens* intergrades with var. *canadensis*.

177. Astragalus oreganus Nuttall in J. Torrey and A. Gray, Fl. N. Amer. 1: 335. 1838 • Wind River milkvetch [E]

Plants somewhat stout and leafy, 6–20(–25) cm, strigose; from deep, subterranean caudex, rhizomes horizontal or obliquely ascending, slender. **Stems** from rhizome buds, internodes short and strongly flexuous, decumbent, ascending distally, 3–10(–14) cm underground, strigose. **Leaves** (2.5–)5–15 cm; stipules bidentate, (2.5–)3.5–11 mm, papery, pallid; leaflets (7 or)9–15(–21), blades broadly obovate or suborbiculate-obcordate, 4–20 mm, apex obtuse or widely and shallowly notched, surfaces strigose, sometimes less densely so adaxially. **Peduncles** erect or divaricate, 1.5–5.5 cm. **Racemes** (15–)20–35-flowered, flowers nodding; axis 3–7.5 cm in fruit; bracts 2–5.5 mm. **Pedicels** 0.6–2.2 mm. **Flowers** 15.5–19 mm; calyx deeply campanulate or subcylindric, 6.5–10 mm, sparsely strigulose, tube 5.5–7.3 mm, lobes subulate, 1–3 mm; corolla ochroleucous, concolorous; keel 11.5–13.5 mm. **Legumes** erect or narrowly ascending, brown, ± straight or incurved through 0.25 spiral, oblong, slightly obcompressed, 1–1.5(–1.8) × (3–)4–6 mm, fleshy becoming leathery, sparsely strigulose; sessile. **Seeds** (17–)20–28.

Flowering mid May–Aug. Barren bluffs, gullied knolls, swales, dunes, detritus under cliffs or buttes, on sandy or sandy-clay soils from weathered sandstone, on alkaline clay flats moist in spring; 1100–2100 m; Mont., Wyo.

Astragalus oreganus is a xeric badland species, probably a recent habitat-specialized derivative of *A. canadensis* var. *brevidens* (R. C. Barneby 1964); it occurs from south-central Wyoming to north-central and south-central Montana.

135ccc. Astragalus Linnaeus sect. Euodmus Bunge, Mém. Acad. Imp. Sci. Saint Pétersbourg, Sér. 7, 11(16): 96. 1868 [I]

Herbs perennial, forming large clumps, caulescent; caudex superficial or shallowly subterranean. **Hairs** malpighian. **Stems** few to several. **Stipules** connate at proximal nodes, at distal nodes distinct. **Leaves** odd-pinnate, petiolate or subsessile; leaflets 19–37. **Racemes** densely flowered, flowers declined. **Calyx tubes** campanulate. **Corollas** greenish white, banner and wing apices often purple-suffused, banner recurved through 20–30°, keel apex obtuse. **Legumes** falling with pedicel, subsessile, deflexed, 3-sided compressed, curved-oblong, bilocular. **Seeds** 12–14.

Species 1 (1 in the flora): introduced; Europe, Asia.

A close affinity exists between the Old World sect. *Euodmus* and sect. *Uliginosi* (R. C. Barneby 1964). D. Podlech and S. Zarre (2013) considered sect. *Euodmus* to be synonymous with sect. *Uliginosi*.

178. Astragalus falcatus Lamarck in J. Lamarck et al., Encycl. 1: 310. 1783 • Russian sickle milkvetch [I]

Plants 40–90 cm, strigulose; from superficial or shallow, subterranean branched caudex. **Stems** ascending to erect, hollow but not fistulose, strigulose. **Leaves** 5–22 cm; stipules 2–12 mm, submembranous, pallid; leaflet blades oblong to elliptic or oblanceolate, 6–35 mm, apex acute to apiculate, surfaces strigose abaxially, glabrous adaxially. **Peduncles** ascending, 6–17 cm. **Racemes** 20–70-flowered, flowers recurved in fruit; axis 3–20 cm in fruit; bracts 2–5 mm; bracteoles 2. **Pedicels** 3.2–6.5 mm. **Flowers** 9–11(–12) mm; calyx 3.6–4.7 mm, strigose, tube 3–3.5 mm, lobes triangular, 0.5–1.2 mm; corolla keel 8–10 mm. **Legumes** stramineous, curved-oblong, 13–23 × 2.5–4.5 mm, thinly fleshy becoming stiffly papery, strigose. $2n = 16$.

Flowering Jun–Aug. Open grasslands, along streams, oak brush and mountain brush to aspen communities; 800–3300 m; introduced; B.C.; Colo., Mont., Oreg., Utah, Wash.; Asia.

Astragalus falcatus was evidently first collected in North America in 1929, near Pullman, Washington. Later it was intentionally introduced as a plant that could occupy stressed environments in the American west that were subject to accelerated erosion. It was suspected of being poisonous to livestock (M. C. Williams and R. C. Barneby 1977) and is now known to contain nitrotoxins (L. F. James and S. L. Welsh 1992).

135ddd. Astragalus Linnaeus sect. Onobrychoidei de Candolle in A. P. de Candolle and A. L. P. P. de Candolle, Prodr. 2: 285. 1825

Herbs perennial, clump-forming, caulescent; caudex superficial or shallowly subterranean. **Hairs** malpighian. **Stems** several to many. **Stipules** connate. **Leaves** odd-pinnate, petiolate or subsessile; leaflets (7–)11–25. **Racemes** subspicate, densely flowered, flowers ascending. **Calyx tubes** short-cylindric. **Corollas** whitish, bluish, reddish lilac, or magenta-purple, often drying bluish, nodding, mainly 13–19 mm, banner recurved through 25°, much surpassing keel, keel apex blunt or sharply deltate. **Legumes** often eventually deciduous, sessile or short-stipitate, erect [ascending], narrowly oblong or oblong-ellipsoid, 3-sided compressed, ± straight, bilocular. **Seeds** 9–16(–18).

Species 75 (1 in the flora): North America, Europe, Asia.

Section *Onobrychoidei* consists of species from Eurasia, except for one extending into the flora area.

179. Astragalus laxmannii Jacquin, Hort. Bot. Vindob. 3: 22, plate 37. 1776 (as laxmanni) • Laxmann's milkvetch

Astragalus adsurgens Pallas

Plants 15–45 cm, strigulose; from branched caudex. **Stems** decumbent-ascending to erect, strigulose. **Leaves** (2–)4–17 cm; stipules 4–13(–16) mm, papery-scarious, pallid; leaflet blades oblong to elliptic, (4–)7–27(–33) mm, apex acute or obtuse, surfaces sparsely to moderately strigose, sometimes glabrous adaxially. **Peduncles** erect or incurved-ascending, (3–)4–14(–16.5) cm. **Racemes** (7–)10–50-flowered; axis (0.6–)1–9(–13) cm in fruit; bracts 2–8 mm; bracteoles 0. **Pedicels** to 0.8 mm. **Flowers** 11.5–19.5 mm; calyx [4.8–]5.6–10.5 mm, strigulose, tube [3–]4–7 × 2–3.2 mm, lobes subulate or subulate-setaceous, 0.4–4.2 mm; corolla keel 8–15 mm. **Legumes** stramineous, ovoid-, oblong-, or lanceoloid-ellipsoid, or narrowly oblong, [5.5–]6–12 × 2.3–4 mm, thin becoming papery, strigulose; stipe 0–1.8 mm.

Varieties ca. 3 (2 in the flora): North America, Asia.

Astragalus laxmannii consists of at least three varieties, with two known to occur in the flora area. For comparison, a key and description were provided for the eastern Asian var. *laxmannii* by S. L. Welsh (2007). R. C. Barneby and Welsh (1996) provided the rationale for the replacement of the long-used name *A. adsurgens*, reviewed also by Welsh.

1. Legumes sessile or subsessile, stipes 0–0.5 mm; calyx lobes 1.4–4.2 mm; widespread. . . . . 179a. *Astragalus laxmannii* var. *robustior*
1. Legumes shortly stipitate, stipes 0.7–1.8 mm; calyx lobes 0.4–1(–2.1) mm; Alaska, Yukon . . . . 179b. *Astragalus laxmannii* var. *tananaicus*

179a. Astragalus laxmannii Jacquin var. **robustior** (Hooker) Barneby & S. L. Welsh, Great Basin Naturalist 56: 85. 1996 • Standing milkvetch E

Astragalus adsurgens Pallas var. *robustior* Hooker, Fl. Bor.-Amer. 1: 149. 1831; *A. adsurgens* subsp. *robustior* (Hooker) S. L. Welsh; *A. striatus* Nuttall

Leaves 4–17 cm; leaflets (9 or) 11–25, blades (4–)8–27(–33) mm. **Peduncles** (3–)4–14(–16.5) cm. **Racemes** (7–)16–50-flowered; axis (0.6–)1.5–9(–13) cm in fruit. **Flowers** 13–19.5 × 4–7(–8) mm; calyx 5.8–10.5 mm, tube (4–)4.4–7 × (2–)2.3–3.2 mm, lobes subulate or subulate-setaceous, 1.4–4.2 mm; corolla magenta-purple, reddish lilac, dull blue, pale milky white. **Legumes** narrowly ovoid-, oblong-, or lanceoloid-ellipsoid, 7–12 × 2.3–3.8 mm, densely strigulose, hairs short and sinuous mixed with longer and straight ones, white or mixed with black; stipes 0–0.5 mm. **Seeds** 9–14(–16). $2n = 32$.

Flowering May–Aug. Plains, prairies, dry hillsides, on bare, rocky or gravelly areas on gravelly or shingly lakeshores or riverbanks, on sedimentary bedrock; 200–2000(–3400) m; Alta., B.C., Man., N.W.T., Ont., Sask., Yukon; Colo., Idaho, Iowa, Minn., Mont., Nebr., N.Mex., N.Dak., S.Dak., Utah, Wash., Wyo.

R. C. Barneby (1964) reviewed, partly in tabular form, the extensive synonymy associated with the widespread var. *robustior*. Some of the variants may ultimately be found to be worthy of taxonomic recognition.

179b. Astragalus laxmannii Jacquin var. **tananaicus** (Hultén) Barneby & S. L. Welsh, Great Basin Naturalist 56: 85. 1996 • Tanana milkvetch E

Astragalus tananaicus Hultén, Fl. Alaska Yukon 10: 1763. 1950, based on *A. viciifolius* Hultén, Ark. Bot. 33B(1): 1, fig. 1. 1947, not de Candolle 1802; *A. adsurgens* Pallas subsp. *viciifolius* S. L. Welsh

Leaves (2–)4–10 cm; leaflets (7–)11–17, blades (4–)7–25 mm. **Peduncles** 4–12 cm. **Racemes** 10–20-flowered; axis 1–3.5 cm in fruit. **Flowers** 11.5–16.2 × 4.5–6.6 mm; calyx 5.6–6.8 mm, tube 4.6–5.7 × 3–3.8 mm, lobes subulate, 0.4–1(–2.1) mm; corolla white. **Legumes** narrowly oblong or oblong-ellipsoid, 6–12 × 2.5–4 mm, densely strigulose, hairs black and relatively short, with ascending, white, straight, longer ones; stipe 0.7–1.8 mm. **Seeds** (9–)12–16(–18).

Flowering Jun–early Aug. Shaley river bluffs, shingle bars, pebbly banks of streams, on disturbed gravelly or sandy soils near highways, airfields, or beaches, dry grassy meadows, hillsides; 100–800 m; Yukon; Alaska.

Variety *tananaicus* is known mostly from the Yukon River drainage in southern Yukon and east-central Alaska.

135eee. Astragalus Linnaeus sect. Hypoglottidei de Candolle in A. P. de Candolle and A. L. P. P. de Candolle, Prodr. 2: 281. 1825

Herbs perennial, caulescent; caudex usually subterranean, rarely superficial. **Hairs** basifixed. **Stems** single or few to many. **Stipules** connate or distally distinct. **Leaves** odd-pinnate, short-petiolate or subsessile; leaflets 13–29(or 31). **Racemes** densely flowered (subcapitate), flowers ascending or erect. **Calyx tubes** cylindric or subcylindric, [deeply campanulate]. **Corollas** pink-purple, whitish, or ochroleucous, banner recurved little, to 25°, keel apex obtuse. **Legumes** persistent, short-stipitate or subsessile, ascending to spreading or erect, oblong-ellipsoid, or obovoid to subglobose, 3-sided and grooved dorsally or inflated, ± straight, bilocular. **Seeds** [8–]14–26.

Species 46 (3 in the flora): w, c North America, Europe, Asia.

Section *Hypoglottidei* includes species from Asia and Europe, with one native to the northwestern United States and two introduced in the flora area as forage or reclamation plants. In addition to *Astragalus cicer*, which is widespread, 355. *A. tibetanus* is also introduced but presently established only in a small area of Wyoming; it is not included in the key to species but will key there to *A. agrestis,* from which it differs in having calyces that are strigulose and sometimes also pilosulous (versus villous); corollas that are blue-violet, often drying yellowish (versus usually pink-purple, sometimes ochroleucous or nearly white); legumes that are 12–15 × 3 mm (versus 7–10 × 2.8–4.5 mm), hirsutulous with white hairs (versus densely silky-villous), and with stipes 0.5 mm (versus 0.3–1 mm).

180. Astragalus agrestis Douglas ex G. Don, Gen. Hist. 2: 258. 1832 • Field milkvetch, astragale rustique [F]

Astragalus goniatus Nuttall

Plants clump-forming, slender, 9–43 cm, strigulose to villous-pilose, sometimes sparsely so; usually from subterranean branched caudex, rarely superficial, branches very long, rhizomatous. **Stems** diffuse or erect to decumbent-clambering, sparsely strigulose-pilosulous. **Leaves** 2–10 cm; stipules (1–)2–11 mm, papery-scarious proximally, submembranous at distal nodes; leaflets 13–23, blades narrowly elliptic to lanceolate-oblong, 4–18 mm, apex obtuse to retuse or acute, surfaces strigulose. **Peduncles** erect or incurved-ascending, 1.5–15 cm. **Racemes** 5–15-flowered, flowers ascending-erect; axis 0.5–2.5 cm in fruit; bracts 3–7 mm; bracteoles 0. **Pedicels** 0.5–1.5 mm. **Flowers** 17–24 mm; calyx cylindric, 7–12.5 mm, villous, tube 5–7.8 mm, lobes linear, 2.5–5.5 mm; corolla usually pink-purple, sometimes ochroleucous or nearly white; keel 11.4–14 mm. **Legumes** erect, green becoming dark, ± straight, oblong-ellipsoid, obtusely 3-sided, 7–10 × 2.8–4.5 mm, sulcate abaxially, scarcely swollen, thinly papery, densely silky-villous; stipe 0.3–1 mm. 2*n* = 16.

Flowering May–early Sep. Meadows, prairies, hillsides, stream banks, openings in sagebrush and aspen communities; 300–3300 m; Alta., B.C., Man., N.W.T., Ont., Que., Sask., Yukon; Alaska, Calif., Colo., Idaho, Iowa, Minn., Mont., Nebr., Nev., N.Mex., N.Dak., Oreg., S.Dak., Utah, Wash., Wyo.; Asia.

Astragalus agrestis is commonly a sod-forming mesophyte. Since the revision of A. Gray (1864), this species has been associated with *A. laxmannii* (as the name is applied here), but each belongs to a different phylogenetically natural group, the centers of which are in central Asia and the Near East (R. C. Barneby 1964). The field milkvetch is taxonomically isolated in the American flora but is sufficiently similar to *A. danicus* Retz from eastern Europe to central Asia (where it overlaps with *A. agrestis* to some extent) that D. Isely (1998) suggested that *A. agrestis* is a regional associate of that species. There are indications that the two intergrade in the Altai region of southern Siberia (Barneby).

Astragalus dasyglottis Fischer ex de Candolle is an illegitimate name that applies here.

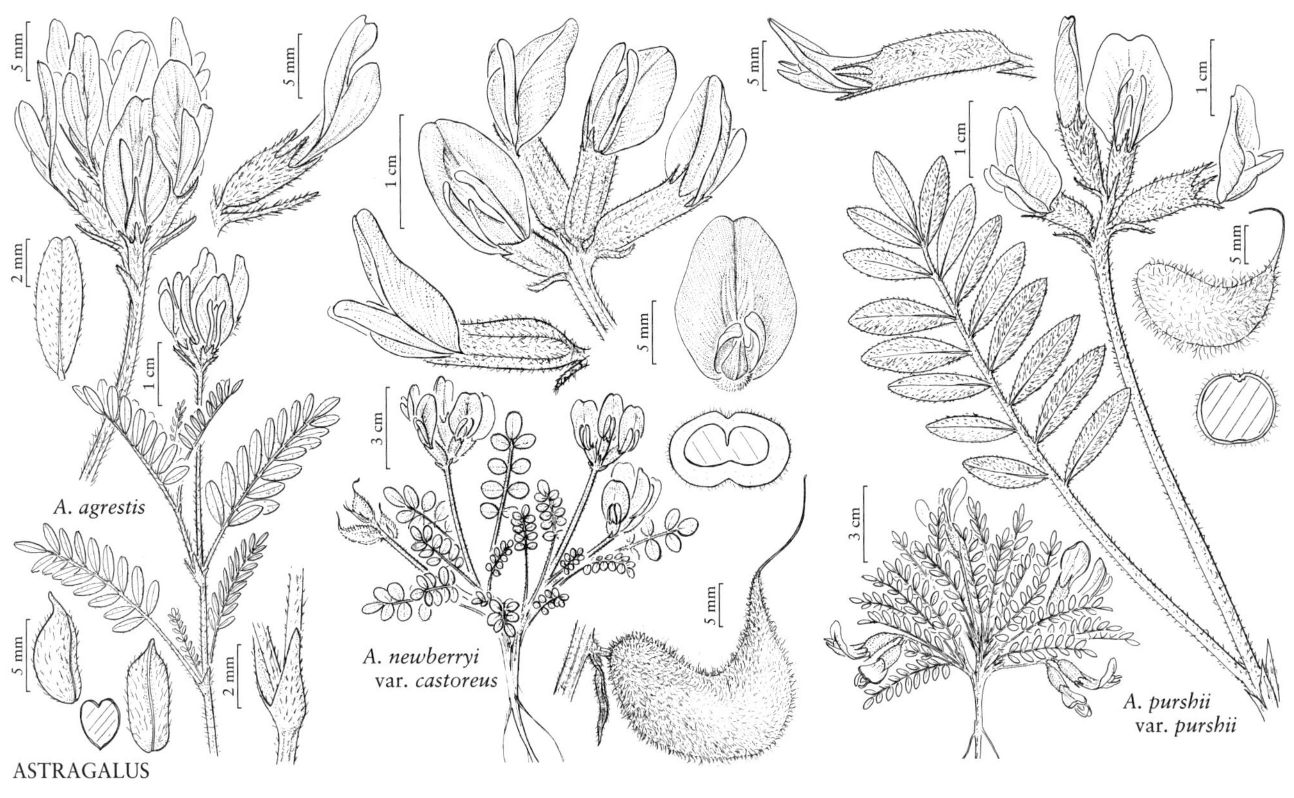

ASTRAGALUS

181. Astragalus cicer Linnaeus, Sp. Pl. 2: 757. 1753 • Chickpea milkvetch, astragale pois-chiche [I]

Plants leafy, 30–90(–130) cm, strigose-pilose; from subterranean branched caudex, branches long, rhizomelike. **Stems** erect or diffuse, flexuous, becoming decumbent-sprawling, sparsely strigose-pilose or glabrate. **Leaves** 2–10 cm; stipules 2–8 mm, herbaceous, becoming membranous; leaflets 17–29(or 31), blades lanceolate-elliptic or oblong, 5–35 mm, apex obtuse, apiculate, or acute, surfaces strigulose, sometimes glabrate adaxially. **Peduncles** incurved-ascending, 3.5–11 cm, together with racemes shorter than leaves. **Racemes** (6–)10–30-flowered, flowers ascending; axis (1.5–)2–5 cm in fruit; bracts 2–6.5 mm; bracteoles 0. **Pedicels** 0.3–1.5 mm. **Flowers** 12.5–16.5 mm; calyx subcylindric, 6.5–9 mm, strigulose, tube 5–6 mm, lobes triangular-acuminate, 1.6–3 mm; corolla ochroleucous; keel 9.6–10.5 mm. **Legumes** ascending to spreading, black, straight, obovoid to subglobose, inflated but firm, hardly bladdery, 6–14 × 5–10(–12) mm, sulcate ventrally, fleshy becoming leathery or stiffly papery, pilose; stipe to 0.8 mm. $2n$ = 16, 32, 48, 64.

Flowering Jun–Sep. Mixed desert shrub, sedge-willow, pinyon-juniper, sagebrush, and aspen communities, gravelly trails, mine tracks; 300–2800 m; introduced; Alta., B.C., Man., Ont., Que., Sask., Yukon; Alaska, Calif., Colo., Idaho, Ind., Mich., Minn., Mont., Nebr., Nev., N.Mex., Okla., Utah, Wash., Wyo.; Europe.

Astragalus cicer is a vigorous European species, now spreading around the American West in reclamation plantings. Its original introduction as a cover or forage crop is not recorded in taxonomic literature, but it has been in North America for at least seven decades. *Astragalus cicer* is somewhat equal to alfalfa in nutrient value.

135fff. Astragalus Linnaeus sect. Argophylli A. Gray, Proc. Amer. Acad. Arts 6: 209. 1864

Herbs perennial (sometimes flowering as annual), usually tuft- or mat-forming, acaulescent, subacaulescent, or caulescent; caudex usually superficial or aerial, sometimes subterranean. **Hairs** basifixed or malpighian. **Stems** (when present) obsolete, single, few, or several to many. **Stipules** distinct (except anomalous forms of *A. missouriensis*, *A. tephrodes*, and *A. zionis*). **Leaves** odd-pinnate, usually petiolate, rarely short-petiolate or subsessile; leaflets (1 or)3–39(–43). **Racemes** subcapitate to loosely flowered, flowers erect, ascending, spreading, declined, or nodding, secund, and retrorsely imbricate. **Calyx tubes** cylindric or deeply campanulate. **Corollas** purple, pink-purple, magenta-purple, violet, bluish, lilac, scarlet, ochroleucous, greenish white, or white, banner barely recurved (*A. phoenix*) or recurved through 20–50° (90–100° in *A. accumbens*), keel apex obtuse. **Legumes** usually deciduous, usually sessile, rarely subsessile or substipitate, gynophore sometimes present, usually ascending (humistrate), less often spreading or pendulous, subglobose to ellipsoid, narrowly lanceoloid, ovoid or oblong-ellipsoid, or lanceoloid-ovoid, straight or usually incurved, usually compressed dorsiventrally, sometimes obcompressed, 3-sided, turgid, or inflated, unilocular, subunilocular, or bilocular. **Seeds** 11–70.

Species 44 (44 in the flora): w North America, n Mexico.

Section *Argophylli* comprises ten subsections, widespread in western North America from southern British Columbia and Saskatchewan southward to northern Baja California, northern Sonora, and western Texas.

The subsections are: subsect. *Argophylli* (A. Gray) M. E. Jones (*Astragalus argophyllus*, *A. callithrix*, *A. columbianus*, *A. cyaneus*, *A. desereticus*, *A. eurylobus*, *A. henrimontanensis*, *A. iodopetalus*, *A. piutensis*, *A. shortianus*, *A. tephrodes*, *A. tidestromii*, *A. uncialis*, *A. zionis*); subsect. *Pseudargophylli* Barneby (*A. feensis*, *A. waterfallii*); subsect. *Neomexicani* Barneby (*A. neomexicanus*); subsect. *Newberryani* M. E. Jones (*A. eurekensis*, *A. loanus*, *A. musiniensis*, *A. newberryi*, *A. phoenix*, *A. welshii*); subsect. *Concordi* S. L. Welsh (*A. concordius*); subsect. *Coccinei* M. E. Jones (*A. coccineus*); subsect. *Eriocarpi* (A. Gray) Barneby (*A. anserinus*, *A. funereus*, *A. inflexus*, *A. leucolobus*, *A. nudisiliquus*, *A. purshii*, *A. subvestitus*, *A. utahensis*); subsect. *Parryani* Barneby (*A. parryi*); subsect. *Missourienses* M. E. Jones (*A. accumbens*, *A. amphioxys*, *A. castaneiformis*, *A. chamaeleuce*, *A. consobrinus*, *A. cymboides*, *A. laccoliticus*, *A. missouriensis*, *A. piscator*); and subsect. *Anisi* Barneby (*A. anisus*).

SELECTED REFERENCE Barneby, R. C. 1947b. Pugillus *Astragalorum* VII. A revision of the *Argophylli*. Amer. Midl. Naturalist 37: 421–516.

182. Astragalus argophyllus Nuttall in J. Torrey and A. Gray, Fl. N. Amer. 1: 331. 1838 • Silveryleaf milkvetch [E]

Plants ± mat-forming, acaulescent or subacaulescent, 1.5–12 cm; from superficial caudex, not or seldom with persistent leaf bases, densely pilose or strigulose, hairs usually basifixed (very unequally malpighian in var. *alvius*). **Stems** prostrate, 0–10(–15) cm, densely pilose or strigulose. **Leaves** 1.5–12(–15) cm; stipules lanceolate, sometimes imbricate, 2–10 mm, submembranous becoming papery; leaflets 7–21, blades usually elliptic, rhombic-elliptic, rhombic-ovate, obovate-cuneate, elliptic-oblong, elliptic-obovate, oblanceolate, or obovate, rarely elliptic-oblanceolate, 2–15 mm, apex acute, obtuse, or acuminate, surfaces pilose. **Peduncles** incurved-ascending, reclined or prostrate in fruit, to 9 cm. **Racemes** 1–6-flowered, flowers ascending; axis 0.2–2(–2.5) cm in fruit; bracts 1.8–6.5 mm; bracteoles 0–2. **Pedicels** 1.2–3.8 mm. **Flowers** 15–25 mm; calyx cylindric, 9–16.8 mm, strigulose, hairs white or black, tube 6.8–11.8 mm, lobes linear, 1.6–5(–5.8) mm; corolla pink-purple or violet to bluish, sometimes fading tan, except keel and wing tips; banner recurved through 40°; keel 12–20.3 mm. **Legumes** ascending, brown or stramineous, straight or incurved, ovoid, lanceoloid-ellipsoid, oblong-ellipsoid, or ovoid-acuminate, ± obcompressed, little or no groove ventrally, 15–32(–37) × 5–12(–13) mm, unilocular, fleshy becoming stiffly leathery or woody, strigulose, strigulose-pilosulous, silky-strigose, or villous, hairs appressed or incumbent (sometimes loosely spreading and contorted in var. *martini*), to 0.4–1(–1.7) mm. **Seeds** 25–43.

Varieties 4 (4 in the flora): w United States.

Astragalus argophyllus varies considerably in hair orientation, in flower size and color, and in ecology. Still, it is only with difficulty that material may be sorted into infraspecific taxa, and sometimes plants cannot be satisfactorily identified.

1. Banners 18.2–24 mm, keel 15.9–20.3 mm; legumes ovoid to broadly lanceoloid-ellipsoid or oblong-ellipsoid, pubescent but not permanently silky-strigose in age; widespread in w United States.
   2. Corollas bright purple, banners 22–24 mm; moist meadows, stream banks, or lakeshores in e California, wc to ec and ne Nevada, e Idaho, sw Montana, c, nc, nw Utah . . . . 182a. *Astragalus argophyllus* var. *argophyllus*
   2. Corollas tinged lilac or dull purple, banners 18–21.5(–22.5) mm; dry gravelly hills and mesas, often among sagebrush, of n Arizona, e Nevada, se Idaho, c to ne Utah, sw Wyoming, nw Colorado . . . . .182b. *Astragalus argophyllus* var. *martini*
1. Banners 15–23.4 mm, keel 12–19.8 mm; legumes lanceoloid-ellipsoid or narrowly and obliquely ovoid-acuminate, silky-strigose even late in season; Arizona, s Utah.
   3. Banners 15–17.5(–18.4) mm, keel 12–15.2 mm; hairs basifixed . . . . .182c. *Astragalus argophyllus* var. *panguicensis*
   3. Banners 20–23.4 mm, keel 17–19.8 mm; hairs unequally malpighian. . . . . 182d. *Astragalus argophyllus* var. *alvius*

182a. Astragalus argophyllus Nuttall var. **argophyllus** E

Hairs basifixed. **Stems** 0–10(–15) cm. **Leaves** (1.5–)2.5–12(–15) cm; leaflets usually distant, sometimes crowded, (7 or) 9–21, blades usually elliptic, rhombic-elliptic, or -ovate, rarely elliptic-oblanceolate, (2–)4–15 mm, apex usually acute, rarely obtuse. **Flowers:** calyx 12.4–16.8 mm, tube (9.4–)10–11.8 mm, lobes 2.4–5(–5.8) mm; corolla bright purple; banner 22–24 mm; keel (17.3–)17.6–20.3 mm. **Legumes** ovoid to broadly lanceoloid-ellipsoid or oblong-ellipsoid, 15–25 × 7–12 mm, strigulose-pilosulous, hairs appressed or subappressed, straight, to (0.4–)0.5–1 mm.

Flowering mid Apr–Jul. Alkaline and saline meadows and in evidently non-saline sites, on stream banks, river terraces, lakeshores; 1300–2300 m; Calif., Idaho, Mont., Nev., Utah, Wyo.

182b. Astragalus argophyllus Nuttall var. **martini** M. E. Jones, Rev. N.-Amer. Astragalus, 207. 1923 • Martin's milkvetch E

Astragalus argophyllus var. *pephragmenoides* Barneby

Hairs basifixed. **Stems** 0–5 cm. **Leaves** 1.5–8.5 cm; leaflets 11–17(or 19), blades usually obovate-cuneate or elliptic-oblong, rarely elliptic-oblanceolate, 2–10 mm, apex usually obtuse, rarely acute. **Flowers:** calyx 10.2–14(–14.7) mm, tube 8.4–10.9 mm, lobes 1.6–3.3 mm; corolla tinged lilac or dull purple; banner 18–21.5(–22.5) mm; keel 15.9–18.5 mm. **Legumes** ovoid to broadly lanceoloid-ellipsoid or oblong-ellipsoid, (17–)20–32(–37) × 8–12(–13) mm, strigulose or villous, hairs appressed to loosely spreading and, sometimes, contorted, to 0.6–1.7 mm.

Flowering Apr–Aug. Dry gravelly or sandy hillsides, stony ridges, mesas, and canyon benches, in sagebrush, mountain brush, aspen, and spruce-fir communities; 1700–3100 m; Ariz., Colo., Idaho, Nev., Utah, Wyo.

Where vars. *martini* and *argophyllus* overlap geographically in southeastern Idaho and adjoining Wyoming and Utah, the former is an obligate xerophyte, whereas the latter is found exclusively in moist ground. Even when closely sympatric, they are ecologically isolated. In this area, habit preferences of these varieties deserves careful field study. Plants of var. *martini* from the desert ranges in Millard County, western Utah, have longer, ascending, and more or less contorted hairs; in that regard, they approach *Astragalus callithrix*.

182c. Astragalus argophyllus Nuttall var. **panguicensis** (M. E. Jones) M. E. Jones, Contr. W. Bot. 8: 5. 1898 • Panguitch milkvetch E

Astragalus chamaeleuce A. Gray var. *panguicensis* M. E. Jones, Proc. Calif. Acad. Sci., ser. 2, 5: 671. 1895; *A. panguicensis* (M. E. Jones) M. E. Jones; *A. sabinarum* (Rydberg) Barneby; *Batidophaca sabinarum* Rydberg

Hairs basifixed. **Stems** rarely developed, 0–5(–10) cm. **Leaves** 1.5–6(–8) cm; leaflets 7–15(or 17), blades elliptic-obovate, 2–9 mm, apex obtuse to very shortly acuminate. **Flowers:** calyx 9–12(–14) mm, tube 6.8–8.7(–10.6) mm, lobes 1.9–3.4(–4.2) mm; corolla light purple; banner 15–17.5(–18.4) mm; keel 12–15.2 mm. **Legumes** lunately lanceoloid-ellipsoid or narrowly and very obliquely ovoid-acuminate, 15–27 × 5–8(–9) mm, silky-strigose, hairs ascending, silvery, to 0.5–0.8 mm.

Flowering Apr–Jul. Gravelly hillsides and benches in ponderosa pine forests, aspen-Douglas-fir-limber pine, white fir, sagebrush, and pinyon-juniper communities; 2000–3200 m; Ariz., Utah.

Variety *panguicensis* is restricted to Coconino and Mohave counties in northwestern Arizona and to south-central and southwestern Utah. Some collections from an outlying population on Mount Emma in Coconino County are typical; others have exceptionally large flowers suggestive of the generally more northern var. *martini*.

182d. Astragalus argophyllus Nuttall var. **alvius** S. L. Welsh, N. Amer. Sp. Astragalus, 204. 2007 • Streambed milkvetch E

Hairs unequally malpighian. **Stems** rarely developed, 0–6 cm. **Leaves** 1.5–9.5 cm; leaflets 11–17, blades elliptic to oblancelate or oblong-elliptic, 4–14 mm, apex acute to obtuse. **Flowers:** calyx 9–12(–14) mm, tube 6.8–8.7(–10.6) mm, lobes 3.9–4.2 mm; corolla purple to violet; banner 20–23.4 mm; keel 17–19.8 mm. **Legumes** lanceoloid-ellipsoid, 23–30 × 6.5–8 mm, silky-strigose, hairs ascending, silvery, to 0.5–0.7 mm.

Flowering May. Oak, ponderosa pine, and juniper communities; 2300–2400 m; Ariz.

Variety *alvius* has been a source of confusion for more than three decades. The type collection has been variously identified as *Astragalus argophyllus* var. *panguicensis* or var. *stocksii*, the latter here included in *A. henrimontanensis*. The malpighian hairs that are attached very close to one end are distinctive. Variety *alvius* is restricted to the Kaibab Plateau and Mount Trumbull vicinity in Coconino and Mohave counties.

183. Astragalus henrimontanensis S. L. Welsh, Great Basin Naturalist 38: 12. 1978 • Dana's milkvetch E

Astragalus stocksii S. L. Welsh, Great Basin Naturalist 34: 307, fig. 2. 1974, not Bentham ex Bunge 1868

Plants: leaves in basal tuft, acaulescent, 4–15 cm, strigose, hairs basifixed; from branching caudex with coarse, persistent leaf bases. **Leaves** 2.7–12.5 cm; stipules 3–8 mm; leaflets 7–17, blades elliptic to oblanceolate, 3–13 mm, apex mucronate, acute to obtuse, or truncate, surfaces strigose. **Peduncles** 1.1–8 cm. **Racemes** 2–11-flowered, flowers ascending; axis 0.8–2.2 cm in fruit; bracts 1.8–5.5 mm; bracteoles 0–2. **Pedicels** 1.3–2.5 mm. **Flowers** 15–25 mm; calyx cylindric, 10.2–15 mm, strigulose, tube 8.2–11.5 mm, lobes subulate, 1.9–3.5 mm; corolla ochroleucous, sometimes tinged or veined purple, wing and keel tips purple; banner recurved through 40°. **Legumes** ascending, humistrate, slightly incurved, lanceoloid-oblong to lanceoloid-ellipsoid or lanceoloid-ovoid, somewhat dorsiventrally compressed, 22–35 × 5–11 mm, unilocular, thinly leathery or woody, strigose.

Flowering Apr–May. Sagebrush, pinyon-juniper, ponderosa pine, aspen, and mixed conifer communities; 2200–2800 m; Utah.

Astragalus henrimontanensis is restricted to the Henry Mountains and Aquarius Plateau, Garfield County. Fruits resemble those of *A. argophyllus* var. *panguicensis*. In flower color, erect, acaulescent habit, and the thatch of persistent leaf bases, it resembles *A. eurekensis*; in growth form, curved fruiting peduncles, and humistrate fruits, it is like *A. welshii*.

184. Astragalus uncialis Barneby, Leafl. W. Bot. 3: 101, plate 1, fig. E. 1942 • Currant milkvetch C E

Plants forming rather dwarf, compact tufts, acaulescent, 1.5–7.5 cm, silvery-strigose, hairs basifixed; from branching caudex. **Stems** obscured by stipules. **Leaves** 1.5–7.5 cm; stipules 3–6.5 mm, membranous, pallid, with green midrib; leaflets 3 or 5, blades oblanceolate, elliptic, or narrowly obovate, 5–17 mm, apex acute to subobtuse, surfaces strigose. **Peduncles** ascending, prostrate in fruit, 0.5–3.5 cm, mostly shorter than leaves. **Racemes** 1–3-flowered, flowers ascending; axis to 0.3 cm in fruit; bracts 1.5–3.5 mm; bracteoles 0 or 1. **Pedicels** 1.5–3 mm. **Flowers** 24.5–32 mm; calyx cylindric, 12–17 mm, strigulose, hairs white, sometimes also black, tube 10.2–13 mm, lobes subulate, 1.8–3.5 mm; corolla pink-purple or purple; banner recurved through 40°; keel 21.5–24.5 mm. **Legumes** ascending, stramineous, ± straight, obliquely lanceoloid-ellipsoid, dorsiventrally compressed, 20–35(–40) × 8–12 mm, unilocular, valves much less than 1 mm thick, thinly fleshy becoming leathery, strigulose, hairs appressed, 0.5–0.7 mm. **Seeds** 38–54.

Flowering Apr–Jun. Shadscale, budsage, horsebrush, and sagebrush and greasewood communities; of conservation concern; 1400–1900 m; Nev., Utah.

The general aspect of *Astragalus uncialis* is that of a small *A. newberryi*, near which R. C. Barneby (1964) placed it. The main area of distribution of this Great

Basin endemic seems to be on the low recessional terraces of ancient Lake Bonneville in Millard County, Utah.

185. Astragalus zionis M. E. Jones, Proc. Calif. Acad. Sci., ser. 2, 5: 652. 1895 • Zion milkvetch [E]

Plants mat- or tuft-forming, subacaulescent or shortly caulescent, 3–23 cm, densely villous-villosulous or strigulose, hairs basifixed; from branched caudex, sometimes with persistent thatch of leaf bases. **Stems** prostrate to ascending, 0–11 cm, internodes often concealed by white-hairy stipules and dense white hairs, villous-tomentulose. **Leaves** 2–15 cm; stipules sometimes shortly connate-sheathing at proximal nodes, 1.5–5.5 mm, submembranous becoming papery-scarious; leaflets 13–25, blades elliptic or ovate, 2–16 mm, apex usually acute, sometimes obtuse, surfaces silvery-villous. **Peduncles** 0.5–15 cm. **Racemes** 1–11-flowered, flowers ascending; axis 0.3–6 cm in fruit; bracts 2–5 mm; bracteoles 0–2. **Pedicels** 1–3 mm. **Flowers** 18–26 mm; calyx cylindric, 8.3–18 mm, villous, tube 6.5–13.5 mm, lobes subulate, 1.5–5.7 mm; corolla often pink-purple, sometimes pale; banner recurved through 40°; keel concealing style, 14.6–18.6(–19) mm. **Legumes** ascending, brightly purple-mottled, usually curved, obliquely ovoid-oblong, dorsiventrally compressed, ventrally grooved proximally, 15–35 × 5.5–12 mm, unilocular, fleshy becoming somewhat woody, strigose or villosulous. **Seeds** 24–30.

Varieties 2 (2 in the flora): w United States.

Astragalus zionis is a variable species, consisting of many isolated populations scattered throughout the deeply dissected sandstones of the Colorado Plateau. The connate stipules are anomalous among its close relatives. It is closely related to *A. argophyllus*, and sometimes differential characters are hard to find. Here it is maintained as a species because the connate stipules and mottled fruits are associated with ecological and distributional patterns.

1. Plants mat- or tuft-forming, usually to 2.5 dm wide; legumes 15–25(–28) × 5.5–9 mm; Arizona, Nevada, New Mexico, Utah . . . . .185a. *Astragalus zionis* var. *zionis*
1. Plants mat-forming, often very large, to 10 dm wide; legumes 25–35 × 9–12 mm; Pine Valley Mountains, Utah. . . 185b. *Astragalus zionis* var. *vigulus*

185a. Astragalus zionis M. E. Jones var. **zionis** [E]

Plants mat- or tuft-forming, usually to 2.5 dm wide. **Legumes** 15–25(–28) × 5.5–9 mm.

Flowering Apr–Jun. On sandstone, on sandy and gravelly soils in blackbrush, sagebrush, *Ephedra*, other mixed desert shrub, sometimes salt desert shrub, mountain brush, ponderosa pine, and riparian communities; 1300–2500 m; Ariz., Nev., N.Mex., Utah.

The caudex of var. *zionis* is often slightly subterranean, being buried in duff or in sand, and the stipules are conspicuously white and white-pilose, mainly concealing the internodes.

185b. Astragalus zionis M. E. Jones var. **vigulus** S. L. Welsh, Rhodora 95: 404, fig. 12. 1993 • Guard station milkvetch [C] [E]

Plants mat-forming, often very large, to 10 dm wide. **Legumes** 25–35 × 9–12 mm.

Flowering Apr–Jun. Pinyon-juniper, mountain mahogany, and oak-*Garrya* communities; of conservation concern; 1800–2500 m; Utah.

Variety *vigulus* is restricted to the eastern slope of the Pine Valley Mountains, Washington County.

186. Astragalus callithrix Barneby, Leafl. W. Bot. 3: 103, plate 1, fig. C. 1942 • Callaway milkvetch [E]

Plants sometimes short-lived, often flowering first year, loosely tuft-forming, subacaulescent, 2–20(–30) cm, densely white-pilose, hairs basifixed, straight, narrowly ascending; from caudex. **Stems** prostrate, 0–15 cm, internodes often concealed by stipules, densely white-pilose. **Leaves** 2–11 cm; stipules 2–5 mm, submembranous; leaflets 9–21, blades obovate, suborbiculate, or lanceolate, 2–13 mm, apex obtuse to truncate or emarginate, surfaces villous. **Peduncles** erect or arcuate-ascending, spreading or procumbent in fruit, 2–8(–12) cm. **Racemes** 5–15-flowered, flowers ascending; axis 0.5–6 cm in fruit; bracts 3–7.5 mm; bracteoles 0–2. **Pedicels** 1–1.5 mm. **Flowers** 16–26 mm; calyx purplish, cylindric, 6.8–13.3 mm, villous-pilose, tube 5.5–10.8 mm, lobes subulate, 1–3.2 mm; corolla bright pink-purple; banner recurved through 40°; keel (12–)13–20.7 mm. **Legumes** ascending-spreading, stramineous, incurved, oblong-ovoid, dorsiventrally compressed, 10–20 × 5–7.5 mm, unilocular, fleshy becoming leathery, hirsute, longest hairs 2–2.5 mm, not obscuring surface. **Seeds** 24–34.

Flowering May–Jun. Sandy flats and dunes in mixed desert shrub and juniper communities; 1500–1800 m; Nev., Utah.

Astragalus callithrix, a Great Basin endemic from Millard County, Utah, and Nye County, Nevada, is associated with the so-called warm point at the south ends of some mountain ranges, where wind-blown sand accumulates along the eastern sides of valleys.

187. Astragalus piutensis Barneby & Mabberley, Taxon 34: 453. 1985 • Sevier milkvetch [E]

Xylophacos marianus Rydberg, Bull. Torrey Bot. Club 52: 233. 1925, not *Astragalus marianus* C. Huber 1872

Plants acaulescent or subacaulescent, 3–10 cm, densely strigulose-strigose, hairs basifixed; from branched caudex. **Stems** prostrate or ascending, 0–6 cm, internodes mostly concealed by stipules, densely to sparsely strigose. **Leaves** 1.2–8.5 cm; stipules 2–7 mm, membranous; leaflets 7–17, blades obovate to oblanceolate, 3–11 mm, apex obtuse to emarginate or acuminate to acute, surfaces strigose, hairs subappressed and silvery-silky. **Peduncles** incurved-ascending, 1–8 cm. **Racemes** 2–10-flowered, flowers ascending; axis 0.2–3.5 cm in fruit; bracts 2–4.5 mm; bracteoles 0–2. **Pedicels** 0.8–3 mm. **Flowers** 17–24 mm; calyx cylindric, 10–13.2 mm, pilosulous, tube 7.3–9.4 mm, lobes subulate, 2–3.5 mm; corolla pink-purple, often pale; banner recurved through 40°; keel 17–19 mm, 2 mm shorter than banner. **Legumes** spreading-ascending (humistrate), sessile or subsessile, gently or abruptly incurved, ovoid-acuminate, obcompressed, 10–23 × 7–12 mm, unilocular, fleshy becoming stiffly leathery, densely shaggy-hirsute, hairs concealing surface, longest hairs 2–3.5 mm. **Seeds** 27–36.

Flowering Apr–Jul. Oak-sagebrush, mixed warm and cool desert shrub, pinyon-juniper, aspen-white fir, and ponderosa pine communities; 900–3100 m; Nev., Utah.

Astragalus piutensis is rather frequent and locally plentiful in the mountains and foothills enclosing the Sevier Basin and surrounding Beaver, Iron, Millard, Piute, Sevier, and Washington counties in Utah, and Lincoln and White Pine counties in Nevada.

As noted by R. C. Barneby (1964, as *Astragalus marianus*), the general form of *A. piutensis* closely matches that of *A. argophyllus* var. *martini*, from which he perceived its derivation. Only when the fruits are sufficiently mature can the nature of the pubescence be determined, and that is still the main diagnostic feature distinguishing the two. Their ranges are largely allopatric.

188. Astragalus desereticus Barneby, Mem. New York Bot. Gard. 13: 634. 1964 • Deseret milkvetch [C] [E]

Plants acaulescent or subacaulescent, 4–15 cm, densely villosulous and hirsute, hairs basifixed; from caudex. **Stems** to 6 cm, internodes ± obscured by stipules, densely villosulous and hirsute. **Leaves** 4–12 cm; stipules 3.5–7 mm, submembranous becoming papery; leaflets 11–17, blades elliptic to obovate, 2–14 mm, apex short-acuminate to acute, surfaces strigulose-villosulous, hairs ascending, dull. **Peduncles** ascending, 2–5.5 cm. **Racemes** 5–10-flowered, flowers ascending; axis 0.5–2 cm in fruit; bracts 3–6 mm; bracteoles 0–2. **Pedicels** 2–3 mm. **Flowers** 18–22.5 mm; calyx cylindric, 8.4–12 mm, villous, tube 6.2–7.5 mm, lobes subulate, 2–4 mm; corolla whitish suffused with pale purple, keel tip purple; banner recurved through 40°; keel 12–13.3 mm, 4.5–9 mm shorter than banner. **Legumes** ascending (not humistrate), sessile or substipitate, incurved, ovoid-ellipsoid, obcompressed, 10–20 × 5–10 mm, unilocular, fleshy becoming stiffly leathery, densely hirsute, hairs lustrous, concealing surface, longest 2–2.5 mm. **Seeds** 14–16.

Flowering May–Jun. Sagebrush-juniper communities on the Moroni Formation; of conservation concern; 1600–1800 m; Utah.

Astragalus desereticus is found on the Moroni Formation where the soil is often ash-flow tuff. It is known from Utah County where it was rediscovered after 60 years growing on roadcuts of a much-travelled highway. It was initially thought to be closely allied to *A. argophyllus*, but it is possibly nearer to *A. purshii*, with which it was compared by R. C. Barneby (1964), but an alliance with *A. argophyllus* was discounted ultimately because of the coarser pubescence of *A. desereticus*. *Astragalus desereticus* shares with *A. purshii* both pale flowers and fruits with thick pubescence. It differs from other species in sect. *Argophylli* in its strongly graduated petals in which the banner and wings much surpass the keel.

Astragalus desereticus is in the Center for Plant Conservation's National Collection of Endangered Plants.

189. Astragalus eurylobus (Barneby) Barneby, Brittonia 36: 169. 1984 • Needle Mountains milkvetch [C] [E]

Astragalus tephrodes A. Gray var. *eurylobus* Barneby, Mem. New York Bot. Gard. 13: 643. 1964

Plants loosely tuft-forming, subacaulescent or shortly caulescent, 10–30 cm, pilosulous, hairs basifixed; from branched caudex. **Stems** prostrate, 0.4–9 cm, internodes less than 1 cm, pilosulous. **Leaves** 3–24 cm; stipules 2.5–8 mm, submembranous becoming papery; leaflets 17–27, blades rhombic- to elliptic-obovate or obovate-cuneate, 3–17 (–27) mm, apex obtuse or emarginate, surfaces pilosulous. **Peduncles** humistrate or procumbent in fruit, 4–18 cm. **Racemes** loosely 7–14(–26)-flowered, flowers ascending; axis 2–5.5(–14) cm in fruit; bracts 1.5–8 mm; bracteoles 0(–2). **Pedicels** 0.6–3 mm. **Flowers** 17–20 (–22) mm; calyx cylindric, 9.5–11(–12) mm, pilosulous, tube 8–9.5 mm, lobes subulate to triangular, 1–1.7 mm; corolla pink-purple; banner recurved through 45°; keel 17–19 mm. **Legumes** ascending (humistrate), green or purplish, straight proximally, incurved distally, obliquely oblong-ellipsoid or lanceoloid-ellipsoid, laterally compressed, abaxially compressed on drying, grooved only along dorsal suture, 21–30(–40) × 7.5–9(–16) mm, semibilocular, fleshy becoming subligneous, strigulose. **Seeds** 30–45.

Flowering Apr–early Jul. Shadscale, matchweed, saltbush, juniper, sagebrush, and grassland communities; of conservation concern; 1300–1900 m; Ariz., Nev.

Astragalus eurylobus has a restricted distribution in Mohave County in Arizona, and Lincoln and Nye counties in Nevada.

Astragalus eurylobus is very similar to *A. tephrodes*, with which it was originally associated as a variety, but from which it differs in its semibilocular (not unilocular or essentially so) thicker fruits with an inflexed septum 1–2 mm wide. Overall, it is a coarser plant than *A. tephrodes*.

190. Astragalus tephrodes A. Gray, Smithsonian Contr. Knowl. 5(6): 45. 1853 • Ashen milkvetch

Plants loosely or densely tuft-forming, acaulescent or shortly caulescent, 10–48 cm, strigulose, pilosulous, or villosulous, hairs basifixed; from branched caudex, branches often with conspicuous thatch of marcescent leaf rachises. **Stems** prostrate, 0–15(–25) cm, internodes to 2(–2.5) cm, strigulose, pilosulous, or villosulous. **Leaves** 4–24 cm; stipules sometimes obscurely connate at proximal nodes, 2–15 mm, submembranous becoming papery-scarious; leaflets 11–27(–31), blades oblanceolate, obovate, obovate-cuneate, rhombic, rhombic-ovate, or rhombic-elliptic, rarely suborbiculate, 2–27 mm, apex usually obtuse or acute, rarely emarginate, surfaces usually pubescent, sometimes glabrescent or glabrous adaxially. **Peduncles** incurved-ascending or erect, 4–40 cm. **Racemes** loosely (9 or)10–25(–35)-flowered, flowers ascending; axis (1.5–)2–20 cm in fruit; bracts 1.5–11 mm; bracteoles usually 0(–2). **Pedicels** 0.6–3.4 mm. **Flowers** 11.8–24 mm; calyx cylindric to deeply campanulate, (5–)6.4–14 mm, loosely strigulose, pilosulous, or villous, tube (3.5–)4.5–10.2 mm, lobes subulate or triangular-subulate, 1.2–3.8 mm; corolla usually pink-purple to dull lilac, rarely white or nearly so; banner recurved through 45°; keel 10.2–20.1 mm. **Legumes** ascending, green or purplish becoming stramineous or brownish, lunately incurved or straight proximally and only beak incurved, obliquely ovoid-acuminate, lanceoloid-, oblong-, or ovoid-ellipsoid, strongly obcompressed, 13–34 × 5–10(–12) mm, ± unilocular, valves less than 1 mm thick, thinly to thickly fleshy becoming thinly leathery, stiffly leathery, or subligneous, usually densely to sparsely strigulose or pilosulous, rarely glabrous. **Seeds** 24–36.

Varieties 3 (3 in the flora): sw United States, nw Mexico.

Astragalus tephrodes consists of two intergrading varieties (var. *brachylobus*, var. *tephrodes*) that are rather widely distributed and one (var. *chloridae*) that is narrowly distributed. R. C. Barneby (1947b, 1964) discussed the taxonomic complexity of the species and described the clinal variation from Arizona to the western limits of the species distribution, resulting in a classification that is necessarily arbitrary.

1. Calyx tubes (3.5–)4.5–6.8(–8) mm, lobes 1.2–2.2 mm; corolla banners 11.8–17.5 mm, keel 10.2–14.5 mm; legumes 13–20 mm, thinly leathery; leaflets mostly conduplicate; sw New Mexico and adjoining Mexico, westward across Arizona to Verde Valley, Yavapai County. . . . . 190a. *Astragalus tephrodes* var. *tephrodes*
1. Calyx tubes 7.1–10.2 mm, lobes 1.7–3.8 mm; corolla banners (14–)16.8–24 mm, keel 14.7–20.1 mm; legumes 17–34 mm, stiffly leathery or subligneous; leaflets mostly flat; Arizona, Nevada, California, and w New Mexico.
    2. Peduncles (4–)5–15(–21) cm; raceme rachis (1.5–)2–8(–11) cm in fruit; broadly distributed from se California and Nevada to New Mexico . . . . 190b. *Astragalus tephrodes* var. *brachylobus*
    2. Peduncles 13–40 cm; raceme rachis (4–)7–20 cm in fruit; nw Arizona, extreme s Nevada . . . . 190c. *Astragalus tephrodes* var. *chloridae*

190a. Astragalus tephrodes A. Gray var. **tephrodes**

Stems 1–12(–15) cm. **Stipules** 2–7 mm. **Leaves** 4.5–10(–19) cm; leaflets (11–)17–27(–31), blades mostly conduplicate, loosely folded, obovate-cuneate or oblanceolate, 3–16 mm, apex obtuse, emarginate, or subacute. **Peduncles** 4–14(–17) cm. **Racemes** (9–)11–20-flowered; axis 2–6(–8.5) cm in fruit. **Flowers** 11.8–17.5 mm; calyx (5–)6.4–8.5(–9.2) mm, tube (3.5–)4.5–6.8(–8) mm, lobes 1.2–2.2 mm; corolla banner 11.8–17.5 mm; keel 10.2–14.5 mm. **Legumes** obliquely ovoid-acuminate, 13–20 × 5–8 mm, beak 3–6 mm, thinly leathery, hardly rigid, not rugulose, densely pilosulous. **Seeds** 26–31. **2*n*** = 22.

Flowering Apr–Jun. Oak brush, among junipers, in yucca-grasslands, edges of ponderosa pine forests, on granitic or volcanic bedrock; 1400–2200 m; Ariz., N.Mex.; Mexico (Sonora).

Variety *tephrodes* is locally plentiful in the foothills of the Mogollon and Pinos Altos mountains in southwestern New Mexico, eastward to the Organ Mountains and southward into Mexico.

190b. Astragalus tephrodes A. Gray var. **brachylobus** (A. Gray) Barneby, Amer. Midl. Naturalist 37: 466. 1947 • Prescott milkvetch [E]

Astragalus shortianus Nuttall var. *brachylobus* A. Gray, Proc. Amer. Acad. Arts 13: 367. 1878

Stems 0–8 cm. **Stipules** 2.5–11 mm, surfaces villosulous, sparsely strigulose, or glabrate abaxially. **Leaves** 4–16 cm; leaflets 11–27(–31), blades mostly flat, usually obovate-cuneate, oblanceolate, or rhombic-elliptic, rarely suborbiculate, (3–)4–17 mm, apex obtuse, acute, or emarginate. **Peduncles** (4–)5–15(–21) cm. **Racemes** 10–25(–35)-flowered; axis (1.5–)2–8(–11) cm in fruit. **Flowers** (14–)18–24 mm; calyx 8.8–12.7(–14) mm, pilosulous to loosely strigulose, sometimes villous, tube 7.1–10 mm, lobes 1.7–2.8 mm; corolla banner (14–)18–24 mm; keel 14.7–20.1 mm. **Legumes** oblong-ellipsoid to lanceoloid-ellipsoid or, sometimes, ovoid-acuminate, 17–30 × 6–10 mm, somewhat fleshy becoming stiffly leathery or subligneous, usually strigulose or pilosulous, sometimes glabrous. **Seeds** 24–35.

Flowering Apr–Jun. Arid grasslands, oak-chaparral, in pinyon-juniper, juniper, or ponderosa pine forests, on volcanic, granitic, or sedimentary bedrock (including limestone); 1000–2000 m; Ariz., Calif., Nev., N.Mex.

The range of var. *brachylobus* extends from the crest of the Mogollon Escarpment northward to the slopes of the Kaibab Plateau, westward to the Colorado River near Needles, California, and southeastward around the edge of the Gila Basin to west-central New Mexico.

The pubescent phases of var. *brachylobus* were aggregated into four groups, three somewhat geographically restricted (R. C. Barneby 1964). Variety *brachylobus* is difficult to distinguish from var. *tephrodes* in west-central New Mexico.

190c. Astragalus tephrodes A. Gray var. **chloridae** (M. E. Jones) Barneby, Mem. New York Bot. Gard. 13: 642. 1964 • Chloride milkvetch [E]

Astragalus remulcus M. E. Jones var. *chloridae* M. E. Jones, Rev. N.-Amer. Astragalus, 210. 1923

Stems 2–15 cm. **Stipules** 2–15 mm, surfaces sparsely strigulose or glabrate abaxially. **Leaves** 10–24 cm; leaflets 19–25, blades flat, rhombic, rhombic-ovate, obovate, or oblanceolate, 6–26 mm, apex usually acute, sometimes obtuse. **Peduncles** 13–40 cm. **Racemes** 13–24-flowered; axis (4–)7–20 cm in fruit. **Flowers** 16.8–20.4 mm; calyx 11.5–14 mm, pilosulous or loosely strigulose, tube 8.3–10.2 mm, lobes 2.1–3.8 mm; corolla banner 16.8–20.4 mm; keel 15.2–18.2 mm. **Legumes** lanceolate- or oblong-ellipsoid, 22–34 × 6–10(–12) mm, beak 3–6 mm, stiffly leathery or subligneous, angles ± rugulose, strigulose-pilosulous. **Seeds** 28–36. **2*n*** = 22.

Flowering Mar–May. *Larrea* and juniper communities; 900–1400 m; Ariz., Nev.

As strictly perceived, var. *chloridae* is restricted to the Cerbat Mountains, Mohave County, Arizona, and the Newberry Mountains, Clark County, Nevada. D. Isely (1998) allowed a somewhat broader range in Mohave County.

191. Astragalus iodopetalus (Rydberg) Barneby, Amer. Midl. Naturalist 37: 471. 1947 • Violet milkvetch [C] [E]

Xylophacos iodopetalus Rydberg, Bull. Torrey Bot. Club 52: 152. 1925

Plants caulescent or subacaulescent, 1.5–10(–18) cm, villous-villosulous, hairs basifixed; from superficial caudex. **Stems** prostrate and radiating, internodes to 0.5–2(–2.5) cm, concealed by stipules or developed, villous-villosulous or glabrate. **Leaves** (4–)5–15(–20) cm; stipules mostly distinct, broadly ovate or triangular, 2.5–12 mm, submembranous; leaflets 7–31, blades oblanceolate, obovate, or elliptic, 3–17(–20) mm, apex obtuse or emarginate, surfaces villous-villosulous abaxially, sometimes glabrate adaxially. **Peduncles** incurved-ascending, prostrate in fruit, (1.5–)3–10 cm. **Racemes** densely (10–)12–20(–25)-flowered, flowers ascending; axis (1.5–)2–8 cm in fruit; bracts 2.5–8.5 mm; bracteoles 0. **Pedicels** 1.3–3.6 mm. **Flowers** 17–23.5 mm; calyx cylindric to deeply campanulate, 10–15 mm, sparsely villous-villosulous, tube (6.8–)7.5–10.5 mm, lobes lanceolate to subulate, 2.5–5.5 mm; corolla bright reddish violet or tinged with violet, white, or whitish; banner incurved 40–50°; keel 12–15.7 mm. **Legumes** ascending (humistrate), brownish then blackish, ± straight, obliquely ovoid, lanceoloid-ellipsoid, oblong-ellipsoid, or lanceoloid, obcompressed, (17–)20–30 × 7–10 mm, subunilocular, fleshy becoming stiffly leathery or subligneous, glabrous; septum to 1.7 mm wide. **Seeds** 30–44.

Flowering May–Jul. Dry, stony hillsides and benches, on granitic bedrock, in oak thickets, oak-pinyon forests, with sagebrush; of conservation concern; 1800–2500 m; Colo., N.Mex.

Astragalus iodopetalus is locally common around the western and southern slopes of the Rocky Mountains.

192. Astragalus shortianus Nuttall in J. Torrey and A. Gray, Fl. N. Amer. 1: 331. 1838 • Short's milkvetch [E]

Plants mostly acaulescent, 10–21 cm, stiffly silvery-strigulose or -strigose, hairs basifixed; from superficial caudex. **Stems** usually reduced to sessile crowns, rarely to 2.5 cm, internodes concealed by stipules, sometimes with thatch of persistent leaf rachises, hairs silvery. **Leaves** (4–)6–21 cm; stipules (3–)5–12 mm, thinly herbaceous becoming papery; leaflets 7–17 (or 19), blades usually obovate, rhombic-obovate, elliptic-ovate, rarely flabellate, 5–20(–25) mm, apex obtuse or subacute, surfaces strigose. **Peduncles** 2–15 cm. **Racemes** loosely (5–)7–16-flowered; axis 1–4(–6) cm in fruit; bracts 4–10 mm; bracteoles 0(–2). **Pedicels** 1.6–3.4 mm. **Flowers** (16–)19–22 mm; calyx cylindric or deeply campanulate, (9.4–)11–14.7 mm, villous (not silvery), tube (6.5–)7.6–9.8 mm, lobes lanceolate-subulate, 2.9–5.6 mm; corolla pink-purple; banner recurved through 40°; keel (13–)15.5–17.2 mm. **Legumes** ascending (humistrate), brown or stramineous then blackish, ± straight in proximal 1/2, obliquely ovoid or ellipsoid, obcompressed, (20–)25–45 × (8–)9–18 mm, unilocular, fleshy becoming woody or very stiffly leathery, densely strigulose. **Seeds** 33–54(–66).

Flowering May–Jul. Prairies, dry hilltops, open stony ridges, cobblestone bluffs, on decomposed granite, on sandstone, coarse alluvia of mixed origins; 1500–2800 m; Colo., Nebr., N.Mex., Wyo.

Astragalus shortianus is common on the eastern slopes of the Rocky Mountains and adjacent plains.

193. Astragalus cyaneus A. Gray, Mem. Amer. Acad. Arts, n. s. 4: 34. 1849 • Cyanic milkvetch [E]

Plants acaulescent or subacaulescent, 10–15 cm, strigulose, hairs basifixed; from superficial caudex. **Stems** reduced to crowns or developed, to 6 cm, internodes to 1.5 cm, strigulose. **Leaves** 6–18 cm; stipules 4–9 mm, papery; leaflets (15 or)17–29, blades obovate to elliptic, 4–19 mm, apex obtuse, acute, or retuse, surfaces strigulose. **Peduncles** ascending, (4–)6–13 cm. **Racemes** loosely (9–)12–22(–25)-flowered, flowers spreading or declined; axis 15–25 cm in fruit; bracts 2.5–6 mm; bracteoles 2. **Pedicels** 1–4.5 mm. **Flowers** 18–22 mm; calyx cylindric to deeply and broadly campanulate, 11.3–15 mm, strigulose, tube 8.2–10.6 mm, lobes subulate or lanceolate-subulate, 2.3–4.6 mm; corolla pink-purple; banner recurved through 40°; keel 16.3–18 mm. **Legumes** ascending (humistrate), green or purple-tinged becoming stramineous or brownish, gently recurved, obliquely oblong-ellipsoid, obcompressed in proximal 1/2, 25–50 × 7–13 mm, unilocular or appearing partially bilocular, valves 1–2 mm thick, thickly fleshy becoming rigidly woody, strongly reticulate, strigulose; didymous, septum forming a narrowly tubular or 3-sided cavity throughout, sutures subcontiguous. **Seeds** (35–)39–48. $2n = 22$.

Flowering late Apr–Jun. Dry hillsides, gullied banks, on sandy or gravelly granitic soils, with pinyon-juniper associations; 2100–2300 m; N.Mex.

Astragalus cyaneus is locally plentiful but uncommon, known only from the eastern side of the Rio Grande in north-central New Mexico.

194. Astragalus columbianus Barneby, Mem. New York Bot. Gard. 13: 649. 1964 • Columbia milkvetch [E]

Plants caulescent, (8–)15–45 cm, strigulose, hairs basifixed; from superficial or barely subterranean caudex. **Stems** decumbent to ascending, diffuse, leafless basally, strigulose. **Leaves** 3.5–5.5 cm; stipules 1–6 mm, membranous at proximal nodes, herbaceous with membranous margins at distal nodes; leaflets 5–13, blades oblong-elliptic, narrowly oblanceolate, or linear-oblong, 3–12 mm, apex obtuse or obtuse and apiculate, surfaces strigulose, sometimes glabrescent adaxially. **Peduncles** ascending, 1.2–2.5 cm. **Racemes** subcapitate, loosely 2–10-flowered, flowers ascending; axis to 1 cm in fruit; bracts 1–5 mm; bracteoles 0–2. **Pedicels** 0.6–1.5 mm. **Flowers** (17–)18.1–19.5(–20) mm; calyx cylindric, (9.5–10–11.5(–13) mm, strigose, tube 7–8.2 mm, lobes narrowly lanceolate-subulate, 2.4–4.5 mm; corolla white or whitish, keel maculate; banner incurved through 35°; keel 13.1–13.6 mm. **Legumes** ascending (humistrate), green, incurved through 0.25–0.5+ spiral, narrowly oblong-ellipsoid or lanceoloid-ellipsoid, dorsiventrally compressed, 25–40 × 8.5–10.5 mm, unilocular, fleshy becoming subligneous, prominently cross-reticulate, glabrous. **Seeds** 48–51.

Flowering Apr–Jun. Rocky slopes in sagebrush and bunchgrass communities, on basalt; 100–700 m; Wash.

Astragalus columbianus, a narrow endemic, is known from only a few kilometers along the Columbia River at Priest Rapids Reservoir in Benton and Yakima counties.

195. Astragalus tidestromii (Rydberg) Clokey, Madroño 6: 214. 1942 • Tidestrom's milkvetch [E]

Xylophacos tidestromii Rydberg, Bull. Torrey Bot. Club 52: 155. 1925

Plants acaulescent or subacaulescent, 5–15 cm, villous-hirsute, sometimes also tomentose, hairs basifixed; from superficial caudex. **Stems** prostrate, mostly obconic crowns with thatch of stipules, or developed, to 4(–7) cm, internodes to 1 cm, villous-hirsute (white-felted), sometimes also tomentose. **Leaves** (3–)4–15 cm; stipules mostly obscuring internodes, 3–8 mm, thinly herbaceous becoming papery-membranous; leaflets (7–)11–19, blades obovate-cuneate, broadly elliptic, or suborbiculate, 4–14 mm, thick, apex usually obtuse or subtruncate, rarely subacute, surfaces villous-hirsute. **Peduncles** ascending, (2.5–)5–13 cm. **Racemes** 5–16-flowered, flowers loosely spreading-ascending; axis (1–)2–7 cm in fruit; bracts 2.5–5.5 mm; bracteoles 2. **Pedicels** 0.8–3.1 mm. **Flowers** 12–17.7 mm; calyx short-cylindric to deeply campanulate, (5.5–)5.8–9.7 mm, villous-hirsute or villosulous, tube 5–7.3 mm, lobes broadly subulate, 0.8–2.7 mm; corolla white, with dull lavender tinge, keel and wings tipped with dark purple; banner recurved through 40°. **Legumes** ascending or incurved-ascending (humistrate), brownish stramineous, not mottled, incurved through 0.5+ spiral, obliquely lanceoloid-acuminate, ± dorsiventrally compressed, laterally compressed at both ends, obcompressed at middle, (15–)20–55 × 6–16 mm, unilocular, fleshy becoming leathery or subligneous, strigulose. **Seeds** 26–49.

Flowering Mar–May. Open, gravelly hillsides, outwash fans, gravelly and sandy playas in foothills of calcareous desert mountains, with *Larrea*, saltbush, oak, and pinyon-juniper associations; (600–)700–1900 m; Calif., Nev.

Astragalus tidestromii may be most closely allied to *A. amphioxys*, though that species has malpighian hairs (R. C. Barneby 1964). An obligate calciphile, it has repeatedly been confused with the rhizomatous calcifuge *A. layneae*. Earliest records were interpreted as being hybrids between *A. amphioxys* and *A. layneae*, a plausible hypothesis as to origin. *Astragalus tidestromii* is restricted to the eastern Mojave Desert in the southern tip of Nevada (Spring [Charleston] and desert mountain ranges in Clark County) and immediately adjacent California (southeastern Inyo and eastern San Bernadino counties).

196. Astragalus waterfallii Barneby, Leafl. W. Bot. 7: 31. 1953 • Waterfall's milkvetch

Plants tuft-forming, subacaulescent or shortly caulescent, 10–28 cm, strigulose, hairs basifixed; from superficial or shallow subterranean caudex. **Stems:** internodes to 1(–1.5) cm or concealed by stipules, strigulose. **Leaves** 3–10(–12.5) cm; stipules 2.5–8 mm, membranous; leaflets 9–25, blades elliptic, ovate-oblong, or oblanceolate, 3–16 mm, apex obtuse or subacute, surfaces strigulose abaxially, glabrous adaxially. **Peduncles** ascending, prostrate in fruit, (1.5–)3–11(–14) cm. **Racemes** loosely (4–)6–18-flowered, flowers ascending; axis (0.5–)1–4 cm in fruit; bracts 2–7 mm. **Pedicels** 1–3.5 mm. **Flowers** 18.5–23 mm; calyx broadly cylindric, 10–14 mm, strigulose, tube 7.9–11.6 mm, lobes subulate or triangular-subulate, 1.3–3(–4) mm; corolla purple; banner recurved through 40°; keel 14.5–19 mm. **Legumes** ascending (humistrate), purple-mottled, somewhat incurved, narrowly oblong-ellipsoid or somewhat clavate-ellipsoid, obtusely 3-sided compressed, (17–) 20–38 × 5–8 mm, bilocular, fleshy becoming stiffly papery or leathery, strigulose. **Seeds** 28–38(–43). **2*n*** = 22.

Flowering Mar–Jun. Stony hillsides, open slopes, on limestone soils, yucca-grassland, *Larrea*, mesquite, and juniper communities; 800–1700 m; N.Mex., Tex.; Mexico (Chihuahua, Coahuila).

Astragalus waterfallii is restricted to southeastern New Mexico, western Texas, and immediately adjacent Mexico. No other *Astragalus* in the region, with the exception of the strongly caulescent, glabrous-ovaried *A. crassicarpus* and *A. gypsodes*, has flowers as large as this species.

197. Astragalus feensis M. E. Jones, Contr. W. Bot. 8: 20. 1898 • Santa Fe milkvetch E

Plants short-lived, subacaulescent or shortly caulescent, 8–22 cm, villous or villosulous, hairs basifixed; from superficial caudex. **Stems** prostrate or ascending, sometimes reduced to crowns, internodes 1–6 cm, concealed by stipules, villous or villosulous. **Leaves** (2.5–)3.5–9.5 cm; stipules 2.5–6 mm, membranous; leaflets (7 or) 9–17(or 19), blades broadly oblanceolate to obovate or cuneate-obovate, 3–13 mm, apex obtuse or truncate, surfaces villous or villosulous abaxially, glabrous or glabrescent adaxially. **Peduncles** ascending, arcuate-procumbent or prostrate in fruit, 2.5–9.5 cm. **Racemes** (6–)8–15-flowered, flowers ascending; axis (0.5–)1–3 cm in fruit; bracts 1.5–3.5 mm; bracteoles 0. **Pedicels** 0.7–2 mm. **Flowers** 13–16 mm; calyx cylindric to deeply campanulate, 5.2–8 mm, villosulous, tube 4.6–6.5 mm, lobes triangular-subulate, 1.2–2 mm; corolla reddish lilac or pale purple; banner recurved through 40°; keel 10.4–13 mm. **Legumes** ascending (humistrate), stramineous, lunate or crescentically incurved through 0.5 spiral, narrowly ellipsoid to lanceoloid-ellipsoid, 3-sided compressed, (13–)20–30 × 3.5–6(–7) mm, bilocular, fleshy, strigulose; septum 1.3–2.3 mm wide. **Seeds** 27–36.

Flowering Apr–early Jun. Open, sandy benches and gravelly hillsides in pinyon-juniper communities, plains-mesa grasslands, on granitic bedrock; 1500–1900 (–2100) m; N.Mex.

D. Isely (1998) questioned the alliance of *Astragalus feensis* and *A. waterfallii* with sect. *Argophylli* because of their three-sided, bilocular fruits. The species is primarily from central to north-central New Mexico, with an outlying population known from a single collection in Hidalgo County.

198. Astragalus neomexicanus Wooton & Standley, Contr. U.S. Natl. Herb. 16: 136. 1913 • New Mexico milkvetch E

Plants caulescent, 10–35(–40) cm, strigulose to pilose, hairs basifixed; from superficial caudex. **Stems** decumbent to incurved-ascending, strigulose to pilose. **Leaves** (5–)8–23 cm; stipules (3–)6–12 mm, submembranous; leaflets (19–)23–39 (–43), blades usually lanceolate-ovate or rhombic-elliptic, sometimes oblong-obovate, (3–)5–20 mm, apex usually acute or subacute, sometimes obtuse or emarginate, surfaces strigulose to pilose abaxially, glabrescent or glabrate adaxially. **Peduncles** incurved-ascending, (5–)6–15 cm. **Racemes** (10–)12–24-flowered, flowers nodding, secund, retrorsely imbricate; axis (3–)5–12 cm in fruit; bracts 3–10 mm; bracteoles 0–2. **Pedicels** 1–3.5 mm. **Flowers** 15.7–19.2 mm; calyx cylindric to broadly campanulate, 9.6–13 mm, strigulose, tube 6.8–9.4 mm, lobes lanceolate or triangular-lanceolate, 2.8–4.4 mm; corolla dull pinkish lavender, greenish purple, or bright magenta-purple; banner recurved through 45°; keel 11.3–12.7 mm. **Legumes** loosely pendulous (from ascending peduncles) or ascending (and humistrate), stramineous then brownish, gently incurved, obliquely oblong-ellipsoid, obcompressed, (17–)20–33 × (4–)7–11 mm, ± unilocular, fleshy becoming leathery, strigulose. **Seeds** 28–33. **2*n*** = 22.

Flowering late May–Oct. Dry, gravelly banks, stony hillsides, talus under cliffs, valley bottoms, roadcuts, in pinyon-juniper, ponderosa pine, or mixed conifer forests; 2000–2600 m; N.Mex.

Astragalus neomexicanus is restricted to the mountains of southern Lincoln and northern Otero counties. It is somewhat isolated in sect. *Argophylli.* R. C. Barneby (1964) observed that it seemed to occupy a position intermediate in some notable technical characters between sects. *Argophylli* and *Gigantei*, suggesting that it may represent a taxon selected and stabilized from progeny of *A. giganteus* × *A. tephrodes*.

199. Astragalus newberryi A. Gray, Proc. Amer. Acad. Arts 12: 55. 1876 • Newberry's milkvetch [E] [F]

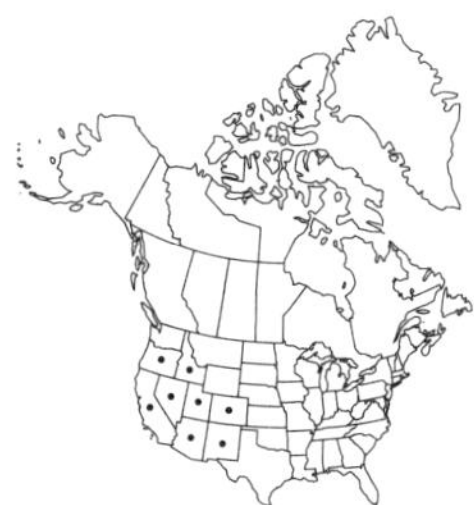

Plants acaulescent, 2–12 cm, silky-pilose, hairs basifixed; from branched, superficial caudex, branches often with thatch of persistent leaf bases. **Stems** reduced to thick crowns. **Leaves** 1.5–14(–15) cm; stipules (2.5–) 4–11 mm, submembranous becoming scarious or papery; leaflets 1–13(or 15), blades obovate to elliptic, oblanceolate, or orbiculate, 3–20 mm, apex acute to obtuse or retuse, surfaces villous-tomentulose. **Peduncles** 0.5–11 cm. **Racemes** 2–8-flowered, flowers ascending; axis 0.2–2.7 cm in fruit; bracts 3.5–10 mm; bracteoles 0–2. **Pedicels** 1.4–5 mm. **Flowers** 14–32 mm; calyx cylindric or campanulate, 7–20 mm, villous, tube 5–16 mm, lobes subulate to lanceolate, 1–4 mm; corolla pink-purple; banner recurved through 40°; keel 12–26 mm. **Legumes** ascending (humistrate), brown-stramineous, incurved, obliquely ovoid, obcompressed, (13–)18–28(–36) × 7–13(–17) mm, unilocular, fleshy becoming leathery, sparsely hirtellous to densely villous-tomentose, usually concealing surfaces. **Seeds** 27–40(–46).

Varieties 4 (4 in the flora): w United States.

Astragalus newberryi is one of several intermountain astragali with fruits so densely villous and tomentulose as to resemble pellets of cotton, a striking feature that tends to overshadow other differences (R. C. Barneby 1964). Except for the uncommon *A. eurekensis*, this is the only *Astragalus* in the region to combine such a fruit with acaulescence, a thatched base, and a vestiture of stiff, shining hairs.

1. Leaflets 1 or 3; Aquarius Mountains, Mohave County, Arizona . . . . 199d. *Astragalus newberryi* var. *aquarii*
1. Leaflets 3–13(or 15); Oregon and Idaho, south- and southeastward to California, Arizona, and New Mexico.
    2. Leaflets 3–13(or 15); c, n Arizona, sw Colorado, nw New Mexico, and se Utah. . . . . 199a. *Astragalus newberryi* var. *newberryi*
    2. Leaflets 7–13; Oregon and Idaho southward to California and Arizona.
        3. Calyces mostly 12–20 mm; banners 21–32 mm; Oregon and Idaho southward to California and Arizona. . . . . 199b. *Astragalus newberryi* var. *castoreus*
        3. Calyces 8–11.5 mm; banners 14–21(–22) mm; w Mohave County, Arizona, s of Colorado River. . . . . 199c. *Astragalus newberryi* var. *blyae*

199a. Astragalus newberryi A. Gray var. **newberryi** [E]

Astragalus newberryi var. *escalantinus* Barneby

Leaflets 3–13(or 15). **Flowers:** calyx cylindric, 11–14.5 mm, tube 9.5–11.5 mm, lobes 1.5–4 mm; corolla banner 21.5–32 mm. $2n = 22$.

Flowering Apr–Jun. Sagebrush, rabbitbrush, matchweed, pinyon-juniper, shadscale, galleta communities; (600–) 1300–2000 m; Ariz., Colo., N.Mex., Utah.

Variety *newberryi* occurs in northern and central Arizona (extending southwestward to Yavapai County), southwestern Colorado (Montezuma County), northwestern New Mexico (McKinley and San Juan counties), and southeastern Utah (Garfield, Kane, and San Juan counties).

Plants described as var. *escalantinus* typically have narrowly elliptic (not ovate to elliptic-obovate) leaflets, differing in no other way from var. *newberryi*. Occasional intermediates are known. The range of the phase with narrow leaflets is contiguous, and partially sympatric, with that of var. *newberryi*.

199b. Astragalus newberryi A. Gray var. **castoreus** M. E. Jones, Proc. Calif. Acad. Sci., ser. 2, 5: 658. 1895 • Beaver Dam Mountains milkvetch [E] [F]

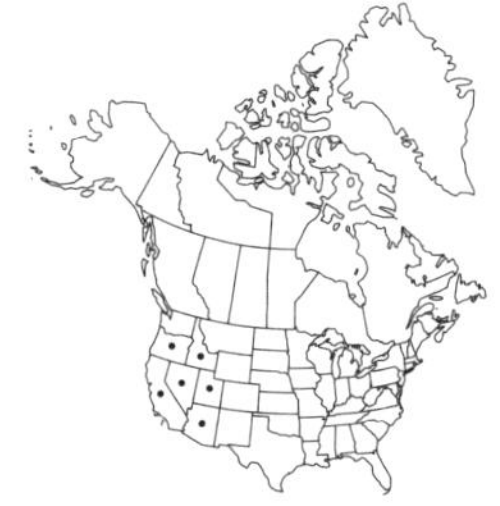

Leaflets 7–11(or 13). **Flowers:** calyx cylindric, 12–20 mm, tube 10–16 mm, lobes 1.5–4 mm; corolla banner 21–32 mm.

Flowering Apr–Jun. Sagebrush, pinyon-juniper, and mixed desert shrub communities, on alluvium consisting of gravel, sand, or silt; 1000–2400(–3100) m; Ariz., Calif., Idaho, Nev., Oreg., Utah.

Of the varieties of *Astragalus newberryi*, var. *castoreus* is the most geographically wide-ranging.

199c. Astragalus newberryi A. Gray var. **blyae** (Rose ex Rydberg) Barneby, Amer. Midl. Naturalist 37: 480. 1947 • Bly milkvetch [E]

Xylophacos blyae Rose ex Rydberg in N. L. Britton et al., N. Amer. Fl. 24: 303. 1929

Leaflets (7 or)9–13. **Flowers:** calyx deeply campanulate, 8–11.5 mm, tube (5–)6–8.5 mm, lobes 2–3 mm; corolla banner 14–21(–22) mm.

Flowering late Mar–May. Dry, rocky hillsides and canyons, on limestone or basaltic gravel, in transitional zone between *Larrea* desert and desert grassland; 1000–1400 m; Ariz.

Variety *blyae*, known in Mohave and Yavapai counties, is distinguished from var. *newberryi* by its smaller flowers and habitat.

199d. Astragalus newberryi A. Gray var. **aquarii** Isely, Syst. Bot. 8: 423. 1983 • Aquarius Mountain milkvetch [C] [E]

Leaflets 1 or 3. **Flowers:** calyx deeply campanulate, 7–8 mm, tube 5–6 mm, lobes 1–2 mm.

Flowering Mar–Apr. Sonoran Desert; of conservation concern; 600–700 m; Ariz.

As presently known, var. *aquarii* is a highly local taxon from Burrow Creek, Mohave County.

200. Astragalus phoenix Barneby, Madroño 20: 395, fig. 1. 1970 • Ash Meadows milkvetch [C] [E]

Plants mound-forming, subacaulescent, 2–5 cm, silvery-pilose-tomentose, hairs basifixed; from branched caudex, branches obscured by persistent leaf bases. **Leaves** 1–3.5(–4) cm; stipules 3–11 mm, membranous or papery; leaflets 3–9, blades ovate to obovate or elliptic, (2–)3–7 mm, apex acute to obtuse, surfaces pilose-tomentose, hairs gray or silvery. **Peduncles** to 1 cm. **Racemes** 1- or 2-flowered, flowers erect-ascending; axis 0.2–0.5 cm in fruit; bracts 3 mm. **Pedicels** 2 mm. **Flowers** 24–25 mm; calyx cylindric, 12.5–15 mm, villous-tomentose, tube 9.5–11 mm, lobes subulate, 3–4 mm; corolla pale lilac, fading ochroleucous, tips purplish; banner only slightly recurved. **Legumes** ascending (humistrate), strongly curved or lunate, obliquely lanceoloid-ovoid, obcompressed, 18 × 10 mm, unilocular, leathery, tomentulose-pilose. **Seeds** 32.

Flowering Apr–May. Calcareous flats and knolls; of conservation concern; 600–700 m; Nev.

Astragalus phoenix, a highly local species, is restricted to Ash Meadows, Nye County. R. C. Barneby proposed that it was derived from *A. newberryi.*

201. Astragalus eurekensis M. E. Jones, Contr. W. Bot. 8: 12. 1898 • Eureka milkvetch [E]

Plants tuft-forming, acaulescent, 2–15 cm, pilose-pilosulous, hairs basifixed; from branched caudex, branches obscured by thatch of persistent leaf bases. **Leaves** 2–15(–17) cm; stipules 3–11 mm, firm becoming papery; leaflets (3 or)5–19, blades elliptic to oblong, 3–35 mm, apex acute, surfaces strigose, hairs gray or silvery. **Peduncles** erect or incurved, 1–13(–14) cm. **Racemes** (1–)3–8-flowered, flowers ascending; axis 0.2–2 cm in fruit; bracts 4–8 mm; bracteoles 0. **Pedicels** 1.2–3 mm. **Flowers** (18–)22–27 mm; calyx cylindric, 10.5–16(–17) mm, pilose-villous, tube (7–)8–12(–13) mm, lobes subulate to narrowly lanceolate, 1.5–5.7 mm; corolla usually ochroleucous, faintly to strongly suffused with purple, rarely pink-purple; banner recurved through 40°; keel 18–22 mm. **Legumes** ascending (humistrate), brown, incurved, obliquely lanceoloid-ovoid, obcompressed, 15–40 × 5–10(–12) mm, unilocular, fleshy becoming leathery or subligneous, villous-hirsute, surface visible through long, shining hairs. **Seeds** 26–36.

Flowering Apr–Jun. Sagebrush, pinyon-juniper, and mountain brush communities; 1300–2200 m; Utah.

Astragalus eurekensis is restricted to Juab, Millard, Sanpete, Sevier, Tooele, Utah, and Wasatch counties in central Utah; it overlaps the eastern margin of the geographic range of *A. newberryi.* The two are distinguished easily by overall appearance, but constant differential criteria are absent. The fruits are hirsute rather than hirsute and tomentose, as in *A. newberryi.*

202. Astragalus welshii Barneby in A. Cronquist et al., Intermount. Fl. 3(B): 130, plate [p. 131], fig. s.n. [lower left]. 1989 • Welsh's milkvetch [E]

Plants acaulescent, 4–20 cm, appressed-pilose, hairs incipiently malpighian, attached shortly distal to base; from branched caudex, branches with thatch of persistent leaf bases. **Leaves** 3–20 cm; stipules 5–15 mm; leaflets 5–11(or 13), blades lanceolate to elliptic or obovate, 6–25 mm, apex acute, surfaces densely strigose. **Peduncles** recurved in fruit, 1.5–11 cm. **Racemes**

(4 or)5–8-flowered, flowers erect-ascending; axis 0.2–1 cm in fruit; bracts 2.5–6 mm; bracteoles 0–2. **Pedicels** 1.2–4 mm. **Flowers** 17.5–23 mm; calyx cylindric, (8.5–)9.5–14 mm, loosely strigulose, tube 7–11 mm, lobes linear-subulate, 1–3.5 mm; corolla ochroleucous or greenish white, often tinged faintly purplish, keel tip purple; banner recurved through 35–45°; keel (14–)15–18.5 mm. **Legumes** ascending (humistrate in fruit), reddish to stramineous, incurved, plumply ovoid, inflated, moderately obcompressed, (15–)17–23 × 10–15 mm, unilocular, leathery, hirsute, hairs lustrous, to 2+ mm. **Seeds** 24–38.

Flowering May–Jul. Sagebrush, pinyon-juniper, and sagebrush-aspen communities, exclusively on igneous gravel; 2100–2800 m; Utah.

Astragalus welshii is known from Garfield, Iron, Kane, Millard, Piute, and Wayne counties in south-central Utah.

Astragalus welshii resembles, and has long been treated as, *A. loanus* when in fruit, and flowering material of *A. welshii* has been placed with uncertainty within *A. eurekensis*. However, *A. welshii* is more robust, its leaflet blades are more acute, and its fruits and flowers are relatively smaller than those two species.

203. Astragalus loanus Barneby, Mem. New York Bot. Gard. 13: 662. 1964 • Glenwood milkvetch [C] [E]

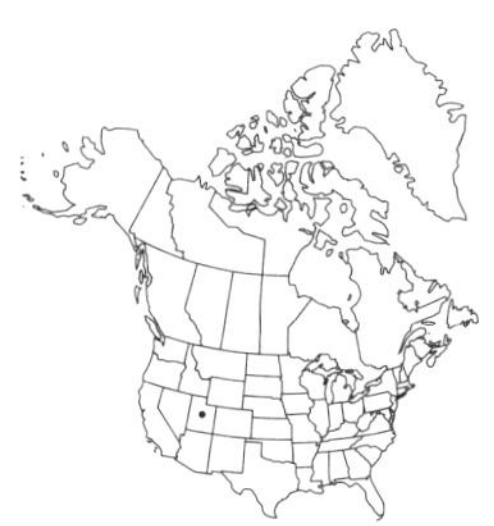

Astragalus newberryi A. Gray var. *wardianus* Barneby, Amer. Midl. Naturalist 37: 481. 1947

Plants tuft-forming, acaulescent, 3–6 cm, appressed-silky-pilose, hairs incipiently malpighian, hairs attached near the end; from branched caudex, branches with thatch of persistent leaf bases. **Leaves** 2–8 cm; stipules 5–10 mm, membranous becoming papery; leaflets (1 or)3 or 5, blades obovate to rhombic or elliptic, 6–25 mm, apex obtuse, surfaces densely strigose. **Peduncles** ascending, 1–3 cm. **Racemes** 2–7-flowered, flowers erect-ascending; axis 0.2–0.8 cm in fruit; bracts 2.5–6 mm; bracteoles 0–2. **Pedicels** 1.2–4 mm. **Flowers** 20–28 mm; calyx cylindric, 12–17 mm, loosely strigulose, tube 10–14 mm, lobes linear-subulate, 1.8–5.5 mm; corolla ochroleucous or greenish white, often tinged faintly purplish, keel tip purple; banner recurved through 40°; keel 18–22 mm. **Legumes** ascending (humistrate), red-purple to stramineous, incurved, ovoid-acuminate, inflated, 17–30(–32) × 10–23 mm, unilocular, fleshy becoming stiffly papery, hirsute, hairs long, lustrous. **Seeds** 28–38.

Flowering May–Jun. Sagebrush and pinyon-juniper communities, exclusively on igneous gravel; of conservation concern; 1900–2100 m; Utah.

Astragalus loanus is a rare and local species from Sevier County. As the species has become better understood, its range has precipitously narrowed. Early specimens were associated with *A. newberryi* and much later segregated as *A. newberryi* var. *wardianus*. That taxon was raised to specific status as *A. loanus*, but within that was yet another nearly sympatric species, later recognized and extracted from the complex as *A. welshii*.

204. Astragalus musiniensis M. E. Jones, Proc. Calif. Acad. Sci., ser. 2, 5: 671. 1895 • Ferron milkvetch [E]

Plants clump-forming, acaulescent, 3–13 cm, strigose to strigulose, hairs basifixed or, incipiently, malpighian; from branched caudex, branches often with thatch of persistent leaf bases. **Stems** reduced to crowns. **Leaves** 1.5–13 cm; stipules 3.5–10 mm, firmly papery; leaflets (1 or)3 or 5, blades elliptic to lanceolate, 5–35(–47) mm, apex acute to obtuse, surfaces strigose. **Peduncles** ascending, 0.5–7 cm. **Racemes** 1–6-flowered, flowers erect-ascending; axis 0.2–1.4 cm in fruit; bracts 1.6–4 mm; bracteoles 0. **Pedicels** 1.2–4 mm. **Flowers** (18.5–)20–28 mm; calyx cylindric, 12–16 mm, strigose-pilose, tube 9.5–13.5 mm, lobes subulate, 1.5–4 mm; corolla pink-purple; banner recurved through 40°; keel (18–)19–22.7 mm. **Legumes** ascending to spreading (humistrate), green or purplish, incurved, obliquely ovoid, dorsiventrally compressed, 15–36 × 8–17 mm, unilocular, thickly succulent becoming alveolate-spongy, spongy-thickened cellular tissue 1.5–2 mm thick, hirsutulous to villous-hirsute, hairs spreading, 0.6–2 mm. **Seeds** 33–53.

Flowering Apr–Jun. Salt desert shrub, mixed desert shrub, and pinyon-juniper communities; 1400–2400 m; Colo., Utah.

Astragalus musiniensis is restricted to Carbon, Emery, Garfield, Grand, Kane, Sevier, and Wayne counties in central and south-central Utah, extending eastward to Garfield and Mesa counties in west-central Colorado.

The pithy texture of the ripe fruit of *Astragalus musiniensis* is similar to that of *A. chamaeleuce*, but that species has malpighian hairs and more numerous leaflets.

205. Astragalus concordius S. L. Welsh, Great Basin Naturalist 58: 387, fig. 1. 1998 • Harmony milkvetch [E]

Plants clump-forming, subacaulescent, 9–15(–25) cm, densely strigose-strigulose, hairs malpighian; from branched caudex. **Stems** 0–6(–20) cm, internodes elongating in shade forms, mostly concealed by stipules. **Leaves** 3–9(–15) cm; stipules 3.5–9 mm; leaflets 11–17, blades obovate to oblanceolate or elliptic, 3.5–13 (–21) mm, apex round to apiculate or acute, surfaces appressed-strigose. **Peduncles** 1–10(–14) cm. **Racemes** 2–8-flowered, flowers ascending; axis 0.5–5 cm in fruit; bracts 2.5–4.5 mm; bracteoles 0. **Pedicels** 1.5–2.5 mm. **Flowers** 21–25 mm; calyx cylindric, 10.5–12 mm, strigulose, tube 8.5–9.5 mm, lobes subulate, 2–3(–5) mm; corolla pink-purple or whitish to lilac-tinged; banner recurved through 40°. **Legumes** spreading-ascending, sessile or subsessile, almost straight to incurved, ovoid to lanceoloid-ovoid, obcompressed, 15–40 × 9–13 mm, unilocular, densely shaggy-hirsute. **Seeds** 30.

Flowering Apr–May(–Jun). Pinyon-juniper, oak-sagebrush, live oak-mountain mahogany, and ponderosa pine-oak communities; (1100–)1600–2500 m; Utah.

Astragalus concordius occurs to the south of *A. piutensis* and is restricted to Pine Valley and Bull Valley mountains and Kolob vicinity in Iron County, and Harmony Mountain in Washington County.

Astragalus concordius had been included within *A. piutensis* primarily on the basis of the shaggy-hirsute fruits. The hairs, however, are strongly malpighian rather than basifixed.

206. Astragalus coccineus (Parry) Brandegee, Zoë 2: 72. 1891 • Scarlet milkvetch

Astragalus purshii Douglas var. *coccineus* Parry, W. Amer. Sci. 7: 10. 1890

Plants tuft-forming, obligately acaulescent, 8–15 cm, villous-tomentose, hairs basifixed; from woody taproot bearing root-crown. **Stems** obsolete (reduced to 1 to several crowns), with persistent thatch of stipules and petioles. **Leaves** (3–)4–10 cm; stipules 6–10 mm, papery-membranous; leaflets 7–15, blades obovate-cuneate to broadly oblanceolate or elliptic, (3–)5–14 mm, thick, apex obtuse or subacute, surfaces villous-tomentose. **Peduncles** ascending, (2–)4–10 cm. **Racemes** (3–)5–10-flowered, flowers ascending; axis 0.5–2.5 cm in fruit; bracts 5–7 mm; bracteoles 0. **Pedicels** 3–5 mm. **Flowers** 35–41 mm; calyx cylindric, 18–24 mm, villous, tube (12–)13.5–16 mm, lobes subulate to lanceolate, 3.5–8 mm; corolla scarlet or crimson; banner and keel nearly same length, recurved through 20–30°; keel 35–40 mm. **Legumes** ascending (humistrate), color concealed by hairs, incurved, obliquely lanceoloid-ovoid or narrowly ovoid-ellipsoid, obcompressed, 25–40 × 9–12 mm, unilocular, fleshy becoming leathery, densely villous-tomentulose, concealing surface. **Seeds** 34–43.

Flowering Mar–early Jun. Open gravelly ridges and canyon benches of desert mountains, on decomposed granite, in mixed warm desert shrub and pinyon-juniper or sagebrush communities; 50–2200 m; Ariz., Calif., Nev.; Mexico (Baja California).

Astragalus coccineus, with its contrasting long and narrow scarlet or crimson flowers and ashy herbage, stands out in the genus. Only two other North American astragali have red flowers, both Mexican and distantly related (*A. helleri* Fenzl and *A. sanguineus* Rydberg). It occurs around the northern and western edges of the Mojave and Sonoran deserts, from Owens Valley and Death Valley to extreme northern Baja California, with an outlying population in the Kofa Mountains, Arizona.

207. Astragalus nudisiliquus A. Nelson, Bot. Gaz. 54: 410. 1912 • Cobblestone milkvetch [E]

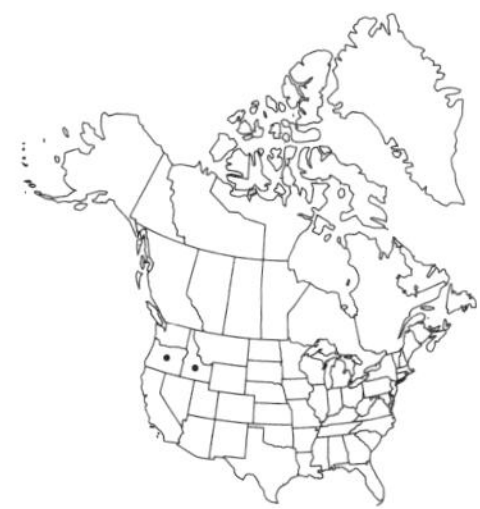

Plants mat-forming, caulescent, (2–)5–25(–30) cm, white-tomentose, hairs basifixed; from root-crown; taproot loosely forked. **Stems** diffuse or prostrate, radiating from root-crown, white-tomentose, white-felted. **Leaves** 3–11 cm; stipules (1.5–)3–7 mm, thinly herbaceous becoming membranous; leaflets (7–)11–17, blades broadly obovate, obovate-cuneate, or broadly oblanceolate, 4–17 mm, apex usually obtuse, sometimes subacute or subretuse, surfaces tomentose. **Peduncles** incurved-ascending, 1–7 cm. **Racemes** (2–)4–8-flowered, flowers ascending; axis 0.5–2.5 cm in fruit; bracts (1.5–) 3–6 mm; bracteoles 0–2. **Pedicels** 1.4–3.4 mm. **Flowers** 19–25.5 mm; calyx cylindric, 12–17(–19) mm, sparsely villosulous, tube (11.3–)12–13.8 mm, lobes subulate-setaceous, (2–)3–5 mm; corolla pink-purple, banner with white or pale eye-spot, this with pink-purple lines; banner recurved through 40°; keel 17.4–21.3 mm. **Legumes** ascending (humistrate), brown or stramineous, strongly incurved, obliquely ovoid or oblong-ellipsoid, strongly obcompressed, (15–)20–40(–45) × (8–)9–13 mm, unilocular, fleshy becoming stiffly leathery, sparsely villous-hirsute, hairs 1+ mm. **Seeds** 30–41.

Flowering late Apr–early Jul. Summits and gullied slopes of river bluffs and terraces, on sand, sandy clay, or cobblestone alluvia; 600–1100 m; Idaho, Oreg.

Astragalus nudisiliquus occurs in east-central Oregon and southwestern Idaho as far east as Cassia County, with greatest abundance along the Snake River and its tributaries.

The specific epithet *nudisiliquus* is a misnomer, although the hairs on the fruit of *Astragalus nudisiliquus* are spaced sufficiently apart that the surface is evident. It may be easily confused, especially when in flower, with two varieties of *A. purshii* in the same region; var. *ophiogenes* is ecologically congruent but has much smaller flowers, and var. *glareosus* is usually at higher elevations and has mostly 2–5-flowered racemes.

208. Astragalus utahensis (Torrey) Torrey & A. Gray in War Department [U.S.], Pacif. Railr. Rep. 2(1): 120. 1857 • Utah milkvetch [E]

Phaca mollissima Nuttall var. *utahensis* Torrey in H. Stansbury, Exped. Great Salt Lake 385, plate 2. 1852

Plants ± mat-forming, subacaulescent, 2–12 cm, pannose-tomentose, hairs basifixed; from branched caudex. **Stems** prostrate and radiating, 0–10 cm, internodes usually concealed by stipules, densely pannose-tomentose. **Leaves** 1.5–12 cm; stipules 3–10 mm, membranous; leaflets 9–19, blades obovate or suborbiculate to ovate, 2–15 mm, apex usually obtuse to emarginate, sometimes acute, surfaces densely villous-tomentose. **Peduncles** ascending, decumbent in fruit, 1–14 cm. **Racemes** 2–8-flowered, flowers ascending; axis 0.4–2.6 cm in fruit; bracts 4–9 mm; bracteoles 0–2. **Pedicels** 2–4.3 mm. **Flowers** 23–31 mm; calyx cylindric, 12–14 mm, villous-tomentose, tube 8.5–13 mm, lobes lanceolate-subulate, 2–4.5 mm; corolla usually pink-purple, rarely white; banner recurved through 45°; keel (16–)17–22 mm. **Legumes** initially ascending (humistrate), color concealed by hairs, ± straight, lanceoloid-ellipsoid or narrowly ovoid-acuminate, obcompressed, 17–30 × 5.5–7.5 mm, unilocular, fleshy becoming stiffly papery or thinly leathery, shaggy-villous, hairs 4–8 mm, obscuring surface; sessile and gynophore 1–2.5 mm. **Seeds** 22–31. 2*n* = 22.

Flowering late Apr–early Jul. Sagebrush, rabbitbrush, pinyon-juniper, mountain brush, and grassland communities; 1200–2200 m; Idaho, Nev., Utah, Wyo.

Astragalus utahensis occurs in southern Idaho, northern and central Nevada, much of Utah, and Lincoln and Uinta counties in southwestern Wyoming.

The fruits of *Astragalus utahensis* have a pubescence that doubles the actual breadth of the valves. The contrast between the large, softly pink-purple petals and the whitish-pannose herbage produces a striking effect. D. Isely (1998) provided a key to distinguish this and sympatric or contiguous varieties of *A. purshii*, with which it has often been confused.

209. Astragalus purshii Douglas in W. J. Hooker, Fl. Bor.-Amer. 1: 152. 1831 • Pursh's milkvetch [E] [F]

Plants tuft-forming, acaulescent, subacaulescent, or shortly caulescent, 4.5–13 cm, usually villous to villous-tomentose, sometimes appearing white or gray, hairs basifixed; from branched, superficial caudex, branches with thatch. **Stems** usually obscured by stipules, or internodes to 2 cm, villous to villous-tomentose. **Leaves** 1–12(–15) cm; stipules (2.5–)3–15 mm, membranous; leaflets (3 or)5–17(–21), blades obovate, obovate-cuneate, elliptic to oblanceolate, or rhombic-elliptic, 2–14(–20) mm, apex usually acute, subacute, acuminate, or obtuse, rarely truncate-emarginate, surfaces densely villous. **Peduncles** ascending or erect, decumbent in fruit, 1.5–10.5 cm. **Racemes** 1–11-flowered, flowers ascending; axis 0.3–2(–4) cm in fruit; bracts 2–9 mm; bracteoles 0. **Pedicels** 1–5 mm. **Flowers** 19–25(–27) mm; calyx cylindric, cylindro-campanulate, or campanulate, (5.5–)6–16(–19) mm, villous-pilose, tube (4–)4.5–12 (–13.6) mm, lobes subulate, 1–6(–7) mm; corolla white, cream, purple, or pink-purple; banner recurved through 40°; keel 8–21.2(–22.5) mm. **Legumes** initially ascending (humistrate), brownish, not mottled or spotted, incurved, ovoid, ovoid-ellipsoid, or lanceoloid-ellipsoid, dorsiventrally compressed, 7–26(–30) × 3.5–11(–13) mm, unilocular, fleshy becoming leathery, mostly shaggy-villous, sometimes tomentose or villous-hirsute, hairs 1.6–4(–5) mm, often concealing surface; sessile or subsessile, or gynophore 0.5+ mm. **Seeds** 14–38(–46).

Varieties 8 (8 in the flora): w North America.

The geographic distribution of *Astragalus purshii*, forming a relatively large triangle in western North America, from southwestern Canada to southern California, northeastward to western North Dakota, makes it the most widely distributed of all astragali with woolly fruits. The case for specific status for such entities as *A. inflexus* and *A. utahensis* may be little stronger than that for several of the taxa included within *A. purshii* (D. Isely 1998). L. Abrams (1944b) often gave an inclusive name of woolly-pod to all of the fuzzy-podded species, sometimes sheep-pod. For consistency they are all called milkvetch here. Isely gave a synopsis that helped to distinguish other woolly fruited species. The treatment of R. C. Barneby (1964) is followed here, and his key to varieties is largely followed.

1. Calyces (5.5–)6–10.1 mm; banners 9–16.5 mm; keel 8–13 mm.
   2. Racemes (3–)5–11-flowered; leaflets (7 or)9–15(or 17); sw Idaho . . . . .209e. *Astragalus purshii* var. *ophiogenes* (in part)
   2. Racemes 1–5(–7)-flowered; leaflets (3 or) 5–9(or 11); California, sw Idaho, nw Nevada, and along foothills and plains adjacent to e slope of Cascades in Oregon.
      3. Legumes incurved only in beak; seeds 24–32; San Bernardino Mountains and Sierra Nevada, California, w Nevada . . . . 209g. *Astragalus purshii* var. *lectulus*
      3. Legumes arched throughout, at least through 0.5–1 spiral; seeds 14–20; plains of ne California to c Oregon, sw Idaho, and nw Nevada . . . . .209h. *Astragalus purshii* var. *lagopinus*
1. Calyces (8–)9–16(–19) mm; banners (14.6–)15.4–25(–26) mm; keel (11.5–)12.4–21.2(–22.5) mm.
   4. Corollas mostly white or cream (keel tip maculate), rarely banners and wings tipped dull, pale bluish purple; widespread from California and British Columbia eastward to North Dakota and Colorado . . . . .209a. *Astragalus purshii* var. *purshii*
   4. Corollas purple or pink-purple throughout; British Columbia to s California (cis- and transmontane), sw Montana, and sc Nevada.
      5. Banners (14.6–)19–25(–26.5) mm; keel (11.5–)12.4–21(–22.5) mm.
         6. Plants acaulescent or subacaulescent; leaflets (5 or)7 or 9(or 11), blades obovate, obovate-cuneate, or broadly elliptic, apices obtuse or truncate; ec Idaho, sw Montana . . . . .209f. *Astragalus purshii* var. *concinnus*
         6. Plants shortly caulescent or subacaulescent; leaflets (3 or)5–17(–21), blades obovate-cuneate, oblanceolate, narrowly elliptic or elliptic-oblanceolate, apices usually acute, subacute, or short-acuminate, rarely obtuse; British Columbia, California, Idaho, Nevada, Oregon, Utah, Washington.
            7. Legumes not or very shallowly sulcate ventrally; leaflets (3 or)5–13(–17), blades usually obovate-cuneate or oblanceolate, rarely elliptic-oblanceolate, apices usually acute or subacute, rarely obtuse; racemes 3–11-flowered; banners (14.6–)15.4–25 mm; cis- and transmontane California, w Nevada, and Oregon . . . . 209b. *Astragalus purshii* var. *tinctus* (in part)
            7. Legumes strongly depressed-sulcate ventrally in proximal 1/2; leaflets (7 or)9–15(or 17), blades usually narrowly elliptic, rarely elliptic-oblanceolate, apices usually acute or short-acuminate; racemes 2–5(–10)-flowered; banners 19–25 (–26.5) mm; Oregon and British Columbia eastward to Utah . . . . 209c. *Astragalus purshii* var. *glareosus*

[5. Shifted to left margin.—Ed.]

5. Banners 11.5–18(–25) mm; keel 10.2–15 (–20.8) mm.
   8. Legumes strongly sulcate ventrally in proximal 1/2; c Nevada . . . . 209d. *Astragalus purshii* var. *pumilio*
   8. Legumes not or shallowly sulcate ventrally; ne California, sw Idaho, nw Nevada, se Oregon.
      9. Legumes 13–23(–27) mm; racemes with relatively short (subcapitate) flowering axes; ne California, nw Nevada, e Oregon . . . . 209b. *Astragalus purshii* var. *tinctus* (in part)
      9. Legumes 8–13 mm; racemes with relatively long flowering axes; along Owyhee, Snake, and lower Bruneau rivers, se Oregon and sw Idaho. . . . . 209e. *Astragalus purshii* var. *ophiogenes* (in part)

209a. Astragalus purshii Douglas var. **purshii** [E] [F]

Astragalus purshii var. *incurvus* (Rydberg) Jepson; *Xylophacos incurvus* Rydberg

Plants subacaulescent or acaulescent. **Stems** 0–10 cm. **Leaves** (1.5–)3–10(–15) cm; leaflets (5 or)7–15(or 17), blades usually elliptic, elliptic-oblanceolate, or rhombic-elliptic, rarely obovate, (2–)4–14(–20) mm, apex usually acute, rarely obtuse. **Racemes** (1 or)2–5(or 6)-flowered. **Flowers** 7.6–12(–13) mm wide; calyx cylindric, (12–)13–16(–19) mm, tube 9.2–12(–13.6) mm, lobes 2.2–6(–7) mm; corolla mostly white or cream, sometimes fading yellowish, keel maculate, rarely banner and wing tips dull, pale bluish purple; banner 19–25(–27) mm; keel (15–)17–21.2 mm. **Legumes** obliquely ovoid or broadly lanceoloid-ellipsoid, not or very shallowly sulcate ventrally, 13–23(–27) × 5–9.5(–13) mm, densely shaggy-villous, hairs to (2–)2.5–4(–5) mm. **Seeds** (20–)22–34. $2n = 22$.

Flowering Apr–Jul. Dry hills and plains, sagebrush steppe and deserts, bunchgrass steppe, pinyon-juniper woodlands and ponderosa pine forests; 300–2900 m; Alta., B.C., Sask.; Calif., Colo., Idaho, Mont., Nev., N.Dak., Oreg., S.Dak., Utah, Wash., Wyo.

Variety *purshii* is the most widely distributed variety of the species. It differs from var. *tinctus* only in the whitish to cream petals.

Astragalus incurvus (Rydberg) Abrams is an illegitimate later homonym of *A. incurvus* Desfontaines and pertains here.

209b. Astragalus purshii Douglas var. **tinctus** M. E. Jones, Zoë 4: 269. 1893 • Dyed milkvetch [E]

Astragalus candelarius E. Sheldon; *A. leucolobus* S. Watson ex M. E. Jones subsp. *consectus* (E. Sheldon) Abrams

Plants shortly caulescent. **Stems** to 9(–12) cm, internodes to 2 cm. **Leaves** 2–8(–11) cm; leaflets (3 or)5–13(–17), blades usually broadly obovate-cuneate or oblanceolate, rarely elliptic-oblanceolate, 2–12(–14) mm, apex usually acute or subacute, rarely obtuse. **Racemes** 3–11-flowered, subcapitate, flowering axis relatively short. **Flowers** 6–12 mm wide; calyx cylindric, (8–)10–14.2(–15.8) mm, tube 6.5–11.8 mm, lobes (1–)1.4–3.5(–4.8) mm; corolla purple; banner (14.6–)15.4–25 mm; keel (11.5–)12.4–20.8 mm. **Legumes** obliquely ovoid or broadly lanceoloid-ellipsoid, not or very shallowly sulcate ventrally, 13–23(–27) × 5–9.5(–13) mm, densely shaggy-villous, hairs to (2–)2.5–4(–5) mm, valves sometimes inflexed as partial or ± complete septum, to 1.4 mm wide. **Seeds** (18–)20–38(–46).

Flowering Apr–Jul. With sagebrush, on basaltic or granitic bedrock; (400–)1100–2500(–3200) m; Calif., Nev., Oreg.

Variety *tinctus* may be the most diverse of the varieties of *Astragalus purshii*; there are six minor variants, each with some morphological and geographical integrity (R. C. Barneby 1964).

Recent collections have been made from Washington state but these have not been verified.

209c. Astragalus purshii Douglas var. **glareosus** (Douglas) Barneby, Amer. Midl. Naturalist 37: 503. 1947 • Gravel milkvetch [E]

Astragalus glareosus Douglas in W. J. Hooker, Fl. Bor.-Amer. 1: 152. 1831

Plants subacaulescent or shortly caulescent. **Stems** to 5–20+ cm. **Leaves** (2–)3–12 cm; leaflets (7 or)9–17(–21), blades usually narrowly elliptic, rarely elliptic-oblanceolate, (2–)4–14(–17) mm, apex usually acute or short-acuminate. **Racemes** 2–5(–10)-flowered. **Flowers** 7–10.5(–12) mm wide; calyx cylindric, 12–16(–18.7) mm, tube (8.5–)9.5–12(–13) mm, lobes 2.3–4.8 mm; corolla purple; banner 19–25(–26.5) mm; keel 16.7–21(–22.5) mm. **Legumes** lunately incurved or sometimes abruptly hooked, obliquely ovoid, ovoid-ellipsoid, or lanceoloid-ellipsoid, strongly depressed-sulcate ventrally in proximal 1/2, sutures contiguous or approximate within, (13–)15–26(–30) × 7–11 mm, villous-hirsute, hairs to (1.2–)1.5–4 mm. **Seeds** (17–)22–30(–35). 2*n* = 22.

Flowering Apr–Jun. Sagebrush associations, ponderosa pine forests, on basaltic bedrock, or granitic and various alluvia; 60–1600(–2100) m; B.C.; Idaho, Nev., Oreg., Utah, Wash.

Variety *glareosus* is a plant primarily of the Columbia and Snake river drainages. In the upper reaches of the Grand Canyon of the Snake River, it superficially resembles *Astragalus inflexus*. R. C. Barneby (1964) provided a key distinguishing the two.

209d. Astragalus purshii Douglas var. **pumilio** Barneby, Amer. Midl. Naturalist 37: 506. 1947 • Dwarf milkvetch [E]

Plants dwarf, acaulescent or subacaulescent. **Stems** obsolete. **Leaves** 2–5.5(–7) cm; leaflets (7 or)9–15(or 17), blades oval or elliptic, 3–8 mm, apex obtuse or acute. **Racemes** loosely (2 or)3–6-flowered. **Flowers** 6.6–9 mm wide; calyx cylindric or cylindro-campanulate, 8.6–12.6 mm, tube 6.5–9 mm, lobes 2.1–4 mm; corolla pink-purple; banner 16–18(–20.5) mm; keel (12–)13–15(–15.3) mm. **Legumes** ± straight, obliquely ovoid-acuminate, strongly sulcate ventrally in proximal 1/2, 8–15 × 3.5–7.5 mm, abruptly incurved through 90° or more into deltoid or lanceoloid-triangular beak, shaggy-villous, hairs to 1.6–2.2 mm. **Seeds** 17–21.

Flowering May–Jun. Dry gravelly flats and hillsides, with pinyon pine and sagebrush; 1600–2100 m; Nev.

Variety *pumilio* is a central Nevada endemic similar to flowered phases of var. *tinctus* except for the fruit. The legumes resemble those of var. *glareosus* but are smaller.

209e. Astragalus purshii Douglas var. **ophiogenes** (Barneby) Barneby in C. L. Hitchcock et al., Vasc. Pl. Pacif. N.W. 3: 256. 1961 • Snake River milkvetch [E]

Astragalus ophiogenes Barneby, Leafl. W. Bot. 4: 232. 1946

Plants low, sometimes diminutive, subacaulescent or shortly caulescent. **Stems** 0–5(–8) cm. **Leaves** 1.5–11 cm; leaflets (7 or) 9–15(or 17), blades elliptic-oblanceolate or obovate-cuneate, 4–12 mm, apex usually acute or obtuse, rarely truncate-emarginate. **Racemes** (3–)5–11-flowered, flowering axis relatively long. **Flowers** 6.5–8.7 mm wide; calyx shortly cylindric, 6.5–10.1 mm, tube 5.5–7.5 mm, lobes 1–2.6 mm; corolla pink-purple; banner 11.5–16.3 mm; keel 10.2–13 mm. **Legumes** very obliquely ovoid-acuminate, shallowly sulcate ventrally, obcompressed, abruptly incurved through 90–180° into the laterally compressed, triangular-acuminate, cuspidate beak, 8–13 × 5–7 mm, densely tomentose and villous-hirsute, hairs to 3–5 mm. **Seeds** 22.

Flowering late Apr–Jun. Gravelly clay and sandy river terraces, gullied bluffs, dunes, sandy pockets in lava flows; 700–1100 m; Idaho.

Variety *ophiogenes* occurs locally along the lower Bruneau and adjacent Snake rivers in southwestern Idaho. Its fruit shape and pubescence approach those of *Astragalus argophyllus* var. *argophyllus*.

209f. Astragalus purshii Douglas var. **concinnus** Barneby, Leafl. W. Bot. 4: 231. 1946 • Neat milkvetch [E]

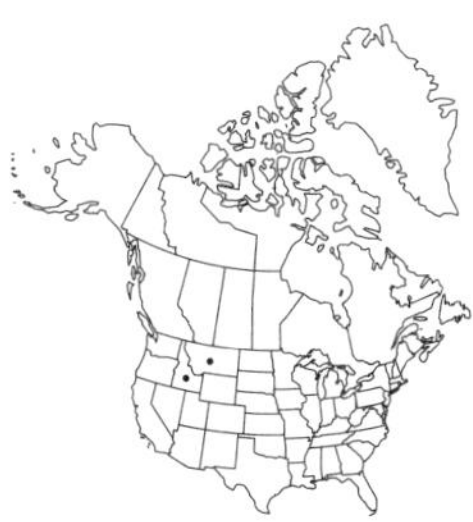

Plants dwarf, acaulescent or subacaulescent, herbage densely pannose. **Stems** obsolete. **Leaves** 1.5–7 cm; leaflets (5 or)7 or 9(or 11), blades obovate, obovate-cuneate, or broadly oval, 3–12 (–15) mm, apex obtuse or truncate. **Racemes** (2 or)3–8-flowered. **Flowers** (11.4–)12–15 mm wide; calyx deeply campanulate to broadly cylindric, 9–13(–14) mm, tube 7.8–10.8 mm, lobes 1.8–3(–4) mm; corolla pink-purple, rhombic- or flabellate-obovate; banner (19–)20–24 mm; keel 15.6–17.6 mm. **Legumes** obliquely ovoid or broadly lanceoloid-ellipsoid, not or very shallowly sulcate ventrally, 13–23(–27) × 5–9.5(–13) mm, densely shaggy-villous, hairs to (2–)2.5–4(–5) mm. **Seeds** 28–38.

Flowering May–Jul. Gravelly hillsides, clay bluffs, valley flats, with sagebrush, on limestone substrates; 1300–2200(–2800) m; Idaho, Mont.

Variety *concinnus* is restricted to east-central Idaho and southwestern Montana.

209g. Astragalus purshii Douglas var. **lectulus** (S. Watson) M. E. Jones, Contr. W. Bot. 10: 61. 1902 • Sierran milkvetch [E]

Astragalus lectulus S. Watson, Proc. Amer. Acad. Arts 22: 471. 1887; *A. jonesii* Abrams

Plants forming small tufts or closely woven mats, subacaulescent. **Stems** obsolete. **Leaves** (1–)1.5–5 cm; leaflets (3 or)5–9(or 11), often crowded, blades usually obovate-cuneate or oblanceolate, sometimes elliptic, 2–10 mm, apex usually obtuse, sometimes subacute. **Racemes** 1–3(–5)-flowered, often embedded in leaves. **Flowers** 5.4–7 mm wide; calyx cylindric, (5.6–)6.1–8.8 mm, tube 4.5–7.2 mm, lobes 1.1–1.6 mm; corolla pink or pale purple; banner 10.3–15 mm; keel 9.4–11.7 mm. **Legumes** obliquely ovoid or broadly lanceoloid-ellipsoid, beak incurved, not or very shallowly sulcate ventrally, 7.5–15 × 4–8 mm, shaggy-villous, hairs to 1.5–3.5 mm. **Seeds** 24–32.

Flowering May–Aug. Dry open flats and benches in pinyon-juniper or ponderosa pine forests, on stony slopes to crests above timberline, on decomposed granite; 1500–3500 m; Calif., Nev.

Variety *lectulus* is found primarily on the eastern slope of the Sierra Nevada, with populations also on the western side in Tuolumne County, and at the eastern end of the San Bernardino Mountains, San Bernardino County in California, and in Humboldt, Lyon, and Washoe counties in Nevada.

209h. Astragalus purshii Douglas var. **lagopinus** (Rydberg) Barneby, Amer. Midl. Naturalist 37: 511. 1947 • Hare's-foot milkvetch [E]

Xylophacos lagopinus Rydberg, Bull. Torrey Bot. Club 52: 372. 1925

Plants forming densely to loosely woven mats, 0.8–3(–3.5) dm wide, shortly caulescent, from root-crown when young, from freely branched caudex when older. **Stems** (of current year) to 8 cm. **Leaves** 1–4.5(–7) cm; leaflets (3 or)5 or 7(–11), blades usually narrowly to broadly obovate-cuneate, rarely elliptic, 5–12(–15) mm, apex usually obtuse, truncate, or shallowly emarginate, rarely subacute. **Racemes** (2 or)3–5(–7)-flowered. **Flowers** (4–)5–6.6 mm wide; calyx short-cylindric or deeply campanulate, (5.5–)6–9 mm, tube (4–)4.5–6.7 mm, lobes (1–)1.4–3 mm; corolla pink-purple; banner 9–13.2 mm; keel 8–11.3 mm. **Legumes** strongly incurved through 0.5–1 spiral, ovoid or lanceoloid-ellipsoid, openly and shallowly sulcate dorsally in proximal 1/2, 7–17 × 3.8–5 (–7) mm, densely shaggy-villous, hairs to 1.8–2.8 mm. **Seeds** 14–20.

Flowering May–Jul. On pumice sand with sagebrush, in dry rushy meadows around lakeshores; 800–1300 m; Calif., Idaho, Nev., Oreg.

Variety *lagopinus* occurs from northeastern California to central Oregon, southwestern Idaho, and northwestern Nevada.

210. Astragalus anserinus N. D. Atwood, Goodrich & S. L. Welsh, Great Basin Naturalist 44: 263, fig. 1. 1984 • Goose Creek milkvetch [C] [E]

Plants dwarf, tuft- or humifusely mat-forming, shortly caulescent, 3–11 cm, densely gray-villous, hairs basifixed; from superficial caudex; taproot slender. **Stems** decumbent-spreading, gray-villous. **Leaves** 1–4 cm; stipules 1.5–3.5 mm, membranous; leaflets 5–15, blades obovate, 3.2–6.5 mm, apex obtuse, surfaces villous. **Peduncles** ascending, decumbent in fruit, (0.7–)1.1–2.4 cm. **Racemes** (2 or)3–7-flowered, flowers ascending; axis 0.1–0.5 cm in fruit; bracts 2 mm; bracteoles 0. **Pedicels** 0.6–1.2 mm. **Flowers** 9–11.2 mm; calyx campanulate, 5.5–6.5 mm, white-villosulous, tube 3.6–4.8 mm, lobes linear-subulate, 1.1–1.8 mm; corolla pink-purple; banner recurved through 40°; keel 8.5 mm. **Legumes** deciduous from within calyx, initially ascending (humistrate), stramineous, falcately incurved, obliquely ellipsoid, dorsiventrally compressed, conspicuously 3-sided beaked, 9–12(–15) × 5–7 mm, unilocular, stiffly papery, sparsely villous. **Seeds** (12–)16–20.

Flowering May–Jun. Sagebrush, rabbitbrush, and juniper communities, on white, tuffaceous outcrops; of conservation concern; 1500–1700(–1800) m; Idaho, Nev., Utah.

Astragalus anserinus is restricted to near the junction of Idaho, Nevada, and Utah.

211. Astragalus leucolobus S. Watson ex M. E. Jones, Zoë 4: 270. 1893 • Whitepod milkvetch [C] [E]

Plants subacaulescent or shortly caulescent, 5–15 cm, villous-villosulous, hairs basifixed; from superficial caudex. **Stems** erect to sprawling, to 7 cm, internodes often shorter than stipules, villous-villosulous. **Leaves** (1.5–)2.5–9 cm; stipules 2–10 mm, submembranous; leaflets (7–)11–19, often crowded, blades elliptic to broadly obovate, 3–13 mm, apex obtuse, acute, or shortly acuminate, surfaces villous. **Peduncles** incurved-ascending, decumbent in fruit, (3–)5–13 cm. **Racemes** 5–13-flowered, flowers ascending; axis (0.5–)2–8 cm in fruit; bracts 2.5–8 mm; bracteoles 2. **Pedicels** 0.8–2.2 mm. **Flowers** 16–18.5 mm; calyx purplish, usually cylindric, sometimes cylindro-campanulate, 8.2–10.7 mm, villosulous, tube 6.6–8.9 mm, lobes subulate or subulate-triangular, 1.5–3.5 mm; corolla pink-purple or pallid; banner recurved through 40°; keel 14.3–16.8 mm. **Legumes** ascending (humistrate), gently incurved, obliquely lanceoloid-oblong, obcompressed to 3-sided compressed, (13–)15–25 × 4.5–9 mm, bilocular, fleshy becoming stiffly leathery, densely villous-tomentulose, hairs to 1 mm; inflexed, especially proximal 1/2, as a narrow, complete septum. **Seeds** 18–24.

Flowering May–Jul. Dry pine woods, gravelly knolls with sagebrush, stony lakeshores in pine belt; of conservation concern; 1500–2800 m; Calif.

Astragalus leucolobus, known from the interior mountains of southern California, is similar to *A. purshii* in fruit but differs in its shorter pubescence that scarcely hides the surface of the fruit. D. Isely (1998) provided keys to distinguish between flowering specimens of *A. leucolobus* and contiguous or partially sympatric *A. purshii* vars. *lectulus* and *tinctus*.

212. Astragalus subvestitus (Jepson) Barneby, Amer. Midl. Naturalist 37: 514. 1947 • Monache milkvetch [E]

Astragalus leucolobus S. Watson ex M. E. Jones var. *subvestitus* Jepson, Fl. Calif. 2: 361. 1936

Plants dwarf, tuft- or depressed mat-forming, to 1–2 dm diam., shortly caulescent, 1–8 cm, villous-tomentose, hairs basifixed; from superficial caudex. **Stems** prostrate, internodes mostly concealed by stipules, villous-tomentose. **Leaves** 1.5–4.5(–6.5) cm; stipules 2–6 mm, membranous; leaflets 7–11(or 13), blades usually obovate-cuneate, rarely elliptic, 2–7(–9) mm, apex obtuse or acute, surfaces villous-tomentose. **Peduncles** decumbent in fruit, 0.3–3(–4.5) cm. **Racemes** 3–8-flowered, flowers ascending; axis 0.3–1.6 cm in fruit; bracts 2–4 mm; bracteoles 0. **Pedicels** 1–2.5 mm. **Flowers** (11–)11.5–13.3 mm; calyx cylindric or deeply campanulate, 7.5–8.9 mm, white-villous, tube 5.3–6.4 mm, lobes subulate, 1.4–2.5 (–3) mm; corolla whitish, keel tip pink or purple; banner recurved through 40°; keel 9.5–10.7 mm. **Legumes** ascending (humistrate), brownish stramineous, incurved, obliquely ovoid, obcompressed, 8–15 × 4.5–6.5 mm, unilocular, fleshy becoming stiffly papery, villous-tomentulose, hairs to 1 mm. **Seeds** 11–14.

Flowering Jun–Jul. Open slopes and gravelly or sandy flats among sagebrush; 2400–2600 m; Calif.

Astragalus subvestitus is known from two small areas on the western slope of the southern Sierra Nevada in Tulare and Kern counties. R. C. Barneby (1964) proposed that *A. subvestitus* and *A. leucolobus* each were derived from a different variety of *A. purshii* (vars. *lectulus* and *tinctus*, respectively).

213. Astragalus funereus M. E. Jones, Contr. W. Bot. 12: 11. 1908 • Funeral Mountain milkvetch [C] [E]

Plants loosely tuft-forming, shortly caulescent, 2–8 cm, hirsute and tomentose, hairs basifixed; from superficial caudex. **Stems** decumbent or prostrate, often with 2+ apparent internodes, internodes to 1–1.5 cm, hirsute or tomentose. **Leaves** 2.5–7 cm; stipules 3–8 mm, submembranous; leaflets (7 or)9–17, blades broadly obovate to oblong-obovate or obovate-cuneate, (2–)3–12 mm, apex obtuse or emarginate, surfaces hirsute and tomentose. **Peduncles** incurved-ascending, decumbent in fruit, 2.5–6.5 cm. **Racemes** (3 or)4–10-flowered, flowers ascending; axis 0.5–3 cm in fruit; bracts 4–6.5 mm; bracteoles 2. **Pedicels** 1.7–4.5 mm. **Flowers** (22–)24–29 mm; calyx cylindro-campanulate, (11.5–)12.5–16 mm, densely hirsute, tube (8–)9.2–12.4 mm, lobes broadly subulate, 3–4.3 mm; corolla pink-purple, wing and keel tips maculate; banner recurved through 40°; keel (21.5–)24–27.5 mm. **Legumes** ascending (humistrate), ± straight proximally, gently incurved distally, obliquely lanceoloid-ellipsoid, obcompressed proximally, (25–)30–50 × 10–15 mm, unilocular, fleshy becoming leathery, densely hirsute, hairs lustrous, wavy or contorted, (1–)2–2.5 mm. **Seeds** 40–50.

Flowering Apr–May. Gravelly, clay ridges among sagebrush, cliff edges, talus under cliffs, on limestone bedrock; of conservation concern; 1000–2300 m; Calif., Nev.

Astragalus funereus, exceptionally striking with pink-purple flowers about the same size as those of *A. coccineus*, is poorly represented in herbaria. It is restricted to the Grapevine Mountains on the eastern side of Death Valley, California, and adjacent Nye County, Nevada.

214. Astragalus inflexus Douglas in W. J. Hooker, Fl. Bor.-Amer. 1: 151. 1831 • Bent milkvetch, grooved woolly-pod [E]

Plants tuft-forming, caulescent, 15–40(–50) cm, villous or tomentose, hairs basifixed; from superficial caudex. **Stems** prostrate and radiating or with incurved-ascending tips, well developed, flexuous, villous or tomentose. **Leaves** (3–)4–12 (–16) cm; stipules 5–12(–16) mm, submembranous; leaflets (9–)17–23(–27), blades obovate-cuneate, rhombic-oval, or broadly oblanceolate, (40–)60–160(–200) mm, apex usually acute, subacute, or shortly acuminate, rarely subobtuse, surfaces villous to tomentose. **Peduncles** divaricate or incurved-ascending, (2–)3–8 cm. **Racemes** (5–)8–18-flowered, flowers ascending; axis (1.5–)2.5–6(–8) cm in fruit; bracts 4.5–10 mm; bracteoles 0. **Pedicels** (1.3–)1.8–3.3 mm. **Flowers** (16.5–)19.5–23 mm; calyx usually purplish, cylindric or cylindro-campanulate, (9.4–)11.3–16.4 mm, villous, tube (6.2–)8.2–10.2 mm, lobes linear-lanceolate or lanceolate-caudate, 3.1–6.6(–7) mm; corolla pink-purple; banner recurved through 40°; keel (12.7–)14.4–17.2 mm. **Legumes** ascending, stramineous or brownish, ± straight proximally, incurved distally, obliquely ovoid, lanceoloid-ovoid, or oblong-ellipsoid, obcompressed, (13–)15–25(–30) × (5–)7–9.5 mm, unilocular, fleshy becoming stiffly leathery, villous-hirsute or tomentose; sutures approximate or contiguous within, cross section deeply cordate or subdidymous; sessile with gynophore (0–)0.7–1.8 mm. **Seeds** 22–28 (–33). $2n = 22$.

Flowering Apr–early Jul. Open, grassy hillsides, dry pastures, valley floors, river terraces, on substrates derived from basalt or granite bedrock, rarely in ponderosa pine forests; (100–)300–1300 m; Idaho, Mont., Oreg., Wash.

Astragalus inflexus occurs in west-central Idaho, western Montana, northeastern Oregon, and south-central and southeastern Washington. It sometimes is confused with *A. purshii* var. *glareosus*, which was historically included within this entity, but *A. inflexus* has longer calyx lobes and a more strongly caulescent habit.

215. Astragalus parryi A. Gray, Amer. J. Sci. Arts, ser. 2, 33: 410. 1862 • Parry's milkvetch [E]

Plants loosely tuft-forming, caulescent, 3–25 cm, hirsute or hirsutulous, hairs basifixed; from superficial caudex. **Stems** decumbent or ascending, hirsute or hirsutulous. **Leaves** (2–)4–14 cm; stipules 5–10 mm, thinly herbaceous becoming papery-membranous; leaflets (9–)15–27, blades broadly ovate, obcordate, obovate to broadly oblanceolate, or elliptic, 4–15 mm, apex usually obtuse, rarely acute, surfaces hirsutulous. **Peduncles** incurved-ascending, 2–5.5 cm. **Racemes** 4–9-flowered, flowers loosely ascending; axis 1–2.5 cm in fruit; bracts 3.5–9 mm; bracteoles 0–2. **Pedicels** 2.5–4 mm. **Flowers** 15–22 mm; calyx usually broadly campanulate, sometimes subcylindric, 9–12 mm, hirsute, tube 5–7 mm, lobes narrowly lanceolate, 4–5 mm; corolla white, veins and keel tip pink; banner recurved through 45°; keel 12.4–16.2 mm. **Legumes** ascending or spreading, brownish, incurved through 0.2–0.5(–1) spiral, lunately lanceoloid, strongly obcompressed, (20–)25–30 × 6–8 mm, unilocular, fleshy becoming stiffly leathery or subligneous, densely hirsutulous. **Seeds** 26–30.

Flowering May–early Jul. Open gravelly or sandy banks and hillsides, with sagebrush, around oak thickets, in open pine forests, on granite or sandstone bedrock; 1700–3100 m; Colo., Wyo.

Astragalus parryi is a species primarily of the eastern slope of the Rocky Mountains that is rarely misidentified. The fruit is one-chambered, but it is deeply sulcate along both sutures and didymous in cross section. It occurs from the Medicine Bow Range in southeastern Wyoming to the Spanish Peaks in south-central Colorado, extending west of the Continental Divide to the headwaters of the Grand River in Grand County, Colorado.

216. Astragalus castaneiformis S. Watson, Proc. Amer. Acad. Arts 20: 361. 1885 (as castaneaeformis) • Chestnut milkvetch [E]

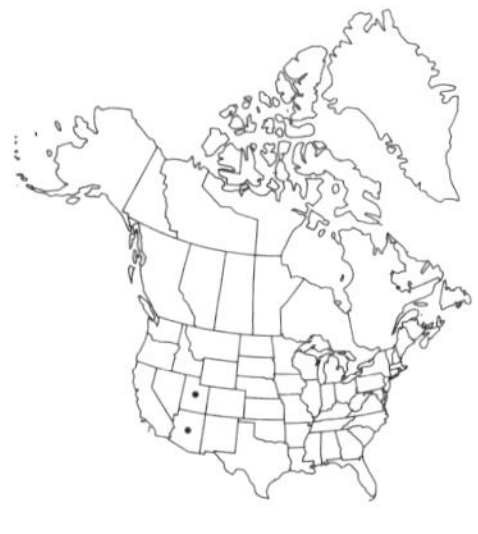

Plants dwarf, clump-forming, acaulescent or subacaulescent, 3–9 cm, silky-strigose to strigulose, hairs malpighian, lustrous; from superficial caudex. **Stems** obsolete, ascending, or prostrate, radiating from root-crown, to 3 cm, internodes mostly obscured by leaf bases, silky-strigose to strigulose. **Leaves** (1.5–)2.5–10 cm; stipules 3–7 mm, submembranous; leaflets 7–13, blades obovate-cuneate or elliptic-oblanceolate, 3–12 mm, apex obtuse or subacute, surfaces strigulose. **Peduncles** ascending, 0.5–3(–5) cm. **Racemes** 2–10-flowered, flowers ascending; axis 0.1–1.5 cm in fruit; bracts 1.5–5.5 mm; bracteoles 0(–2), exceptionally conspicuous. **Flowers** (14.5–)15–18.5 mm; calyx cylindric or vase-shaped, 6–10.5 mm, strigulose, hairs black or white, tube 6.5–8 mm, lobes subulate, 1.3–2.5 mm; corolla white, whitish, or ochroleucous; banner recurved through 40°; keel 8.3–14.3 mm. **Legumes** spreading-ascending (humistrate), green or purplish becoming brownish or stramineous, scarcely to moderately incurved, obliquely ovoid, lanceolate-ovoid, or lunately ellipsoid, obcompressed becoming laterally compressed distally, 9–20(–22) × 4–8 mm, unilocular, distinctly beaked, leathery, walls much less than 1 mm thick, densely strigulose. **Seeds** 18–33.

Flowering May–early Jul. Gentle slopes and flats in ponderosa pine and pinyon-juniper forests, rarely in oak woodlands, in dry stony soils of basaltic or, rarely, calcareous substrates; (1800–)1900–2500 m; Ariz., Utah.

Astragalus castaneiformis is a species of the Kaibab and Mogollon plateaus, Coconino County, Arizona, extending southeastward to the Natanes Plateau, in Gila County. To the north, it just enters Kane County, Utah, in the Buckskin Mountains.

217. Astragalus consobrinus (Barneby) S. L. Welsh, Great Basin Naturalist 38: 271. 1978 • Bicknell milkvetch [E]

Astragalus castaneiformis S. Watson var. *consobrinus* Barneby, Amer. Midl. Naturalist 41: 496. 1949 (as castaneaeformis)

Plants sometimes flowering first year, tuft-forming, acaulescent, 1–5 cm, strigulose, hairs malpighian; from branched caudex, branches obscured by persistent leaf bases and stipules. **Leaves** 1–6 cm; stipules 3–7 mm; leaflets 3–11, blades obovate to oblanceolate or orbiculate, 1.5–8 mm, apex round to obtuse or acute, surfaces strigose. **Peduncles** ascending, 0.4–3 cm. **Racemes** 2–10-flowered; axis to 1 cm in fruit; bracts 1.5–3.5 mm; bracteoles 0. **Pedicels** ascending, 1–2 mm. **Flowers** 10–15.5(–17.5) mm; calyx cylindric, 5.5–8.9 mm, strigose, tube 4.1–6.8 mm, lobes subulate, 1.4–1.7 mm; corolla usually white or ochroleucous, sometimes fading yellowish, suffused with purple, sometimes purple, keel tip maculate; banner recurved through 40°; keel (9–)10–12.5 mm. **Legumes** ascending, green, straight or slightly incurved, obliquely ovoid or lanceoloid-ovoid, somewhat dorsiventrally compressed,

(8–)11–19 × 3–8 mm, unilocular, distinctly beaked, thinly fleshy becoming papery, sometimes incipiently alveolate-spongy, walls much less than 1 mm thick, strigose. **Seeds** 18–33.

Flowering Jun–Jul. Sagebrush-grassland and pinyon-juniper communities, among basalt boulders or gravel derived from ash-flow tuffs of Tertiary Marysvale volcanic centrum; 1800–2600 m; Utah.

Astragalus consobrinus is a delicate, diminutive species of south-central Utah in Emery, Garfield, Sevier, and Wayne counties.

218. Astragalus chamaeleuce A. Gray in J. C. Ives, Rep. Colorado R. 4: 10. 1861 • Cicada milkvetch [E]

Phaca pygmaea Nuttall in J. Torrey and A. Gray, Fl. N. Amer. 1: 349. 1838, not *Astragalus pygmaeus* Pallas 1800

Plants tuft-forming, acaulescent to subacaulescent, 2–10 cm, strigose to strigulose, hairs malpighian; from superficial caudex. **Stems** prostrate or reduced to sessile crowns, 0–6 cm, internodes mostly obscured by stipules, strigose to strigulose. **Leaves** 2–10 cm; stipules 2–7 mm, submembranous becoming papery; leaflets (1–)5–17, blades obovate to oblanceolate, (2–)4–15 mm, apex obtuse to truncate or emarginate, surfaces strigose. **Peduncles** incurved-ascending, 1–8 cm. **Racemes** 2–11-flowered, flowers spreading-ascending; axis (0.3–)1–2 cm in fruit; bracts 2–5 mm; bracteoles 0(–2). **Pedicels** 1–3.5 mm. **Flowers** 17–24 (–25.5) mm; calyx cylindric, 9–13 mm, strigulose, tube 6.5–9.5(–12) mm, lobes subulate, 1.5–3 mm; corolla ochroleucous or tinged purplish to pink-purple; banner recurved through 45°; keel 14.6–20(–22) mm. **Legumes** ascending (humistrate), purple-mottled, definitely incurved, oblong-ovoid or ellipsoid, 20–40(–45) × 7–16 mm, unilocular, contracted into distinct, conic-cuspidate beak, fleshy becoming alveolate-spongy, walls 1+ mm thick, exocarp and endocarp separated by thick, pulpy mesocarp, strigose. **Seeds** 37–60. **2*n*** = 22.

Flowering late Apr–Jul. Juniper-pinyon, sagebrush, mixed desert shrub, and grassland communities; 1500–2400 m; Colo., Mont., Utah, Wyo.

Astragalus chamaeleuce is known from western Colorado from Montrose County northward, the Uinta Basin southward to Emery and Grand counties in Utah, southwestern to north-central Wyoming, and Carbon County in Montana.

The thick-walled but relatively light-weight fruits of *Astragalus chamaeleuce* have a spongy, thickened mesocarp that exfoliates with the exocarp at maturity. The fruits are windblown after separation from racemes.

219. Astragalus laccoliticus (M. E. Jones) S. L. Welsh, Great Basin Naturalist 58: 53. 1998 • Laccolite milkvetch [E]

Astragalus cicadae M. E. Jones var. *laccoliticus* M. E. Jones, Proc. Calif. Acad. Sci., ser. 2, 5: 672. 1895

Plants clump-forming, acaulescent, 4–8 cm, strigulose, hairs malpighian; from superficial caudex. **Stems** ± obsolete, internodes obscured by stipules. **Leaves** 2–9 cm; stipules 2–5 mm; leaflets (5–)9 or 11, blades oblanceolate to obovate, (4.5–)5–11 mm, apex obtuse, surfaces strigose. **Peduncles** 1.3–6 cm. **Racemes** 3–8-flowered, flowers spreading-ascending; axis 3–15 cm in fruit; bracts 2–5 mm. **Pedicels** 1–2.5 mm. **Flowers** 19–27 mm; calyx cylindric, 10–11.5 mm, strigulose, tube 8.5–10 mm, lobes 1–2 mm; corolla pink-purple, fading or drying ochroleucous; banner recurved through 45°. **Legumes** ascending (humistrate), green or purplish (not mottled), turgidly lanceoloid-ovoid (much broader basally), 15–25(–27) × 7–15 mm, unilocular, distinctly beaked, fleshy becoming alveolate-spongy, walls 1+ mm thick, exocarp and endocarp separated by thick, pulpy mesocarp, strigulose. **Seeds** 38.

Flowering Apr–Jun. Salt desert shrub, Bigelow sagebrush, and juniper communities; 1500–1900 m; Utah.

Previously considered a synonym of *Astragalus chamaeleuce*, *A. laccoliticus* has lanceolate-ovoid (not ellipsoid) fruits without purple mottling. The species occurs in western Garfield and western Wayne counties. M. E. Jones (1923) suggested that this taxon might be a hybrid between *A. chamaeleuce* (*A. pygmaeus* in the sense of Jones) and *A. musiniensis*. Hybrids between *Astragalus* species are rare, but Jones hypothesized hybridity as the solution to explain intermediates in numerous instances in the genus.

220. Astragalus piscator Barneby & S. L. Welsh, Great Basin Naturalist 45: 551. 1985 • Fisher milkvetch [C] [E]

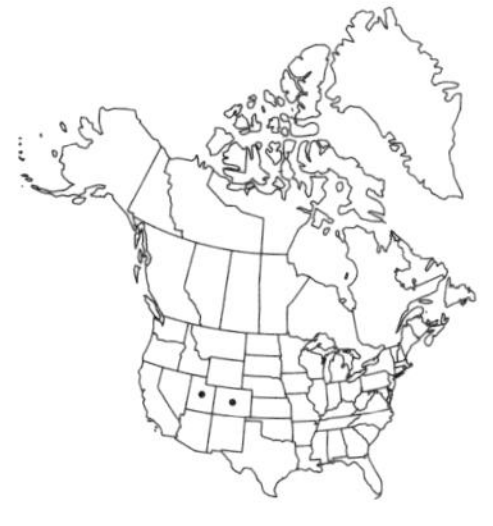

Plants short-lived, sometimes flowering first year, tuft-forming, acaulescent or subacaulescent, strigose, hairs malpighian; from caudex, with persistent leaf bases. **Stems** obsolete, obscured by stipules. **Leaves** (3–)4–10(–16) cm; stipules 3–9 mm; leaflets (1–)5–11 (or 13), blades elliptic or lanceolate-elliptic, (5–)7–17 (–32) mm, apex acute or subobtuse, surfaces pubescent. **Peduncles** (1–)2–6(–9) cm. **Racemes** 3–10-flowered, flowers ascending; axis 0.4–1.5(–2) cm in fruit. **Flowers** 18–24 mm; calyx cylindric, 11–14.5 mm, strigose, tube 8.5–11 mm, lobes subulate, 2–3.5(–4) mm; corolla ochroleucous, suffused or lined with purple, or suffused with pink fading purple; banner recurved through 40°; keel 16–18 mm. **Legumes** deciduous from receptacle, dehiscent through gaping beak after falling, ascending (humistrate), purplish-mottled, shallowly lunate-incurved, lanceoloid-ellipsoid, somewhat laterally compressed, 24–40 × 8–15 mm, unilocular, moderately fleshy becoming stiffly papery or leathery, not pithy, densely strigose, hairs short. **Seeds** 40.

Flowering late Apr–early Jun. Sandy soils of valley benches, in gullied foothills, on rocks of Cretaceous Mancos Shale formation, Triassic Moenkopi and Cutler formations, and Permian White Rim formation, with *Atriplex*, shadscale, woody aster, budsage, blackbrush, and pinyon-juniper; of conservation concern; 1300–1800 m; Colo., Utah.

Astragalus piscator occurs in southeastern Grand, northern San Juan, eastern Wayne, and central Emery counties in Utah, and adjacent Mesa County in Colorado.

The habit and laterally-compressed legumes (at maturity) of *Astragalus piscator* are similar to those of *A. cymboides* but it is distinguished by larger flowers and fruit.

Astragalus piscator is in the Center for Plant Conservation's National Collection of Endangered Plants.

221. Astragalus amphioxys A. Gray, Proc. Amer. Acad. Arts 13: 366. 1878 • Crescent milkvetch [F]

Plants short-lived, sometimes flowering first year, tuft- or loosely mat-forming, subacaulescent to shortly caulescent, 2–35 cm, densely strigose-strigulose, hairs malpighian; from weakly developed caudex. **Stems** usually prostrate or weakly ascending, sometimes erect, 0–20 cm, internodes often concealed by stipules, densely strigose-strigulose. **Leaves** 2–13 cm; stipules sometimes connate-sheathing at proximal nodes, 2–13 mm, submembranous becoming papery; leaflets (1–)5–21, blades elliptic to obovate or oblanceolate, 3–20 mm, apex obtuse to acute, surfaces strigose. **Peduncles** ascending, (1–)2–15(–20) cm. **Racemes** 2–13-flowered, flowers ascending; axis (0.5–)1–6.5 cm in fruit; bracts 2.5–8 mm; bracteoles 0–2. **Pedicels** 0.6–2.5 mm. **Flowers** 10.3–27(–28) mm; calyx usually purplish, cylindric, campanulate, or cylindro-campanulate, 6.3–14.2 mm, strigose, tube (3.4–)5.8–13.2 mm, lobes subulate, 1.1–3.7(–4.5) mm; corolla usually pink-purple, rarely white; banner recurved through 40°; keel 8–23.6 mm. **Legumes** readily deciduous, ascending, green, sometimes mottled, usually incurved, crescentic, mostly dorsiventrally compressed, 15–40 × 5–12 mm, unilocular, distinctly beaked, fleshy becoming stiffly leathery or subligneous, walls much less than 1 mm thick, strigose. **Seeds** 42–70.

Varieties 4 (4 in the flora): w United States, n Mexico.

Astragalus amphioxys is a widely distributed and complex species consisting of a series of morphological and geographical varieties that are fairly distinctive. The species is common in the middle Colorado Basin and adjoining regions. *Astragalus missouriensis*, mostly of the Missouri drainage, is a major related species; the ranges of the two are essentially allopatric, but they slightly conjoin in southwestern Colorado and northwestern New Mexico. Flowering material is difficult to identify in the Four Corners area of the Southwest.

1. Calyx tubes (5.8–)7–13.2 mm; banners (16.2–)19–27(–28) mm; keel (13.2–)14.3–23.6 mm; Arizona, Colorado, Nevada, New Mexico, Texas, Utah.
   2. Calyx tubes (5.8–)7–10.5 mm; banners (16.2–)19–24.5 mm; keel (13.2–)14.3–18.8(–19.6) mm; Arizona, Colorado, Nevada, New Mexico, Texas, Utah . . . . .221a. *Astragalus amphioxys* var. *amphioxys*
   2. Calyx tubes 8.8–13.2 mm; banners 23–27(–28) mm; keel 19–23.6 mm; extreme n Arizona, sw Colorado, nw New Mexico, se Utah. . . 221d. *Astragalus amphioxys* var. *vespertinus*
1. Calyx tubes 3.4–9.3 mm; banners 10.3–16 mm; keel 8–12.7 mm; Mohave and Coconino counties, Arizona, se Nevada, sc Utah.
   3. Calyces cylindro-campanulate, tubes 6.1–9.3 mm; keel 11–12.7 mm; seeds 44–58; nc, nw Arizona, Lincoln County, Nevada, and Kane County, Utah . . . . .221b. *Astragalus amphioxys* var. *modestus*
   3. Calyces campanulate, tubes 3.4–4.8 mm; keel 8–11.5 mm; seeds 26–36; Mohave County, Arizona, Clark County, Nevada . . . . 221c. *Astragalus amphioxys* var. *musimonum*

221a. Astragalus amphioxys A. Gray var. **amphioxys** [F]

Flowers: calyx cylindric, tube (5.8–)7–10.5 mm, lobes 1.5–3.7(–4.5) mm; corolla banner (16.2–)19–24.5 mm; keel (13.2–)14.3–18.8(–19.6) mm. **Legumes** 15–40 mm, curved. **Seeds** (42–)44–56. $2n = 22$.

Flowering late Mar–Jun. Sandy valleys, plains, gravelly hillsides, on dunes, rarely on gumbo-clay flats, in creosote bush, Joshua tree, blackbrush, indigo bush, salt desert shrub, pinyon-juniper, and mountain brush communities; 400–2100 m; Ariz., Colo., Nev., N.Mex., Tex., Utah; Mexico (Chihuahua).

Variety *amphioxys* is variable and includes elements that may be taxonomically significant (D. Isely 1998).

221b. Astragalus amphioxys A. Gray var. **modestus** Barneby, Leafl. W. Bot. 9: 89. 1960 • Modest milkvetch E

Flowers: calyx cylindro-campanulate, tube 6.1–9.3 mm, lobes 1.1–2.6 mm; corolla banner 12.8–16 mm; keel 11–12.7 mm. **Legumes** 16–40 mm, crescentic or incurved through 1/2 their length. **Seeds** 44–58.

Flowering Mar–May. Dry gravelly hillsides, in blackbrush, four-wing saltbush, Indian ricegrass, needle-and-thread grass, old man sagebrush, mixed grass communities, on sandy silt, limestone, or cindery volcanic debris; 1100–1500 m; Ariz., Nev., Utah.

The small-flowered var. *modestus* forms the other major extreme in flower size within the species, contrasting with the large-flowered var. *vespertinus*. It is local, forming uniform colonies within the range of var. *amphioxys* but only from valleys affluent to the Colorado River from San Juan and eastern Kane counties, Utah, and northern Mohave County, Arizona, with disjunct populations in Lincoln County, Nevada. Some plants from northeastern Arizona and northwestern New Mexico have similarly small flowers and might represent an eastward extension of var. *modestus*; however, in this case introgression from *Astragalus missouriensis* cannot be ruled out.

221c. Astragalus amphioxys A. Gray var. **musimonum** (Barneby) Barneby in A. Cronquist et al., Intermount. Fl. 3(B): 138. 1989 • Sheep Mountain milkvetch E

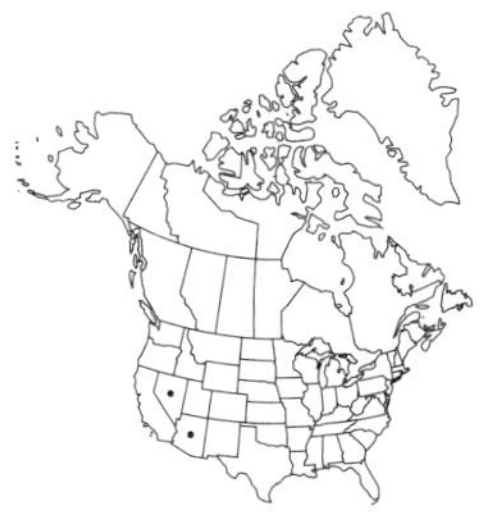

Astragalus musimonum Barneby, Proc. Calif. Acad. Sci., ser. 4, 25: 150, plate 17, figs. 1–9. 1944

Flowers: calyx campanulate, tube 3.4–4.8 mm, lobes 1.8–2.5 mm; corolla banner 10.3–13.4 mm; keel 8–11.5 mm. **Legumes** 15–20(–25) mm, crescentic or incurved through 1/2 their length. **Seeds** 26–36.

Flowering Apr–Jun. Limestone gravel and outcrops with blackbrush; 1100–1800 m; Ariz., Nev.

Variety *musimonum* is found on the Shivwits Plateau in Mohave County, Arizona, westward to the Sheep Mountain Range in Clark County, Nevada.

The combination of a sharply curved tip of the fruit, short petal claws, and small calyx has been considered sufficient to recognize this taxon as a distinct species, *Astragalus musimonum* (D. Isely 1998).

221d. Astragalus amphioxys A. Gray var. **vespertinus** (E. Sheldon) M. E. Jones, Rev. N.-Amer. Astragalus, 215. 1923 • Evening milkvetch E

Astragalus vespertinus E. Sheldon, Minnesota Bot. Stud. 1: 150. 1894

Flowers: calyx cylindric, tube 8.8–13.2 mm, lobes 1.3–3 mm; corolla banner 23–27(–28) mm; keel 19–23.6 mm. **Legumes** 30–35 mm, gently incurved. **Seeds** 50–70.

Flowering Apr–Jun. Sandy valley floors, ledges under cliffs, gravelly hillsides, in sagebrush or mountain brush communities, pinyon-juniper forests, usually on sandstone; 600–1800 (–2000) m; Ariz., Colo., N.Mex., Utah.

Variety *vespertinus* is found locally within the Colorado Basin and occurs from northwestern New Mexico to southwestern Colorado, through southeastern Utah, extending to the Grand Canyon and Kanab Plateau of northwestern Arizona. It is a large-flowered, more or less northern form of the species that is, otherwise, poorly characterized.

222. Astragalus cymboides M. E. Jones, Proc. Calif. Acad. Sci., ser. 2, 5: 650. 1895 • Canoe milkvetch E

Plants tuft-forming, acaulescent or subacaulescent, 2.5–8 cm, strigulose or strigose, hairs malpighian; from simple or branched caudex. **Stems** usually reduced to sessile crowns, sometimes prostrate, 0–3 cm, internodes mostly obscured by stipules, strigulose or strigose. **Leaves** 2.5–8(–10) cm; stipules 3–8 mm, submembranous becoming firmly papery; leaflets (1–)5–18, blades obovate, elliptic, or oblanceolate, 3–13(–20) mm, apex obtuse to acute, surfaces strigulose or strigose. **Peduncles** ascending, 2–8 cm. **Racemes** 3–9(–12)-flowered, flowers ascending; axis 0.5–2(–2.5) cm in fruit; bracts 1–4 mm; bracteoles 0. **Pedicels** 0.7–2.5 mm. **Flowers** 15–18.5 mm; calyx cylindric, 7.6–10.2(–14.6) mm, strigose, tube 5.9–8(–11) mm, lobes subulate, 1–2.3(–3.4) mm; corolla ochroleucous, suffused purplish, or pink-purple; banner recurved through 40°; keel 12.6–15.1(–20.2) mm. **Legumes** ascending, stramineous, straight, oblong to oblong-ellipsoid, initially cylindroid, finally laterally compressed, (12–)15–24(–30) × 6–9.5 mm, unilocular,

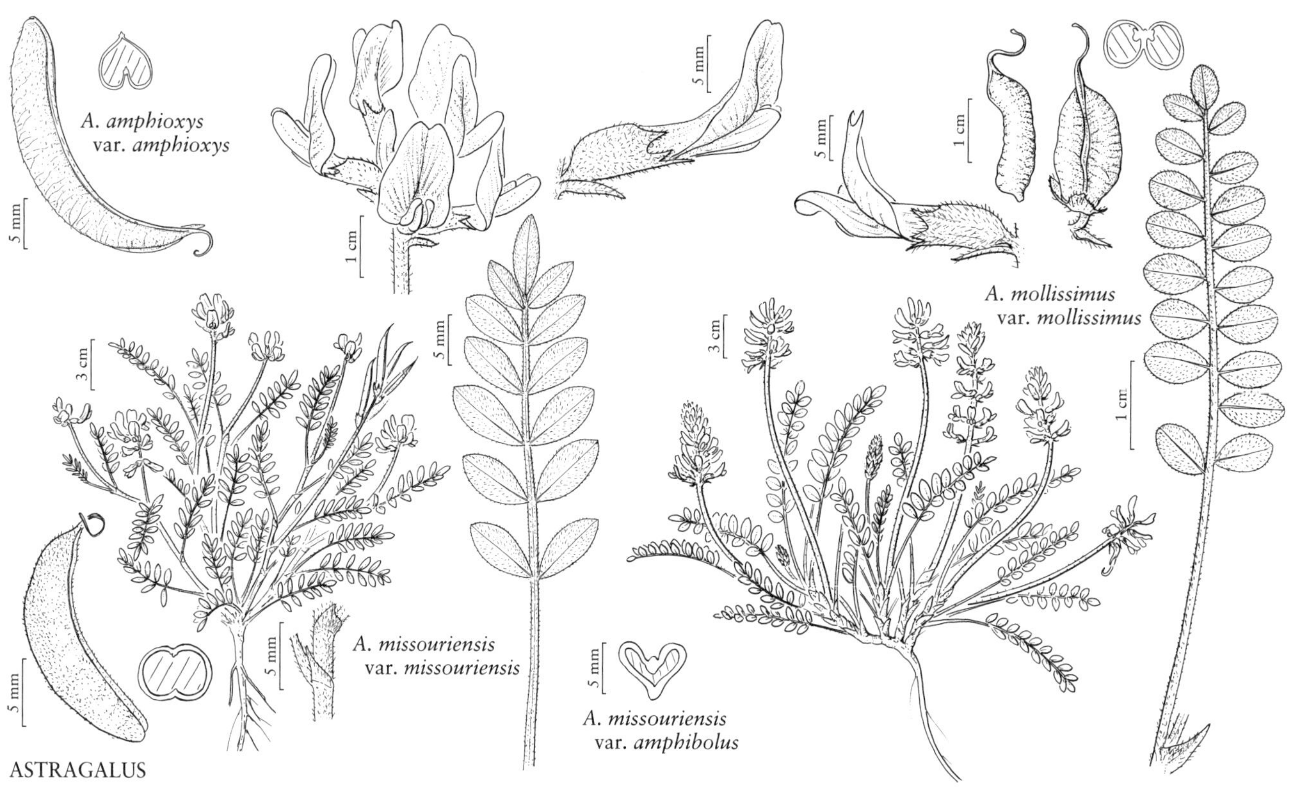

papery or cellular-spongy, exocarp in time exfoliating, strigose, hairs short. **Seeds** 39–57. **2*n*** = 24.

Flowering Apr–Jun. Salt desert shrub and pinyon-juniper communities, on cobblestone pedimental bluffs, river terraces, on saddles or along draws in gullied clay hills, in loose gravelly clay alluvia often on Cretaceous Mancos Shale, on gravelly ridges held up by that formation; 1500–2300 m; Utah.

Astragalus cymboides is the common, low *Astragalus* on pedimental gravel overlying the Mancos Shale clays in east-central Utah. There is a cline from short, thick, and blunt fruits on the western side of the San Rafael Swell to long, slender, and ellipsoid fruits in Grand County; whether this merits taxonomic consideration is undetermined.

223. Astragalus missouriensis Nuttall, Gen. N. Amer. Pl. 2: 99. 1818 • Missouri milkvetch [E] [F]

Plants sometimes loosely tuft-forming, shortly caulescent, subacaulescent, or caulescent, 5–15 (–20) cm, strigose or strigulose, hairs malpighian; from subterranean caudex. **Stems** prostrate and radiating, to 15(–20) cm, internodes often concealed by stipules, strigose or strigulose. **Leaves** (2–)4–14 cm; stipules sometimes connate-sheathing at proximal nodes (vars. *humistratus* and *missouriensis*), (2–)3–9 mm, firm or submembranous becoming scarious or papery; leaflets (5–)11–17(–21), blades elliptic to obovate, 3.5–13(–17) mm, apex acute, apiculate, or obtuse, surfaces strigose to strigulose. **Peduncles** ascending, (1.5–)3.5–11 cm. **Racemes** (3–)4–15-flowered, flowers ascending to spreading; axis (0.5–) 1–4 cm in fruit; bracts 2.5–8 mm; bracteoles 0–2. **Pedicels** 1–3.5 mm. **Flowers** 9.5–22(–24) mm; calyx purple-tinged, cylindric or deeply campanulate, 5–13 (–14.3) mm, strigulose, tube 4.1–10 mm, lobes subulate, (0.7–)1.4–4.5(–5.3) mm; corolla usually pink-purple, purple, lavender, or violet-red, rarely white; banner recurved through 45°; keel 8.9–17.3(–18.5) mm. **Legumes** usually persistent, ascending or descending, brownish becoming black, straight or slightly incurved, subsymmetrically or obliquely oblong, oblong-ellipsoid, or ellipsoid, subterete, or dorsiventrally or ± laterally compressed, (11–)14–28(–30) × (4–)5–9(–10) mm, unilocular or subunilocular, distinctly beaked, fleshy becoming stiffly leathery or subligneous, walls much less than 1 mm thick, strigulose, strigose, or glabrous. **Seeds** (33–)35–55(or 56). **2*n*** = 22.

Varieties 4 (4 in the flora): w North America.

From the central Canadian provinces to trans-Pecos Texas and western Iowa, *Astragalus missouriensis* is remarkably uniform morphologically. In the Four Corners region of the Southwest, it has undergone considerable differentiation.

1. Calyces 5–5.8 mm; banners 9.5–11.8 mm; keel 8.9–10.6 mm; wc New Mexico, ne Arizona . . . . 223d. *Astragalus missouriensis* var. *mimetes*
1. Calyces 6–13(–14.3) mm; banners 14.5–22(–24) mm; keel (11.5–)12.8–17.3(–18.5) mm; Prairie Provinces southward to Arizona and Texas, eastward to Iowa and Minnesota.
   2. Legumes subsymmetrically oblong-ellipsoid, ± straight, initially subterete or ± dorsiventrally compressed, at maturity ± laterally compressed and obtuse-angled; Prairie Provinces southward to Arizona and Texas, eastward to Iowa and Minnesota. . . . . 223a. *Astragalus missouriensis* var. *missouriensis*
   2. Legumes ellipsoid or oblong-ellipsoid, lunately incurved, dorsiventrally compressed, apices obcompressed proximal to incurved beak; Four Corners area.
      3. Plants subacaulescent to shortly caulescent; stems to 10 cm; racemes 4–8-flowered; Apache County, Arizona, Garfield to La Plata and Montezuma counties, Colorado, San Juan County, New Mexico, Grand and San Juan counties, Utah . . . . 223b. *Astragalus missouriensis* var. *amphibolus*
      3. Plants caulescent; stems 10–15(–20) cm; racemes 9–12-flowered; Archuleta, Hinsdale, and La Plata counties, Colorado, adjacent Rio Arriba County, New Mexico . . . . 223c. *Astragalus missouriensis* var. *humistratus*

223a. Astragalus missouriensis Nuttall var. **missouriensis** E F

Plants usually shortly caulescent, sometimes subacaulescent. **Stems** to 15 cm. **Racemes** (3–)5–15-flowered. **Flowers:** calyx 9–12(–14.3) mm, tube 6.3–9(–9.3) mm, lobes 1.4–4.5(–5.3) mm; corolla usually pink-purple, rarely white; banner (14.5–)16–22(–24) mm; keel (11.5–)12.8–17.3(–18.5) mm. **Legumes** ascending, initially subterete or ± dorsiventrally compressed, ± straight, subsymmetrically oblong-ellipsoid, ± laterally compressed and obtuse-angled when mature, 15–28(–30) × (4–)5–9(–10) mm, subunilocular, base obtuse or sometimes cuneate, apex abruptly contracted into subulate, pungent beak, sutures prominent, strigulose. **Seeds** (33–)40–50(–56). $2n = 22$.

Flowering late Mar–Jul. Prairies, valleys, hillsides, dry open places, on limestone, shale, sandstone, or gypsum substrates; 300–2400 m; Alta., Man., Sask.; Ariz., Colo., Iowa, Kans., Minn., Mont., Nebr., N.Mex., N.Dak., Okla., S.Dak., Tex., Wyo.

There is an irregular cline in flower size of var. *missouriensis*, from smallest in the north to largest in the south; caulescent forms appear to be more common southward (D. Isely 1998).

223b. Astragalus missouriensis Nuttall var. **amphibolus** Barneby, Amer. Midl. Naturalist 37: 447. 1947 • Mancos milkvetch E F

Plants subacaulescent to shortly caulescent. **Stems** to 10 cm. **Racemes** 4–8-flowered. **Flowers:** calyx 8.5–13 mm, tube 7–10 mm, lobes 1.5–3 mm; corolla usually pink-purple, rarely white; banner (14.5–)16–22(–24) mm; keel (11.5–)12.8–17.3(–18.5) mm. **Legumes** sometimes deciduous, ascending to descending, dorsiventrally compressed, lunately incurved, ellipsoid, (11–)15–25 × 7–9 mm, unilocular, apex obcompressed proximal to incurved beak, strigose. **Seeds** 35–55.

Flowering May–Jul. Pinyon-juniper and sagebrush communities, on igneous or sandstone outcrops or substrates; 1600–2500 m; Ariz., Colo., N.Mex., Utah.

The fruits of var. *amphibolus* are initially dorsiventrally compressed, and ultimately dehisce apically while still attached to the inflorescence (though sometimes deciduous). The fruits have a lateral ridge down each valve, with the valves separated by more or less prominent bicarinate keels. In these features, along with the typically persistent fruits, the plants can be distinguished from the similar *Astragalus amphioxys* var. *amphioxys* where their ranges are contiguous, as in northwestern New Mexico and vicinity. R. C. Barneby (1947b, 1964) suggested that hybridization occurs between the two taxa.

223c. Astragalus missouriensis Nuttall var. **humistratus** Isely, Syst. Bot. 8: 423. 1983 • Archuleta milkvetch C E

Plants caulescent. **Stems** 10–15(–20) cm. **Racemes** 9–12-flowered. **Flowers:** calyx 7.8–10 mm, tube 6–10 mm, lobes 1.5–3 mm; corolla lavender, purple, or almost white, wing tips often white; banner (17–)19–20.5 mm. **Legumes** ascending to descending, dorsiventrally compressed, lunately incurved, oblong-ellipsoid, (12–)17–20 × 6–9 mm, unilocular, apex obcompressed proximal to incurved beak, glabrous or sparsely strigulose. **Seeds** 33–40.

Flowering May–Jul. Oak brush with scattered ponderosa pine on clay knolls, pinyon-juniper woodlands, associated with Lewis and Mancos formations; of conservation concern; 2100–2500 m; Colo., N.Mex.

Variety *humistratus* is locally distributed in Archuleta, Hinsdale, and La Plata counties, Colorado, and adjacent Rio Arriba County, New Mexico. It is anomalous in its strongly caulescent but mat-forming habit, and the slightly or plainly connate stipules. R. C. Barneby (1964) suggested a hybrid origin between *Astragalus missouriensis* and *A. humistratus*.

Variety *humistratus* is in the Center for Plant Conservation's National Collection of Endangered Plants.

223d. Astragalus missouriensis Nuttall var. **mimetes** Barneby, Mem. New York Bot. Gard. 13: 716. 1964 • Mimic milkvetch [E]

Plants shortly caulescent or, sometimes, subacaulescent. **Stems** to 15 cm. **Racemes** (3–)5–15-flowered. **Flowers:** calyx 5–5.8 mm, tube 4.1–4.8 mm, lobes 0.7–1.1 mm; corolla bright pink-purple or violet-red, wings darker, banner with pale center; banner 9.5–11.8 mm; keel 8.9–10.6 mm. **Legumes** ascending, initially subterete or ± dorsiventrally compressed, incurved, subsymmetrically oblong-ellipsoid, somewhat laterally compressed and obtuse-angled when mature, 14–24 × 5–7.5(–9) mm, subunilocular, base obtuse or, sometimes, cuneate, apex abruptly contracted into subulate, pungent beak, sutures prominent, strigulose. **Seeds** 36–46.

Flowering Apr–May (Sep). *Larrea* and juniper communities on barren limey knolls, with juniper and matchweed; 1400–1800 m; Ariz., N.Mex.

Variety *mimetes* occurs in the Rio Grande Valley in Valencia and Socorro counties, New Mexico, and in northeastern Arizona. In its small flowers and fruits, it resembles *Astragalus accumbens*, with which it has been confused.

224. Astragalus accumbens E. Sheldon, Minnesota Bot. Stud. 1: 20. 1894 • Zuñi milkvetch [E]

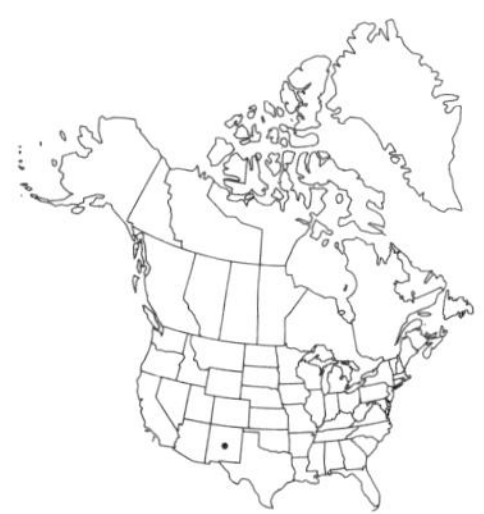

Astragalus procumbens S. Watson, Proc. Amer. Acad. Arts 20: 361. 1885, not Miller 1768; *A. missouriensis* Nuttall var. *accumbens* (E. Sheldon) Isely

Plants tuft-forming, acaulescent or shortly caulescent, 4(–6) cm, strigulose, hairs malpighian; from superficial caudex. **Stems** prostrate, 0–4(–6) cm, internodes to 8 mm, strigulose. **Leaves** (1–)2–6.5 cm; stipules (2–)2.5–5 mm, submembranous; leaflets 7–15, blades obovate, oval, or elliptic-oblanceolate, 2–8(–11) mm, apex usually obtuse, sometimes subacute or obscurely emarginate, surfaces strigulose. **Peduncles** incurved-ascending, 3–6.5 cm. **Racemes** (3–)5–14-flowered, flowers ascending; axis 0.4–1.5 cm in fruit; bracts 1.5–2.7 mm; bracteoles 0. **Pedicels** 0.7–1.6 mm. **Flowers** 7–8.3 mm; calyx campanulate, 4.6–5.1 mm, strigulose, tube 3.5–3.9 mm, lobes subulate, 1–1.6 mm; corolla ochroleucous or purple-veined or -margined; banner abruptly recurved through 90–100°; keel 6.9–7.8 mm. **Legumes** long-persistent on receptacle, spreading or ascending, brown or black, ± straight, plumply ovoid or oblong-ellipsoid, 9–18 × 4–7(–8) mm, unilocular or subunilocular, distinctly beaked, fleshy becoming leathery, strigulose. **Seeds** 22–32.

Flowering (Mar–)May–Jul(–Aug). Gravelly clay banks and knolls, on stiff, dry, alkaline soils derived from sandstone, pinyon-juniper woodlands; 1900–2500 m; N.Mex.

D. Isely placed *Astragalus accumbens* as a variety within *A. missouriensis*, which has merit; it differs from its close geographic congener principally in the comparatively broader calyx and shortly clawed petals. *Astragalus accumbens* is known only from the Zuni Mountains in northwestern New Mexico.

225. Astragalus anisus M. E. Jones, Zoë 4: 34. 1893 • Gunnison milkvetch [C] [E]

Plants dwarf, loosely tuft-forming, subacaulescent or shortly caulescent, to 5 cm, gray-strigose, hairs basifixed; from superficial caudex. **Stems** usually obsolete, 0–5 cm, internodes mostly concealed by stipules, gray-strigose. **Leaves** 2–8(–10) cm; stipules 4–6 mm, submembranous; leaflets (7–)11–15(–19), blades obovate, obovate-cuneate, or subrhombic, 4–10 mm, apex obtuse, surfaces strigose. **Peduncles** 1.5–4(–5) cm. **Racemes** 3–7-flowered, flowers ascending; axis 0.5–2.5 cm in fruit; bracts 2.5–4.5 mm; bracteoles 0–2. **Pedicels** 1.5 mm. **Flowers** 18.8–21 mm; calyx cylindric, base obliquely obconic-attenuate, 11–13 mm, densely strigose-strigulose, tube 9–10.5 mm, lobes subulate, 1.5–3 mm; corolla pink-purple; banner recurved through 40°; keel 16.5–18.5 mm. **Legumes** ascending or loosely spreading (humistrate), stramineous, straight or slightly incurved, obliquely globose, oblong-globose, or broadly obovoid, turgid or moderately inflated, dorsiventrally compressed, (1–)1.3–1.8 × 8–13 mm, bilocular, apex minutely cuspidate, not or scarcely beaked, fleshy becoming spongy, strigulose; septum 3–6 mm wide. **Seeds** 28–40.

Flowering May–Jul. Dry gravelly flats and hillsides, on sandy clay soils overlying granitic bedrock, among or sheltering under low sagebrush; of conservation concern; 2300–2600 m; Colo.

Astragalus anisus is restricted to the Gunnison River valley, Gunnison County. Label data for the type specimen, indicating its origin near Pueblo, is probably in error. It has moved readily onto gravel hauled from nearby deposits to bury radioactive wastes near the town of Gunnison.

Astragalus anisus is in the Center for Plant Conservation's National Collection of Endangered Plants.

135ggg. Astragalus Linnaeus sect. Desperati Barneby, Mem. New York Bot. Gard. 13: 720. 1964 [E]

Herbs perennial (sometimes flowering as annual), tuft-forming, acaulescent, subacaulescent, or short-caulescent; caudex superficial. **Hairs** basifixed (incipiently malpighian in *A. cottamii*, sometimes shortly malpighian in *A. monumentalis*). **Stems** obsolete or few. **Stipules** connate or distinct. **Leaves** odd-pinnate, petiolate; leaflets (3–)7–19(or 21). **Racemes** loosely flowered or subcapitate, flowers ascending, spreading, or declined. **Calyx tubes** campanulate or cylindric. **Corollas** purple, pink-purple, whitish tipped with purple, or ochroleucous, often purple-veined, banner recurved through 40–45°, keel apex round to narrowly deltate. **Legumes** deciduous, sessile, gynophore short or absent, declined, deflexed, spreading, or ascending (humistrate), obliquely ovoid to narrowly oblong-ellipsoid or linear-lanceoloid, straight or incurved, dorsally or 3-sided compressed, unilocular, subunilocular, or bilocular. **Seeds** 8–31.

Species 7 (7 in the flora): w United States.

Section *Desperati* consists of two subsections, with distribution on sandstone rimrock in northern Arizona, western Colorado, northwestern New Mexico, and southeastern Utah. The subsections are: subsect. *Desperati* Barneby (*Astragalus barnebyi*, *A. desperatus*, *A. equisolensis*); and subsect. *Naturitenses* Barneby (*A. cottamii*, *A. deterior*, *A. monumentalis*, *A. naturitensis*).

226. Astragalus desperatus M. E. Jones, Zoë 2: 243. 1891 • Rimrock milkvetch [E]

Plants acaulescent or shortly caulescent, 1–12 cm, strigulose, hairs basifixed; from branched caudex. **Stems** prostrate, when developed, to 8 cm, internodes often obscured by stipules, strigulose. **Leaves** 1–12 cm; stipules connate-sheathing at proximal nodes, connate or distinct at distal nodes, 1.5–7 mm, submembranous becoming papery-scarious; leaflets (3–)7–17, blades elliptic to oblanceolate or obovate, 2–13 mm, apex acute to obtuse, surfaces strigose abaxially, strigose or glabrate adaxially. **Peduncles** erect and ascending, 0.5–13 cm. **Racemes** 3–16(–18)-flowered, flowers ascending to declined; axis 0.4–13 cm in fruit; bracts (1–)1.5–5 mm; bracteoles 0–2. **Pedicels** 0.5–1.4(–2) mm. **Flowers** 6–9 mm; calyx campanulate, 3.5–6 mm, strigose-pilose, tube 2.5–4.2 mm, lobes subulate, 0.8–2.6 mm; corolla pink-purple or bicolored; keel 5.9–12.5 mm. **Legumes** declined to deflexed, green, usually red-mottled or -spotted, becoming stramineous, ± straight or lunately to very strongly incurved through 0.75(–1) spiral, obliquely ovoid to lanceoloid-ellipsoid, dorsiventrally compressed, 6–19 × 3–6 mm, unilocular, papery-membranous, hirsute, hairs lustrous; sessile, gynophore 0–1.2 mm. **Seeds** 16–28.

Varieties 2 (2 in the flora): sw United States.

Two former varieties of *Astragalus desperatus* are recognized here as species (*A. barnebyi* and *A. equisolensis*).

1. Plants shortly caulescent; racemes 6–16(–18)-flowered; legumes lunately curved, 11–19 mm; Arizona, Colorado, New Mexico, Utah . . . . 226a. *Astragalus desperatus* var. *desperatus*
1. Plants acaulescent; racemes 3–6-flowered; legumes ± straight, 6–11 mm; e, se portions of San Rafael Swell, Emery and Wayne counties, Utah . . . . . 226b. *Astragalus desperatus* var. *petrophilus*

226a. Astragalus desperatus M. E. Jones var. **desperatus** E

Plants shortly caulescent. **Racemes** 6–16(–18)-flowered. **Legumes** lunately curved, 11–19 mm.

Flowering Apr–Jun. Mixed desert shrub and pinyon-juniper communities, on rimrock on sandy substrates; 1100–1900 m; Ariz., Colo., N.Mex., Utah.

Variety *desperatus* occurs in Apache, Coconino, and Navajo counties in northeastern Arizona, Delta and Mesa counties in west-central Colorado, San Juan County in northwestern New Mexico, and Emery, Garfield, Grand, Kane, San Juan, and Washington counties in southeastern Utah.

226b. Astragalus desperatus M. E. Jones var. **petrophilus** M. E. Jones, Rev. N.-Amer. Astragalus, 204. 1923 • Rockloving milkvetch E

Plants acaulescent. **Racemes** 3–6-flowered. **Legumes** ± straight, 6–11 mm.

Flowering Apr–Jun. Pinyon-juniper and mixed desert shrub communities; 1400–2200 m; Utah.

Variety *petrophilus* is distinguished by its short stature and small fruit, and occurs along the eastern margin of the San Rafael Swell in Emery and Wayne counties.

227. Astragalus barnebyi S. L. Welsh & N. D. Atwood, Great Basin Naturalist 35: 346. 1976 (as barneby) • Barneby's milkvetch E

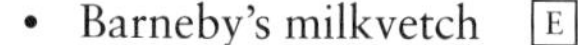

Astragalus desperatus M. E. Jones var. *conspectus* Barneby, Leafl. W. Bot. 5: 87. 1948

Plants acaulescent or subacaulescent, 1.5–5 cm, strigulose, hairs basifixed; from branched caudex. **Stems** prostrate, when developed, 0–5 cm, mostly obscured by stipules, strigulose. **Leaves** 1.5–5 cm; stipules connate-sheathing or distinct, 2–7 mm, membranous; leaflets 7–17, blades elliptic to oblanceolate, 3–9 mm, apex acute to obtuse, surfaces strigose. **Peduncles** ascending, 0.5–5.2 cm. **Racemes** 2–8-flowered, flowers ascending; axis 0.5–2.5 cm in fruit; bracts 2–4 mm; bracteoles 0–2. **Pedicels** 0.5–1.5 mm. **Flowers** 12.2–15 mm; calyx short-cylindric, 6.1–7.7 (–8.4) mm, pilose, hairs black and white, tube 5.2–6.5 mm, lobes subulate, 0.9–1.7 mm; corolla pink-purple or bicolored; keel 9.8–12.5 mm. **Legumes** declined, green, usually red-mottled or -spotted, becoming stramineous, lunately incurved, ovoid-ellipsoid, dorsiventrally compressed, 12–19 × 5–6 mm, subunilocular, thin becoming papery, long silky-pilose; sessile, gynophore 0–0.5+ mm. **Seeds** 20.

Flowering Apr–Jun. Pinyon-juniper woods and mixed desert shrublands on platy shales of the Carmel Formation, on sandstone of Jurassic and Cretaceous ages; 1400–1900 m; Ariz., Utah.

Astragalus barnebyi is known in northern and northeastern Arizona to south-central Utah.

228. Astragalus equisolensis Neese & S. L. Welsh, Rhodora 83: 457, fig. [p. 458]. 1981 • Horseshoe milkvetch C E

Astragalus desperatus M. E. Jones var. *neeseae* Barneby

Plants acaulescent or subacaulescent, 5–18 cm, strigulose, hairs basifixed; from branched caudex. **Stems** prostrate, when developed, 0–2.5 cm, mostly obscured by stipules, strigulose. **Leaves** 1.5–9 cm; stipules connate-sheathing at proximal nodes, connate or distinct at distal nodes, 2–5 cm, membranous; leaflets 5–17, blades elliptic, oblanceolate, or obovate, 3–12 mm, apex acute to obtuse, surfaces strigose. **Peduncles** erect, 2–9 cm. **Racemes** 4–13-flowered, flowers ascending or spreading; axis 1.5–8 cm in fruit; bracts 2–4.5 mm; bracteoles 0. **Pedicels** 0.5–2 mm. **Flowers** 12–16 mm; calyx cylindric, 6–8.5 mm, strigose, tube 4.5–6 mm, lobes subulate, 1.2–2.5 mm; corolla purplish; keel 9.5–12.5 mm. **Legumes** declined to deflexed, green, usually red-mottled or -spotted, becoming stramineous, lunately incurved, obliquely ovoid or lanceoloid-ellipsoid, dorsiventrally compressed, 10–14 × 3.5–6.5 mm, unilocular or subunilocular, thickly papery, hirsute, hairs lustrous; sessile, gynophore 0.3–0.8 mm. **Seeds** 20.

Flowering May–Jun. Sagebrush, shadscale, horsebrush, and other mixed desert shrub communities on Duchesne River Formation; of conservation concern; 1400–1800 m; Colo., Utah.

Astragalus equisolensis lies north of its close ally, *A. desperatus*, in Uintah County, Utah, and in extreme western Mesa County, Colorado.

229. Astragalus naturitensis Payson, Bot. Gaz. 60: 377. 1915 • Naturita milkvetch [E]

Plants subacaulescent, 4.5–16 cm, loosely strigulose, hairs basifixed; from branched caudex, branches with persistent leaf bases. **Stems** obsolete (0–6 cm), internodes to 0.5 cm, mostly concealed by stipules, loosely strigulose. **Leaves** 1.5–7 cm; stipules distinct throughout, imbricate, broadly ovate, 2–7 mm, mostly broader than stem, submembranous becoming papery-scarious; leaflets 9–17, blades elliptic to obovate or oblanceolate, 2–8 mm, apex obtuse, surfaces strigulose abaxially, strigulose or glabrescent adaxially. **Peduncles** ascending, 1–6.5 cm. **Racemes** 3–8(–11)-flowered, flowers ascending; axis 0.5–2.5 cm in fruit; bracts 1.5–4 mm; bracteoles 0. **Pedicels** 0.7–1.8 mm. **Flowers** (11.2–)13–15.5 mm; calyx cylindro-campanulate, 5–7.4 mm, strigulose, tube 4–6.2 mm, lobes triangular-subulate, 1–1.5(–2) mm; corolla bicolored, banner whitish or suffused or lined with lilac, wing and keel tips purple; keel 10–12.5 mm. **Legumes** ascending (humistrate), green, usually red-mottled, becoming stramineous, incurved, obliquely ellipsoid, dorsiventrally to ± 3-sided compressed, 13–22 × 4–6 mm, unilocular, usually leathery, sparsely strigulose, hairs appressed, to 1 mm; sessile, gynophore to 0.8 mm. **Seeds** 22–31.

Flowering Apr–Jun. Sandstone outcrops in sagebrush and pinyon-juniper communities; 1500–3000 m; Colo., N.Mex., Utah.

Astragalus naturitensis is found from west-central Colorado to northeastern San Juan County, Utah, and southward to northwestern New Mexico.

230. Astragalus monumentalis Barneby, Leafl. W. Bot. 7: 35. 1953 • Monument milkvetch [E]

Plants dwarf, acaulescent or subacaulescent, 3–18 cm, strigulose, hairs basifixed or shortly malpighian; from branching caudex, often with thatch of marcescent leaf bases. **Stems** obsolete, ascending, 0.5–6 cm, internodes usually concealed by stipules, strigulose. **Leaves** 1.5–8(–11) cm; stipules distinct throughout, 2–4 mm, membranous becoming papery, stramineous; leaflets (5–)9–17(–21), blades oval to obovate or oblanceolate, 2–9 mm, apex obtuse, acute, or emarginate, surfaces strigulose abaxially, glabrous or glabrate adaxially. **Peduncles** ascending, 1–12 cm. **Racemes** 3–9-flowered, flowers ascending; axis 0.5–7 cm in fruit; bracts 1.5–5 mm; bracteoles 0. **Pedicels** 0.8–2.2 mm. **Flowers** 7–10.5 mm; calyx purplish, campanulate, 3.6–4.5 mm, strigose, tube 3–3.5(–4.5) mm, lobes subulate, 0.5–1.4 mm; corolla pink-purple; keel 7.8–12.4 mm. **Legumes** separating from receptacle at maturity, ascending (humistrate), green, often purple-mottled, becoming stramineous, straight or incurved, narrowly oblong to lanceoloid, 3-sided compressed, 12–17(–21) × 2–3 mm, ± bilocular, thinly fleshy becoming papery, strigose; sessile or subsessile. **Seeds** 16–30.

Flowering Apr–Jun. Rimrock and other slickrock in mixed desert shrub and pinyon-juniper communities; 1200–1900 m; Utah.

Astragalus monumentalis, *A. cottamii*, and *A. deterior* are exploiters of crevices in sandstone rimrock. They are allopatric except for confluence of the first two in the vicinity of Natural Bridges National Monument, San Juan County, Utah. The three differ from each other to about the same degree. *Astragalus monumentalis* is restricted to Garfield and San Juan counties.

231. Astragalus cottamii S. L. Welsh, Rhodora 72. 189, figs. 1, 2. 1970 • Cottam's milkvetch [E]

Astragalus monumentalis Barneby var. *cottamii* (S. L. Welsh) Isely

Plants sometimes flowering first year, acaulescent or subacaulescent, 1.2–15 cm, strigulose, hairs incipiently malpighian or basifixed; from branched caudex. **Stems** osolete, 0–6 cm, internodes mostly obscured by stipules, strigulose. **Leaves** 1.2–8 cm; stipules distinct throughout, 2–6 mm; leaflets (5–)9–19(or 21), blades elliptic to oval or oblanceolate, 2–9 mm, apex acute to obtuse, surfaces strigose abaxially, strigose or glabrous adaxially. **Peduncles** 0.7–9(–10) cm. **Racemes** 3–9(–12)-flowered, flowers ascending; axis 0.5–2 cm in fruit; bracteoles 0–2. **Flowers** 11–17 mm; calyx purplish, cylindric, 6.2–8 mm, strigulose, tube 4.8–6.7 mm, lobes subulate, 1.2–2 mm; corolla pink-purple or bicolored; keel 9–11.5 mm. **Legumes** spreading-descending (humistrate), green, usually purple-mottled, becoming stramineous, incurved, oblong to oblong-lanceoloid, 3-sided compressed, 15–27(–37) × 3–4(–5) mm, ± bilocular, thinly fleshy becoming papery, strigose; sessile. **Seeds** 16–28. $2n = 22$.

Flowering Apr–May. Rimrock, hogbacks, and ledges, sandy canyons, in shadscale, pinyon-juniper and blackbrush communities; 1300–1900 m; Ariz., Colo., N.Mex., Utah.

Astragalus cottamii is closely allied to, and contiguous with, *A. monumentalis*, but its distribution is to the east and southeast in the Four Corners area. *Astragalus cottamii* is associated with the Cedar Mesa, Entrada, Kayenta, Mesa Verde, and Navajo formations.

232. Astragalus deterior (Barneby) Barneby, Leafl. W. Bot. 7: 35. 1953 • Cliff-palace milkvetch [C] [E]

Astragalus naturitensis Payson var. *deterior* Barneby, Leafl. W. Bot. 5: 88. 1948

Plants forming small tufts, subacaulescent or shortly caulescent, slender, 4–7(–10) cm, strigulose, hairs basifixed; from caudex, ± with persistent leaf bases; taproot slender. **Stems** prostrate, 0.5–3(–7) cm, internodes short, length slightly 2 times stipules, strigulose. **Leaves** 2–10 cm; stipules distinct throughout, 1–4 mm, papery-scarious; leaflets 11–15(or 17) blades linear-elliptic or oblanceolate, 3–10 mm, apex acute or obtuse, surfaces usually strigulose, sometimes glabrescent adaxially. **Peduncles** ascending, (1.5–)2.5–8 cm. **Racemes** 2–5-flowered, flowers ascending; axis 0.5–2 cm in fruit; bracts 1.5–2.5 mm. **Pedicels** 1.5–2 mm. **Flowers** 9.5–11 mm; calyx purplish, cylindric or campanulate, 5–5.5 mm, strigulose, tube 3–3.5 mm, lobes subulate, 1.5–2 mm; corolla ochroleucous, banner and keel with purple tips or veins; keel 7–7.5 mm. **Legumes** separating from receptacle at maturity, ascending (humistrate), red-mottled, gently incurved, narrowly oblong, slightly 3-sided compressed, 12–20 × 3.5–5 mm, sub-bilocular, thin becoming papery, sparsely strigulose; septum partial, 0.2–0.6 mm wide; sessile, gynophore to 1 mm. **Seeds** 8–10.

Flowering May–Jun. Ledges of sandstone cliffs, sand-filled depressions of flat or shelving rock, on loose, sandy talus on slopes below rimrock; of conservation concern; 2000–2100 m; Colo.

Astragalus deterior is known only from the southern end of Mesa Verde, on Chapin Mesa, in Montezuma County. It was initially mistaken for the related *A. naturitensis*, but differs in its smaller, ochroleucous flowers, connate stipules, and narrower fruits of thinner texture that are borne on distinct gynophores.

Astragalus deterior is in the Center for Plant Conservation's National Collection of Endangered Plants.

135hhh. Astragalus Linnaeus sect. Layneani Barneby, Mem. New York Bot. Gard. 13: 729. 1964 [E]

Herbs perennial, clump-forming, acaulescent or subacaulescent; caudex deeply subterranean, with horizontal rhizomes. **Hairs** basifixed. **Stems** single or few. **Stipules** distinct. **Leaves** odd-pinnate, petiolate; leaflets (11 or)13–21(or 23). **Racemes** loosely flowered, flowers initially ascending, later horizontal or slightly declined. **Calyx tubes** deeply or broadly campanulate. **Corollas** whitish, lavender- or purple-tipped, banner recurved through 50°, keel apex obtuse. **Legumes** deciduous, sessile, usually ascending or incurved-ascending, rarely declined, obliquely linear-ellipsoid, usually straight, sometimes crescent-incurved, 3-sided compressed, ± bilocular. **Seeds** 26–36.

Species 1: w United States.

233. Astragalus layneae Greene, Bull. Calif. Acad. Sci. 1: 156. 1885 • Layne's milkvetch [E]

Plants short-lived, somewhat coarse, 15–35 cm, pilosulous to gray-strigulose; from branching caudex, branches becoming rhizomatous. **Stems** erect or nearly so, 1–7(–10) cm underground, becoming abruptly stouter on emergence, clump-forming at irregular intervals along subterranean rhizome, gray-strigulose to pilosulous. **Leaves** (4–)6–16 cm; stipules 3–10(–12) mm, membranous throughout or herbaceous at distal nodes; leaflet blades ovate, obovate, rhombic-ovate, obovate-cuneate, broadly elliptic, or suborbiculate, 5–18(–23) mm, apex obtuse or shallowly retuse, surfaces strigulose-pilosulous. **Peduncles** erect, 4.5–10(–14) cm. **Racemes** (12–)15–45-flowered; axis (3–)5–20(–30) cm in fruit; bracts 2.5–6 mm; bracteoles 2. **Pedicels** 0.6–2.8 mm. **Flowers** 12.5–17.5(–18) mm; calyx 6–8.8 mm, densely hirsutulous, tube 5–7.5 mm, lobes deltate or subulate, 1–2 mm; corolla whitish and suffused, veined, or tipped with purple; keel 10.4–15.4(–16.5) mm. **Legumes** green, sometimes purplish, usually red-mottled, (20–)30–65 × 3.5–8 mm, fleshy becoming leathery, villosulous. $2n = 44$.

Flowering Mar–May. Sandy flats, washes and gentle slopes or outwash fans in foothills of desert mountains; 400–1600 m; Ariz., Calif., Nev.

Astragalus layneae, named for Katharine Layne Brandegee, western American botanist, is the only extensively rhizomatous *Astragalus* in the Mojave Desert; however, the rhizomes are rarely collected. This is one of the few North American *Astragalus* with a reported tetraploid chromosome number ($x = 22$), and this with meiotic abnormalities in at least one population (R. Spellenberg 1976).

135iii. Astragalus Linnaeus sect. Mollissimi A. Gray, Proc. Amer. Acad. Arts 6: 195. 1864

Herbs perennial, tuft- or clump-forming, acaulescent or caulescent; caudex superficial. **Pubescence** copious and commonly villous-tomentose, with shorter, usually curly, and longer spirally twisted hairs, usually turning rusty brown on drying. **Hairs** basifixed. **Stems** obsolete, single, or few to several. **Stipules** distinct. **Leaves** odd-pinnate, petiolate; leaflets (9 or)11–35. **Racemes** initially densely flowered, flowers spreading or ascending. **Calyx tubes** cylindric or deeply campanulate. **Corollas** purple, pinkish, pink-purple, yellowish suffused with lilac, or ochroleucous, banner recurved through 30°, keel apex round or triangular. **Legumes** deciduous, sessile, spreading or ascending, (usually humistrate), obliquely ovoid, lanceoloid-ellipsoid, or linear-oblong, straight or incurved, terete to obcompressed, bilocular. **Seeds** 12–38[–41].

Species 3 (2 in the flora): c, sw United States, n Mexico.

Section *Mollissimi* consists of three monospecific subsections: subsect. *Mollissimi* (A. Gray Barneby (*Astragalus mollissimus*); subsect. *Nutriosenses* S. L. Welsh (*A. nutriosensis*); and subsect. *Orthanthi* Barneby (*A. helleri* Fenzl). The last occurs only in Mexico.

234. Astragalus mollissimus Torrey, Ann. Lyceum Nat. Hist. New York 2: 178. 1827 • Woolly locoweed F

Plants densely or loosely tuft-forming, acaulescent to subacaulescent or shortly caulescent, (6–)10–30(–45) cm, villous-tomentose. **Stems** usually few or several, sometimes single, decumbent to ascending, when developed, with several, short internodes, to 2 cm, villous-tomentose. **Leaves** (2–)5–32 cm; stipules (3–)4–20 mm; leaflets (9 or)11–35, blades elliptic, suborbiculate, ovate, obovate, rhombic-elliptic, rhombic-obovate, rhombic-ovate, oblong-elliptic, oblanceolate, or oval, (2–)3–30 (–45) mm, apex acute, obtuse, retuse, or subacute, surfaces villous-tomentose, sometimes densely so. **Peduncles** ascending, (1.5–)2.5–24 cm. **Racemes** (5–)7–45-flowered; axis (0.5–)1–18 cm in fruit; bracts 2.5–10(–12) mm; bracteoles 0(–2). **Pedicels** 0.5–3 mm. **Flowers** 11.8–25 mm; calyx cylindric to deeply campanulate, 6.8–15.5 mm, villous-tomentose, tube (4.5–)5–13 mm, lobes lanceolate to subulate or subulate-setaceous, 1.6–5.5(–6.8) mm; corolla pink-purple, pale purple, pinkish, cream, or yellowish suffused with dull lavender, or tipped and suffused or margined with dull purple; keel 9–20.5 mm. **Legumes** spreading or ascending, ± straight to incurved through 0.25+ spiral, oblong-ellipsoid, lanceoloid-ellipsoid, ovoid, or ovoid-ellipsoid, sometimes decidedly inflated (not bladdery), terete when narrow, obcompressed when broad, (6–)9–24 × (3–)4–13 mm, fleshy, stiffly papery, leathery, or subligneous, glabrous, puberulent, hispidulous, villosulous, villous-hirsute, villous-tomentulose, or villous-tomentose; beaks sometimes unilocular. **Seeds** 12–38[–41]. $2n = 22$.

Varieties 10 (8 in the flora): w United States, Mexico.

The *Astragalus mollissimus* complex has been variously interpreted as belonging to several species, or has been combined in varietal status under one or more species, or has been split into species each with segregate varieties, and with peripheral taxa still represented at specific rank (D. Isely 1998). Isely (1983) recognized three species within the complex, restricting *A. mollissimus* to those phases with glabrous or sparsely puberulent fruits, *A. bigelovii* to the bulk of the remainder with shaggy-hairy fruits, and with *A. thompsoniae* (whose fruit has a unilocular beak) standing by itself, remote from the remainder of *A. bigelovii* in the broad sense. Two varieties are exclusive to Mexico: var. *irolanus* (M. E. Jones) Barneby occurs from Durango and Nuevo León southward to Puebla, and var. *nitens* Barneby is known from Coahuila. The present treatment follows R. C. Barneby (1964). Some of the varieties, possibly all, are poisonous to domestic livestock, especially to horses (N. Ritter 1917; L. F. James and S. L. Welsh 1992; M. H. Ralphs et al. 2002).

1. Legumes glabrous or sparsely pubescent (hispidulous, villous-tomentose, or loosely strigulose).
   2. Corollas cream, immaculate; Edwards Plateau, Texas . . . . 234b. *Astragalus mollissimus* var. *coryi*
   2. Corollas pinkish, pink-purple, pure pale yellow or yellowish suffused with dull lavender, or tipped and suffused or margined with dull purple; not of Edwards Plateau, Texas.
      3. Calyx tubes 3.4–4.5 mm wide; plains from Nebraska to New Mexico and w Texas . . . 234a. *Astragalus mollissimus* var. *mollissimus*
      3. Calyx tubes 0.8–3(–3.2) mm wide; se New Mexico, trans-Pecos Texas, southward . . . . 234c. *Astragalus mollissimus* var. *earlei*
1. Legumes densely pubescent (villous-tomentose, villous-hirsute, or villous-tomentulose).
   4. Racemes (5–)7–12-flowered; peduncles (1.5–)2.5–8 cm; legumes broadly ovoid, 7–13 mm wide; e Arizona (Apache County), nw New Mexico (Santa Fe to McKinley County). . . . . 234g. *Astragalus mollissimus* var. *matthewsii*
   4. Racemes 7–45-flowered; peduncles 2.5–24 cm; legumes ovoid, lunately ellipsoid, or lanceoloid-ellipsoid, 3–8(–11) mm wide; Arizona, Colorado, Idaho, Nevada, New Mexico, Texas, Utah.
      5. Legumes ovoid, turgid, 6–11 mm wide, beaks unilocular; Arizona and New Mexico northward to Idaho . . . . 234h. *Astragalus mollissimus* var. *thompsoniae*
      5. Legumes ovoid, lunately ellipsoid or lanceoloid-ellipsoid, usually solid, rarely slightly turgid, 3–8 mm wide, beaks bilocular; Arizona, New Mexico, Texas.
         6. Plants acaulescent; calyces 6.8–9.9 mm; banners 11.8–16.3 mm, keel 10.3–12.5 mm; legumes 6–10 mm; seeds 12–16; trans-Pecos Texas (Presidio and Jeff Davis counties) . . . . 234e. *Astragalus mollissimus* var. *marcidus*
         6. Plants acaulescent or shortly caulescent; calyces 10–15.3 mm; banners 16–22.5 mm, keel 12.3–18.6 mm; legumes 9–15 mm; seeds 19–31; Arizona, New Mexico, Texas.

[7. Shifted to left margin.—Ed.]

7. Plants usually robust, shortly caulescent, stems (0 or)3–17 cm; leaves 9–26 cm, leaflet blades 6–25 mm; keel 13.5–18.5 mm; legume hairs to 1–1.6 mm; se Arizona to extreme w Texas; 1200–1900(–2300) m . . . . 234d. *Astragalus mollissimus* var. *bigelovii*
7. Plants usually dwarf, acaulescent; stems reduced to thick crowns; leaves (4–)6–16 cm, leaflet blades 3–13 mm; keel 12.5–14.5 mm; legume hairs to 1.6–2.6 mm; plateaus of n Arizona and wc New Mexico, on and near Mogollon Escarpment or north; 1800–2300 m . . . . 234f. *Astragalus mollissimus* var. *mogollonicus*

234a. Astragalus mollissimus Torrey var. **mollissimus** E F

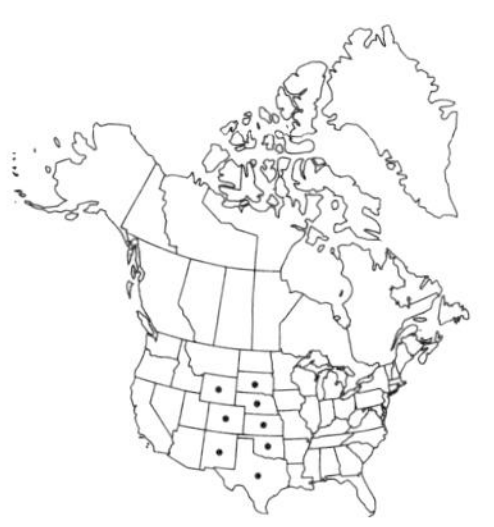

Plants usually shortly caulescent, sometimes subacaulescent, to 45 cm. **Stems** 1.5–18 cm, internodes to 4 cm or obscured by imbricate stipules. **Leaves** (7–)10–20(–25) cm; stipules (5–)7–17 mm; leaflets 15–27(–33), blades usually oval, ovate, or obovate, sometimes rhombic-elliptic, 5–22 mm. **Peduncles** 6–23 cm. **Racemes** (10–)15–40-flowered; axis elongating, (2–)4–17 cm in fruit. **Flowers:** calyx (8.8–)10.5–14 mm, tube 6.8–9.5 × 3.4–4.5 mm, lobes (2–)3–5 mm; corolla pinkish, pink-purple, pale yellow, or yellowish suffused with dull lavender; banner (16–)17.5–21.5 mm; keel 14–18 mm. **Legumes** shallowly crescentic or abruptly incurved near middle through ± 90°, contracted distally, narrowly oblong-ellipsoid to lanceoloid-ellipsoid, 14–24 × 4–7 mm, mostly glabrous and apex usually puberulent or hispidulous, rarely puberulent, sometimes shortly villosulous throughout; beak unilocular. **Seeds** 26–37. $2n = 22$.

Flowering Apr–Jul. Prairies, plains, valley floors, stony mesas, and fallow fields on alluvial loams, loess, on outcrops of shale, limestone, or sandstone, most abundant where vegetation is low and sparse; 500–1900 m; Colo., Kans., Nebr., N.Mex., Okla., S.Dak., Tex., Wyo.

Flowers of var. *mollissimus* are normally dull purplish, but in some New Mexico populations they are a pure pale yellow, the basis of forma *flavus* McGregor.

234b. Astragalus mollissimus Torrey var. **coryi** Tidestrom, Proc. Biol. Soc. Wash. 50: 21. 1937 • Cory's woolly locoweed [E]

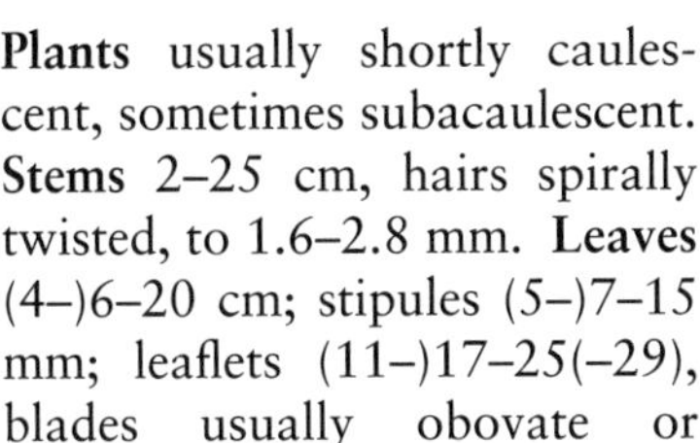

Astragalus argillophilus Cory, Rhodora 32: 5. 1930

Plants usually shortly caulescent, sometimes subacaulescent. **Stems** 2–25 cm, hairs spirally twisted, to 1.6–2.8 mm. **Leaves** (4–)6–20 cm; stipules (5–)7–15 mm; leaflets (11–)17–25(–29), blades usually obovate or oblong-oval, sometimes rhombic-obovate, 5–18 mm. **Peduncles** 8–21 cm. **Racemes** densely 15–45-flowered; axis 3.5–9 cm in fruit. **Flowers:** calyx 10.5–14 mm, tube 7–8.7 × 3–4 mm, lobes (3.3–)3.7–5.5 mm; corolla cream; banner (14.4–)15–20.3 mm; keel 12–17.4 mm. **Legumes** narrowly ovoid or oblong-ellipsoid, 10–17 × 4.5–7 mm, glabrous or sparsely hispidulous (distally); beak unilocular.

Flowering Mar–May. Calcareous clay flats and depressions on rolling plains; 500–1000 m; Tex.

Variety *coryi* is locally abundant on the northwestern Edwards Plateau in Crockett, Howard, Irion, Martin, Reagan, Schleicher, Sterling, and Upton counties.

234c. Astragalus mollissimus Torrey var. **earlei** (Greene ex Rydberg) Tidestrom, Proc. Biol. Soc. Wash. 48: 40. 1935 • Earle's woolly locoweed [W]

Astragalus earlei Greene ex Rydberg in N. L. Britton et al., N. Amer. Fl. 24: 444. 1929

Plants subacaulescent or shortly caulescent. **Stems** to 10(–16) cm. **Leaves** 8–32 cm; stipules 5–15 mm; leaflets 19–35, blades oblanceolate, rhombic-ovate, or rhombic-obovate, (5–)10–30(–45) mm. **Peduncles** (5–)8–17 cm. **Racemes** 15–36-flowered; axis elongating, 4–15 cm in fruit. **Flowers:** calyx (8.5–)8.8–10.5 mm, tube (4.5–)5–7 × 0.8–3 (–3.2) mm, lobes 2.4–4 mm; corolla pink-purple or yellowish tipped and suffused or margined with dull purple; banner 12–17.5 mm; keel 9–13 mm. **Legumes** ± incurved, abruptly contracted distally, obliquely ovoid-ellipsoid or lanceoloid-ellipsoid, 9–14 × 4–6.5 (–9) mm, usually sparsely villous-tomentulose or loosely strigulose, rarely glabrate or glabrous, hairs ascending and almost straight, or subappressed and curly, less than 1 mm; beak bilocular. **Seeds** 20–30. **2*n*** = 22, 24.

Flowering Mar–Jun. Dry hills and grassy plains, on volcanic and calcareous soils; 1100–1800 m; N.Mex., Tex.; Mexico (Chihuahua).

Within the flora area, var. *earlei* is a plant common in the trans-Pecos region of Texas and southeastern New Mexico.

234d. Astragalus mollissimus Torrey var. **bigelovii** (A. Gray) Barneby, Mem. New York Bot. Gard. 13: 742. 1964 • Bigelow's woolly locoweed [E]

Astragalus bigelovii A. Gray, Smithsonian Contr. Knowl. 5(6): 42. 1853

Plants shortly caulescent, robust. **Stems** (0 or)3–17 cm. **Leaves** 9–26 cm; stipules 6–20 mm; leaflets (13–)19–27, blades ovate, obovate, oval, or broadly elliptic, 6–25 mm. **Peduncles** (5–)8–22 cm. **Racemes** somewhat densely (15–)20–45-flowered, flowers subcontiguous or interrupted proximally; axis (4–)5–11 cm in fruit. **Flowers:** calyx 10.5–13.5 cm, tube (8–)8.3–10.3 × (3.2–)4–5.2 mm, lobes (1.7–)2.6–4.4 mm; corolla pink-purple; banner 17–22.5 mm; keel 13.5–18.5 mm. **Legumes** gently incurved or ± straight, ovoid-acuminate or lanceoloid-ellipsoid, sometimes slightly turgid, 10–15 × (4–)4.5–8 mm, stiffly papery or leathery, densely villous-tomentulose, hairs to 1–1.6 mm; beak bilocular. **Seeds** 20–31. **2*n*** = 22.

Flowering (Jan–)Mar–Jun. Dry plains and foothills, in desert- or mesquite-grasslands, among junipers, on calcareous soils, sandy loams, basalt gravel, over-grazed and badly eroded cattle ranges; 1200–1900(–2300) m; Ariz., N.Mex., Tex.

Variety *bigelovii* is known from extreme western Texas to southeastern Arizona and in New Mexico as far north as Socorro County and the Plains of San Augustin in Catron County.

D. Isely (1998) recognized var. *bigelovii* at the species level, and included with it vars. *marcidus*, *matthewsii*, and *mogollonicus*, primarily on the basis of the completely bilocular fruits.

234e. Astragalus mollissimus Torrey var. **marcidus** (Greene ex Rydberg) Barneby, Mem. New York Bot. Gard. 13: 743. 1964 • Davis Mountains locoweed [C] [E]

Astragalus marcidus Greene ex Rydberg in N. L. Britton et al., N. Amer. Fl. 24: 446. 1929; *A. bigelovii* A. Gray var. *marcidus* (Greene ex Rydberg) Isely

Plants acaulescent or subacaulescent. **Stems** reduced to crowns. **Leaves** 5–15 cm; leaflets 15–19(or 21), blades ovate, obovate, or broadly elliptic, 4–15(–20) mm. **Peduncles** 3.5–11 cm. **Racemes** 10–45-flowered; axis 3–10 cm in fruit. **Flowers:** calyx 6.8–9.9 mm, tube 5.2–6.4 × 2.8–3.5 mm, lobes 1.6–3.5 mm; corolla pink-purple; banner 11.8–16.3; keel 10.3–12.5 mm. **Legumes** ovoid-acuminate to lanceolate-ellipsoid, usually solid, rarely slightly turgid, 6–10 × 3–5 mm, villous-hirsute, hairs 1+ mm; beak bilocular. **Seeds** 12–16.

Flowering Apr–Jul. Open gravelly hillsides and rocky stream beds, on volcanic soils; of conservation concern; 1500–2000 m; Tex.

Variety *marcidus* is known from Jeff Davis and Presidio counties of the trans-Pecos region.

234f. Astragalus mollissimus Torrey var. **mogollonicus** (Greene) Barneby, Mem. New York Bot. Gard. 13: 745. 1964 • Mogollon woolly locoweed [E]

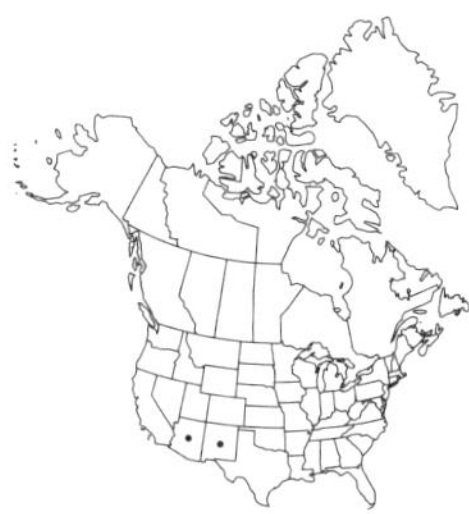

Astragalus mogollonicus Greene, Bull. Torrey Bot. Club 8: 97. 1881; *A. bigelovii* A. Gray var. *mogollonicus* (Greene) Barneby

Plants acaulescent, usually dwarf. **Stems** reduced to thick crowns, closely invested with stipules. **Leaves** (4–)6–16 cm; stipules 5–12 mm; leaflets (9–)13–23, blades broadly elliptic to suborbiculate, 3–13 mm. **Peduncles** scapiform, 4–10 cm. **Racemes** densely 12–32-flowered; axis 1.5–6 cm in fruit. **Flowers:** calyx 10–15.3 mm, tube 6.6–8.5 × 3.2–5 mm, lobes 3.3–6.8 mm; corolla pink-purple; banner 16–21.5 mm; keel 12.5–14.5 mm. **Legumes** ± straight to gently incurved, narrowly ovoid or lunately ellipsoid, 9–13 × 4.5–6 mm, densely villous-tomentose, hairs to 1.6–2.6 mm; beak bilocular. **Seeds** 19–28.

Flowering Apr–Jul. Stony flats and hilltops, on pebbly, volcanic soils of open ponderosa pine forests, on limestone substrates, rocky knolls in pinyon-juniper belt; 1800–2300 m; Ariz., N.Mex.

D. Isely (1998) viewed var. *mogollonicus* as a reduced phase of var. *bigelovii*, but var. *mogollonicus* is distinguished by its acaulescent growth habit and scapiform peduncles. It occurs from the Kaibab Plateau south of the Grand Canyon in Arizona to the southeast along the Mogollon Escarpment to western New Mexico.

234g. Astragalus mollissimus Torrey var. **matthewsii** (S. Watson) Barneby, Mem. New York Bot. Gard. 13: 746. 1964 • Matthews woolly locoweed [E]

Astragalus matthewsii S. Watson, Proc. Amer. Acad. Arts 18: 192. 1883; *A. bigelovii* A. Gray var. *matthewsii* (S. Watson) M. E. Jones

Plants acaulescent or subacaulescent. **Stems** to 1.5 cm, obscured by imbricate stipules. **Leaves** (3–)5–12 cm; stipules (3–)4–8 mm; leaflets 11–23, blades obovate, 3–12 mm. **Peduncles** scapiform, (1.5–)2.5–8 cm. **Racemes** (5–)7–12-flowered; axis (0.5–)1–4.5 cm in fruit, not or scarcely surpassing foliage. **Flowers:** calyx 10–13 mm, tube 7–8.6 × 3.4–4.7 mm, lobes 2.4–5.2 mm; corolla pale purple; banner 18.5–22.5 mm; keel 14.2–18 mm. **Legumes** gently or abruptly incurved distally, broadly ovoid, turgid, 12–18 × 7–13 mm, widest near obtuse or truncate base, densely villous-tomentose; beak bilocular. **Seeds** 24–31.

Flowering Apr–Jun. Open slopes and hilltops, in ponderosa pine forests, along canyons to juniper-pinyon belt, on light, sandy or gravelly, sedimentary, granitic, or volcanic soils; 1900–2600 m; Ariz., N.Mex.

Variety *matthewsii* is scattered and uncommon in Apache County in eastern Arizona and from Santa Fe to McKinley counties in the mountains of north-central and northwestern New Mexico.

234h. Astragalus mollissimus Torrey var. **thompsoniae** (S. Watson) Barneby, Mem. New York Bot. Gard. 13: 747. 1964 (as thompsonae) • Thompson's woolly locoweed [E]

Astragalus thompsoniae S. Watson, Proc. Amer. Acad. Arts 10: 345. 1875 (as thompsonae)

Plants acaulescent, 6–45 cm, from caudex. **Stems** mostly obscured by stipules. **Leaves** 2–28 cm; stipules 4–13 mm; leaflets 15–35, blades obovate to suborbiculate or elliptic, 2–18 mm. **Peduncles** 2.5–24 cm. **Racemes** 7–25-flowered; axis 1.5–18 cm in fruit. **Flowers:** calyx 11–15.5 mm, tube 7.7–13 mm, lobes 2–4.2 mm; corolla pink-purple; banner 18–25 mm; keel 15–18.5(–20.5) mm. **Legumes**

curved, ovoid, turgid, 11–23 × 6–11 mm, densely villous-tomentose; beak unilocular. **Seeds** 28–38.

Flowering Mar–Jun (Oct). Salt desert shrub, mixed desert shrub, grasslands, and pinyon-juniper communities, usually on sandy substrates; (700–)1100–2400 m; Ariz., Colo., Idaho, Nev., N.Mex., Utah.

Variety *thompsoniae* is transitional with var. *matthewsii* in northwestern New Mexico.

235. Astragalus nutriosensis M. J. Sanderson, Madroño 35: 325, fig. 1. 1989 • Nutrioso milkvetch [E]

Plants dwarf, clump-forming, acaulescent, 3–11 cm, pilose to strigulose. **Stems** obsolete. **Leaves** 3–11 cm; stipules 3–9 mm; leaflets 11–19, blades obovate or elliptic, 4–8 mm, apex acute or obtuse, surfaces hairy abaxially, glabrescent adaxially. **Peduncles** (0–)1–2(–5) cm. **Racemes** (1 or)2–5(–7)-flowered; axis to 0.6 cm in fruit; bracts 2–5 mm; bracteoles 0. **Pedicels** 2–4 mm. **Flowers** 20–23 mm; calyx cylindric, 11–14 mm, pilose; corolla white to lavender-pink or veined pink-purple, keel tip lavender-pink. **Legumes** ascending, brownish gray, ± straight, semi-ellipsoid, subterete to slightly obcompressed, 8–10 × 6–8 mm, thin and papery, pilose. **Seeds** 20.

Flowering May–Jun. Volcanic silt-clay soils on gently sloping hillsides, with juniper, blue grama and matchweed; 2200–2400 m; Ariz., N.Mex.

Astragalus nutriosensis is known from the border region between Arizona and New Mexico in Apache and Catron counties, respectively. It is still relatively poorly known and may ultimately be placed outside sect. *Mollissimi*.

135jjj. ASTRAGALUS Linnaeus sect. GIGANTEI Barneby, Mem. New York Bot. Gard. 13: 749. 1964

Herbs perennial, caulescent; caudex superficial. **Hairs** basifixed, pilose and tomentulose. **Stems** single or few. **Stipules** distinct. **Leaves** odd-pinnate, petiolate; leaflets 17–35. **Racemes** densely flowered, flowers initially horizontal, later declined. **Calyx tubes** deeply campanulate or subcylindric. **Corollas** pale yellow, banner recurved through 45°, keel apex obtuse. **Legumes** persistent, sessile, erect, plumply ovoid- or ellipsoid-acuminate, swollen but somewhat obcompressed, slightly incurved, ± bilocular. **Seeds** 28–45.

Species 1: sw United States, n Mexico.

236. Astragalus giganteus S. Watson, Proc. Amer. Acad. Arts 17: 370. 1882 • Giant milkvetch

Plants robust, (7–)20–60 cm; taproot coarse, woody. **Stems** erect or stiffly ascending, stout, with 5–10 well-developed internodes, pilose and tomentulose. **Leaves** (9–)13–35 cm; stipules distinct 6–17 mm, herbaceous; leaflet blades broadly to narrowly elliptic, ovate, oblong-elliptic, or rhombic-elliptic, (7–)10–55 mm, apex acute or abruptly short-acuminate, often callous-apiculate, surfaces pilose and tomentulose. **Peduncles** erect, (8–)10–27 cm, together with racemes shorter than stems. **Racemes** (15–)20–55(–65)-flowered; axis (3–)5–20(–24) cm in fruit; bracts 2–6 mm; bracteoles 0. **Pedicels** (1.2–)1.5–9 mm. **Flowers** (14.4–)15.5–22 mm; calyx (7.8–)10–14.7 mm, silky-pilose or tomentulose, tube (6–)7–8.7 mm, lobes lanceolate-acuminate or linear-lanceolate, 3–6.5 mm; corolla immaculate; keel (11.5–)12–15.1 mm. **Legumes** stiffly erect, becoming brownish stramineous then blackish, 15–25 × 8–13 mm, fleshy becoming leathery, glabrous. $2n = 22$.

Flowering (mid May–)Jun–Sep. Gravel bars, stream banks, in pine or oak forests, on open, moist, grassy banks, hillsides, weedy roadsides, on volcanic or granitic soils, apparently not on limestone substrates; 1800–2500 m; N.Mex., Tex.; Mexico (Chihuahua).

Astragalus giganteus may have the largest leaves of any North American *Astragalus* (D. Isely 1998). It occurs in the mountains of south-central New Mexico, western Texas, and western Chihuahua, Mexico.

135kkk. Astragalus Linnaeus sect. Sarcocarpi A. Gray, Proc. Amer. Acad. Arts 6: 192. 1864

Herbs perennial, caulescent; caudex usually subterranean, sometimes superficial; taproot woody. **Hairs** basifixed. **Stems** single or few to several. **Stipules** distinct or connate at proximal nodes. **Leaves** odd-pinnate, petiolate to subsessile; leaflets (11–)15–33. **Racemes** loosely flowered, flowers ascending to spreading. **Calyx tubes** campanulate or cylindric. **Corollas** usually red- or lilac-purple, pink-purple, or white with maculate keel apex, banner recurved through 40–45°, keel apex obtuse. **Legumes** deciduous, at least eventually, sessile, spreading or ascending, humistrate, usually straight, rarely incurved, broadly ovoid, globose, subglobose, or oblong-cylindroid or -ellipsoid, terete or ± obcompressed, bilocular. **Seeds** 26–77.

Species 5 (4 in the flora): c, w North America, n Mexico.

Section *Sarcocarpi* consists of two subsections: subsect. *Sarcocarpi* (A. Gray) Barneby with the four species in the flora area and subsect. *Sanguinei* Barneby only in Mexico.

237. Astragalus crassicarpus Nuttall, Cat. Pl. Upper Louisiana, no. 6. 1813 • Common groundplum, buffalo bean [E] [F]

Geoprumnon crassicarpum (Nuttall) Rydberg

Plants (5–)10–50(–60) cm, pubescent; from subterranean or superficial, woody caudex or root-crown, caudex determinate, shortly forking (except var. *berlandieri*). **Stems** ascending or decumbent, 1–9 cm underground, sparsely strigulose. **Leaves** (2–)3.5–18 cm; stipules distinct, 3–10 mm, submembranous, glabrous abaxially; petiolate or subsessile; leaflets (11–)15–33, blades oblanceolate, oblong-oblanceolate, obovate, suborbiculate, or broadly oval to linear-elliptic, (2–)3–24 mm, apex obtuse, acute, subacute, or truncate-emarginate, sometimes apiculate, surfaces pubescent abaxially, glabrous or glabrescent adaxially. **Peduncles** ascending to spreading, (1.5–)2–16 cm. **Racemes** (5–)6–25(–35)-flowered, flowers ascending or slightly arched; axis 1–7(–14) cm in fruit; bracts 2.5–7.5 mm; bracteoles 0–2. **Pedicels** 2–7.5 mm. **Flowers** (16–)16.5–25(–27) mm; calyx usually broadly or deeply campanulate or cylindro-campanulate, rarely cylindric, (6.6–)7.7–14 mm, densely strigulose, pilosulous, ascending-pilose, or villosulous-tomentulose, tube (5.2–)5.6–9.7 mm, lobes subulate or triangular-subulate, (1.3–)1.7–4.2(–5.8) mm; corolla pink-purple, red-purple, white, whitish (faintly lilac-tinged), lilac, ochroleucous, or suffused pinkish lilac; keel (10.7–)12–20.7 mm. **Legumes** green, often red-mottled or suffused with red on adaxial surface, becoming brown or blackish, straight, globose, subglobose, broadly and plumply oblong-ellipsoid, oblong-ovoid, or oblong-obovoid, ± obcompressed, 15–40 × 12–27 mm, fleshy becoming alveolate-spongy or pithy, wrinkled on drying, mesocarp at least 1.2 mm thick, glabrous. **Seeds** 34–77.

Varieties 5 (5 in the flora): w, c North America.

The fleshy fruits of *Astragalus crassicarpus* are burnished with red or purple and resemble small plums prior to maturity. Early travelers valued the immature fruits as a summer vegetable. Ultimately, the surface collapses as the mesocarp dries. The fruits are frequently broader than long (S. L. Welsh 1960).

1. Calyces usually densely villosulous-tomentulose, hairs entangled, cream or brownish; corollas usually ochroleucous or suffused with pinkish lilac; racemes 13–25-flowered; peduncles 6–16 cm; stems usually ascending, rarely decumbent, (2.5–)3.5–6 cm; legumes 25–32 mm . . . . 237e. *Astragalus crassicarpus* var. *trichocalyx*
1. Calyces strigulose, pilosulous, or ascending-pilose, hairs mixed black and white or all black; corollas pink- or red-purple, lilac, or whitish; racemes (5–)6–23(–35)-flowered; peduncles (1.5–)2–9(–11) cm; stems usually decumbent (sometimes ascending in var. *cavus*), 5–40(–50) cm; legumes 15–40 mm.
    2. Stems arising singly or few from subterranean caudex, branches creeping, forming loose mats or colonial; seeds 34–50; Balcones Escarpment and vicinity, c, e Texas . . . . 237d. *Astragalus crassicarpus* var. *berlandieri*
    2. Stems clustered from root-crown or superficial or subterranean caudex, not forming mats or colonial, caudex determinate; seeds 38–68; Alberta to Arizona eastward to Oklahoma panhandle.
        3. Corollas pink- or red-purple; herbage bright green (under vestiture) . . . . 237a. *Astragalus crassicarpus* var. *crassicarpus*
        3. Corollas white or whitish and faintly lilac-tinged; herbage pallid green or yellowish.

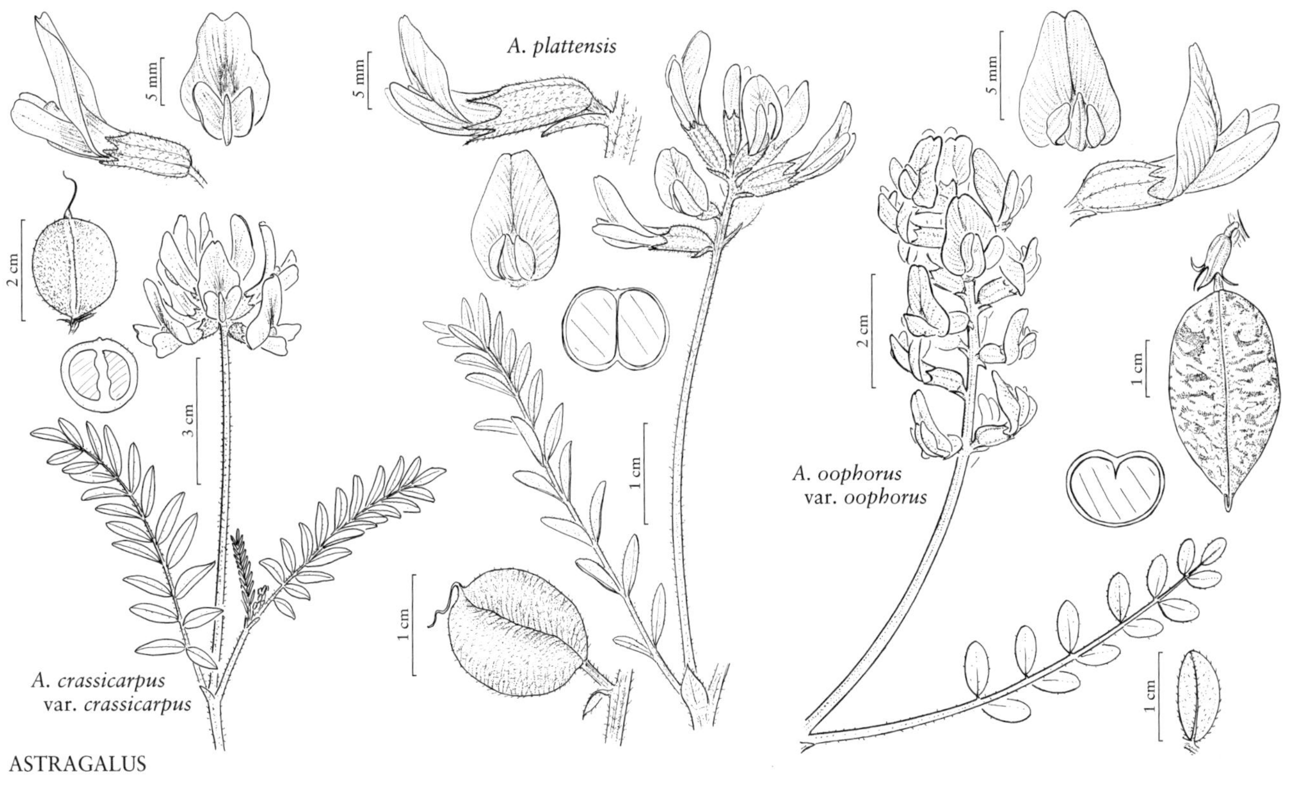

ASTRAGALUS

[4. Shifted to left margin.—Ed.]

4. Legumes globose or plumply ovoid-oblong or obovoid-oblong; Alberta southward to Oklahoma panhandle and adjacent New Mexico .237b. *Astragalus crassicarpus* var. *paysonii*
4. Legumes broadly and plumply oblong-ovoid, oblong-obovoid, or subglobose; ec Arizona, c New Mexico. . . . . 237c. *Astragalus crassicarpus* var. *cavus*

237a. Astragalus crassicarpus Nuttall var. **crassicarpus** E F

Astragalus caryocarpus Ker Gawler

Herbage bright green (under vestiture). **Stems** clustered from root-crown or subterranean to superficial caudex, decumbent (with ascending tips), (8)10–40 (–50) cm. **Leaves** 3.5–13(–18) cm; leaflets (11–)15–29(–31), blades oblanceolate, elliptic, oblong-elliptic, narrowly obovate-cuneate, obovate or suborbiculate, 3–19(–22) mm, apex acute or obtuse. **Peduncles** (1.5–)2–6(–10) cm. **Racemes** (5–)7–15(–35)-flowered; axis 1–3.5(–14) cm in fruit. **Pedicels** 2.7–4.5 mm. **Flowers:** calyx (6.7–)7.7–11.3(–14) mm, strigulose, pilosulous, or ascending-pilose, hairs mixed black and white or all black, tube (5.2–)5.8–7.8(–8.6) mm, lobes (1.3–)1.7–4.2(–5.8) mm; corolla pink- or blue-purple; banner (16–)16.5–23.5(–25) × (7–)8–12.5 mm. **Legumes** globose or plumply ovoid-oblong or obovoid-oblong, 15–27 × 12–25 mm. **Seeds** 52–68. $2n = 22$.

Flowering Mar–Jul. Prairies, rolling plains, old pastures, roadsides, railroad rights-of-way, on calcareous stony hillsides, in open oak thickets; 200–1200 (–1800) m; Alta., B.C., Man., Sask.; Ark., Colo., Iowa, Kans., Minn., Mo., Mont., Nebr., N.Mex., N.Dak., Okla., S.Dak., Tex., Wis., Wyo.

Diversity in the widely distributed var. *crassicarpus* was discussed in detail by R. C. Barneby (1964). The plants in fruit, with the upper side suffused with red or red-purple, are truly beautiful and remarkable, supporting in their very appearance the designation of groundplum. The legumes vary from globose to ellipsoid or quadrate, but the apex in all cases is abruptly acuminate. The legumes are frequently broader than long (S. L. Welsh 1960). This is truly a plant of the prairies and plains of low to moderate elevations, a component of shortgrass to tallgrass prairies, whose total extent has been impacted by development of much of its habitat for growth of grains mainly.

237b. Astragalus crassicarpus Nuttall var. **paysonii** (E. H. Kelso) Barneby, Amer. Midl. Naturalist 55: 497. 1956 (as paysoni) • Mountain groundplum [E]

Astragalus succulentus Richardson var. *paysonii* E. H. Kelso, Rhodora 39: 151. 1937 (as paysoni)

Herbage pallid or yellowish. **Stems** clustered from root-crown or subterranean to superficial caudex, decumbent, (5–)10–35 cm. **Leaves** (2–)4–11(–16) cm; leaflets 15–25, blades obovate-cuneate, oval, or oblanceolate, 4–16 mm, apex usually obtuse or acute, rarely truncate-emarginate. **Peduncles** (1.5–)2–6.5(–8) cm. **Racemes** (5–)8–20-flowered; axis (1–)2–7 cm in fruit. **Pedicels** (2–)2.8–5.5 mm. **Flowers:** calyx 9.6–14 mm, strigulose, pilosulous, or ascending-pilose, hairs mixed black and white or all black, tube 7–9.7 mm, lobes (1.9–)2.3–4(–4.4) mm; corolla white; banner (18.3–)20–24 × (8.6–)9–12 mm. **Legumes** globose or plumply ovoid-oblong or obovoid-oblong, 15–27 × 12–25 mm. **Seeds** (40–)47–59. **2*n*** = 22.

Flowering Apr–Jul. Prairies, grassy hillsides, open knolls, on granite, shale, sandstone, or limestone, with sagebrush; 1000–2700 m; Colo., Mont., Nebr., N.Mex., Okla., S.Dak., Wyo.

Variety *paysonii*, not sharply demarcated from var. *crassicarpus*, is a plant of lower elevations along the eastern slope and valleys of the Rocky Mountain chain from southwestern Montana southward to the Oklahoma panhandle and adjacent New Mexico.

237c. Astragalus crassicarpus Nuttall var. **cavus** Barneby, Mem. New York Bot. Gard. 13: 759. 1964 • Hollow groundplum [E]

Herbage pallid green or yellowish. **Stems** clustered from root-crown or subterranean to superficial caudex, decumbent and ascending, 5–30 cm, sometimes short, closely tuft-forming, elongating as fruit matures. **Leaves** (4–)5–15 cm; leaflets (13–)17–31(or 33), blades broadly to narrowly elliptic, oblong-oblanceolate, or obovate, (2–)4–17 mm, apex obtuse or subacute, sometimes callous-apiculate. **Peduncles** 2–9(–11) cm. **Racemes** 10–23(–30)-flowered; axis (1–)1.5–7(–9) cm in fruit. **Pedicels** 2–4 mm. **Flowers:** calyx (8.6–)9.6–12.6 mm, strigulose, pilosulous, or ascending-pilose, hairs mixed black and white or all black, tube (6.3–)7.5–9.2 mm, lobes (1.9–)2.3–3.6 mm; corolla whitish (faintly lilac-tinged); banner 17–25 × (8.2–)9–14 mm. **Legumes** broadly and plumply oblong-ovoid, oblong-obovoid, or subglobose, 15–35(–40) × 12–25 mm. **Seeds** 38–51. **2*n*** = 22.

Flowering May–Jul. Arid sandy plains, dry stony meadows, gravelly banks, canyon benches, on granitic and various alluvial soils, in grasslands, juniper-pinyon forests; (1500–)1700–2400 m; Ariz., N.Mex.

Variety *cavus* is a xeric plant, more so than its prairie and foothills counterparts to the east and north. It occurs from central New Mexico to east-central Arizona.

237d. Astragalus crassicarpus Nuttall var. **berlandieri** Barneby, Amer. Midl. Naturalist 55: 498. 1956 • Berlandier's groundplum [E]

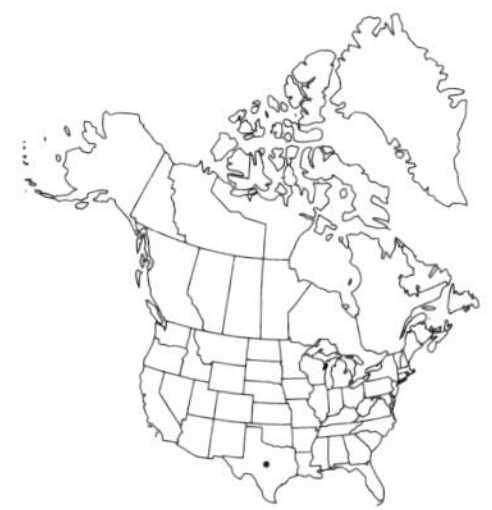

Astragalus mexicanus A. De Candolle, Mém. Soc. Phys. Genève 6: 224, plate 3. 1833

Herbage bright green (under vestiture). **Stems** single or few from subterranean caudex, branches widely creeping, forming loose mats or colonial, decumbent, 7–30 cm, usually quite slender, 1–15 cm underground. **Leaves** (2.5–)5–12(–14) cm; leaflets (15 or)17–29, blades narrowly elliptic to elliptic-obovate, (3–)5–18 mm, apex obtuse, obtuse and apiculate, or sometimes acute. **Peduncles** 3–8(–11) cm. **Racemes** 6–14-flowered; axis 1–4(–5) cm in fruit. **Pedicels** 2.8–4.5 mm. **Flowers:** calyx (7.5–)7.9–12.7 mm, strigulose, pilosulous, or ascending-pilose, hairs mixed black and white or all black, tube (5.3–)5.6–9.6 mm, lobes (2–)2.2–4 mm; corolla lilac or pink-purple; banner (18–)18.5–25(–27) × (6.5–)7–10(–11.2) mm. **Legumes** globose or broadly and plumply oblong-ovoid or oblong-obovoid, 20–40 × 17–27 mm. **Seeds** 34–50. **2*n*** = 22.

Flowering Mar–May. Hillsides and flats in oak thickets, on bluffs or prairies, on substrates overlying limestone or clays; 100–500 m; Tex.

Variety *berlandieri* is found from the southeastern edge of the Edwards Plateau eastward to the West Coastal Plain.

237e. Astragalus crassicarpus Nuttall var. **trichocalyx** (Nuttall) Barneby in H. A. Gleason, Ill. Fl. N.E. U.S. 2: 421. 1952 • Ozark groundplum [E]

Astragalus trichocalyx Nuttall in J. Torrey and A. Gray, Fl. N. Amer. 1: 332. 1838; *A. mexicanus* A. De Candolle var. *trichocalyx* (Nuttall) Fernald

Herbage green (or grayish in youth). **Stems** clustered from root-crown or subterranean to superficial caudex, usually ascending, rarely decumbent, usually coarse, rarely slender, fistulose, (2.5–)3.5–6 cm, mostly glabrous, sometimes glabrate basally. **Leaves** (5–)7–18 cm; leaflets 21–33, blades elliptic to broadly elliptic, lanceolate-elliptic, or lanceolate-oblong, (4–)7–24 mm, apex acute, subacute, obtuse, or truncate-emarginate. **Peduncles** 6–16 cm. **Racemes** 13–25-flowered. **Pedicels** 4–7.5 mm. **Flowers:** calyx (6.6–)8.3–11 mm, usually densely villosulous-tomentulose throughout, sometimes basally, hairs entangled, cream or brownish, tube pallid green, (5.2–)6–8.1 mm, lobes (1.4–)1.9–3.3 mm; corolla ochroleucous or suffused pinkish lilac; banner (16–)17.8–24.5 × 7.4–10.8 mm. **Legumes** broadly oblong-ellipsoid, plumply ovoid, plumply obovoid, or globose, 25–32 × 13.5–24 mm. **Seeds** 48–77. $2n = 22$.

Flowering Mar–Jul. Open rocky woodlands, edges of prairies and pastures, along roadsides; 150–500 m; Ark., Ill., Kans., La., Mo., Okla., Tex.

Variety *trichocalyx*, the easternmost variety of the species, is scattered but locally plentiful in the limestone regions of south-central Missouri into west-central Illinois, and southwestward across northwestern Arkansas and eastern Oklahoma to eastern Texas.

238. Astragalus bibullatus Barneby & E. L. Bridges, Brittonia 39: 359, fig. 1. 1987 • Limestone Glades groundplum [C] [E]

Plants 5–15 cm, strigulose; from shallow, subterranean caudex. **Stems** ascending and radiating, to 6(–9) cm underground, strigulose. **Leaves** 5–10 cm; stipules connate-sheathing at proximal nodes, distinct at distal nodes, (3–)5–11 mm, membranous; petiolate; leaflets 19–27, blades elliptic or elliptic-obovate, 7–16 mm, apex shallowly emarginate, surfaces sparsely strigose abaxially, glabrous or glabrescent adaxially. **Peduncles** ascending, 4.5–7.5 cm. **Racemes** 10–16-flowered, flowers ascending to spreading; axis 1–2 cm in fruit; bracts 6–10 mm; bracteoles 2. **Pedicels** 2–2.5 mm. **Flowers** 17–19 mm; calyx purplish, short-cylindric, 9–10.5 mm, sparsely pilosulous, tube 7–8.5 mm, lobes subulate, 2 mm; corolla bright pink-purple; keel 13–14 mm. **Legumes** pale green or reddish becoming stramineous suffused with brown-purple, straight, globose to plumply oblong-ellipsoid, terete or slightly dorsiventrally compressed, 14–26 × 12–16 mm, bilocular, somewhat fleshy, glabrous; valves differentiated into double envelope separated by air space 1.5–2 mm wide. **Seeds** 26–28.

Flowering Jun–Jul. Limestone juniper glades, edges of shrub thickets; of conservation concern; 200–300 m; Tenn.

Astragalus bibullatus, restricted to three sites in Rutherford County, is nearest to *A. crassicarpus*, but disjunct by approximately 750 km. A population from Davidson County was apparently extirpated by construction of the Percy Priest Reservoir. In comparison to *A. crassicarpus*, it has a reduced ovule number and specialized fruits, particularly the double-envelope of the valves upon which the taxon is based in large part.

Astragalus bibullatus is in the Center for Plant Conservation's National Collection of Endangered Plants.

239. Astragalus gypsodes Barneby, Amer. Midl. Naturalist 55: 499. 1956 • Gypsum milkvetch [C] [E]

Plants robust, coarse, (5–)10–30(–35) cm, strigulose; from subterranean caudex. **Stems** ascending and radiating, to 6(–9) cm underground, strigulose. **Leaves** (4–)6–18 cm; stipules distinct throughout, 2–7(–9) mm, membranous or subherbaceous, strigulose abaxially; petiolate; leaflets (11–)15–25(–29), blades elliptic, narrowly ovate-lanceolate, rhombic-elliptic, or oblong-obovate, 5–20 mm, apex obtuse, subacute, or retuse, surfaces cinereous-strigulose. **Peduncles** erect or ascending, 3.5–10 cm. **Racemes** (10–)15–30-flowered, flowers ascending to spreading; axis (2.5–)3.5–11.5 cm in fruit; bracts 2.5–6 mm; bracteoles 2. **Pedicels** 1.3–3.4 mm. **Flowers** 16–23 mm; calyx purplish or reddish, cylindro-campanulate, 10.4–14.7 mm, finely strigulose, tube 7.3–10 mm, lobes subulate or lanceolate, (2.6–)3–5 mm; corolla bright pink-purple, keel maculate; keel 15.4–18.1 mm. **Legumes** pale green or suffused purple becoming stramineous suffused with brown-purple, usually straight, rarely slightly incurved, broadly and plumply oblong-cylindroid, oblong-ellipsoid, or more narrowly cylindro- or clavate-ellipsoid, terete or slightly laterally or dorsiventrally compressed, 25–45(–50) × (8–)10–21 mm, bilocular, fleshy and succulent, becoming thick and plump, mesocarp at least 1.5 mm, glabrous. **Seeds** (41–)45–66. $2n = 24$.

Flowering Mar–May. Creosote bush and mesquite communities, in dry flats, gullied knolls, low rolling hills, on gypsum or stiff gypsum-clay soils; of conservation concern; 700–1300 m; N.Mex., Tex.

Astragalus gypsodes has thick, plump fruits that, upon drying, are light enough to be wind dispersed (R. C. Barneby 1964). It is found along the Pecos River and tributaries in southern Eddy County, New Mexico, and northern Culberson and adjacent Reeves counties, Texas.

240. Astragalus plattensis Nuttall in J. Torrey and A. Gray, Fl. N. Amer. 1: 332. 1838 • Platte River milkvetch [E] [F]

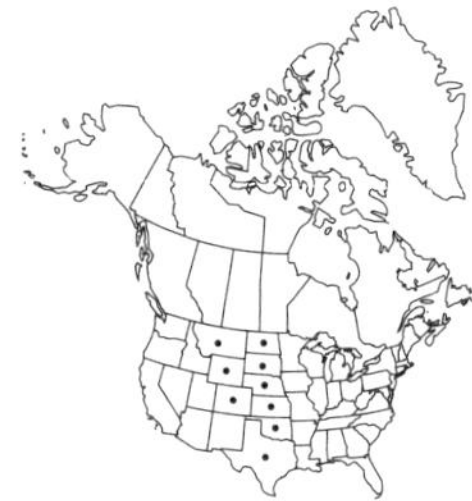

Geoprumnon plattense (Nuttall) Rydberg

Plants (5–)10–30(–37) cm, sparsely to densely pilose; from subterranean, rhizomatous, widely branched caudex. **Stems** sprawling-decumbent, 1–20 cm underground, sparsely to densely pilose. **Leaves** 2.5–11.5(–15) cm; stipules distinct throughout, 1.5–7 mm, scarious at proximal nodes, herbaceous at distal nodes; short-petiolate or subsessile; leaflets (11–)15–29, blades usually broadly to narrowly elliptic or oblong, rarely oblong-obovate, (2–)4–13(–17) mm, apex usually obtuse or acute, rarely truncate-emarginate, surfaces sparsely pilose or glabrescent, sometimes glabrous adaxially. **Peduncles** ascending, (1–)2–8(–9) cm. **Racemes** (3–)6–15-flowered, flowers ascending or spreading; axis 0.7–2.5(–3.2) cm in fruit; bracts (2–)3–7.5 mm; bracteoles (0 or)2. **Pedicels** 1.4–2.8 mm. **Flowers** (14.3–)16.5–20(–21.5) mm; calyx purplish, deeply campanulate, 7.8–12.2(–13.7) mm, pilose or shortly pilosulous, tube 5.4–7.8 mm, lobes subulate or lanceolate-subulate, (2–)2.6–4.7(–6.1) mm; corolla pink-purple or lilac-purple, sometimes pale, wings and keel maculate; keel (11.5–)12–15.5(–16) mm. **Legumes** long persisting then finally disjointing from receptacle, green, often purple-mottled, straight, obliquely ovoid-oblong or subglobose, ± obcompressed, 10–17(–20) × 10–13 mm, bilocular, fleshy becoming stiffly leathery, mesocarp 1.5–2 mm thick, not separated into 2 layers, strigulose or pilosulous. **Seeds** (28–)32–48(–52).

Flowering Mar–Jul. Plains, low rolling hills, on clay-loam or sandy clay prairies, abandoned pastures, fallow fields, gravelly gullies, openings in oak woodlands, mowed prairie-remnant cemeteries; (30–)100–1400 m; Colo., Kans., Mont., Nebr., N.Dak., Okla., S.Dak., Tex., Wyo.

Astragalus plattensis is included within the range of *A. crassicarpus*, and in flower the two species may be confused. When flowering, *A. plattensis* will have ovaries with hairs, whereas *A. crassicarpus* has glabrous ovaries.

135lll. Astragalus Linnaeus sect. Tennesseenses Barneby, Mem. New York Bot. Gard. 13: 768. 1964 [E]

Herbs perennial, clump-forming, caulescent; caudex superficial or shallowly subterranean; taproot woody. **Hairs** basifixed. **Stems** several to many. **Stipules** distinct or connate, conspicuous, several-veined, pale green. **Leaves** odd-pinnate, short-petiolate or subsessile; leaflets (15–)23–33. **Racemes** densely flowered, flowers ascending to spreading or declined. **Calyx tubes** deeply campanulate or cylindric. **Corollas** ochroleucous, banner recurved through 40°, keel apex obtuse. **Legumes** deciduous, sessile, short gynophore present, ascending, humistrate, oblong- or lanceoloid-ellipsoid, slightly obcompressed, nearly straight or slightly incurved, bilocular. **Seeds** 26–36.

Species 1: c, se United States.

241. Astragalus tennesseensis A. Gray ex Chapman, Fl. South. U.S., 98. 1860 • Tennessee milkvetch [E]

Geoprumnon tennesseense (A. Gray) Rydberg

Plants (5–)10–50 cm, pilose to pilose-hirsute. **Stems** decumbent to ascending, densely pilose to pilose-hirsute. **Leaves** (6–)8–15 cm; stipules often connate-sheathing at proximal nodes, connate or distinct at distal nodes, 5–20 mm, submembranous becoming papery-scarious; leaflet blades oblong-elliptic or obovate-obcordate, (4–)6–23 mm, apex obtuse, emarginate, or apiculate-acute, surfaces sparsely pilose or pilose-hirsute abaxially, glabrous adaxially. **Peduncles** incurved-ascending, 5–10(–14) cm. **Racemes** 9–20-flowered; axis 2–5(–6) cm in fruit; bracts 5–12 mm; bracteoles 0. **Pedicels** 1.5–3.5 mm. **Flowers** 14–19 mm; calyx 8.3–15.1 mm, sparsely white-hirsute, tube gibbous-saccate behind pedicel, 5.9–11.4 mm, lobes lanceolate-subulate, 2.4–4 mm; corolla whitish or pale cream, drying yellow, immaculate; keel 11–13.6 mm. **Legumes** green or pink-tinged becoming stramineous, 25–40 × 7–13 mm, fleshy becoming spongy, walls 2.5–3 mm thick, translucent, alveolate-rugulose, sparsely hirsute; gynophore stout, (1–)1.3–2 mm, glabrous.

Flowering Apr–Jun. Openings in cedar barrens, edges of thickets, on limestone pavement, stony calcareous hillsides; 200–300 m; Ala., Ill., Tenn.

Astragalus tennesseensis is the only species of the genus between the Mississippi River and the Appalachian Mountains with pilose indumentum (D. Isely 1998). It is locally abundant on the cedar glades of middle Tennessee, but many of these unique communities have been lost in recent decades due to the rapid growth of metropolitan Nashville. Extant populations also occur in Lawrence and Morgan counties in northern Alabama and Tazewell County in central Illinois. It has been extirpated from four counties in Illinois, from its only known site in Indiana, from one county in Tennessee, and from one county in Alabama (J. M. Baskin and C. C. Baskin 2005).

Astragalus tennesseensis is in the Center for Plant Conservation's National Collection of Endangered Plants.

135mmm. Astragalus Linnaeus sect. Megacarpi (Rydberg) Barneby, Mem. New York Bot. Gard. 13: 771. 1964 [E]

Phaca Linnaeus sect. *Megacarpi* Rydberg in N. L. Britton et al., N. Amer. Fl. 24: 338. 1929 (as Megacarpae)

Herbs perennial, caulescent or subacaulescent; caudex superficial or slightly subterranean. **Hairs** basifixed. **Stems** several to many. **Stipules** distinct. **Leaves** odd-pinnate, petiolate; leaflets 9–27. **Racemes** loosely flowered, flowers ascending or spreading. **Calyx tubes** deeply campanulate or cylindric. **Corollas** ochroleucous, whitish, pink-purple, or purple, banner recurved through 45–90°, keel apex obtuse. **Legumes** deciduous, sessile, gynophore present, ascending (humistrate), spreading, pendulous, or declined, ellipsoid, ovoid-ellipsoid, or semi-ovoid, dorsiventrally compressed or bladdery-inflated, straight or slightly or sharply incurved, unilocular or semibilocular. **Seeds** 18–54.

Species 3 (3 in the flora): w, c North America.

Section *Megacarpi* is distributed in the Colorado, Columbia, and Great basins.

242. Astragalus megacarpus (Nuttall) A. Gray, Proc. Amer. Acad. Arts 6: 215. 1864 • Great bladdery milkvetch [E]

Phaca megacarpa Nuttall in J. Torrey and A. Gray, Fl. N. Amer. 1: 343. 1838; *Astragalus megacarpus* var. *neeseae* S. Welsh

Plants densely tuft-forming, 1–4 dm diam., subacaulescent or shortly caulescent, 3–15(–20) cm, strigulose; from superficial or slightly subterranean caudex; taproot thick. **Stems** erect-ascending, 1–7 cm, internodes mostly concealed by imbricate stipules and marcescent leaf remains, strigulose. **Leaves** (2–)5–17 cm; stipules 2–7 mm, submembranous; leaflets 7–19 (–23), blades obovate, ovate, elliptic, or suborbiculate, 3–21 mm, apex usually obtuse or retuse and mucronate, rarely abruptly cuspidate-acuminate, surfaces strigose or glabrous abaxially, glabrous adaxially. **Peduncles** 0.5–6(–7) cm, together with racemes shorter than leaves. **Racemes** 1–7(or 8)-flowered, flowers ascending; axis 0.2–2.5 cm in fruit; bracts 2–5 mm; bracteoles 0–2. **Pedicels** 3.5–8 mm. **Flowers** 15–23(–26) mm; calyx cylindric, (7–)8.5–13.5(–16) mm, strigulose, tube (5.2–)6–10 mm, lobes subulate or lanceolate-subulate, 1.8–4.5(–6) mm; corolla pink-purple or white with pale pink veins; banner recurved through 45°; keel 11.5–17.5 mm. **Legumes** appearing radical, forming ring on ground beneath tufted foliage, ascending, greenish, brightly mottled reddish purple, becoming brownish stramineous, straight or slightly incurved, symmetrically or somewhat obliquely ellipsoid or ovoid-ellipsoid, bladdery-inflated, 35–70(–90) × 15–45 mm, papery, surface lustrous, sparsely strigulose; gynophore 2–4 mm. **Seeds** 38–54.

Flowering Apr–Jul. Clay or gravel derived from limestone, shale, or red sandstone, in mixed desert shrub, pinyon-juniper, sagebrush, oak, and ponderosa pine communities; 1400–2400(–3100) m; Colo., Nev., Utah, Wyo.

R. C. Barneby (1964) discussed the problem of relating potential infraspecific taxa to flower color within *Astragalus megacarpus*. Plants from Wyoming, northwestern Colorado, and some from northeastern Utah have white or whitish petals. Those from elsewhere are mostly pale to dark pink-purple, and var. *neeseae* has been proposed for the pink-flowered populations. Flower color in many populations needs to be determined, and since the flowering season for the species is early and short, the majority of herbarium specimens are in fruit. *Astragalus megacarpus* has the largest legumes in the genus.

243. Astragalus oophorus S. Watson, Botany (Fortieth Parallel), 73. 1871 • Egg milkvetch [E] [F]

Plants caulescent, 15–30(–40) cm, glabrous or sparsely hairy; from superficial caudex. **Stems** decumbent to ascending, (2–) 15–25 cm, 1 to several internodes elongated and longer than stipules, glabrous or sparsely hairy. **Leaves** 3–21 cm; stipules 1.5–7 mm, thinly herbaceous becoming papery; leaflets 9–21(–25), blades oval to obovate or orbiculate, 3–20 mm, apex obtuse to retuse or mucronate, surfaces glabrous, ciliate. **Peduncles** ascending or incurved, 4–13 cm, together with racemes shorter than leaves. **Racemes** 3–14-flowered, flowers spreading; axis 1–8 cm in fruit; bracts 1.5–5 mm; bracteoles 0–2. **Pedicels** 2–6 mm. **Flowers** 11–24 mm; calyx cylindric or campanulate, 6–12 mm, glabrous or sparsely strigulose, tube 4–8.5 mm, lobes subulate, 2–6(–7.7) mm; corolla ochroleucous (concolorous) or pink-purple and wing tips white (bicolored); banner recurved through 85°; keel 9.5–16 mm. **Legumes** spreading to pendulous, often red-mottled, straight or slightly incurved, ellipsoid, semi-ellipsoid, or semi-ovoid, bladdery-inflated, (20–)25–55(–63) × 10–30 mm, thin becoming papery, glabrous; seed-bearing flange narrow or obsolete, 0.2–0.7 mm wide; gynophore 3.5–11 mm. **Seeds** 28–54.

Varieties 6 (6 in the flora): w United States.

D. Isely (1998) viewed *Astragalus oophorus* as having two major varieties (var. *caulescens* to the east, var. *oophorus* to the west) and several comparatively local, named phases. He noted that *A. oophorus* was closely related to *A. megacarpus* and *A. beckwithii*, but it differs from *A. megacarpus* by its caulescent habit and usually smaller, more strongly stipitate fruits. From *A. beckwithii*, it is often distinguished by range, though, technically, it is distinguished by its bladdery-inflated fruit. Variety *caulescens* and *A. beckwithii* var. *beckwithii* co-occur in north-central Utah and, when in flower, are essentially indistinguishable.

1. Calyces cylindric, tubes 7.8–8.5 × 3.6–4.4 mm; gynophores 10–11 mm; corollas bicolored; se Nevada, adjoining Utah .... 243c. *Astragalus oophorus* var. *lonchocalyx*
1. Calyces usually campanulate, tubes 4–7.8 × 2.6–5.5 mm; gynophores 3.5–8(–10.5) mm; corollas white, ochroleucous, or pink-purple and white and bicolored; Arizona, California, Colorado, Nevada, Utah.

[2. Shifted for left margin.—Ed.]

2. Corollas pink-purple, wing tips white, bicolored; legumes subsymmetric, ellipsoid, sutures convexly arched, sometimes less strongly so ventrally; se California, s, wc Nevada.
   3. Calyx tubes (4.6–)5–6.5 mm, lobes 2–4.2 mm; corollas 16–23 mm; California and Nevada but not of Spring (Charleston) Mountains . . . . 243a. *Astragalus oophorus* var. *oophorus*
   3. Calyx tubes 4–4.3 mm, lobes 2 mm; corollas 11–16 mm; Spring (Charleston) Mountains, Clark and Nye counties, Nevada . . . . 243b. *Astragalus oophorus* var. *clokeyanus*
2. Corollas usually ochroleucous, concolorous, (rarely banners and wings suffused purple); legumes subsymmetric and ellipsoid or asymmetric and semi-ovoid or semi-ellipsoid, sutures subequally concave or gently concave ventrally and straight or strongly convex (in profile); Arizona, California, Colorado, Nevada, Utah.
   4. Legumes subsymmetric, ellipsoid, sutures subequally concave (in profile); leaflets 7–11; Mono County, California, wc Nevada. . . . . 243d. *Astragalus oophorus* var. *lavinii*
   4. Legumes asymmetric, semi-ovoid or semi-ellipsoid, ventral suture gently concave, straight or strongly convex (in profile); leaflets 9–21(–25); Utah plateaus, and nw to ec and s Nevada to n Arizona and w Colorado.
      5. Gynophores 5–9 mm; calyces short-cylindric or campanulate, tubes 4.5–6 × 3.3–5.5 mm, lobes 2.3–6(–7.7) mm; n Arizona, ec Nevada, sw, w Utah . . . . 243e. *Astragalus oophorus* var. *caulescens*
      5. Gynophores 6–10.5 mm; calyces broadly campanulate, tubes 5.8–7.8 × 5 mm, lobes 3.6–5 mm; w Colorado. . . . . 243f. *Astragalus oophorus* var. *wilkenii*

243a. Astragalus oophorus S. Watson var. **oophorus** E F

Leaflets 9–19(or 21). **Flowers** 16–23 mm; calyx often purplish, campanulate, glabrous, tube (4.6–)5–6.5 × 3.4–4.5 mm, lobes 2–4.2 mm; corolla usually pink-purple and wing tips white (bicolored), less often concolorous. **Legumes** subsymmetric, ellipsoid, (25–)35–55(–63) mm, sutures convexly arched, sometimes less strongly so ventrally; gynophore 3.5–8(–10) mm.

Flowering May–Jul. Open hillsides, gullied banks, on dry, gravelly or sandy soils derived from various sedimentary and eruptive rocks, pinyon pine and sagebrush communities; (1500–)1600–3200 m; Calif., Nev.

Variety *oophorus* ranges from the Panamint Mountains and upper Owens Valley of southeastern California to west-central and central Nevada.

243b. Astragalus oophorus S. Watson var. **clokeyanus** Barneby, Leafl. W. Bot. 7: 194. 1954 • Clokey's egg milkvetch C E

Leaflets 9–19(or 21). **Flowers** 11–16 mm; calyx campanulate, glabrous, tube 4–4.3 × 2.6–3.3 mm, lobes 2 mm; corolla pink-purple and wing tips white (bicolored). **Legumes** subsymmetric, ellipsoid, 20–37 mm, sutures convexly arched, sometimes less strongly so ventrally; gynophore 3.5–5.5 mm.

Flowering Jun–Jul. Open slopes in ponderosa pine forests, on gravelly limestone soils; of conservation concern; 1600–2800 m; Nev.

Variety *clokeyanus* is restricted to the eastern slope of Mount Charleston, Clark County, and adjacent southern Nye County. It is closely allied to var. *oophorus*, differing mainly in having smaller flowers.

243c. Astragalus oophorus S. Watson var. **lonchocalyx** Barneby, Leafl. W. Bot. 7: 194. 1954 • Pink egg milkvetch C E

Leaflets 7–11. **Flowers** 20.5–24 mm; calyx cylindric, glabrous, tube 7.8–8.5 × 3.6–4.4 mm, lobes 2.5–4 mm; corolla pink-purple and wing tips white or whitish (bicolored). **Legumes** subsymmetric, ellipsoid, (25–)35–55(–63) mm, sutures convexly arched, sometimes less strongly so ventrally; gynophore 10–11 mm.

Flowering May–Jun. Pinyon-juniper, sagebrush, and mixed desert shrub communities; of conservation concern; 1700–2300 m; Nev., Utah.

Variety *lonchocalyx* is restricted to eastern Lincoln County, Nevada, and western Beaver and Iron counties, Utah.

243d. Astragalus oophorus S. Watson var. **lavinii** Barneby, Brittonia 36: 168. 1984 • Lavin's egg milkvetch [C] [E]

Leaflets 7–11. **Flowers** 17–20 mm; calyx campanulate, glabrous, tube 4.7–6.5 × 3.4–4.5 mm, lobes 2.3–6 mm; corolla white (concolorous), drying ochroleucous. **Legumes** subsymmetric, ellipsoid, 25–40 mm, sutures subequally concave in profile; gynophore 3.5–8 (–10) mm.

Flowering May–Jun. Sagebrush and bitterbrush communities; of conservation concern; 1400–2300 m; Calif., Nev.

Variety *lavinii* is found in the Pine Nut Mountains and Wellington Hills, Douglas and southern Lyon counties, Nevada, and in the Bodie Hills, Mono County, California.

243e. Astragalus oophorus S. Watson var. **caulescens** (M. E. Jones) M. E. Jones, Rev. N.-Amer. Astragalus, 121 [line 38]. 1923 • Pallid egg milkvetch [E]

Astragalus megacarpus (Nuttall) A. Gray var. *caulescens* M. E. Jones, Proc. Calif. Acad. Sci., ser. 2, 5: 643. 1895

Leaflets 9–19(–25). **Flowers** 17–21 mm; calyx campanulate or short-cylindric, often sparsely black-strigulose, sometimes glabrous, tube 4.5–6 × 3.3–5.5 mm, lobes 2.3–6(–7.7) mm; corolla usually ochroleucous (concolorous), rarely banner and wings suffused with purple, or purple throughout. **Legumes** asymmetric, semi-ovoid or semi-ellipsoid, (25–)30–40(–45) mm, sutures gently concave ventrally, straight or strongly convex in profile; gynophore 5–9 mm.

Flowering May–Jul. Sagebrush, pinyon-juniper, and mountain brush communities; 1300–2500 m; Ariz., Nev., Utah.

As noted by R. C. Barneby (1964), plants with bicolored (purple and white) flowers occur occasionally within the range of var. *caulescens* in Mohave County, Arizona. From near the southern limit of the variety in Arizona, plants sometimes have petals suffused or lined with lilac. Plants from the Arizona plateaus also tend to have more numerous leaflets (to 21–25) than found elsewhere within the variety, and the fruit is generally less oblique in outline and with a shorter, less well-defined beak.

243f. Astragalus oophorus S. Watson var. **wilkenii** S. L. Welsh, N. Amer. Sp. Astragalus, 257. 2007 • Wilken's milkvetch [E]

Leaflets 9–21. **Flowers** 16–20 mm; calyx broadly campanulate, often sparsely black-strigulose, sometimes glabrous, tube 5.8–7.8 × 5 mm, lobes 3.6–5 mm; corolla ochroleucous (concolorous). **Legumes** asymmetric, semi-ovoid or semi-ellipsoid, (25–)30–40 mm, sutures gently concave ventrally, straight or strongly convex in profile; gynophore 6–10.5 mm.

Flowering May–Jun. Sagebrush, oak, pinyon-juniper, and mountain brush communities; 1800–2500 m; Colo.

Variety *wilkenii* occurs in western Colorado and is supported by a more or less convincing subset of specimens placed historically within var. *caulescens*. That variety is distantly disjunct by more than 200 km, with its entire range in western and southwestern Utah, north-central and northwestern Arizona, and east-central Nevada.

244. Astragalus beckwithii Torrey & A. Gray in War Department [U.S.], Pacif. Railr. Rep. 2(1): 120, plate 3. 1857 • Beckwith's milkvetch [E] [F]

Plants caulescent, 5–40(–70) cm, glabrous or strigose; from superficial caudex. **Stems** decumbent to ascending or erect, glabrous or strigose. **Leaves** 2–15 cm; stipules 2–10 mm, papery at proximal nodes, herbaceous at distal nodes; leaflets (7–)11–27, blades orbiculate, suborbiculate, elliptic, rhombic-elliptic, rhombic-ovate, oblong-ovate, ovate, or obovate, 3–25 mm, apex obtuse, truncate, retuse, or apiculate, surfaces glabrous or glabrate. **Peduncles** erect or incurved-ascending, 3–15 cm. **Racemes** 7–16-flowered, flowers ascending; axis 1–7 cm in fruit; bracts 1–7 mm; bracteoles 2. **Pedicels** 1–3.5 mm. **Flowers** (16–)16.5–21 mm; calyx short-cylindric to deeply campanulate, 7–13.5 mm, sparsely strigulose or glabrous, tube 3.5–6.8 mm, lobes subulate to lanceolate, 2–7.1 mm; corolla ochroleucous, yellowish, whitish, cream, or purple (wing tips sometimes pale or white); banner recurved through 90°; keel 11.5–15.5 mm. **Legumes** ascending to declined, pale green, often purple-mottled, becoming brownish or stramineous, sharply incurved, obliquely ellipsoid, dorsiventrally compressed, (15–)20–30 × 6–12 mm, fleshy becoming leathery, glabrous; septum narrow, subobsolete, to 1.5 mm wide; gynophore 1.5–5 mm. **Seeds** 18–41.

Varieties 4 (4 in the flora): w North America.

Mature fruit is necessary to distinguish *Astragalus beckwithii* from *A. oophorus*. A geographical key to varieties of both species was presented by D. Isely (1984).

1. Corollas purple or bicolored, wings then with pale or white tips; Nevada, extreme w Utah . . . . 244b. *Astragalus beckwithii* var. *purpureus*
1. Corollas yellowish or whitish to ochroleucous, cream, purple, or bicolored; s British Columbia to ne Nevada and Utah.
    2. Legumes dorsally sulcate nearly throughout; Salmon River, Lemhi County, Idaho . . . . 244d. *Astragalus beckwithii* var. *sulcatus*
    2. Legumes dorsally flattened or shallowly and openly sulcate; not of upper Salmon River, ec Idaho.
        3. Calyx lobes 2.5–3.7 mm; leaflets (13–) 17–27, blades 3–13(–17) mm, apices truncate or retuse; se Idaho, ne Nevada, w Utah . . . . 244a. *Astragalus beckwithii* var. *beckwithii*
        3. Calyx lobes (3.6–)5–7 mm; leaflets (7–) 11–17, blades (6–)10–25 mm, apices obtuse; s British Columbia southward to c Nevada, eastward to se Idaho . . . . 244c. *Astragalus beckwithii* var. *weiserensis*

244a. Astragalus beckwithii Torrey & A. Gray var. **beckwithii** E F

Stems usually slender, (0.2–)1–3 cm. **Leaves:** stipules 2–7 mm; leaflets (13–)17–27, blades usually suborbiculate or broadly oval rarely ovate or obovate, 3–13(–17) mm, apex truncate or retuse; bracts 2.5–4 mm; brac teoles 0.2 mm. **Flowers** 16.5–21 mm; calyx 7.2–8.2(–9) mm, usually black-strigulose, tube 3.5–5.3 mm, lobes 2.5–3.7 mm; corolla yellowish or whitish to ochroleucous. **Legumes** usually mottled, sometimes faintly so, (15–) 20–30 × 7–12 mm, dorsal face flattened or shallowly and openly sulcate.

Flowering Apr–Jun. Juniper-pinyon, sagebrush, bunchgrass, and mountain brush communities; 1300–2600 m; Idaho, Nev., Utah.

Variety *beckwithii* is known from southern Idaho, to Elko and White Pine counties in Nevada, and to the western half of Utah as far south as Iron County.

Plants of var. *beckwithii* are indistinguishable in anthesis from those of *Astragalus oophorus* var. *caulescens*, with which they are sympatric in part of their ranges, yet they were placed in different segregate genera by P. A. Rydberg (1929b). The dorsiventrally collapsed, leathery fruits of *A. beckwithii*, the basis of the segregate genus *Phacomene* Rydberg, easily distinguishes the two species in fruit.

244b. Astragalus beckwithii Torrey & A. Gray var. **purpureus** M. E. Jones, Zoë 3: 288. 1893 • Sagebrush milkvetch E

Stems (2–)15–25 cm. **Leaves:** stipules 1.5–6 mm; leaflets (11 or)13–27, blades oval, orbiculate, or obovate, 3–12 mm, apex truncate or retuse; bracts 1.5–3.5 mm; bracteoles 0–1 mm. **Flowers** 17–21 mm; calyx 7–9.5 mm, very sparsely black-strigulose, tube 4.7–5.7 mm, lobes 2–4.3 mm; corolla purple or bicolored and wings tipped pale or white. **Legumes** usually brightly mottled, (15–)20–30 × 7–12 mm, dorsal face flattened or shallowly and openly sulcate.

Flowering Apr–Jun. Pinyon-juniper, sagebrush, and other cool-desert shrublands, on alluvial gravel, sand, and silt, on limestone and dolomite outcrops; 1300–2300(–2600) m; Nev., Utah.

The range of var. *purpureus* overlaps that of *Astragalus oophorus* var. *clokeyanus* in southern Nevada, and care must be taken in identification of specimens from there. The calyx tube of *A. oophorus* var. *clokeyanus* is shorter than that of *A. beckwithii* var. *purpureus*.

244c. Astragalus beckwithii Torrey & A. Gray var. **weiserensis** M. E. Jones, Zoë 5: 47. 1900 • Weiser milkvetch E

Stems (1–)1.5–3.5(–7) cm. **Leaves:** stipules (3–)4–10 mm; leaflets (7–)11–17, blades broadly ovate to rhombic-elliptic, (6–)10–25 mm, apex obtuse; bracts 3–7.5 mm; bracteoles (0.4–)1–4 mm. **Flowers** (16–)17–20.5 mm; calyx (8.5–) 10.2–13.5 mm, mostly glabrous, sometimes margins and lobes with few hairs, tube (4.6–)5.1–6.3 mm, lobes (3.6–)5–7.1 mm; corolla purple or bicolored and wings tipped pale or white. **Legumes** usually mottled, sometimes faintly so, (15–) 20–30 × 7–12 mm, dorsal face flattened or shallowly and openly sulcate. $2n = 22$.

Flowering May–Jul. Sagebrush, bunchgrass, and juniper communities, on sandy, gravelly, or heavy clay soils; 600–1900 m; B.C.; Idaho, Nev., Oreg., Wash.

Variety *weiserensis* is known from the lower Fraser River in southern British Columbia southward to the lower Humboldt River valley in Pershing County, Nevada, and eastward to Franklin County in Idaho.

The long calyx lobes of var. *weiserensis* are apparently diagnostic, but where var. *beckwithii* approaches this variety in the Raft River Mountains of northern Utah, adjacent to the Idaho border, there appears to be a gradual transition.

244d. Astragalus beckwithii Torrey & A. Gray var. **sulcatus** Barneby, Mem. New York Bot. Gard. 13: 784. 1964 • Grooved milkvetch [E]

Stems (20–)30–40 cm. **Leaves:** stipules 3–8 mm; leaflets (7–)11–17, blades broadly rhombic-ovate or oblong-ovate, 7–24 mm, apex obtuse or apiculate; bracts 2–4 mm; bracteoles 0–2 mm. **Flowers** 18–20 mm; calyx 10.8–12.8 mm, mostly glabrous, sometimes lobes with few, black hairs, tube 6.2–6.8 mm, lobes 4–6.6 mm; corolla cream. **Legumes** mottled, 20–25 × 6–7.5 mm, dorsal face sulcate nearly throughout.

Flowering May–Jul. Open, brushy slopes with sagebrush and rabbitbrush, on volcanic gravelly clay soils; 1100–1500 m; Idaho.

Variety *sulcatus* occurs from the banks of the Salmon River in eastern Lemhi County, from North Fork upstream about 60 km.

135nnn. Astragalus Linnaeus sect. Lutosi (Rydberg) Barneby, Mem. New York Bot. Gard. 13: 784. 1964 [E]

Phaca Linnaeus [unranked] *Lutosae* Rydberg in N. L. Britton et al., N. Amer. Fl. 24: 349. 1929

Herbs perennial, caulescent; caudex subterranean caudex; taproot thickened. **Hairs** basifixed. **Stems** several. **Stipules** ± distinct. **Leaves** odd-pinnate, petiolate; leaflets (9 or)11–27. **Racemes** loosely flowered, flowers ascending-spreading. **Calyx tubes** short-cylindric. **Corollas** whitish, with keel apex pink or purplish, banner recurved through 45°, keel apex obtuse. **Legumes** persistent, sessile, gynophore present, spreading to ascending (humistrate), subsymmetrically ovoid-ellipsoid, straight, bladdery-inflated, unilocular. **Seeds** 24–30.

Species 1: w United States.

245. Astragalus lutosus M. E. Jones, Contr. W. Bot. 13: 7. 1910 • Dragon milkvetch [E]

Plants shortly caulescent (aboveground), 2–10 cm, strigulose; from deeply subterranean, often soboliferous, caudex. **Stems** prostrate to ascending and radiating, (0.5–)2–18(–24) cm underground, frequently exceeding aerial stem length, strigulose. **Leaves** 1–5.5 cm; stipules distinct throughout or shortly connate-sheathing at proximal nodes, 2–5 mm, subherbaceous; leaflets closely spaced on rachis, blades obovate to elliptic or oblong, 1–12 mm, apex obtuse to retuse, surfaces gray-strigulose, sometimes glabrous adaxially. **Peduncles** ascending, 0.5–4 cm. **Racemes** (1 or)2–10-flowered; axis 0.3–1 cm in fruit; bracts 1.5–2.5 mm; bracteoles 0. **Pedicels** 1.2–3 mm. **Flowers** 9–17 mm; calyx 4.8–10.5 mm, strigulose, tube 3.5–7.6 mm, lobes subulate, 1.2–3 mm; corolla white or ochroleucous, or banner and wings tinged lavender, keel tip pink or purplish; keel 7.4–13.2 mm. **Legumes** pale green and red-cheeked, 15–38 × 8–23 mm, thin becoming papery, strigose; gynophore 1–4.5 mm.

Flowering May–Jun. Barrens, often with other mound-forming species in mixed desert shrub, pinyon-juniper, mountain brush, and limber pine-Douglas-fir communities, on outcrops of the Green River Shale Formation; 1500–2900 m; Colo., Utah.

Astragalus lutosus, a highly specialized endemic to shale knolls and ridgetops almost bare of other plants, has its distribution aligned along, and within, a few miles of the fortieth parallel in northwestern Colorado and northeastern Utah. R. C. Barneby (1964) noted that it is one of the rarest of North American astragali.

Astragalus lutosus is in the Center for Plant Conservation's National Collection of Endangered Plants.

135ooo. Astragalus Linnaeus sect. Pterocarpi S. Watson, Botany (Fortieth Parallel), 439. 1871 [E]

Herbs perennial, caulescent; caudex subterranean or superficial. **Hairs** basifixed. **Stems** few to several. **Stipules** distinct. **Leaves** odd-pinnate, short-petiolate; leaflets 3–23, terminal leaflet jointed or confluent. **Racemes** loosely flowered, flowers ascending sometimes spreading or declined in age. **Calyx tubes** cylindric or deeply campanulate. **Corollas** purple, pink-purple, or yellowish to white, banner recurved through 45°, keel apex obtuse. **Legumes** deciduous, sessile, pendulous or deflexed, lanceoloid- or oblong-ellipsoid, oblong-oblanceoloid, or obliquely or clavately oblong, slightly to strongly obcompressed or 4-sided, straight, curved (sometimes sigmoidally), or coiled, unilocular. **Seeds** 28–60.

Species 3 (3 in the flora): w United States.

Section *Pterocarpi* distribution is centered in Nevada.

246. Astragalus casei A. Gray in W. H. Brewer et al., Bot. California 1: 154. 1876 • Case's milkvetch [E]

Plants usually slender, somewhat wiry, (10–)15–50 cm, strigulose; from subterranean caudex. **Stems** erect or decumbent to ascending, ± strongly flexuose aboveground, (0–)2–6 cm underground, strigulose. **Leaves** 30–100 cm; stipules (1–)2–5 mm, membranous at proximal nodes, herbaceous at distal nodes; leaflets (5–)9–15, blades elliptic-oblong, oblanceolate, or linear, 3–25 mm, apex usually obtuse or retuse, rarely subacute, surfaces strigulose. **Peduncles** erect or divaricate, 3–9(–12) cm. **Racemes** (5–)8–20(–26)-flowered, flowers ascending becoming declined; axis (1.5–)3–12(–17) cm in fruit, elongating; bracts 2–3.5(–5) mm; bracteoles 0–2. **Pedicels** 1–2.3 mm. **Flowers** (12–)13.5–18 mm; calyx pallid or purplish, cylindric or deeply campanulate, (5.8–)7.5–9 mm, strigulose, tube (4.6–)5.8–7.5 mm, lobes subulate or triangular-subulate, 1.2–1.8 mm; corolla usually pink-purple and wing tips white, rarely white throughout; keel 10.6–13.3 mm. **Legumes** promptly deciduous, deflexed, red- or brownish-mottled becoming stramineous or brownish, usually ± sigmoid-arcuate, rarely straight, lanceoloid-ellipsoid or oblong-ellipsoid, obcompressed, 20–55 × (5–)6–10 mm, fleshy becoming stiffly leathery, strigulose. **Seeds** 32–42.

Flowering Apr–Jun. Alkaline gravelly soils overlying granite or basaltic bedrock, with sagebrush, in pinyon-juniper forests, rarely on dunes; 1200–2500 m; Calif., Nev.

Astragalus casei occurs near the California-Nevada border from Death Valley, Inyo County, California, northward to Pyramid Lake and the lower Humboldt River in Pershing and Washoe counties, Nevada, with a disjunct population in northeastern Nye County, Nevada.

247. Astragalus tetrapterus A. Gray, Proc. Amer. Acad. Arts 13: 369. 1878 • Four-wing milkvetch [E] [F]

Plants relatively robust, 10–35 cm, strigulose; from subterranean caudex. **Stems** erect, ascending, or decumbent, 2–8 cm underground, strigulose. **Leaves** 1.5–8.5 cm; stipules 2–5.5 mm, herbaceous; leaflets 9–23, blades linear, narrowly oblong, or elliptic, 1–33 mm, apex obtuse to acute, surfaces strigose or glabrous; terminal leaflet sometimes decurrent distally, not jointed to rachis. **Peduncles** ascending, 1–6.5 cm. **Racemes** 6–15-flowered, flowers ascending; axis 1–4 cm in fruit; bracts 1.5–3.5 mm; bracteoles 0–2. **Pedicels** 1.4–4.3 mm. **Flowers** 15–19 mm; calyx cylindric, 5.5–8.7 mm, strigose, tube 4.7–7 mm, lobes subulate, 0.8–2.8 mm; corolla white to yellowish and tinged faintly with pink, sometimes lightly suffused with pink-purple on drying, keel tip faintly to darkly purple; keel 10.2–13 mm. **Legumes** pendulous, green or purple-mottled becoming stramineous or brownish, strongly incurved or coiled, obliquely oblong, sharply 4-sided compressed, 20–40 × 6–10 mm, fleshy becoming stiffly papery, glabrous or strigose. **Seeds** 28–38.

Flowering Apr–Jul. Pinyon-juniper and sagebrush communities; 1000–2200 m; Ariz., Idaho, Nev., Oreg., Utah.

Astragalus tetrapterus contains nitrotoxins that are poisonous to livestock (L. F. James and S. L. Welsh 1992), but it is seldom sufficiently abundant as to result in large-scale loss. The fresh fruit is fleshy, with the dorsal suture essentially flat and the ventral suture raised in a low ridge; it becomes four-winged upon drying.

Astragalus cinerascens (Rydberg) Tidestrom is an illegitimate name that pertains here.

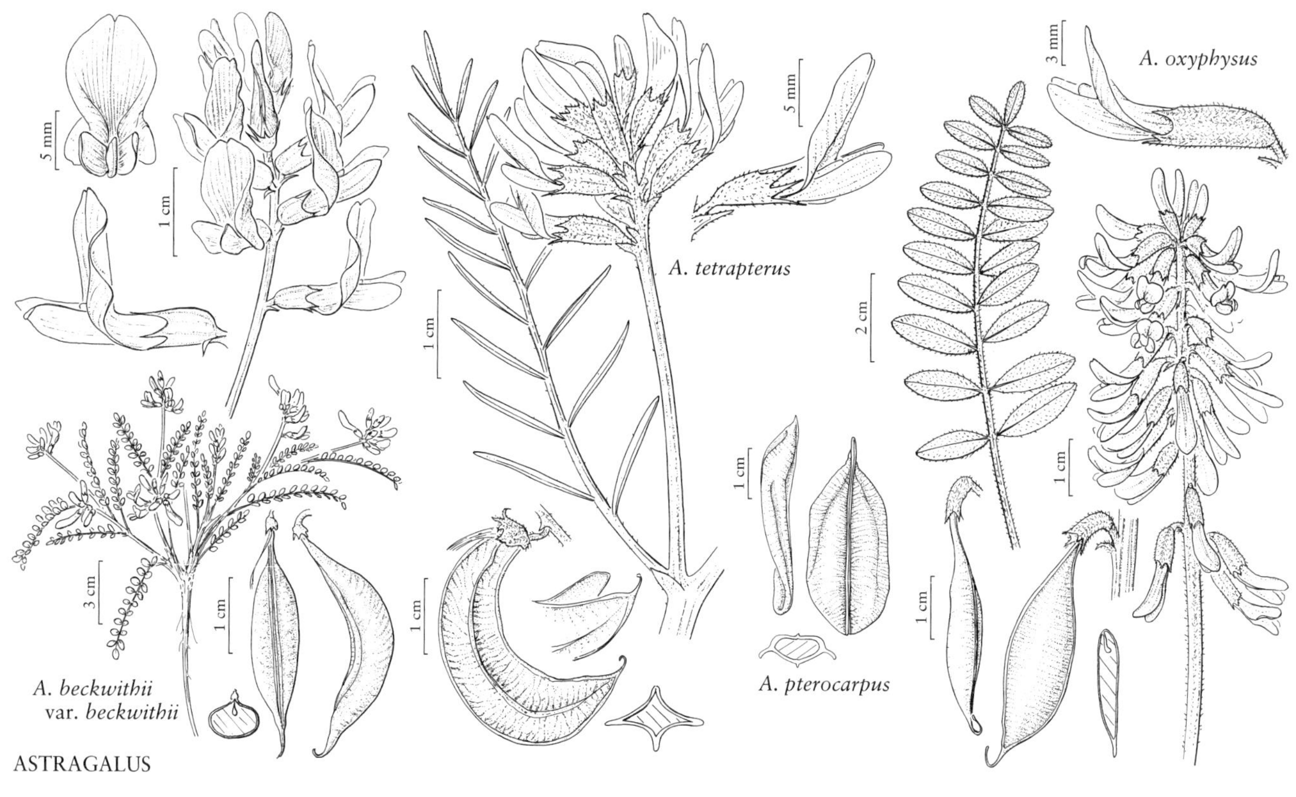

ASTRAGALUS

248. **Astragalus pterocarpus** S. Watson, Botany (Fortieth Parallel), 71, plate 12, figs. 1, 2. 1871 • Winged milkvetch E F

Plants (10–)15–35(–40) cm, strigulose; from superficial to slightly subterranean caudex. **Stems** erect or decumbent to ascending, (0–)1–5 cm underground, sparsely strigulose. **Leaves** (3.5–)5–10 cm; stipules 2.5–7 mm, scarious at proximal nodes, herbaceous at distal nodes; leaflets 3–7(or 9), blades linear, 10–50 mm, apex acute or subacute, surfaces sparsely strigulose abaxially, silvery-canescent adaxially; terminal leaflet decurrent distally, not jointed to rachis. **Peduncles** ascending, (4–) 5–11(–15) cm. **Racemes** 5–15-flowered, flowers ascending becoming horizontal; axis (1–)2–8 cm in fruit; bracts 1–5 mm; bracteoles 0–2. **Pedicels** 1.2–2.8 mm. **Flowers** 16.3–19 mm; calyx pallid, cylindric, 9–12 mm, pilosulous, tube 7–8.5 mm, lobes subulate, 2–4 mm; corolla purple or whitish with purple tips; keel 12.8–15.5 mm. **Legumes** pendulous, very pale green becoming stramineous, ± straight or obscurely sigmoid-arcuate, ellipsoid or broadly oblong-oblanceoloid, strongly obcompressed, (25–)30–45 × (11–)13–17(–23) mm, fleshy becoming leathery, translucent, lustrous, smooth, transversely rugulose-reticulate, glabrous. **Seeds** 42–60.

Flowering Apr–Jun. Saline hills and flats in saltgrass meadows and openings among shadscale and greasewood; 1200–1500 m; Nev.

Astragalus pterocarpus is known from the Black Rock Desert southward to the Carson Sink, and eastward to the Humboldt Valley and to Battle Mountain in Churchill, Humboldt, Lander, and Pershing counties.

R. C. Barneby (1964) discussed the final phases of development of the striking fruits of *Astragalus pterocarpus* from smooth, shieldlike green pods that were suggestive of worked jade, to the rigidly biwinged, leathery, cross-reticulate pods that are unique in the sum of their characteristics. He noted that laterally-winged fruits, though much smaller, have independently evolved in two annual astragali, the Mexican *A. scutaneus* Barneby and the central Asiatic *A. thlaspi* Lipsky.

135ppp. Astragalus Linnaeus sect. Anemophili Barneby, Mem. New York Bot. Gard. 13: 794. 1964

Herbs perennial, caulescent; caudex superficial. **Hairs** basifixed. **Stems** several to many. **Stipules** connate or distinct at distal nodes. **Leaves** odd-pinnate, short-petiolate; leaflets (17–)21–27 [–35]. **Racemes** compactly flowered, flowers ascending, spreading, or somewhat declined in age. **Calyx tubes** campanulate. **Corollas** whitish or ochroleucous, or lilac-tinged, banner recurved through 45°, keel apex obtuse. **Legumes** deciduous, sessile, spreading, obliquely ovoid-acuminate, straight, bladdery-inflated, unilocular. **Seeds** 27–40.

Species 3 (1 in the flora): California, nw Mexico.

Section *Anemophili* is distributed in northern Baja California and insular southern California.

249. Astragalus miguelensis Greene, Pittonia 1: 33. 1887 • Channel island milkvetch [E]

Plants (15–)20–30 cm, woolly-tomentulose. **Stems** decumbent and ascending, woolly-tomentulose. **Leaves** (2.5–)4–12 cm; stipules connate-sheathing at proximal nodes, mostly connate at distal nodes, 2–5.5 mm, submembranous; leaflet blades oblong-oblanceolate, oblong-obovate, or oblong-ovate, (3–)6–12(–22) mm, apex retuse or obtuse, surfaces white-pannose. **Peduncles** ascending, (3–)5–13 cm. **Racemes** 10–30-flowered; axis (1–)2–9 cm in fruit; bracts 2–3.5 mm; bracteoles 0–2. **Pedicels** 0.8–3 mm. **Flowers** 12.5–16 mm; calyx 6.6–7.9 mm, white-tomentulose, tube 4.1–4.8 mm, lobes broadly subulate, 2.3–3.5 mm; corolla whitish or ochroleucous, concolorous, drying yellowish; keel (9–)9.3–12 mm. **Legumes** pale green or purplish becoming stramineous, 16–26 × (9–)13–23 mm, papery, somewhat translucent, finely tomentulose.

Flowering Mar–Jul. Rocky slopes, wind-swept sea bluffs, beaches or sandy talus beneath sea cliffs; 0–200 m; Calif.

The insular *Astragalus miguelensis* is unique among those in its area in having inflated, sessile fruits. It is locally common on Anacapa, San Clemente, San Miguel, Santa Cruz, and Santa Rosa islands.

135qqq. Astragalus Linnaeus sect. Densifolii (Rydberg) Barneby, Mem. New York Bot. Gard. 13: 801. 1964

Phaca Linnaeus [unranked] *Densifoliae* Rydberg in N. L. Britton et al., N. Amer. Fl. 24: 346. 1929

Herbs perennial, stems often fistulose, caulescent; caudex usually superficial, rarely subterranean. **Hairs** basifixed. **Stems** several to many. **Stipules** connate or distinct at distal nodes (except *A. pomonensis* ± distinct throughout). **Leaves** odd-pinnate, subsessile to petiolate; leaflets (11–)17–43. **Racemes** usually densely flowered, flowers horizontal, declined, or nodding, sometimes retrorsely imbricate. **Calyx tubes** campanulate or cylindric, sometimes gibbous proximally. **Corollas** greenish white, cream, or ochroleucous, keel apex sometimes faintly lilac-tipped, banner recurved through 35–50°, keel apex obtuse. **Legumes** eventually deciduous, sessile, gynophore sometimes present, loosely ascending, spreading, or declined, obliquely ovoid, semi-ovoid, ovoid-lenticular, obovoid, rhombic-ellipsoid, or ovoid-ellipsoid, straight or slightly curved, usually bladdery inflated, sometimes barely inflated, or laterally or dorsiventrally compressed, unilocular. **Seeds** (2 or)3–12 or 12–55.

Species 5 (5 in the flora): California, nw Mexico.

Section *Densifolii* is complex, composed of three subsections. Distribution is mainly in or near coastal central to southern California and Baja California.

The subsections are: subsect. *Crotalarii* M. E. Jones (*Astragalus curtipes*, *A. nuttallii*, *A. pomonensis*); subsect. *Pycnostachyi* (Rydberg) Barneby (*A. pycnostachyus*); and subsect. *Oxyphysi* (M. E. Jones) Barneby (*A. oxyphysus*).

250. Astragalus nuttallii (Torrey & A. Gray) J. T. Howell, Leafl. W. Bot. 5: 107. 1948 • Nuttall's milkvetch [E]

Phaca nuttallii Torrey & A. Gray, Fl. N. Amer. 1: 343. 1838

Plants densely mat-forming or bushy or mounded or, sometimes, erect clumps, 20–100 cm, sparsely villosulous; from superficial caudex. **Stems** diffuse, prostrate, ascending, or erect, sparsely villosulous. **Leaves** (2.5–)4–17 cm; stipules connate-sheathing at proximal nodes, mostly connate at distal nodes, 3–14 mm, membranous; short-petiolate or subsessile; leaflets (21 or)23–43, blades obovate, obovate-cuneate, oblong-obovate, narrowly to broadly oblong, or oblanceolate, (2–)3.5–25(–28) mm, apex retuse, emarginate, obtuse, or obtuse and apiculate, surfaces villosulous, sometimes sparsely so or glabrous adaxially, rarely puberulent. **Peduncles** erect or incurved-ascending, (4–)6–15(–18) cm. **Racemes** (15–)20–90(–125)-flowered, flowers nodding; axis 3–19 cm in fruit; bracts 1.5–4(–5) mm; bracteoles 0–2. **Pedicels** 0.8–5.5(–7) mm. **Flowers** (10–)11–15 mm; calyx campanulate or ovoid-campanulate, gibbous abaxially, (5.5–)5.8–8.2(–9) mm, sparsely to densely villosulous or loosely strigulose, tube (4–)4.3–5.7(–5.9) mm, lobes broadly subulate or triangular, (1.1–)1.3–3(–3.1) mm; corolla greenish white or cream; keel (9.7–)10.5–14 mm. **Legumes** loosely spreading, ascending, or declined, pale green or minutely purple-dotted, becoming stramineous, obliquely ovoid, ovoid-ellipsoid, or semi-ovoid, semi-obovoid, or semi ovoid-ellipsoid, bladdery-inflated, (20–)25–55(–60) × 15–27 mm, thin becoming papery, lustrous, glabrous or villosulous; sessile. **Seeds** (14–)16–38. **2*n*** = 22.

Varieties 2 (2 in the flora): California.

Astragalus nuttallii is the only *Astragalus* with sessile, bladdery fruits found at the shoreline or on sea bluffs in central California.

1. Legumes villosulous; stems diffuse or prostrate; herbage green, cinereous, or canescent; leaflet blades equally pubescent or sparsely so adaxially; seeds (22–)28–38; maritime, Monterey Bay southward to Point Conception, California. . . . . 250a. *Astragalus nuttallii* var. *nuttallii*
1. Legumes glabrous or sparsely villosulous; stems strongly ascending or erect; herbage green or greenish cinereous; leaflet blades usually glabrous adaxially, rarely puberulent; seeds (14–)16–21; maritime or slightly inland, San Francisco Peninsula (and formerly on Bay shore) and maritime northward to Mendocino County, California . . . . . . 250b. *Astragalus nuttallii* var. *virgatus*

250a. Astragalus nuttallii (Torrey & A. Gray) J. T. Howell var. **nuttallii** [E]

Herbage green, cinereous, or canescent. **Stems** diffuse or prostrate, 20–75 cm. **Leaves** 2.5–15 cm; leaflet blade surfaces equally pubescent or sparsely so adaxially, rarely ciliate, midrib prominent abaxially, hairs sparse. **Racemes** (15–)20–50-flowered; axis 3–8(–10) cm in fruit. **Flowers** (10.5–)11–14.5 mm; calyx (5.6–)5.8–8.2 mm, tube (4–)4.3–5.7 mm, lobes 1.3–3 mm. **Legumes** (23–)26–55(–60) × 17–27 mm, villosulous. **2*n*** = 22.

Flowering Jan–Nov (year-round). Ocean bluffs, dunes, rocky or sandy shores; 0–60 m; Calif.

Variety *nuttallii* is locally abundant from Monterey Bay southward to Point Conception.

250b. Astragalus nuttallii (Torrey & A. Gray) J. T. Howell var. **virgatus** (A. Gray) Barneby, Aliso 4: 135. 1958 • San Francisco milkvetch [C] [E]

Astragalus crotalariae A. Gray var. *virgatus* A. Gray in W. H. Brewer et al., Bot. California 1: 149. 1876

Herbage green or greenish cinereous. **Stems** strongly ascending or erect, (40–)60–100 cm, sometimes relatively slender and prostrate or mounded along immediate coast. **Leaves** (4–)5.5–17 cm; leaflet blade surfaces usually glabrous adaxially, rarely puberulent, sometimes sparsely ciliate, midrib sparsely hairy abaxially. **Racemes** (25–)40–90(–125)-flowered; axis (4.5–)6–19 cm in fruit. **Flowers** (10–)11–15 mm; calyx (5.5–)6–8(–9) mm, tube (4.4–)4.7–5.5(–5.9) mm, lobes (1.1–)1.3–2.5(–3.1) mm. **Legumes** (20–)25–40 × 15–25 mm, glabrous or sparsely villosulous.

Flowering Apr–Jul (year-round). Ocean bluffs, sandy fields, brushy or grassy banks, in temporarily moist, sandy bottomlands; of conservation concern; 0–200 m; Calif.

Many of the habitats of var. *virgatus* have been destroyed by development; it occurs around San Francisco Bay and northward to Mendocino County.

251. Astragalus pomonensis M. E. Jones, Contr. W. Bot. 10: 59, plate 9. 1902 • Pomona milkvetch

Plants coarse, (25–)40–80 cm, sparsely strigulose or glabrate; from superficial caudex. **Stems** decumbent and ascending, sometimes fistulose, sparsely strigulose or glabrous. **Leaves** (5–)8–20 cm; stipules mostly distinct, (2–)4–10 mm, papery at proximal nodes, herbaceous at distal nodes; sessile or subsessile to short-petiolate; leaflets 25–41, blades narrowly oblong, ovate-cuneate, or rhombic-ovate, (3–)6–30(–37) mm, apex truncate, emarginate and apiculate, or subacute, surfaces sparsely strigulose or glabrous abaxially, glabrous adaxially. **Peduncles** erect or incurved-ascending, 5.5–14 cm. **Racemes** (10–)20–45-flowered, flowers horizontal or declined; axis 3.5–9 cm in fruit; bracts 1.5–3.5 mm; bracteoles 0. **Pedicels** 0.6–3.5 mm. **Flowers** 11.1–15.3 mm; calyx broadly campanulate, obliquely truncate or subgibbous abaxially, 5–7.2(–7.7) mm, strigulose, tube 3.5–4.8(–5) mm, lobes subulate or triangular-subulate, (1–)1.3–2.6(–3) mm; corolla white, greenish white, or ochroleucous; keel 9.4–13.2 mm. **Legumes** readily deciduous, horizontal or ascending, pale green or purplish stramineous, obliquely ovoid or semi-ovoid, bladdery-inflated, (18–)23–45(–50) × (10–)12–20 mm, thin becoming papery, translucent, sublustrous, sparsely strigulose or glabrate; sessile. **Seeds** 34–55. $2n = 22$.

Flowering Mar–May. Grassy or brushy hillsides, openings in chaparral, fallow fields, valley floors, sometimes weedy in orchards; 0–700(–1200) m; Calif.; Mexico (Baja California).

Astragalus pomonensis occurs in the interior valleys of southern California, extending to the desert near Morongo Pass, southward to extreme northwestern Baja California and northward along the coast to Cambria in San Luis Obispo County.

The relationship between *Astragalus pomonensis* and *A. nuttallii* has long been inferred. Where closely adjacent, the Pomona milkvetch can be distinguished by its sparsely strigulose or glabrate, not softly villous, herbage. *Astragalus pomonensis* has distinct stipules and, in this character and in the form of the fruits, it resembles *A. douglasii*. R. C. Barneby (1964) provided a detailed key to distinguish these last two species.

252. Astragalus curtipes A. Gray, Proc. Calif. Acad. Sci. 3: 103. 1864 • Morro milkvetch [E]

Plants clump-forming, caulescent, 25–60+ cm, strigulose and often minutely tomentulose; from superficial caudex. **Stems** erect or ascending, strigulose and often minutely tomentulose. **Leaves** (4–)5–16 cm; stipules connate-sheathing at proximal nodes, connate or distinct at distal nodes, 2–12 mm, papery-membranous; petiolate or subsessile; leaflets 25–39, blades linear-oblong to narrowly obovate, (2–)5–25 mm, apex obtuse or truncate-emarginate, surfaces strigulose abaxially, glabrous adaxially. **Peduncles** erect, (5.5–)7–25 cm. **Racemes** 15–35-flowered, flowers spreading becoming declined; axis 2–11 cm in fruit; bracts 1.4–3.7 mm; bracteoles 0 or 1. **Pedicels** 1–6 mm. **Flowers** 13–16 mm; calyx campanulate, 6–8.6 mm, densely strigulose, tube (3.7–)4–5 mm, lobes subulate or lanceolate, (1.5–)1.8–3.6 mm; corolla creamy white (concolorous), or keel tip faintly lilac; keel 10.7–12.7 mm. **Legumes** ascending, loosely spreading, or declined, stramineous, not bicarinate, obliquely obovoid or semi-obovoid-ellipsoid, bladdery-inflated, 23–36 × 12–18(–20) mm, thin becoming papery-membranous, translucent, lustrous, sparsely strigulose; gynophore 2.3–5.5(–6) mm. **Seeds** (26–)28–37.

Flowering Feb–Jun. Grassy and brushy hillsides, rocky bluffs and fallow fields near the coast; 10–200 m; Calif.

Astragalus curtipes is known from San Simeon Creek, San Luis Obispo County, to near Point Arguello in Santa Barbara County, and on San Miguel and Santa Rosa islands. Populations from the mainland nearly always have conspicuously whitened stems with dense pubescence of straight and curled hairs and uniformly white flowers, whereas the common phase on the islands is more sparsely pubescent and with a lilac keel apex. In San Benito County, there is a rarely collected phase with very large fruits, 4.5–7 cm.

253. Astragalus pycnostachyus A. Gray, Proc. Amer. Acad. Arts 6: 527. 1865 (as pycnostachius) • Brine milkvetch [C] [E]

Plants clump-forming, 40–90 cm, pilose-tomentulose; from superficial or shallow, subterranean caudex. **Stems** erect or ascending, fistulose, pilose-tomentulose or white-lanate, rarely white-tomentulose. **Leaves** 3–13(–15) cm; stipules connate-sheathing at proximal nodes, connate or distinct at distal nodes, 3–12 mm, papery-membranous becoming scarious; mostly sessile; leaflets (23–)27–41, blades narrowly oblong to oblong, oblong-elliptic, or linear-lanceolate, (2–)5–30 mm, apex obtuse or emarginate and apiculate, surfaces pilose-tomentulose. **Peduncles** erect or incurved-ascending, 2–10 cm. **Racemes** many-flowered, flowers declined and retrorsely imbricate in spikelike heads, 20–70(–90) × 18–23 mm; axis 2.5–8(–9.5) cm in fruit; bracts (1.2–)1.6–4 mm; bracteoles 0. **Pedicels** 0.7–1.8 mm. **Flowers** 7–10 mm; calyx ovoid-campanulate, 5.4–7.8 mm, villosulous, tube 3.7–5.2 mm, lobes ± subulate, 1.2–3 mm; corolla greenish white or cream; keel 7.1–9.1 mm. **Legumes** deflexed or declined, green becoming stramineous or brownish, ovoid-lenticular, slightly inflated, somewhat compressed laterally, 6–11 × 3.5–6 mm, thin becoming papery, somewhat lustrous, glabrous or sparsely strigulose; sessile. **Seeds** (2 or)3–12.

Varieties 2 (2 in the flora): California.

1. Peduncles (3–)4–10 cm; calyx tubes 3.7–5.2 mm, lobes subulate, 1.7–3 mm; legumes 6–9(–10) mm; seeds (2 or)3–5; Humboldt to San Mateo counties, California . . . . 253a. *Astragalus pycnostachyus* var. *pycnostachyus*
1. Peduncles 2–4 cm; calyx tubes 3–3.5 mm, lobes broader and shorter, 1.2–1.5 mm; legumes 8–11 mm; seeds 8–12; Ventura to Orange counties, California . . . . 253b. *Astragalus pycnostachyus* var. *lanosissimus*

253a. Astragalus pycnostachyus A. Gray var. **pycnostachyus** [C] [E]

Herbage usually cinereous or subcanescent, rarely white-tomentulose. **Leaflets** (23–)27–41, blades flat or loosely folded, narrowly oblong, oblong-elliptic, or linear-lanceolate, (2–)5–30 mm. **Peduncles** (3–)4–10 cm. **Calyces:** tube 3.7–5.2 mm, lobes subulate, 1.7–3 mm. **Legumes** 6–9(–10) mm, glabrous. **Seeds** (2 or)3–5.

Flowering Jun–Sep. Salt marshes within reach of high tide or protected by barrier beaches, rarely near seeps on sandy sea bluffs, in springy spots along creeks opening to the sea; of conservation concern; 0–40 m; Calif.

Variety *pycnostachyus* occurs along the immediate coastline of central and northwestern California in Marin and San Mateo counties and is apparently disjunct in central Humboldt County.

R. C. Barneby (1964) noted of var. *pycnostachyus* that he had not observed any convincing example of a natural legume fall or dehiscence of this late-flowering, tardily maturing, small-podded taxon.

253b. Astragalus pycnostachyus A. Gray var. **lanosissimus** (Rydberg) Munz & McBurney, Bull. S. Calif. Acad. Sci. 31: 66. 1932 • La Bolsa milkvetch [C] [E]

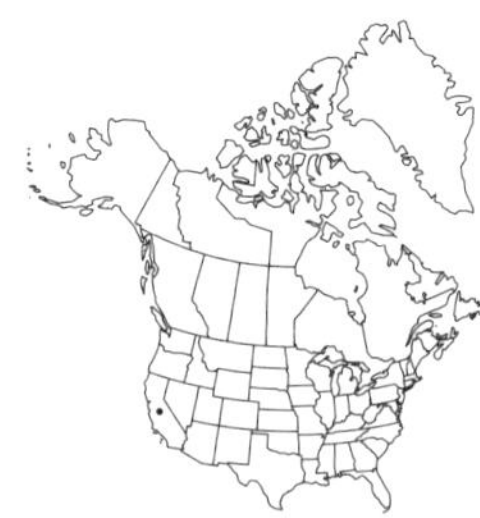

Phaca lanosissima Rydberg in N. L. Britton et al., N. Amer. Fl. 24: 357. 1929

Herbage usually white-lanate, almost silvery when young. **Leaflets** 27–39, blades flat, oblong, (3–)5–20 mm. **Peduncles** 2–4 cm. **Calyces:** tube 3–3.5 mm, lobes broader and shorter, 1.2–1.5 mm. **Legumes** 8–11 mm, usually sparsely strigulose, sometimes glabrous. **Seeds** 8–12.

Flowering Jun–Oct. Salt marshes within reach of high tide or protected by barrier beaches, more rarely near seeps on sandy sea bluffs, in springy spots along creeks opening to the sea; of conservation concern; 0–60 m; Calif.

Because of habitat loss, var. *lanosissimus* was assumed to be extinct, but in 1997 a population of 30 to 50 plants was located on an abandoned oil-field waste site near Oxnard in Ventura County. It formerly occurred from Point Hueneme in Ventura County southward to the now drained Ballona Marshes in Los Angeles County and perhaps extreme northern Orange County.

Variety *lanosissimus* is federally listed and in the Center for Plant Conservation's National Collection of Endangered Plants.

254. Astragalus oxyphysus A. Gray, Proc. Calif. Acad. Sci. 3: 103. 1864 • Stanislaus milkvetch [E] [F]

Plants forming bushy clumps, (15–)30–80(–100) cm, almost as wide, villosulous; from superficial caudex. **Stems** erect or ascending, sparsely villosulous, often glabrous basally. **Leaves** (4.5–)7–17 cm; stipules connate-sheathing at proximal nodes, distinct at distal nodes, (3–)4–12 mm, submembranous; short-petiolate or subsessile; leaflets (11–)17–29(or 31), blades broadly to narrowly lanceolate-elliptic or oblong-elliptic, or oblong-obovate, (4–)7–32 mm, apex obtuse, subacute, truncate and apiculate, or retuse, surfaces villosulous, sometimes glabrescent adaxially. **Peduncles** erect, (4–)7–17 cm. **Racemes** 20–60(–65)-flowered, flowers ascending becoming loosely declined or nodding; axis (4.5–)6–22(–25) cm in fruit; bracts 2–3.5 mm. **Pedicels** 1.2–4 mm. **Flowers** 15.3–18(–19) mm; calyx cylindric or deeply campanulate, (5.5–)8.7–10.3 mm, villosulous, tube 5.9–8.4 mm, lobes subulate or triangular-subulate, 1.6–3.7 mm; corolla pale cream, white, or whitish; keel 13.1–14.7 mm. **Legumes** spreading or loosely pendulous, stramineous, bicarinate, obliquely elliptic, semielliptic, or rhombic-elliptic, bladdery-inflated, laterally compressed, (21–)25–45 × (6–)8–15.5 mm, thin becoming papery, translucent, lustrous, sparsely strigulose; gynophore 3–11 mm, densely villosulous. **Seeds** 11–18. **2*n*** = 22.

Flowering Mar–Jun. Rolling plains, grassy hillsides, canyon banks, arid grasslands; 80–700(–1000) m; Calif.

Astragalus oxyphysus occurs in the inner South Coast Ranges and adjacent Great Valley from Mount Hamilton, Stanislaus County, southward to the upper Cuyama Valley and foothills of the Tehachapi Mountains and extreme southern Sierra Nevada in Santa Barbara and Kern counties, and also the eastern slope of the Santa Lucia Mountains in northern San Luis Obispo County.

Since early settlement, *Astragalus oxyphysus* has been known to cause rapid fatality in sheep, severe poisoning in cattle, and addiction and ultimate poisoning in horses; it is sometimes called Diablo loco (R. C. Barneby 1964). Plants of *A. oxyphysus* contain swainsonine (L. F. James and S. L. Welsh 1992). It closely resembles another southern California species, *A. asymmetricus*. Barneby provided a key contrasting the two, noting that *A. oxyphysus* has a gynophore whereas *A. asymmetricus* has a genuine stipe emanating from the receptacle.

135rrr. Astragalus Linnaeus sect. Trichopodi (Rydberg) Barneby, Mem. New York Bot. Gard. 13: 816. 1964

Phaca Linnaeus [unranked] *Trichopodae* Rydberg in N. L. Britton et al., N. Amer. Fl. 24: 335. 1929

Herbs perennial, clump-forming, caulescent; caudex superficial. **Hairs** basifixed. **Stems** several to many. **Stipules** distinct or at proximal nodes connate. **Leaves** odd-pinnate, short-petiolate or subsessile; leaflets (15–)21–35(–39). **Racemes** loosely flowered, flowers spreading or nodding. **Calyx tubes** campanulate. **Corollas** whitish, cream, or ochroleucous, banner purple-veined, or keel apex slightly purplish, banner slightly recurved or recurved through 40–45°, keel apex blunt or sharply deltate. **Legumes** persistent, stipitate, pendulous or spreading, linear-ellipsoid to broadly and obliquely ovoid-ellipsoid or semi-ovoid, compressed laterally and 2-sided, or bladdery-inflated, unilocular. **Seeds** (10–)12–30.

Species 2 (2 in the flora): California, nw Mexico.

Section *Trichopodi* consists of two species, with distribution in the South Coast Ranges, western edge of the Great Valley, and in southern California coast and islands, southward to northern Baja California.

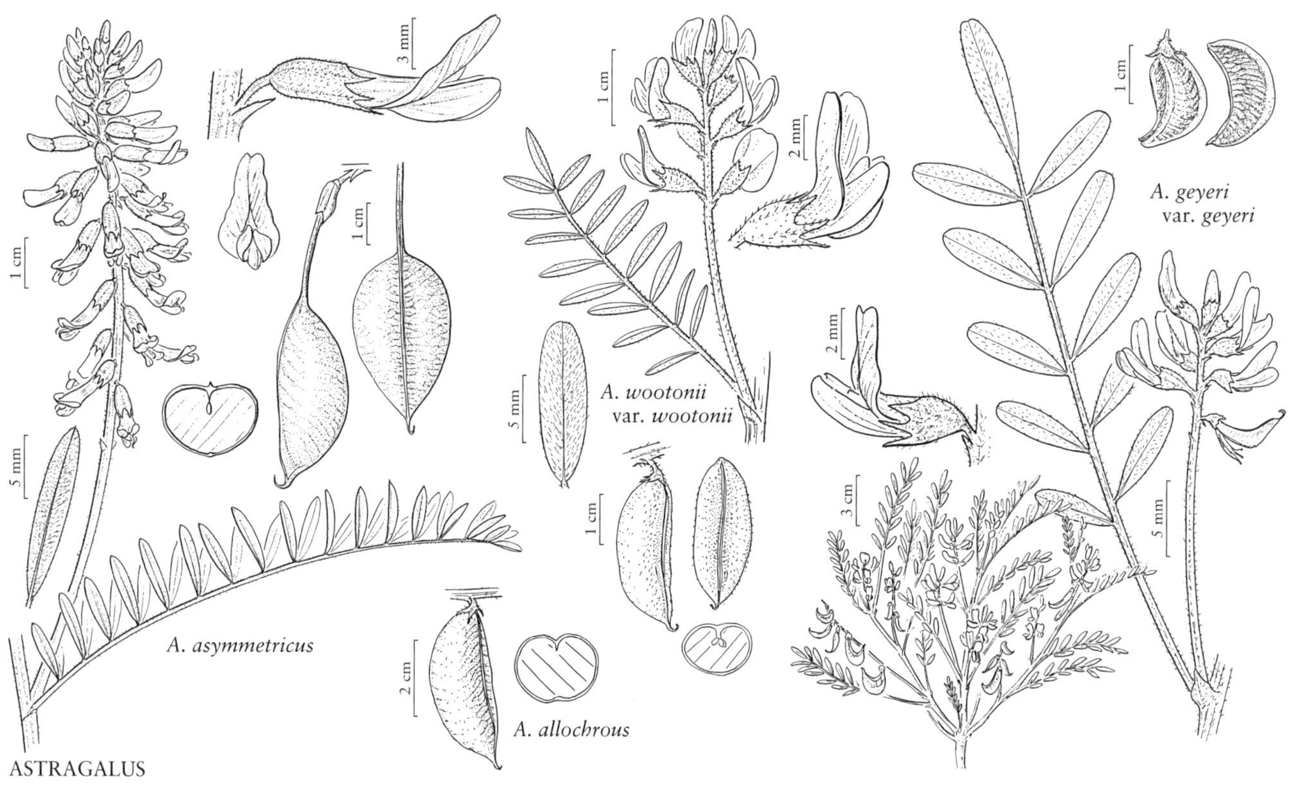

ASTRAGALUS

255. Astragalus asymmetricus E. Sheldon, Minnesota Bot. Stud. 1: 23. 1894 • Horse milkvetch E F W

Astragalus leucophyllus Torrey & A. Gray, Fl. N. Amer. 1: 336. 1838, not Willdenow 1802

Plants 50–120 cm, densely silky-strigulose. **Stems** erect or ascending, densely silky-strigulose. **Leaves** (5–)7–17(–20) cm; stipules connate-sheathing at proximal nodes, distinct at distal nodes, 2–14 mm, scarious; leaflets (17–)21–35, blades linear, linear-oblong, -elliptic, -lanceolate, or -oblanceolate, (3–)6–26 mm, apex obtuse and apiculate or emarginate, surfaces strigulose, sometimes glabrous adaxially. **Peduncles** erect, 6–24 cm. **Racemes** 15–45-flowered, flowers nodding; axis (5–)7–17 cm in fruit; bracts 1.5–4 mm; bracteoles 0–2. **Pedicels** 1.2–5 mm. **Flowers** 12.6–17.6 mm; calyx (6.5–)8–11.4 mm, densely silky-strigulose, hairs white, tube 5–7.2 mm, lobes lanceolate-subulate, (1.5–)2–4.2 mm; corolla ochroleucous, immaculate; banner gently and slightly recurved; keel 11.5–14.7 mm. **Legumes** spreading to pendulous, stramineous, obliquely ovoid-ellipsoid or semi-ovoid, bladdery-inflated, somewhat compressed laterally, (20–)25–43 × 13–18 mm, thin becoming papery-membranous, translucent, lustrous, sparsely strigulose; stipe filiform, 14–40 mm, pubescent. **Seeds** (16–)18–30. **2*n*** = 22.

Flowering Apr–Jul. Dry, grassy hills, fields, roadside banks, rolling plains; 50–1000 m; Calif.

Astragalus asymmetricus is known from the inner South Coast Ranges and adjoining Great Valley, from western Kern County and the Salinas Valley, San Luis Obispo County, northward through the hill country east of San Francisco Bay to Solano County.

Astragalus asymmetricus, *A. oxyphysus*, and *A. trichopodus* form a trio of very similar southern California species. R. C. Barneby (1964) contrasted the first and last in a key. *Astragalus asymmetricus* has connate proximalmost stipules, longer calyces, and slightly graduated petals. It is also well known in California as poisonous to stock, containing swainsonine (L. F. James and S. L. Welsh 1992).

256. Astragalus trichopodus (Nuttall) A. Gray, Proc. Amer. Acad. Arts 6: 218. 1864 • Santa Barbara milkvetch

Phaca trichopoda Nuttall in J. Torrey and A. Gray, Fl. N. Amer. 1: 343. 1838

Plants (5–)25–80(–100) cm, strigulose to villosulous. **Stems** erect, ascending, or trailing, strigulose to villosulous. **Leaves** (2.5–)5–16(–20) cm; stipules usually distinct, rarely connate at proximal nodes, (2–)3–7 mm, herbaceous; leaflets (15–)21–35(–39), blades ovate- or lanceolate-oblong, oblong-elliptic or -oblanceolate, (2–)5–20(–25) mm, apex emarginate, surfaces pubescent, sometimes glabrous adaxially. **Peduncles** erect or incurved-ascending, (4–)6–26(–30) cm. **Racemes** (10–)15–50-flowered, flowers spreading becoming nodding; axis (2–)3.5–13(–16) cm in fruit; bracts 1–3.3 mm; bracteoles 2. **Pedicels** 1.2–5.2 mm. **Flowers** 11.3–19 mm; calyx pallid, obliquely turbinate, 5–8.7 mm, strigulose or strigulose-villosulous, tube 3.6–5.4 mm, lobes subulate, (0.9–)1.1–3.7 mm; corolla greenish white or cream, rarely veined pale pink or purple; banner recurved through 40–45°; keel 8.6–13.3 mm. **Legumes** pendulous, pale green or purplish-tinged becoming stramineous, straight or decurved, linear-ellipsoid, fusiform-ellipsoid, semi-ovoid, semi-ellipsoid, ovoid, or oblanceoloid, ± greatly inflated, often bladdery, laterally compressed when narrow, (13–)15–40(–45) × 4.8–18(–21) mm, thin becoming papery, lustrous, glabrous or strigulose; stipe filiform, (6–)6.5–17 mm, flexible, strigulose-villosulous. **Seeds** (10–)12–30.

Varieties 3 (3 in the flora): California, nw Mexico.

With ample material available, R. C. Barneby (1964) noted that differences between taxa within *Astragalus trichopodus*, in the past based in part on variation in indumentum, existed only in the fruits, and even then variation was more or less continuous. *Astragalus trichopodus* is easily confused with *A. asymmetricus* or *A. oxyphysus*.

In the northern Channel Islands, care is required to distinguish *Astragalus trichopodus* from *A. curtipes*, which has a true gynophore that is shorter than the stipe of *A. trichopodus*.

1. Legumes usually laterally compressed, symmetric (straight) or rarely somewhat oblique distally, 15–36 × 4.8–9 mm, usually glabrous, rarely finely strigulose; inland from Los Angeles and Riverside counties to San Luis Obispo County, to coastal bluffs in sw Santa Barbara County . . . . 256c. *Astragalus trichopodus* var. *antisellii*
1. Legumes not or slightly laterally compressed, bladdery-inflated or strongly tumid, lateral faces convexly rounded, asymmetric, (13–)15–40(–45) × (5–)6–18(–21) mm, glabrous or strigulose; San Luis Obispo County, California, to n Baja California and adjacent islands.
    2. Legumes (13–)15–35 × (5–)6–10(–13) mm, bladdery-inflated or strongly tumid, symmetric or strongly oblique, sutures equally convex, or dorsally low-convex, ventrally straight, usually glabrous, very rarely strigulose; Orange and immediately adjoining counties, Kern and s San Luis Obispo counties, Catalina Island. . . . . 256a. *Astragalus trichopodus* var. *trichopodus*
    2. Legumes (17–)20–40(–45) × (8–)10–18(–21) mm, bladdery-inflated, greatly oblique, sutures more convex dorsally, usually openly sulcate ventrally and straight, shallowly concave, or low-convex, usually finely strigulose, rarely glabrous distally or throughout; coastal, rarely somewhat inland along seaward-running canyons, n Baja California to San Luis Obispo County, California, and Channel Islands . . . . 256b. *Astragalus trichopodus* var. *lonchus*

256a. Astragalus trichopodus (Nuttall) A. Gray var. **trichopodus** [E]

Astragalus trichopodus var. *capillipes* (Rydberg) Munz & McBurney

Peduncles (4–)6–26(–30) cm. **Racemes** (10–)20–50-flowered; axis (2–)3.5–13(–16) cm in fruit. **Flowers** 11.5–15.4 mm. **Legumes** not or slightly compressed, bladdery-inflated or strongly tumid, lateral faces convexly rounded, symmetric or, sometimes, strongly oblique, fusiform-ellipsoid or semi-ellipsoid, (13–)15–35 × (5–)6–10(–13) mm, sutures equally convex or dorsally low-convex, ventrally straight, usually glabrous, very rarely strigulose; gynophore 6.5–17 mm, minutely pubescent.

Flowering Mar–Jun (fall–winter). Shale or sandstone outcrops on sea bluffs or low grassy hills; 10–90 (–700) m; Calif.

Variety *trichopodus* is known from three restricted areas in southern California from Kern and San Luis Obispo counties southward to San Diego County.

256b. Astragalus trichopodus (Nuttall) A. Gray var. **lonchus** (M. E. Jones) Barneby, Mem. New York Bot. Gard. 13: 821. 1964 • Ocean milkvetch

Astragalus leucopsis (Torrey & A. Gray) Torrey var. *lonchus* M. E. Jones, Rev. N.-Amer. Astragalus, 119. 1923

Peduncles (5.5–)8–20(–30) cm. **Racemes** (12–)15–36-flowered; axis (2–)3.5–11 cm in fruit. **Flowers** 11.3–19 mm; corolla rarely veined pale pink or purple. **Legumes** not or slightly laterally compressed, bladdery-inflated, lateral faces convexly rounded, greatly oblique, ovoid, semi-ovoid, semi-ellipsoid, or lunately so, (17–)20–40(–45) × (8–)10–18(–21) mm, sutures more convex dorsally, usually openly sulcate ventrally and straight, shallowly or low-convex, usually finely strigulose, rarely glabrous distally or throughout, hairs often white, sometimes fuscous; gynophore mostly 8–12 mm. $2n$ = 22.

Flowering Feb–Jun (fall–winter). Coastal bluffs, mesas, and sandy fields near the sea, shale cliffs or descending to shingle banks behind barrier beaches; 0–80(–500) m; Calif.; Mexico (Baja California).

Variety *lonchus* has a largely coastal distribution from Morro Bay in San Luis Obispo County southward to the Santa Maria Plains in northern Baja California.

256c. Astragalus trichopodus (Nuttall) A. Gray var. **antisellii** (A. Gray) Jepson, Man. Fl. Pl. Calif., 572. 1925 • Antisell's milkvetch or rattleweed [E]

Astragalus antisellii A. Gray in W. H. Brewer et al., Bot. California 1: 152. 1876 (as antiselli); *A. antisellii* var. *gaviotus* (Elmer) Munz & McBurney; *A. antisellii* var. *phoxus* M. E. Jones; *A. gaviotus* Elmer; *A. hasseanus* E. Sheldon; *A. trichopodus* var. *gaviotus* (Elmer) Jepson; *A. trichopodus* var. *phoxus* (M. E. Jones) Barneby; *Homalobus antisellii* (A. Gray) Rydberg; *H. gaviotus* (Elmer) Rydberg

Peduncles (4–)6–26(–30) cm. **Racemes** (10–)20–50-flowered; axis (2–)3.5–13(–16) cm in fruit. **Flowers** (11.4–)12.4–16.7 mm. **Legumes** usually laterally compressed, symmetric (straight) or rarely somewhat oblique distally, oblanceoloid or linear-ellipsoid, (15–)20–36 (–40) × 4.8–9(–11) mm, keeled by both sutures, usually glabrous, rarely finely strigulose; gynophore (6–)7–13 (–15) mm.

Flowering Feb–Jun (fall–winter). Disturbed sites and openings in chaparral; 30–1300 m; Calif.

Variety *antisellii* occurs from Kern and San Luis Obispo counties southward to western Riverside county.

Variety *antisellii* is a relatively tall taxon with ample leaves and elongate, loosely-flowered racemes, which do not much elongate in fruit. The long-stipitate, pendulous, laterally compressed legumes bicarinate by the sutures are diagnostic for this variety.

135sss. Astragalus Linnaeus sect. Inflati A. Gray, Proc. Amer. Acad. Arts 6: 213. 1864

Herbs perennial, biennial, or annual, caulescent; caudex usually superficial (shallowly subterranean in *A. perianus*). **Hairs** basifixed. **Stems** single, few, or several to many. **Stipules** usually distinct, rarely connate at proximal nodes. **Leaves** odd-pinnate, subsessile to petiolate; leaflets (3 or)5–35. **Racemes** loosely or densely flowered, flowers spreading to ascending or declined. **Calyx tubes** campanulate, turbinate-campanulate, or obconic-campanulate. **Corollas** white, whitish, yellowish, lilac, blue-violet, or pink-purple, often drying violet, banner recurved through 40–125°, keel apex rounded, deltate, or narrowly triangular, often beaklike. **Legumes** usually deciduous, sessile, gynophore sometimes present, spreading, ascending, or declined, globose to ovoid, lanceoloid-oblong, or -ellipsoid, bladdery-inflated or slightly swollen, usually unilocular, rarely semibilocular. **Seeds** (3–)6–58(–76).

Species 35 (28 in the flora): w, c United States, n Mexico, South America.

Section *Inflati* consists of five subsections: subsect. *Macrodontes* M. E. Jones (*Astragalus deanei*, *A. douglasii*, *A. macrodon*, *A. oocarpus*); subsect. *Proriferi* M. E. Jones (*A. magdalenae*, *A. palmeri*); subsect. *Aridi* M. E. Jones (*A. allochrous*, *A. aquilonius*, *A. aridus*, *A. beatleyae*, *A. cerussatus*, *A. endopterus*, *A. geyeri*, *A. gilmanii*, *A. insularis*, *A. nutans*, *A. pardalinus*,

A. perianus, *A. pubentissimus*, *A. sabulonum*, *A. serpens*, *A. thurberi*, *A. wardii*, *A. wootonii*); subsect. *Sparsiflori* (M. E. Jones) Barneby (*A. diaphanus*, *A. sparsiflorus*, *A. wetherillii*); and subsect. *Horniani* Barneby (*A. hornii*).

257. Astragalus douglasii (Torrey & A. Gray) A. Gray, Proc. Amer. Acad. Arts 6: 215. 1864 • Douglas's milkvetch

Phaca douglasii Torrey & A. Gray, Fl. N. Amer. 1: 346. 1838

Plants perennial, (15–)20–100 cm, strigulose or villosulous; from superficial caudex. **Stems** decumbent, trailing, erect, or ascending, mostly strigulose or villosulous, often glabrous or glabrate at proximal nodes. **Leaves** 5–16(–18) cm; stipules distinct 1.5–6.5 mm, papery at proximal nodes, firm or submembranous at distal nodes; leaflets (11 or)13–25, blades ovate, obovate, oblong-elliptic, elliptic, lanceolate-oblong, oblanceolate, or linear-oblong, 5–25(–30) mm, apex usually obtuse, retuse, or truncate and apiculate, rarely subacute, surfaces glabrous. **Peduncles** erect, 2.5–13 cm. **Racemes** (10–)12–30(–35)-flowered, flowers subhorizontal or ascending; axis (2–)2.5–12(–17) cm in fruit; bracts 1–3 mm. **Pedicels** 0.8–4(–4.8) mm. **Flowers** (6.4–)7.8–13 mm; calyx campanulate or ovoid-campanulate, 4–6.6 mm, strigulose, tube (2.5–)2.6–4.3 mm, lobes subulate, deltate, or triangular, 0.7–2.6 mm; corolla ochroleucous, yellowish, or greenish white; banner abruptly recurved through 60–90°, (6.4–)7.8–13 mm; keel (6.2–)7.1–10.8 mm, apex narrowly deltate and triangular, subacute, somewhat beaklike. **Legumes** spreading or ascending (sometimes humistrate), pale green, sometimes purple-tinged or -speckled, becoming stramineous, obliquely ovoid, semi-ovoid or semi-ellipsoid, bladdery-inflated, somewhat obcompressed, 25–60 × 12–32 mm, beak prominent, papery, ± lustrous, usually strigulose, rarely glabrescent. **Seeds** 42–71(–76).

Varieties 3 (3 in the flora): California, n Mexico.

Astragalus douglasii is a closely knit group of races; the varieties are weakly marked and intergradient. It is considered part of a taxonomically difficult group of perennial species in sect. *Inflati*, with racemes of numerous (ten to about sixty) flowers with petals strongly recurved and poorly or irregularly graduated. The center of variation of the species is in interior southern California and adjacent Mexico, coinciding with the center of diversity of the group as a whole (R. C. Barneby 1964).

1. Calyces uniformly pubescent, lobes usually subulate, rarely triangular-subulate, 1.4–2.6 mm; Los Angeles County and San Bernardino County northward. . . . . 257a. *Astragalus douglasii* var. *douglasii*
1. Calyces sparsely pubescent, lobes broadly triangular or triangular-subulate, 0.7–1.9(–2.2) mm; San Bernardino County southward.
   2. Stems decumbent with ascending tips, trailing, or weakly assurgent, (15–)20–60(–70) cm; peduncles incurved-ascending; legumes humistrate, 25–40(–50) mm; San Bernardino County, southward to n Baja California . . . . 257b. *Astragalus douglasii* var. *parishii*
   2. Stems erect or stiffly ascending, 40–100 cm; peduncles erect; legumes not humistrate, (35–)40–60 mm; near international boundary in se San Diego County . . . . 257c. *Astragalus douglasii* var. *perstrictus*

257a. Astragalus douglasii (Torrey & A. Gray) A. Gray var. **douglasii** [E]

Stems decumbent with ascending tips, trailing, or weakly assurgent, (15–)20–60(–70) cm. **Leaflets** (11–)15–25, blades ovate, obovate, oblong-elliptic, oblanceolate, or linear-oblong, 5–25(–30) mm, apex usually obtuse or retuse, sometimes truncate and apiculate or subacute. **Peduncles** incurved-ascending, 2.5–9 cm. **Racemes** (10–)15–30(–35)-flowered; axis (2–)2.5–12(–17) cm in fruit. **Flowers:** calyx (4.7–)4.9–6.6 mm, uniformly strigulose, tube (2.5–)2.9–4.3 mm, lobes usually subulate, rarely triangular-subulate, 1.4–2.6mm; corolla banners (6.4–)7.8–13 × (5.8–)6.8–10.2 mm. **Legumes** humistrate, 25–60 mm, usually sparsely strigulose, rarely glabrescent; seed-bearing flange 0.7–1.8 mm wide. **Seeds** (46–)51–71. $2n = 22$.

Flowering Apr–Jul (late Oct). Gray pine and live oak woodlands; 100–2100 m; Calif.

Variety *douglasii* is the only small-flowered *Astragalus* with fruits at once greatly swollen and sessile that is at all common in the California coast ranges between the lower Sacramento River and Santa Barbara (R. C. Barneby 1964). It overlaps in range with *A. macrodon*, which is distinctly villous.

257b. Astragalus douglasii (Torrey & A. Gray) A. Gray var. **parishii** (A. Gray) M. E. Jones, Contr. W. Bot. 8: 6. 1898 • Parish's milkvetch

Astragalus parishii A. Gray, Proc. Amer. Acad. Arts 19: 75. 1883

Stems decumbent with ascending tips, trailing, or weakly assurgent, (15–)20–60(–70) cm. **Leaflets** (11–)15–25, blades ovate, obovate, oblong-elliptic, oblanceolate, or linear-oblong, 5–25(–30) mm, apex usually obtuse or retuse, sometimes truncate and apiculate or subacute. **Peduncles** incurved-ascending, 2.5–9 cm. **Racemes** (10–)15–30(–35)-flowered; axis (2–)2.5–12 (–17) cm in fruit. **Flowers:** calyx 4–6 mm, sparsely strigulose, tube 2.6–4.1 mm, lobes triangular, 0.7–1.9 (–2.2) mm; corolla banners 8.1–12 × 6–9 mm. **Legumes** humistrate, 25–40(–50) mm, strigulose; seed-bearing flange 1–2.5 mm wide. **Seeds** 42–62(–76). $2n$ = 22.

Flowering May–Oct. Gravelly flats and openings in pine or oak forests; 400–2400 m; Calif.; Mexico (Baja California).

Variety *parishii* is restricted to the mountains of interior southern California and adjacent Baja California.

257c. Astragalus douglasii (Torrey & A. Gray) A. Gray var. **perstrictus** (Rydberg) Munz & McBurney, Bull. S. Calif. Acad. Sci. 31: 65. 1932 (as perstricta) • Campo milkvetch [C] [E]

Phaca perstricta Rydberg in N. L. Britton et al., N. Amer. Fl. 24: 344. 1929; *Astragalus parishii* A. Gray subsp. *perstrictus* (Rydberg) Abrams

Stems erect or stiffly ascending, 40–100 cm. **Leaflets** (11 or)13–19, blades narrowly elliptic, lanceolate-oblong, or narrowly obovate, 7–25 mm, apex obtuse or truncate-emarginate and apiculate. **Peduncles** erect, 7–13 cm. **Racemes** 12–20-flowered; axis 4–10 cm in fruit. **Flowers:** calyx 4.1–5 mm, sparsely strigulose, tube (2.5–)2.9–4.3 mm, lobes broadly triangular or triangular-subulate, 0.7–1.1 mm; corolla banners 8.5–10 × 7–8.4 mm. **Legumes** not humistrate, (35–)40–60 mm, strigulose; seed-bearing flange 1 mm wide. **Seeds** (48–)58–67. $2n$ = 22.

Flowering late Apr–Jun. Stony hillsides, gravelly or sandy flats, decomposed granitic soils, open oak woodlands; of conservation concern; 900–1300 m; Calif.

Variety *perstrictus* is restricted to southeastern San Diego County (and probably adjacent Baja California) and is more or less intermediate between two other local taxa, *Astragalus douglasii* var. *parishii* and *A. oocarpus*. R. C. Barneby (1964) suggested possible amphidiploidy, but R. Spellenberg (1976) reported $2n$ = 22 in all varieties of *A. douglasii* and also in *A. oocarpus*.

258. Astragalus macrodon (Hooker & Arnott) A. Gray, Proc. Amer. Acad. Arts 6: 216. 1864 • Long-toothed milkvetch [E]

Phaca macrodon Hooker & Arnott, Bot. Beechey Voy., 333. 1838

Plants perennial, clump-forming, 15–50(–80) cm, villosulous; from superficial caudex. **Stems** decumbent or ascending, villosulous. **Leaves** 5.5–15 cm; stipules distinct, 1.5–8(–12) mm, herbaceous; leaflets (11–)17–27(or 29), blades oblong-oblanceolate to narrowly elliptic, or obovate, (4–)7–22(–25) mm, apex acute or truncate and apiculate, or shallowly retuse, surfaces villosulous, sometimes sparsely so adaxially. **Peduncles** divaricate or incurved-ascending, 3.5–10(–12) cm. **Racemes** (8–)10–30(–35)-flowered, flowers declined; axis 3–15(–20) cm in fruit; bracts 1.5–3.5 mm; bracteoles 2. **Pedicels** 1–6.4 mm. **Flowers** 8.3–11.4 mm; calyx campanulate, 6.5–8.7 mm, densely villosulous, tube 3.6–4.5 mm, lobes lanceolate or subulate, 2.5–4.3 mm; corolla pale or greenish yellow; banner abruptly recurved through 90°; keel 7.5–9.1 mm, apex sharply triangular, sometimes obscurely beaklike. **Legumes** spreading to declined or ascending, pale green, usually red-cheeked, becoming stramineous, straight, broadly ovoid-ellipsoid, bladdery-inflated, somewhat obcompressed, 20–40 × 14–20 mm, thin becoming papery, sparsely to quite densely villosulous or strigulose-villosulous, hairs 1+ mm. **Seeds** 29–52.

Flowering Apr–Jun. Open hillsides, chaparral burn sites, bare ridges, along gullied draws in grassy hillsides, on shale or sandstone substrates; 200–1000 m; Calif.

Astragalus macrodon is known from the inner South Coast Ranges from Monterey and San Benito counties southward to Ventura County.

Astragalus macrodon, a close match to *A. douglasii* and especially to var. *parishii*, grows on yellowish to tan weathered shale, a habitat not known to support any phase of *A. douglasii*.

259. Astragalus oocarpus A. Gray, Proc. Amer. Acad. Arts 6: 213. 1864 • Egg-pod milkvetch [C] [E]

Plants perennial, stout, 60–130 cm, glabrate to strigulose; from superficial caudex. **Stems** stiffly erect or ascending, or finally straggling and supported on bushes, fistulose, glabrous. **Leaves** (4.5–)6–17 cm; stipules distinct, 2–14 mm, herbaceous becoming papery; leaflets (17 or)19–35, blades broadly lanceolate to oblong-ovate or oblong-obovate, 6–33 mm, apex retuse or truncate-obtuse, surfaces mostly glabrous, margins and midribs sparsely strigulose. **Peduncles** erect or incurved-ascending, 1.5–6(–7) cm. **Racemes** (15–)20–60(–75)-flowered, flowers ascending; axis (3–)4–19 cm in fruit; bracts 1.2–3 mm; bracteoles 0–2. **Pedicels** 1–3.5 mm. **Flowers** 10.5–12.5 mm; calyx campanulate, 4.5–6 mm, sparsely strigulose, tube 3.5–4.6 mm, lobes deltate or subulate, 0.8–1.8 mm; corolla ochroleucous, rarely tinged purplish, drying brownish; banner abruptly recurved through 70–90°; keel 9–10.8 mm, apex sharply triangular. **Legumes** persistent on receptacle, erect, stramineous, straight, obliquely ovoid-acuminate, greatly inflated, scarcely bladdery, terete or somewhat dorsiventrally compressed, 15–25 × (8.5–)10–16 mm, fleshy becoming stiffly papery, glabrous or minutely strigulose. **Seeds** 44–58. **2*n*** = 22.

Flowering May–Aug. Openings in chaparral, gravelly flats and slopes in thin oak woodlands; of conservation concern; (400–)800–1600 m; Calif.

Astragalus oocarpus is known primarily in the mountains of interior San Diego County. It differs from *A. douglasii* mainly by a thickening and coarsening of all its tissues, especially the petals, which are fleshy and turn brown upon drying (unless dried quickly). D. Isely (1998) provided a key by flower, by fruit, and by geography, to the four similar and related taxa of *Astragalus* in San Diego County (*A. deanei*, *A. douglasii* vars. *parishii* and *perstrictus*, and *A. oocarpus*).

260. Astragalus deanei (Rydberg) Barneby, Aliso 4: 133. 1958 • Deane's milkvetch [C] [E]

Phaca deanei Rydberg in N. L. Britton et al., N. Amer. Fl. 24: 355. 1929

Plants perennial, coarse, (15–)30–60 cm, sparsely hairy or glabrous; from superficial caudex. **Stems** erect or ascending, fistulose, glabrous. **Leaves** 8–18 cm; stipules distinct, (2–)3.5–7.5 mm, submembranous; leaflets (19 or)21–29, blades ovate-oblong to lanceolate or lanceolate-elliptic, (4–)8–21 mm, apex obtuse or truncate, usually apiculate, surfaces sparsely strigose. **Peduncles** erect or incurved-ascending, (6–)12–20 cm. **Racemes** (13–)18–25-flowered, flowers spreading or weakly ascending; axis (5–)9–16 cm in fruit; bracts 1.5–2.5 mm; bracteoles (0–)2. **Pedicels** 0.9–3.5 mm. **Flowers** (9.5–)12–15 mm; calyx purplish, campanulate, (4.7–)5–7.2 mm, sparsely strigulose, tube (2.7–)3–4.5 mm, lobes subulate, 1.8–2.7 mm; corolla whitish, drying ochroleucous; banner recurved through 45°, 12–15 mm; keel 8–10.5 mm, apex blunt and narrowly deltate. **Legumes** ascending, pale green and purplish-tinged becoming stramineous, straight or slightly incurved, obliquely semi ovoid-ellipsoid, bladdery-inflated, somewhat obcompressed, (15–)20–28 × (8–)10–15(–18) mm, beak prominent, papery, sparsely strigulose. **Seeds** 29–40.

Flowering Mar–May. Open, brushy slopes, in oak chaparral, on recently burned hillsides; of conservation concern; 200–400 m; Calif.

Astragalus deanei is restricted to tributaries of the upper Otay and Sweetwater rivers, southwestern San Diego County.

261. Astragalus palmeri A. Gray, Proc. Amer. Acad. Arts 7: 398. 1868 • Palmer's milkvetch

Astragalus palmeri var. *johnstonii* (Munz & McBurney) Barneby; *A. vaseyi* S. Watson; *A. vaseyi* var. *johnstonii* Munz & McBurney; *A. vaseyi* var. *metanus* (M. E. Jones) Munz & McBurney

Plants perennial (sometimes flowering first year), (10–)15–50 cm, silvery-strigulose; from superficial root-crown. **Stems** prostrate or weakly ascending, silvery-strigulose. **Leaves** (2–)3–13(–16) cm; stipules distinct, (1.5–)2–6.5 mm, submembranous; leaflets (9 or)11–21, blades oblong, oblong-ovate or -obovate, or broadly to narrowly elliptic, (3–)5–25 mm, apex usually acute or obtuse and apiculate, rarely retuse-emarginate, surfaces sparsely strigulose abaxially, usually densely to sparsely strigulose adaxially, rarely glabrous or glabrescent. **Peduncles** ascending or incurved, 4–13 cm. **Racemes** (10–)20–40-flowered, flowers widely ascending or spreading; axis (3.5–)4–21 cm in fruit; bracts 0.8–2.6 mm; bracteoles 2. **Pedicels** 0.5–3(–3.4) mm. **Flowers** 7–10.3 mm; calyx campanulate or ovoid-campanulate, 3.6–6.6 mm, strigulose, tube (2.2–)2.7–3.8 mm, lobes subulate or triangular-subulate, (0.9–)1–2.8 mm; corolla bright pink-purple, or ochroleucous with purple tips or veins; banner recurved through 90°, 7–10.3 mm; keel 6.2–8.8 mm, apex round or narrowly triangular and beaklike. **Legumes** ascending, spreading, or declined, pale green or purple-specked or -suffused becoming stramineous, straight or slightly incurved, obliquely ovoid-ellipsoid or ovoid-acuminate, moderately to strongly bladdery-inflated, ± dorsiventrally or laterally compressed, 9–23 × (4–)5–15(–17) mm, beak prominent, papery, sparsely to densely strigulose. **Seeds** (7–)12–31.

Flowering Dec–Jun. Open gravelly or sandy flats, hillsides, canyon benches and boulder-strewn slopes or washes, with pinyon pine, Joshua tree, scrub-oak or manzanita, sometimes on desert floor, on granitic bedrock; (100–)300–1300(–1700) m; Ariz., Calif.; Mexico (Baja California).

Astragalus palmeri is restricted to the Colorado Desert region in California; though the type is reputed to have come from Arizona, the species has only been collected there once since. Plants of the northern portion of the range have larger fruits and a greener aspect; the more southern forms are silvery. Individual populations differ in a polymorphic manner, but variation is more or less continuous.

262. Astragalus magdalenae Greene, Pittonia 1: 162. 1888 • Satiny or Pierson's milkvetch C

Phaca candidissima Bentham, Bot. Voy. Sulphur, 13. 1844, not *Astragalus candidissimus* Ledebour 1831

Varieties 3 (1 in the flora): sw United States, nw Mexico.

262a. Astragalus magdalenae Greene var. **peirsonii** (Munz & McBurney) Barneby, Aliso 4: 135. 1958 C E

Astragalus peirsonii Munz & McBurney, Bull. S. Calif. Acad. Sci. 31: 67. 1932

Plants perennial (sometimes short-lived, flowering first season), sometimes clump-forming, 20–70 cm, silvery- or satiny-strigulose; from superficial root-crown, ultimately woody at base. **Stems** erect or ascending, strigulose (silvery-canescent or satiny). **Leaves** (1–)2–15 cm; stipules distinct, (1–)2–5.5 mm, submembranous; leaflets distant and scattered, (3–)9–13, blades oblanceolate, linear-oblong, oblong-obovate, obovate-cuneate, or broadly obovate, 1.5–14 mm, apex usually obtuse or emarginate, rarely obtuse and apiculate, surfaces strigulose; terminal leaflet confluent to rachis, larger than laterals. **Peduncles** erect or incurved-ascending, (2–)3.5–15 cm. **Racemes** 10–37-flowered, flowers ascending to spreading; axis 2.5–6.5 cm in fruit; bracts 1–3 mm; bracteoles 0–2. **Pedicels** 0.4–1.5 mm. **Flowers** 9.4–14.2 mm; calyx campanulate, 4.3–7.5(–9.2) mm, densely silky-strigulose, tube 3–4 mm, lobes subulate, 1.3–3.6(–5.2) mm; corolla pink-purple or tips whitish and margins pinkish lavender; banner recurved 40°; keel 7.4–10 mm, apex bluntly deltate. **Legumes** spreading, pale green or purple-cheeked becoming stramineous, straight or slightly incurved, usually broadly ovoid, ovoid-ellipsoid, or ovoid-acuminate, sometimes semi-ellipsoid or subglobose, bladdery-inflated, 10–35 × 5–21 mm, thin becoming papery, translucent, strigulose. **Seeds** 10–20.

Flowering Dec–Apr. Slopes and hollows in mobile dunes, usually to lee of prevailing winds; of conservation concern; 50–300 m; Calif.

Variety *peirsonii* is locally plentiful west of Yuma in Imperial County. It is peculiar among sect. *Inflati* species in having the terminal leaflet confluent with the rachis.

263. Astragalus allochrous A. Gray, Proc. Amer. Acad. Arts 13: 366. 1878 • Hassayampa milkvetch E F W

Plants biennial or perennial (short-lived), coarse, 10–50(–60) cm, strigulose; from superficial root-crown. **Stems** ascending and radiating, strigulose. **Leaves** 4–10 cm; stipules usually distinct throughout, rarely connate at proximal nodes, 1.5–7 mm, papery at proximal nodes, herbaceous or submembranous at distal nodes; leaflets (9 or)11–21, blades oblong-obovate, oblanceolate, elliptic, or narrowly oblong-elliptic, (4–)6–21 mm, apex acute, obtuse, or retuse and apiculate, surfaces strigulose abaxially, strigulose or glabrous adaxially. **Peduncles** incurved-ascending, 3–9(–11) cm. **Racemes** 10–20-flowered, flowers ascending; axis (1.5–)3.5–12 cm in fruit; bracts 1.2–2.5 mm; bracteoles 2. **Pedicels** 1–4 mm. **Flowers** 7.2–9.4 mm; calyx campanulate or turbinate-campanulate, (3.6–)4.1–5.7 mm, strigulose, tube 2.4–3.5 mm, lobes lanceolate-subulate, (1.1–)1.6–2.5 mm; corolla pink-purple or reddish purple; banner recurved through 50°; keel 6.2–7.5 mm, apex blunt or subacute, slightly beaklike. **Legumes** spreading or declined, or humistrate and ascending, pale green or purple-cheeked becoming stramineous, straight or slightly incurved, obliquely ellipsoid or semi-ellipsoid, bladdery-inflated, (20–)25–40(–45) × 10–17 mm, beak prominent, clearly differentiated from body, thin becoming papery, translucent, lustrous, finely strigulose. **Seeds** (10–)14–21. $2n = 22$.

Flowering Apr–Jul. Plains, foothills, open valleys, in desert-grasslands, scattered scrub-oak or juniper forests, rarely on dunes; 600–1900(–2300) m; Ariz., N.Mex., Tex.

Astragalus allochrous occurs throughout much of central and southeastern Arizona, southern New Mexico as far north as Valencia County, and just into extreme western trans-Pecos Texas.

Astragalus allochrous contains swainsonine and can result in the poisoning of livestock (C. D. Allison 1984).

264. Astragalus wootonii E. Sheldon, Minnesota Bot. Stud. 1: 138. 1894 (as wootoni) • Wooton's milkvetch F W

Varieties 2 (1 in the flora): sw United States, n Mexico.

D. Isely (1983) regarded the widespread *Astragalus wootonii* as intergradient with *A. allochrous*, and the two are sympatric over much of the range of the latter. He placed *A. wootonii* into *A. allochrous* as var. *playanus*. The proposal has merit but merely moves the resolution of the problem of distinction to another level. The plants contain swainsonine and are potentially poisonous to livestock (L. F. James and S. L. Welsh 1992).

Variety *candollianus* (Kunth) Barneby is disjunct in Mexico.

264a. Astragalus wootonii E. Sheldon var. **wootonii** F

Astragalus allochrous A. Gray var. *playanus* (M. E. Jones) Isely

Plants winter-annual or biennial, coarse, (10–)15–50 cm, strigulose; from superficial root-crown. **Stems** decumbent to incurved-ascending or almost prostrate, strigulose. **Leaves** (2–)4–10(12) cm; stipules usually distinct, very rarely connate at proximal nodes, (1.5–)2.5–7(–10) mm, submembranous becoming papery; leaflets (7–)11–19[–23], blades narrowly oblanceolate, linear-oblong, or oblong-obovate, 5–20 mm, apex retuse-truncate or obtuse, often callous-apiculate, surfaces strigulose abaxially, strigulose or glabrous adaxially. **Peduncles** incurved-ascending, (0.5–)1.5–5.5(–7) cm. **Racemes** [2 or](3–)5–10(–15)-flowered, flowers ascending to spreading or declined; axis (0.5–)1–4(–5) cm in fruit; bracts 1–3.2 mm; bracteoles 2. **Pedicels** 1–3.5 mm. **Flowers** 4.6–7.5 mm; calyx campanulate or turbinate-campanulate, 4.3–6.4 mm, strigulose or villosulous, tube 2.1–2.9(–3.2) mm, lobes lanceolate-subulate, 2–3.5 mm; corolla whitish, sometimes tinged pink or lavender, or pale to vivid reddish lilac; banner recurved through 50°; keel (4.1–)4.4–6.4 mm, apex usually broad and blunt, rarely triangular and subacute, sometimes obscurely beaklike. **Legumes** spreading or declined (usually humistrate), green or purplish-tinged, rarely lightly mottled, becoming stramineous, straight or slightly incurved, broadly and subsymmetrically, or somewhat obliquely, ovoid, ovoid-ellipsoid, ellipsoid, or subglobose, bladdery-inflated, (10–)15–37(–43) × (8–)12–20 mm, beak short and obscure, not well differentiated from body, thin becoming papery, lustrous, sparsely strigulose, hairs straight, [subvillosulous, or glabrate]. **Seeds** (10–)13–21. $2n = 22$.

Flowering Mar–Jul. Desert- and mesquite-grasslands, in pinyon-juniper communities; 600–2300 m; Ariz., Calif., Colo., N.Mex., Tex.; Mexico (Chihuahua, Durango, Sonora).

Variety *wootonii* occurs from extreme eastern Mojave Desert in San Bernardino County, California, through most of Arizona and the western half of New Mexico to extreme southern Colorado and trans-Pecos Texas, southward into Mexico.

The plants contain the indolizidine alkaloid swainsonine, and are potentially poisonous to livestock (L. F. James and S. L. Welsh 1992).

265. Astragalus thurberi A. Gray, Pl. Nov. Thurb., 312. 1854 • Thurber's milkvetch

Plants perennial (short-lived, often flowering first year), forming bushy clumps, somewhat coarse, (7–)15–40 cm, strigulose; from superficial root-crown. **Stems** decumbent to ascending, strigulose. **Leaves** (2–)4–10(–11.5) cm; stipules distinct, (2–)3–8 mm, papery at proximal nodes, submembranous at distal nodes; leaflets (9–)13–21, blades oblong-elliptic, oblanceolate, or linear-elliptic, 5–15(–18) mm, apex obtuse, truncate and apiculate, or shallowly retuse, surfaces strigulose abaxially, glabrous adaxially. **Peduncles** erect or incurved-ascending, 0.3–0.9 cm. **Racemes** (7–)10–25(–32)-flowered, flowers spreading; axis (2–)3–7(–11) cm in fruit; bracts 1–2.4 mm. **Pedicels** 0.5–1.8 mm. **Flowers** 5.7–7.1 mm; calyx campanulate, 3.3–5 mm, strigulose, tube 2.2–2.9 mm, lobes subulate or lanceolate-subulate, (1–)1.3–2.3 mm; corolla reddish lilac or reddish purple; banner recurved through 50°; keel 4.7–5.6 mm, apex obtusely deltate, sometimes obscurely beaklike. **Legumes** spreading or declined, green or minutely purple-dotted becoming stramineous, straight or slightly incurved, broadly and plumply ovoid- or obovoid-ellipsoid, obovoid, or subglobose, bladdery-inflated, 6–13 × 6–10 mm, beak nearly obsolete, thin becoming papery, sparsely strigulose. **Seeds** 8–11. $2n = 22$.

Flowering Mar–May. Plains, valleys, open hillsides, on dry sandy or gravelly soils, on semistabilized dunes, with *Larrea* and *Prosopis*, oak brush and juniper, in mesquite-grasslands; 900–1900 m; Ariz., N.Mex.; Mexico (Sonora).

With its compact, small, rounded, inflated fruits and small flowers, *Astragalus thurberi* is one of the more distinctive species of the large and difficult sect. *Inflati*. It contains swainsonine and is considered poisonous (L. F. James and S. L. Welsh 1992). It is a species of southeastern Arizona, southwestern New Mexico, and adjacent Mexico.

266. **Astragalus wardii** A. Gray, Proc. Amer. Acad. Arts 12: 55. 1876 (as wardi) • Ward's milkvetch [E]

Plants perennial, 9–50 cm, sparsely strigulose; from usually superficial, rarely subterranean, branched caudex. **Stems** decumbent to erect, sparsely strigulose. **Leaves** 3–10 cm; stipules distinct, 1–3 mm, papery at proximal nodes, submembranous at distal nodes; leaflets (11–)15–23, blades oblanceolate to elliptic or narrowly oblong to linear, 3–11 mm, apex obtuse to retuse or emarginate, surfaces glabrous or strigose on midrib abaxially and margins. **Peduncles** incurved-ascending, 1.5–5 cm. **Racemes** loosely 5–15-flowered, flowers ascending to declined; axis 1–5 cm in fruit; bracts 1–2.2 mm; bracteoles 0–2. **Pedicels** 1–3.4 mm. **Flowers** 5–8 mm; calyx campanulate, 2.9–4.6 mm, strigose, hairs usually black, sometimes also white, tube 1.7–2.3 mm, lobes subulate, 1–2.4 mm; corolla whitish or ochroleucous; banner abruptly recurved through 100–110°; keel 3.9–4.6 mm, apex bluntly deltate, often obscurely beaklike. **Legumes** deciduous from receptacle, pendulous to spreading, green, sometimes purple-mottled, becoming stramineous, straight, subsymmetrically ovoid-ellipsoid, bladdery-inflated, slightly obcompressed, 15–28 × 9–17 mm, thin becoming papery-membranous, translucent, glabrous; sessile or on a gynophore about as broad as long. **Seeds** 12–17.

Flowering May–Sep. Sagebrush, cottonwood, pinyon-juniper, ponderosa pine, spruce-fir, and less commonly, in grassland and salt desert shrub communities; 1500–2800 m; Utah.

Astragalus wardii is known from several counties in south-central Utah.

267. **Astragalus aquilonius** (Barneby) Barneby, Mem. New York Bot. Gard. 13: 876. 1964 • Lemhi milkvetch [E]

Astragalus wootonii E. Sheldon var. *aquilonius* Barneby, Amer. Midl. Naturalist 41: 499. 1949 (as wootoni)

Plants perennial (short-lived), somewhat coarse, 5–35(–50) cm, strigulose-villosulous; from superficial root-crown; taproot slender. **Stems** decumbent or weakly ascending, strigulose-villosulous. **Leaves** 4–9 cm; stipules distinct, 2–4 mm, submembranous; leaflets (11–)15–19(–23), blades oval, elliptic-obovate, or broadly oblanceolate, (4–)5–18 mm, apex obtuse or shallowly retuse, surfaces pubescent abaxially, glabrescent adaxially. **Peduncles** incurved-ascending, (3–)4–6.5 cm. **Racemes** loosely 5–9-flowered, flowers ascending becoming declined; axis 1.5–5.5 cm in fruit; bracts 1.5–2.5 mm; bracteoles 0–2. **Pedicels** 2–4 mm. **Flowers** 9.5–11 mm; calyx campanulate, 6.7–7.8 mm, loosely strigulose, tube 3.7–3.9 mm, lobes slenderly subulate, 2.8–4 mm; corolla greenish white, often tinged or veined dull lilac; banner abruptly recurved through 90°; keel 7.8–8.9 mm, apex triangular, subacute, often obscurely beaklike. **Legumes** loosely spreading, declined, or ascending, pale green and purple-cheeked becoming stramineous, straight, subsymmetrically ellipsoid or ovoid-ellipsoid, bladdery-inflated, somewhat obcompressed, 25–40 × 13–17 mm, thin, translucent, lustrous, glabrous or strigulose. **Seeds** (27–)30–39.

Flowering May–Jul. Washes in gullied clay bluffs, steep eroded banks in canyons, sand or gravel bars along streams, on shale, clay, or alluvial debris, with shadscale or sagebrush; 1700–2000 m; Idaho.

Astragalus aquilonius occurs along the lower Lemhi and upper Salmon rivers in Butte, Custer, and Lemhi counties. It is closely related and technically similar to *A. wootonii* but has larger flowers and more than twice the number of seeds per fruit (R. C. Barneby 1964). *Astragalus aquilonius* is the only *Astragalus* within its range with large, bladdery-inflated, unilocular fruits.

268. Astragalus cerussatus E. Sheldon, Minnesota Bot. Stud. 1: 139. 1894 • Powdered milkvetch [E]

Plants perennial (short-lived, often flowering in first year), slender, 3–25 cm, sparsely villosulous; from superficial root-crown; taproot slender. **Stems** ascending or decumbent, sparsely villosulous. **Leaves** 2.5–8 cm; stipules distinct, 2–4 mm, herbaceous; leaflets 13–21, blades narrowly oblanceolate to oblong-oblanceolate, 4–13(–18) mm, thin, apex often retuse, sometimes obtuse, surfaces sparsely villosulous abaxially, sparsely villosulous or glabrescent adaxially. **Peduncles** incurved-ascending, 2–4.5 cm. **Racemes** (1 or)2–7-flowered, flowers ascending becoming declined; axis 0.5–3.5 cm in fruit; bracts 1.5–2.5 mm; bracteoles 0–2. **Pedicels** 1–2.5 mm. **Flowers** 5.2–6 mm; calyx campanulate or obconic-campanulate, 3.4–4.2 mm, villosulous, tube 1.7–2 mm, lobes narrowly lanceolate-subulate, 1.4–2.5 mm; corolla pale lilac, or whitish and tips lilac; banner recurved through 90°; keel 3.6–4.3 mm, apex round or narrowly triangular and beaklike. **Legumes** spreading or declined, greenish, sometimes purplish, becoming stramineous, straight or slightly incurved, obliquely ovoid or ovoid-ellipsoid, bladdery-inflated, somewhat obcompressed, 10–22 × 5–14 mm, thin becoming papery-membranous, sparsely strigose-villosulous, hairs spreading, incumbent or curly. **Seeds** 18–22.

Flowering Apr–Aug. Dry sandy banks and hillsides, sandbars and shingle bars along rivers and torrents, with grama grass, sagebrush, in pinyon pine forests; 1600–2600 m; Colo., N.Mex.

Astragalus cerussatus ranges from southern Colorado as far north as Fremont, Rio Grande, and Saguache counties. Specimens from New Mexico have been reported but have not been verified.

269. Astragalus endopterus (Barneby) Barneby, Mem. New York Bot. Gard. 13: 879. 1964 • Sandbar milkvetch [E]

Astragalus wootonii E. Sheldon var. *endopterus* Barneby, Amer. Midl. Naturalist 41: 498. 1948 (as wootoni)

Plants annual or biennial, coarse, 10–20 cm, strigulose; from slender taproot. **Stems** few, erect or ascending, strigulose, cinereous. **Leaves** 4.5–8.5 cm; stipules distinct, 1–2.5 mm, submembranous; leaflets 7–11, blades lanceolate, oblong, or narrowly oblong-elliptic, 8–16 mm, apex obtuse or truncate, surfaces strigulose abaxially, glabrescent adaxially. **Peduncles** ascending or incurved, 1.5–2 cm. **Racemes** 4–7-flowered, flowers ascending becoming declined; axis 1.5–3 cm in fruit; bracts 1.5 mm; bracteoles 0. **Pedicels** 1–2 mm. **Flowers** 6–6.3 mm; calyx campanulate, 4 mm, strigulose, tube 2.1–2.3 mm, lobes subulate, 1.8–2 mm; corolla whitish faintly lined pink; banner recurved through 80°; keel 4.3–4.4 mm, apex bluntly deltate, obscurely beaklike. **Legumes** spreading to declined, pale green and faintly brown-mottled, becoming stramineous, straight, subsymmetrically ovoid or ovoid-ellipsoid, bladdery-inflated, slightly obcompressed, 20–27 × 11–15 mm, thin, lustrous, finely strigulose, hairs straight, appressed; seed-bearing flange 3–3.5 mm wide. **Seeds** 28–30.

Flowering May–Jun. Gravelly washes and sandbars of summer-dry streams, on sand dunes; 1100–1300 m; Ariz.

Astragalus endopterus is rare and local, known only from the lower Little Colorado River and Moenkopi Wash near Cameron, Coconino County. R. C. Barneby (1964) noted the similarity to *A. wootonii*. He and D. Isely (1998) reviewed the small but significant differences that distinguish *A. endopterus* and *A. wootonii*, including the exceptionally broad seed-bearing flange within the fruits and the higher ovule number in *A. endopterus*.

270. Astragalus serpens M. E. Jones, Proc. Calif. Acad. Sci., ser. 2, 5: 641. 1895 • Plateau milkvetch [E]

Plants perennial, loosely tuft-forming, 3–23 cm; from weak superficial caudex or root-crown; strigose-pilosulous. **Stems** ascending to erect, diffuse, strigulose. **Leaves** 1.5–4.5 cm; stipules distinct, 1.5–3.5 mm, papery at proximal nodes, subherbaceous at distal nodes; leaflets (7 or)9–15, blades obovate to oblanceolate or elliptic, 2–9 mm, apex obtuse to emarginate, surfaces strigose-pilosulous abaxially, strigose-pilosulous or glabrate adaxially. **Peduncles** incurved-ascending, 0.7–2.5 cm. **Racemes** subumbellate, 2–9-flowered, flowers spreading; axis 0.2–1 cm in fruit; bracts 1–1.5 mm; bracteoles 0. **Pedicels** 1–1.8 mm. **Flowers** 6.6–8.6 mm; calyx campanulate, 4.2–5.3 mm, strigulose, tube 2.7–3.5 mm, lobes subulate, 1.1–2.2 mm; corolla purplish to pink-purple or whitish; banner recurved through 90–100°; keel 6.6–7.2 mm, apex narrowly triangular, sometimes beaklike. **Legumes** deciduous from receptacle, ascending to declined, red or purple throughout or mottled, straight, ovoid or ellipsoid, bladdery-inflated, 13–29 × 7–17 mm, thin becoming papery, strigose; gynophore 0.7–1.5 mm. **Seeds** 7–22.

Flowering May–Jul. Sagebrush, pinyon-juniper, aspen, and aspen-fir communities mainly on igneous gravel; 2000–2800 m; Utah.

Astragalus serpens is an uncommon plant of the Marysvale volcanic centrum in eastern Piute, western Wayne, and southern Sevier counties.

271. Astragalus perianus Barneby, Mem. New York Bot. Gard. 13: 972. 1964 • Rydberg's milkvetch [E]

Plants perennial, dwarf, very slender, 1–6 cm, pilosulous; from shallow, subterranean branched caudex. **Stems** prostrate, 3–12 cm, (0–)1–8 cm underground, pilosulous. **Leaves** 1–3 cm; stipules connate-sheathing and papery at proximal nodes, distinct and submembranous at distal nodes, 1–2.5 mm; leaflets 7–19, blades oval to obovate, 1–5 mm, apex retuse, surfaces strigulose, sometimes glabrous adaxially. **Peduncles** incurved-ascending, 0.3–2.2 cm. **Racemes** 2–6-flowered, flowers spreading; axis 0.2–0.8 cm in fruit; bracts 0.8–1.2 mm; bracteoles 0. **Pedicels** 1.4–2.5 mm. **Flowers** 6.8–8.5 mm; calyx purplish, campanulate, 3.5–4.2 mm, pilosulous, tube 2.3–3 mm, lobes subulate, 1–1.4 mm; corolla whitish, faintly suffused with pink or purple; banner abruptly recurved through 80°; keel 4.8–5 mm, apex round or narrowly triangular and beaklike. **Legumes** ascending to declined, purple-mottled, ovoid, bladdery-inflated, 10–23 × 8–14 mm, thin, translucent, strigose; gynophore 0.1–0.8 mm. **Seeds** 18–20.

Flowering late Jun–Sep. Tertiary igneous gravel, frequently thermally or chemically altered, often on varicolored barrens in alpine or montane sites in tundra and spruce-fir communities, montane sagebrush sites; 2100–3500 m; Utah.

Astragalus perianus, initially obscure and thought to be extinct (but recollected after six decades), is known to be rather widely distributed and locally abundant in south-central Utah. Initially placed by R. C. Barneby (1964) in the disjunct sect. *Monoenses*, it is apparently most closely allied to *A. serpens*, which occurs adjacent to its range.

272. Astragalus pubentissimus Torrey & A. Gray, Fl. N. Amer. 1: 693. 1840 • Green River milkvetch [E]

Astragalus multicaulis Nuttall in J. Torrey and A. Gray, Fl. N. Amer. 1: 335. 1838, not Ledebour 1831

Plants annual or perennial, loosely tuft-forming, 9–45 cm, strigulose-villosulous; from weak caudex or root-crown. **Stems** ascending to erect or spreading-decumbent, diffuse, radiating, strigulose. **Leaves** 2–9 cm; stipules distinct, 1–4.5 mm, papery at proximal nodes, herbaceous at distal nodes; leaflets 5–15, blades oblong to ovate, obovate, or elliptic, 2–14 mm, apex obtuse to retuse, mucronate, or acute, surfaces villosulous. **Peduncles** incurved, 1–4 cm. **Racemes** 3–12-flowered, flowers spreading; axis 0.4–3.5 cm in fruit; bracts 1–3 mm; bracteoles 0. **Pedicels** 0.5–2 mm. **Flowers** 8.8–12.2 mm; calyx campanulate, 4.8–6.3 mm, villosulous, tube 2.8–4.2 mm, lobes subulate, 1.8–2.8 mm; corolla pink-purple or ochroleucous; banner incurved through 90–110°; keel 7.3–8.7 mm, apex bluntly triangular or deltate. **Legumes** deciduous from receptacle, spreading-declined, green or reddish becoming stramineous, incurved through 0.25–0.5 spiral, obliquely lanceoloid-ellipsoid, inflated, 12–20 × 4–8(–9) mm, thin becoming papery, shaggy-pilose, hairs lustrous, 1–2 mm. **Seeds** 9–18.

Varieties 2 (2 in the flora): w United States.

1. Stems ascending to erect; corollas bright pink-purple; Colorado, Utah, Wyoming . . . . 272a. *Astragalus pubentissimus* var. *pubentissimus*
1. Stems spreading-decumbent; corollas ochroleucous or pale to dark pink-purple (varicolored, often in same inflorescence); Tavaputs Plateau, Book Clifs, Emery and Grand counties, Utah . . . . 272b. *Astragalus pubentissimus* var. *peabodianus*

272a. Astragalus pubentissimus Torrey & A. Gray var. **pubentissimus** [E]

Stems ascending to erect. **Corollas** bright pink-purple, fading blue-purple. **Legumes** 5–8(–9) mm wide.

Flowering May–Jul. Pinyon-juniper, sagebrush, and mixed desert shrub communities; 1500–2200 m; Colo., Utah, Wyo.

When precipitation arrives propitiously and abundantly, var. *pubentissimus* responds in such abundance as to appear similar to an alfalfa patch in openings in pinyon-juniper woodland, or it successfully pioneers areas that have been cleared by mechanical chaining. The plants contain swainsonine (L. F. James and S. L. Welsh 1992) and have been implicated in poisoning of sheep in the Uinta Basin in Utah.

272b. Astragalus pubentissimus Torrey & A. Gray var. **peabodianus** (M. E. Jones) S. L. Welsh, Great Basin Naturalist 38: 297. 1978 • Peabody's milkvetch [E]

Astragalus peabodianus M. E. Jones, Zoë 3: 295. 1893

Stems spreading-decumbent. **Corollas** ochroleucous or pale to dark pink-purple, often fading yellowish (varicolored, often in same inflorescence). **Legumes** 4–5 mm wide.

Flowering (late Apr–)May–Jun. Pinyon-juniper and mixed desert shrub communities; 1300–1800(–2100) m; Utah.

Variety *peabodianus* occurs in entrenched channels affluent to both the Colorado and Green rivers along the southern and western flanks of the East Tavaputs Plateau in Emery and Grand counties; it is perhaps a connecting link between var. *pubentissimus* and *Astragalus pardalinus*.

273. Astragalus pardalinus (Rydberg) Barneby, Mem. New York Bot. Gard. 13: 884. 1964 • Panther milkvetch [E]

Phaca pardalina Rydberg in N. L. Britton et al., N. Amer. Fl. 24: 352. 1929

Plants annual or perennial (short-lived), clump-forming, 8–30(–35) cm, strigulose-villosulous; from superficial caudex. **Stems** decumbent to ascending, diffuse, clumps often as tall as wide, strigulose-villosulous. **Leaves** 3–8.5 cm; stipules mostly distinct, some shortly connate-sheathing, 2–6 mm, papery at proximal nodes, subherbaceous at distal nodes; leaflets 11–17, blades oblong to oblanceolate or obovate, 3–20 mm, apex truncate to retuse, mucronate, or acute, surfaces strigulose. **Peduncles** incurved, 1–4 cm. **Racemes** 3–9-flowered, flowers ascending; axis 1–4 cm in fruit; bracts 1–3.5 mm; bracteoles 0–2. **Pedicels** 0.8–3.6 mm. **Flowers** 6.3–8.2 mm; calyx campanulate, 4.8–6.6 mm, villous, tube 2.3–3 mm, lobes subulate, 2.2–3.5 mm; corolla pink-purple, fading yellowish; banner recurved through 60–90°; keel 5.8–6.8 mm, apex bluntly or sharply triangular, often beaklike. **Legumes** deciduous from receptacle, declined, green, often brightly purple- or red-mottled, straight or slightly incurved, obliquely ovoid-ellipsoid, inflated, not strongly bladdery, gently obcompressed, 13–21 × 7–11 mm, firmly papery, villosulous, hairs spreading, incurved, to 0.7 mm. **Seeds** 20–28.

Flowering May–Jun. Mixed desert shrub and pinyon-juniper communities; 1200–1900 m; Utah.

The main area of distribution of *Astragalus pardalinus* is the sandy eastern foot of the San Rafael Swell. There it forms a geographic link to the closely related *A. pubentissimus* to the north and *A. sabulonum* to the south. D. Isely (1998) provided a key distinguishing these three species. R. C. Barneby (1964) also discussed its distinction from *A. wootonii* var. *candollianus* (Kunth) Barneby of central Mexico.

274. Astragalus sabulonum A. Gray, Proc. Amer. Acad. Arts 13: 368. 1878 • Gravel milkvetch

Plants annual, winter-annual, or biennial, coarse, 4–35 cm, villous-hirsutulous; from root-crown. **Stems** single or few, usually decumbent to ascending, rarely erect, villous-hirsutulous. **Leaves** 1.5–7 cm; stipules distinct, 1–4 mm, subherbaceous becoming papery; leaflets (5–)9–15, blades oblanceolate to oblong or obovate, 2–13 mm, apex retuse to truncate or obtuse, surfaces loosely villous, sometimes glabrate adaxially. **Peduncles** incurved-ascending, 0.5–4 cm. **Racemes** 2–7-flowered, flowers ascending-spreading; axis 0.3–2.5 cm in fruit; bracts 1–2.5 mm; bracteoles 0. **Pedicels** 0.8–2 mm. **Flowers** 5.2–8 mm; calyx campanulate, 3.3–6.2 mm, hirsutulous, tube 1.8–2.5 mm, lobes subulate, 1.8–3.5 mm; corolla usually pink-purple, rarely ochroleucous and tinged with purple; banner recurved 50–70°; keel (5–)5.4–6.5 mm, apex narrowly triangular, sometimes slightly beaklike. **Legumes** spreading-declined, green or purple-cheeked or -dotted, becoming brownish or stramineous, lunately incurved or hooked, obliquely ovoid, turgid or somewhat inflated, 9–17(–20) × (4–)5–8(–11) mm, thinly fleshy becoming leathery or stiffly papery, white-villous or hirsute, hairs spreading, curved, 0.7–2.2 mm. **Seeds** 10–19. $2n = 24$.

Flowering Nov–Jul. *Larrea* and other warm-desert shrub, mixed cool desert shrub, salt-desert shrub, and lower pinyon-juniper communities, on sandy substrates; (60–)500–2200 m; Ariz., Calif., Nev., N.Mex., Utah; Mexico (Baja California, Sonora).

Astragalus sabulonum is known from San Juan County in northwestern New Mexico, northern Arizona, north to Emery County in east-central Utah and Mineral County in southwestern Nevada, and southward through southeastern California to Baja California and Sonora in northern Mexico.

Although *Astragalus sabulonum* has a wide ecological amplitude, from warm-desert shrubland to pinyon-juniper woodland, it is reasonably uniform morphologically. It can be distinguished from its closest relatives, *A. pubentissimus* and *A. pardalinus*, by characteristics of the calyx (size), ovules (number) and fruit (size, pubescence, texture, and curvature) (D. Isely 1998).

275. Astragalus nutans M. E. Jones, Rev. N.-Amer. Astragalus, 108. 1923 • Chuckwalla milkvetch [E]

Astragalus chuckwallae Abrams

Plants annual, biennial, or perennial (short-lived), 6–15 cm, strigulose; from superficial caudex; taproot slender. **Stems** single, erect or prostrate to ascending, strigulose. **Leaves** (2–)3–8 cm; stipules distinct, 1–4 mm, papery; leaflets 7–13, blades broadly or narrowly elliptic or oblanceolate, (3–)5–15 mm, apex obtuse, shallowly emarginate, or subacute, surfaces strigulose, sometimes glabrescent adaxially. **Peduncles** ascending, 2–5 cm. **Racemes** 6–10-flowered, flowers loosely ascending or in age declined; axis (1–)1.5–3.5(–4) cm in fruit; bracts 1–2 mm; bracteoles 0–2, minute when present. **Pedicels** 1–2 mm. **Flowers** 7.8–10.4 mm; calyx often purplish, campanulate, 4–4.6 mm, strigulose, tube 2.5–3.2 mm, lobes subulate, 1.2–2 mm; corolla pink-purple; banner recurved through 90°; keel 5.9–6.6 mm, apex blunt. **Legumes** horizontal or declined, stramineous, straight or slightly incurved, plumply ovoid or broadly oblong-ellipsoid, bladdery-inflated, subterete, (13–)15–25 × 11–15 mm, thin becoming papery-membranous, translucent, somewhat lustrous, sparsely strigulose, hairs straight, appressed; seed-bearing flange 1–2.5 mm wide; gynophore to 2 mm. **Seeds** 19–24. $2n = 22$.

Flowering Mar–Jun. Sandy flats and stony washes in the foothills of desert mountains, with *Larrea* or *Yucca brevifolia*; 400–2000 m; Calif.

Astragalus nutans is known from the eastern Mojave and extreme northern Colorado deserts of San Bernardino and Riverside counties. R. C. Barneby (1964) postulated a close relationship to *A. gilmanii*.

276. Astragalus gilmanii Tidestrom, Proc. Biol. Soc. Wash. 50: 20. 1937 (as gilmani) • Gilman's milkvetch [C] [E]

Plants winter-annual or biennial, (3–)8–25 cm, strigulose to villosulous; from superficial root-crown; taproot slender. **Stems** incurved-ascending to decumbent, strigulose to villosulous. **Leaves** 1.5–4 cm; stipules distinct, 1–4 mm, membranous or herbaceous with membranous margins; leaflets (7 or)9–15(or 17), blades linear-elliptic, 5–12.5 mm, apex obtuse, surfaces pubescent. **Peduncles** incurved-ascending, (0.6–)1.4–3.5 cm. **Racemes** loosely (3 or)4–9-flowered, flowers ascending becoming spreading, ultimately declined; axis 0.4–3 cm in fruit; bracts 0.7–1.5 mm; bracteoles 0. **Pedicels** (1.2–)1.6–4.3 mm. **Flowers** 6.5–7.5 mm; calyx campanulate, 4.2–5 mm, gray-strigulose, tube 2.5–3 mm, lobes subulate, 1.4–2 mm; corolla pink-purple; banner recurved through 90°; keel 4.7–6.1 mm, apex bluntly deltate. **Legumes** deciduous from receptacle, horizontal or declined, green or minutely purple-dotted, becoming stramineous, straight, obliquely ovoid or ovoid-ellipsoid, bladdery-inflated, terete or somewhat obcompressed, 13–26 × 8–16 mm, thin becoming papery-membranous, somewhat lustrous, strigulose, hairs spreading, incumbent or curly; gynophore to 0.8 mm. **Seeds** 10–14.

Flowering May–Jul. On volcanic, gravelly flats, brushy hillsides, canyon slopes, on volcanic tuff; of conservation concern; 1600–3100 m; Calif., Nev.

Astragalus gilmanii is restricted to the Panamint Mountains in Inyo County, California, and the Groom Range in Lincoln County, Nevada.

Astragalus gilmanii simulates some of the small-flowered phases of *A. lentiginosus*, but the annual or winter annual habit and unilocular legumes easily distinguish it from that species.

277. Astragalus beatleyae Barneby, Aliso 7: 161. 1970 • Beatley's milkvetch [C] [E]

Plants perennial (short-lived), clump-forming, 1.5–13 cm, strigulose; from superficial root-crown; taproot slender. **Stems** prostrate to incurved-ascending, strigulose. **Leaves** 1.5–3.5 cm; stipules distinct, 1–3 mm; leaflets (3 or)5–9, blades obovate-cuneate to broadly oblanceolate, 1.5–7 mm, apex emarginate, surfaces strigulose, sometimes glabrescent adaxially. **Peduncles** incurved-ascending, 0.2–1.5 cm. **Racemes** loosely 2–7-flowered, flowers spreading or declined; axis to 1 cm in fruit; bracts 0.4–1 mm; bracteoles 0. **Pedicels** 1–2 mm. **Flowers** 6–7 mm; calyx campanulate, 3–4.5 mm, white-strigulose, tube 2–2.8 mm, lobes subulate, 0.8–1.8 mm; corolla blue-violet; banner recurved through 60–80°; keel 5–5.5 mm, apex sharply triangular and beaklike. **Legumes** deciduous from receptacle, pendulous (sometimes humistrate), green or minutely purple-dotted becoming stramineous, straight, obliquely ovoid, bladdery-inflated, terete or somewhat obcompressed, 7–14 × 4.5–7.5 mm, papery-membranous, somewhat lustrous, minutely strigulose. **Seeds** 10–14.

Flowering May–Jun. Igneous low outcrops with black sagebrush; of conservation concern; 1600–2100 m; Nev.

Astragalus beatleyae is known from the summit of Pahute Mesa, south-central Nye County. It is a delicate, small clump-forming plant with small flowers and pale, small, bladdery-inflated pods with valves of thin texture.

278. Astragalus insularis Kellogg, Bull. Calif. Acad. Sci. 1: 6. 1884 • Cedros milkvetch

Varieties 3 (1 in the flora): sw United States, nw Mexico.

Astragalus insularis is a Baja California species that includes vars. *insularis* and *quentinus* M. E. Jones south of the international boundary, and var. *harwoodii* northward into the Colorado Desert in southern California and southwestern Arizona; it is similar to *A. nutans*, which does not extend south of the Chuckwalla Mountains in eastern Riverside County, California.

278a. Astragalus insularis Kellogg var. **harwoodii** Munz & McBurney, Bull. S. Calif. Acad. Sci. 31: 66. 1932

Astragalus harwoodii (Munz & McBurney) Abrams

Plants annual, [3–](4–)15–55 cm, strigulose; from superficial root-crown; taproot slender. **Stems** erect, incurved-ascending, or prostrate, strigulose. **Leaves** (2–)3–12 cm; stipules distinct, (1–)1.5–4(–5) mm, thinly herbaceous becoming papery; leaflets (9 or)11–19(or 21), blades broadly to narrowly elliptic, narrowly oblong, or lanceolate, 3–19 mm, apex acute, obtuse, or emarginate, surfaces strigulose abaxially, strigulose, glabrescent, or glabrous adaxially. **Peduncles** incurved-ascending or divaricate, 0.8–7 cm. **Racemes** 3–9-flowered, flowers horizontal becoming declined; axis (0.5–)1–4(–6) cm in fruit; bracts 0.6–1.3 mm; bracteoles 0. **Pedicels** 0.4–2.2 mm. **Flowers** 5.5–7.4 mm; calyx campanulate or turbinate-campanulate, 3.2–4.5 mm, strigulose, tube 1.8–2.7(–2.9) mm, lobes subulate, 1.3–2.2(–3) mm; corolla reddish purple; banner recurved through 50–60°; keel 4.8–6 mm, apex deltate or triangular-acuminate, sometimes obscurely beaklike. **Legumes** spreading or declined, pale green and purple-suffused or -dotted, becoming stramineous, straight, very obliquely to subsymmetrically ovoid-ellipsoid, lanceoloid-ellipsoid, or subglobose, bladdery-inflated, [9–]14–23 × (5–)6–12(–15) mm, thin becoming papery, translucent, somewhat lustrous, sparsely strigulose, hairs straight, appressed; seed-bearing flange to 2.5 mm wide. **Seeds** 7–12(–14). $2n = 22$.

Flowering Jan–May. Open sandy flats, sandy or stony desert washes, with *Larrea*; 0–400 m; Ariz., Calif.; Mexico (Baja California).

279. Astragalus geyeri A. Gray, Proc. Amer. Acad. Arts 6: 214. 1864 • Geyer's milkvetch [E] [F]

Phaca annua Geyer ex Hooker, London J. Bot. 6: 213. 1847, not *Astragalus annuus* De Candolle 1802

Plants annual or biennial, (3–)6–27(–30) cm, strigulose; from superficial root-crown; taproot slender. **Stems** single or to 3, prostrate to ascending or erect, strigulose. **Leaves** (1.5–)2–10.5(–12) cm; stipules distinct, 1.5–4 mm, thinly herbaceous or submembranous; leaflets (3–)7–13, blades linear, linear-oblong, oblanceolate, or linear-elliptic, rarely obcordate, 3–18 mm, apex obtuse to retuse, surfaces strigose abaxially, strigose or glabrous adaxially. **Peduncles** incurved-ascending, 0.6–2.5 cm. **Racemes** 2–8-flowered, flowers ascending; axis 0.3–1.5 cm in fruit; bracts 0.7–2 mm; bracteoles 0–2. **Pedicels** 0.6–1.5 mm. **Flowers** 5–7.6 mm; calyx campanulate, (2–)2.7–3.8(–4) mm, strigose, tube 1.5–2.5 mm, lobes subulate to lanceolate, 0.6–1.5 mm; corolla whitish, suffused with purple, or pink-purple; banner recurved through 45°; keel 3.8–4.8 mm, apex obtuse, deltate. **Legumes** spreading to declined, green or suffused purple, becoming stramineous, straight or slightly incurved, obliquely ovoid, bladdery-inflated, 15–24 × 6–12 mm, unilocular or semibilocular, thin becoming papery, strigose, hairs straight, appressed; seed-bearing flange 0.2–1.5 mm wide. **Seeds** 7–18.

Varieties 2 (2 in the flora): w United States.

The drab flowers and inflated fruits of *Astragalus geyeri* are mostly tucked among the leaves. Of all the species of sect. *Inflati*, *A. geyeri* has the largest geographic range.

1. Legume not inflexed, unilocular, sutures rounded dorsally; leaflet blades usually linear-oblong, narrowly oblanceolate, or linear-elliptic, rarely obcordate; Washington and Montana southward to California and Colorado but not nw Arizona or adjoining s Nevada . . . . 279a. *Astragalus geyeri* var. *geyeri*
1. Legume inflexed, semibilocular, sutures sulcate dorsally; leaflet blades broadly oblanceolate or elliptic; nw Arizona, adjoining s Nevada . . . . 279b. *Astragalus geyeri* var. *triquetrus*

279a. Astragalus geyeri A. Gray var. **geyeri** E F

Plants annual, rarely biennial. Leaflets (3–)7–13, blades usually linear-oblong, narrowly oblanceolate, or linear-elliptic, rarely obcordate, 3–17 mm; terminal leaflet usually longer than last pair. **Legumes** not inflexed, unilocular; sutures rounded dorsally. **Seeds** 10–18.

Flowering Apr–Jul. Salt deserts; 700–1700(–2200) m; Calif., Colo., Idaho, Mont., Nev., Oreg., Utah, Wash., Wyo.

Variety *geyeri* is known only as far south as Nye County, northwest of the range of var. *triquetrus*. Greenhouse-grown plants of var. *geyeri* can produce mature seeds in 58 days (S. L. Welsh 2007). In years when growing conditions are suitable, this species may cover the ground like a planted crop.

279b. Astragalus geyeri A. Gray var. **triquetrus** (A. Gray) M. E. Jones, Contr. W. Bot. 8: 7. 1898 • Muddy River milkvetch E

Astragalus triquetrus A. Gray, Proc. Amer. Acad. Arts 13: 367. 1878

Plants annual. Leaflets (5 or)7 or 9, blades broadly oblanceolate or elliptic, 4–15 mm; terminal leaflet not conspicuously longer than last pair. **Legumes** inflexed as narrow, partial septum 0.6–1.2 mm wide, semibilocular; sutures sulcate dorsally (3-sided). **Seeds** 7–11.

Flowering Apr–May. Sandy flats and washes, with *Ambrosia* and *Larrea*; 300–700 m; Ariz., Nev.

Variety *triquetrus* is a rare and local taxon from extreme northwestern Mohave County, Arizona, and southern Clark County, Nevada.

280. Astragalus aridus A. Gray, Proc. Amer. Acad. Arts 6: 223. 1864 • Parched milkvetch

Plants annual (short-lived, of 2–4 months duration), slender or coarse, 2.5–30 cm, densely strigulose-pilose; from superficial root-crown; taproot slender. **Stems** single or few, decumbent with ascending tips or trailing and diffuse, densely white-strigulose-pilose. **Leaves** (2–)3–9(–10) cm; stipules distinct, 1.5–5(–6.5) mm, herbaceous becoming papery; leaflets (7 or)9–17, blades oblanceolate, oblong-oblanceolate, or elliptic, 4–16 mm, apex obtuse, truncate, or emarginate, surfaces pubescent. **Peduncles** incurved-ascending, 2–5.5 cm. **Racemes** (3 or)4–9-flowered, flowers ascending; axis 1.5–5.5 cm in fruit; bracts 0.8–2.2 mm; bracteoles 0. **Pedicels** 0.2–1 mm. **Flowers** (3.3–)3.5–6.5 mm; calyx turbinate-campanulate, 3.3–4.3 mm, densely silvery-pilose, tube 2.1–2.7 mm, lobes broadly subulate, 1–1.6 mm; corolla whitish, faintly tinged with pink-lilac or cream-pink; banner recurved through 40°; keel 3.6–5 mm, apex round or narrowly triangular and beaklike. **Legumes** ascending, incurved, semi-ellipsoid or lunately ellipsoid, slightly inflated, scarcely bladdery, 10–17 × 4.5–7 mm, thin becoming papery, opaque, canescently strigulose-pilosulous. **Seeds** (3 or)4–6(or 7).

Flowering Feb–May. Desert dunes, open sandy plains, valley floors; -60–400 m; Ariz., Calif.; Mexico (Baja California, Sonora).

Astragalus aridus is a species of the Colorado Desert in southern California and adjacent Arizona. It is vaguely similar to *A. insularis*, but the flowers of *A. aridus* are smaller than those of any similar species.

281. Astragalus wetherillii M. E. Jones, Zoë 4: 34. 1893 (as wetherilli) • Wetherill's milkvetch E

Plants perennial (short-lived), clump-forming, 4–26 cm, strigulose; from branched, superficial caudex; taproot slender. **Stems** decumbent to ascending. strigulose. **Leaves** 2–10 cm; stipules distinct, 1–3.5 mm, thinly herbaceous becoming papery or membranous; leaflets 7–15, blades obovate to oval, 3–14 mm, apex obtuse to emarginate or mucronate, surfaces sparsely strigose abaxially, glabrous adaxially. **Peduncles** ascending or incurved, 1.5–4.5 cm. **Racemes** 2–9-flowered, flowers ascending to declined; axis 0.3–2.3 cm in fruit; bracts 1–2.5 mm; bracteoles 0. **Pedicels** 1–2.5 mm. **Flowers** 7.5–11 mm; calyx campanulate, 4.5–6.2 mm, strigose, tube 2.5–3.8 mm, lobes subulate, 1.8–2.4 mm; corolla whitish or tinged lavender; banner recurved through 45°; keel 6.5–8 mm, apex deltate, sometimes obscurely beaklike. **Legumes** spreading to declined, greenish, often purple-mottled, becoming stramineous or brownish, slightly incurved, ovoid-ellipsoid, inflated, 14–22 × 6–13 mm, thin becoming papery, minutely strigulose to glabrate; gynophore 1–2.5 mm. **Seeds** 9–13.

Flowering May–Jun. Greasewood-sagebrush, mountain brush and pinyon-juniper communities, on fine-textured substrates associated with sandstone outcrops (Mesaverde Group) and canyon bottoms; 1600–2300 m; Colo.

Astragalus wetherillii is endemic to west-central Colorado (near the Grand and lower Gunnison rivers in Garfield, Mesa, and Montrose counties). A historical report from Grand County in Utah cannot be substantiated; that collection, attributed to Alice Eastwood, is presumed to have been lost when the California Academy of Sciences was destroyed in the 1906 San Francisco fire.

Early-formed flowers on racemes at the proximalmost nodes produce maturing fruit while later ones are still fresh at distal nodes, and still in bud at the distalmost nodes. Thus, the flowering and fruiting season is extended by the growth habit of the plant, a feature not common in closely allied taxa, but found sporadically in other parts of *Astragalus* in North America.

Gynophores, such as in *Astragalus wetherillii*, have evolved multiple times and so have little value in establishing evolutionary relationships (R. C. Barneby 1964). The closely related *A. sparsiflorus*, a species from the opposite side of the Continental Divide, has nearly identical flowers but has fruits that are sessile or nearly so, not inflated, and bear a partial septum. Such differences in the fruit may arise rather easily, as apparently they have within the different fruit forms of the closely related *A. diaphanus*.

282. Astragalus sparsiflorus A. Gray, Proc. Amer. Acad. Arts 6: 205. 1864 • Front Range milkvetch [C] [E]

Plants annual or perennial (short-lived), 3.5–33 cm, sparsely strigulose; from superficial caudex; taproot slender. **Stems** prostrate or decumbent, sparsely strigulose. **Leaves** 1.5–10.5 cm; stipules distinct, 1–4 mm, mostly herbaceous or submembranous; leaflets 9–19, blades obovate, oblong-oblanceolate to -obovate, obcordate, suborbiculate, or elliptic, 2–15 mm, apex obtuse or emarginate, surfaces sparsely strigulose abaxially, glabrous adaxially. **Peduncles** ascending, 1–7.5 cm. **Racemes** (1 or)2–10-flowered, flowers ascending or spreading; axis (0–)1–4 cm in fruit; bracts 1–2.5 mm; bracteoles 2. **Pedicels** 1–3.5 mm. **Flowers** 5.5–8 mm; calyx campanulate, 3–4.3 mm, strigulose, hair white or partly black, tube 1.5–2.8 mm, lobes subulate, 1.2–2 mm; corolla white, banner with pink veins; banner recurved through 45–90°; keel 3.6–5 mm, apex bluntly deltate. **Legumes** ascending, spreading, or loosely declined, green, purplish, or purple- or red-mottled becoming brownish or stramineous, incurved, narrowly oblanceoloid or obliquely semi-ovoid, ± inflated, ± 3-sided compressed, (5–)6–26 × 2.7–5 mm, thin becoming papery, finely strigulose, hairs straight, appressed; gynophore conical, short. **Seeds** 6–15.

Varieties 2 (2 in the flora): Colorado.

The two abruptly different varieties of *Astragalus sparsiflorus* sometimes occur in close proximity without apparent intergradation and may deserve specific rank (R. C. Barneby 1964).

1. Leaves 1.5–5 cm, leaflet blades broadly elliptic, obovate, or suborbiculate, 2–7 mm; calyces 3–3.5 mm, tubes 1.5–1.9 × 1.6–2 mm, lobes 1.5–2 mm; banners 5.5–6.6 mm; legumes (5–)6–8 × 2.7–4 mm; seeds 6–8 . . . . 282a. *Astragalus sparsiflorus* var. *sparsiflorus*
1. Leaves 2.5–10.5 cm, leaflet blades mostly oblong-oblanceolate or -obovate, 4–15 mm; calyces 3.2–4.3 mm, tubes 2–2.8 × 2–2.4 mm, lobes 1.2–1.7 mm; banners 6.2–8 mm; legumes 11–26 × 3–5 mm; seeds 10–15. . . . . 282b. *Astragalus sparsiflorus* var. *majusculus*

282a. Astragalus sparsiflorus A. Gray var. **sparsiflorus** [C] [E]

Pubescence sometimes copious. **Leaves** 1.5–5 cm; leaflets 9–15, blades broadly elliptic, obovate, or suborbiculate, 2–7 mm. **Racemes** (1 or)2–6-flowered; axis (0–)1.5–2.5 cm in fruit. **Flowers:** calyx 3–3.5 mm, tube 1.5–1.9 × 1.6–2 mm, lobes 1.5–2 mm; corolla banner recurved through 90°, 5.5–6.6 mm. **Legumes** purplish-tinged or -mottled, obliquely semi-ovoid, carinate ventrally by the concavely arched suture, openly sulcate dorsally in proximal 1/2–2/3, (5–)6–8 × 2.7–4 mm, contracted distally into a broadly triangular, laterally flattened beak; septum very narrow or obsolete, to 0.2 mm wide.

Flowering late May–Aug. Dry gravelly banks, open hillsides, sandy canyon bottoms, roadcuts, natural talus, on loose granitic sand or gravel; of conservation concern; 1600–3000 m; Colo.

Variety *sparsiflorus* is known from the upper canyon of the South Platte River, southward through the foothills of Pike's Peak to the upper Arkansas River, in Denver, El Paso, Fremont, Park, and Teller counties.

282b. Astragalus sparsiflorus A. Gray var. **majusculus** A. Gray, Proc. Amer. Acad. Arts 6: 206. 1864 • Tium milkvetch [C] [E]

Pubescence sparse. **Leaves** 2.5–10.5 cm; leaflets (at least distally) 9–19, blades mostly oblong-oblanceolate or oblong-obovate, 4–15 mm. **Racemes** 2–10-flowered; axis 1–4 cm in fruit. **Flowers:** calyx 3.2–4.3 mm, tube 2–2.8 × 2–2.4 mm, lobes 1.2–1.7 mm; corolla banner recurved through 45°, 6.2–8 mm. **Legumes** red- or purple-mottled, gently incurved, narrowly oblanceoloid, 11–26 × 3–5 mm, contracted distally into short, triangular, compressed beak; septum narrow, 0.2–0.6 mm wide.

Flowering May–Jul. Dry gravelly banks, open hillsides, sandy canyon bottoms, roadcuts, natural talus, on loose granitic sand or gravel; of conservation concern; 1500–3000 m; Colo.

Variety *majusculus* apparently is restricted to the valley of the South Platte River from near Denver and upstream approximately 80 km. R. C. Barneby (1964) considered it the more primitive of the two varieties, having much in common with *A. diaphanus* and *A. wetherillii*.

283. Astragalus diaphanus Douglas in W. J. Hooker, Fl. Bor.-Amer. 1: 151. 1831 • Transparent milkvetch [E]

Astragalus diurnus S. Watson; *A. drepanolobus* A. Gray

Plants annual or biennial, slender, 5–15 cm, strigulose; from superficial root-crown; taproot slender. **Stems** usually 3–10, decumbent to ascending, strigulose. **Leaves** 2–5(–6) cm; stipules distinct, 1.5–4 mm, papery at proximal nodes, herbaceous or submembranous at distal nodes; leaflets (5 or)7–13, blades oblong-obovate, -ovate, or obovate-cuneate, (2–)3–12 mm, apex obtuse, truncate, or retuse, surfaces glabrous. **Peduncles** divaricate, 1–4(–5.5) cm. **Racemes** (3–)7–15-flowered, flowers ascending becoming spreading, later declined; axis (0.4–)1–3.5(–4.5) cm in fruit; bracts 0.8–1.8 mm; bracteoles 0. **Pedicels** 0.6–1.8 mm (in fruit). **Flowers** 6.7–9.1 mm; calyx campanulate, 3.5–4.5 mm, strigulose, tube 2–2.6 mm, lobes lanceolate-subulate, 1.3–1.9 mm; corolla whitish, banner with lavender veins; banner incurved through 45°; keel 4.1–5.7 mm, apex obtuse, sometimes obscurely beaklike. **Legumes** deflexed or declined, purplish green becoming stramineous then brownish, lunately incurved, usually obliquely linear-oblong, oblanceoloid, or semi-ellipsoid, rarely semi-ovoid, somewhat inflated, almost bladdery, usually ± 3-sided compressed, (10–)15–28 × 3–9 mm, unilocular or subunilocular, thin becoming papery-membranous, translucent, sparsely and minutely strigulose, hairs straight, appressed; seed-bearing flange to 2.5 mm wide, septum 0.5–1 mm. **Seeds** (6–)8–14. $2n = 28$.

Flowering Apr–Jun. Gravelly soils overlying basalt, sandbars, sandy banks; 50–600 m; Oreg.

Astragalus diaphanus occurs along the John Day River from near Dayville in Grant County, Oregon, westward along the Columbia River to slightly south of The Dalles, but is considered extirpated in Washington. R. C. Barneby (1964) discussed variation in this species in detail and compared it with *A. wetherillii*, a species disjunct by hundreds of kilometers in west-central Colorado.

284. Astragalus hornii A. Gray, Proc. Amer. Acad. Arts 7: 398. 1868 • Horn's milkvetch

Varieties 2 (1 in the flora): sw United States, nw Mexico.

Astragalus hornii has an unusual geographic distribution: the upper San Joaquin Valley and the western edge of the Mojave Desert in California, and the western shore of Pyramid Lake in Nevada. The habitat for the species in the United States has been largely destroyed, with most collections more than 50 years old (D. Isely 1998). Variety *minutiflorus* M. E. Jones is known from Baja California.

284a. Astragalus hornii A. Gray var. **hornii** [E]

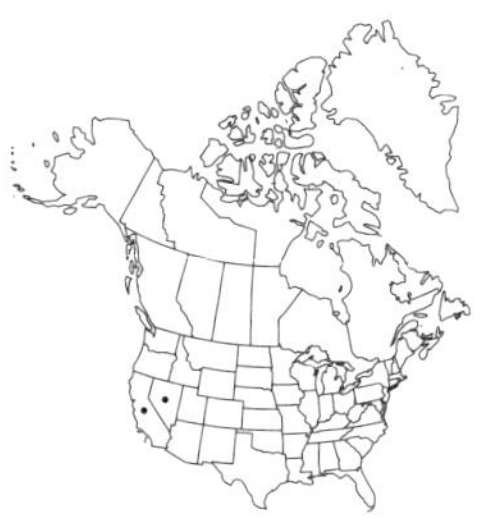

Plants annual (long-lived), 30–120 cm, villosulous or strigulose; from superficial caudex; taproot slender. **Stems** ascending to decumbent, slender to stout and fistulose, glabrous, sometimes glabrate at proximal nodes. **Leaves** (1.5–)2.5–13 cm; stipules distinct, 2–7 mm, membranous becoming papery; leaflets (11–)15–31, blades narrowly elliptic, oblong-elliptic, or oblong-obovate, (3–)5 mm, apex acute, obtuse, obtuse and apiculate, or, sometimes, emarginate, surfaces pubescent abaxially, pubescent or glabrous adaxially. **Peduncles** incurved-ascending, 2–13 cm. **Racemes** in subglobose or oblong heads, densely (8–)10–35-flowered, flowers spreading and ascending; axis 0.7–7 cm in fruit; bracts 1.2–2 mm; bracteoles 0(or 1). **Pedicels** 0.2–1.3 mm. **Flowers** 7.8–10.2 mm; calyx campanulate, 3.8–6 mm, villosulous or loosely strigulose, tube 2.3–4.4 mm, lobes subulate or subulate-triangular, 1–2.5 mm; corolla whitish or cream, sometimes tinged with pale lilac; banner recurved through 40°; keel 5.9–8.4 mm, apex blunt, deltate. **Legumes** subpersistent or very tardily disjointing, spreading and ascending, crowded into dense, subglobose or oblong-cylindric heads, 2.5–3.5 cm diam., pale green or faintly pink-tinged becoming stramineous, straight or slightly incurved, obliquely ovoid-acuminate or inversely pyriform, bladdery-inflated, 9–18 × 5–9 mm, thin becoming papery-membranous, hirsute. **Seeds** 11–14(–17).

Flowering Apr–Sep(–Nov). Alkaline substrates, on clay soils moist in spring and dry in summer, along irrigation ditches, lakeshores, with salt-grass, chenopods, and other halophytes; 60–900(–1200) m; Calif., Nev.

Historically, var. *hornii* occurred from Kings to San Bernardino counties. It was especially abundant in the upper San Joaquin Valley, but much of its original habitat has been destroyed. A disjunct population occurs on the western shore of Pyramid Lake in Washoe County, Nevada. A historical collection from Washington County in Utah (*Palmer s.n.*, in 1879) lacks specific locality information.

135ttt. Astragalus Linnaeus sect. Diphysi A. Gray, Proc. Amer. Acad. Arts 6: 192. 1864

Herbs annual, biennial, or perennial, caulescent or subacaulescent; caudex superficial or subterranean. **Hairs** basifixed. **Stems** single or few to many. **Stipules** distinct. **Leaves** odd-pinnate, petiolate to subsessile; leaflets (3–)7–27(or 29). **Racemes** loosely or remotely flowered or subumbellate, flowers ascending to spreading or declined. **Calyx tubes** cylindric or campanulate. **Corollas** usually white, lilac, purple, or pink- to magenta-purple, lavender, or violet, sometimes ochroleucous or yellowish, keel apex usually purple, banner recurved through 30–50°, keel apex round, obtuse, or bluntly deltate. **Legumes** usually deciduous, sometimes persistent, usually sessile, rarely short-stipitate, ascending, spreading, deflexed, or declined, linear, narrowly lanceoloid to oblanceoloid or ellipsoid, oblong, ovoid to obovoid, subglobose, or triangular-obcordate, ventral suture deeply grooved and appearing ± didymous, strongly inflated, terete, dorsiventrally compressed, or 3-sided compressed, straight or curved, usually bilocular, sometimes semibilocular or unilocular. **Seeds** (7–)10–42.

Species 3 (3 in the flora): w North America, nw Mexico.

Section *Diphysi* has wide distribution in western North America, from British Columbia southward to northwestern Mexico. One of the species, *Astragalus lentiginosus*, consists of 42 varieties and is as complex an assemblage as occurs in many genera.

285. Astragalus lentiginosus Douglas in W. J. Hooker, Fl. Bor.-Amer. 1: 151. 1831 • Freckled milkvetch F

Plants annual, biennial, or perennial, subacaulescent to caulescent, (0.4–)1–100 cm, glabrous or pubescent; from superficial or slightly subterranean root-crown. **Stems** prostrate, creeping, decumbent, ascending, or erect, glabrous, strigulose, villosulous, or pilose. **Leaves** 1–17 cm; stipules (1–)2–7 mm, submembranous; leaflets (3–)11–27(or 29), blades suborbiculate, elliptic, oblong, ovate, obovate, lanceolate, oblanceolate, or linear, (1–)2–21(–25) mm, apex acute to emarginate, surfaces glabrous, glabrate, strigose, strigulose, strigulose-villosulous, pilosulous, tomentulose, or silvery-silky. **Peduncles** 0.5–11(–14) cm. **Racemes** (2 or)3–35(–48)-flowered, flowers ascending or spreading; axis (0.3–)0.5–18(–26) cm in fruit, elongating only slightly; bracteoles usually 0. **Flowers** 5.5–23 mm; calyx cylindric or campanulate, (3.4–)3.8–12.5 mm, strigose, strigulose, or villosulous, tube 2.7–10 mm, lobes subulate or triangular, 0.5–5 mm; corolla pink-purple to purple, ochroleucous, yellowish, or whitish, sometimes veined, suffused, or tipped with lavender or pink; banner recurved 30–50°; keel 6–16.4 mm. **Legumes** readily deciduous from receptacle when mature, except vars. *mokiacensis* and *trumbullensis* where firmly attached and falling while still attached to pedicel, ascending or spreading and incurved, green, sometimes red- or purple-mottled, usually becoming stramineous or brownish, usually incurved, sometimes ± straight, usually ± ovoid, less often oblong, lanceoloid, or linear, usually strongly inflated or bladdery-inflated, rarely not or scarcely so, 8–40(–48) × (3–)4–18(–19) mm, usually bilocular, sometimes semibilocular, leathery, papery, or papery-membranous, usually glabrous, sometimes puberulent, strigose, strigulose, villosulous, or villous-tomentulose; usually inflexed as a complete septum, rarely incomplete, seed-bearing flange either conspicuous or subobsolete; usually sessile, rarely shortly stipitate. **Seeds** (7–)10–42.

Varieties 42 (42 in the flora): w North America, n Mexico.

P. A. Rydberg (1929) placed what is here treated as *Astragalus lentiginosus* in the broad sense in *Cystium*, recognizing 33 species. M. E. Jones (1923) treated it as a single species, *A. lentiginosus*, with 18 varieties. The numerous varieties occur in geologically young habitats in the western United States, barely entering northwestern Mexico and southwestern Canada (B. J. Knaus et al. 2005). Fruits and flowers both are needed to key most varieties successfully. D. Isely (1998) presented keys to the species by geographic region. Amplified fragment length polymorphism (AFLP) analysis discriminates varieties despite potentially confounding geographic patterns and has proven effective at inferring relationships (Knaus et al.).

At least some, and perhaps all, of the varieties contain swainsonine and are toxic to livestock (L. F. James and S. L. Welsh 1992).

1. Legumes not or scarcely inflated, ovoid, lanceoloid, ellipsoid, or oblong, 10–32(–35) × (3–)3.7–8.5(–10) mm wide (longer than wide).
   2. Flowers 7.4–11 mm; corollas whitish or yellowish, sometimes faintly lilac; British Columbia, California, Idaho, Nevada, Oregon, Washington . . . . .285a. *Astragalus lentiginosus* var. *lentiginosus* (in part)
   2. Flowers (10–)12–20 mm; corollas pink- or red-purple, ochroleucous, or white, sometimes suffused or tipped with white, pink, or pink-purple; Arizona, California, Colorado, Nevada, Utah.
      3. Herbage silvery- or satiny-pubescent; legumes densely pubescent; Yuma Desert, Arizona, adjoining Colorado Desert of se California . . . . 285kk. *Astragalus lentiginosus* var. *coulteri*
      3. Herbage green or subglabrescent; legumes glabrous, strigulose, minutely pubescent, or puberulent; Arizona, Colorado, Nevada, Utah.
         4. Raceme axis elongating or not, (1–)2–12(–14.5) cm in fruit (if to 14.5 cm, then plants of Flagstaff, Arizona, and vicinity).
            5. Corollas pink-purple; Coconino, Mohave, and Navajo counties, Arizona (but not upper Verde Valley or Coconino Plateau), sw Colorado to s Utah . . . . 285mm. *Astragalus lentiginosus* var. *palans* (in part)
            5. Corollas white or suffused or tipped with pink or pink-purple; upper Verde Valley and Coconino Plateau, Coconino, Gila, and Yavapai counties, Arizona. . . . . 285pp. *Astragalus lentiginosus* var. *wilsonii*
         4. Raceme axis usually elongating, (1–)3–22 cm in fruit.
            6. Corollas ochroleucous; Maricopa County, Arizona. . . . . 285ll. *Astragalus lentiginosus* var. *maricopae*
            6. Corollas pink- or red-purple, sometimes with pale or white wing tips; Nevada to w Texas including Arizona.
               7. Legumes papery-membranous, valves translucent.
                  8. Plants clump-forming; seeds 18–22 . . . . 285z. *Astragalus lentiginosus* var. *australis* (in part)
                  8. Plants not clump-forming; seeds 21–31 . . . . 285cc. *Astragalus lentiginosus* var. *vitreus* (in part)
               7. Legumes stiffly papery or leathery, not translucent.

[9. Shifted to left margin.—Ed.]

9. Legumes subsessile to shortly stipitate, stipe 0.1–1 mm; leaflet blade surfaces usually strigose to strigulose, less commonly glabrate or glabrous adaxially; Mt. Trumbull, Mohave County, Arizona . . . . 285oo. *Astragalus lentiginosus* var. *trumbullensis*
9. Legumes sessile; leaflet blade surfaces glabrous adaxially; Arizona, Colorado, Nevada, Utah.
   10. Legumes spreading, declined, or spreading-ascending, ± straight to uniformly or hamately incurved, dehiscent on ground; corollas with purple wing tips; sw Colorado, n Arizona along and north of Colorado River to se Utah . . . . 285mm. *Astragalus lentiginosus* var. *palans* (in part)
   10. Legumes usually ascending-erect to ascending, rarely spreading, usually ± straight to incurved, rarely decurved, dehiscent on plant; corollas with usually pale or white wing tips; Beaver Dam Mountains, Washington County, Utah, Virgin Mountains, nw Mohave County, Arizona, and adjacent Clark County, Nevada . . . . 285nn. *Astragalus lentiginosus* var. *mokiacensis*

1. Legumes inflated to strongly or bladdery-inflated, usually globose, subglobose, or ovoid, rarely ellipsoid, obovoid, or lanceoloid, (6–)10–35(–48) × (4–)6–20 mm (length less than 1/2 width).
   11. Legumes obscurely stipitate, stipe 0.5–1.5 mm; corollas whitish; leaflet blades broadly obovate-cuneate or suborbiculate; Tooele County, Utah. . . . . . . 285p. *Astragalus lentiginosus* var. *pohlii*
   11. Legumes sessile; corollas pink-purple, yellow, ochroleucous, or whitish, often tipped, veined, or suffused purple or pink; leaflet blades linear-elliptic to obovate, oval, or suborbiculate; California to Texas including sw Utah.
       12. Racemes lax in fruit, axes (2.5–)4–15(–16) cm.
           13. Flowers 9.1–12(–12.4) mm; nw Arizona, sw Utah, s Nevada, adjacent California. . . . . 285ee. *Astragalus lentiginosus* var. *fremontii*
           13. Flowers 11–17(–18.5) mm; California to Texas including Nevada and Utah.
               14. Legumes stiffly papery or almost leathery, usually glabrous, rarely puberulent; Mohave County, nw Arizona . . . . . . 285dd. *Astragalus lentiginosus* var. *ambiguus*
               14. Legumes thinly or stiffly papery, usually glabrous, strigulose, strigose, villosulous, or villous-tomentulose, rarely puberulent; California to w Texas including Arizona.

[15. Shifted to left margin.—Ed.]

15. Corollas usually white, ochroleucous, creamy yellow, or greenish yellow to greenish white, sometimes pink-purple or pale.
    16. Petals poorly graduated, banner only slightly longer than nearly equal wings and keel; legumes usually glabrous, rarely minutely strigulose; Arizona, Nevada . . . . 285aa. *Astragalus lentiginosus* var. *yuccanus*
    16. Petals well-graduated, banner much longer than wings, wings well surpassing keel; legumes villosulous; California . . . . 285hh. *Astragalus lentiginosus* var. *nigricalycis*
15. Petals pink-purple.
    17. Plants of deserts in California and Nevada.
        18. Herbage usually cinereous, sometimes green or silky-canescent (not silvery); calyx lobes 1–1.4(–1.5) mm . . . . .285gg. *Astragalus lentiginosus* var. *variabilis* (in part)
        18. Herbage silvery-canescent or silvery- or white-silky; calyx lobes 1.4–2.9 mm.
            19. Plants winter annual or short-lived perennial; herbage hairs to 0.7–1.2 mm; Coachella Valley, California . . . . .285ii. *Astragalus lentiginosus* var. *coachellae*
            19. Plants perennial; herbage hairs to 1.1–2 mm; Eureka Valley, Inyo County, California, and Nye County, Nevada . . . . . .285jj. *Astragalus lentiginosus* var. *micans*
    17. Plants of interior states (Arizona, Nevada, New Mexico, Texas, Utah).
        20. Plants clump-forming; flowers (13.2–) 14.5–18 mm; s of Mogollon Rim, s Arizona, eastward to w Texas. . . . . 285z. *Astragalus lentiginosus* var. *australis* (in part)
        20. Plants not clump-forming; flowers 11–17 mm; north and west of Colorado River in Arizona, to Utah, Nevada, and California.
            21. Legumes usually glabrous, rarely puberulent; herbage villosulous; wc Nevada . . . . 285ff. *Astragalus lentiginosus* var. *kennedyi*
            21. Legumes glabrous, strigulose, or strigose-villosulous; herbage not villosulous; Arizona, California, Nevada, Utah.

[22. Shifted to left margin.—Ed.]

22. Herbage green, stems glabrous or glabrate; legumes glabrous, subtranslucent; w Kane and e Washington counties, Utah, and Mohave and Coconino counties, Arizona, not extending onto North Rim of Grand Canyon . . . . 285cc. *Astragalus lentiginosus* var. *vitreus* (in part)
22. Herbage cinereous or green, stems ashy-canescent or green; legumes strigulose or strigose-villosulous, opaque; Arizona, California, Nevada, Utah.
    23. Corollas pale purple; Arizona, Clark County, Nevada, Utah. . . . . 285bb. *Astragalus lentiginosus* var. *stramineus*
    23. Corollas pink- or magenta-purple; California, Nye County, Nevada . . . . 285gg. *Astragalus lentiginosus* var. *variabilis* (in part)

[12. Shifted to left margin.—Ed.]

12. Racemes compact in fruit (except var. *salinus*, sometimes var. *wahweapensis*), axes (0.3–)1–5.5(–9) cm.
    24. Flowers 7.4–15 mm.
        25. Plants of the Columbia and Great basins, ne California and Nevada north and eastward of Lake Tahoe, north to British Columbia and east to Montana, Wyoming, and Utah.
            26. Stems prostrate; racemes floriferous from all but proximalmost nodes; Ruby Mountains, Nevada . . . . 285c. *Astragalus lentiginosus* var. *multiracemosus*
            26. Stems decumbent, prostrate, diffuse, erect, or ascending; racemes floriferous from middle to distalmost nodes or throughout; not Ruby Mountains, Nevada.
                27. Legumes stiffly papery, opaque, or nearly so.
                    28. Legumes usually thinly strigulose, rarely puberulent; British Columbia to ne California and s Idaho . . . . 285a. *Astragalus lentiginosus* var. *lentiginosus* (in part)
                    28. Legumes glabrous; mountains of e Nevada, extreme w Utah. . . . . .285b. *Astragalus lentiginosus* var. *scorpionis*
                27. Legumes thinly papery or papery-membranous, often translucent.

[29. Shifted to left margin.—Ed.]

29. Leaflet blade surfaces strigulose-villosulous, some hairs spreading or sinuous; n Nevada. . . . . 285f. *Astragalus lentiginosus* var. *macrolobus*
29. Leaflet blade surfaces glabrate to densely strigulose, hairs appressed or subappressed; widespread, including n Nevada.
    30. Plants 6–30(–45) cm; racemes comparatively loose, not cylindric or globose in fruit; stems ascending to erect, mostly unbranched; widespread. . . . . 285d. *Astragalus lentiginosus* var. *salinus*
    30. Plants 20–50 cm; racemes dense, cylindric or globose in fruit; stems prostrate to weakly ascending, branched proximally; nw Nevada, adjoining California and Oregon . . . . 285e. *Astragalus lentiginosus* var. *floribundus*

[25. Shifted to left margin.—Ed.]

25. Plants of ec, se California (southward from Lake Tahoe) and sw Nevada (Spring [Charleston] and White mountains).
    31. Legumes with linear- or subulate-tubular, cusplike beaks; s Sierra Nevada, California, and Charleston Peak, Nevada . . . . 285n. *Astragalus lentiginosus* var. *kernensis*
    31. Legumes with deltoid or triangular beaks; California, Nevada.
        32. Plants 30–100 cm; legumes with decurved beaks; alkaline flats at eastern foot of Sierra Nevada from Inyo southward to Los Angeles County, California . . . . . 285k. *Astragalus lentiginosus* var. *albifolius*
        32. Plants (1–)3–30 cm; legumes with incurved or erect beaks; mountain slopes and flats, California, Nevada.
            33. Plants of Sierra Nevada and Inyo and White mountains.
                34. Herbage loosely strigulose or villosulous; leaves 1.5–5.5 cm; leaflets (9–)15–21, crowded; Sierra Nevada. . . . . 285g. *Astragalus lentiginosus* var. *ineptus*
                34. Herbage subappressed-strigulose; leaves 4–9 cm; leaflets (13–)17–27, distant; Inyo and White mountains . . . . . . 285h. *Astragalus lentiginosus* var. *semotus*
            33. Plants of San Gabriel and San Bernardino mountains.
                35. Flowers 10.4–13(–14.5) mm; herbage green or greenish; San Bernardino Mountains . . . . . . .285i. *Astragalus lentiginosus* var. *sierrae* (in part)
                35. Flowers 9–10.5 mm; herbage cinereous or silvery-canescent; San Gabriel Mountains . . . . .285j. *Astragalus lentiginosus* var. *antonius*

[24. Shifted to left margin.—Ed.]

24. Flowers 10.4–21.4 mm.
    36. Plants of South Coast Ranges and San Bernardino Mountains, California.
        37. Legumes papery; San Bernardino Mountains . . . . .285i. *Astragalus lentiginosus* var. *sierrae* (in part)
        37. Legumes leathery or stiffly papery; South Coast Ranges (Mount Hamilton to Mount Pinos) . . . . 285s. *Astragalus lentiginosus* var. *idriensis*
    36. Plants not of South Coast Ranges or San Bernardino Mountains, Californa.
        38. Corollas usually white, rarely purple; ne California, nw Colorado, s Idaho, ne Nevada, e Oregon to w Wyoming, n Utah . . . . 285o. *Astragalus lentiginosus* var. *platyphyllidius*
        38. Corollas usually pink-purple, rarely whitish; Arizona, California, Colorado, Nevada, New Mexico, Texas, Utah.
            39. Corollas pale violet; ec New Mexico, Texas Panhandle . . . . 285y. *Astragalus lentiginosus* var. *higginsii*
            39. Corollas usually purple or pink-purple, rarely whitish, sometimes with pale, striate eye; Arizona, California, Colorado, Nevada, Utah.
                40. Plants 70–100 cm; stems prostrate; plants of moist, alkaline flats, w Nevada, adjacent California.
                    41. Leaflets (9–)15 or 17, terminal leaflet 7–15 mm . . .285l. *Astragalus lentiginosus* var. *sesquimetralis*
                    41. Leaflets 3 or 5, terminal leaflet 14–30 mm . . . . .285m. *Astragalus lentiginosus* var. *piscinensis*
                40. Plants 5–40(–80) cm; stems usually ascending, spreading, or decumbent, rarely prostrate; plants of dry habitats, Arizona, Colorado, Nevada, New Mexico, Utah.

[42. Shifted to left margin.—Ed.]

42. Stems decumbent or weakly ascending; calyx lobes (2.5–)3–5 mm; plants often growing with ponderosa pine, North Rim and n wall of Grand Canyon, Coconino County, Arizona . . . . 285t. *Astragalus lentiginosus* var. *oropedii*
42. Stems decumbent, spreading, prostrate, or incurved-ascending; calyx lobes (1.2–)1.4–3.8 (–4) mm; Arizona, Colorado, Nevada, New Mexico, Utah.
    43. Legumes plumply ovoid or subglobose, beaks 2.5–5 mm, bilocular; limestone mountains of ec Nevada . . . . 285r. *Astragalus lentiginosus* var. *latus*
    43. Legumes usually ovoid-acuminate, ellipsoid, ovoid, or lanceoloid-ovoid, rarely subglobose, beaks (3–)4–15 mm, usually unilocular; Arizona, Colorado, Nevada, New Mexico, Utah.
        44. Legumes thinly papery; seeds 13–20; elevations (1800–)2400–3500 m; c, wc Nevada . . 285q. *Astragalus lentiginosus* var. *toyabensis*
        44. Legumes thinly or stiffly papery or leathery (sometimes thinly papery in var. *wahweapensis*); seeds (20–)24–40; elevations 1400–2300 m; Arizona, Colorado, Nevada, New Mexico, Utah.

[45. Shifted to left margin.—Ed.]

45. Legumes 23–34 × 6–15 mm, stiffly papery or almost leathery; Box Elder, Millard, and Tooele counties, Utah . . . . 285u. *Astragalus lentiginosus* var. *negundo*
45. Legumes (10–)14–30(–40) × (6.5–)8–18 mm; thinly or stiffly papery or leathery; Arizona, Colorado, Nevada, New Mexico, Utah.
    46. Legumes usually strongly incurved, beaks lanceoloid-acuminate, 6–15 mm; c Utah to c Nevada . . . . 285v. *Astragalus lentiginosus* var. *chartaceus*
    46. Legumes slightly or strongly incurved, beaks broadly triangular or deltoid, (3–)4–15 mm; n Arizona to c New Mexico, extreme sw Colorado, se Utah.
        47. Legumes thinly papery to almost leathery; racemes compact to loose, axes 1.5–5.5(–7) cm in fruit; sc Utah and n Arizona . . . . . 285w. *Astragalus lentiginosus* var. *wahweapensis*
        47. Legumes stiffly papery or leathery; racemes compact, axes 1–4(–6) cm in fruit; c to n Arizona to c New Mexico and extreme sw Colorado . . . . 285x. *Astragalus lentiginosus* var. *diphysus*

285a. Astragalus lentiginosus Douglas var. **lentiginosus** [E] [F]

Astragalus lentiginosus var. *carinatus* M. E. Jones

Plants perennial, 10–30(–50) cm, sparsely strigulose. **Leaves** 3–10 cm; leaflets (5–)9–17(or 19), blades broadly obovate, obovate-cuneate, or oblong-elliptic to suborbiculate or oblanceolate, (3–)5–15 mm, apex retuse or obtuse. **Peduncles** 1–3.5 cm. **Racemes** 8–18(–22)-flowered; axis 0.5–3(–3.5) cm in fruit. **Flowers** 7.4–11 mm; calyx 4.1–6.4 mm, tube 2.8–4.2 mm, lobes 1–2.2 mm; corolla whitish or yellowish, sometimes faintly lilac. **Legumes** green, usually mottled, becoming stramineous or brownish, obliquely ovoid-acuminate to lanceoloid-acuminate, strongly to scarcely inflated, 10–23 × (3–)4.5–10 mm, semibilocular, stiffly papery, opaque or nearly so, usually thinly strigulose, rarely puberulent; beak 4–9 mm, unilocular. **Seeds** (15 or)16–21. $2n = 22$.

Flowering May–early Jul. Often on volcanic soils, on basalt, with sagebrush and bunchgrass, in ponderosa pine and western juniper communities; 200–1500 m; B.C.; Calif., Idaho, Nev., Oreg., Wash.

Variety *lentiginosus* is widespread in the northern part of its range and is partially sympatric with vars. *platyphyllidius* and *salinus* in the southern part of its range. It is transitional to both.

285b. Astragalus lentiginosus Douglas var. **scorpionis** M. E. Jones, Rev. N.-Amer. Astragalus, 124. 1923 • Scorpion milkvetch [E]

Plants perennial, 5–30 cm. **Leaves** 3–10 cm; leaflets 13–19, blades oval, obovate, or elliptic-oblanceolate, 5–15 mm, apex subacute, truncate, or retuse. **Peduncles** 1.5–6(–8) cm. **Racemes** 8–18-flowered, short and compact in fruit; axis 1.5–4(–5) cm in fruit. **Flowers** 8.5–12.2 mm; calyx 4.2–7(–8.4) mm, tube 2.7–4.2(–5.3) mm, lobes 1.5–3.2 mm; corolla whitish or faintly lavender. **Legumes** green, usually mottled, becoming stramineous, broadly ovoid-acuminate, usually strongly inflated, 8–20(–25) × 4.5–12(–15) mm, stiffly papery, ± opaque, glabrous; beak 3–10 mm, unilocular. **Seeds** (7–)16–25.

Flowering Jun–Aug. Rocky crests, meadows, brushy hillsides, limber pine woodlands, mostly on limestone or limey clay soils, with sagebrush, to timberline; 2100–3400 m; Nev., Utah.

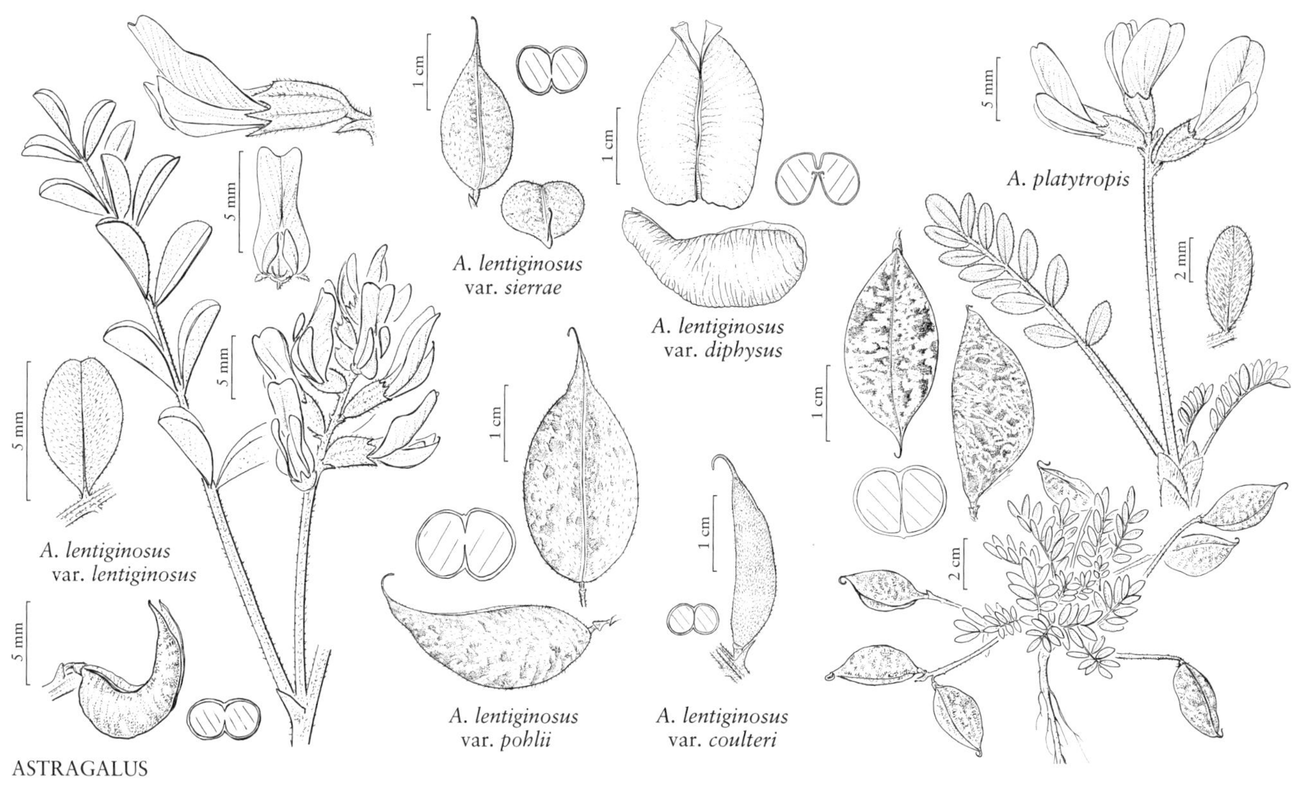

ASTRAGALUS

Variety *scorpionis* resembles forms of var. *lentiginosus* that have thin-walled, well-inflated fruits but is disjunct from that northern, lower elevation variety. Variety *scorpionis* is seemingly the only member of its species present in several Nevada ranges (Deep Creek, Diamond, Grant, Ruby, and White Pine). It is contiguous to two usually purple-flowered montane varieties, vars. *latus* and *toyabensis* (D. Isely 1998).

285c. Astragalus lentiginosus Douglas var. **multiracemosus** S. L. Welsh & N. D. Atwood in S. L. Welsh, N. Amer. Sp. Astragalus, 294, fig. 285c. 2007 • Lamoille Canyon milkvetch [E]

Plants perennial, 25–48 cm. **Stems** prostrate, radiating from root-crown. **Leaves** 6.5–12 cm; leaflets 15 or 17, blades lanceolate to oblong-elliptic, 7–18 mm, apex truncate or round. **Peduncles** 1.3–2 cm. **Racemes** 12–14-flowered, floriferous from all but proximalmost nodes, short and compact in fruit; axis 4–4.5 cm in fruit. **Flowers** 12–15 mm; calyx 7–7.5 mm, tube 4–4.5 mm, lobes 3–3.2 mm; corolla whitish or faintly lavender. **Legumes** purple-mottled becoming stramineous, broadly ovoid-acuminate, strongly inflated, 8–12 × 5–6 mm, opaque-papery, glabrous; beak 3–5 mm, unilocular. **Seeds** not determined.

Flowering Jul–Sep. Moist seeps; 2500–2600 m; Nev.

Variety *multiracemosus* is known only from Lamoille Canyon in the Ruby Mountains in Elko County. The proliferous habit of producing numerous racemes along prostrate stems is shared with disjunct vars. *floribundus*, *ineptus*, *piscinensis*, and *sesquimetralis*. The nearest relationship is most likely with var. *salinus*, which sometimes produces racemes from middle as well as distal nodes, producing new flowers distally while proximal racemes are in fruit. Flower size is similar to that of var. *salinus*; fruit is similar to that of var. *scorpionis*.

285d. Astragalus lentiginosus Douglas var. **salinus** (Howell) Barneby, Leafl. W. Bot. 4: 86. 1945 • Harney milkvetch [E]

Astragalus salinus Howell, Erythea 1: 111. 1893

Plants perennial, 6–30(–45) cm. **Stems** ascending to erect, mostly unbranched. **Leaves** 4–10 cm; leaflets (9 or)11–19, blades broadly obovate, obovate-cuneate, obcordate, or oblong to oblanceolate, 5–20 mm, apex usually retuse or emarginate, surfaces glabrate to densely strigulose, hairs appressed or subappressed. **Peduncles** 2–4.5(–5) cm. **Racemes** 10–25-flowered, floriferous from middle to distalmost nodes, short and compact in fruit; axis 1.5–4(–9) cm in fruit. **Flowers** 9.5–11.5 mm; calyx 5–6.4 mm, tube 3.6–4.2(–4.6) mm, lobes 1.2–2.2 mm; corolla whitish, sometimes wings and keel with lavender tips. **Legumes** green or mottled becoming stramineous, obliquely ovoid or subglobose, strongly inflated, 14–26(–30) × (6–)7.5–14 mm, papery-membranous, translucent, glabrous or puberulent; beak 3–9 mm, unilocular. **Seeds** (7–)16–25. **2*n*** = 22.

Flowering Apr–Jun. Saline flats and playas upward to mountain slopes in sagebrush, oak, and other montane communities; 700–2600 m; B.C.; Calif., Idaho, Mont., Nev., Oreg., Utah, Wyo.

Variety *salinus*, widespread in the northern and eastern portions of the Great Basin, occupies a crucial position in the *Astragalus lentiginosus* complex, serving to link many superficially disparate lines of differentiation (R. C. Barneby 1964). On the one hand, one can trace a sequence passing through var. *floribundus* to var. *ineptus*, and then to vars. *antonius*, *idriensis*, and *sierrae*. On the other hand, another strand leads through vars. *lentiginosus* and *platyphyllidius* to vars. *chartaceus*, *diphysus*, and finally *australis*.

285e. Astragalus lentiginosus Douglas var. **floribundus** A. Gray, Proc. Amer. Acad. Arts 6: 524. 1865 • Carson City milkvetch [E]

Plants perennial, 20–50 cm. **Stems** prostrate to weakly ascending, branched proximally. **Leaves** 3–8(–11) cm; leaflets 11–15(–19), blades obovate or oblanceolate, 5–15 mm, apex retuse, surfaces glabrate to densely strigulose, hairs appressed or subappressed. **Peduncles** 1–4(–7) cm. **Racemes** (11–)15–30(–37)-flowered, short and dense, cylindric or globose in fruit; axis 1–4(–7) cm in fruit. **Flowers** 8.8–11 mm; calyx 4–6.5 mm, tube 3–4 mm, lobes 0.6–1.4(–2) mm; corolla whitish, sometimes wings and keel with lavender tips. **Legumes** faintly mottled becoming stramineous, obliquely ovoid or subglobose, strongly inflated, (8–)12–21 × (6–)7–12 mm, thinly papery, translucent, glabrous or strigulose; beak 3–7 mm, unilocular. **Seeds** 15–21(–25).

Flowering May–Jun. Sagebrush communities, on sandy, granitic, or basaltic substrates; 1100–1600 (–2100) m; Calif., Nev., Oreg.

Variety *floribundus* is the only member of *Astragalus lentiginosus* in the Lake Tahoe area; it occurs along the eastern flanks of the Sierra Nevada, passing into var. *ineptus* in Mono County, and extends northward into southeastern Oregon, where it grades into var. *salinus*.

285f. Astragalus lentiginosus Douglas var. **macrolobus** (Rydberg) Barneby, Leafl. W. Bot. 4: 89. 1945 • West Humboldt milkvetch [E]

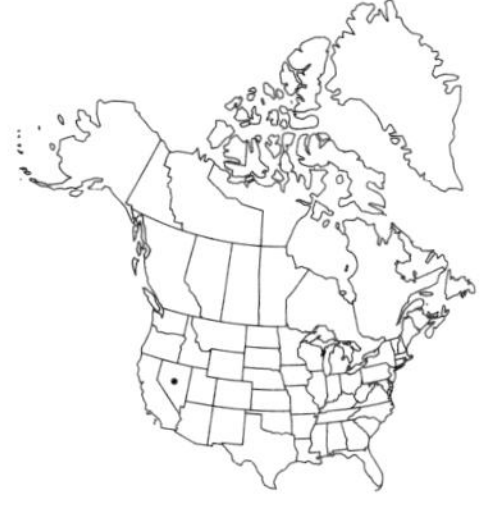

Cystium macrolobum Rydberg in N. L. Britton et al., N. Amer. Fl. 24: 408. 1929

Plants perennial (rarely flowering first year), 6–30 cm. **Leaves** 4–11 cm; leaflets (9–)13–19, blades obovate or oblanceolate, 4–20 mm, apex mostly retuse, surfaces strigulose-villosulous, some hairs spreading or sinuous. **Peduncles** 2.5–7 cm. **Racemes** (8–)12–30-flowered, short and compact in fruit; axis (2–)3–7(–9) cm in fruit. **Flowers** 9.3–11.3 mm; calyx (4.5–)5–7.1 mm, tube 3–3.8 mm, lobes (1.5–)2–3.3 mm; corolla usually whitish, sometimes purple or pink-purple. **Legumes** green, faintly mottled, or stramineous, obliquely ovoid or subglobose, strongly inflated, 15–25 × (6–)8–14 mm, thinly papery, translucent, glabrous or strigulose; beak 3–7 mm, unilocular. **Seeds** 18–26.

Flowering Apr–Jul. On sand, with sagebrush; 1100–1800 m; Nev.

Specimens of var. *macrolobus*, apparently flowering the first year, have been misidentified as *Astragalus geyeri*, which is clearly annual and has straight, appressed (not villosulous) indumentum. Variety *macrolobus* occurs in northern Nevada. To the north and east, it grades into var. *salinus* and to the west into var. *floribundus*.

285g. Astragalus lentiginosus Douglas var. **ineptus** (A. Gray) M. E. Jones, Rev. N.-Amer. Astragalus, 124. 1923 • Homely milkvetch [E]

Astragalus ineptus A. Gray, Proc. Amer. Acad. Arts 6: 525. 1865

Plants perennial, (1–)3–30 cm, herbage loosely strigulose or villosulous. **Leaves** 1.5–5.5 cm; leaflets (9–)15–21, crowded, blades obovate or oblanceolate, (1–)2–10 mm, apex obtuse or retuse. **Peduncles** 0.5–2 cm. **Racemes** (4–)10–21-flowered, short and compact in fruit; axis (0.3–)1–2.5 cm in fruit. **Flowers** (8.8–)9.8–12 mm; calyx (4.8–)5.4–7.3 mm, tube (3.6–)3.9–4.9 mm, lobes (1–)1.2–2.4 mm; corolla whitish or cream, sometimes with pink tips. **Legumes** usually faintly mottled becoming stramineous, plumply ovoid- or ellipsoid-acuminate, strongly inflated, 10–18 × (5–)6–12 mm, thinly papery, strigulose or, sometimes, glabrous; beak erect or incurved, deltoid, 3–5 mm, unilocular. **Seeds** (12–)14–19.

Flowering Jun–Aug. Gravelly slopes, ridges, and talus, on coarse granitic sand or volcanic tuff, in bristlecone pine and alpine tundra communities; 1800–3700 m; Calif.

Variety *ineptus* occurs along the eastern face of the Sierra Nevada from Alpine County southward to the Inconsolable Range, Inyo County, Sweetwater Mountains, Mono County, and Bonita Meadows, Tulare County.

285h. Astragalus lentiginosus Douglas var. **semotus** Jepson, Fl. Calif. 2: 357. 1936 • White Mountains milkvetch E

Plants perennial, 5–10(–20) cm, herbage subappressed-strigulose. **Leaves** 4–9 cm; leaflets (13–)17–27, distant, blades oblanceolate, oblong-oval, or oblong-elliptic, 2–9 mm, apex obtuse or emarginate. **Peduncles** 0.6–1.5 cm. **Racemes** 6–10-flowered, short and compact in fruit; axis 1–3 cm in fruit. **Flowers** 10.4–12 mm; calyx 5.2–7.3 mm, tube 3.6–5 mm, lobes 1.5–2.6 mm; corolla whitish. **Legumes** mottled, ovoid-acuminate, bladdery-inflated, 11–20(–23) × 6–12 mm, papery, sparsely strigulose; beak incurved, deltoid, 4–7 mm, unilocular. **Seeds** 13–15. $2n = 22$.

Flowering Jun–Aug. Among sagebrush, with bristlecone pine; 2100–3500 m; Calif., Nev.

Variety *semotus*, similar to var. *ineptus*, occurs in the Inyo and White mountains in Inyo and Mono counties, California, and Esmeralda County, Nevada.

285i. Astragalus lentiginosus Douglas var. **sierrae** M. E. Jones, Rev. N.-Amer. Astragalus, 124. 1923 • San Bernardino Mountains milkvetch C E F

Plants perennial, 10–30 cm, herbage green or greenish. **Leaves** 2–5 cm; leaflets 15–21, blades obovate or broadly oblanceolate, 3–8 mm, apex obtuse or emarginate. **Peduncles** (0.7–)1–3 cm. **Racemes** (5–)7–15-flowered, short and compact in fruit; axis 0.5–3 cm in fruit. **Flowers** 10.4–13(–14.5) mm; calyx 5–6(–6.6) mm, tube 4.3–4.8(–5.2) mm, lobes 0.5–1.4 mm; corolla whitish or with pink tinge. **Legumes** mottled becoming stramineous, plumply ovoid-acuminate or subglobose, bladdery-inflated, 15–22 × 8–15 mm, papery, strigulose; beak erect, triangular, 3–6 mm, unilocular. **Seeds** 17–24.

Flowering Apr–Aug. Meadows, pine forests; of conservation concern; 1800–2200(–2600) m; Calif.

Variety *sierrae* is restricted to the eastern margin of the San Bernardino Mountains in San Bernardino County, where it is local and common.

285j. Astragalus lentiginosus Douglas var. **antonius** Barneby, Leafl. W. Bot. 4: 100, plate 2, figs. 7–9. 1945 • Mount San Antonio milkvetch C E

Plants perennial, 7–30 cm, herbage cinereous or silvery-canescent. **Leaves** 3–8 cm; leaflets 11–19(or 21), blades obovate or elliptic, 2.5–11 mm, apex obtuse or emarginate. **Peduncles** (1–)2–5.5 cm. **Racemes** 10–15-flowered, short and compact in fruit; axis 0.5–4(–5) cm in fruit. **Flowers** 9–10.5 mm; calyx 4.2–5.5 mm, tube 3.2–4 mm, lobes 0.8–1.4 mm; corolla purple. **Legumes** mottled becoming stramineous, plumply ovoid-acuminate or subglobose, bladdery-inflated, 14–22(–30) × 10–16(–18) mm, papery, strigulose; beak erect, triangular, 3–6 mm, unilocular. **Seeds** 20–26.

Flowering late Apr–Jul. Ponderosa pine forests; of conservation concern; 1500–2600 m; Calif.

Variety *antonius*, from the eastern end of the San Gabriel Mountains in eastern Los Angeles and adjacent San Bernardino counties, is the homologue of var. *sierrae*, from which it differs by its much denser pubescence and mostly flat leaflets (D. Isely 1998).

285k. Astragalus lentiginosus Douglas var. **albifolius** M. E. Jones, Rev. N.-Amer. Astragalus, 124. 1923 • Owens Valley milkvetch C E

Plants perennial, halophyte, 30–100 cm. **Leaves** 2–9 cm; leaflets (9 or)11–17(–21), blades oblanceolate, elliptic, or narrowly oblong, (3–)5–15(–18) mm, apex obtuse or subacute. **Peduncles** (1–)1.5–6.5 cm. **Racemes** (9–)12–35-flowered, crowded into subglobose or cylindric heads, short and compact in fruit; axis obscured, (0.5–)1–4 cm in fruit. **Flowers** 8.2–11.5 mm; calyx 5–7.3 mm, tube 3.2–4.5 mm, lobes 1.5–2.8 mm; corolla whitish, sometimes with purple veins, or pink-purple with white wing tips. **Legumes** pale green and purple-mottled becoming stramineous, plumply ovoid-acuminate, bladdery-inflated, 9–17 × 8–14 mm, papery-membranous, subtranslucent, strigulose; beak decurved, triangular, 3–5 mm, unilocular. **Seeds** 10–15.

Flowering Apr–Jul. Saline, summer-dry flats about seepage areas in lower foothills, on clay soils moist in springtime; of conservation concern; 600–1500 m; Calif.

Variety *albifolius* was described as an elongate, ungainly, trailing or scrambling halophyte (D. Isely 1998); it occurs at the eastern base of the Sierra Nevada in Inyo County near Big Pine and Lone Pine, near Muroc in Kern County, and near Lancaster in Los Angeles County.

Astragalus albifolius (M. E. Jones) Abrams is an illegitimate later homonym of *A. albifolius* Freyn & Sintenis 1893.

285l. Astragalus lentiginosus Douglas var. **sesquimetralis** (Rydberg) Barneby, Leafl. W. Bot. 4: 116. 1945 • Soda Springs milkvetch [C] [E]

Cystium sesquimetrale Rydberg in N. L. Britton et al., N. Amer. Fl. 24: 414. 1929

Plants perennial, to 70–80 cm. **Stems** prostrate. **Leaves** 2–5 cm; leaflets 9–15(or 17), blades oblanceolate, 6–18 mm, terminal leaflet 7–15 mm, apex obtuse or subacute. **Peduncles** 1.5–4 cm. **Racemes** shortly and loosely 6–12-flowered, short and compact in fruit; axis 1–2 cm in fruit. **Flowers** 14–14.5 mm; calyx 7–8 mm, tube 4.8–5.5 mm, lobes 2.2–2.5 mm; corolla purple. **Legumes** mottled, ovoid or broadly lanceoloid, moderately inflated, 16–26 × 9–12 mm, semibilocular, stiffly papery, strigulose; beak incurved, 4–8 mm, unilocular. **Seeds** 12–20.

Flowering May–Jun. Saline, seasonally moist clay flats, around seeps and springs; of conservation concern; 900–1400 m; Calif., Nev.

The branches of var. *sesquimetralis* radiate, forming large, round plants that hug the ground. This habit, coupled with a long season of available water, is evidently conducive to long-continuing flowering and fruiting but is not necessarily an indication of a near relationship to other taxa that are similar (see discussion under 285c. var. *multiracemosus*). The variety is restricted to southern Mineral County, Nevada, and northern Inyo County, California.

285m. Astragalus lentiginosus Douglas var. **piscinensis** Barneby, Brittonia 29: 378, fig. 2. 1977 • Fish Slough milkvetch [C] [E]

Plants perennial, to 100 cm. **Stems** prostrate. **Leaves** 2–5 cm; leaflets 3 or 5, blades linear-oblanceolate, 7–15 mm, terminal leaflet 14–30 mm, apex obtuse or subacute. **Peduncles** 2–5.5 cm. **Racemes** shortly 5–12-flowered, short and compact in fruit; axis 1.5–4 cm in fruit. **Flowers** 13 mm; calyx 7 mm, tube 4.5 mm, lobes 2.5 mm; corolla purple. **Legumes** mottled, ovoid-acuminate, moderately inflated, 20–24 × 8–12 mm, stiffly papery, strigulose; beak incurved, 4.5–7 mm, bilocular. **Seeds** 18.

Flowering Jun–Jul. Saline seep, moist at least in springtime, growing with *Ivesia*, *Juncus*, and other herbs; of conservation concern; 1200–1300 m; Calif.

Variety *piscinensis* is known from Fish Slough northwest of Bishop in Mono County. It is similar in habit to vars. *multiracemosus* and *sesquimetralis*.

285n. Astragalus lentiginosus Douglas var. **kernensis** (Jepson) Barneby, Leafl. W. Bot. 4: 102. 1945 • Kern River milkvetch [E]

Astragalus kernensis Jepson, Man. Fl. Pl. Calif., 569. 1925

Plants perennial, 2.5–12 cm. **Stems** prostrate or decumbent. **Leaves** 1–5 cm; leaflets (7–)11–19, mostly conduplicate, blades elliptic-oblanceolate, oval, or obovate, 1.5–7 mm, apex obtuse or emarginate. **Peduncles** 0.6–2.5 cm. **Racemes** shortly and loosely (2 or)3–9-flowered, short and compact in fruit; axis 0.3–1.5 cm in fruit. **Flowers** 9.3–11.3 mm; calyx 4.1–5.3 mm, tube 3.5–4.6 mm, lobes 0.6–1.2 mm; corolla whitish or suffused purplish. **Legumes** in loose or compact, humistrate clusters, pale green or stramineous, purple-mottled, becoming brownish, globose or very broadly and plumply ovoid or obovoid, bladdery-inflated, 6–13 × 6–10 mm, papery, subtranslucent, sparsely and loosely strigulose; beak linear- or subulate-tubular, cusplike, bilocular. **Seeds** (7–)10–18.

Flowering Jun–Jul. Dry, gravelly or sandy slopes and flats, with sagebrush, in lodgepole pine forests on granite, with bristlecone pine, on limestone; (1900–)2300–3100 m; Calif., Nev.

The relatively small fruit size of var. *kernensis* coupled with a narrow, tubular beak resembling a persistent style are the main features of this delicate, montane plant. It is locally plentiful in two widely separate and restricted areas: the Kern Plateau just west of the Sierra Nevada crest in Tulare County, California, and about the summit of Charleston Peak in Clark County, Nevada.

285o. Astragalus lentiginosus Douglas var. **platyphyllidius** (Rydberg) M. Peck, Man. Pl. Oregon, 449. 1941 (as platyphyllidium) • Broad-leaved milkvetch [E]

Cystium platyphyllidium Rydberg in N. L. Britton et al., N. Amer. Fl. 24: 410. 1929; *Astragalus lentiginosus* var. *cornutus* (Rydberg) M. Peck; *A. merrillii* (Rydberg) Tidestrom; *C. cornutum* Rydberg; *C. merrillii* Rydberg

Plants perennial, (7–)10–30(–35) cm. **Leaves** (4–)5–11 cm; leaflets (7–)11–17(or 19), blades usually broadly obovate-cuneate, elliptic, or suborbiculate, rarely rhombic-elliptic, (4–)7–20 mm, apex usually obtuse, retuse, truncate, or apiculate, rarely acute. **Peduncles** 1–5 cm. **Racemes** shortly and loosely (5–)7–15-flowered, flowering from near or proximal to middle nodes, short and compact in fruit; axis little elongating, 1–3.5 cm in fruit. **Flowers** (12.6–)14–21.4 mm; calyx (8–)8.5–12.5 mm, tube (5–)5.5–8(–9) mm, lobes 2.4–5 mm; corolla usually whitish, rarely purple. **Legumes** variable in length, outline, and curvature, pale green or purple-speckled becoming stramineous or brownish, plumply ovoid or narrowly lanceoloid-ellipsoid, (13–)15–40 (–48) × 7–14 mm, ± bilocular, strongly or slightly inflated, ± fleshy becoming leathery or stiffly papery, usually glabrous, sometimes minutely strigulose; beak deltoid or lanceolate-acuminate, 5–15 mm, unilocular. **Seeds** (21–)24–32(–38).

Flowering May–Jul. Arid plains, hillsides, and valley floors, on basalt, with sagebrush; 600–1900(–2100) m; Calif., Colo., Idaho, Nev., Oreg., Utah, Wyo.

Variety *platyphyllidius* is dispersed widely from eastern Oregon and northeastern California, across southern Idaho into western Wyoming, northeastern Nevada, and barely into northern Utah and northwestern Colorado. It is apparently common only locally, distinguished by its typically pale flowers and thick-textured fruits (approximate length of two times width or less).

285p. Astragalus lentiginosus Douglas var. **pohlii** S. L. Welsh & Barneby, Iselya 2: 1. 1981 • Pohl's milkvetch [C] [E] [F]

Plants perennial, 7–20 cm. **Leaves** (4–)5–9 cm; leaflets 11–17, blades broadly obovate-cuneate or suborbiculate, 4–11 mm, apex obtuse or retuse to emarginate. **Peduncles** 1–4 cm. **Racemes** shortly and loosely 3–9-flowered, short and compact in fruit; axis 1–3.5 cm in fruit. **Flowers** 20–23 mm; calyx 8.5–10.5 mm, tube 8–10 mm, lobes 2.4–3 mm; corolla whitish tinged with violet. **Legumes** pale green or purple-speckled becoming stramineous or brownish, plumply ovoid, strongly inflated, 23–33 × 10–15 mm, ± bilocular, leathery or stiffly papery, minutely strigulose; beak 5–15 mm, unilocular; stipe 0.5–1.5 mm. **Seeds** 24–32.

Flowering May–Jun. Greasewood, shadscale, horsebrush, and big sagebrush communities, vegetated sand dunes; of conservation concern; 1300–1700 m; Utah.

Variety *pohlii* is restricted to the Rush and Skull valleys in Tooele County. The shortly stipitate fruit is unusual among varieties of *Astragalus lentiginosus.*

285q. Astragalus lentiginosus Douglas var. **toyabensis** Barneby, Leafl. W. Bot. 4: 106, plate 3, figs. 1–4. 1945 • Toyabe milkvetch [E]

Plants perennial, 10–30 cm. **Stems** usually ascending, rarely prostrate. **Leaves** 3–13(–16) cm; leaflets (7–)15–25, blades oval-obovate, broadly oblanceolate, or narrowly elliptic-oblanceolate, (2–)6–16(–21) mm, apex obtuse and apiculate, truncate, acute, or subacute. **Peduncles** 1.5–4.5(–6.5) cm. **Racemes** 7–18-flowered, short and compact in fruit; axis 1–2.5(–5) cm in fruit. **Flowers** 12.6–17 mm; calyx (6.2–)6.7–10 mm, tube 5–6.5 mm, lobes (1.2–)1.6–3.5(–4) mm; corolla usually pink-purple, rarely whitish. **Legumes** usually mottled becoming stramineous, narrowly to broadly ovoid-acuminate, ± strongly inflated, 8–20 × 4–11 mm, thinly papery, glabrous or exceptionally puberulent; beak triangular-acuminate, (3–)4–11 mm, unilocular. **Seeds** 13–20.

Flowering Jun–Aug. Dry, stony hillsides with sagebrush, open, treeless crests within timber belt, rarely above timber belt, on cool, loamy soils among aspens, on igneous bedrock; (1800–)2400–3500 m; Nev.

Usually a montane plant of central and west-central Nevada, var. *toyabensis* sometimes descends into the foothills as low as 1830 m, where it enters the habitat of, and apparently grades into, var. *chartaceus*, a form that differs typically in its leathery or at least much more stiffly papery fruit (R. C. Barneby 1964).

285r. Astragalus lentiginosus Douglas var. **latus** (M. E. Jones) M. E. Jones, Rev. N.-Amer. Astragalus, 125. 1923 • Schell Creek milkvetch [C] [E]

Astragalus diphysus A. Gray var. *latus* M. E. Jones, Zoë 3: 287. 1893

Plants perennial, 5–17 cm. **Stems** usually ascending, rarely prostrate. **Leaves** (4–)6–13 cm; leaflets 11–17(–23), blades broadly obovate, ovate, or broadly oblanceolate, (4–)6–15 mm, apex shallowly notched or obtuse. **Peduncles** 1.5–6 cm. **Racemes** shortly and loosely 5–12(–18)-flowered, short and compact in fruit; axis 0.7–2(–4) cm in fruit. **Flowers** (11.3–)15–19 mm; calyx (6.5–)7–12.5 mm, tube (4.5–)5.6–8.2 mm, lobes (1.4–)2–4 mm; corolla pink-purple. **Legumes** green, red-mottled, becoming stramineous, plumply ovoid or subglobose, strongly inflated, 1–2.5 × 0.7–1.6 cm, leathery, glabrous; beak 2.5–5 mm, bilocular. **Seeds** (12–)22–28.

Flowering May–Jul. Open, gravelly slopes in timber belt; of conservation concern; (1700–)2200–3000 m; Nev.

Variety *latus* is known from the Schell Creek and Egan ranges in White Pine County.

285s. Astragalus lentiginosus Douglas var. **idriensis** M. E. Jones, Contr. W. Bot. 10: 63. 1902 • New Idria milkvetch [E]

Astragalus idriensis (M. E. Jones) Abrams; *A. tehachapiensis* (Rydberg) Tidestrom

Plants perennial, (10–)15–40 cm. **Leaves** (2–)3–11 cm; leaflets (7–)17–27(or 29), blades oval-obovate, obovate-cuneate, or broadly oblanceolate, (2–)3–15(–18) mm, apex truncate or emarginate. **Peduncles** (1.5–)3–6 cm. **Racemes** 7–20-flowered, short and compact in fruit; axis (0.5–)1–4 cm in fruit. **Flowers** (12–)14–19(–20) mm; calyx (5–)6.2–11 mm, tube (4.2–)4.7–7.2 mm, lobes (0.5–)1.3–3.4 mm; corolla brilliant or pale pink-purple. **Legumes** green, usually red-mottled, obliquely ovoid or lunately semi-ovoid, greatly or slightly inflated, 12–30 × 5-16 mm, semibilocular, somewhat fleshy becoming leathery or stiffly papery, strigulose, hairs usually white, rarely black; beak 3–10 mm, unilocular. **Seeds** 21–30.

Flowering Apr–Jun. Dry, grassy hillsides, canyon floors and benches, on shale or sandstone outcrops, in arid grasslands with blue oak, with foothill pine, among sagebrush; 300–2100 m; Calif.

Variety *idriensis* occurs in and around the head of the San Joaquin Valley and in the South Coast ranges, where it is the only form of *Astragalus lentiginosus* with shortly racemose purple flowers that is native (R. C. Barneby 1964).

285t. Astragalus lentiginosus Douglas var. **oropedii** Barneby, Leafl. W. Bot. 4: 135. 1945 • Kaibab Plateau milkvetch [E]

Plants perennial, (10–)20–80 cm. **Stems** decumbent or weakly ascending, flexuous or zigzag in age, glabrous or glabrate. **Leaves** 5–15 cm; leaflets 15–21(–25), blades broadly oblong-elliptic, ovate-oblong, or suborbiculate, 5–20(–25) mm, apex rounded, truncate, or retuse. **Peduncles** (2–)3–10 cm. **Racemes** shortly (8–)10–25-flowered, compact in fruit; axis little elongating, 1.5–4(–5) cm in fruit. **Flowers** (12.5–)13.2–20 mm; calyx 7.5–10.8 mm, tube (4.5–)5–7.5 mm, lobes (2.5–)3–5 mm; corolla purple or pale pink-purple. **Legumes** mottled, obliquely ovoid or semi-ovoid, ± strongly inflated, 13–25(–30) × 6.5–14 mm, ± bilocular, stiffly papery, glabrous; beak 5–8 mm, unilocular. **Seeds** 20–33.

Flowering Jun–Sep. Openings in ponderosa pine forests; 2100–2500 m; Ariz.

Variety *oropedii* is locally common but apparently confined to the Kaibab Plateau, especially the North Rim and upper levels of the northern wall of the Grand Canyon in Coconino County. Specimens with thin-textured, subdiaphanous fruits that occur within or near known localities of var. *oropedii* have been tentatively placed with var. *vitreus*.

285u. Astragalus lentiginosus Douglas var. **negundo** S. L. Welsh & N. D. Atwood in S. L. Welsh, N. Amer. Sp. Astragalus, 302, fig. 285u. 2007 [E]

Plants perennial, 19–32 cm. **Stems** diffuse and incurved-ascending, often red- or purple-tinged. **Leaves** (2.5–)4–11 cm; leaflets (7–)13–19, blades elliptic-oblanceolate, broadly oblong-oblanceolate, or obovate, (2–)5–17 mm, apex obtuse or emarginate. **Peduncles** 2.2–5 cm. **Racemes** 5–11-flowered, flowering from middle and distally, short and compact in fruit; axis 0.5–5 cm in fruit. **Flowers** 12.5–14.5 mm; calyx 7.5–10.2 mm, tube 5.2–5.8 mm, lobes 1.8–4.4 mm; corolla bright pink-purple with pale, striate eye. **Legumes** purplish, often red-mottled, becoming stramineous, ellipsoid to lanceoloid-ovoid or ellipsoid-acuminate, moderately inflated, 23–34 × 6–15 mm, bilocular, stiffly papery or almost leathery, usually glabrous, rarely puberulent; beak well-defined, triangular or deltoid, 7–12 mm, unilocular. **Seeds** 40.

Flowering late Apr–Jun. Salt and sand desert shrub communities with shadscale, greasewood, sagebrush, and horsebrush, in pinyon-juniper communities; 1400–1700(–2300) m; Utah.

Variety *negundo*, which is known from Box Elder, Millard, and Tooele counties, fills a portion of the gap in distribution between var. *platyphyllidius*, with which it shares relatively thick-textured fruits, and var. *chartaceus*, with which it is transitional to the south. From either taxon, the elongated fruit is evidently diagnostic, apparent only as fruits approach maturity. The lower flower number is characteristic of var. *negundo* and is more or less diagnostic.

285v. Astragalus lentiginosus Douglas var. **chartaceus** M. E. Jones, Proc. Calif. Acad. Sci., ser. 2, 5: 673. 1895 • Cobweb milkvetch [E]

Astragalus araneosus E. Sheldon, Minnesota Bot. Stud. 1: 170. 1894; *A. lentiginosus* var. *araneosus* (E. Sheldon) Barneby

Plants perennial, 10–35 cm. **Stems** diffuse and incurved-ascending, often red-tinged. **Leaves** (2.5–)4–11 cm; leaflets (9 or)11–23, blades elliptic-oblanceolate, broadly oblong-oblanceolate, or obovate, (3–)5–17(–20) mm, apex obtuse or emarginate. **Peduncles** (1–)2.5–6(–7.5) cm. **Racemes** (5–)10–20-flowered, flowering from middle and distally, short and compact in fruit; axis (0.5–)1.5–4(–5.5) cm in fruit. **Flowers** (12.5–)15–18.2 mm; calyx (6.2–)7.5–10.5 mm, tube (4.6–)5.2–6.7 mm, lobes 1.4–3.8 mm; corolla bright pink-purple with pale, striate eye. **Legumes** green, often red-mottled, becoming stramineous, usually strongly incurved, ovoid, lanceoloid-ovoid, or ovoid-acuminate, moderately inflated, 15–30(–40) × (7–)9–15 mm, bilocular, stiffly papery or almost leathery, usually glabrous, rarely puberulent; beak well-defined, triangular or deltoid, 6–15 mm, unilocular. **Seeds** 24–34(–38).

Flowering May–Jul. Sagebrush, pinyon-juniper, and mixed desert shrub communities, on alluvial silt, igneous gravel; 1400–2200 m; Nev., Utah.

Variety *chartaceus* is widespread from central to western Utah into northeastern and central Nevada, there intergrading with vars. *fremontii*, *kennedyi*, and *toyabensis*. S. L. Welsh (2007) discussed the problems of including this variety in an expanded var. *diphysus* and its complex relationships to other varieties.

285w. Astragalus lentiginosus Douglas var. **wahweapensis** S. L. Welsh, Great Basin Naturalist 38: 286. 1978 • Wahweap freckled milkvetch [E]

Plants perennial (short-lived, sometimes flowering first year), 10–25(–35) cm. **Stems** diffuse and incurved-ascending. **Leaves** (2.5–)4–11 cm; leaflets 13–23, blades elliptic-oblanceolate, broadly oblong-oblanceolate, or obovate, (3–)5–17(–20) mm, apex obtuse or emarginate. **Peduncles** 2.5–6(–7.5) cm. **Racemes** 10–20-flowered, flowering from middle and distally, compact to loose in fruit; axis 1.5–5.5(–7) cm in fruit. **Flowers** (12.5–)15–18.2 mm; calyx (6.2–)7.5–10.5 mm, tube (4.6–)5.2–6.7 mm, lobes 1.4–3.8 mm; corolla usually bright pink-purple with pale, striate eye, rarely white (concolorous). **Legumes** green, sometimes stramineous or purple-mottled, almost always very strongly incurved, very obliquely ovoid-acuminate, moderately or greatly inflated, 15–30(–40) × (7–)9–15 mm, bilocular, thinly papery, semitranslucent, seeds visible, to almost leathery, opaque, usually glabrous, rarely puberulent; beak well-defined, triangular or deltoid, 6–15 mm, unilocular. **Seeds** (20–)24–28.

Flowering Apr–Jul. Pinyon-juniper, sagebrush, and mixed desert shrub communities; 1400–1900 m; Ariz., Utah.

Variety *wahweapensis* may be very abundant in wetter years, filling the interspaces in pinyon-juniper woodland much like an alfalfa field. It is found on the plateaus and drainages affluent to Lake Powell in eastern Kane and Garfield counties in Utah, and in northern Arizona. Variety *wahweapensis* grades into the slender-podded var. *palans* to the east and the ovoid-fruited var. *diphysus* southward.

285x. Astragalus lentiginosus Douglas var. **diphysus** (A. Gray) M. E. Jones, Proc. Calif. Acad. Sci., ser. 2, 5: 673. 1895 • Double-bladder freckled milkvetch [E] [F] [W]

Astragalus diphysus A. Gray, Mem. Amer. Acad. Arts, n. s. 4: 34. 1849; *A. lentiginosus* var. *albiflorus* (A. Gray) Schoener; *A. lentiginosus* var. *macdougalii* (E. Sheldon) M. E. Jones

Plants perennial, (10–)15–35 (–40) cm. **Stems** usually ascending, rarely prostrate. **Leaves** 3–10(–14) cm; leaflets (11–)15–21(or 23), blades oblong-oblanceolate, obovate, rhombic-obovate, elliptic, or ovate-cuneate, 4–20 mm, apex truncate-emarginate. **Peduncles** (1.5–)2.5–8.5 cm. **Racemes** ± densely becoming shortly (9–)12–24-flowered, short and compact in fruit; axis not or little elongating, 1–4(–6) cm in fruit. **Flowers** (12.6–)14.5–19 mm; calyx 7–10.4 mm, tube (5.1–)5.5–8 mm, lobes 1.5–3.2 mm; corolla pink-purple. **Legumes** green, purple- or red-tinged, or brightly mottled, slightly incurved, mostly plumply ovoid or subglobose, (10–)14–27(–30) × (6.5–)8–18 mm, semi-bilocular, stiffly papery or leathery, glabrous; beak well-defined, triangular or deltoid, (3–)4–10 mm, unilocular or bilocular. **Seeds** 28–35. $2n = 22$.

Flowering Mar–Jun(–Aug). Yucca-grasslands, pinyon-juniper forests, other xeric communities; 1400–2300 m; Ariz., Colo., N.Mex.

Variety *diphysus* is widespread, ranging across the northern parts of Arizona and New Mexico, extending northward into western Colorado. D. Isely (1998) recognized var. *macdougalii*, here considered a form with diminutive fruits, from the San Francisco Peaks area of Arizona.

285y. Astragalus lentiginosus Douglas var. **higginsii** S. L. Welsh & K. H. Thorne, Brittonia 33: 296, fig. 2. 1981 • Higgins's freckled milkvetch [E]

Plants perennial, 15–25 cm. **Leaves** 3–11 cm; leaflets 15–21, blades lanceolate-elliptic to obovate, 8–18 mm, apex emarginate. **Peduncles** 3–6.5 cm. **Racemes** 7–17-flowered, short and compact in fruit; axis 1–4 cm in fruit. **Flowers** 17–20 mm; calyx 7–10.4 mm, tube 6–6.8 mm, lobes 3–3.5 mm; corolla pale violet. **Legumes** green, sometimes mottled, becoming stramineous, ovoid, greatly inflated, 19–27 × 11–16(–19) mm, semibilocular, stiffly papery, thinly translucent, glabrous. **Seeds** 30–35.

Flowering Apr–early Jun. Sandy to loamy soils, with *Ptelea-Rhus-Prosopis*, and yucca, oak, mesquite communities; 800–1100 m; N.Mex., Tex.

Variety *higginsii*, from Chaves County in New Mexico, and Hudspeth, Hutchinson, and Potter counties in Texas, almost certainly is a derivative of var. *diphysus*, differing only in its pale flowers.

285z. Astragalus lentiginosus Douglas var. **australis** Barneby, Leafl. W. Bot. 4: 117, plate 3, figs. 15–19. 1945 • Southern freckled milkvetch

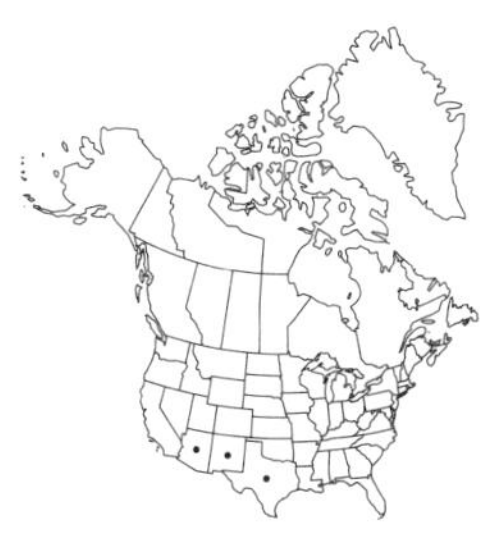

Plants perennial (short-lived), clump-forming, 25–40(–60) cm. **Stems** decumbent and ascending. **Leaves** (5–)6–17 cm; leaflets (13 or)15–21(or 23), blades usually obovate, broadly elliptic, or rhombic-ovate, rarely suborbiculate, (4–)6–25 mm, apex emarginate or retuse. **Peduncles** 3–7(–9) cm. **Racemes** loosely (10–)15–33-flowered, lax and open in fruit; axis (3.5–)4–12 cm in fruit. **Flowers** (13.2–)14.5–18 mm; calyx (5.3–)6.4–10.8 mm, tube (4.5–)4.8–7 mm, lobes (0.8–)1.6–3.8 mm; corolla pink-purple, sometimes pale. **Legumes** green or faintly mottled becoming stramineous or purplish, narrowly to broadly ovoid-acuminate or broadly lanceoloid-acuminate, slightly or greatly inflated, 12–22 × (4–)5–13(–15) mm, bilocular, thinly papery, usually glabrous, rarely sparsely pubescent; beak 4–8 mm, unilocular. **Seeds** 18–22. $2n$ = 22.

Flowering Feb–May. Open desert, sandy playas and outwash fans, plains, washes in foothills of desert mountains, with *Larrea*, *Carnegiea gigantea*, in yucca-grasslands; 600–1300 m; Ariz., N.Mex., Tex.; Mexico (Chihuahua, Sonora).

Variety *australis* is common and abundant in southeastern Arizona and southwestern New Mexico, grading into var. *yuccanus* to the north in Arizona. Eastward it extends to far western trans-Pecos Texas and becomes similar to var. *diphysus*.

285aa. Astragalus lentiginosus Douglas var. **yuccanus** M. E. Jones, Contr. W. Bot. 8: 3. 1898 • Yucca freckled milkvetch [E]

Plants winter-annual or short-lived perennial, clump-forming, 15–60(–100) cm. **Stems** erect and ascending. **Leaves** (5–)7–16 cm; leaflets 13–21(–25), blades broadly elliptic, oval, rhombic-obovate, or obovate, (4–)6–21 mm, apex retuse or emarginate. **Peduncles** (3–)5–10 cm. **Racemes** loosely (12–)15–32-flowered, lax and open in fruit; axis early elongating, (4.5–)6–14 cm in fruit. **Flowers** 11–15.6 mm; calyx 6–7.5 mm, tube 4.4–5.7 mm, lobes (1.3–)1.5–2.4 mm; corolla white or ochroleucous, concolorous, sometimes fading pale bluish, petals poorly graduated, banner slightly longer than wings, wings and keel nearly equal length. **Legumes** stramineous, plumply ovoid-acuminate or subglobose, strongly inflated, 15–25(–32) × 10–18 mm, bilocular, papery-membranous, subtranslucent, usually glabrous, rarely minutely strigulose; beak 3–7 mm, unilocular. **Seeds** 17–26. $2n$ = 22.

Flowering Feb–May. Open sandy plains, sandy or rocky washes, gulches in foothills of desert mountains, with *Larrea* and in yucca-grasslands; 500–1100 m; Ariz., Nev.

Variety *yuccanus* occurs in west-central Arizona, barely entering Nevada in the southern tip of Clark County.

285bb. Astragalus lentiginosus Douglas var. **stramineus** (Rydberg) Barneby, Leafl. W. Bot. 4: 122. 1945 • Straw milkvetch [E]

Cystium stramineum Rydberg in N. L. Britton et al., N. Amer. Fl. 24: 409. 1929

Plants perennial (short-lived), 12–40(–65) cm, herbage cinereous or green. **Stems** ashy canescent or green. **Leaves** (2.5–)4–11(–13) cm; leaflets (9 or)11–15, blades broadly oblanceolate or obovate-cuneate, (3–)5–18 mm, apex openly notched. **Peduncles** 3.5–9 cm. **Racemes** loosely or remotely 15–25(–30)-flowered, lax and open in fruit; axis 5–18 cm in fruit. **Flowers** 11–12 mm; calyx 5–6.6 mm, tube 3.8–4.5 mm, lobes 1.2–2.1 mm; corolla pale purple. **Legumes** greenish, usually mottled, becoming stramineous, obliquely ovoid-acuminate, bladdery-inflated, (10–)17–26 × 10–16 mm, bilocular, somewhat stiffly papery, opaque, strigulose; beak (2–)3–7 mm, unilocular. **Seeds** 20–26.

Flowering Apr–May. Mixed warm-desert shrub communities; 900–1000 m; Ariz., Nev., Utah.

Variety *stramineus* is the only member of the species with moderate-sized, pale purple flowers known to occur in Washington County in Utah, and adjacent Arizona and Nevada; it is similar to the slightly smaller-flowered var. *fremontii* and to var. *ambiguus*.

285cc. Astragalus lentiginosus Douglas var. **vitreus** Barneby, Leafl. W. Bot. 4: 119, plate 3, figs. 30–33. 1945 • Glass freckled milkvetch E

Plants perennial, 15–40 cm. **Stems** glabrous or glabrate. **Leaves** 4.5–10 cm; leaflets (7–)13–19, blades obovate-cuneate or oblong-obovate, (5–)7–17(–21) mm, apex obtuse or truncate-emarginate. **Peduncles** 4–9.5 cm. **Racemes** loosely (10–)15–27-flowered, lax and open in fruit; axis 4–8.5 cm in fruit. **Flowers** 13.2–17 mm; calyx 6.5–8 mm, tube 4.6–5.7 mm, lobes (1.5–)1.7–2.3 mm; corolla pink-purple or lavender with white wing tips. **Legumes** pale green and unmottled turning pallid, usually broadly ovoid, rarely lunately lanceoloid-acuminate, usually strongly inflated, rarely less so, 15–25 × (7–)9–15 mm, papery-membranous, subtranslucent, lustrous, glabrous; beak triangular, short, unilocular. **Seeds** 21–31. $2n = 22$.

Flowering Apr–Jun. Gullied badlands and desert flats, on sand or clay derived from sandstone or limestone, on volcanic gravel; 800–1500(–2000) m; Ariz., Utah.

Variety *vitreus* is found in the valleys of the upper Virgin River and Kanab Creek, southward to the northern slope of the Kaibab Plateau, and Toroweap and House Rock valleys in eastern Washington and western Kane counties in Utah, and northern Mohave and northwestern Coconino counties in Arizona.

285dd. Astragalus lentiginosus Douglas var. **ambiguus** Barneby, Mem. New York Bot. Gard. 13: 945. 1964 • Peach Springs freckled milkvetch C E

Plants perennial, 3–5 cm. **Leaves** 7–14 cm; leaflets 13–21, blades oblanceolate or oblong-obovate, (3–)7.5–15 mm, apex retuse-emarginate. **Peduncles** 7–11 cm. **Racemes** loosely (7–)15–20-flowered, lax and open in fruit; axis (4–)5.5–9 cm in fruit. **Flowers** (13–)15–16.7 mm; calyx 6.7–8 mm, tube 5–5.7 mm, lobes 1.6–2.3 mm; corolla purple. **Legumes** green and unmottled becoming stramineous, plumply ovoid or subglobose, inflated but firm, 15–22 × 9–13 mm, stiffly papery or almost leathery, usually glabrous, rarely puberulent; beak 2–5 mm, unilocular. **Seeds** 22–34.

Flowering Apr–May. Open limestone or granite hillsides; of conservation concern; 1200–1500 m; Ariz.

Variety *ambiguus* is known from Mohave County south of the Colorado River.

285ee. Astragalus lentiginosus Douglas var. **fremontii** (A. Gray) S. Watson, Botany (Fortieth Parallel), 66. 1871 • Frémont's freckled milkvetch E

Astragalus fremontii A. Gray in War Department [U.S.], Pacif. Railr. Rep. 4(5): 80. 1857; *A. fremontii* subsp. *eremicus* (E. Sheldon) Abrams

Plants annual, biennial, or perennial (short-lived), (4–)8–35(–40) cm. **Leaves** (3–)4–9(–12) cm; leaflets (9 or)11–19, blades ovate- or obovate-cuneate, broadly oblanceolate, or rhombic-elliptic, 5–19 mm, apex usually obtuse or emarginate, rarely subacute. **Peduncles** 2.5–8.5(–10) cm. **Racemes** loosely (8–)10–30-flowered, lax and open in fruit; axis (2.5–)4–11(–16) cm in fruit. **Flowers** 9.1–12(–12.4) mm; calyx (3.4–)3.8–6(–7.9) mm, tube (2.8–)3–4.5 mm, lobes (0.6–)0.9–2(–3.5) mm; corolla usually bright purple, rarely pink-lilac to pure white. **Legumes** pale green, often purple-freckled or purple-mottled, usually broadly and plumply ovoid-acuminate, rarely quite narrowly so, nearly always bladdery-inflated, 14–27(–36) × (5–)8–18 mm, ± bilocular, papery-membranous, subtranslucent, glabrous or sparsely strigulose-villosulous; beak (2–)3–7(–10) mm, unilocular. **Seeds** (17–)19–31.

Flowering late Mar–Jul (Sep–Oct). Braided stream gravel in riparian communities, gravelly slopes in creosote bush, Joshua tree, juniper, pinyon-juniper, and Jeffrey pine communities; 700–2500(–2800) m; Ariz., Calif., Nev., Utah.

Variety *fremontii* is common from southeastern California across southern Nevada to southwestern Utah and northwestern Arizona and may be very abundant when adequate moisture is available at an appropriate time. To the south and west, it grades into the larger-flowered var. *variabilis*; to the north in western Nevada, it grades into var. *kennedyi*.

285ff. Astragalus lentiginosus Douglas var. **kennedyi** (Rydberg) Barneby, Leafl. W. Bot. 4: 121. 1945 • Kennedy's freckled milkvetch [E]

Cystium kennedyi Rydberg in N. L. Britton et al., N. Amer. Fl. 24: 407. 1929

Plants biennial or perennial (short-lived), (10–)15–40(–50) cm; herbage villosulous. **Stems** decumbent and ascending. **Leaves** 4.5–12(–15) cm; leaflets (9–)15–21(or 23), blades obovate-cuneate to broadly oblong-oblanceolate, (5–)7–20 mm, apex obtuse, emarginate, or retuse. **Peduncles** (3–)4.5–7.5 cm. **Racemes** loosely (10–)15–35-flowered, lax and open in fruit; axis (3.5–)5–12 cm in fruit. **Flowers** (11.8–)12.5–17 mm; calyx 6.1–8.8 mm, tube 4.1–5.7 mm, lobes 1.6–3.1 mm; corolla bright pink. **Legumes** stramineous, usually narrowly ovoid-acuminate, more rarely plumply so, bladdery-inflated, (20–)25–30 × 9–15 mm, papery-membranous, usually lustrous, usually glabrous, rarely puberulent; beak 5–9 mm, unilocular. **Seeds** (24–)26–36. **2*n*** = 22.

Flowering Apr–Jun. Alkaline dunes, sandy valleys, dry stony knolls, sometimes on volcanic gravel or cinders; 1100–1800 m; Nev.

Variety *kennedyi* is a locally abundant endemic of west-central Nevada, blending with var. *fremontii* in the south.

285gg. Astragalus lentiginosus Douglas var. **variabilis** Barneby, Leafl. W. Bot. 4: 123, plate 4, figs. 1–8. 1945 • Victorville freckled milkvetch [E]

Plants usually short-lived perennial, sometimes annual, (4–)10–40 cm, herbage usually cinereous, sometimes green or silky-canescent. **Stems** diffuse and ascending; ashy canescent or green. **Leaves** (2.5–)4–13 cm; leaflets (7–)11–21(–25), blades obovate-cuneate to broadly oblanceolate or rhombic-elliptic, 4–15(–17) mm, apex usually obtuse or emarginate, rarely acute or subacute. **Peduncles** 3–8(–9) cm. **Racemes** loosely (10–)12–25-flowered, lax and open in fruit; axis (3–)4–15(–17) cm in fruit. **Flowers** 11.1–15 mm; calyx 4.7–6.5 mm, tube 3.7–5.2 mm, lobes 1–1.4(–1.5) mm, adaxial pair usually shortest; corolla pink- or magenta-purple. **Legumes** pale green or mottled becoming stramineous, obliquely ovoid or subglobose, bladdery-inflated, (12–)15–27(–30) × 8–14(–15) mm, bilocular, stiffly papery, opaque, sparsely strigulose to densely and canescently strigose-villosulous; beak (3–)4–9 mm, unilocular. **Seeds** 23–29. **2*n*** = 22.

Flowering (Feb–)Mar–Jun. Sandy flats, washes, desert playas, sometimes on dunes, usually with *Larrea*; 100–1000(–2100) m; Calif., Nev.

Variety *variabilis* is common and locally abundant in the southern and southwestern Mojave Desert, replacing var. *fremontii*, which is usually found to the north and east. Vestiture varies from ashy white to greenish. To the north in southern Inyo County, California, it intergrades with var. *fremontii* to the point that differentiation of the varieties is subjective. At low elevations in the central Mojave Desert it grades into var. *coachellae*. It also occurs on the floor of the upper San Joaquin Valley in Kern County, California, where it closely resembles var. *nigricalycis* except for the purple flowers. White-canescent plants of this variety also occur in Nye County in Nevada, west of Beatty. R. C. Barneby (1964) discussed intergradient populations more thoroughly.

285hh. Astragalus lentiginosus Douglas var. **nigricalycis** M. E. Jones, Proc. Calif. Acad. Sci., ser. 2, 5: 674. 1895 • Bakersfield freckled milkvetch [E]

Astragalus nigricalycis (M. E. Jones) Abrams

Plants perennial, 25–55 cm. **Stems** decumbent to ascending. **Leaves** (4–)6–16 cm; leaflets 19–25, blades oblong-oblanceolate to broadly obovate or rhombic-obovate, (3–)7–25 mm, apex usually retuse. **Peduncles** 4–11 cm. **Racemes** closely becoming loosely (10–)15–32-flowered, lax and open in fruit; axis (2.5–)4.5–11(–13) cm in fruit. **Flowers** 12–17(–18.5) mm; calyx 6.4–8.2 mm, tube 4.7–6.2 mm, lobes 1.4–2.5 mm; corolla creamy yellow or greenish yellow to greenish white (immaculate), yellow when dry, petals well-graduated, banner longer than wings, wings well exceeding keel. **Legumes** mottled, obliquely ovoid-acuminate, greatly inflated, (17–)20–35 × 10–20 mm, bilocular, papery, villosulous; beak 4–8 mm, unilocular.

Flowering Mar–May (or fall). Rolling hills, plains, gravelly banks, roadcuts; 90–800(–1300) m; Calif.

Variety *nigricalycis* is known from the inner South Coast Ranges and foothills at the southern end of the Central Valley from San Benito and Fresno to Kern and Ventura counties.

The yellowish corollas with blackish calyces and the large, inflated but firm fruits distinguish var. *nigricalycis* in its region. In Kern County, it intergrades somewhat with var. *variabilis*.

285ii. Astragalus lentiginosus Douglas var. **coachellae** Barneby in F. Shreve and I. L. Wiggins, Veg. Fl. Sonoran Desert, 695. 1964 • Palm Springs freckled milkvetch [C] [E]

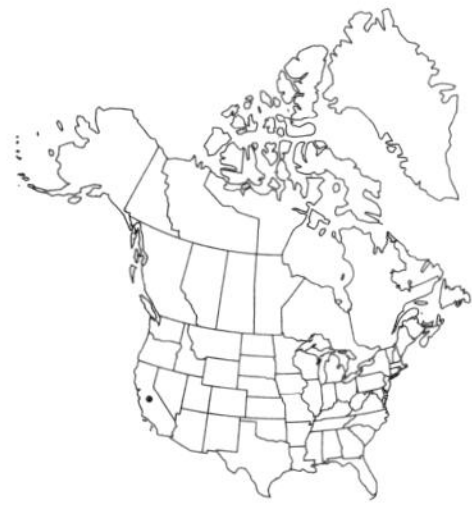

Plants winter-annual or perennial (short-lived, often flowering first year), clump-forming, (10–)15–30(–55) cm, herbage silvery-canescent, hairs to 0.7–1.2 mm. **Stems** erect and ascending. **Leaves** 5–11.5 cm; leaflets (7–)11–17(–21), blades broadly oval to obovate-cuneate or oblong-elliptic, 5–15(–17) mm, apex emarginate, or obtuse and apiculate. **Peduncles** 3.5–8 cm. **Racemes** loosely 11–25-flowered, lax and open in fruit; axis (3–)4–10 cm in fruit. **Flowers** 12.7–14.5 mm; calyx 6.6–7.8 mm, tube 4.5–5.3 mm, lobes 1.7–2.9 mm; corolla pink-purple. **Legumes** usually mottled, broadly and obliquely ovoid-acuminate, greatly inflated, 16–21 × 9–14 mm, bilocular, stiffly papery, canescent-strigulose; beak 3.5–6 mm, unilocular. **Seeds** 24–30.

Flowering Feb–May. Sandy flats, washes, outwash fans, on dunes, in *Larrea* belt; of conservation concern; -10–400 m; Calif.

Variety *coachellae* occurs at low elevations in and around the Coachella Valley in Riverside County.

285jj. Astragalus lentiginosus Douglas var. **micans** Barneby, Leafl. W. Bot. 8: 22. 1956 • Shining freckled milkvetch [C] [E]

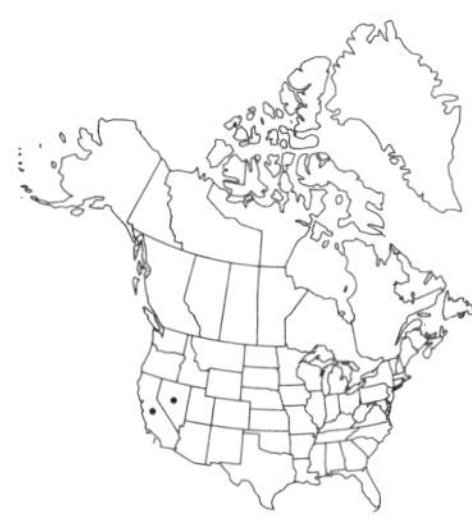

Plants perennial, clump-forming, 20–40 cm, herbage silvery- or white-silky, hairs 1.1–2 mm. **Leaves** 4.5–9.5 cm; leaflets 11–17, blades usually narrowly to broadly obovate or ovate, rarely rhombic-suborbiculate, 5–14 mm, apex truncate-emarginate to subacute. **Peduncles** 4.5–9 cm. **Racemes** loosely (12–)20–35-flowered, lax and open in fruit; axis (3.5–)4.5–10(–15) cm in fruit. **Flowers** 12.2–14.3 mm; calyx 6–7.6 mm, tube 4.5–4.9 mm, lobes 1.4–2.6 mm; corolla pink-lavender. **Legumes** green, unmottled, obliquely ovoid, inflated, 15–20 × 8–10 mm, bilocular, stiffly papery, densely silky-villous-tomentulose; beak 2.5–4 mm, unilocular. **Seeds** 23–28.

Flowering Apr–Jun. Forming large clumps over low slopes of mobile dunes; of conservation concern; 900–1000 m; Calif., Nev.

Variety *micans* is a local adjunct of the variable var. *variabilis* (D. Isely 1998), restricted to the southern end of Eureka Valley in Inyo County, California, and adjacent to Big Dune and in the Amargosa Desert, near Lathrop Wells in Nye County, Nevada. Isely questioned its recognition at varietal rank, initially considering it a local dune-specialized ecotype. Although it is ordinarily a strong perennial, some plants are evidently short-lived, a feature shared with var. *coulteri*.

Variety *micans* is in the Center for Plant Conservation's National Collection of Endangered Plants.

285kk. Astragalus lentiginosus Douglas var. **coulteri** (Bentham) M. E. Jones, Contr. W. Bot. 8: 4. 1898 • Borrego Springs milkvetch [F]

Astragalus coulteri Bentham, Pl. Hartw., 307. 1849; *A. agninus* Jepson; *A. arthurschottii* A. Gray; *A. lentiginosus* var. *borreganus* M. E. Jones

Plants winter-annual, 10–30 cm, herbage densely pubescent). **Leaves** 6–10(–16) cm; leaflets (7–)15–19, blades broadly obovate-cuneate to elliptic-oblanceolate, 4–14(–21) mm, apex obtuse or emarginate to retuse. **Peduncles** 5–10 cm. **Racemes** loosely 13–35(–48)-flowered; axis (4.5–)6–18(–26) cm in fruit. **Flowers** 12–14.8 mm; calyx 5.2–6.6 mm, tube 4–5.1 mm, lobes 1–2.3 mm; corolla pink-purple. **Legumes** greenish stramineous, sometimes faintly mottled, lanceoloid to ovoid-acuminate, not or scarcely inflated, slightly turgid, 15–23 × 4.5–6 mm, ± bilocular, thin becoming papery, silky-strigulose-villosulous; beak short, unilocular. **Seeds** (10–)13–20.

Flowering late Feb–May. Sandy flats and semi-stabilized dunes, with *Larrea*; 30–900 m; Ariz., Calif.; Mexico (Sonora).

Variety *coulteri* is found in the southern Colorado Desert, extending from eastern San Diego County in California, to the Yuma Desert in extreme southwestern Yuma County in Arizona, and adjacent Sonora, Mexico.

285ll. Astragalus lentiginosus Douglas var. **maricopae** Barneby, Leafl. W. Bot. 4: 140. 1945 • Maricopa milkvetch [E]

Plants perennial (short-lived), 45–65 cm, herbage green or subglabrescent. **Leaves** (4–)6–16 cm; leaflets 17–25, blades ovate, broadly oval, oblong-elliptic, or obovate-cordate, (3–)5–22 mm, apex obtuse and apiculate or emarginate. **Peduncles** 5–14 cm. **Racemes** loosely 13–30-flowered; axis elongating, (3–)5–20 cm in fruit. **Flowers** 15–16.5 mm; calyx 7.2–8.6 mm, tube 5.6–6.4 mm, lobes 1.6–2.6 mm; corolla ochroleucous (immaculate). **Legumes** green becoming stramineous, narrowly oblong- or linear-ellipsoid, not inflated, 20–30

× 3.7–5 mm, bilocular, somewhat fleshy becoming leathery or stiffly papery, glabrous; beak 3–5 mm, unilocular. **Seeds** 22–26.

Flowering Mar–May. Washes, roadsides with *Larrea*; 300–700 m; Ariz.

Variety *maricopae* is common in the Cave Creek and Fish Creek areas in Maricopa County. In years with higher rainfall it is weedy in subdivisions where desert vegetation remains intact.

285mm. Astragalus lentiginosus Douglas var. **palans** (M. E. Jones) M. E. Jones, Contr. W. Bot. 8: 4. 1898 • Straggling milkvetch [E]

Astragalus palans M. E. Jones, Zoë 4: 37. 1893; *A. bryantii* Barneby

Plants perennial (sometimes short-lived), (10–)15–35(–40) cm, herbage green or subglabrescent. **Leaves** (3.5–)5–11cm; leaflets 13–21(or 23), blades broadly obovate-cuneate, oblong-elliptic, oblong-oblanceolate, or suborbiculate-obcordate, (3–)5–17 (–23) mm, apex obtuse, emarginate, or subacute, adaxial surface glabrous. **Peduncles** (3.5–)5–11 cm. **Racemes** loosely (6–)10–28-flowered; axis elongating or not, (1–)2–12(–14.5) cm in fruit. **Flowers** 13.5–17.5(–18.3) mm; calyx 6.3–9.4 mm, tube 4.7–6.8 mm, lobes (0.9–)1.1–3(–4) mm; corolla pink-purple. **Legumes** spreading, declined, or spreading-ascending, green becoming stramineous then blackish, ± straight to uniformly or hamately incurved, obliquely linear-lanceoloid to narrowly ovoid-acuminate, not or scarcely inflated, dehiscent on ground, (12–)15–27 × 4–8.5 mm, ± bilocular, somewhat fleshy becoming leathery or stiffly papery, glabrous or strigulose; beak 5–8 mm, unilocular. **Seeds** 20–42. **2*n*** = 22.

Flowering Apr–Jun. Salt-desert shrub, blackbrush, juniper, pinyon-juniper, and mixed desert shrub communities; 1100–1900 m; Ariz., Colo., Utah.

Variety *palans* is known from northern Arizona, excluding the Coconino Plateau and upper Verde Valley, and from southwestern Colorado and southeastern Utah.

There is no substantial difference between material included within the concept of var. *palans* and *Astragalus bryantii*, which R. C. Barneby (1964) included within sect. *Leptocarpi*. S. L. Welsh (2007) considered it significant that fallen fruits, characteristic of var. *palans*, are included with the type collection of *A. bryantii*.

285nn. Astragalus lentiginosus Douglas var. **mokiacensis** (A. Gray) M. E. Jones, Rev. N.-Amer. Astragalus, 126. 1923 • Mokiak milkvetch [E]

Astragalus mokiacensis A. Gray, Proc. Amer. Acad. Arts 13: 367. 1878; *A. lentiginosus* var. *ursinus* (A. Gray) Barneby

Plants perennial, 20–60 cm, herbage green or subglabrescent. **Leaves** 3–10(–13) cm; leaflets (7 or)9–17(–21), blades broadly obovate-obcordate, lanceolate, elliptic, or suborbiculate-obcordate, 5–13(–19) mm, apex emarginate or retuse to truncate, adaxial surface glabrous. **Peduncles** 4–11(–14) cm. **Racemes** loosely 12–20-flowered; axis elongating, 3.5–18(–22) cm in fruit. **Flowers** (10–)14–18(–19) mm; calyx 5–8(–9.2) mm, tube (3.5–)4–6.5 mm, lobes 1–2(–2.7) mm; corolla pink- to red-purple, usually with pale or white wing tips. **Legumes** dehiscent on plant, usually ascending-erect to ascending, rarely spreading, green becoming stramineous, usually ± straight to incurved, rarely decurved, oblong-ellipsoid, not or scarcely inflated, slightly turgid, 14–28(–32) × 4.5–6.5 mm, ± bilocular, somewhat fleshy becoming leathery or stiffly papery, glabrous or minutely pubescent; beak 3–4 mm, unilocular. **Seeds** (22–)25–36. **2*n*** = 22.

Flowering Mar–Jun. Limestone on outcrops and gravel, on basaltic or granitic gravel and/or outcrops, with *Hymenoclea*, bursage, Joshua tree, *Larrea*, and *Ferocactus*; 700–1800 m; Ariz., Nev., Utah.

The placement of var. *mokiacensis* has challenged generations of botanists. R. C. Barneby (1945) regarded var. *mokiacensis* as part of the *lentiginosus* complex but later (Barneby 1964) recognized it as a species within sect. *Preussiani*. In Washington County in Utah, var. *mokiacensis* has been consistently confused with var. *palans*. S. L. Welsh (2007) extensively discussed problems revolving around interpretation and distinction of var. *mokiacensis*. J. A. Alexander (2005) considered the taxon to be best recognized at the species level, as *A. mokiacensis*, the persistent fruit being otherwise unknown in *A. lentiginosus*. Alexander also presented a key to similar taxa and to minor variants within *A. mokiacensis*. As recognized here, the variety is found in Washington County in southwestern Utah, northwestern Mohave County in Arizona, and eastern Clark County in Nevada.

285oo. Astragalus lentiginosus Douglas var. **trumbullensis** S. L. Welsh & N. D. Atwood, Rhodora 103: 81, fig. 3. 2001 • Mount Trumbull milkvetch [E]

Plants perennial, 30–45(–65) cm, herbage green or subglabrescent. **Leaves** 2–9.5(–10.5) cm; leaflets (7–)13–17, blades broadly obovate to oblanceolate or elliptic, 5–15 mm, apex retuse to round or subacute, adaxial surface usually strigose to strigulose, sometimes glabrate or glabrous. **Peduncles** 4.5–7.5 cm. **Racemes** loosely 4–15(–17)-flowered; axis elongating, 3–9.5 cm in fruit. **Flowers** 13–17 mm; calyx 6.3–7.4 mm, tube 4.8–5.5 mm, lobes 1.7–2 mm; corolla pink- or red-purple, sometimes with pale or white wing tips. **Legumes** evidently persistent, stramineous or mottled, linear-oblong to oblong or narrowly ellipsoid, not or scarcely inflated, 17–32 × 4–5.5(–7.5) mm, ± bilocular, somewhat fleshy becoming leathery or stiffly papery, strigulose; beak 3–5 mm, unilocular; stipe 0.1–1 mm. **Seeds** 14–28.

Flowering Apr (Sep). Sandstone outcrops and gravel, with *Agave*, *Ephedra*, *Mortonia*, *Purshia*, and other warm-desert shrubs; 900–1800 m; Ariz.

Variety *trumbullensis* is restricted to Mohave County. It is closely related to vars. *mokiacensis* and *palans*, weakly differentiated by a series of features that intergrade insensibly but taken in combination are more or less diagnostic (as is true for most members of the *lentiginosus* complex). J. A. Alexander (2005) provided statistical evidence that this variety is indistinguishable from var. *mokiacensis* (as *Astragalus mokiacensis*), and he considered the two synonymous.

285pp. Astragalus lentiginosus Douglas var. **wilsonii** (Greene) Barneby, Leafl. W. Bot. 4: 139. 1945 • Wilson's milkvetch [E]

Astragalus wilsonii Greene, Pittonia 3: 196. 1897

Plants perennial, 20–50 cm, herbage green or subglabrescent. **Leaves** (3.5–)6–16 cm; leaflets (11–)17–25, blades ovate, broadly elliptic, or oblong-obovate, (4–)6–20(–25) mm, apex obtuse to emarginate. **Peduncles** 2.5–7(–8) cm. **Racemes** shortly and loosely (7–)10–17(–22)-flowered; axis not elongating, 1.5–4 (–13) cm in fruit. **Flowers** (14.2–)15–20 mm; calyx (7–) 7.7–9.4 mm, tube (5.5–)5.7–7.7 mm, lobes 1.5–3 mm; corolla white or suffused or tipped pink or pink-purple. **Legumes** green or mottled becoming stramineous or brownish, narrowly lanceoloid-acuminate, scarcely to moderately inflated, (15–)20–35 × 3.8–7 mm, ± bilocular, stiffly papery, glabrous or puberulent; beak 5–10 mm, unilocular. **Seeds** (29–)32–41. $2n = 22$.

Flowering Feb–Jun. Ponderosa pine forests, oak and juniper communities on volcanic substrates; 900–2200 m; Ariz.

Variety *wilsonii* occurs on the Coconino Plateau near Flagstaff and near the head of the Verde River in southwestern Coconino, northwestern Gila, and eastern Yavapai counties. Some plants share features with the closely adjacent, but still disjunct, var. *maricopae*, as discussed by S. L. Welsh (2007). M. E. Jones (1923) placed these in var. *palans*, a taxon well to the north. Provisionally, these unusual plants form a portion of what has traditionally been understood as var. *wilsonii*.

286. Astragalus iodanthus S. Watson, Botany (Fortieth Parallel), 70. 1871 • Humboldt River milkvetch [E]

Plants perennial, caulescent, (3–)8–35 cm, ± densely strigulose or glabrate, exceptionally villosulous, hairs 0.3–0.7 mm; from branched, superficial caudex; taproot woody. **Stems** prostrate to decumbent, finely cinereous, glabrous, or glabrate. **Leaves** 2–8 cm; stipules 2–6 mm, membranous or thinly herbaceous; leaflets (7 or)9–19(or 21), blades obovate to oblong or oblanceolate to elliptic, 3–18 mm, apex truncate to retuse, obtuse, or mucronate, surfaces sparsely strigose abaxially, usually glabrous adaxially. **Peduncles** ascending or incurved, 1–4.5 cm. **Racemes** 7–17-flowered, flowers ascending to spreading; axis 0.5–4.5 cm in fruit; bracts 1–3 mm; bracteoles 2. **Pedicels** 0.3–2 mm. **Flowers** 9–15.5 mm; calyx shortly cylindric, (3.3–)5–8 mm, strigose, tube 2.6–5 mm, lobes subulate, (0.6–)1–3 mm; corolla usually purple, lilac, or whitish, rarely cream (concolorous), sometimes keel tips purple; banner recurved through 45°; keel 7.5–12 mm. **Legumes** disjointing from receptacle when mature, ascending to declined, green, often red-mottled, becoming stramineous or purplish, curved through 0.25–0.5+ spiral, obliquely lanceoloid, dorsiventrally or 3-sided compressed, (20–)25–40 × (2.5–)3–8.5 mm, unilocular to semibilocular, fleshy becoming leathery or stiffly papery, strigose; sessile. **Seeds** 14–30.

Varieties 2 (2 in the flora): w United States.

Astragalus iodanthus is widespread from east-central California across Nevada to southeastern Oregon, southwestern Idaho, and northeastern Utah. *Astragalus iodanthus* and *A. cibarius* are sometimes confounded, particularly where their ranges overlap in eastern Nevada. *Astragalus iodanthus* has a truly sessile fruit, and the proximal stipules are small and inconspicuous, contrasting with the short, thick stipe of the fruit and large, conspicuous, veiny stipules of *A. cibarius* (R. C. Barneby 1964).

Calyx tube measurements in these descriptions are from the margin of the calycine (hypanthium) disc to the sinus between the two lateral lobes.

1. Calyx tubes (3.4–)3.7–5 mm; banners (10–)12–15.5 mm; wings longer than keel; legumes (4.5–)5–8.5 mm wide, curved to recurved . . . . 286a. *Astragalus iodanthus* var. *iodanthus*
1. Calyx tubes 2.6–3.2 mm; banners 9–11.5 mm; wings shorter or slightly longer than keel; legumes (2.5–)3–5.5 mm wide, folded back on itself . . . . 286b. *Astragalus iodanthus* var. *diaphanoides*

286a. Astragalus iodanthus S. Watson var. **iodanthus** E

Stems glabrous or glabrate. **Leaflets** (7–)11–19(or 21). **Flowers:** calyx (5–)5.5–8 mm, tube (3.4–)3.7–5 × 2.1–2.7 mm, lobes (1.3–)1.5–3 mm; corolla usually wine-purple, drying violet, lilac, or whitish with purple keel tip, rarely cream (concolorous); banner (10–)12–15.5 mm; wings longer than keel. **Legumes** curved to recurved, mostly dorsiventrally compressed, (20–)25–40 × (4.5–)5–8.5 mm. **Seeds** 18–30. **2*n*** = 22.

Flowering Apr–early Jul. Sagebrush communities, sometimes in pinyon-juniper communities; 1500–2400 m; Calif., Idaho, Nev., Oreg., Utah.

Variety *iodanthus* is known from Mono County in California, southwestern Idaho, Malheur County in southeastern Oregon, northern and central Nevada, and Box Elder and Tooele counties in northwestern Utah.

286b. Astragalus iodanthus S. Watson var. **diaphanoides** Barneby, Leafl. W. Bot. 4: 50, figs. 20–23. 1944 • Viper milkvetch E

Astragalus iodanthus var. *vipereus* Barneby

Stems usually finely cinereous. **Leaflets** (7 or)9–13(or 15). **Flowers:** calyx (3.3–)3.7–5.3 mm, tube 2.6–3.2 × 1.7–2.6(–2.9) mm, lobes (0.6–)1–2.2 mm; corolla pale lilac, keel tip usually darker lilac; banner 9–11.5 mm; wings shorter or slightly longer than keel. **Legumes** folded back on itself, mostly 3-sided compressed, (20–)25–35(–40) × (2.5–)3–5.5(–6) mm. **Seeds** 14–24. **2*n*** = 22.

Flowering Apr–Jun. Alkaline clay or loam soils, often with sagebrush or juniper; 700–2100 m; Calif., Idaho, Nev., Oreg.

Variety *diaphanoides* is known from Lassen County in California, along the Bruneau, Malheur, Owyhee, and Snake rivers in Elmore, Owyhee, and Twin Falls counties in Idaho, Washoe County in Nevada, and Deschutes, Harney, and Malheur counties in Oregon.

287. Astragalus pseudiodanthus Barneby, Leafl. W. Bot. 3: 99, plate 1, fig. B. 1942 • Tonopah milkvetch E

Astragalus iodanthus S. Watson var. *pseudiodanthus* (Barneby) Isely

Plants perennial, caulescent, 20–30 cm, villosulous or villous, hairs 0.7–1.2 mm; from shallow to deep subterranean branched caudex. **Stems** prostrate to decumbent, radiating, villosulous or villous. **Leaves** 2.5–5 cm; stipules 2–5 mm, membranous; leaflets (7–)11–19, blades obovate-cuneate, 3–10 mm, apex obtuse to retuse, surfaces villous abaxially, glabrous adaxially. **Peduncles** ascending or incurved, 2–3.5 cm. **Racemes** (7–)12–25-flowered, flowers spreading to declined; axis 2.5–8(–11) cm in fruit; bracts 0.6–1.5 mm; bracteoles 0. **Pedicels** 0.5–1.8 mm. **Flowers** 9–10 mm; calyx campanulate, 3.8–4.7 mm, loosely villous, tube 2.8–3.8 mm, lobes triangular-subulate, 1–1.7 mm; corolla reddish lilac; banner recurved through 45°; keel 8.5–9.3 mm. **Legumes** disjointing from receptacle when mature, deflexed, green or faintly mottled, incurved through 0.5+ spiral, obliquely ellipsoid to lanceoloid-ellipsoid, dorsiventrally compressed, (16–)20–30 × (4.5–)5–8 mm, semibilocular, somewhat fleshy becoming leathery, villosulous; sessile. **Seeds** 14–19.

Flowering May–Jun. Dunes, sandy sites, often with *Sarcobatus baileyi* and *Hilaria jamesii*, less commonly on old beaches; 1300–2100 m; Calif., Nev.

Astragalus pseudiodanthus occurs in Esmeralda, Lyon, and Nye counties in southwestern Nevada, and Mono County in California. It is sufficiently close to the geographically adjacent *A. iodanthus* that the two taxa have been considered as varieties of *A. iodanthus* (D. Isely 1983, 1998).

135uuu. Astragalus Linnaeus sect. Monoenses Barneby, Mem. New York Bot. Gard. 13: 964. 1964 [E]

Herbs perennial, low, caulescent; caudex subterranean. **Hairs** basifixed. **Stems** few or several to many. **Stipules** connate or distinct. **Leaves** odd-pinnate, petiolate to subsessile; leaflets 7–13 (or 15). **Racemes** loosely flowered or rather densely flowered and subumbellate, flowers spreading. **Calyx tubes** campanulate. **Corollas** whitish or lilac-tinged, banner recurved through 50–90°, keel apex blunt or deltate. **Legumes** deciduous, sessile, ascending (humistrate) or spreading, ovoid to lanceoloid-ovoid, bladdery-inflated or ± dorsiventrally compressed, subunilocular to bilocular. **Seeds** 16–28.

Species 2 (2 in the flora): California.

Section *Monoenses*, as defined here, consists of two species of the Sierra Nevada in Mono, eastern Fresno, and western Inyo counties. Other species sometimes placed in this section are *Astragalus perianus* (whose alliance is apparently with *A. serpens* in central Utah) and *A. pulsiferae* (which has been removed to sect. *Pulsiferani*, with distribution in the northern Sierra Nevada, adjacent Nevada, and disjunct Washington).

288. Astragalus monoensis Barneby, Leafl. W. Bot. 4: 55, figs. 7–15. 1944 • Mono milkvetch [C] [E]

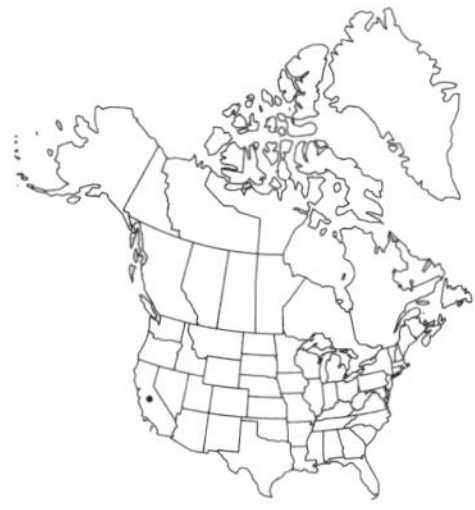

Plants mat-forming, 7–20 cm, densely silky-villosulous; from slender-branched caudex. **Stems** prostrate or decumbent with ascending tips, 1.5–12+ cm underground, densely silky-villosulous. **Leaves** (0.7–)1–3 cm; stipules mostly connate throughout, sometimes distinct at distal nodes, 1–3 mm, scarious at proximal nodes, herbaceous at distal nodes; leaflets 9–13(or 15), blades oval, obovate-cuneate, or oblong-obovate, 2–8 mm, apex obtuse, surfaces villous abaxially, glabrous adaxially. **Peduncles** incurved-ascending, (1–)2–4.5 cm. **Racemes** 6–12-flowered; axis 0.5–1.2 cm in fruit; bracts 1.5–3 mm; bracteoles 2. **Pedicels** 0.8–2 mm. **Flowers** 10–13 mm; calyx 4.8–6.6 mm, loosely villosulous, tube 3–4.6 mm, lobes broadly subulate, 1.2–2.1 mm; corolla whitish, tinged with pinkish lavender, fading cream; banner recurved through 50°; keel 6.7–8 mm. **Legumes** spreading or ascending (sometimes humistrate), green or purplish-cheeked becoming stramineous, almost straight to incurved through 0.3 spiral, obliquely ovoid-acuminate or lanceoloid-ovoid, somewhat dorsiventrally compressed, 15–20 × 6–9 mm, ± bilocular, slightly fleshy becoming papery, shortly villosulous. **Seeds** 18–28. $2n = 22$.

Flowering late Jun–Aug. On pumice sand or gravel, ponderosa pine communities, under sagebrush; of conservation concern; 2200–3400 m; Calif.

Astragalus monoensis is locally common with a limited range south of Mono Lake in Mono County.

289. Astragalus ravenii Barneby, Aliso 4: 131. 1958 • Raven's milkvetch [C] [E]

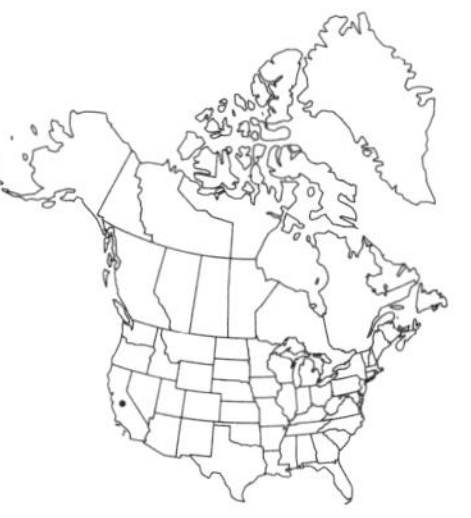

Astragalus monoensis Barneby var. *ravenii* (Barneby) Isely

Plants delicate, 1.5–10 cm, strigulose; from slender-branched caudex. **Stems** prostrate to decumbent, very slender, underground for 1–6 cm, strigulose. **Leaves** 0.5–2.5(–3) cm; stipules connate, 0.8–1.5(–2) mm, papery at proximal nodes, herbaceous at distal nodes; leaflets 7–11(or 13), blades broadly oblong-obovate or suborbiculate, (1–)1.5–3.5(–4) mm, apex retuse, surfaces villous abaxially, sparsely so adaxially. **Peduncles** (1–)1.5–5.5 cm. **Racemes** rather densely (1–)3–6(–8)-flowered; axis 0.2–0.7 cm in fruit; bracts 0.7–1.5 mm; bracteoles 0. **Pedicels** 0.5–2 mm, disjointing in age. **Flowers** (5.5–)6–8.4 mm; calyx 3.4–4 mm, strigulose, tube 2.5–3.3 mm, lobes subulate or triangular-subulate, 0.6–1.2 mm; corolla whitish, banner veins lilac; banner recurved through 80–90°; keel 4.5–5.5 mm. **Legumes** ascending (humistrate), mottled, gently incurved, obliquely ovoid, moderately inflated, somewhat dorsiventrally compressed, 8–13 × 5–8.5 mm, subunilocular, thin becoming papery, shortly villosulous. **Seeds** 16–20. $2n = 22$.

Flowering Jul–early Sep. Alpine fields, red fir forests; of conservation concern; 3400–3500 m; Calif.

Astragalus ravenii is known from at least four populations high in the Sierra Nevada in eastern Fresno, western Inyo, and western Mono counties. It can be treated at the varietal level within *A. monoensis* but differs in smaller stature, high elevational distribution, and more nearly unilocular fruit (D. Isely 1983, 1998). The Mono County population shows stronger resemblance to *A. monoensis*.

135vvv. Astragalus Linnaeus sect. Pulsiferani S. L. Welsh, N. Amer. Sp. Astragalus, 316. 2007 [E]

Herbs perennial, mat- or cushion-forming, prostrate or tufted, caulescent; caudex subterranean or superficial. **Hairs** basifixed. **Stems** few to several. **Stipules** connate or distinct. **Leaves** odd-pinnate, petiolate; leaflets (3–)7–15. **Racemes** densely or loosely flowered, flowers ascending, spreading, or declined. **Calyx tubes** obconic-campanulate or shallowly campanulate. **Corollas** whitish or yellowish, banner lilac-veined or rose-purple, keel apex lilac, banner recurved through 60–100°, keel apex broadly deltate, obtuse, or bluntly triangular, sometimes obscurely beaked. **Legumes** deciduous, sessile, spreading or declined (often humistrate), ovoid-lenticular, ovoid-ellipsoid, semi-ovoid, or lunately ellipsoid-obovoid, compressed laterally, both laterally and dorsiventrally and somewhat 3-sided, or bladdery-inflated, unilocular or subunilocular. **Seeds** 2–9.

Species 3 (3 in the flora): w United States.

Section *Pulsiferani* is more diminutive (*Astragalus tegetarioides*, *A. tiehmii*) than sect. *Monoenses*, or if of about the same habit and morphology, then the indumentum of the pod is thinly long-villous to villosulous.

290. Astragalus tegetarioides M. E. Jones, Contr. W. Bot. 10: 66. 1902 • Bastard kentrophyta [E]

Plants 5–15+ cm, 1–3(–4) dm wide, strigose-strigulose or villous to pilosulous; from branched caudex superficial or shallowly subterranean. **Stems** prostrate, strigose-strigulose or villous to pilosulous. **Leaves** 1–4(–6) cm; stipules connate-sheathing at proximal nodes, mostly connate at distal nodes, sometimes distinct, 0.8–3(–5) mm, thinly herbaceous becoming papery; leaflets 7–15, blades obovate-cuneate, 1.5–9 mm, apex obtuse, truncate, or emarginate, surfaces sparsely villosulous abaxially, glabrescent adaxially. **Peduncles** 0.3–2.5 cm. **Racemes** densely or loosely 2–13(–15)-flowered, flowers ascending then declined; axis 0.3–1.5 cm in fruit; bracts 1.2–2.7 mm; bracteoles 0. **Pedicels** 0.4–1.3 mm. **Flowers** 4.4–10(–12) mm; calyx obconic-campanulate, (2.2–)2.6–4.7(–5) mm, sparsely villosulous, tube 1.1–2 mm, lobes subulate, 1–2.7 mm; corolla whitish and banner veins faintly lilac, or rose-purple with pale basal eye; banner recurved through 60–100°; keel 3.5–3.7 mm, apex broadly deltate. **Legumes** spreading, yellowish, straight, ovoid-lenticular, obscurely 3-sided, 3.3–4.5 × 1.5–4.2 mm, unilocular, thinly papery, minutely strigulose to silky-villous. **Seeds** 2 or 3(or 4).

Varieties 2 (2 in the flora): nw United States.

Astragalus tegetarioides is mat-forming, a habit unique within the region where it occurs (nearly similar to *A. pulsiferae* in northeastern California), and has small flowers that are included within the foliage or barely extending beyond the leaves.

1. Racemes loosely 2–6(–8)-flowered; flowers 4.4–6(–7) mm; corollas whitish, banners with pale lilac veins; legumes 1.5–2.8 mm wide; Deschutes, Grant, and Harney counties, Oregon . . . . 290a. *Astragalus tegetarioides* var. *tegetarioides*
1. Racemes densely (7–)9–15-flowered; flowers (6–)6.5–10(–12) mm; corollas rose-purple, banners with pale basal eyes; legumes 3.2–4.2 mm wide; Lassen County, California . . . . .290b. *Astragalus tegetarioides* var. *anxius*

290a. Astragalus tegetarioides M. E. Jones var. **tegetarioides** [E]

Pubescence strigose-strigulose. **Leaflets** 7–11; blades 1.5–5.5 mm. **Racemes** loosely 2–6(–8)-flowered, axis 13–18 mm. **Flowers** 4.4–6(–7) mm; calyx (2.2–)2.6–3.7 mm, lobes 1–1.9 mm; corolla whitish, banner with pale lilac veins; banner recurved 70–100°. **Legumes** 3.3–4.5 × 1.5–2.8 mm.

Flowering Jun–Jul. Dry, pine forests and sagebrush communities; 1300–1600 m; Oreg.

Variety *tegetarioides* is known from Deschutes, Grant, and Harney counties. This variety superficially resembles *Astragalus kentrophyta* var. *tegetarius*, which is widespread from the Rocky Mountains to northeastern Oregon, and southward to Mono County, California.

290b. Astragalus tegetarioides M. E. Jones var. **anxius** (Meinke & Kaye) S. L. Welsh, Great Basin Naturalist 58: 51. 1998 • Ash Valley milkvetch [E] [C]

Astragalus anxius Meinke & Kaye, Madroño 39: 194, figs. 1, 2A,C,E. 1992

Pubescence loosely villous to pilosulous. **Leaflets** 9–15; blades 4–9 mm. **Racemes** densely 7–13 (–15)-flowered, axis 8–22 mm. **Flowers** (6–)6.5–10(–12) mm; calyx 3.2–4.7(–5) mm, lobes 1.7–2.7 mm; corolla rose-purple, banner with pale basal eye; banner recurved 60–80°. **Legumes** 3.5–4.5 × 3.2–4.2 mm.

Flowering Jun–Jul. Arid flats on or near juniper-sagebrush steppes or *Pinus jeffreyi* woodlands; of conservation concern; 1500–1700 m; Calif.

Variety *anxius* is known only from Ash Valley in Lassen County. The report of *Astragalus tegetarioides* (T. W. Nelson and J. P. Nelson 1982) from here is assigned to this variety.

Variety *anxius* is listed as *Astragalus anxius* in NatureServe as a G1 plant of conservation concern.

291. Astragalus tiehmii Barneby, Brittonia 36: 169, fig. 1. 1984 • Tiehm's milkvetch [E]

Plants 4–15+ cm, 1–3.5(–4.5) dm wide, gray-pilosulous; from branched caudex. **Stems** prostrate, gray-pilosulous. **Leaves** 0.8–2.6 cm; stipules distinct, 1–2.5 mm; leaflets 7 or 9, blades folded, obovate-cuneate, 2–6 mm, apex emarginate, surfaces pilosulous. **Peduncles** 0.3–0.7 cm, often paired at a node. **Racemes** (3 or)4–7(or 8)-flowered, flowers declined; axis 0.3–1 cm in fruit; bracts 0.5–1.2 mm; bracteoles 0. **Pedicels** 0.8–1.8 mm. **Flowers** 4.8–5.3 mm; calyx obconic-campanulate, 3.6–4.2 mm, white-pilosulous, tube 1.3–1.8 mm, lobes slenderly subulate, 1.3–1.8 mm; corolla whitish, banner tinged or veins faint lilac; banner recurved through 90°; keel 3.3–3.6 mm, apex obtuse. **Legumes** spreading-declined, lunately ellipsoid-obovoid, laterally compressed, somewhat depressed but not grooved dorsally, lateral faces with shallow longitudinal groove, 4.5–5 × 2–2.5 mm, unilocular, sparsely pilosulous. **Seeds** 2 or 3.

Flowering Jun–Jul. White volcanic ash deposits; 1600–1800 m; Nev.

Astragalus tiehmii is diminutive in all its parts, appearing as a small *A. pulsiferae*, but it is essentially similar, and probably more closely allied, to *A. tegetarioides*. R. C. Barneby (1984), however, considered its kinship with the former. It is known from the western side of the Black Rock Desert in Washoe County.

292. Astragalus pulsiferae A. Gray, Proc. Amer. Acad. Arts 10: 69. 1874 (as pulsiferi) • Pulsifer's milkvetch [E]

Plants sometimes short-lived, delicate, (4–)10–25(–30) cm, strigose-strigulose, villous-hirsute, or villosulous; from subterranean or ± branched, superficial caudex, with many naked, slender branches below ground. **Stems** prostrate to decumbent, (0–)2–9(–12) cm underground, strigose-strigulose, villous-hirsute, or villosulous. **Leaves** 1–4.5(–5.5) cm; stipules usually connate-sheathing at proximal nodes, sometimes distinct throughout, 1–4.5(–5) mm, papery-scarious at proximal nodes, thinly herbaceous at distal nodes; leaflets (3–)7–13, blades oblanceolate- or obovate-cuneate, 2–12 mm, apex retuse or truncate and apiculate, surfaces villous abaxially, sparsely so adaxially. **Peduncles** incurved-ascending, 0.4–2.5 cm. **Racemes** (2 or)3–13-flowered, flowers spreading; axis (0.2–)0.4–1.2 cm in fruit; bracts 0.8–2.4 mm; bracteoles 0. **Pedicels** 0.7–1.8 mm, disjointing in age. **Flowers** (5.2–)6–8.5 mm; calyx shallowly campanulate, 3.2–5.8(–6.2) mm, villous or villosulous, tube 1.3–2.6 mm, lobes linear-lanceolate or setaceous, (1–)1.4–3.6 mm; corolla whitish or yellowish, banner and keel tips with lilac veins; banner abruptly recurved through 90–100°; keel 3.4–5.3 mm, apex bluntly triangular, obscurely beaklike. **Legumes** spreading or declined (often humistrate), pale green or minutely purple-dotted becoming stramineous, straight or slightly incurved, semi-ovoid or ovoid-ellipsoid, bladdery-inflated, somewhat dorsiventrally compressed, 8–20 × (5–)6–11(–13) mm, unilocular or subunilocular, papery-membranous, sparsely long-villous or villosulous. **Seeds** (3–)5–9.

Varieties 3 (3 in the flora): nw United States.

Most populations of *Astragalus pulsiferae* are in northeastern California and adjacent Nevada, with an outlying population in south-central Washington. Relationships of the species are ambiguous (R. C. Barneby 1964, 1984).

1. Caudices superficial; stipules distinct at proximal nodes; legumes villosulous, hairs 1–1.7 mm . . . . 292c. *Astragalus pulsiferae* var. *coronensis*
1. Caudices subterranean or superficial; stipules connate-sheathing at proximal nodes; legumes hirtellous, hairs 0.4–0.9 mm.
   2. Stems 6–10(–12) cm underground, internodes villous or villous-hirsute, hairs widely spreading . . . . .292a. *Astragalus pulsiferae* var. *pulsiferae*
   2. Stems (0–)1–2.5(–3.5) cm underground, internodes loosely strigose to strigulose, hairs ascending, subappressed, and sinuous . . . . 292b. *Astragalus pulsiferae* var. *suksdorfii*

292a. Astragalus pulsiferae A. Gray var. **pulsiferae** C E

Caudices usually subterranean. **Stems** (6–)10–12 cm underground, usually branched at emergence from soil; foliose internodes villous or villous-hirsute, hairs widely spreading. **Stipules** connate-sheathing at proximal nodes. **Flowers:** calyx lobes (1–)1.4–3.6 mm. **Legumes** hirtellous, hairs 0.6–0.9 mm. $2n = 22$.

Flowering May–Aug. Loose sandy sites and interdunal valleys, often with sagebrush, mostly on basalt; of conservation concern; 1300–1900 m; Calif., Nev.

Variety *pulsiferae* is known from the foothills of the northern Sierra Nevada in Lassen, Plumas, and Shasta counties in California, and Washoe County in Nevada.

292b. Astragalus pulsiferae A. Gray var. **suksdorfii** (Howell) Barneby, Aliso 4: 131. 1958 • Suksdorf's milkvetch C E

Astragalus suksdorfii Howell, Erythea 1: 111. 1893

Caudices usually superficial, rarely subterranean. **Stems** (0–)1.5–2.5 cm underground, mostly simple, sometimes branched (or spurred at 1 or 2 nodes preceding first peduncle); foliose internodes loosely strigose to strigulose, hairs ascending, subappressed, and sinuous. **Stipules** connate-sheathing at proximal nodes. **Flowers:** calyx lobes 1.4–2.5 mm. **Legumes** hirtellous, hairs 0.4–0.7 mm.

Flowering May–Jul. Open pine forests, in loose volcanic substrates; of conservation concern; 1300–1400 m; Calif., Wash.

Variety *suksdorfii* occurs in Plumas, Lassen, and Shasta counties in California, with an outlier in Falcon Valley in Klickitat County, Washington. The disjunct distribution of var. *suksdorfii* suggests a longer history than that of var. *pulsiferae*, which R. C. Barneby (1964) considered to be derived.

292c. Astragalus pulsiferae A. Gray var. **coronensis** S. L. Welsh, Ondricek & G. Clifton, Rhodora 104: 276, fig. 1. 2002 • Ram's horn milkvetch E

Caudices superficial. **Stems** emergent at soil level; foliose to the base, internodes villosulous. **Stipules** distinct at proximal nodes. **Flowers:** calyx lobes 1.5–2.5 mm. **Legumes** villosulous, hairs 1–1.7 mm.

Flowering Jun–Jul. Gravelly volcanic duff and hard-packed soils, with juniper, sagebrush, and Jeffrey pine; 1500–1900 m; Calif., Nev.

Variety *coronensis* is known from California in the Modoc Plateau in Lassen and Modoc counties and from a volcanic inclusion in the Sierra Nevada of Plumas County. A disjunct population occurs in Washoe County in Nevada.

Variety *coronensis* is similar in flower and fruit characteristics to vars. *suksdorfii* and *pulsiferae* but differs in features provided in the key.

135www. Astragalus Linnaeus sect. Cystiella Barneby, Proc. Calif. Acad. Sci., ser. 4, 25: 166. 1944 [E]

Herbs perennial, dwarf, forming loose tufts, subacaulescent to shortly caulescent; caudex subterranean. **Hairs** basifixed. **Stems** few. **Stipules** connate. **Leaves** odd-pinnate, short-petiolate; leaflets 5–13. **Racemes** subumbellate, flowers ascending. **Calyx tubes** campanulate. **Corollas** pink-purple or whitish, keel tip purple, banner recurved through 45°, keel apex long-attenuate and beaklike, style at anthesis exserted. **Legumes** deciduous, sessile, spreading (humistrate), broadly ellipsoid or subglobose, bladdery-inflated, bilocular. **Seeds** 20–28.

Species 1: sw United States.

293. Astragalus striatiflorus M. E. Jones, Proc. Calif. Acad. Sci., ser. 2, 5: 643. 1895 • Escarpment milkvetch [E]

Plants 1.5–6 cm, densely canescent-hirsutulous; from branched caudex; taproot slender becoming stout and deep set. **Stems** only tips produced aboveground, 0–5 cm, 2–30 cm underground, often with marcescent leaf rachises, densely canescent-hirsutulous. **Leaves** 1–4 cm; stipules ± obscuring stem, 2–4 mm, papery-scarious; leaflet blades ovate to obovate or oblanceolate, 1–7 mm, apex obtuse, mucronate, or emarginate, surfaces pilosulous. **Peduncles** ascending, 1–3 cm. **Racemes** 2–5-flowered; axis 0.2–1 cm in fruit; bracts 1.5–2.5 mm; bracteoles 0. **Pedicels** 1–1.5 mm. **Flowers** 9–12 mm; calyx 5.5–7 mm, hirsutulous, tube 3–4 mm, lobes subulate, 1.8–3 mm; corolla pink-purple or whitish, usually suffused with purple, keel tip purple; keel not concealing style, 9–11 mm, apex long-attenuate and beaklike. **Legumes** mottled, straight, 12–18 × 8–15 mm, papery, spreading-hairy.

Flowering Apr–Jul. Interdunal valleys, sandy depressions on ledges, bars and terraces in stream channels, in pinyon-juniper, ponderosa pine, and sandy desert shrub communities; 1500–2000 m; Ariz., Utah.

The distribution of *Astragalus striatiflorus* is almost exclusively in a narrow strip of land in Kane and Washington counties in Utah, and adjacent Coconino County in Arizona, on substrates derived from the Vermilion and White Cliffs formation.

135xxx. Astragalus Linnaeus sect. Platytropia (Rydberg) Barneby, Mem. New York Bot. Gard. 13: 978. 1964 (as Platytropides) [E]

Cystium Steven [unranked] *Platytropia* Rydberg in N. L. Britton et al., N. Amer. Fl. 24: 405. 1929

Herbs perennial, acaulescent or subacaulescent and tuft-forming, or caulescent; caudex superficial or subterranean. **Hairs** basifixed. **Stems** single or few, or reduced to crowns. **Stipules** usually connate at proximal nodes, distinct at distal nodes, rarely distinct throughout. **Leaves** odd-pinnate, petiolate or subsessile; leaflets 5–15. **Racemes** subumbellate or loosely flowered, flowers ascending, spreading, or declined. **Calyx tubes** campanulate. **Corollas** pink-purple, whitish infused or veined with purple, or stramineous, keel apex commonly dark, banner recurved through 30–50°, keel apex deltate, broadly rounded, or obtuse. **Legumes** deciduous, sessile, spreading or ascending (humistrate), ovoid to ellipsoid or subglobose, inflated, bilocular or semibilocular. **Seeds** 16–34.

Species 3 (3 in the flora): w United States.

Section *Platytropia* is distributed from southeastern Oregon, east-central Idaho, western Montana, and north-central Wyoming southward to western Utah, southern Nevada, and east-central California.

294. Astragalus platytropis A. Gray, Proc. Amer. Acad. Arts 6: 526. 1865 • Broad-keeled milkvetch E F

Plants closely tuft-forming, acaulescent or subacaulescent, 2–7 cm, strigulose; from branched, superficial caudex, branches often with thatch of persistent leaf bases. **Stems** mostly reduced to crowns, prostrate-ascending or erect, 0–2 cm, (0–)1–3 cm underground, often with thatch of marcescent leaf bases, strigulose. **Leaves** 1–7 cm; stipules usually connate at proximal nodes, distinct at distal nodes, 1.5–5 mm, subherbaceous becoming papery; leaflets 5–15, blades elliptic to obovate, oblong, or oval, 2–11 mm, apex acute to obtuse or retuse, surfaces silvery-strigose. **Peduncles** ascending, 1.5–6.5 cm. **Racemes** 2–9-flowered, flowers ascending; axis 0.2–0.6 cm in fruit; bracts 0.6–2 mm; bracteoles 0–2. **Pedicels** 0.7–1.9 mm. **Flowers** 7–9.5 mm; calyx 3–5.4 mm, strigose, tube 2–3.4 mm, lobes subulate, 0.2–2.1 mm; corolla pink-purple; keel 7.8–8.6 mm. **Legumes** ascending, purple-mottled, straight, ovoid to subglobose, bladdery-inflated, 15–33 x 10–22 mm, bilocular or semibilocular, thin becoming papery, strigulose. **Seeds** 26–34.

Flowering Jul–Aug. Ridge tops and scree in shrub and forest communities; 2400–3500 m; Calif., Idaho, Mont., Nev., Oreg., Utah, Wyo.

The easily recognizable *Astragalus platytropis* is marked by its tufted, silvery-gray foliage and subcapitate racemes of small, purplish corollas with petals of nearly equal length. It is found in scattered populations from east of the Sierra Nevada in Califoirnia eastward through Nevada to far western Utah, and northward to Malheur County, Oregon, north-central Idaho, and west-central Montana, with an isolated population in north-central Wyoming.

295. Astragalus amnis-amissi Barneby in C. L. Hitchcock et al., Vasc. Pl. Pacif. N.W. 3: 219, plate [p. 221], fig. s.n. [upper left]. 1961 • Lost River milkvetch E

Plants caulescent, slender, 10–25 cm, strigulose; from branched, superficial caudex. **Stems** few, weakly ascending, 2–10 cm underground, strigulose. **Leaves** (3–)4–9.5 cm; stipules usually distinct, rarely very obscurely connate, 1.5–5 mm, papery-membranous at proximal nodes, herbaceous at distal nodes; leaflets (7 or) 9–13, blades broadly ovate-oblong or oblong-elliptic, (3–)4–15(–18) mm, apex retuse or emarginate to obcordate, surfaces sparsely strigose or glabrous. **Peduncles** incurved-ascending, (2–)3–6(–8) cm. **Racemes** 5–12-flowered, flowers spreading to declined; axis 1–3 cm in fruit; bracts 1–2 mm; bracteoles 0–2. **Pedicels** 1–2.2 mm. **Flowers** 8.8–10.4 mm; calyx 4–5.9 mm, strigose, tube 2–3 mm, lobes subulate, 1.8–2.9 mm; corolla whitish, suffused purplish, keel tip maculate; keel 7.8–9.8 mm. **Legumes** ascending to spreading, green or purplish becoming stramineous, straight, subsymmetrically ellipsoid or ovoid-ellipsoid, moderately inflated, dorsiventrally compressed, 15–17 x 7–8 mm, semibilocular, thin becoming papery, strigulose; septum partial, to 1.6 mm wide. **Seeds** 16–20. $2n = 24$.

Flowering late Jun–Aug. Limestone rock crevices and talus; 1800–2100 m; Idaho.

Astragalus amnis-amissi, a close relative of *A. amblytropis*, is known from few populations in the Lost River Mountains in Custer County, and Lemhi Range in Butte County.

296. Astragalus amblytropis Barneby, Amer. Midl. Naturalist 41: 501. 1949 • Challis milkvetch E

Plants caulescent, slender, 10–40 cm, densely strigulose; from subterranean branched caudex. **Stems** few or single, prostrate, 2–10 cm underground, densely strigulose. **Leaves** 1–3(–4.5) cm; stipules connate at proximal nodes, distinct at distal nodes, 1–2.5 mm, scarious at proximal nodes, herbaceous at distal nodes; leaflets 9–13, blades obovate, cuneate-obovate, or oblanceolate, 3–9(–14) mm, apex obtuse or retuse to obcordate, surfaces ashy-strigose. **Peduncles** spreading or incurved, (0.3–)0.5–2.2 cm. **Racemes** (4–)6–10(–13)-flowered, flowers spreading; axis 0.5–1.5(–2) cm in fruit; bracts 0.6–1.5 mm; bracteoles 0. **Pedicels** 1–2 mm. **Flowers** 6.4–8.3 mm; calyx (2.8–)4.1–5 mm, strigulose, tube 1.9–2.7 mm, lobes subulate, (0.9–)1.5–2.3 mm; corolla dull stramineous, banner veins lilac, keel tip maculate; keel 8.8–8.3 mm. **Legumes** spreading or ascending (humistrate), green or purplish becoming stramineous, straight, ovoid or ellipsoid, bladdery-inflated, somewhat dorsiventrally compressed, 20–35 x 12–26 mm, bilocular, thin becoming papery, sparsely strigulose. **Seeds** 25–32.

Flowering late May–early Jul. Clay, shale, or volcanic gravel slopes or talus, in *Atriplex*-sagebrush communities; 1400–1800 m; Idaho.

Astragalus amblytropis, restricted to the upper gorges of the Salmon River and its tributaries in Custer and Lemhi counties, is known by its neat, divaricately branched stems, and large, bladdery fruits that scarcely exceed the foliage. It is unusual in sect. *Platytropia* for its subterranean root-crown, which is evident whether on steep, mobile slopes or on stable flats of canyon floors.

135yyy. Astragalus Linnaeus sect. Villosi (Rydberg) Barneby, Mem. New York Bot. Gard. 13: 992. 1964 [E]

Batidophaca Rydberg [unranked] *Villosae* Rydberg in N. L. Britton et al., N. Amer. Fl. 24: 318. 1929

Herbs perennial (sometimes flowering as annual), caulescent; caudex usually superficial, rarely subterranean. **Hairs** basifixed. **Stems** few to many. **Stipules** usually distinct, rarely connate at proximal nodes. **Leaves** odd-pinnate, petiolate; leaflets (3–)9–27. **Racemes** densely or loosely flowered, flowers spreading to declined. **Calyx tubes** campanulate. **Corollas** white, greenish white, cream, yellow, or pinkish to purple with wing apices pale, banner recurved through 45–80°, keel apex blunt, round, or sharply deltate, sometimes beaklike. **Legumes** deciduous, sessile, short gynophore present, spreading or ascending (humistrate), some eventually declined, crescentic, semi-ellipsoid, or semi-obovoid, compressed laterally or dorsiventrally, sometimes slightly 3-sided, subunilocular or sub-bilocular. **Seeds** 12–37.

Species 4 (4 in the flora): c, se United States.

Section *Villosi* consists of two subsections: subsect. *Austro-orientales* (A. Gray) Barneby (*Astragalus distortus*, *A. obcordatus*, *A. soxmaniorum* Lundell) and subsect. *Villosi* (Rydberg) Barneby (*A. villosus*).

297. Astragalus distortus Torrey & A. Gray, Fl. N. Amer. 1: 333. 1838 • Ozark milkvetch [E] [F]

Holcophacos distortus (Torrey & A. Gray) Rydberg

Plants (2.5–)5–40(–60) cm, sparsely strigulose, hairs subappressed, to 0.7 mm; from branched, superficial caudex. **Stems** decumbent or prostrate, sparsely strigulose, sometimes glabrous proximally. **Leaves** (2–)4–10(–12) cm; stipules (1.5–)2–8 mm, papery at proximal nodes; leaflets (9–)13–25(or 27), blades firm, oval, obovate, elliptic-oblanceolate, or suborbiculate, (2–)3–11(–13) mm, veins not apparent, apex round, truncate, or retuse, surfaces sparsely strigose abaxially, glabrous adaxially. **Peduncles** decumbent or prostrate, (2–)5–15 cm. **Racemes** (5–)10–21-flowered; axis 1.5–5(–7.5) cm in fruit; bracts 0.8–1.4 mm; bracteoles 0–2. **Pedicels** 0.8–2.4 mm. **Flowers** 8.2–15.5 mm; calyx 3.1–6.3 mm, strigulose, tube 2.4–4 mm, lobes subulate, 1–2 mm; corolla pink-purple, purplish, or whitish, fading yellowish, sometimes wing tips whitish, banner veins lilac, keel tip maculate; banner recurved through 45°; keel 5.5–9.3 mm, apex blunt. **Legumes** usually ascending, rarely declined (humistrate), green becoming brown then blackish, incurved, narrowly lunate-ellipsoid to obliquely oblong-, ovoid-, or obovoid-ellipsoid, somewhat dorsiventrally compressed, 13–25 × 3.5–7 mm, subunilocular, thinly fleshy becoming leathery, not especially reticulate, glabrous; gynophore 0.4–1.4 mm. **Seeds** 16–37.

Varieties 2 (2 in the flora): c, se United States.

Among perennial species, *Astragalus distortus* substantially overlaps in range with *A. soxmaniorum*, a closely related endemic from eastern Texas, and *A. crassicarpus*, mostly more western. *Astragalus lotiflorus* resembles *A. distortus* in flower but is also more western and has evident or obscure malpighian hairs versus the basifixed hairs in *A. distortus*.

1. Flowers (10.5–)11–15.5 mm; legumes: sutures deeply sulcate, cross section didymous; Oklahoma and Louisiana northward to Iowa, eastward to West Virginia . . .297a. *Astragalus distortus* var. *distortus*
1. Flowers 8.2–11.6(–12) mm; legumes: sutures shallowly sulcate dorsally, not or obscurely so ventrally, cross section obcordate or suborbiculate; Texas and adjacent Louisiana, Arkansas, Mississippi . . . . 297b. *Astragalus distortus* var. *engelmannii*

297a. Astragalus distortus Torrey & A. Gray var. distortus [E] [F]

Flowers (10.5–)11–15.5 mm; calyx tube 2.8–3.8 mm, lobes 1.2–1.9(–2.5) mm. **Legumes** 13–25 × 4–7 mm, sutures deeply sulcate, cross section didymous.

Flowering late Mar–Jul. Prairies, open pine and oak woods, shale slopes; 40–400 m; Ark., Ill., Iowa, Kans., La., Md., Miss., Mo., Okla.,Va., W.Va.

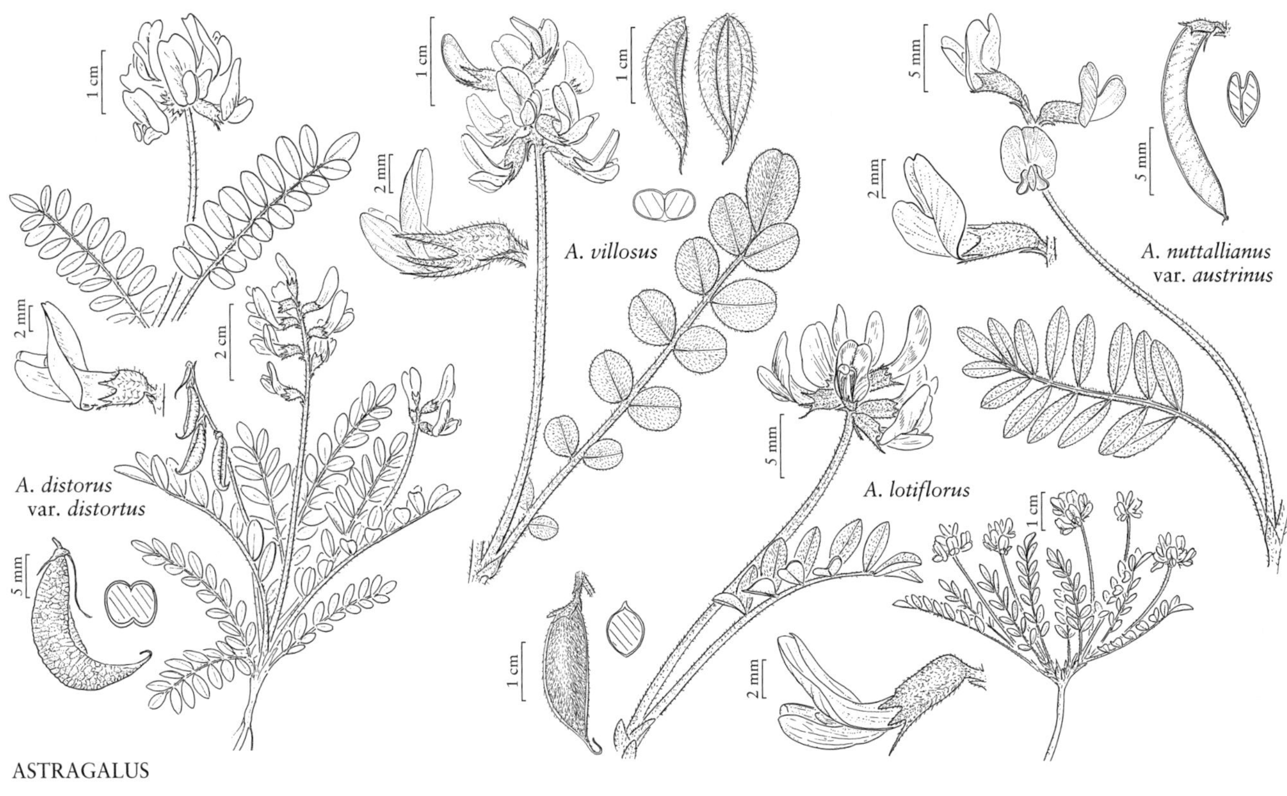

ASTRAGALUS

D. Isely (1998) pointed out that the widely disjunct Appalachian populations of var. *distortus* doubtless have been isolated for some time. Its physiological differentiation perhaps exceeds that between the two varieties, which are not clearly defined. There are no morphological differences between the Appalachian populations and those more western that justify formal taxonomic recognition.

297b. Astragalus distortus Torrey & A. Gray var. **engelmannii** (E. Sheldon) M. E. Jones, Rev. N.-Amer. Astragalus, 256. 1923 (as engelmanni) • Engelmann's milkvetch [E]

Astragalus engelmannii E. Sheldon, Minnesota Bot. Stud. 1: 152. 1894 (as engelmanni)

Flowers 8.2–11.6(–12) mm; calyx tube (2–)2.4–3.4 mm, lobes 0.7–1.5(–1.8) mm. **Legumes** 13–20 × 3.5–5.5(–6) mm, sutures shallowly sulcate dorsally, not or obscurely so ventrally, cross section obcordate or subglobose. $2n = 26$.

Flowering Feb–May. Prairie relicts, open woodlands, old fields or pastures, on limestone, slate, or clay substrates, in pine or oak woodlands; 0–300 m; Ark., La., Miss., Tex.

Variety *engelmannii* is known from northeastern Texas as far south as Matagorda County and adjacent northwestern Louisiana and southwestern Arkansas, with a population in Forrest County in southern Mississippi.

298. Astragalus soxmaniorum Lundell, Field & Lab. 13: 3. 1945 • Soxmans' milkvetch [E]

Plants short-lived, (3–)7–40 cm, sparsely strigulose-hirsutulous, hairs subappressed, to 0.7 mm; from branched, superficial caudex. **Stems** prostrate (and radiating) or weakly ascending, sparsely strigulose-hirsutulous. **Leaves** (2.5–)3.5–9(–11.5) cm; stipules 2.5–6.5 mm, thinly herbaceous becoming papery; leaflets (9–)13–19(or 21), blades firm, obovate, obovate-cuneate, or oblong-obovate, (2–)4–15 mm, veins not apparent, apex deeply emarginate, surfaces glabrous and sparsely strigose on margins and midrib abaxially, glabrous adaxially. **Peduncles** incurved-ascending becoming procumbent, (3–)4.5–9.5 cm. **Racemes** 8–20-flowered; axis (1–)1.5–4(–4.5) cm in fruit; bracts 2–4 mm; bracteoles 0–2. **Pedicels** 0.5–2.6 mm. **Flowers** 11.4–17.4 mm; calyx (5.8–)6.1–9 mm, strigulose, tube 3.3–4.8 mm, lobes lanceolate to lanceolate-caudate, (2–)2.4–4 mm; corolla white to greenish white or cream, keel tip immaculate;

banner recurved through 45°; keel 8.6–12.7 mm, apex round or sharply deltate, sometimes beaklike. **Legumes** ascending (humistrate), stramineous or blackish brown, straight or gently incurved, semi-obovoid or lunately oblanceoloid, somewhat laterally compressed, 15–21 × 5–8 mm, sub-bilocular, somewhat fleshy becoming leathery, not especially reticulate, glabrous; gynophore 0.6–1.6 mm. **Seeds** 18–26.

Flowering Mar–early May. Sandy openings in oak and oak-hickory woods, along sandy roadsides, in abandoned fields and clearings; 70–200 m; Ark., La., Tex.

Astragalus soxmaniorum, primarily of eastern Texas extending into adjacent Louisiana and Arkansas, appears to be a local derivative of *A. distortus* var. *engelmannii* and is fully contained within the range of that variety. Though the differences are what might be expected in allopatric varieties of a single species, there is no evidence of intergradation (R. C. Barneby 1964; D. Isely 1998).

299. Astragalus obcordatus Elliott, Sketch Bot. S. Carolina 2: 227. 1823 • Florida milkvetch [E]

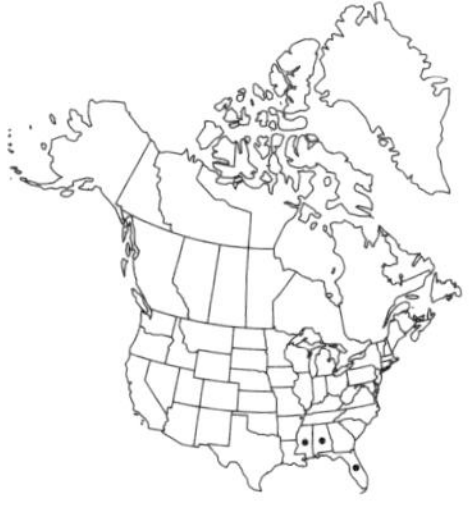

Plants slender, 4–40(–50) cm, glabrous or glabrate, hairs subappressed, to 0.7 mm; from branched, superficial caudex. **Stems** prostrate or decumbent, glabrate. **Leaves** 5–12(–30) cm; stipules distinct throughout, subulate to ovate-triangular, 2.4–6 mm, usually thinly herbaceous, sometime papery at proximal nodes; leaflets (9–)15–27, blades firm, oblong-obovate or cuneate-obcordate, 2–7(–11) mm, veins not apparent, apex retuse or obcordate with small, blunt mucro, surfaces glabrous, sparsely strigose on midrib abaxially, glabrous adaxially and frequently on margins. **Peduncles** incurved-ascending, (1.5–)3–10(–12.5) cm. **Racemes** 5–15(–18)-flowered; axis 1–4.5(–6) cm in fruit; bracts 1.2–2.5(–3.5) mm; bracteoles 0–2. **Pedicels** 1–2.8 mm. **Flowers** 8.5–11 mm; calyx 4.7–6.5 mm, strigulose, tube 2.7–3.5 mm, lobes lanceolate to broadly subulate, (1.8–)2.2–2.8 mm; corolla pinkish or bluish lilac, soon fading; banner recurved through 45–50°; keel 6.5–8 mm, apex round. **Legumes** ascending or spreading (humistrate), green or purple-tinged becoming stramineous or brownish, incurved, lunately semi-ellipsoid to semi-obovoid, somewhat laterally compressed, (13–)16–25(–32) × 4–7.5 mm, subunilocular, thinly fleshy becoming stiffly papery, coarsely reticulate, glabrous; gynophore to 0.6 mm. **Seeds** 13–18.

Flowering Feb–Jul. Sandy pine woods; 0–100 m; Ala., Fla., Miss.

Astragalus obcordatus is one of two *Astragalus* species known to occur in Florida (the other is *A. villosus*); it also occurs in Dallas County in Alabama, and Jackson County in Mississippi. D. Isely (1998) noted that it has the essential characteristics of *A. distortus* and is perhaps a Coastal Plain derivative.

300. Astragalus villosus Michaux, Fl. Bor.-Amer. 2: 67. 1803 • Bearded milkvetch [E] [F]

Plants short-lived, slender, 2–20 cm, hirsute, hairs spreading-ascending, often spirally twisted, to 1.1–2 mm; from superficial to subterranean branched caudex. **Stems** prostrate or decumbent, 0–7 cm underground, hirsute. **Leaves** (1.5–)3–10(–12) cm; stipules rarely connate at proximal nodes, 2–8.5 mm, mostly thinly herbaceous, sometimes papery at proximal nodes; leaflets (3–)7–15, blades thin, obovate, broadly oblanceolate, or suborbiculate, (2–)5–22 mm, larger ones pinnately veined, apex cuneate to emarginate, surfaces villous-pilose abaxially, glabrous adaxially. **Peduncles** incurved-ascending, (2–)3–11 cm. **Racemes** densely (5–)8–24-flowered; axis 1–3(–4) cm in fruit; bracts (2–)2.5–5 mm; bracteoles 0. **Pedicels** 0.7–2.5 mm. **Flowers** 8.8–11.2 mm; calyx 5.5–7.8(–8.2) mm, pilose, tube 2.7–3.7 mm, lobes lanceolate to lanceolate-attenuate, (2.7–)3–4.5(–5) mm; corolla pale yellow to greenish ochroleucous, fading yellowish, keel immaculate; banner recurved through 50–80°; keel 7.2–9.7 mm, apex narrowly deltate, acute or subacute, often beaklike. **Legumes** ascending or spreading (humistrate), pale yellow green becoming stramineous then brownish, incurved or ± straight, slenderly lunate-ellipsoid or semi-ellipsoid, bluntly 3-sided compressed, (15–)17–25 × (2.8–)3.2–5.2 mm, subunilocular, thinly fleshy becoming stiffly papery, densely hirsute, hairs spreading-ascending, to 1.2–1.8 mm, lustrous white; gynophore to 0.8 mm. **Seeds** 12–18.

Flowering late Feb–Jun. Glades, savannas, openings in sandy oak and pine woods, roadsides; 0–100 m; Ala., Fla., Ga., S.C.

Astragalus villosus, as with many astragali, readily grows in secondary habitats. It is especially common in northern Florida and occurs in southern Alabama through eastern and southern Georgia, and just into Aiken County in southern South Carolina.

135zzz. Astragalus Linnaeus sect. Lotiflori A. Gray, Proc. Amer. Acad. Arts 6: 208. 1864 [E]

Herbs perennial, tuft-forming, caulescent to subacaulescent; caudex superficial. **Hairs** malpighian. **Stems** single or few to several. **Stipules** distinct. **Leaves** odd-pinnate, petiolate; leaflets (3–)7–19. **Racemes** dimorphic, chasmogamous densely (3–)5–17-flowered, flowers ascending, cleistogamous reduced to 1–3 sessile flowers in leaf axils. **Calyx tubes** campanulate. **Corollas** (chasmogamous) greenish white to ochroleucous or purple, banner recurved through 45–80°, keel apex blunt or deltate, cleistogamous petals minute. **Legumes** deciduous, sessile, spreading or ascending (humistrate), ovoid to narrowly oblong-ellipsoid or lanceoloid, compressed dorsally or 3-sided, unilocular. **Seeds** 24–40.

Species 1: c, nw North America.

301. Astragalus lotiflorus Hooker, Fl. Bor.-Amer. 1: 152. 1831 • Lotus milkvetch [E] [F]

Plants short-lived, loosely or densely tuft-forming, 2–17 cm, strigose to villous; from branched caudex. **Stems** prostrate or decumbent to erect, strigose to villous. **Leaves** 2.5–12(–14) cm; stipules (2.5–)3–8(–9) mm, submembranous becoming papery-scarious; leaflet blades narrowly to broadly elliptic, oblanceolate, or obovate-cuneate, 4–20(–26) mm, apex acute to obtuse, surfaces strigulose, pilosulous, or hirsute, sometimes glabrescent or glabrous adaxially. **Inflorescences** dimorphic, pedunculate in chasmogamous flowers, sessile in cleistogamous flowers, on same or different plants. **Peduncles** ascending, chasmogamous (2–)4–10(–12) cm, cleistogamous 0–2 cm. **Racemes:** chasmogamous (3–)5–17-flowered, ; axis 0.7–2.5 cm in fruit; bracts 1.8–5 mm; bracteoles 0; cleistogamous 1–3-flowered, very short. **Pedicels** 0.5–2.4 mm. **Chasmogamous flowers** 8.5–14 mm; calyx shallowly campanulate, 5–9.7 mm, strigose, tube 3.2–4.5 mm, lobes lanceolate, 2.2–5.2 mm; corolla greenish white, ochroleucous, or tinged or veined lavender or purple, keel without darker apex; banner recurved through 45+°; keel 6.6–9.8 mm. **Cleistogamous flowers** 4.3–7.2 mm; calyx shorter than in chasmogamous flowers at anthesis, accrescent in fruit; corolla whitish, drying yellowish, petals not expanding, much shorter than calyx lobes; banner little recurved; keel 4.2–6 mm. **Legumes** (of both) ascending or spreading (humistrate), stramineous or purplish brown, usually straight or incurved, rarely decurved, ovoid-acuminate, ovoid-, lanceoloid-, or narrowly oblong-ellipsoid, abaxially or 3-sided compressed, 12–37 × 5–8 mm, somewhat fleshy becoming leathery or stiffly papery, strigulose, villosulous, or long-villous. $2n = 26$.

Flowering Apr–Jul. Prairies, barren hilltops or bluffs, lakeshores; 200–1900(–2400) m; Alta., B.C., Man., Sask.; Colo., Iowa, Kans., Minn., Mo., Mont., Nebr., N.Mex., N.Dak., Okla., S.Dak., Tex., Wyo.

The affinities of *Astragalus lotiflorus*, a variable and polymorphic species, are not clear. It was associated by A. Gray (1864) with *A. villosus* because of the similar forms of calyces and petals, but the basifixed hairs and three-sided compressed, narrow fruits are important differences. M. E. Jones (1923) excluded *A. villosus* from sect. *Lotiflori* but introduced other extraneous elements (R. C. Barneby 1964). *Astragalus lotiflorus* is unusual, if not unique, among North American astragali in that it has floral dimorphism (some plants completely cleistogamous, others chasmogamous) or the floral form varies on the same plant at different times of the year. Frequency of cleistogamous plants increases northward from Nebraska.

135aaaa. Astragalus Linnaeus sect. Panamintenses Barneby, Mem. New York Bot. Gard. 13: 998. 1964 [E]

Herbs perennial, mat- or tuft-forming, caulescent or subacaulescent; caudex superficial. **Hairs** basifixed. **Stems** few to many. **Stipules** distinct. **Leaves** odd-pinnate, petiolate; leaflets 5–9(or 11). **Racemes** loosely flowered, flowers ascending. **Calyx tubes** campanulate. **Corollas** pink-purple, banner recurved through 45°, keel apex bluntly deltate. **Legumes** deciduous, sessile, ascending or spreading (humistrate), oblong-ellipsoid or oblong-oblanceoloid, somewhat 3-sided, sub-bilocular. **Seeds** 12–19.

Species 1: California.

302. Astragalus panamintensis E. Sheldon, Contr. U.S. Natl. Herb. 4: 87. 1893 • Panamint milkvetch [E]

Plants 5–18 cm, silvery-canescent; from branched caudex, branches intricate, usually with sparse thatch of marcescent petioles. **Stems** erect or ascending, internodes elongate or not, usually white-strigulose. **Leaves** (1.5–)2–12 cm; stipules 1–3(–4) mm, herbaceous becoming papery; leaflet blades linear-elliptic or subulate, 2–12(–14) mm, apex acute and apiculate, surfaces silvery-canescent. **Peduncles** ascending, (0.5–)1–6(–8) cm. **Racemes** 1–4(–6)-flowered; axis (0–)1.5–3.5 cm in fruit; bracts 0.8–2 mm; bracteoles 0. **Pedicels** 1–2.5 mm. **Flowers** 8.2–14 mm; calyx 4.6–8.5 mm, strigulose, tube (2.7–)3–4.6 mm, lobes lanceolate- to linear-subulate, 1.5–4.4 mm; corolla pink-purple, banner with white in middle, wing tips white, keel maculate; keel 6.6–8.7 mm. **Legumes** pale green and purple spotted becoming stramineous, slightly decurved or ± straight, bluntly 3-sided compressed, 8–18 × (2.3–)3.4–4.7 mm, thin becoming papery, densely strigulose.

Flowering Apr–Jun. Forming mats on ledges and crevices in limestone outcrops and talus, less commonly in canyon bottoms; (1000–)1200–2200 m; Calif.

Astragalus panamintensis is restricted to the mountains of Inyo County. The leaflets appear to be early deciduous, falling more or less synchronously with the fruits.

135bbbb. Astragalus Linnaeus sect. Humillimi (M. E. Jones) Barneby, Mem. New York Bot. Gard. 13: 1000. 1964 [E]

Astragalus subsect. *Humillimi* M. E. Jones, Rev. N.-Amer. Astragalus, 68. 1923

Herbs perennial, matted, tufted, or pulvinate, ± acaulescent; caudex superficial, often with persistent stipules and leaf bases. **Hairs** malpighian or basifixed. **Stems** obscured by stipules and leaf bases. **Stipules** distinct, rarely connate at distal nodes. **Leaves** odd-pinnate, petiolate; leaflets (3 or)5–21(–25), sessile but jointed. **Racemes** subcapitate and densely flowered, or loosely flowered, flowers ascending, spreading, or erect, sometimes most proximal becoming declined. **Calyx tubes** campanulate or cylindric. **Corollas** pink to purple or reddish, sometimes wing tips whitish, banner recurved through 20–50°, wing apices obscurely emarginate, keel apex blunt or bluntly deltate, sometimes beaklike. **Legumes** ultimately deciduous, sessile, spreading to ascending or erect, subglobose, ovoid, or oblong-ellipsoid, compressed laterally, terete, or somewhat 3-sided, unilocular. **Seeds** 4–12.

Species 6 (6 in the flora): sw United States.

Section *Humillimi* comprises three subsections with distribution in northern Arizona, southwestern Colorado, and New Mexico. The subsections are: subsect. *Troglodyti* Barneby (*Astragalus troglodytus*); subsect. *Humillimi* (*A. gilensis*, *A. siliceus*); and subsect. *Nothorophaca* Barneby (*A. cremnophylax*, *A. humillimus*, *A. wittmannii*).

303. Astragalus troglodytus S. Watson, Proc. Amer. Acad. Arts 20: 362. 1885 • Cliff-dweller's milkvetch [C] [E]

Plants tuft-forming, acaulescent or subacaulescent, 6–25 cm, silky-pilose, hairs basifixed. **Stems** obscured by stipules. **Leaves** 3.5–11.5 cm; stipules distinct, 3–11 mm, papery-membranous; leaflets (7–)11–19, blades obovate, obovate-cuneate, rhombic, or broadly oblanceolate, 4–13 mm, apex subacute, obtuse and apiculate, or obtuse, surfaces pilose abaxially, glabrous adaxially. **Peduncles** scapiform, incurved-ascending, 4.5–15(–20) cm. **Racemes** 10–30-flowered, flowers in compact cluster, ascending to spreading becoming declined proximally; axis not elongating in fruit; bracts 3–8.5 mm; bracteoles 0–2. **Pedicels** 0.4–1 mm. **Flowers** 9.5–11.4 mm; calyx campanulate, 5.9–8.2 mm, sparsely hirsute, tube 3.4–5.2 mm, lobes lanceolate-linear to setaceous, 1.9–3 mm; corolla dull reddish purple, keel maculate; banner recurved through 45°; keel 7.9–9.1 mm, apex blunt. **Legumes** in oblong or globose, headlike clusters, spreading and ascending, green or purple-tinged becoming stramineous or brownish, plumply ovoid or subglobose, terete or somewhat laterally compressed, 5–7 × 4–4.5 mm, thinly fleshy becoming stiffly papery, sparsely long-hirsute. **Seeds** 8–12.

Flowering May–Aug. Dry slopes and flats, ponderosa pine forests; of conservation concern; 1900–2200 m; Ariz.

Astragalus troglodytus, a probable relative of *A. gilensis*, is restricted to the Coconino Plateau and adjacent Mogollon Rim in Coconino County.

304. Astragalus gilensis Greene, Bull. Torrey Bot. Club 8: 97. 1881 • Gila milkvetch [E]

Plants tuft-forming, acaulescent or subacaulescent, 6–25 cm, ashen-strigulose, hairs malpighian; branched caudex with thatch of marcescent leaf bases. **Stems** obscured by stipules and leaf bases. **Leaves** (1.5–)2.5–9 cm; stipules distinct, 4–9 mm, submembranous becoming papery; leaflets (7–)11–21(–25), blades elliptic, oblong-elliptic, or oblanceolate, (2–)3–12 mm, apex acute, obtuse, or emarginate, surfaces ashen-strigulose. **Peduncles** ±scapelike, incurved-ascending, (2.5–)3.5–15(–22) cm. **Racemes** densely 7–26-flowered, flowers in subcapitate cluster, ascending to spreading becoming declined proximally; axis slightly elongating to 0.5–2.5 cm in fruit; bracts 1.5–4 mm; bracteoles 0–2. **Pedicels** 0.6–1.6 mm. **Flowers** 6.2–10.4 mm; calyx campanulate, 3.7–6 mm, strigulose, tube 2.3–4 mm, lobes subulate, 1.3–2.7 mm; corolla pink to pink-purple, wing tips white, keel maculate; banner recurved through 45–50°; keel 4.3–6.8 mm, apex bluntly deltate, sometimes beaklike. **Legumes** in oblong or globose, headlike clusters, spreading and ascending, reddish-tinged becoming brownish, slightly incurved, obliquely-ovoid or oblong-ellipsoid, obscurely 3-sided and somewhat laterally compressed, 4.5–7.5 × 2–4.2 mm, fleshy and firm becoming stiffly papery or somewhat leathery, strigulose. **Seeds** 7–11. $2n = 22$.

Flowering (Apr–)May–Sep. Dry sites in xeric ponderosa pine forests, pinyon-juniper woodlands; 1700–2700 m; Ariz., N.Mex.

Astragalus gilensis is reminiscent of the larger *A. troglodytus* in growth form and subcapitate inflorescences that remain compact in fruit, but the hairs of *A. troglodytus* are basifixed. It occurs in the Mogollon Mountain system in east-central Arizona and west-central New Mexico, with an outlying population in the Jemez Mountains of northern New Mexico.

305. Astragalus siliceus Barneby, Leafl. W. Bot. 8: 14. 1956 • Flint milkvetch [E]

Plants tuft- or mat-forming, mounds 1–3 dm wide, acaulescent or subacaulescent, 1–2.5 cm, ashen-strigulose, hairs malpighian; branched caudex with thatch of marcescent stipules and leaf bases. **Stems** obscured by stipules and leaf bases. **Leaves** 0.5–3 cm; stipules distinct, 1.5–3 mm, submembranous becoming papery; leaflets (3 or)5–9, blades elliptic, oblanceolate, or obovate, 1.5–5 mm, apex obtuse or subacute, surfaces ashen-strigulose. **Peduncles** axillary, ascending, 0.2–0.6 cm. **Racemes** (1 or)2(or 3)-flowered, flowers ascending; axis 0.1–0.3(–0.4) cm in fruit, slightly elongating; bracts 0.7–2.2 mm; bracteoles 0. **Pedicels** 2.2–3.5 mm. **Flowers** 9–11.5 mm; calyx campanulate, 4–5.9 mm, silky-strigulose, tube 3.2–4.2 mm, lobes subulate, 0.8–1.8 mm; corolla pink-purple, wing tips whitish, keel maculate, or near-white; keel 7.5–8.7 mm, apex blunt. **Legumes** ascending or spreading, green, slightly incurved, obliquely-ovoid, laterally compressed, 5–7.5 × 2.8–3.8 mm, thinly fleshy becoming stiffly papery, densely strigulose. **Seeds** 8–10. $2n = 22$.

Flowering May–Jun. Rocky knolls on high rolling plains, arid grasslands, on granitic or calcareous substrates; 1800–2000 m; N.Mex.

Astragalus siliceus is a narrow endemic of Guadalupe, Santa Fe, and Torrance counties in central New Mexico, where it is locally common, especially on rocky areas exposed by disturbance years earlier. Hundreds of dense, mounded mats provide a spectacular spring display of various whitish to pink-lavender hues when covered by low, close flowers. The extent of the population recently discovered in Santa Fe County is not documented; the plants collected there have measurements in the small end of the range for *A. siliceus*.

306. Astragalus wittmannii Barneby, Brittonia 31: 459, fig. 1. 1979 • Wittmann's milkvetch [E]

Plants tuft-forming, flattened cushions 1–3 dm wide, acaulescent or subacaulescent, 1–3 cm, ashen-strigulose or sparsely hairy, hairs malpighian; caudex much-branched, branches with thatch of marcescent stipules and soft leaf bases. **Stems** obscured by stipules and leaf bases, sometimes shortly elongating following anthesis. **Leaves** 0.5–8 cm; stipules distinct at proximal nodes, connate at distal nodes, (2–)3–5 mm, membranous; leaflets (3 or)5 or 7, blades oblanceolate to linear-oblanceolate or linear-elliptic, (2–)5–12 mm, apex obtuse or acute, surfaces ashen-strigulose. **Peduncles** obsolete. **Racemes** 1-flowered, flowers erect; bracts 2.5 mm; bracteoles 0. **Pedicels** obsolete. **Flowers** 14–18 (–21) mm; calyx cylindric, 8–10 mm, strigulose to subglabrous, tube 6–6.7 mm, lobes linear-subulate, 2–3.3 mm; corolla bright pink-purple, keel maculate; banner recurved to 20°; keel apex blunt. **Legumes** erect, green, straight, inversely plumply pyriform, subglobose, subterete, 3 × 3 mm, thinly fleshy becoming papery, strigulose. **Seeds** 7 or 8. **2*n*** = 22.

Flowering May–Jun. Sandy hollows, in short-grass prairies, on shale-limestone outcrops; 1700–2000 m; N.Mex.

Astragalus wittmannii, known from Colfax, Harding, and Mora counties, is similar to *A. siliceus*; it was placed by R. C. Barneby (1964) in subsect. *Nothorophaca* Barneby rather than *Humillimi*, thus allying it with *A. cremnophylax*, because of the depauperate racemes, elongated flowers, and globose, non-compressed fruits.

307. Astragalus cremnophylax Barneby, Leafl. W. Bot. 5: 83. 1948 • Sentry milkvetch [C] [E]

Plants tuft- or cushion-forming, to 2 dm wide, acaulescent or subacaulescent, 0.5–2(–3.2) cm, silvery-strigulose, hairs malpighian; branched caudex with thatch of marcescent stipules and leaf bases. **Stems** obscured by stipules and leaf bases. **Leaves** 0.3–2(–3.5) cm; stipules distinct, 1–3 mm, submembranous becoming papery; leaflets (3 or)5–9(or 11), blades elliptic, obovate, or suborbiculate, 1.5–5 mm, apex obtuse or subacute, surfaces silvery-strigulose. **Peduncles** axillary, ascending, to 0.5 cm. **Racemes** (1 or)2(or 3)-flowered, flowers ascending; axis 0.1–0.2 cm; bracts 0.6–1 mm; bracteoles 0. **Pedicels** 0.7–1 mm. **Flowers** 3.7–8 mm; calyx campanulate, 2.7–3.6 mm, silky-strigulose, tube 1.7–2.3 mm, lobes subulate, 0.8–1.4 mm; corolla borne within surface of cushion, pale pink-purple, wing tips whitish, keel maculate; banner recurved through 45°; keel 3.7–5.7 mm, apex bluntly deltate, minutely beaklike. **Legumes** ascending (humistrate), green or purple dotted becoming stramineous, straight, obliquely-ovoid, slightly flattened or basally compressed dorsally, 3–4.5 (–4.8) × 2.5 mm, thinly fleshy becoming papery, densely strigulose. **Seeds** 4–6.

Varieties 3 (3 in the flora): Arizona.

Astragalus cremnophylax, as interpreted here, consists of three (possibly more) obscure and disjunct populations, all within Coconino County. There are few collections of the taxa and measurements presented here are tentative.

1. Leaf rachises lax, soft; plants forming soft cushions; North and South Rim, Grand Canyon, Arizona . . . . 307a. *Astragalus cremnophylax* var. *cremnophylax*
1. Leaf rachises erect or ascending, stiff; plants forming tufts or prickly cushions; Buckskin Mountain, e rim of Marble Canyon, Arizona.
   2. Banners 7–8 × 5.4–6 mm; keel 5.2–5.7 mm . . . . . . 307b. *Astragalus cremnophylax* var. *hevronii*
   2. Banners 3.7–6.3 × 4–4.6 mm; keel 3.7–4.5 mm . . . . 307c. *Astragalus cremnophylax* var. *myriorrhaphis*

307a. Astragalus cremnophylax Barneby var. **cremnophylax** [C] [E]

Plants forming soft cushions. **Leaves:** rachis lax, soft. **Corollas:** banner 5.3–6.1 × 4.3–4.6 mm; keel 3.7–4.3 mm.

Flowering May–Jun. Crevices of limestone pavement, in pinyon pine belt; of conservation concern; 2100–2200 m; Ariz.

Variety *cremnophylax* is restricted to the North and South rims of the Grand Canyon. S. E. Travis et al. (1996) found genetic variation between plants in populations (one very low in a small South Rim population) and comparatively substantial variation between populations. Greater genetic variation occurred in the North Rim plants, which constitute the largest population.

Variety *cremnophylax* is in the Center for Plant Conservation's National Collection of Endangered Plants.

SELECTED REFERENCE Travis, S. E., J. Maschinski, and P. Keim. 1996. An analysis of genetic variation in *Astragalus cremnophylax* var. *cremnophylax*, a critically endangered plant, using AFLP markers. Molec. Ecol. 5: 735–745.

307b. Astragalus cremnophylax Barneby var. **hevronii** Barneby, Brittonia 44: 238. 1992 • Hevron's milkvetch [C] [E]

Plants forming tufts or prickly cushions. **Leaves:** rachis erect or ascending, stiff. **Corollas:** banner 7–8 × 5.4–6 mm; keel 5.2–5.7 mm.

Flowering Apr. In Kaibab Limestone crevices; of conservation concern; 1500–1600 m; Ariz.

Variety *hevronii* is known only from the eastern rim of Marble Canyon along the Colorado River.

307c. Astragalus cremnophylax Barneby var. **myriorrhaphis** Barneby, Brittonia 31: 463, fig. 2. 1979 • Buckskin Mountain milkvetch [C] [E]

Plants forming tufts or prickly cushions. **Leaves:** rachis erect or ascending, stiff. **Corollas:** banner 3.7–6.3 × 4–4.6 mm; keel 3.7–4.5 mm.

Flowering May–Jul. Crevices of rimrock and limestone cliffs in Kaibab Limestone; of conservation concern; 1800–2000 m; Ariz.

Variety *myriorrhaphis* is known from several collections, all from Buckskin Mountain, east of Fredonia in Coconino County.

308. Astragalus humillimus A. Gray, Bull. U.S. Geol. Geogr. Surv. Territ. 2: 235. 1876 • Mesa Verde milkvetch [C] [E]

Plants tuft- or mat-forming, cushions to 3 dm wide, acaulescent, 0.5–2 cm, ashy-strigulose, hairs malpighian; from sand-impacted, branched caudex with thatch of marcescent stipules and leaf bases, these spinose-persistent, often extending above foliage of current season. **Stems** obscured by stipules and leaf bases. **Leaves** 0.8–4 cm; stipules distinct, 1–1.5 mm, submembranous becoming papery; leaflets 7–11, blades obovate-cuneate to oblong-elliptic, 1–5 mm, apex obtuse or subacute, surfaces silvery-strigulose. **Peduncles** axillary, 0.2–0.4 cm. **Racemes** 1–3-flowered, flowers ascending; axis 0.1–0.2 cm in fruit; bracts 0.6–0.8 mm; bracteoles 0. **Pedicels** 1–2.5 mm. **Flowers** 9–12 mm; calyx campanulate to subcylindric, 3.3–4.5 mm, strigulose, tube 2.2–3.8 mm, lobes subulate, 0.5–1.3 mm; corolla pink-purple, keel maculate; banner recurved through 45°; keel apex bluntly deltate. **Legumes** ascending to spreading, greenish becoming stramineous, oblong-ellipsoid, laterally compressed, 4.5–5.5 × 2–2.5 mm, thinly fleshy becoming stiffly papery, densely strigulose. **Seeds** 4–9. $2n = 22$.

Flowering May–Jul. Channel sandstone in hogbacks within the Cretaceous Mancos Shale Formation, on barrier sandstone ledges and mesa tops of Mesaverde Group formations, with Bigelow sagebrush, matchweed, and widely spaced junipers; of conservation concern; 1500–1900 m; Colo., N.Mex.

Astragalus humillimus was known only from the type collection for more than a century. It was rediscovered in 1980 in San Juan County, New Mexico, and subsequently has been found at more than a dozen sites there and in Montezuma County, Colorado. It is often locally common, forming showy, tight mounds of pink-purple flowers in late spring.

Astragalus humillimus is in the Center for Plant Conservation's National Collection of Endangered Plants.

135cccc. Astragalus Linnaeus sect. Leptocarpi M. E. Jones, Rev. N.-Amer. Astragalus, 266. 1923

Herbs annual, biennial, or perennial, caulescent; caudex superficial. **Hairs** basifixed or malpighian. **Stems** single or few to many. **Stipules** distinct. **Leaves** odd-pinnate, petiolate to subsessile; leaflets (3 or)5–25(or 27). **Racemes** subumbellate or loosely flowered, flowers ascending, spreading, or declined. **Calyx tubes** campanulate. **Corollas** usually pink-purple, purple or purple-tinged or -tipped, ochroleucous, or lilac, rarely whitish, banner recurved through 20–80°, keel apex acute, round, deltate, or triangular-acuminate, sometimes slightly beaklike. **Legumes** deciduous, usually sessile, rarely short-stipitate, short gynophore sometimes present, ascending, spreading to declined, incurved-ascending, or pendulous, mostly linear to linear-oblanceoloid, oblong, or crescentic, sometimes 3-sided, rarely ellipsoid or fleshy, straight or incurved, rarely slightly decurved, compressed laterally, slightly 3-sided or subterete, bilocular. **Seeds** (2–)4–30.

Species 24 (18 in the flora): se, w United States, n Mexico.

Section *Leptocarpi* is complex morphologically, with eight subsections recognized, one of them, subsect. *Coahuilani* Barneby, occurring only in northern Mexico. The subsections within the flora area are: subsect. *Pringleani* Barneby (*Astragalus nothoxys*); subsect. *Arizonici* Barneby (*A. arizonicus*); subsect. *Mohavenses* Barneby (*A. albens*, *A. mohavensis*); subsect. *Parvi* Barneby (*A. hypoxylus*); subsect. *Tricarinati* (Rydberg) Barneby (*A. bernardinus*, *A. tricarinatus*); subsect. *Californici* (A. Gray) Barneby (*A. acutirostris*, *A. breweri*, *A. claranus*, *A. emoryanus*, *A. pauperculus*, *A. rattanii*, *A. tener*); and subsect. *Leptocarpi* (M. E. Jones) Barneby (*A. leptocarpus*, *A. lindheimeri*, *A. nuttallianus*, *A. nyensis*).

309. Astragalus nothoxys A. Gray, Proc. Amer. Acad. Arts 6: 232. 1864 • Beaked milkvetch

Plants perennial (short-lived, sometimes flowering first year), (1.5–)2.5–35(–45) cm, strigulose, hairs basifixed. **Stems** decumbent or prostrate with ascending tips, strigulose. **Leaves** (2–)3–9(–11.5) cm; stipules 2–5 mm, submembranous; leaflets (7 or)9–21, blades obovate, oblong-obovate, broadly oblanceolate, oval, or oval-suborbiculate, 2–12(–15) mm, apex obtuse or emarginate, surfaces strigulose abaxially, glabrous or glabrescent adaxially. **Peduncles** incurved-ascending, (3–)4–14(–15) cm. **Racemes** (4–)6–20(–25)-flowered, flowers ascending to spreading; axis (1–)1.5–9 cm in fruit; bracts 0.8–3(–3.5) mm; bracteoles 0 or 1. **Pedicels** 0.5–3.2 mm. **Flowers** 8.5–12 mm; calyx 5–7 mm, strigulose, tube 3.6–4.9 mm, lobes lanceolate-subulate, 0.5–1.3 mm; corolla pink-purple, wing tips often whitish, keel maculate; banner recurved through 45°; keel 6.5–8.4 mm, apex bluntly deltate, beak narrowly triangular or subulate. **Legumes** ascending, green or purplish becoming stramineous or brownish, slightly incurved, linear-lanceoloid to linear, 3-sided compressed, (13–)15–22 × 2.3–3.5(–4) mm, papery, strigulose. **Seeds** (17 or)18–26. $2n = 28$.

Flowering (Jan–)Mar–Jun (summer). Among live oaks, mesquite, cholla, in juniper forests, common on caliche soils in live oak woodlands; 800–2000 m; Ariz., N.Mex.; Mexico (Chihuahua, Sonora).

Astragalus nothoxys occurs from east-central Arizona to southwestern New Mexico, and into northwestern Mexico. The keel beak has been compared, irrelevantly, to that of *Oxytropis* (S. Watson 1871), in which the cusp is terminal, not lateral as in this species. *Astragalus nothoxys* contains swainsonine and is known to be poisonous to livestock (L. F. James and S. L. Welsh 1992).

310. Astragalus arizonicus A. Gray, Proc. Amer. Acad. Arts 7: 398. 1868 • Arizona milkvetch

Plants perennial (short-lived, sometimes flowering as annual), clump-forming, (5–)15–40(–55) cm, silvery- to gray-strigulose, hairs malpighian. **Stems** decumbent or prostrate with ascending tips, silvery-canescent or silvery- to gray-strigulose. **Leaves** 2–8(–10) cm; stipules 2–4 mm, submembranous becoming papery; leaflets (5–)9–15(or 17), blades linear, linear-oblong, linear-elliptic, narrowly lanceolate, or oval, (1.5–)3–17(–21) mm, apex obtuse to apiculate or acute, surfaces strigulose. **Peduncles** erect or divaricate and incurved, (1.5–)2.5–10(–15) cm. **Racemes** (7–)10–30-flowered, flowers ascending; axis (1.5–)2.5–10 cm in fruit; bracts 0.8–2(–3) mm; bracteoles 0–2. **Pedicels** 0.5–2.2 mm. **Flowers** (8.7–)9–12 mm; calyx (4.5–)5–7 mm, strigulose, tube 3.3–4.1 mm, lobes broadly to slenderly subulate, (1.2–)1.4–3 mm; corolla pink-purple, wing tips pale or white and ± suffused with greenish yellow, keel maculate; banner recurved through 50°; keel 8.2–10.4 mm, apex narrowly triangular, acute, beaklike. **Legumes** erect or ascending, straight or gently incurved, linear-oblong or linear, obtusely 3-sided compressed, 15–30 × (2.2–)2.5–4.5 mm, thin becoming papery, strigulose. **Seeds** 14–22. $2n$ = 16, 26.

Flowering Mar–Jun. Desert grasslands, thorn-scrub, oak scrub, or juniper forests; 800–1500 m; Ariz.; Mexico (Sonora).

Astragalus arizonicus occurs from west-central to southeastern Arizona and into northern Sonora. The hairs vary from definitely malpighian to ones with the attachment very near the base; careful observation and good magnification are required. Within its area of distribution, *A. arizonicus* is the only member of its genus with narrowly oblong leaflets and widely-spaced flowers.

311. Astragalus albens Greene, Bull. Calif. Acad. Sci. 1: 156. 1885 • Cushenbury milkvetch [C] [E]

Plants winter-annual, delicate, (2–)5–30 cm, silvery-strigulose, hairs basifixed. **Stems** prostrate to ascending, silvery-strigulose. **Leaves** (1–)1.5–4(–5.5) cm; stipules 1.8–3.5 mm, submembranous; leaflets (5 or)7 or 9, blades obovate, oblong-oval, or rhombic-obovate, 2–11 mm, apex subacute, obtuse, or emarginate, surfaces silvery-strigulose, appearing frosted. **Peduncles** ascending, 1.5–4.5(–8) cm. **Racemes** 5–14-flowered, flowers spreading to declined; axis 2.5–4.5(–8) cm in fruit; bracts 0.8–1.5 mm; bracteoles 0. **Pedicels** 0.8–2.5 mm. **Flowers** 7.3–9.5 mm; calyx 3.9–4.5 mm, strigulose, tube 2.2–2.7 mm, lobes subulate, 1.4–2.3 mm; corolla pink-purple; banner recurved through 40°; keel 7–8.4 mm, apex bluntly deltate. **Legumes** spreading to declined, green or purple-tinged becoming stramineous or brownish, incurved through 0.25–0.5 spiral, narrowly lunate-oblanceoloid, 3-sided compressed, 13–18 × 2.8–3.5 mm, thinly papery, strigulose; gynophore slender, 0.5–0.9 mm. **Seeds** 8–11.

Flowering late Mar–May. Mainly on granitic or calcareous gravel; of conservation concern; 1200–1900 m; Calif.

Astragalus albens is one of the most narrowly localized astragali, restricted to, but common in, Cushenbury Canyon in the northeastern foothills of the San Bernardino Mountains in San Bernardino County. Similar to its relative *A. mohavensis*, *A. albens* is a short-lived perennial, usually flowering precociously, often persistent from season to season by dormant seeds (R. C. Barneby 1964).

Astragalus albens is in the Center for Plant Conservation's National Collection of Endangered Plants.

312. Astragalus mohavensis S. Watson, Proc. Amer. Acad. Arts 20: 361. 1885 • Mohave milkvetch [E]

Plants annual, winter-annual, or perennial (short-lived), sometimes loosely tuft-forming, 5–40(–65) cm, silvery-strigulose, hairs basifixed. **Stems** decumbent to weakly ascending; silvery-strigulose. **Leaves** 2–10 (–12.5) cm; stipules 1.8–3.5 mm, membranous or thinly herbaceous; leaflets (3 or)5–11, blades rhombic-elliptic, obovate-cuneate, or suborbiculate, 3–18 mm, apex obtuse or shallowly retuse, surfaces silvery-strigulose, appearing frosted. **Peduncles** erect or divaricate and ascending, often humistrate in fruit, 1.5–7(–10) cm. **Racemes** loosely 3–16-flowered, flowers ascending to declined; axis 0.8–7 cm in fruit; bracts 1–2.2 mm; bracteoles 0–2. **Pedicels** 0.6–3 mm. **Flowers** 7–12.5 mm; calyx 4–7.2 mm, strigulose, tube 2.5–4.4 mm, lobes subulate, 1.5–2.8 mm; corolla pink-purple; banner recurved through 45; keel 6.8–10.7 mm, apex round. **Legumes** declined or pendulous, stramineous or brownish, straight or incurved, oblong, or broadly and plumply so to oblong-ellipsoid or clavately oblong, (13–)15–28(–32) × 3.5–8.5 mm, fleshy becoming leathery or subligneous, densely strigulose; gynophore to 0.8 mm. **Seeds** 20–30.

Varieties 2 (2 in the flora): w United States.

The distinctive fruit of *Astragalus mohavensis*, leathery when mature and ventrally crested, has long funiculi extending into the cavity bearing the ovules or seeds. The two varieties can be distinguished only in fruit.

1. Legumes 15–28(–32) × (5–)5.5–8.5 mm, broadly and plumply oblong to oblong ellipsoid or clavately oblong in profile, usually straight or somewhat incurved, rarely lunately so; Mojave Desert, California, s Nevada . . . . 312a. *Astragalus mohavensis* var. *mohavensis*
1. Legumes (13–)15–25(–30) × 3.5–5.5(–6.5) mm, oblong, lunately to strongly and hamately incurved; Death Valley and Spring (Charleston) Mountains vicinity in California and Nevada . . . . 312b. *Astragalus mohavensis* var. *hemigyrus*

312a. Astragalus mohavensis S. Watson var. **mohavensis** E

Flowers (8.8–)9–12.5 mm; calyx 4.9–7.2 mm, tube 2.7–4.4 mm, lobes 1.8–2.8 mm. **Legumes** broadly and plumply oblong to oblong-ellipsoid or clavately oblong in profile, usually straight or somewhat incurved, rarely lunately so, 15–28(–32) × (5–)5.5–8.5 mm. 2*n* = 24.

Flowering (Mar–)Apr–Jun. Foothills of desert mountains, along washes, on rock ledges; (300–)700–2300 m; Calif., Nev.

Variety *mohavensis* occurs in the Mojave Desert in Inyo, Riverside, and San Bernardino counties in California, and Clark and southern Nye counties in Nevada.

312b. Astragalus mohavensis S. Watson var. **hemigyrus** (Clokey) Barneby, Aliso 2: 207. 1950 • Indian Springs milkvetch E

Astragalus hemigyrus Clokey, Madroño 6: 220, plate 27, figs. p–z. 1942

Flowers: calyx 4–5.7 mm, tube 2.5–3.2 mm, lobes 1.5–2.5 mm; corolla 7–9 mm. **Legumes** oblong, lunately to strongly and hamately incurved, (13–)15–25(–30) × 3.5–5.5(–6.5) mm. 2*n* = 24.

Flowering Apr–Jun. Limestone outcrops and gravelly slopes in *Larrea* belt; 900–1600 m; Calif., Nev.

Variety *hemigyrus* occurs near Indian Springs, Spring (Charleston) Mountains in Clark County, Nevada, and on Darwin Mesa in Inyo County, California.

313. Astragalus hypoxylus S. Watson, Proc. Amer. Acad. Arts 18: 192. 1883 • Huachuca Mountain milkvetch C

Plants perennial, 4–11 cm, cinereous-strigulose, hairs basifixed. **Stems** decumbent, strigulose. **Leaves** 1.5–4 cm; stipules 1–1.5 mm, herbaceous becoming papery; leaflets 11 or 13, blades obovate, 2–4.5 mm, apex obtuse, surfaces strigulose abaxially, glabrous adaxially. **Peduncles** prostrate and radiating in fruit, 5–7 cm. **Racemes** 8–18-flowered, flowers ascending; axis 1–2.5 cm in fruit; bracts 1.3–2.5 mm; bracteoles 0. **Pedicels** 1.5 mm. **Flowers** 7.5–8 mm; calyx 6 mm, strigulose-villosulous, tube 3 mm, lobes subulate, 2.8 mm; corolla pink-purple or bluish lavender; banner recurved through 45°; keel 5.8–6.2 mm, apex bluntly deltate. **Legumes** disjointing from receptacle when mature, ascending, stramineous, slightly incurved, narrowly lanceoloid, 3-sided compressed, 7–9 × 2–2.5 mm, thin becoming stiffly papery, loosely strigulose. **Seeds** 6.

Flowering Jun–Jul. Pinyon-juniper and oak communities in open rocky clearings on limestone substrates; of conservation concern; 1500–1700 m; Ariz.; Mexico (Sonora).

Astragalus hypoxylus is restricted to southeastern Arizona and northern and south-central Sonora, Mexico. Known only from the type collection for nearly a century, it has been collected several times since the mid 1980s.

Astragalus hypoxylus is in the Center for Plant Conservation's National Collection of Endangered Plants.

314. Astragalus tricarinatus A. Gray, Proc. Amer. Acad. Arts 12: 56. 1876 • Three-keeled milkvetch C E

Plants perennial, loosely tuft-forming, vigorous, 5–35(–45) cm, strigulose, hairs basifixed. **Stems** erect and ascending, in clumps, sparsely strigulose. **Leaves** 7–20 cm; stipules 1–4 mm, membranous becoming papery; leaflets (17 or)19–25 (or 27), blades ovate, elliptic, or obovate to obcordate, 3–12 mm, apex retuse or obtuse, surfaces sparsely strigulose abaxially, silvery-canescent adaxially. **Peduncles** arising from near or proximal to middle of stem, erect and ascending, 9–20 cm, together with racemes as long as or longer than stems. **Racemes** (5–)7–12(–15)-flowered, flowers spreading-ascending; axis (4–)6–18 cm in fruit; bracts 1–2.4 mm; bracteoles 0–2. **Pedicels** 1–4.8 mm. **Flowers** 12.6–15.7 mm; calyx 6.1–7.6 mm, strigulose-villosulous, tube 4.1–5 mm, lobes subulate, 2–2.8 mm; corolla ochroleucous; banner recurved through 45°; keel 9.7–11 mm, apex bluntly deltate. **Legumes** ascending, stramineous, slightly incurved, linear-lanceoloid, 3-sided compressed, 24–42 × 3.5–5.5 mm, thin becoming papery, glabrous; gynophore stout, (0.8–)1.2–2.5 mm. **Seeds** 20–24.

Flowering Feb–May. Gravelly slopes and canyons, with *Larrea* and *Encelia farinosa*; of conservation concern; 400–600(–1300) m; Calif.

Leaflets of *Astragalus tricarinatus* are numerous and irregularly spaced, early deciduous, the basal leaves often naked by anthesis, persisting as stiff, sharp, rachises. It occupies a range of approximately 80 km in Riverside and San Bernardino counties.

315. Astragalus bernardinus M. E. Jones, Proc. Calif. Acad. Sci., ser. 2, 5: 661. 1895 • Lesser three-keeled milkvetch [E]

Plants perennial, tuft-forming, slender, wiry, 15–50(–60) cm, strigulose, hairs basifixed. **Stems** ascending, in clumps, sparsely strigulose. **Leaves** (3–)4–12(–14) cm; stipules (1–)1.5–4 mm, submembranous becoming papery; leaflets (7–)11–17 (or 19), blades lanceolate or oblong-elliptic, (3–)5–20(–25) mm, apex obtuse or retuse, surfaces strigulose, densely so adaxially. **Peduncles** arising from stem distally, erect or incurved-ascending, (1.5–)3–10 cm, together with racemes much shorter than stems. **Racemes** 10–25-flowered, flowers ascending (to spreading); axis (2.5–)4–15(–17) cm in fruit; bracts 1–1.7 mm; bracteoles 0–2. **Pedicels** 0.4–2 mm. **Flowers** 7.1–10.2 mm; calyx campanulate, 3.6–6.7 mm, strigulose, tube 2.7–4.1 mm, lobes subulate, 0.9–3 mm; corolla pale to dark lilac; banner recurved through 45–80°; keel 6.8–9.4 mm, apex sharply triangular. **Legumes** erect or incurved-ascending, pale or purple-tinged becoming stramineous, straight or slightly incurved, narrowly oblanceoloid, 3-sided compressed, (20–)25–31 × 3.7–5 mm, thin becoming papery, glabrous; gynophore stout, 0.7–1.5 mm. **Seeds** 19–28.

Flowering Apr–Jun. Granitic or calcareous substrates, beneath shrubs; 900–2100 m; Calif.

As noted by D. Isely (1998), the fruits of *Astragalus bernardinus* and *A. tricarinatus* are virtually identical, but the latter species occurs at lower elevations. *Astragalus bernardinus* is one of the few species in the Mojave Desert that shelters under shrubs, with the flowers and fruits held at the level of the distalmost twigs (see also 119b. *A. atratus* var. *mensanus* and 126. *A. jaegerianus*).

316. Astragalus emoryanus (Rydberg) Cory, Rhodora 38: 406. 1936 • Emory's milkvetch

Hamosa emoryana Rydberg, Bull. Torrey Bot. Club 54: 327. 1927

Plants annual or winter-annual, rarely biennial, (2.5–)4–45(–60) cm, strigulose, hirsutulous, or subvillosulous, hairs basifixed; taproot slender. **Stems** prostrate, radiating from crown, strigulose, hirsutulous, or subvillosulous. **Leaves** 1–4.5(–8) cm; stipules mostly distinct, 1.5–3.5(–5) mm, membranous; leaflets (7–)11–19(or 21), blades oval-obovate, obcordate, cuneate-oblanceolate, or elliptic-oblanceolate, 2–10(–14) mm, apex obtuse or retuse, surfaces strigulose abaxially, strigulose or glabrous adaxially. **Peduncles** (1–)2–6(–10) cm. **Racemes** (1 or)2–10-flowered, flowers spreading to declined; axis (0–)0.3–2.5(–3.5) cm in fruit; bracts 0.5–1.8 mm; bracteoles 0 or 1. **Pedicels** 0.5–2 mm. **Flowers** (6–)7.3–11.2 mm; calyx 3.6–6 mm, strigulose, tube 1.9–3.5 mm, lobes lanceolate-subulate to subulate, 1.3–2.5(–2.9) mm; corolla pink-purple; banner recurved through 45°; keel (4.5–)4.8–6.6 mm, apex bluntly deltate. **Legumes** spreading, declined, or ascending, green or purple-tinged becoming pale brown or stramineous, straight or incurved through 0.25–0.5 spiral, linear-oblong to lanceoloid-oblong, 3-sided compressed, falling before splitting, dehiscent on ground, 8–20(–22) × (2–)2.2–3.7 mm, ± bilocular, papery, glabrous. **Seeds** (8–)10–15.

Varieties 2 (2 in the flora): sw, sc United States, n Mexico.

Astragalus emoryanus and *A. nuttallianus* are difficult to distinguish, differing definitively only by the deciduous fruits of *A. emoryanus*. The latter also usually has larger and showier flowers, an apically broad and commonly obtuse keel, and an elongating raceme axis. D. Isely (1998) provided a series of geographically restricted short keys that distinguish these species.

1. Legumes 12–20(–22) × (2–)2.2–3.3 mm, length 5–6.5 times width; Arizona, New Mexico, Texas, Utah . . . . . .316a. *Astragalus emoryanus* var. *emoryanus*
1. Legumes 8–14 × (2.5–)3–3.7 mm, length 3–4 times width; s trans-Pecos Texas . . . . 316b. *Astragalus emoryanus* var. *terlinguensis*

316a. Astragalus emoryanus (Rydberg) Cory var. **emoryanus**

Hairs mostly appressed or subappressed. **Peduncles** equaling or surpassing leaves. **Legumes** 12–20(–22) × (2–)2.2–3.3 mm, length 5–6.5 times width. $2n$ = 22, 24.

Flowering Feb–Jun. *Larrea*, mesquite, grassland, juniper, and mixed desert shrub communities; 10–2200 m; Ariz., N.Mex., Tex., Utah; Mexico (Chihuahua, Coahuila, Nuevo León, Tamaulipas).

The range of var. *emoryanus* is unusual and tripartite: Kane County, Utah, and northern Arizona; central New Mexico, western Texas, and southward to Nuevo León, Mexico; and Maverick County in the Rio Grande Valley and more or less continuously to near the mouth of the Rio Grande. In the Big Bend region of Texas and adjacent Mexico, it sometimes occurs with var. *terlinguensis*, without apparent hybridization.

316b. Astragalus emoryanus (Rydberg) Cory var. **terlinguensis** (Cory) Barneby, Amer. Midl. Naturalist 55: 494. 1956 • Big Bend milkvetch

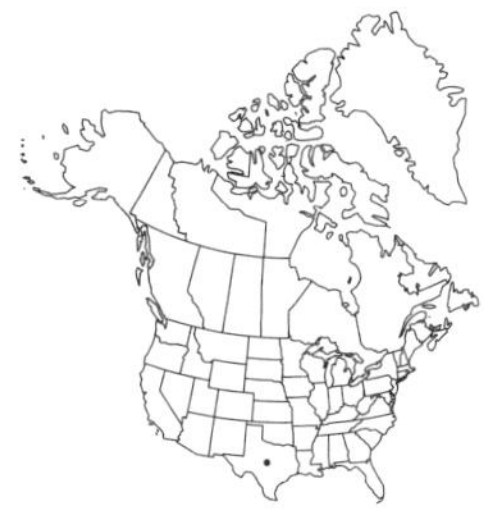

Astragalus terlinguensis Cory, Rhodora 39: 419. 1937

Hairs straight and spreading or incurved-ascending, pubescence cinereous-hirsute. **Peduncles** shorter than leaves proximally. **Legumes** 8–14 × (2.5–)3–2.7 mm, length 3–4 times width. 2*n* = 24.

Flowering Feb–Apr. Mixed shrub and shrub-grass communities; 700–1300 m; Tex.; Mexico (Coahuila).

Variety *terlinguensis* is sufficiently distinct that it might be given species status if there were not intermediate plants (D. Isely 1998). It is restricted to the Big Bend area of Texas and adjacent Mexico.

317. Astragalus acutirostris S. Watson, Proc. Amer. Acad. Arts 20: 360. 1885 • Sharp-keeled milkvetch

Oxytropis acutirostris (S. Watson) M. E. Jones

Plants annual or winter-annual, slender, 2–25(–30) cm, strigulose to pilosulous, hairs basifixed; taproot slender. **Stems** prostrate to decumbent or ascending, strigulose to pilosulous. **Leaves** (1–)1.5–4.5 cm; stipules 0.8–2.5(–3) mm, membranous; leaflets (7 or)9–13(or 15), blades oblong-oblanceolate, obovate, or cuneate, 2–10 mm, apex retuse, surfaces pubescent abaxially, glabrescent adaxially. **Peduncles** erect or spreading and incurved, (1.5–)2.5–7 cm. **Racemes** (1–)3–8-flowered, flowers spreading or declined; axis (0–)1–3.5 cm in fruit; bracts 0.7–1.3 mm; bracteoles 0. **Pedicels** 0.4–0.9 mm. **Flowers** (4.7–)5–7 mm; calyx (2.6–)2.8–3.5(–4.1) mm, strigulose, tube 1.6–2.1 mm, lobes lanceolate-subulate, (1–)1.2–1.5(–2.3) mm; corolla whitish, banner tinged or veins purple; banner recurved through 45°; keel 4.3–5.8 mm, apex narrowly triangular, acute or subacute, often slightly beaklike. **Legumes** pendulous, spreading, or ascending and resupinate, green or purple-tinged becoming brownish stramineous, gently incurved, lunately linear-ellipsoid, 3-sided compressed, falling before splitting, dehiscent on ground, 12–30 × (2.2–)2.5–3.1 mm, thin becoming papery, usually strigulose, sometimes glabrous; gynophore obscure, 0.4–0.8 mm. **Seeds** 12–26. **2*n*** = 24.

Flowering late Mar–May. *Larrea* and Joshua tree communities; 600–1600 m; Ariz., Calif., Nev.; Mexico (Baja California).

Astragalus acutirostris is known from the Mojave Desert from the lower Owens Valley and Death Valley, southward to the New York and San Bernardino mountains, eastward to the Belted Range in southern Nye County in Nevada, and southward to Mexico. There are also disjunct populations at lower elevations in Baja California.

Despite its desert habitat, the relationships of *Astragalus acutirostris* seem to be among the cismontane species, among which *A. pauperculus* is technically similar (R. C. Barneby 1964). It is often confused with western races of *A. nuttallianus*, which have persistent fruits and mostly acute leaflet blades. The upwardly curved keel apex was the basis for its inclusion in *Oxytropis*, but the keel shape is unmatched in that genus.

318. Astragalus tener A. Gray, Proc. Amer. Acad. Arts 6: 206. 1864 • Delta milkvetch [C] [E]

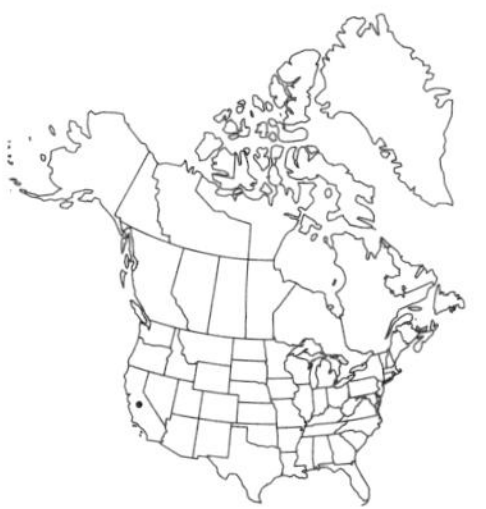

Astragalus hypoglottis Linnaeus var. *strigosus* Kellogg, Proc. Calif. Acad. Sci. 2: 115, fig. 37. 1861 (as strigosa), not *A. strigosus* J. M. Coulter & Fisher 1893

Plants annual or winter-annual, (2–)6–30(–35) cm, strigulose or glabrate, hairs basifixed; taproot slender. **Stems** erect or ascending, strigulose or glabrate. **Leaves** 2–9 cm; stipules 1.5 mm, membranous; leaflets 7–17, blades obovate-cuneate, obcordate to lanceolate, narrowly oblong, or linear-elliptic, 3–16 mm, apex retuse, truncate, obtuse, or acute, surfaces strigulose abaxially, glabrous adaxially. **Peduncles** erect, incurved-ascending, or divaricate, 2.5–7 cm. **Racemes** 2–12-flowered, subcapitate, flowers loosely spreading; axis 0.2–0.8 cm in fruit; bracts 0.7–2 mm; bracteoles 0 or 1. **Pedicels** 0.5–2.3 mm. **Flowers** 5–11.8 mm; calyx 2.7–5.4 mm, strigulose-villosulous, tube 1.6–3.2 mm, lobes broadly subulate, 0.9–2.3 mm; corolla pink-purple, keel maculate; banner recurved 30–40°; keel 3.4–6.4 mm, apex bluntly deltate, sometimes obscurely beaklike. **Legumes** ascending, spreading, or declined, stramineous, straight or curved, linear- or narrowly lanceoloid-oblong, obscurely 3-sided compressed, falling before splitting, dehiscent on ground, (6–)10–50 × 1.7–3.5 mm, base round, thinly fleshy becoming stiffly papery, strigulose, villosulous, or glabrous; bearing seeds near middle; stipe 2.7–5 mm. **Seeds** 5–14.

Varieties 3 (3 in the flora): California.

1. Flowers 5–6 mm; legumes pubescent; seeds 5–11; coastal from Monterey Bay s to San Diego, California . . . . .318c. *Astragalus tener* var. *titi*
1. Flowers 7.8–11.8 mm; legumes glabrous or pubescent; seeds (10 or)11–14; Sacramento and San Joaquin valleys, San Francisco Bay region, and Salinas Valley, California.
   2. Legumes 10–16(–20) mm, straight or incurved, bases round; s Sacramento Valley, n San Joaquin Valley, San Francisco Bay region, and Salinas Valley. . . . . . 318a. *Astragalus tener* var. *tener*
   2. Legumes 27–50 mm, incurved (crescentic), bases tapered; Sacramento Valley, Butte to Solano counties . . . . 318b. *Astragalus tener* var. *ferrisiae*

318a. Astragalus tener A. Gray var. **tener** C E

Stems single to several, (4–)6–30(–35) cm. **Leaves** (2–)3–9 cm; leaflets 7–17. **Racemes** (3–)5–10(–12)-flowered. **Flowers** 8.8–11.8 mm; calyx 3.5–5.4 mm. **Legumes** straight or incurved, 10–16(–20) mm, base round, glabrous or pubescent; stipe 0 mm. **Seeds** (10–)11–14. $2n = 22$.

Flowering Mar–early Jun. Saline flats and low meadows moist in spring; of conservation concern; 0–60 m; Calif.

Most of the habitat of var. *tener*, restricted to the San Francisco Bay area, the adjacent Central Valley, and the lower valleys of the San Benito and Salinas rivers, has been destroyed by urbanization and agriculture. The plant is now uncommon. Intra-plant and -population leaf variation, first reported by A. Kellogg (1861), has been reviewed by R. C. Barneby (1964).

318b. Astragalus tener A. Gray var. **ferrisiae** Liston, Brittonia 42: 100, fig. 1. 1990 • Ferris's milkvetch C E

Stems single to several, 6–26 cm. **Leaves** 2–6 cm; leaflets 7–15. **Racemes** 3–12-flowered. **Flowers** 7.8–9.6 mm; calyx 2.8–3.6 mm. **Legumes** incurved (crescentic), 27–50 mm, base tapered, glabrous or pubescent; stipe 2.7–5 mm. **Seeds** (10 or) 11–16.

Flowering Apr. Subalkaline fields and vernally moist meadows; of conservation concern; 0–60 m; Calif.

Variety *ferrisiae* from the Sacramento Valley, now very rare, shares about as much with *Astragalus rattanii* as it does with *A. tener*. It is retained here with reservation. Plants included in this variety were placed with *A. rattanii* var. *jepsonianus* by R. C. Barneby (1964), in which leaflet number averages greater (7–15 versus 7 or 9). In addition, A. Liston noted that var. *ferrisiae* can be distinguished from *A. rattanii* var. *jepsonianus* by its smooth seeds, deflexed pedicels, and crescentic, pseudostipitate fruits.

318c. Astragalus tener A. Gray var. **titi** (Eastwood) Barneby, Aliso 2: 209. 1950 • Titus's milkvetch C E

Astragalus titi Eastwood, Bull. Torrey Bot. Club 32: 195. 1905

Stems 1–3, (2–)3–12 cm. **Leaves** 2–7 cm; leaflets 7–11(or 13). **Racemes** 2–7-flowered. **Flowers** 5–6 mm; calyx 2.7–3.5 mm. **Legumes** straight or slightly decurved, base round, (6–)7–14 mm, pubescent; stipe 0 mm. **Seeds** 5–11. $2n = 22$.

Flowering late Mar–May. Moist depressions on coastal bluffs and dunes; of conservation concern; 0–20 m; Calif.

The coastal var. *titi* once occurred in Los Angeles, Monterey, and San Diego counties. It was thought extinct, but one population was discovered on a bluff in Monterey County.

Variety *titi* is in the Center for Plant Conservation's National Collection of Endangered Plants.

319. Astragalus pauperculus Greene, Pittonia 3: 224. 1897 • Bruce's milkvetch E

Astragalus bruceae (M. E. Jones) Abrams

Plants annual or winter-annual, slender, delicate, (1–)8–11 cm, strigulose or glabrate, hairs basifixed; taproot slender. **Stems** incurved-ascending, strigulose or glabrate. **Leaves** 1.5–5 cm; stipules 1–3 mm, submembranous; leaflets (5 or)7–11, blades oblong-oblanceolate, obovate-cuneate, or cuneate, 2–8 mm, apex truncate or retuse, surfaces strigulose abaxially, glabrous or margins sparsely hairy adaxially. **Peduncles** ascending or incurved-ascending, 2.5–7 cm. **Racemes** loosely 2–5(–7)-flowered, flowers ascending to declined; axis (0.4–)0.7–2 cm in fruit; bracts 0.8–1.5 mm; bracteoles 0 or 1. **Pedicels** 0.5–1.5 mm. **Flowers** 5.4–10.5 mm; calyx 2.9–4.3 mm, strigulose, tube 2.2–2.9 mm, lobes subulate, 0.7–1.5 mm; corolla pink- or violet-purple, wings margined white, keel maculate; banner recurved through 40°; keel 4.3–5.8 mm, apex broadly deltate, sometimes minutely beaklike. **Legumes** deflexed, declined, or ascending (resupinate), mottled or suffused with purple, incurved, narrowly crescentic, bluntly 3-sided compressed, falling before splitting, dehiscent on ground, 12–20 × 2.6–3.4 mm, thin becoming papery, base round, strigulose or glabrous; bearing seeds near middle. **Seeds** 8–12. **2*n*** = 24.

Flowering Mar–early May. Moist, open sites, foothill oak woodlands, treeless summits, on igneous-derived, clay substrates from disintegrated lava rock; 40–1200 m; Calif.

Astragalus pauperculus differs from *A. rattanii* and *A. tener* by its comparatively loose fruiting racemes (often more than 10 mm) and is found along the western margin of the southern Cascade Range and the northern Sierra Nevada in Butte, Shasta, and Tehama counties.

320. Astragalus rattanii A. Gray, Proc. Amer. Acad. Arts 19: 75. 1883 (as rattani) • Rattan's milkvetch [E]

Plants annual or winter-annual, usually slender, (2.5–)4–30 cm, sparsely strigulose or glabrate, hairs basifixed; taproot slender. **Stems** erect, incurved-ascending, or decumbent, sparsely strigulose or glabrate. **Leaves** (1.5–)2–5(–6) cm; stipules (1–)1.2–4 mm, submembranous becoming papery; leaflets (5 or)7–11(or 13), blades broadly obovate, obovate-cuneate to oblanceolate, or suborbiculate-obcordate, 2–12 mm, apex emarginate or retuse, surfaces strigulose abaxially, glabrous adaxially. **Peduncles** erect, (1.5–)2–7 cm. **Racemes** 2–10-flowered, flowers spreading; axis 0.1–0.4(–0.5) cm in fruit, not elongating; bracts 0.5–0.8 mm; bracteoles 0–2. **Pedicels** 0.3–1.3 mm. **Flowers** 7.2–12 mm; calyx 2.5–5 mm, strigulose, tube (1.8–)2.7–3.4 mm, lobes subulate, 0.6–1.7 mm; corolla pink-purple, wing tips pale or banner and keel tips maculate; banner recurved through 40°; keel 3.8–8.1 mm, apex broadly rounded or deltate, often obscurely beaklike. **Legumes** ascending, green or purple-tinged becoming brownish stramineous, gently incurved or straight, very narrowly linear, terete to obscurely 3-sided compressed, falling before splitting, dehiscent on ground, (15–)18–50(–57) × 1.7–2.7(–3.1) mm, thinly fleshy becoming papery, base cuneate or cuneate-tapered, then sometimes pseudostipitate, strigulose; bearing seeds near middle. **Seeds** 8–20.

Varieties 2 (2 in the flora): California.

Astragalus rattanii is distinguished from other northern California annuals of sect. *Leptocarpi* by its long, capitate-clustered, acicular-tipped fruits that taper at both ends (D. Isely 1998).

1. Calyx tubes 2.7–3.4 mm, lobes 0.9–1.7 mm; banners (9.2–)10–12 mm; legumes (21–)25–50 (–57) mm; seeds (11–)14–20 . . . . 320a. *Astragalus rattanii* var. *rattanii*
1. Calyx tubes 1.8–2.4 mm, lobes 0.6–1.2 mm; banners 7.2–9.6 mm; legumes (15–)18–30 mm; seeds 8–12. . . . 320b. *Astragalus rattanii* var. *jepsonianus*

320a. Astragalus rattanii A. Gray var. **rattanii** [E]

Leaflets (5 or)7–11(or 13). **Racemes** 2–10-flowered. **Flowers:** calyx tube 2.7–3.4, lobes 0.9–1.7 mm; corolla pink-purple, wing tips pale; banner (9.2–)10–12 × 4.9–6.4 mm. **Legumes** (21–)25–50(–57) mm. **Seeds** (11–)14–20. **2*n*** = 22.

Flowering mid Apr–Jul. Grassy sites, gravel bars, river beds; 30–800 m; Calif.

Variety *rattanii* is a taxon of primarily the outer North Coast Ranges from Humboldt County southward to western Tehama and northwestern Lake counties.

320b. Astragalus rattanii A. Gray var. **jepsonianus** Barneby, Aliso 4: 137. 1958 (as rattani) • Jepson's milkvetch [E]

Leaflets 7 or 9. **Racemes** 4–9-flowered. **Flowers:** calyx tube 1.8–2.4 mm, lobes 0.6–1.2 mm; corolla bicolored, banner and keel tips purple-maculate; banner 7.2–9.6 × 3.5–5(–5.4) mm. **Legumes** (15–)18–30 mm. **Seeds** 8–12. **2*n*** = 22.

Flowering Apr–early Jun. Meadows, chaparral, on or near serpentine outcrops; 300–600 m; Calif.

Two closely related entities are morphologically similar to var. *jepsonianus*: *Astragalus claranus* (fruits on a gynophore, generally curved), and *A. tener* var. *tener* (fruits round basally, usually less than 16 mm versus usually greater than 18 mm). Removing plants now classified as *A. tener* var. *ferrisiae* from *A. rattanii* var. *jepsonianus*, where they were included by R. C. Barneby (1964), means that var. *jepsonianus* is characterized by wrinkled or pitted seeds, upright pedicels, and fruits that are straight or incurved, 1.5–3.5 cm, and shortly pseudostipitate (A. Liston 1990).

321. Astragalus claranus Jepson, Man. Fl. Pl. Calif., 578, fig. 570. 1925 (as clarianus) • Napa milkvetch [C] [E]

Plants annual or winter-annual, ephemeral, very slender, (2–)3–10(–23) cm, sparsely strigulose, hairs basifixed; taproot slender. **Stems** erect or ascending, sparsely strigulose. **Leaves** 1.5–5 cm; stipules 1–2.5 mm, submembranous becoming papery; leaflets 5–9, blades cuneate-obovate to narrowly cuneate, 2–10 mm, apex retuse, surfaces sparsely strigulose abaxially, glabrous adaxially. **Peduncles** ascending becoming declined or divaricate, 2–7 cm. **Racemes** 2–7-flowered, flowers spreading to declined; axis 0.2–1(–1.3) cm in fruit, scarcely elongating; bracts 0.7–1.2 mm; bracteoles 0. **Pedicels** 0.4–2.2 mm. **Flowers** 8.9–12 mm; calyx 2.8–4 mm, strigulose, tube 2.1–2.6 mm, lobes triangular to subulate, 0.6–1.4 mm; corolla whitish, banner and keel tips purple; banner recurved through 20°; keel 7.4–9.1 mm, apex round. **Legumes** horizontal or declined, green or faintly brown-mottled becoming brownish, incurved, crescentic and linear, obscurely 3-sided compressed, falling before splitting, dehiscent on ground, 17–25 × (1.6–)2–3.1 mm, thinly fleshy becoming stiffly papery, base and apex acuminate, strigulose; bearing seeds near middle; gynophore pseudostipitate, slender, 1.4–2.5 mm. **Seeds** 6–12. $2n = 22$.

Flowering Apr–May. Grassy slopes, especially on thin volcanic clay substrates moist in springtime; of conservation concern; 90–200 m; Calif.

Astragalus claranus occurs in the North Coast Ranges in Napa and Sonoma counties; it is sometimes confused with *A. tener* var. *ferrisiae*. Both taxa are pseudostipitate, but *A. claranus* has, in addition, a slender gynophore from which the fruit disarticulates. No other species has both a pseudostipe and a gynophore (R. C. Barneby 1964). The keel also exceeds the wings in *A. claranus*, but not in var. *ferrisiae* (A. Liston 1990).

322. Astragalus breweri A. Gray, Proc. Calif. Acad. Sci. 3: 103. 1864 • Brewer's milkvetch [E]

Plants annual or winter-annual, slender, (1.5–)4–30 cm, sparsely strigulose, hairs basifixed; taproot slender. **Stems** erect or ascending, sparsely strigulose. **Leaves** (1.5–)2–6(–7.5) cm; stipules 1.5–4.5 mm, membranous becoming papery; leaflets 7–13, blades cuneate-obovate to oblong-elliptic, 3–10(–12) mm, apex retuse or obtuse, surfaces sparsely strigulose abaxially, glabrous adaxially. **Peduncles** erect or divaricate and ascending, (2–)3–9(–11) cm. **Racemes** densely 3–10-flowered, flowers ascending to spreading; axis to 0.5 cm, not or scarcely elongating; bracts 0.6–2 mm; bracteoles 0 or 1. **Pedicels** 0.4–1.4 mm. **Flowers** 7.8–11.4 mm; calyx 3.8–5.1 mm, strigulose, tube 2.5–3.5 mm, lobes subulate, 1–2 mm; corolla whitish, banner and, sometimes, wings veined or suffused lilac, keel tip purple; banner recurved through 35–45°; keel (5–)5.4–7.8 mm, apex round. **Legumes** stellately ascending, green, straight, ovoid, ovoid-oblong, or fusiform, obscurely 3-sided compressed, falling before splitting, dehiscent on ground, 5.5–10 × (2.5–)2.8–4 mm, thinly fleshy becoming stiffly papery, apex acuminate-tapered or cuneately contracted into a straight, elongate-subulate, spinelike, glabrescent beak (3.5–)4–10 mm, densely silvery-strigulose; bearing seeds in proximal 1/2. **Seeds** 2–6. $2n = 22$.

Flowering late Mar–Jun. Grassy sites, chaparral; 50–700 m; Calif.

Astragalus breweri is a taxon of the North Coast Ranges from southeastern Mendocino County southward to Marin County. As A. Gray noted, the long-beaked, tightly-clustered fruits distinguish this from other annual species.

323. Astragalus nuttallianus de Candolle in A. P. de Candolle and A. L. P. P. de Candolle, Prodr. 2: 289. 1825 • Small-flowered milkvetch [F] [W]

Astragalus micranthus Nuttall, J. Acad. Nat. Sci. Philadelphia 2: 122. 1821, not Desvaux 1814

Plants annual or winter-annual, usually slender, (1–)2–30(–45) cm, strigose, strigulose, pilosulous, or hirsutulous, hairs basifixed; taproot slender. **Stems** rarely more than 15, erect, ascending, prostrate, or decumbent, glabrate, sparsely strigulose, villosulous, or pilose. **Leaves** 1–6.5(–9.5) cm; stipules (1–)1.5–6(–9) mm, papery at proximal nodes, herbaceous at distal nodes; leaflets (5 or)7–19(–23), blades linear-elliptic and linear-oblong to obovate, 2–14(–17) mm, apex acute to emarginate, surfaces pubescent abaxially, glabrous or pubescent adaxially. **Peduncles** erect or incurved-ascending, (0.2–)0.5–9(–10) cm. **Racemes** (1 or)2–10(–27)-flowered, flowers ascending to declined; axis 0–2(–)3 cm in fruit; bracts 0.5–2.5 mm; bracteoles 0 or 1. **Pedicels** 0.4–1.6 mm. **Flowers** 3.7–13 mm; calyx (1.7–)3–5.6(–5.7) mm, strigulose, hirsutulous, or pilose, tube (1–)1.3–3.1 mm, lobes linear-setaceous to narrowly lanceolate, (0.7–)1–3.2 mm; corolla whitish, lilac, or pink-purple; banner recurved through 40–45°; keel 3.7–6.8(–9.3) mm, apex obtusely round to sharply deltate, beaklike or not. **Styles** glabrous. **Legumes** ascending, spreading, or declined, green or purple-tinged becoming stramineous or brownish then black, ± straight or incurved through 0.3–0.5 spiral, linear or linear-oblanceoloid, 3-sided compressed, dehiscent on plant, (7–)10–26 × (1.6–)2.1–3.5 mm, usually bilocular, rarely ± unilocular, thin becoming papery, glabrous, strigulose, or villosulous, hairs straight; stipe (0–)0.5–0.9 mm. **Seeds** 10–22.

Varieties 9 (9 in the flora): w United States, n Mexico.

The *Astragalus nuttallianus* complex is a series of forms found in a wide region of the southwestern and south-central United States and adjacent Mexico. There are two groups discernable: a western phalanx wherein varietal differentiation is apparently ecologically and geographically controlled, and there is intergradation where one form meets another; and the central and eastern Texas group where several varieties are sympatric, but apparently do not form intermediates. *Astragalus nuttallianus* is often confused with *A. emoryanus* (see discussion under 316. *A. emoryanus*).

1. Leaflet blade apex often retuse or truncate-emarginate, sometimes acute.
    2. Herbage hirsutulous; legumes loosely strigulose; banners (4–)4.9–6.7 mm; s Texas. . . . . 323i. *Astragalus nuttallianus* var. *zapatanus*
    2. Herbage sparsely strigulose or strigose-pilosulous; legumes glabrous; banners (4.3–)4.8–13 mm; Alabama, Arkansas, Kansas, Louisiana, Oklahoma, Texas.
        3. Banners (4.3–)4.8–7.3 mm, keel apex triangular-acute or sharply deltate; raceme axis to 0.8(–1) cm in fruit; Oklahoma to sc, e Texas, Kansas, Arkansas, Louisiana, and Alabama . . . . . 323a. *Astragalus nuttallianus* var. *nuttallianus*
        3. Banners (6.4–)8.5–13 mm, keel apex obtusely rounded; raceme axis to (0.5–)1–3 cm in fruit; c, w Texas . . . . 323c. *Astragalus nuttallianus* var. *macilentus* (in part)
1. Leaflet blade apex acute, obtuse, round, retuse, or emarginate, usually not retuse or truncate-emarginate for all leaflets.
    4. Keel apex obtusely rounded; raceme axis (0–)0.5–3 cm in fruit; legumes usually glabrous, sometimes minutely strigulose; n Arizona, se Colorado, New Mexico, c, w Texas, and s Utah.
        5. Banners 6.3–7.6(–9.2) mm; Four Corners area . . . . 323b. *Astragalus nuttallianus* var. *micranthiformis*
        5. Banners (6.4–)8.5–13 mm; c, w Texas . . . . 323c. *Astragalus nuttallianus* var. *macilentus* (in part)
    4. Keel apex sharply deltate or triangular-acute or -subacute, sometimes beaklike; raceme axis (0–)0.2–1(–2) cm in fruit; legumes glabrous, strigulose, or hirsutulous; Arizona, California, Louisiana, Nevada, New Mexico, Oklahoma, Texas, Utah.

[6. Shifted to left margin.—Ed.]

6. Calyces strigulose or hirsutulous, lobes (0.7–)1–1.7(–2) mm; s, c Arizona to Utah, se California, s Nevada.
    7. Leaflets monomorphic, blades elliptic throughout; calyx tube 1.9–2.8 mm; e Mojave Desert, California, to Utah and w, c Arizona, s Nevada . . . . 323g. *Astragalus nuttallianus* var. *imperfectus*
    7. Leaflets dimorphic, blades of proximal leaves cuneate or obcordate, blades of distal leaves linear-elliptic; calyx tube (1–)1.4–1.7 mm; sw Colorado Desert, California, to s Arizona . . . . . .323h. *Astragalus nuttallianus* var. *cedrosensis*
6. Calyces hirsute, hirsutulous, or pilose, lobes 1.8–2.1(–3.1) mm; Arizona, Louisiana, New Mexico, Oklahoma, Texas.
    8. Banners 7–9(–9.5) mm; racemes 4–9(–12)-flowered; legumes glabrous; Cameron Parish, Louisiana, e Texas, from Red River to Edwards Plateau and Sabine River. . . . . 323d. *Astragalus nuttallianus* var. *pleianthus*
    8. Banners (4–)5–7 mm; racemes (1 or)2–6(–8)-flowered; legumes glabrous, strigulose, or hirsutulous; s Kansas to s Texas, westward to s California.
        9. Legumes hirsutulous; leaflets 11 or 13; e, s Texas, mostly on Coastal Plain, and w Oklahoma to sw New Mexico . . . . .323e. *Astragalus nuttallianus* var. *trichocarpus*
        9. Legumes glabrous or strigulose; leaflets 7–11(–17); s Kansas to s Texas, westward to s California. . . . . .323f. *Astragalus nuttallianus* var. *austrinus*

323a. **Astragalus nuttallianus** de Candolle var. **nuttallianus** [E]

Plants sparsely strigulose, hairs appressed, to 0.6(–0.7) mm. **Stems** (2–)5–30(–40) cm. **Leaves** 2–6(–7.5) cm; leaflets (7–)11–19(–23), blades linear-oblong, oblong, oblong-cuneate, ovate-cuneate, or obcordate, apex retuse to truncate-emarginate. **Peduncles** 2–7(–8.5) cm. **Racemes** (1 or)2–6(or 7)-flowered; axis to 0.8(–1) cm in fruit. **Flowers:** calyx (3.5–)3.7–5.4 mm, sparsely strigulose, tube 1.3–2.4 mm, lobes (1.7–)1.9–3.2 mm; corolla banner (4.3–)4.8–7.3 mm; keel apex triangular-acute or sharply deltate, erect or beaklike. **Legumes** (12–)16–26 × (2–)2.4–3.5 mm, glabrous. **Seeds** 10–16. $2n$ = 22.

Flowering Mar–Jun. Prairies, roadsides, open pine or oak woods; 0–700 m; Ala., Ark., Kans., La., Okla., Tex.

Variety *nuttallianus* is the common phase of the species in Oklahoma and central Texas. The Alabama occurrence is thought to be a recent introduction (B. R. Keener 2013).

323b. Astragalus nuttallianus de Candolle var. **micranthiformis** Barneby, Mem. New York Bot. Gard. 13: 1064. 1964 • Montezuma milkvetch [E]

Plants sparsely pilosulous, hairs to 0.7(–0.8) mm. **Stems** 3–25 (–39) cm. **Leaves** 1.5–4.5(–6.5) cm; leaflets (7 or)9–15(or 17), blades proximally obovate, oblong, or obcordate, distally oblanceolate, elliptic, or linear-oblong, apex proximally retuse or emarginate, distally obtuse to subacute, terminal one sometimes emarginate. **Peduncles** (1.5–)2.5–5.5(–6.5) cm. **Racemes** (1–)3–7-flowered; axis (0–)0.5–2 cm in fruit. **Flowers:** calyx 3.4–4.7 mm, loosely strigulose, tube 2–2.8 mm, lobes (1.2–)1.5–2.2 (–2.5) mm; corolla banner 6.3–7.6(–9.2) mm; keel apex obtusely rounded. **Legumes** somewhat hamate, (12–) 14–20 × 2.1–3.3 mm, glabrous or minutely strigulose. **Seeds** 13–17.

Flowering Apr–Jun. Mixed salt-desert and desert shrub, sagebrush, and pinyon-juniper communities; (1000–)1100–1900 m; Ariz., Colo., N.Mex., Utah.

D. Isely (1998) suggested that large-flowered individuals within the range of var. *micranthiformis* are intermediates with var. *austrinus*. Ranges of these varieties are discrete, however, and larger-flowered plants may be part of normal variation. Variety *micranthiformis* occurs in approximately one-fourth of each state around the Four Corners area.

323c. Astragalus nuttallianus de Candolle var. **macilentus** (Small) Barneby, Mem. New York Bot. Gard. 13: 1065. 1964 • Small milkvetch [E]

Hamosa macilenta Small, Fl. S.E. U.S., 618, 1332. 1903; *Astragalus macilentus* (Small) Cory

Plants strigose-pilosulous, hairs to 0.8 mm. **Stems** 8–30(–38) cm. **Leaves** (1.5–)2–9.5 cm; leaflets 7–23, blades sometimes dimorphic, distal ones more narrow, linear-elliptic, oblong-oblanceolate, broadly elliptic, or obovate, apex acute or truncate-emarginate. **Peduncles** 2.5–9 cm. **Racemes** (2 or)3–27-flowered; axis to (0.5–)1–3 cm in fruit. **Flowers:** calyx 3.4–5.6 mm, loosely sparsely strigulose-pilosulous, tube 2–3.1 mm, lobes 1.1–3 mm; corolla banner (6.4–)8.5–13 mm; keel apex obtusely rounded. **Legumes** (10–)13–25 × 1.8–2.7 mm, glabrous; substipitate. **Seeds** 12–22.

Flowering Mar–May. Dry gravelly or rocky sites, disturbed soils; 200–1400 m; Tex.

Variety *macilentus* occurs from south-central Texas to the western tip of the state. Species level recognition may be justified because of its elongating inflorescences, substipitate fruits, obtuse keels, and absence of intergradation with sympatric *Astragalus nuttallianus* (D. Isely 1998). It is easily confused with *A. emoryanus* in flower, which is distinguished by its sessile and deciduous fruits.

323d. Astragalus nuttallianus de Candolle var. **pleianthus** (Shinners) Barneby, Mem. New York Bot. Gard. 13: 1066. 1964 • Richland milkvetch [E]

Astragalus austrinus (Small) E. D. Schulz var. *pleianthus* Shinners, Field & Lab. 25: 33. 1957; *A. pleianthus* (Shinners) Isely

Plants strigose or hirsutulous, hairs 0.6–1.4 mm. **Stems** 10–30(–45) cm. **Leaves** 1–6.5(–8) cm; leaflets 13–17(–21), blades broadly elliptic, apex proximally obtuse or emarginate, distally subacute or obtuse. **Peduncles** longer or shorter than leaves. **Racemes** 4–9(–12)-flowered; axis to 0.8(–1.2) cm in fruit. **Flowers:** calyx 4–5.4(–5.7) mm, hirsute or hirsutulous, tube 2–3.1 mm, lobes 1.8–2.1(–3.1) mm; corolla banner 7–9(–9.5) mm; keel apex triangular-acute or sharply deltate, usually beaklike. **Legumes** 13–24 × 1.8–2.8(–3) mm, glabrous. **Seeds** 14–18.

Flowering Mar–May. Prairies, roadsides, and open woods; 0–800 m; Tex.

Variety *pleianthus* is widespread in Texas east of the one hundredth meridian. It is sympatric with several congeners but does not intergrade with them so justification exists for elevating this taxon to species (see D. Isely 1998 for key to related sympatric species).

323e. Astragalus nuttallianus de Candolle var. **trichocarpus** Torrey & A. Gray, Fl. N. Amer. 1: 334. 1838 • Hairypod milkvetch [E]

Astragalus austrinus (Small) Schultz var. *trichocarpus* (Torrey & A. Gray) B. L. Turner

Plants strigose or hirsutulous. **Stems** 10–30(–35) cm. **Leaves** 1–6.5 cm; leaflets 11 or 13, blades broadly elliptic, apex subacute or obtuse, rarely emarginate proximally. **Peduncles** longer or shorter than leaves. **Racemes** (1–)3–6-flowered; axis very short in fruit. **Flowers:** calyx 4–5.4 mm, hirsutulous, tube 2–3 mm, lobes 1.8–2.1 mm; corolla banner (4–)5–7 mm; keel apex triangular-acute or sharply deltate, usually beaklike. **Legumes** 13–24 × 1.8–2.8(–3) mm, hirsutulous. **Seeds** 14–18.

Flowering Mar–May. Prairies, roadsides, and woodlands; 0–500 m; N.Mex., Okla., Tex.

Variety *trichocarpus* is widespread in eastern and southern Texas, but is not clearly distinguished from var. *austrinus* where their ranges overlap (R. C. Barneby 1964).

323f. Astragalus nuttallianus de Candolle var. **austrinus** (Small) Barneby in F. Shreve and I. L. Wiggins, Veg. Fl. Sonoran Desert, 709. 1964 • Rio Fronteras milkvetch [F]

Hamosa austrina Small, Fl. S.E. U.S., 618, 1332. 1903; *Astragalus austrinus* (Small) E. D. Schulz

Plants strigulose or hirsutulous. **Stems** (1–)3–25(–35) cm. **Leaves** 1–6.5 cm; leaflets 7–11(–17), blades often narrowly elliptic, sometimes broader proximally, apex rounded. **Peduncles** 3–10 cm. **Racemes** (1–)2–5(–8)-flowered; axis very short in fruit. **Flowers:** calyx 3.7–5.4 mm, silvery-pilose, tube (1.5–)2–3 mm, lobes 1.8–2.1 mm; corolla white or tipped pink or purple, banner (4–)5.5–7 mm; keel apex triangular-acute or sharply deltate, usually beaklike. **Legumes** 13–24 × 1.8–2.8(–3) mm, glabrous or strigulose. **Seeds** 14–18. **2*n*** = 24.

Flowering Mar–May (summer–fall). On limestone substrates, in various vegetative types; 600–2200 m; Ariz., Calif., Colo., Kans., N.Mex., Okla., Tex.; Mexico (Baja California, Chihuahua, Coahuila, Durango, Nuevo León, Puebla, Sonora).

Variety *austrinus* occurs from southern Kansas to the southern tip of Texas and northern Mexico, and westward to Arizona and southern California, where it grades into var. *imperfectus* (D. Isely 1998).

323g. Astragalus nuttallianus de Candolle var. **imperfectus** (Rydberg) Barneby, Leafl. W. Bot. 3: 109. 1942 • Imperfect milkvetch

Hamosa imperfecta Rydberg, Bull. Torrey Bot. Club 54: 329. 1927

Plants strigulose or hirsutulous. **Stems** 2–30(–45) cm. **Leaves** 1.5–4.5(–5.5) cm; leaflets 7–11 (or 13), blades broadly to narrowly elliptic or oval, apex acute, subacute, or round. **Peduncles** (1–)2–8(–9.5) cm. **Racemes** 1–4-flowered; axis (0–)0.2–1 cm in fruit. **Flowers:** calyx 3.2–4.5 mm, strigulose or hirsutulous, tube 1.9–2.8 mm, lobes 1–1.7(–2) mm; corolla banner 4.1–6.5(–7.3) mm; keel apex triangular-subacute. **Legumes** (10–)12–21 × 1.9–3.1 mm, bilocular or ± unilocular, glabrous or strigulose. **Seeds** 12–16. **2*n*** = 22.

Flowering Mar–Jun. Mainly in *Larrea* and Joshua tree desert communities; 200–1600(–2100) m; Ariz., Calif., Nev., Utah; Mexico (Baja California).

Variety *imperfectus* was circumscribed to include forms of the species with imperfectly bilocular fruits (D. Isely 1998) but, as characterized here, fruits range from bilocular to nearly unilocular. It is somewhat distinct in northwestern Arizona, southwestern Utah, southern Nevada, and southeastern California, but merges with var. *austrinus* to the southeast and to the south and west it is confluent with var. *cedrosensis*. Recommendations have been made to merge vars. *cedrosensis* and *imperfectus* (R. C. Barneby 1964; Isely). The disjunction on Stansbury Island in Great Salt Lake might be due to transport of sheep from the Mojave Desert.

323h. Astragalus nuttallianus de Candolle var. **cedrosensis** M. E. Jones, Rev. N.-Amer. Astragalus, 270. 1923 • Cedros Island milkvetch

Astragalus pertenuis Greene; *Hamosa pertenuis* (Greene) Rydberg

Plants strigulose. **Stems** 2–30 cm. **Leaves** 1.5–4.5 cm; leaflets (5 or)7–11, blades proximally cuneate or obcordate, distally linear-elliptic, apex proximally retuse or emarginate, distally acute. **Peduncles** (0.8–)1.5–8.5 cm. **Racemes** 1–3-flowered; axis 0–2 cm in fruit. **Flowers:** calyx 1.7–3 mm, strigulose, tube (1–)1.4–1.7 mm, lobes (0.7–)1–1.6 mm; corolla banner 3.7–6 mm; keel apex triangular-subacute. **Legumes** (7–)10–20 × 1.6–2 mm, bilocular or ± unilocular, minutely strigulose. **Seeds** 12–16. **2*n*** = 22.

Flowering Dec–Apr. In *Larrea* communities; 100–600 m; Ariz., Calif.; Mexico (Baja California, Sonora).

Variety *cedrosensis* occurs on the Sonoran Desert in southern California and southwestern Arizona, and southward into northwestern Mexico. It is characterized in large part by the dimorphic proximal leaves with retuse leaflet apices.

323i. Astragalus nuttallianus de Candolle var. **zapatanus** Barneby, Field & Lab. 24: 36. 1956 • Loredo milkvetch

Plants hirsutulous, hairs 0.4–0.8 mm. **Stems** 2–30 cm. **Leaves** 1.5–4.5(–5) cm; leaflets (7 or)9–17, blades narrowly cuneate to oblong, oval, or oblong-cuneate, apex retuse or deeply emarginate. **Peduncles** (0.2–)0.5–4.5 cm. **Racemes** 1–4-flowered; axis very short in fruit. **Flowers:** calyx 3–4.6 mm, pilosulous, tube 1.6–2.7 mm, lobes 1.5–2.1 mm; corolla banner (4–)4.9–6.7 mm; keel apex triangular, slightly beaklike. **Legumes** 13–18 × 2.6–3.2 mm, loosely strigulose. **Seeds** 10–16.

Flowering Feb–Mar. Sandy, frequently disturbed sites; 0–200 m; Tex.; Mexico (Tamaulipas).

Variety *zapatanus* occurs in the lower Rio Grande Valley from Laredo to the Gulf Coast and into northeastern Mexico.

324. Astragalus nyensis Barneby, Leafl. W. Bot. 7: 195. 1954 • Nye milkvetch [E]

Astragalus nuttallianus de Candolle var. *piliferus* Barneby, Leafl. W. Bot. 3: 110, plate 1, fig. F1–3. 1942

Plants annual or winter-annual, slender, 1–28 cm, hirsutulous, hairs basifixed; taproot slender. **Stems** prostrate, spreading from root-crown, hirsutulous. **Leaves** 1–4 cm; stipules 1–2.2 mm, papery-membranous at proximal nodes, thinly herbaceous at distal nodes; leaflets 7–13, blades oblong-obovate or ovate-lanceolate, 2–7 mm, apex retuse, surfaces hirsutulous, sometimes glabrous adaxially. **Peduncles** 0.3–2.5(–3.8) cm. **Racemes** 1–4-flowered, flowers declined; axis 0–1.5(–2.3) cm in fruit; bracts 0.6–1 mm; bracteoles 0. **Pedicels** 0.8–1 mm. **Flowers** 4.2–5.4 mm; calyx 3–4 mm, hirsutulous, tube 1.6–2.3 mm, lobes lanceolate-subulate, 1.3–2 mm; corolla whitish, banner veins purple; banner recurved through 40°; keel 3.7–4.5 mm, apex bluntly deltate. **Styles** glabrous. **Legumes** dehiscent on plant, declined, stramineous or brownish, gently incurved or incurved through 0.2–0.3 spiral, linear-oblong, 3-sided compressed, 13–18 × 2.8–4.1 mm, thin becoming papery, hirsutulous, hairs curved. **Seeds** 12–14. $2n = 26$.

Flowering Apr–Jun. Calcareous desert mountains, with desert shrubs and grasses; 300–1700 m; Calif., Nev., Utah.

Astragalus nyensis is known from extreme southeastern Inyo County in California, southern Nevada, and southwestern Utah.

Astragalus nyensis was placed among the California annual group (sect. *Leptocarpi*, subsect. *Californici*) by R. C. Barneby (1964) because of its easily disarticulated fruits. Anatomical characteristics of the fruit, and allozyme similarities, ally it with *A. nuttallianus* (A. Liston 1990). In addition, the overall similarity in flower structure and size also indicates a close relationship. *Astragalus nyensis* forms flat sprays on the ground, the prostrate stems radiating from the root-crown, quite unlike *A. nuttallianus*. In specimens seen, the fruits seldom are more than gently and evenly curved, not forming 1/4–1/3 circle as described by Barneby.

325. Astragalus leptocarpus Torrey & A. Gray, Fl. N. Amer. 1: 334. 1838 • Bodkin milkvetch [E]

Plants annual, (1.5–)3–20(–30) cm, sparsely strigulose or glabrate, hairs basifixed; taproot slender. **Stems** erect, ascending, decumbent, or prostrate, sparsely strigulose. **Leaves** 1–6(–7) cm; stipules distinct throughout, triangular or lanceolate, (1–)1.5–5 mm, submembranous; leaflets (7–)11–17(or 19), blades oblong-, obovate-, or oblanceolate-cuneate, 2–11(–12) mm, apex retuse or emarginate, surfaces glabrous, sometimes hairs present on margins and midrib abaxially. **Peduncles** erect or divaricate, (2–)2.5–9(–10) cm. **Racemes** (1 or) 2–7(–12)-flowered, flowers spreading to ascending; axis 0–1.2(–2) cm in fruit; bracts 0.8–2 mm; bracteoles 0. **Pedicels** 0.4–1.7 mm. **Flowers** (5.2–)8.3–12(–13.2) mm; calyx (3–)3.6–4.5(–5.3) mm, strigulose, tube (1.8–) 2–2.4(–2.8) mm, lobes broadly subulate, 1.2–2.2(–2.8) mm; corolla pink-purple, wings often marked with white; banner recurved through 40°; keel (4.5–)6–7.8 (–9) mm, apex narrowly acute-triangular, often beaklike. **Styles** style glabrous. **Legumes** dehiscent on plant, spreading or ascending, green or purplish becoming brownish then black, straight or slightly incurved, linear or linear-oblanceoloid, 3-sided compressed, (17–)20–37 × 2.2–3.1 mm, slightly fleshy becoming papery, glabrous; stipe 0 mm or pseudostipe to 0.5 mm. **Seeds** (17–)20–26. $2n = 26$.

Flowering Mar–May. Open, oak woodlands, mesquite thickets, sandy sites; 0–400 m; Ark., La., Okla., Tex.

Astragalus leptocarpus occurs in southwestern Arkansas, south-central Louisiana, southern Oklahoma, and eastern Texas. D. Isely (1998) compared it to other Texas annuals in a key with his treatment of *A. pleianthus*.

326. Astragalus lindheimeri Engelmann ex A. Gray, Smithsonian Contr. Knowl. 3(5): 52. 1852 • Lindheimer's milkvetch [E]

Plants annual, (2–)5–30(–40) cm, sparsely strigulose or glabrate, hairs basifixed; taproot slender. **Stems** erect, incurved-ascending, or prostrate, sparsely strigulose. **Leaves** (1–)2–6.5 (–9) cm; stipules 1.5–5 mm, herbaceous or submembranous becoming papery; leaflets (11 or)13–21(or 23), blades broadly to narrowly cuneate, cuneate-oblong, or -oblanceolate, 2–12(–17) mm, apex truncate-emarginate to deeply retuse, surfaces sparsely strigulose abaxially, glabrous adaxially. **Peduncles** ascending or incurved-ascending, (2–)2–6.5 cm. **Racemes** (1 or)2–6(–8)-flowered, flowers spreading; axis 0.2–1.5(–2.4) cm in fruit; bracts 1.3–5 mm; bracteoles 2. **Pedicels** 1–3 mm. **Flowers** (12–)13–18.5 mm; calyx (4–)5–8 mm, strigulose, tube (2–)2.4–3.3 mm, lobes narrowly lanceolate-subulate, (2–)2.3–5 mm; corolla bicolored, banner margined purple around a prominent white (purple-veined) eye, wings white, fading yellowish, keel tip maculate; banner recurved through 35°; keel 9.5–13 mm, apex obtusely deltate. **Styles** puberulent proximal to stigma. **Legumes** dehiscent on plant, spreading to declined, brown then blackish, incurved, linear-oblong or linear-oblanceoloid, 3-sided compressed, 17–27 × 3.5–6(–6.5) mm, thinly fleshy becoming thinly leathery or stiffly papery, glabrous; stipe (0.8–)1–2.6(–3) mm. **Seeds** 8–12(–14).

Flowering late Mar–early Jun. Prairies, disturbed sites; 0–700 m; Okla., Tex.

Widespread in central Texas, northward to the panhandle, and eastward into central Oklahoma, *Astragalus lindheimeri* is thought to be the most attractive of the annual astragali in Texas because of its relatively large, brightly colored flowers.

135dddd. Astragalus Linnaeus sect. Succumbentes A. Gray, Proc. Amer. Acad. Arts 6: 200. 1864 [E]

Herbs perennial, caulescent; caudex shallowly subterranean. **Hairs** basifixed. **Stems** several. **Stipules** distinct. **Leaves** odd-pinnate, short-petiolate; leaflets (7 or)9–17. **Racemes** densely flowered, flowers spreading-ascending. **Calyx tubes** cylindric-campanulate. **Corollas** bicolored, banner and keel pink-purple, wings whitish, banner recurved through 45–50°, keel apex triangular or obtusely deltate. **Legumes** deciduous, sessile, ascending or erect, lunately linear-lanceoloid or -oblong, 3-sided compressed, bilocular. **Seeds** 27–38.

Species 1: nw United States.

327. Astragalus succumbens Douglas in W. J. Hooker, Fl. Bor.-Amer. 1: 151. 1831 • Crouching milkvetch [E]

Plants robust, (2–)5–30(–40) cm, hirsute or hirsutulous; taproot long. **Stems** erect or ascending, usually flexuous and abruptly angled distal to each node, hirsute or hirsutulous. **Leaves** 3–10(–11) cm; stipules lanceolate-attenuate, (1.5–)2.5–8(–9) mm, herbaceous, sometimes papery at proximal nodes; leaflet blades obovate to elliptic, (3–)5–19 mm, apex acute to obtuse or retuse, surfaces pubescent abaxially, sometimes glabrous adaxially. **Peduncles** erect, 1.5–5.5 cm. **Racemes** 10–25-flowered; axis (1–)2–5 cm in fruit; bracts (2.5–)4–12 mm; bracteoles 0–2. **Pedicels** 0.5–2.3 mm. **Flowers** 12–15.3 mm; calyx 9.5–13 mm, hirsute to hirsutulous, tube 7–8.6 mm, lobes subulate to linear-subulate, 2.5–5.5 mm; corolla bicolored, keel tip maculate. **Legumes** stramineous, incurved, (20–)25–40 × (4–)5–7(–8) mm, thin becoming papery, glabrous. **2*n*** = 24.

Flowering Apr–Jul. Dunes, other sandy sites; 70–800 m; Oreg., Wash.

Astragalus succumbens is restricted to central to southeastern Washington and adjacent Oregon along and near the Columbia River.

135eeee. Astragalus Linnaeus sect. Scaposi (Rydberg) Barneby, Mem. New York Bot. Gard. 13: 1081. 1964 [E]

Hamosa Medikus [unranked] *Scaposae* Rydberg, Bull. Torrey Bot. Club 54: 16. 1927

Herbs perennial, tuft- or mound-forming, acaulescent; caudex superficial. **Hairs** malpighian. **Stems** usually obsolete. **Stipules** distinct. **Leaves** odd-pinnate, petiolate; leaflets (1 or)3–13. **Racemes** subumbellate or loosely flowered, flowers ascending to spreading. **Calyx tubes** campanulate to short-cylindric. **Corollas** whitish, or pink-purple and wing tips whitish, banner recurved through 45–90°, wings deeply cleft, keel apex round or bluntly deltate. **Legumes** deciduous, sessile, ascending, narrowly oblong, 3-sided compressed, bilocular. **Seeds** 13–28.

Species 1: w United States.

328. Astragalus calycosus Torrey ex S. Watson, Botany (Fortieth Parallel), 66, plate 10, figs. 4–7. 1871 • Torrey's milkvetch [E] [F]

Plants xerophytic, 1–12(–23) cm, densely silvery-strigulose; from branched caudex, branches often with well-developed thatch of persistent leaf bases. **Stems** rarely 2, 0–2 cm, internodes concealed by stipules. **Leaves** 1–7(–12) cm; stipules 1.5–6 mm, submembranous becoming papery; leaflet blades obovate, oblanceolate, or elliptic, 2–19 mm, apex obtuse to acute, surfaces silvery-strigose. **Peduncles** scapelike, ascending, 1–7+ cm. **Racemes** (1 or)2–7(or 8)-flowered; axis 0.2–2(–2.5) cm in fruit; bracts 0.5–2 mm; bracteoles 0 or 1, minute. **Pedicels** 0.7–3 mm. **Flowers** 7.4–11.6(–12.7) mm; calyx 5–10.6 mm, strigose, tube 4–6.4(–6.7) mm, lobes subulate, 1–4.2 mm. **Legumes** brown, usually straight or slightly incurved, 8–25 × 3–4.5 mm, thin becoming papery, strigose.

Varieties 4 (4 in the flora): w United States.

Astragalus calycosus includes two major multiracial and confluent varieties, var. *calycosus* to the north and northwest, and var. *scaposus* to the southeast; included also are two minor varieties.

1. Leaflets 1(or 3); ec Nevada, sc Utah . . . . 328b. *Astragalus calycosus* var. *monophyllidius*
1. Leaflets (1 or)3–13; California to Colorado, northward to Idaho, including Nevada and Utah.
    2. Leaflets (1 or)7–13; rachis usually 1+ cm; peduncles erect-ascending, 7+ cm; n Arizona, sw Colorado, se Nevada, nw New Mexico, s Utah . . . . 328d. *Astragalus calycosus* var. *scaposus*
    2. Leaflets 3–13; rachis to 1 cm; peduncles ascending or decumbent, 1–7 cm; Arizona, California to Colorado, northward to Idaho, including Nevada and Utah.

[3. Shifted to left margin.—Ed.]

3. Leaflets 3–7, blades 5–19 mm; elevation (1200–)1400–2800(–3500) m; California and Oregon eastward to New Mexico and Wyoming . . . . 328a. *Astragalus calycosus* var. *calycosus*
3. Leaflets 7–13, blades 2–6 mm; elevation 2300–4000 m; Nevada, w Utah . . . . 328c. *Astragalus calycosus* var. *mancus*

328a. Astragalus calycosus Torrey ex S. Watson var. **calycosus** [E] [F]

Plants tuft- or mound-forming. **Leaves:** rachis to 1 cm; leaflets 3–7, blades 5–19 mm. **Peduncles** ascending or decumbent, 1–7 cm, shorter or longer than leaves. **Racemes** (1 or)2–6(–8)-flowered; axis 0.2–2(–2.5) cm in fruit. **Flowers** 10–16.5(–20.8) mm; calyx 5.2–10.6 mm, tube 4–6.4(–6.7) mm, lobes (1–)1.5–4.2 mm; corolla whitish to pink-purple. $2n = 22$.

Flowering May–early Jul. Mixed desert shrublands, sagebrush, pinyon-juniper, and ponderosa pine woodlands, on gravel, sand, and silt; (1200–)1400–2800(–3500) m; Ariz., Calif., Idaho, Nev., N.Mex., Oreg., Utah, Wyo.

Variety *calycosus* is found from east-central California to north-central Idaho, eastern Utah, and southwestern Wyoming. In northwestern New Mexico, southern Utah, and adjacent Arizona, var. *calycosus* grades into var. *scaposus*.

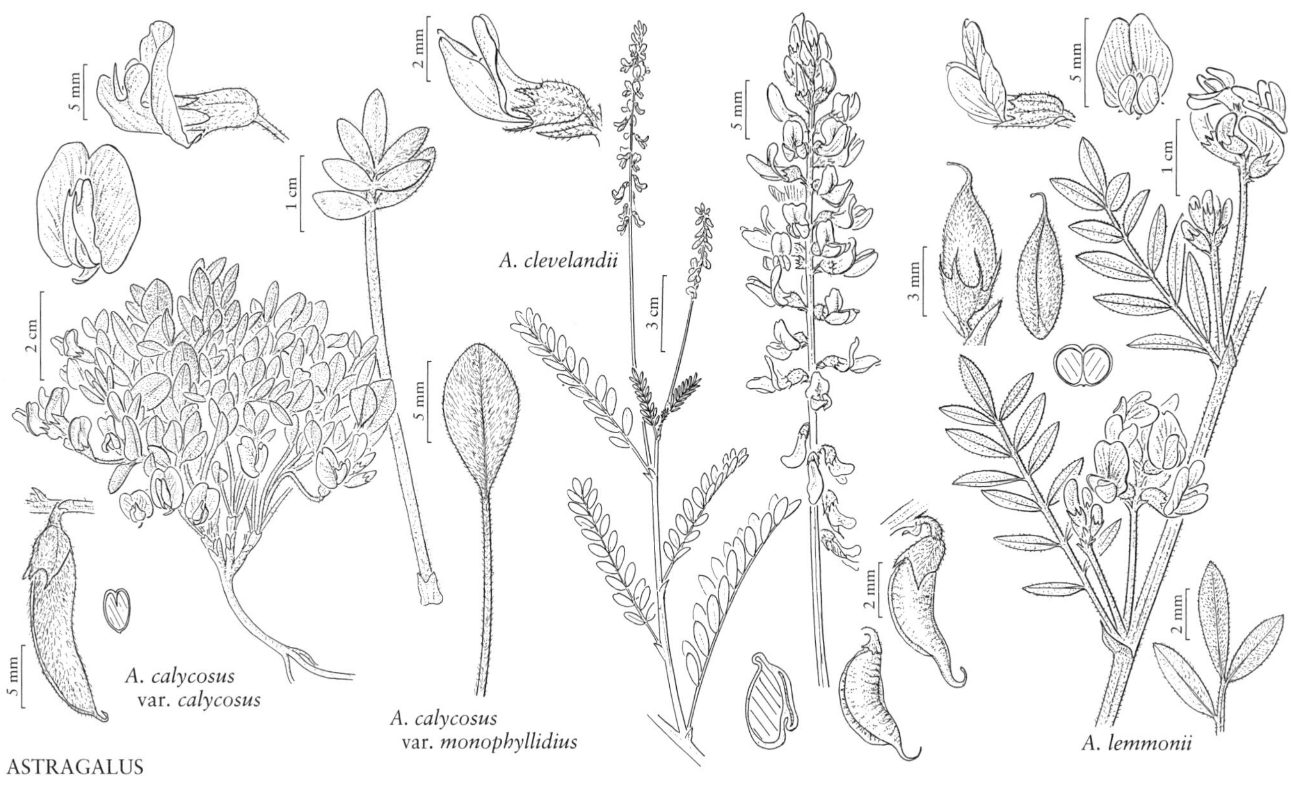

ASTRAGALUS

328b. Astragalus calycosus Torrey ex S. Watson var. **monophyllidius** (Rydberg) Barneby, Leafl. W. Bot. 3: 107. 1942 • One-leaf milkvetch [E] [F]

Hamosa monophyllidia Rydberg in N. L. Britton et al., N. Amer. Fl. 24: 421. 1929

Plants tuft- or mound-forming. **Leaves:** rachis 0–0.8 cm; leaflets 1(or 3), blades 4–16 mm. **Peduncles** weakly ascending, 1–7 cm, shorter or longer than leaves. **Racemes** (1 or)2–7-flowered; axis 0.2–1.2 cm in fruit. **Flowers** 10–14.5 mm; calyx 5.2–7.5 mm, tube 4–6.4(–6.7) mm, lobes (1–)1.5–4.2 mm; corolla whitish to pink-purple. $2n = 22$.

Flowering May–Jun. Gravelly sites in pinyon-juniper forests, mainly on limestone; 1600–2300 m; Nev., Utah.

At first glance var. *monophyllidius* is distinctive, but it is intergradient in leaflet number with var. *calycosus*. Variety *monophyllidius* occurs in Eureka, Lincoln, and Nye counties in Nevada, and Sevier County in Utah.

328c. Astragalus calycosus Torrey ex S. Watson var. **mancus** (Rydberg) Barneby, Leafl. W. Bot. 7: 195. 1954 • Defective milkvetch [E]

Hamosa manca Rydberg, Bull. Torrey Bot. Club 54: 17. 1927

Plants tuft- or mound-forming. **Leaves:** rachis to 1(–1.3) cm; leaflets 7–13, blades 2–6 mm. **Peduncles** ascending or decumbent, 1–7 cm, shorter or longer than leaves. **Racemes** (1 or)2–4-flowered; axis 0.2–1 cm in fruit. **Flowers** 11–13(–14) mm; calyx 5–8.5 mm, tube 4–5.5 mm, lobes 1–3 mm; corolla whitish to pink-purple. $2n = 22$.

Flowering May–Aug. Ridge tops in alpine communities with scattered limber pine, *Geum rossii*, or sometimes with ponderosa pine, on limestone; 2300–4000 m; Nev., Utah.

Variety *mancus* is a diminutive, comparatively foliose, high-elevation phase from Clark, Elko, Nye, and White Pine counties in Nevada, and Juab County in Utah.

328d. Astragalus calycosus Torrey ex S. Watson var. **scaposus** (A. Gray) M. E. Jones, Zoë 4: 26. 1893 • Scapose milkvetch E

Astragalus scaposus A. Gray, Proc. Amer. Acad. Arts 13: 366. 1878

Plants tuft-forming. **Leaves:** rachis usually 1+ cm; leaflets (1–)7–13, blades 8–11 mm. **Peduncles** erect-ascending, 7+ cm, longer than leaves. **Racemes** (1 or)2–6(–8)-flowered; axis 0.2–2(–2.5) cm in fruit. **Flowers** 10.5–14 mm; calyx 5.2–10.6 mm, tube 4–6.4(–6.7) mm, lobes 1–2 mm; corolla pink-purple, wing-tips whitish. $2n = 22$.

Flowering Apr–Jun. Juniper, pinyon-juniper, and mixed desert shrub communities; 1300–1900 m; Ariz., Colo., Nev., N.Mex., Utah.

With its contrasting white/pink-purple pattern on the petals, var. *scaposus* is the showiest phase of the species. It occurs from southeastern Nevada, across northern Arizona and southern Utah, to southwestern Colorado and northwestern New Mexico.

135ffff. ASTRAGALUS Linnaeus sect. MICRANTHI A. Gray, Proc. Amer. Acad. Arts 6: 198. 1864

Herbs perennial, caulescent; caudex superficial or slightly subterranean. **Hairs** basifixed. **Stems** few to many. **Stipules** distinct. **Leaves** odd-pinnate, short-petiolate or subsessile; leaflets (9–) 13–25(or 27). **Racemes** densely becoming loosely flowered, flowers deflexed. **Calyx tubes** campanulate. **Corollas** whitish or yellow to green, suffused pale lavender, banner recurved through 45–90°, keel apex round or sharply or bluntly deltate, sometimes slightly beaklike. **Legumes** deciduous, at least eventually, sessile, reflexed, linear to narrowly lanceoloid or obliquely ovoid, 3-sided compressed, incurved, bilocular or sub-bilocular. **Seeds** (2–)4–10.

Species ca. 6 (2 in the flora): sw United States, n Mexico.

In the flora area, *Astragalus clevelandii* and *A. vaccarum* occur in Arizona (only historically), New Mexico, and the Inner Coast Ranges of California.

329. Astragalus vaccarum A. Gray, Smithsonian Contr. Knowl. 5(6): 43. 1853 • Cow Spring milkvetch

Plants slender, (10–)15–45 cm, strigulose; from superficial caudex. **Stems** prostrate to decumbent or ascending, strigulose. **Leaves** 4–12 cm; stipules 2–8 mm, subherbaceous or papery; leaflets (9 or)11–21(or 23), blades linear-oblong to narrowly elliptic, (3–)5–20(–24) mm, apex acute to obtuse, surfaces strigulose abaxially, glabrous or glabrate adaxially. **Peduncles** erect or incurved-ascending, (2–)5–12 cm. **Racemes** (10–)15–50-flowered; axis (1.5–)3–8 cm in fruit; bracts 1–3 mm; bracteoles 0–2. **Pedicels** 0.3–1.2 mm. **Flowers** 4.2–6.2 mm; calyx 2.5–3.6 mm, strigulose, tube 1.7–2 mm, lobes subulate, 0.8–1.8 mm; corolla yellow to green, suffused pale lavender, fading ochroleucous, wing tips pale or white; banner recurved through 45–90°; keel 3.7–5 mm, apex round. **Legumes** stramineous, narrowly lanceoloid or linear-ellipsoid, 6–12 × 1.3–2 mm, bilocular or sub-bilocular, thin becoming papery, strigulose. **Seeds** 6–10. $2n = 28$.

Flowering (Apr–)Jun–Oct. Oak-pine forests, along drainages, flats, foothills; 1200–2300 m; N.Mex.; Mexico (Chihuahua, Coahuila, Sonora).

Astragalus vaccarum is a northern member of the primarily Mexican sect. *Micranthi*, long known from only a few old collections from southeastern Arizona and southwestern New Mexico. Thought extirpated in the United States, it was rediscovered in Hidalgo County, New Mexico, in the 1980s. *Astragalus vaccarum* is fairly common in northern Mexico.

330. Astragalus clevelandii Greene, Bull. Torrey Bot. Club 9: 121. 1882 (as clevelandi) • Cleveland's milkvetch [E] [F]

Perennials, forming bushy clumps, usually robust, rarely slender, 30–100 cm, strigulose; from slightly subterranean caudex; taproot woody. **Stems** erect or ascending, glabrous. **Leaves** (2–)4–14 cm; stipules (2–)3–7 mm, papery-scarious proximally, submembranous distally; leaflets 13–25(or 27), blades elliptic, narrowly oblong, lanceolate, or oblanceolate, (3–)5–23 mm, apex obtuse to acute, surfaces strigulose abaxially, glabrous or glabrate adaxially. **Peduncles** incurved-ascending, 5–15 cm. **Racemes** (10–)20–95-flowered; axis 8–30 cm in fruit; bracts 1.2–3 mm; bracteoles 0. **Pedicels** 0.6–3 mm. **Flowers** 4.8–6 mm; calyx 3.5–4.4 mm, strigulose, tube 1.8–2.2 mm, lobes narrowly subulate, 1.4–2.2 mm; corolla whitish, immaculate, drying ochroleucous; banner abruptly recurved through 45°; keel 3.8–4.6 mm, apex sharply or bluntly deltate, slightly beaklike. **Legumes** stramineous, lunately semi-ovoid or lanceoloid-ovoid (in outline), 4.5–7 × 1.3–2.3 mm, bilocular, stiffly papery, glabrous. **Seeds** (2–)4–6. **2*n*** = 26.

Flowering Jun–Sep. Stream banks, gravel bars, seeps, marshy areas, on serpentine soils; 200–1600 m; Calif.

Astragalus clevelandii, an apparent serpentine endemic, is found in two widely separated areas in the inner Coast Ranges (Colusa, Lake, and Napa counties) and San Benito County. R. Spellenberg (1976) reported a chromosome number of 2*n* = 26, a number more characteristic of southern species of North American *Astragalus*, consistent with the hypothesis by R. C. Barneby (1964) that this is a relict of a northward migration.

135gggg. ASTRAGALUS Linnaeus sect. CHAETODONTES A. Gray, Proc. Amer. Acad. Arts 6: 194. 1864 [E]

Herbs perennial, usually caulescent (sometimes subacaulescent in *A. austiniae*); caudex superficial or subterranean. **Hairs** usually basifixed, rarely malpighian. **Stems** several to many. **Stipules** distinct or connate. **Leaves** odd-pinnate, petiolate to subsessile; leaflets (5 or)7–25 (–29). **Racemes** subumbellate, spicate or loosely flowered, flowers erect, ascending, spreading, or declined and secund. **Calyx tubes** campanulate or turbinate, sometimes accrescent. **Corollas** whitish, pinkish, grayish lavender, or pale yellow, banner recurved through 35–85°, keel apex round, obtuse, or deltate, sometimes obscurely beaklike. **Legumes** deciduous, at least eventually, sessile or subsessile, widely spreading to declined, ovoid to oblong, ellipsoid, or lenticular-oblong, compressed laterally or 3-sided, straight, incurved, or falcate, bilocular. **Seeds** 4–20.

Species 9 (9 in the flora): nw United States.

Section *Chaetodontes* is made up of five subsections with its distribution mainly in the Columbia Basin, the lower Snake River Plains, northern Great Basin to the Sierra Nevada, eastern Washington to south-central Idaho, and northeastern and east-central California.

The subsections are: subsect. *Chaetodontes* (A. Gray) Barneby (*Astragalus spaldingii*, *A. tyghensis*); subsect. *Lyalliani* Barneby (*A. lyallii*); subsect. *Lemmoniani* Barneby (*A. lemmonii*); subsect. *Lentiformes* (Rydberg) Barneby (*A. caricinus*, *A. lentiformis*); and subsect. *Andersoniani* Barneby (*A. andersonii*, *A. austiniae*, *A. sepultipes*).

331. Astragalus spaldingii A. Gray, Proc. Amer. Acad. Arts 6: 524. 1865 • Spalding's milkvetch [E]

Astragalus chaetodon Torrey ex A. Gray, Proc. Amer. Acad. Arts 6: 194. 1864, not Bunge 1851

Plants somewhat slender, (5–)10–35(–48) cm, villous; from superficial caudex. **Stems** prostrate or decumbent to ascending, villous. **Leaves** 2.5–13 cm; stipules distinct, 2.5–7 mm, herbaceous becoming membranous; leaflets (9–)15–25(–29), blades narrowly elliptic to oblanceolate, 4–16 mm, apex obtuse to acute, surfaces villous or villous-pilose. **Peduncles** erect or incurved-ascending, 3–10 cm. **Racemes** (6–)12–30-flowered, flowers spreading; axis (1–)1.5–5(–7) cm in fruit; bracts 1.5–4.5 mm; bracteoles 0. **Pedicels** 0.2–0.8 mm. **Flowers** 7–11(–11.7) mm; calyx campanulate, (5–)5.6–8.3 mm, villous or villous-tomentose, tube (2.5–)3.1–4.5 × (2.4–)2.6–3.6 mm, lobes narrowly subulate, (2.4–)2.6–3.6 mm, somewhat accrescent, covering most or all of mature legume; corolla whitish, often tinged lavender, immaculate or keel tip maculate, drying ochroleucous; banner recurved through 50°; keel 5.2–7.4 mm, apex obtuse, sometimes obscurely beaklike. **Legumes** spreading to ascending, straight, obliquely ovoid, somewhat laterally compressed, (3.5–)4–6 × 2.5–3.5 mm, stiffly papery, densely villous-tomentulose, hairs 1+ mm. **Seeds** 4–10. $2n$ = 24.

Flowering May–Jul. Sagebrush-grass and bunchgrass communities, mostly on basaltic substrates; 300–900(–1200) m; B.C.; Idaho, Oreg., Wash.

Astragalus spaldingii is a species of central and southeastern Washington, northeastern Oregon, and adjacent Idaho. A disjunct population also occurs in south-central British Columbia. Plants are often grazed and are said to provide good forage (R. C. Barneby 1964).

332. Astragalus tyghensis M. Peck, Proc. Biol. Soc. Wash. 49: 110. 1936 • Tygh Valley milkvetch [C] [E]

Astragalus spaldingii A. Gray var. *tyghensis* (M. Peck) C. L. Hitchcock

Plants (10–)15–55 cm, densely villous-tomentose; from superficial caudex; taproot woody. **Stems** prostrate or decumbent to ascending, densely villous-tomentose. **Leaves** 5–14 cm; stipules distinct, 3–6 mm, herbaceous becoming membranous; leaflets (7–)15–21, blades oval-obovate, 6–17 mm, apex obtuse to subacute, surfaces villous-tomentose. **Peduncles** erect or incurved-ascending, 5–12 cm. **Racemes** (10–)20–40-flowered, flowers spreading; axis (1–)1.5–12 cm in fruit; bracts 2–5 mm; bracteoles 0. **Pedicels** 0.5–1 mm. **Flowers** 9–12 mm; calyx broadly campanulate, 6.6–7.8 mm, silky-villous, tube 3.9–4.5 × 3.5–4.1 mm, lobes narrowly subulate, 2.7–3.5 mm, somewhat accrescent, covering most or all of mature legume; corolla pale yellow, drying ochroleucous, pubescent abaxially; banner recurved through 50°; keel 7.1–8.2 mm, apex obtuse-deltate. **Legumes** spreading or somewhat declined, straight, obliquely ovoid, obscurely 3-sided compressed, 4.5–6 × 3 mm, stiffly papery, tomentulose, hairs 1+ mm; contracted basally into pseudostipe, 0.4–0.6 mm. **Seeds** 6–8.

Flowering May–Jul. Sagebrush and open oak woodlands, on basaltic substrates; of conservation concern; 400–600 m; Oreg.

Astragalus tyghensis is known from the eastern foothills of the Cascade Range in Wasco County.

333. Astragalus lyallii A. Gray, Proc. Amer. Acad. Arts 6: 195. 1864 (as lyalli) • Lyall's milkvetch [E]

Plants somewhat slender, (10–)15–40 cm, gray-villous; from superficial caudex; taproot woody. **Stems** decumbent to ascending, gray-villous. **Leaves** (3–)4–11 cm; stipules distinct, 3–8 mm, submembranous; leaflets 11–19, blades elliptic to linear-elliptic or oblanceolate, 6–16 mm, apex acute, surfaces villous. **Peduncles** erect or narrowly ascending, 1.5–6.5 cm. **Racemes** (7–)10–21-flowered, flowers spreading, later declined or nodding; axis (2–)3.5–9(–11) cm in fruit; bracts 1.5–4.5 mm; bracteoles 0 or 1. **Pedicels** 0.5–1.8 mm. **Flowers** 5.3–7.4 mm; calyx campanulate or turbinate, 3.8–5.6 mm, densely villous, tube 1.6–2.5 × 1.8–2.6 mm, lobes setaceous, 1.7–3.4 mm, not accrescent and covering 1/2 of mature legume; corolla whitish and lilac-tinged, banner veins purple; banner recurved through 50°; keel 3.8–4.9 mm, apex obtuse. **Legumes** declined or deflexed, stramineous, straight, subsymmetrically ellipsoid or ovoid-ellipsoid, 3-sided compressed, 5–8 × (2–)2.5–3.5 mm, papery, villous-tomentulose, hairs 1+ mm; stipe (0.1–)0.3–0.5 mm. **Seeds** 4–8.

Flowering May–early Jul. Low hills and rolling plains, on sandy or loamy basaltic soils, with sagebrush; 100–700 m; Wash.

Astragalus lyallii occurs in central and southeastern Washington. R. C. Barneby (1964) called this a species of great theoretical interest because of its presumed close relationship to two species, *A. caricinus* and *A. spaldingii*, which are not closely related to each other.

He postulated that it was more similar to the latter in its diffuse growth-habit and distinct stipules, and similar to the former in its loosely racemose, nodding flowers and declining, exserted fruits. He proposed a hybrid origin for *A. lyallii* involving these two species, followed by generations of selection, an argument supported by morphological intermediacy and the geographical distribution of the species.

334. Astragalus lemmonii A. Gray, Proc. Amer. Acad. Arts 8: 626. 1873 (as lemmoni) • Lemmon's milkvetch [C] [E] [F]

Plants delicate, 10–40(–50) cm, villous-tomentose; from superficial caudex; taproot woody. **Stems** prostrate, usually villous-tomentose, sometimes glabrous. **Leaves** (1–)1.5–4.5 cm; stipules distinct, 2–5 mm, submembranous becoming scarious; leaflets (7 or)9–15, blades flat or loosely folded, narrowly elliptic to elliptic-oblanceolate, 2–11 mm, apex obtuse to subacute, surfaces strigulose abaxially, strigulose, glabrous, or glabrate adaxially. **Peduncles** ascending, 0.6–1.7 cm, sometimes 2 or 3 per node. **Racemes** (2–)5–13-flowered, subcapitate, flowers loosely ascending; axis 0.2–1 cm per fruit; bracts 0.8–2 mm; bracteoles 0. **Pedicels** 0.7–2.5 mm. **Flowers** 4.8–6.1 mm; calyx campanulate, 3–3.9 mm, strigulose, tube 1.7–2.2 mm, lobes subulate, 1.1–1.7 mm; corolla whitish, sometimes tinged lilac, banner veins purple; banner recurved through 45–85°; keel 3.4–4 mm, apex triangular, obtuse, somewhat beaklike. **Legumes** spreading or somewhat declined, stramineous or brownish, straight or somewhat incurved, ellipsoid or oblong-ellipsoid, 3-sided compressed, grooved dorsally, lateral faces flat, 4–7 × 1.5–2.5 mm, thin becoming papery, strigulose. **Seeds** 4–8.

Flowering late May–Aug. Meadows and rushy flats along stream and lakeshores; of conservation concern; 1200–2900 m; Calif., Nev., Oreg.

Astragalus lemmonii is one of a small number of North American astragali to occupy truly mesic communities, those that are at least seasonally moist. The typically two or three small, shortly pedunculate racemes borne per node is diagnostic for this species. It occurs from central Oregon to northeastern and east-central California and western Washoe County in Nevada.

335. Astragalus caricinus (M. E. Jones) Barneby, Amer. Midl. Naturalist 55: 502. 1956 • Buckwheat milkvetch [E]

Astragalus lyallii A. Gray var. *caricinus* M. E. Jones, Rev. N.-Amer. Astragalus, 174. 1923

Plants clump-forming, slender, stiff, wiry, (10–)15–30 cm, villous or pilose, densely gray-villosulous basally, hairs basifixed, sub-basifixed, or malpighian; from superficial caudex; taproot woody. **Stems** erect or ascending, subappressed-pilose, densely white-tomentose basally. **Leaves** 3.5–9 (–10.5) cm; stipules connate-sheathing at proximal nodes, distinct at distal nodes, (2–)3–8 mm, submembranous; leaflets 11–19(–23), blades narrowly elliptic to lanceolate-elliptic or narrowly oblong, (3–)5–15 (–18) mm, apex acute to obtuse or apiculate, surfaces villous. **Peduncles** erect, 0.5–5(–7) cm. **Racemes** (5–)10–25-flowered, flowers spreading and declined; axis (1.5–)3–10.5 cm in fruit; bracts 1–2.5 mm; bracteoles 0. **Pedicels** 0.4–1.5 mm. **Flowers** 4.5–6(–7) mm; calyx campanulate, 3.5–5.5 mm, villous-villosulous, tube 1.7–2.2 mm, lobes subulate-setaceous, (1.3–)1.5–3 mm; corolla whitish or tinged lilac, drying yellowish; banner recurved through 50°; keel (3.6–)4–5 mm, apex bluntly deltate, sometimes obscurely beaklike. **Legumes** reflexed, pale green, straight, subsymmetrically lanceoloid-ellipsoid or ellipsoid, 3-sided or laterally compressed, 6–8.5(–9) × 2–2.7(–3) mm, papery, tomentulose. **Seeds** 6–8.

Flowering May–Jul. Sandy substrates or dunes derived from basalt, on clay, in sagebrush, bitterbrush, and hopsage communities; 100–1400 m; Idaho, Oreg., Wash.

Astragalus caricinus occurs from south-central Idaho to eastern Oregon, and in south-central and central Washington, where it apparently intergrades with *A. lyallii* (D. Isely 1998).

336. Astragalus lentiformis A. Gray in W. H. Brewer et al., Bot. California 1: 156. 1876 • Lentil milkvetch [C] [E]

Plants slender, 9–18(–25) cm, gray-villosulous; from superficial caudex; taproot woody. **Stems** ascending, diffusely spreading, densely gray-villosulous. **Leaves** 1.2–3.5 cm; stipules connate-sheathing at proximal nodes, distinct at distal nodes, to 7 mm, submembranous proximally, firm or herbaceous distally; leaflets 7–15, blades narrowly obovate or elliptic, 2–10 mm, apex obtuse to subacute, surfaces villosulous abaxially, glabrate adaxially. **Peduncles** incurved-ascending, 0.4–1.6 cm. **Racemes** 5–10-flowered, flowers declined; axis 0.4–1.6 cm in fruit; bracts 1.5–3 mm; bracteoles 0. **Pedicels** 1–1.8 mm. **Flowers** 6.2–7 mm; calyx campanulate, 3.6–4.5 mm, white-villosulous, tube 2.2–2.9 mm, lobes subulate, 1.3–2.3 mm; corolla ivory-yellow, drying yellowish; banner recurved through 50°; keel 4–4.9 mm, apex deltate, obscurely beaklike. **Legumes** declined, stramineous, straight, symmetrically or subsymmetrically lenticular-oblong, 3-sided compressed, 5–8.5 × 2.5–3 mm, thin becoming papery, villosulous. **Seeds** 6–10.

Flowering May–Jul. Sagebrush and Jeffrey pine communities; of conservation concern; 1400–1800 m; Calif.

Astragalus lentiformis, locally common, is restricted to the eastern foot of the Sierra Nevada in Plumas and Sierra counties.

337. **Astragalus andersonii** A. Gray, Proc. Amer. Acad. Arts 6: 524. 1865 • Anderson's milkvetch [E]

Plants loosely tuft-forming, 7–20(–24) cm, gray-villosulous or villous; from superficial caudex; taproot woody. **Stems** decumbent to incurved-ascending or erect, densely gray-villous, densely white-tomentose basally. **Leaves** (2–)3–10 cm; stipules connate-sheathing at proximal nodes, connate or distinct at distal nodes, (1.5–)2–7 mm, scarious proximally, herbaceous distally; leaflets (9–)13–21, blades elliptic-oblanceolate to oval-obovate, 3–10(–14) mm, apex acute to abruptly short-acuminate, apiculate, or obtuse, surfaces villosulous or villous abaxially, glabrate adaxially. **Peduncles** erect or incurved-ascending, (2–)3–7 cm. **Racemes** 12–20(–26)-flowered, flowers ascending becoming declined; axis 2.5–8 cm in fruit; bracts 2–4 mm; bracteoles 0. **Pedicels** 0.6–1.7 mm. **Flowers** 9–14.5 mm; calyx campanulate, 6.2–8.2 mm, villous, tube 3.5–4.3 mm, lobes subulate or setaceous, 2.4–4.3 mm; corolla whitish or ochroleucous, tinged or veins purple; banner recurved through 45°; keel 6.6–9 mm, apex bluntly deltate. **Legumes** spreading to declined, stramineous, gently incurved or falcate, obliquely oblong, linear-oblong, or narrowly lanceoloid, 3-sided compressed, (10–)12–18 × 3–4.5 mm, thin becoming papery, villous or villous-villosulous. **Seeds** (10–)12–16. $2n = 24$.

Flowering Apr–Jun(–Jul). Sandy or gravelly sites on granitic or basaltic substrates; 1300–2200 m; Calif., Nev.

Astragalus andersonii occurs along the eastern base of the Sierra Nevada from Mono County northward to Modoc County in California, and in adjacent western Nevada. R. C. Barneby (1964) noted that it was quick to establish in secondary habitats.

338. **Astragalus sepultipes** (Barneby) Barneby, Aliso 4: 136. 1958 • Bishop milkvetch [E]

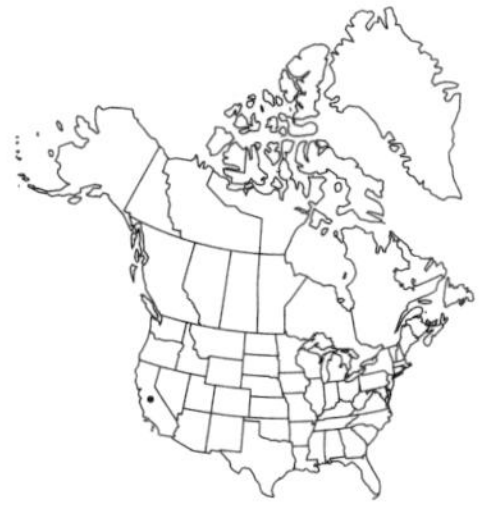

Astragalus andersonii A. Gray var. *sepultipes* Barneby, Aliso 2: 209. 1950

Plants moderately stout or slender, 15–35(–45) cm, densely gray-villosulous, strigulose-villosulous, or villous-pilose; from subterranean caudex; taproot woody. **Stems** decumbent to ascending, 0.5–5.5 cm underground, glabrous underground. **Leaves** 2–8 cm; stipules connate-sheathing at proximal nodes, connate distally, (2–) 3–7.5 mm, scarious proximally, herbaceous distally; leaflets (7–)11–17, blades obovate-cuneate or broadly oblanceolate, (3–)4–14 mm, apex retuse or truncate and apiculate, surfaces strigulose-villosulous. **Peduncles** incurved-ascending, (3–)5–12.5 cm. **Racemes** (10–)15–30-flowered, flowers spreading to ascending; axis (2–)4–11 cm in fruit; bracts 3–5 mm; bracteoles 0–2. **Pedicels** 0.8–1.5 mm. **Flowers** (12.7–)14.5–17.5 mm; calyx campanulate, 8.6–13 mm, villous, tube (4.7–) 5.1–6.5 mm, lobes linear-caudate, margins plumose-ciliate, 3.5–5.7(–6.5) mm; corolla pinkish white or pale lilac with whitish wing tips; banner recurved through 40°; keel 10–12.2 mm, apex round. **Legumes** spreading-ascending to declined, stramineous, gently incurved, narrowly oblong, 3-sided compressed, 15–20 × 3.5–5.5 mm, thinly fleshy becoming stiffly papery, villous. **Seeds** (14–)16–20.

Flowering May–Jul. Sagebrush and pinyon communities; 1400–2000 m; Calif.

Astragalus sepultipes is found in the eastern foothills of the Sierra Nevada in Inyo County. D. Isely (1998) suggested that it is a derivative of *A. andersonii* and questioned its specific status.

339. Astragalus austiniae A. Gray in W. H. Brewer et al., Bot. California 1: 156. 1876 (as austinae) • Austin's milkvetch [E]

Tragacantha austiniae (A. Gray) Kuntze

Plants densely tuft-, mat-, or cushion-forming, caulescent or subacaulescent, 0–11(–15) cm, villous or villosulous; from superficial caudex; taproot woody. **Stems** concealed by stipules or some with elongate internodes. **Leaves** (0.7–)1–4(–5) cm; stipules connate-sheathing, 2–6.5 mm, scarious; leaflets (5 or)7–13(–17), blades elliptic to oblanceolate, 1.5–9 mm, apex acute to subobtuse, surfaces villous. **Peduncles** erect or ascending, 1.4–4(–5) cm. **Racemes** densely 4–15-flowered, subglobose and ovoid, flowers erect or ascending; axis 0.2–1 (–1.5) cm in fruit; bracts 3–5.5 mm; bracteoles 0. **Pedicels** 0.4–0.8 mm. **Flowers** 8.4–11.3 mm; calyx campanulate, (6.6–)7–9.3 mm, villous-hirsute, tube 3.3–5.3 mm, lobes narrowly subulate, 2.9–4.6 mm; corolla whitish, tinged or veined purple, banner and wings villosulous abaxially; banner recurved through 35°; keel 6.2–8.1 mm, apex round, or triangular and obscurely beaklike. **Legumes** ascending or spreading, straight, subsymmetrically oblong-ovoid, 3-sided compressed, ± included in calyx, 5–7 × 3–3.5 mm, ± bilocular, papery, densely tomentulose; gynophore to 0.5 mm. **Seeds** (5 or)6–8.

Flowering Jul–Sep. Alpine sites, at or above timberline; 2600–3200 m; Calif., Nev.

Astragalus austiniae is restricted to peaks in the vicinity of Lake Tahoe from El Dorado County to Nevada County, both in California, and Washoe County in Nevada; it is closely allied to *A. andersonii* but easily distinguished by the silky pubescent banners and wings, and the very short fruits.

135hhhh. Astragalus Linnaeus sect. Brauntoniani (Rydberg) Barneby, Mem. New York Bot. Gard. 13: 1119. 1964 [C] [E]

Brachyphragma Rydberg [unranked] *Brauntoniana* Rydberg in N. L. Britton et al., N. Amer. Fl. 24: 399. 1929

Herbs perennial, caulescent; caudex superficial, trunklike. **Hairs** basifixed. **Stems** several to many. **Stipules** distinct. **Leaves** odd-pinnate, short-petiolate or subsessile; leaflets 25–33. **Racemes** densely flowered, flowers retrorsely imbricate. **Calyx tubes** ovoid-campanulate. **Corollas** pink-purple, banner recurved through 40°, keel apex round. **Legumes** deciduous, sessile, short gynophore present, deflexed, oblong to plumply lanceoloid-oblong, bluntly 3-sided compressed, straight or gently incurved, bilocular, separating into halves but held in place by invested calyx. **Seeds** 6–9.

Species 1: California.

340. Astragalus brauntonii Parish, Bull. S. Calif. Acad. Sci. 2: 26, plate 1. 1903 • Braunton's milkvetch [C] [E]

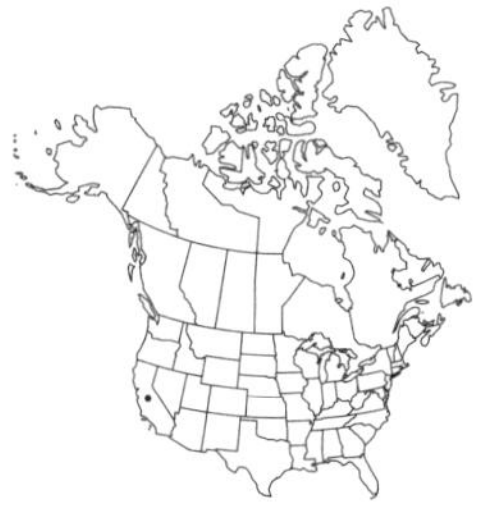

Plants coarse, 70–150 cm, villous-tomentulose. **Stems** erect or ascending, fistulose, white and villous-tomentulose. **Leaves** (3–)4–16 cm; stipules 3–10 mm, submembranous becoming papery; leaflet blades oblong-ovate or -obovate to lanceolate-elliptic, 3–20 mm, apex acute, obtuse and apiculate, or apiculate, surfaces villous-tomentulose. **Peduncles** spreading or incurved-ascending, 2.5–9 cm. **Racemes** 35–60-flowered; axis 3.5–10(–14) cm in fruit; bracts 2.5–5 mm; bracteoles 0. **Pedicels** 0.5–1.5 mm. **Flowers** 9.1–11.7 mm; calyx 6.2–8.1 mm, villous-villosulous, tube 3.3–4.1 mm, lobes lanceolate-acuminate to caudate, 2.5–5(–6) mm; corolla keel 6.4–8.5 mm. **Legumes** stramineous, 6.5–9 × (2.5–)3–4 mm, thinly fleshy becoming stiffly papery, villous or villous-tomentulose; gynophore 0.5–0.7 mm.

Flowering Mar–Jul. Disturbed sites and openings in chaparral, on granitic or sandstone substrates; of conservation concern; 10–600 m; Calif.

Astragalus brauntonii, distinguished by ligneous stems that develop after a year or two and a covering of spreading and entangled white hairs, is found near Los Angeles in Los Angeles and Orange counties. It is in the Center for Plant Conservation's National Collection of Endangered Plants.

135iiii. Astragalus Linnaeus sect. Reflexi A. Gray, Proc. Amer. Acad. Arts 6: 197. 1864 [E]

Herbs annual or winter-annual, caulescent; root-crown superficial. **Hairs** basifixed. **Stems** single or few to several. **Stipules** distinct. **Leaves** odd-pinnate, short-petiolate or subsessile; leaflets (9 or)11–15(–19). **Racemes** loosely flowered, flowers spreading becoming declined. **Calyx tubes** shallowly campanulate. **Corollas** bicolored, banner and keel bluish violet or reddish violet, wings pale or white on margins or apex, banner recurved through 40°, keel apex narrowly obtuse, beaklike. **Legumes** deciduous, sessile, short gynophore present, declined, narrowly to broadly ovoid or triangular-ovoid, 3-sided compressed, straight, bilocular. **Seeds** 4–6(–8).

Species 1: Texas.

341. Astragalus reflexus Torrey & A. Gray, Fl. N. Amer. 1: 334. 1838 • Texas milkvetch [E]

Plants annual or winter-annual, usually slender, 10–35(–45) cm, sparsely hirsute-hirsutulous; taproot slender. **Stems** erect to spreading or ascending, sparsely hirsute-hirsutulous. **Leaves** 2–8 cm; stipules (2–)2.5–7 mm, papery-scarious proximally, herbaceous distally; leaflet blades oblong-ovate, oblong-obovate, or obovate-cuneate, (3–)5–15 mm, apex retuse, surfaces hirsute-hirsutulous abaxially, glabrous adaxially. **Peduncles** erect or incurved-ascending, (3–)4–8.5 cm. **Racemes** 3–10-flowered; axis 0.4–1 cm in fruit; bracts 0.5–1.1 mm; bracteoles 0. **Pedicels** 0.5–1.4 mm. **Flowers** 4.2–5.2 mm; calyx 1.9–2.7 mm, white pilosulous, tube 1.1–1.5 mm, lobes subulate, 0.7–1.2 mm; corolla keel 4.3–5 mm. **Legumes** green, usually with purple spots, becoming brownish, 5.5–9 × 2.5–5.5 mm, stiffly papery, glabrous; gynophore 0.1–0.5 mm.

Flowering Feb–May. Prairies, roadsides; 10–300 m; Tex.

Astragalus reflexus is a diminutive annual that is known from east-central Texas. The population in Cameron County, in the Rio Grande Valley, may be introduced (D. Isely 1998).

135jjjj. Astragalus Linnaeus sect. Scutanei Barneby, Mem. New York Bot. Gard. 13: 1127. 1964

Herbs annual or winter-annual, caulescent; root-crown superficial. **Hairs** basifixed. **Stems** few to several. **Stipules** distinct. **Leaves** odd-pinnate, petiolate or subsessile; leaflets (9–)13–19 [–23]. **Racemes** densely flowered, flowers spreading becoming declined. **Calyx tubes** shallowly campanulate. **Corollas** whitish with lilac tips, or bicolored, banner purple margined, wing tips white and keel tip maculate, banner recurved through 45°, keel apex triangular, acute or subacute, usually slightly beaklike. **Legumes** deciduous, sessile, gynophore present, deflexed, broadly ovoid, subglobose, or transversely oblong in dorsiventral view, very strongly obcompressed, peltiform or scutiform, straight or gently incurved, bilocular. **Seeds** 4[–12].

Species 2 (1 in the flora): Texas, n Mexico.

Section *Scutanei* consists of one species in southern Texas and Tamaulipas, and another, *Astragalus scutaneus* Barneby, in Jalisco, Mexico. Both have the strongly obcompressed fruits that are peltiform or scutiform. The two species may not be closely related (R. C. Barneby 1964).

342. Astragalus brazoensis Buckley, Proc. Acad. Nat. Sci. Philadelphia 13: 452. 1862 • Brazos milkvetch

Plants dwarf and slender, or coarse and robust, (5–)10–35 (–45) cm, sparsely strigulose; taproot slender. **Stems** ascending to decumbent, sparsely strigulose. **Leaves** (2–)2.5–7.5(–9) cm; stipules 1.5–4.5 mm, papery proximally, herbaceous distally; leaflet blades narrowly to broadly obovate-cuneate or obcordate, 3–10(–13) mm, apex retuse, surfaces strigulose abaxially, glabrous adaxially. **Peduncles** erect or incurved-ascending, (3–) 4–9(–11) cm. **Racemes** 7–20(–25)-flowered; axis 0.7–2.5(–3.5) cm in fruit; bracts 0.8–2 mm; bracteoles 0. **Pedicels** 0.5–1.5 mm. **Flowers** (5.4–)6.7–8 mm; calyx (2.7–)3–4.1 mm, strigulose, tube 1.6–2.4 mm, lobes subulate, 1.1–1.8 mm; corolla keel 4.5–4.9 mm. **Legumes** green or purple-tinged becoming brownish or stramineous, subglobose (almost round in dorsiventral profile), 3.5–7 × 4.5–7.5(–9) mm, firm becoming stiffly papery, glabrous; gynophore 1.5–2.3 mm. **2*n*** = 22.

Flowering Feb–Apr. Prairies, disturbed sites, often weedy; 0–300 m; Tex.; Mexico (Tamaulipas).

The Brazos milkvetch occurs in southern Texas and adjacent Mexico.

135kkkk. Astragalus Linnaeus [unranked] Microlobium Nuttall, Proc. Acad. Nat. Sci. Philadelphia 4: 9. 1848

Herbs annual or winter-annual, very slender, spring-flowering, caulescent; root-crown superficial. **Hairs** basifixed. **Stems** single or few to several. **Stipules** distinct. **Leaves** odd-pinnate, sessile or petiolate; leaflets 7–17. **Racemes** densely flowered, flowers erect, ascending, spreading, or declined. **Calyx tubes** campanulate or turbinate, becoming ovoid-campanulate. **Corollas** usually whitish and lilac-tinged or pink-purple, sometimes violet, banner recurved through 25°, keel apex blunt, obtuse, deltate, or triangular-acute, sometimes beaklike. **Legumes** deciduous, sessile, short gynophore sometimes present, deflexed, spreading, or erect, ovoid, rhombic-ovoid, or subglobose, obcompressed or slightly laterally compressed, straight or gently incurved, ± bilocular. **Seeds** 2.

Species 2 (2 in the flora): w United States, nw Mexico.

The unranked group *Microlobium* consists of two monospecific subsections, *Gambeliani* Barneby and *Microlobium* (Nuttall) Barneby. Their range is from southern Oregon to Baja California and eastward to southern Nevada, southern Arizona, and northern Sonora.

343. Astragalus gambelianus E. Sheldon, Minnesota Bot. Stud. 1: 21. 1894 (as gambellianus) • Gambel's milkvetch, Little Bill loco

Astragalus nigrescens Nuttall, Proc. Acad. Nat. Sci. Philadelphia 4: 9. 1848, not Pallas 1800–1803; *A. gambelianus* subsp. *elmeri* (Greene) Abrams

Plants 3–23(–30) cm, pilosulous; taproot slender. **Stems** erect to ascending or decumbent, pilosulous. **Leaves** 1–3.5(–4) cm; stipules (1–)1.5–3 mm, submembranous becoming papery; leaflets 7–13(or 15), blades oblanceolate, linear-oblanceolate, or broadly to narrowly cuneate, (1–) 2–9 mm, apex retuse, surfaces pilosulous abaxially, pilosulous or glabrate adaxially. **Peduncles** erect, divaricate, or incurved-ascending, (1–)2–5(–6) cm. **Racemes** 4–15-flowered, flowers ascending becoming spreading or declined, curved; axis 0.3–2(–2.7) cm in fruit, elongating; bracts 1.5–1.3 mm; bracteoles 0. **Pedicels** 0.2–0.9 mm. **Flowers** 2.5–3.3 mm; calyx 1.8–2.3(–2.5) mm, pilosulous, tube 1.1–1.7 mm, lobes subulate to triangular-subulate, 0.5–0.9 mm; corolla whitish, tinged or veins or margins bluish lilac, sometimes bright violet; keel 2–2.5(–4.2) mm. **Legumes** deflexed, stramineous or brownish, straight or gently incurved, broadly ovoid, rhombic-ovoid, or subglobose, strongly obcompressed, 2.8–4.2 × 2.4–3.6 mm, thin becoming papery, hirsutulous to strigulose. **2*n*** = 22.

Flowering Mar–Jul. Grassy sites, roadsides, chaparral, with live oaks, often on serpentine substrates; 10–1300 m; Calif., Oreg.; Mexico (Baja California).

Astragalus gambelianus and *A. didymocarpus* are annuals that are superficially similar and sometimes sympatric, with similar dehiscence of the fruits by fracture through both sutures and the septum, the

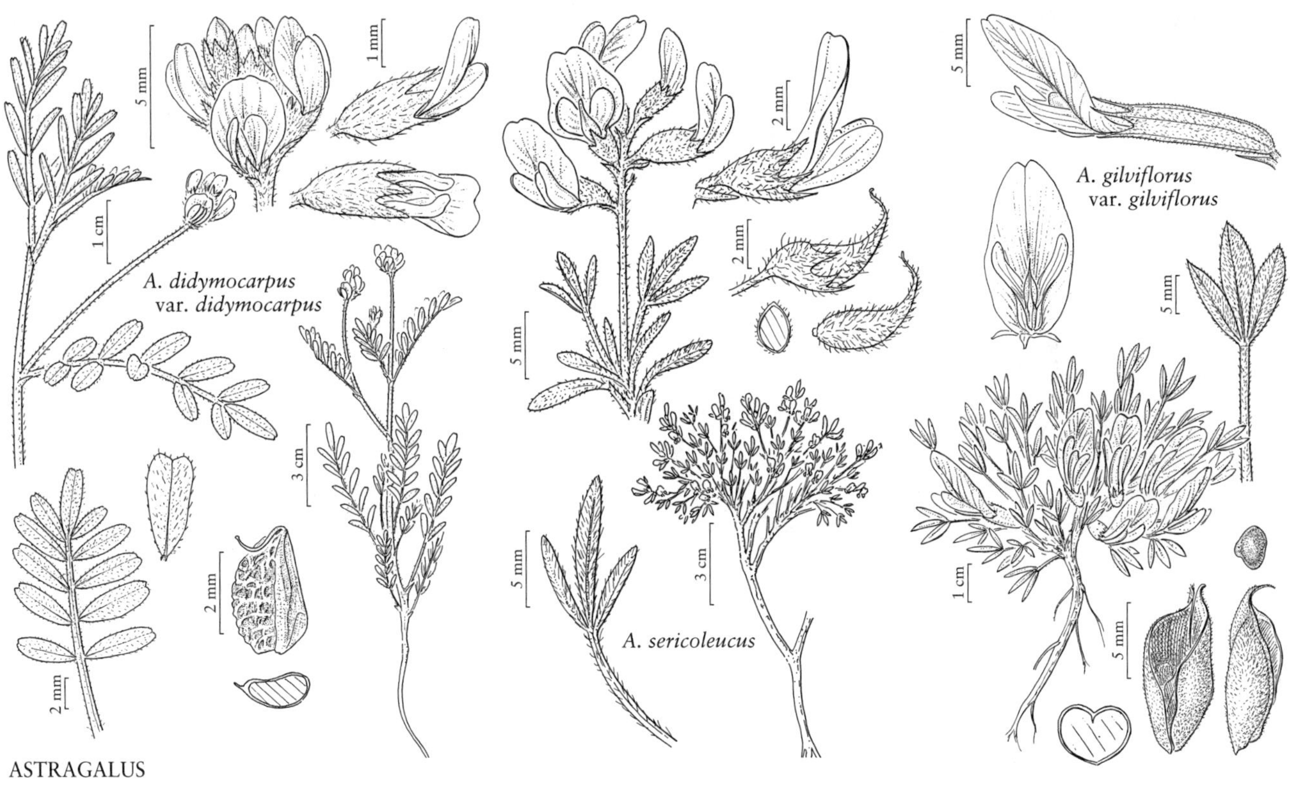

ASTRAGALUS

fruit halves separating into two lobes that assume the character of sacs, each containing one proportionately very large seed. *Astragalus gambelianus* occurs from south-central Oregon to northern Baja California. A. Liston (1992) found the species to be predominantly self-pollinating.

344. Astragalus didymocarpus Hooker & Arnott, Bot. Beechey Voy., 334, plate 81. 1838 • Two-seeded milkvetch [F]

Plants (1.5–)3–35(–45) cm, sparsely strigose; taproot slender. **Stems** erect, ascending, diffuse, or prostrate, sparsely strigose. **Leaves** (0.8–)1–7.5 cm; stipules (0.5–)1–5 mm, thinly herbaceous becoming papery-membranous; leaflets (7 or)9–17, blades linear-oblanceolate, -elliptic, oblanceolate, oblong-cuneate, or cuneate, 1.5–14 mm, apex deeply retuse, surfaces strigose abaxially, strigose, glabrate, or glabrous adaxially. **Peduncles** erect or incurved-ascending, (0.5–)1–8 cm. **Racemes** (5–)7–30-flowered, flowers erect or ascending, straight; axis 0.2–2(–2.2) cm in fruit, not elongating; bracts 0.6–3 mm; bracteoles 0. **Pedicels** 0.1–0.5(–0.6) mm. **Flowers** 2.8–10 mm; calyx 2.5–5.7 mm, pilosulous or villosulous, tube 1.5–3.8 mm, lobes subulate to subulate-setaceous, 0.8–2.5 mm; corolla whitish and tinged lavender, or pink-purple with white or pale wing tips; keel 2.4–7.2 mm. **Legumes** erect or spreading, green or purple-tinged becoming brownish, straight, plumply ovoid or subglobose, somewhat laterally compressed, (2–)2.3–4 × 1.5–3 mm, thinly fleshy becoming stiffly papery, coarsely reticulate or ridged, strigulose, strigulose-hirsutulous, pilosulous, or glabrous; gynophore slender, 0–0.5 mm.

Varieties 4 (4 in the flora): sw United States, nw Mexico.

Astragalus didymocarpus has erect flowers and fruits, which contrast with the late anthesis nodding flowers and declined fruits of *A. gambelianus*.

1. Keel petals 2.4–4.5 mm.
   2. Calyces: hairs mostly black, lobes 0.8–1.4(–2) mm, tubes 1.5–2.8 mm; stems usually erect or ascending, rarely diffuse; Sacramento and San Joaquin valleys s from Contra Costa County and s Coast Ranges, foothills of s California and Channel Islands to Baja California, e Inyo County and adjacent Nevada. . . . . 344a. *Astragalus didymocarpus* var. *didymocarpus*
   2. Calyces: hairs mostly white, lobes (1.3–) 1.6–2.4 mm, tubes 1.7–2.3 mm; stems diffuse, weakly ascending, or prostrate; s Mojave and Colorado deserts, California and Nevada, to c, s Arizona and Mexico . . . . 344c. *Astragalus didymocarpus* var. *dispermus*

1. Keel petals (4.7–)5.3–7.2 mm.
   3. Keel petals abruptly incurved, apex broadly rounded; coastal San Luis Obispo and Santa Barbara counties . . . 344b. *Astragalus didymocarpus* var. *milesianus*
   3. Keel petals incurved, apex narrowly triangular, acute or subacute, slightly beaklike; interior s California, Los Angeles County to Baja California . . . . 344d. *Astragalus didymocarpus* var. *obispensis*

344a. Astragalus didymocarpus Hooker & Arnott var. **didymocarpus** [F]

Astragalus catalinensis Nuttall; *A. didymocarpus* var. *daleoides* Barneby

Stems usually erect or ascending, rarely diffuse, (2.5–)4–35 (–45) cm. **Leaves** (0.8–) 1.5–7.5 cm; leaflets (9 or)11–17, blades 1.5–14 mm. **Racemes** (5–)7–25-flowered; axis 0.2–1.5 (–2.2) cm. **Flowers** 2.8–5.3(–6.1) mm; calyx tube 1.5–2.8 mm, lobes subulate, 0.8–1.4(–2) mm, hairs mostly black, sometimes also white; corolla keel abruptly incurved, 2.4–4.3(–4.5) mm, apex bluntly deltate. **Legumes** (2–)2.3–3.4(–4) × 1.5–3 mm, strongly wrinkled transversely or diagonally, strigulose. 2*n* = 24.

Flowering Mar–May. Hillsides, plains, valley floors; 100–1600 m; Calif., Nev.; Mexico (Baja California).

Variety *didymocarpus* is the most widely dispersed form of the species, apparently having geographic contact with all of the other varieties and more or less blending with them. It occurs from the Sacramento Valley southward through the San Joaquin Valley, then nearer the coast (including the Channel Islands) to Baja California, with eastern populations in eastern Inyo County and adjacent Nevada.

344b. Astragalus didymocarpus Hooker & Arnott var. **milesianus** (Rydberg) Jepson, Fl. Calif. 2: 376. 1936 • Miles's milkvetch [C] [E]

Hesperastragalus milesianus Rydberg, Bull. Torrey Bot. Club 53: 169. 1926

Stems erect, 4–35 cm. **Leaves** (0.8–)1.5–7.5 cm; leaflets 9–15, blades 1.5–14 mm. **Racemes** (5–)7–25-flowered; axis 0.2–1.5 (–2.2) cm. **Flowers** 7.5–10 mm; calyx tube (2.5–)3–3.8 mm, lobes subulate, 1–2.4 mm; corolla keel abruptly incurved, (4.7–)5.3–6.9 mm, apex broadly round. **Legumes** 3–4 × 1.5–3 mm, glabrous or pilosulous.

Flowering Mar–May. Grassy hillsides, meadows, along and near Pacific Ocean; of conservation concern; 0–60 m; Calif.

Variety *milesianus* occurs near the Pacific Ocean in San Luis Obispo and Santa Barbara counties.

344c. Astragalus didymocarpus Hooker & Arnott var. **dispermus** (A. Gray) Jepson, Fl. Calif. 2: 376. 1936 • Wickenburg milkvetch

Astragalus dispermus A. Gray, Proc. Amer. Acad. Arts 13: 365. 1878

Stems diffuse, weakly ascending, or prostrate, (1.5–)4–27 cm. **Leaves** 1–3.5 cm; leaflets (7 or) 9–15, blades 2–8 mm. **Racemes** 7–20-flowered; axis 0.3–1.2 cm. **Flowers** (3.4–)4.3–5.4 mm; calyx tube 1.7–2.3 mm, lobes subulate or subulate-setaceous, (1.3–)1.6–2.4 mm, hairs mostly white, sometimes also black; corolla keel abruptly incurved, (3.4–) 3.8–4.5 mm, apex usually bluntly deltate, sometimes obscurely beaklike. **Legumes** 2.3–4 × 1.6–2.5 mm, deeply sulcate, strongly wrinkled transversely or diagonally, strigulose-hirsutulous. 2*n* = 26.

Flowering Feb–May. Foothills of desert mountains, on arid sandy soils, with *Larrea*; 30–1100(–1300) m; Ariz., Calif., Nev.; Mexico (Baja California).

Variety *dispermus* occurs from the western edge of the California deserts across southern Nevada to central and southern Arizona.

344d. Astragalus didymocarpus Hooker & Arnott var. **obispensis** (Rydberg) Jepson, Fl. Calif. 2: 376. 1936 (as obispoensis) • San Luis Obispo milkvetch

Hesperastragalus obispensis Rydberg, Bull. Torrey Bot. Club 53: 167. 1926

Stems mostly erect or ascending, (2.5–)3–25 cm. **Leaves** 1–5 cm; leaflets 9–17, blades 1.5–10 mm. **Racemes** (5–)8–30-flowered; axis 0.2–2 cm. **Flowers** (6.2–) 7–8.6 mm; calyx tube 2.1–2.8 mm, lobes subulate-setaceous, (0.9–)1.1–2.5 mm, hairs white, sometimes also black; corolla keel incurved, (5.2–)5.5–7.2 mm, apex narrowly triangular, acute or subacute, slightly beaklike. **Legumes** (2–)2.3–3.4(–4) × 1.5–3 mm, strigulose.

Flowering Mar–May. Grassy sites, chaparral; 400–1100 m; Calif.; Mexico (Baja California).

Variety *obispensis* occurs mostly inland but west of the deserts, from Los Angeles County southward to Baja California.

135llll. Astragalus Linnaeus sect. Sesamei de Candolle in A. P. de Candolle and A. L. P. P. de Candolle, Prodr. 2: 287. 1825

Herbs annual, caulescent; root-crown superficial. **Hairs** basifixed. **Stems** single or few. **Stipules** distinct. **Leaves** odd-pinnate, petiolate or subsessile; leaflets 7–13. **Racemes** subcapitate-verticillate, flowers suberect. **Calyx tubes** turbinate-campanulate. **Corollas** reddish violet, lilac, or whitish and lilac-tinged, [purple], banner recurved through 30°, keel apex bluntly triangular. **Legumes** persistent, sessile, erect, lanceoloid-oblong or narrowly oblong, 3-sided compressed, ± straight, bilocular. **Seeds** 5–9.

Species 26 (1 in the flora): Texas, Europe, Asia, n Africa.

Section *Sesamei* is distributed in the Mediterranean Old World region and east to India and south-central Asia, in the Canary Islands, and in Texas.

345. **Astragalus wrightii** A. Gray, Boston J. Nat. Hist. 6: 176. 1850 • Wright's milkvetch [E]

Plants slender, becoming stiff or rigid, (2–)4–30(–35) cm, silky-pilose; taproot slender. **Stems** erect to ascending, silky-pilose. **Leaves** 1.5–5.5(–7.5) cm; stipules 3–6 mm, herbaceous becoming papery; leaflet blades usually broadly to narrowly elliptic or oblanceolate, rarely obovate, 4–17(–20) mm, apex acute to obtuse, surfaces pilose. **Peduncles** erect and ascending, 0.7–7 cm. **Racemes** 3–7-flowered; axis to 0.4 cm in fruit; bracts 1.5–5.5 mm; bracteoles 0. **Pedicels** 0.6–1 mm. **Flowers** 5.2–6.2 mm; calyx 5.2–6.2 mm, pilose, tube 2–2.6 mm, lobes linear-lanceolate, 3.2–3.8 mm; corolla keel 4.7–5.5 mm. **Legumes** brown or blackish, 7–13 × 2.5–3.5 mm, scarcely fleshy becoming stiffly papery, pilose-hirsute. $2n$ = 22.

Flowering Mar–May. Live oak and juniper woodlands, prairies; 100–400 m; Tex.

Astragalus wrightii is the sole North American representative in sect. *Sesamei.* The reported chromosome counts in this section are mostly based on $x = 8$, with none based on $x = 11$ (as reviewed by R. Spellenberg 1976). G. F. Ledingham (1960b) reported $2n = 22$ for *A. wrightii*, consistent with chromosome numbers for species of American lineages.

135mmmm. Astragalus Linnaeus sect. Cycloglottis Bunge, Mém. Acad. Imp. Sci. Saint Pétersbourg, Sér. 7, 11(16): 17. 1868 [I]

Herbs annual, caulescent; root-crown superficial. **Hairs** basifixed. **Stems** several. **Stipules** distinct. **Leaves** odd-pinnate, petiolate; leaflets 13–21. **Racemes** subcapitate, flowers ascending. **Calyx tubes** campanulate. **Corollas** whitish, banner straight or recurved slightly, keel apex blunt. **Legumes** deciduous, sessile, spreading, forming an oblong to globose head, narrowly oblong, 3-sided compressed, coiled, bilocular.

Species 1 (1 in the flora): introduced, Massachusetts; Europe, Asia.

Introduced in the flora area, sect. *Cycloglottis* is known otherwise from east-central Europe eastward to Balochistan, northwestern Pakistan, and central Asia.

346. Astragalus contortuplicatus Linnaeus, Sp. Pl. 2: 758. 1753 • Coil-legumes milkvetch [I]

Plants coarse, 20–40 cm, hirsute; taproot slender. **Stems** prostrate-ascending, hirsute. **Leaves** 5–15 cm; stipules 3–6 mm, herbaceous; leaflet blades oblong-obovate or -ovate, 4–17 mm, apex retuse, surfaces hirsute. **Peduncles** 1.5–4 cm. **Racemes** 5–15-flowered; axis scarcely elongating; bracts 1.5–3 mm; bracteoles 0. **Pedicels** 0.6–1 mm. **Flowers** 5–6.5 mm; calyx 5–6.5 mm, densely white or white and black hairy, lobes filiform, 2–5 mm (longer than tube); corolla keel 5–6.5 mm. **Legumes** blackish brown at maturity, coiled through 0.75–1.25 spiral into a ring, 6–8 mm diam., 2–3 mm wide, papery, grooved dorsally, sparsely hirsutulous. $2n = 16$.

Flowering May–Aug. Riversides, saline meadows; 0 m; introduced; Mass.; Eurasia.

Astragalus contortuplicatus, native from east-central Europe to central Asia, was collected in Westport in the nineteenth century; it apparently has not been recollected in North America.

135nnnn. Astragalus Linnaeus sect. Glycyphyllus Bunge, Mém. Acad. Imp. Sci. Saint Pétersbourg, Sér. 7, 11(16): 25. 1868 [I]

Herbs perennial, caulescent; caudex shallowly subterranean. **Hairs** basifixed. **Stems** several. **Stipules** distinct or connate at proximal nodes. **Leaves** odd-pinnate, short-petiolate; leaflets 9–13(or 15)[or 17]. **Racemes** subcapitate to loose, flowers ascending. **Calyx tubes** campanulate. **Corollas** greenish white, often suffused purple, banner recurved through 40°, keel apex round. **Legumes** persistent, short-stipitate, incurved-ascending [erect], linear-ellipsoid, somewhat 3-sided compressed, ± straight or gently incurved, bilocular. **Seeds** 19–25.

Species 6 (1 in the flora): introduced; Europe, Asia.

Section *Glycyphyllus* has a rather broad distribution in Eurasia.

347. Astragalus glycyphyllos Linnaeus, Sp. Pl. 2: 758. 1753 • Liquorice milkvetch [I]

Plants coarse, 40–90 cm, sparsely strigulose. **Stems** ascending or sprawling, sparsely strigulose. **Leaves** (6–)8–20 cm; stipules connate-sheathing at proximal nodes, connate or distinct at distal nodes, 10–20 mm, thinly herbaceous or foliaceous becoming papery; leaflet blades ovate to oblong or broadly elliptic, 10–45(–60) mm, apex obtuse and apiculate, surfaces strigulose abaxially, glabrous adaxially. **Peduncles** 1.5–8 cm. **Racemes** 10–20-flowered; axis (1–)1.5–3.5 cm in fruit; bracts 2–6 mm; bracteoles 0. **Pedicels** 0.5–3 mm. **Flowers** 11.5–13.5 mm; calyx 5.2–6.5 mm, glabrate to sparsely strigulose, tube 3.5–4.2 mm, lobes subulate, 1.2–2.9 mm; corolla keel 9.5–11 mm. **Legumes** brownish stramineous, (27–)30–37(–40) × 4–5 mm, fleshy becoming leathery, minutely strigulose; stipe 2–3.5 mm. $2n = 16$.

Flowering May–Aug. Deciduous woodlands, hedgerows, thickets, fallow fields; 0–300 m; introduced; Ont.; Conn., Ind., Mass., N.J., N.Y.; Eurasia.

Astragalus glycyphyllos, native from Europe to the Caucasus and Altai in Asia, has been sparsely introduced in northeastern North America. The species has no close relative in North America. R. C. Barneby (1964) and D. Isely (1998) reviewed its distribution in more detail.

135oooo. Astragalus Linnaeus sect. Sericoleuci Barneby, Mem. New York Bot. Gard. 13: 1143. 1964 [E]

Herbs perennial, mat- or cushion-forming, caulescent or acaulescent; caudex superficial. **Hairs** malpighian. **Stems** several to numerous, sometimes obscured by stipules. **Stipules** connate-sheathing. **Leaves** palmately trifoliolate (except sometimes 5-foliolate in *A. sericoleucus*), petiolate. **Racemes** subumbellate or loosely flowered, exserted or included in stipular sheath, flowers ascending. **Calyx tubes** campanulate, campanulate-turbinate, or subcylindric. **Corollas** usually pink-purple, rarely white, banner recurved through 40–90°, keel apex round, bluntly deltate, or subacutely triangular, sometimes ± beaklike. **Legumes** deciduous, sessile, ascending to recurved, invested by calyx or partly exserted, lanceoloid- or ovoid-ellipsoid, straight, slightly compressed or obscurely 3-sided compressed, unilocular. **Seeds** (2 or)6–12.

Species 4 (4 in the flora): c, w United States.

Section *Sericoleuci* is distributed in northeastern Colorado, western Kansas, southeastern Montana, western Nebraska, western South Dakota, northeastern Utah, and Wyoming.

D. Isely (1998) placed the species in sect. *Sericoleuci* and sect. *Orophaca* in the genus *Orophaca* (Torrey & A. Gray) Britton, emphasizing the isolated nature of the group, the trifoliolate leaves, and the base chromosome number of $x = 12$. M. F. Wojciechowski et al. (1999) found that *A. aretioides* and *A. sericoleucus*, and presumably other species Isley treated in *Orophaca*, are clearly nested within North American *Astragalus* and not distinct from it.

348. Astragalus sericoleucus A. Gray, Amer. J. Sci. Arts, ser. 2, 33: 410. 1862 • Silky orophaca [E] [F]

Phaca sericea Nuttall in J. Torrey and A. Gray, Fl. N. Amer. 1: 343. 1838, not *Astragalus sericeus* Lamarck 1779; *Orophaca sericea* (Nuttall) Britton

Plants cushion- or mat-forming, 1.5–9 dm wide, caulescent, 1–8 cm, silvery-pilose; from branched caudex, branches with thatch of persistent petioles; taproot stout. **Stems** prostrate, silvery-pilose. **Leaves** 1–4 cm; stipules 2–8 mm, hyaline, densely pilose abaxially; leaflets usually 3, rarely 5, blades narrowly to broadly oblanceolate or obovate-cuneate, 3–13 mm, apex subacute, surfaces silvery-pilose. **Peduncles** 0.5–2.5 cm. **Racemes** (2 or) 3–5-flowered; axis to 1 cm in fruit; bracts 1–2.5 mm. **Pedicels** 1–3.5 mm. **Flowers** 5–6.2(–8) mm; calyx campanulate, 2.4–4.2 mm, densely pilose, tube 2–3 mm, lobes triangular-subulate, 1–1.2 mm; corolla pink-purple or white, often drying yellowish; banner recurved through 90°; keel 4–4.5 mm, apex bluntly deltate. **Legumes** ascending or recurved, ovoid-ellipsoid, slightly compressed, 3–4.5 × 2 mm, papery, densely silky-strigose or silky-pilose. **Seeds** 6–10.

Flowering late May–Jul. Barren ridges, knolls, hilltops, on gravelly clay, shale outcrops in higher prairies; 1100–1700 m; Colo., Kans., Nebr., N.Mex., Wyo.

Astragalus sericoleucus occurs on Niobrara Shale outcrops from southeastern Wyoming to western Nebraska, northwestern Kansas, and northeastern Colorado, with a disjunct population in Union County in northeastern New Mexico.

349. Astragalus aretioides (M. E. Jones) Barneby, Amer. Midl. Naturalist 55: 505. 1956 • Cushion orophaca [E]

Astragalus sericoleucus A. Gray var. *aretioides* M. E. Jones, Contr. W. Bot. 8: 13. 1898; *Orophaca aretioides* (M. E. Jones) Rydberg

Plants cushion-forming, 1–3 dm wide, acaulescent or subacaulescent, 0–1.5(–2) cm, silvery-pilose; from branched caudex; taproot stout. **Stems** obscured by stipules. **Leaves** 0.6–2 cm; stipules 3.5–7 mm, hyaline, glabrate or glabrous abaxially, ciliate; leaflet blades spatulate to elliptic, 3–7.5 mm, apex acute, surfaces silvery-pilose. **Peduncles** 0.7–1.5 cm. **Racemes** 2- or 3-flowered; axis very short; bracts 2–3 mm; bracteoles 0. **Pedicels** 1–1.5 mm. **Flowers** (5.8–) 6.6–8 mm; calyx campanulate, 3.3–4.2 mm, densely pilose, tube 2.1–2.3 mm, lobes triangular-subulate, 1.2–2 mm; corolla usually pink-purple, rarely white; banner recurved through 90°, obovate-cuneate, (5.8–)6.6–8 mm; wings (5.7–)6–6.8 mm; keel 4.1–4.5 mm, apex bluntly deltate. **Legumes** ascending, ovoid-ellipsoid, slightly compressed, 4–5 × 1.2–2 mm, papery, densely silky-strigose or silky-pilose. **Seeds** 6–10.

Flowering Jun–Aug. Clay bluffs, eroded banks, on sandstone or limestone bedrock; 1200–2400 m; Colo., Mont., Utah, Wyo.

Astragalus aretioides is similar to *A. sericoleucus*, but has slightly larger flowers borne mostly in pairs. It occurs mostly to the west of *A. sericoleucus* in south-central Montana, western Wyoming, northeastern Utah, and Moffat County in northwestern Colorado.

350. Astragalus tridactylicus A. Gray, Proc. Amer. Acad. Arts 6: 527. 1865 • Foothill orophaca [E]

Orophaca tridactylica (A. Gray) Rydberg

Plants cespitose, mat- or cushion-forming, (0.5–)1–4 dm wide, acaulescent or subacaulescent, 0–1.5 cm, silvery-pilose; taproot stout; from branched caudex, branches with thatch of persistent petioles and stipules. **Stems** obscured by stipules. **Leaves** 0.5–6(–6.5) cm; stipules 5–10 mm, hyaline, proximally pilose abaxially; leaflet blades spatulate to narrowly lanceolate, 2–20 mm, apex acute, surfaces silvery-pilose. **Peduncles** 0–1 cm. **Racemes** 2–6(–10)-flowered; axis very short; bracts 1.5–5 mm; bracteoles 0. **Pedicels** 1–3.5 mm. **Flowers** 8.2–11.5 mm; calyx campanulate to turbinate-campanulate, 4.5–6.9 mm, densely silvery-pilose, tube 1.8–3.5(–3.8) mm, lobes lanceolate-subulate, 1.8–3.5 mm; corolla usually pink-purple, rarely white; banner recurved through 90°; keel 4.4–7.2 mm, apex obtuse. **Legumes** ascending, ovoid-ellipsoid, slightly compressed, 4–5 × 1.2–2 mm, papery, densely silky-strigose or silky-pilose. **Seeds** 6–12.

Flowering late May–Jul. Bluffs and knolls on rolling plains, on sand or gravelly clay, shale, sandstone, or limestone, especially on red sand of the Chugwater Formation; 1400–2300 m; Colo., Wyo.

Astragalus tridactylicus occurs from near Denver, Colorado, northwestward to the Laramie Plains and northward to near Casper, Wyoming.

351. Astragalus barrii Barneby, Amer. Midl. Naturalist 55: 506. 1956 • Barr's orophaca [E]

Orophaca barrii (Barneby) Isely

Plants cespitose, cushion- or mat-forming, (0.5–)1–5 dm wide, acaulescent or subacaulescent, 0–1.5 cm, silvery-strigose; from branched caudex, branches with thatch of marcescent petioles and stipules; taproot stout. **Stems** obscured by stipules. **Leaves** 1–4(–5) cm; stipules 4–8 mm, hyaline, glabrous abaxially; leaflet blades narrowly spatulate to narrowly lanceolate, 3–12 mm, apex acute, surfaces silvery-strigose. **Peduncles** erect, 0.7–2.2 cm. **Racemes** (1 or)2–4-flowered; axis 0.5–1.5 cm in fruit; bracts 1.8–3.5 mm; bracteoles 0. **Pedicels** 0.7–1.5 mm. **Flowers** (9.5–)10.5–16.7 mm; calyx deeply campanulate to subcylindric, (4.8–)5–7.1 mm, densely strigose to pilose, hairs white, tube 3.6–5.1 mm, lobes subulate to linear-subulate, (1.4–)1.9–5.1 mm; corolla usually pink-purple, rarely white, wing tips white or pale; banner recurved through 40°; keel 7.5–10.5 mm, apex acute-triangular, often somewhat beaklike. **Legumes** mostly enclosed in marcescent calyx, ascending, lanceoloid-ellipsoid, obscurely 3-sided compressed, 4.5–7.5 × 1.2–2.2 mm, thin becoming papery, densely silver-strigulose. **Seeds** 2.

Flowering (late Apr–)May–Jun. Knolls, buttes, barren hilltops; 900–1800 m; Mont., S.Dak., Wyo.

Astragalus barrii occurs in southeastern Montana, southwestern South Dakota, and northeastern Wyoming.

Astragalus barrii is in the Center for Plant Conservation's National Collection of Endangered Plants.

135pppp. ASTRAGALUS Linnaeus sect. OROPHACA (Torrey & A. Gray) Barneby, Mem. New York Bot. Gard. 13: 1150. 1964 [E]

Phaca Linnaeus [unranked] *Orophaca* Torrey & A. Gray, Fl. N. Amer. 1: 342. 1838

Herbs perennial, tuft-, cushion-, or mound-forming, acaulescent or subacaulescent; root-crown or caudex superficial. **Hairs** malpighian. **Stems** obscured by stipules and leaf bases. **Stipules** connate-sheathing. **Leaves** trifoliolate or unifoliolate, leaflets caducous when dried, petiolate. **Racemes** reduced to 1–3 flowers, flowers erect, ± sessile in leaf axils. **Calyx tubes** cylindric. **Corollas** usually whitish to ochroleucous, rarely purple, banner nearly erect, little recurved, keel apex bluntly triangular or obtuse. **Legumes** often concealed by stipules, deciduous, sessile, erect, at first enclosed by calyx, finally rupturing tube, subsymmetrically ovoid-ellipsoid or narrowly ellipsoid, laterally compressed, straight or slightly decurved, unilocular. **Seeds** 8–17.

Species 3 (3 in the flora): w, c North America.

Section *Orophaca* is distributed from southern Alberta to southwestern Manitoba southward to Wyoming, northeastern Colorado, and northeastern Utah. The case was made by D. Isely (1983) for assignment of the species placed here in sect. *Sericoleuci* and sect. *Orophaca* to the genus *Orophaca*. One consideration was the lack of any near relatives among the vast number of *Astragalus* species in North America, and another was the base chromosome number of 12 in *Orophaca*, not 11–15 as for members of *Astragalus*.

352. Astragalus gilviflorus E. Sheldon, Minnesota Bot. Stud. 1: 21. 1894 (as Atsragalus) • Plains orophaca [E] [F]

Astragalus triphyllus Pursh, Fl. Amer. Sept. 2: 740. 1813, not Pallas 1800–1803

Plants tuft-, cushion-, or mound-forming, 0.5–3+ dm wide, appearing acaulescent, silvery-strigose; from branched caudex, branches with thatch of persistent petioles. **Stems** obscured by stipules and marcescent leaf bases. **Leaves** palmately trifoliolate, 1–13 cm; stipules sometimes ruptured in age, 6–18 mm, hyaline; leaflet blades spatulate to elliptic, (3–)7–27(–37) mm, apex acute to obtuse, surfaces silvery-strigose. **Peduncles** obsolete. **Racemes** 1–3-flowered, capitate; axis very short in fruit; bracts tridentate, 4.5–7.6 mm; bracteoles 0(or 1). **Pedicels** 0–1.6 mm. **Flowers** 16–29 mm; calyx 9.3–18(–20) mm, loosely villous, tube (6.5–)10–14(–16) mm, lobes linear or narrowly subulate, 1.6–4 mm; corolla usually whitish to ochroleucous, rarely purple, petals usually glabrous, banner rarely puberulent adaxially; banner not differentiated into blade and claw; keel 10.4–21.8 mm. **Legumes** straight, ovoid-ellipsoid, 6–10 × 2.5–5 mm, fleshy becoming leathery, densely strigose-hirsutulous. **Seeds** 10–17.

Varieties 2 (2 in the flora): w, c North America.

Astragalus gilviflorus is found from southern Alberta, southern Saskatchewan, and southwestern Manitoba southward to northeastern Utah, southern Wyoming, through the Dakotas to western Nebraska and northeastern Colorado.

Astragalus gilviflorus is a rather common species in the prairie-steppe communities of the high plains.

Phaca caespitosa Nuttall (1818) (not *Astragalus caespitosus* Pallas, 1800–1803) and *Orophaca triphylla* Isely are illegitimate names that pertain here.

1. Corollas ochroleucous. . . . . 352a. *Astragalus gilviflorus* var. *gilviflorus*
1. Corollas purple. . . . . 352b. *Astragalus gilviflorus* var. *purpureus*

352a. Astragalus gilviflorus E. Sheldon var. **gilviflorus** [E] [F]

Corollas ochroleucous. **2*n*** = 22, 24.

Flowering late Apr–May (–Jun). Prairies, plains, knolls, hilltops, badlands, less commonly in sagebrush and juniper woodlands; 500–2500 m; Alta., Man., Sask.; Colo., Idaho, Mont., Nebr., N.Dak., S.Dak., Utah, Wyo.

Recent collections of var. *gilviflorus* from western Tooele County in Utah may represent a recent introduction.

352b. Astragalus gilviflorus E. Sheldon var. **purpureus** Dorn, Vasc. Pl. Wyoming, 297. 1988 [C] [E]

Corollas purple.

Flowering May–Jul. Cushion plant and bunchgrass communities on sandy-clay soils with gravel surface; of conservation concern; 1900–2700 m; Wyo.

Variety *purpureus* is restricted to the Dubois Badlands in Fremont County. The specimens examined seem, on the whole, to be somewhat smaller and more compact than for most of the species, in which plant size and compactness varies greatly. The flowers are somewhat smaller than for var. *gilviflorus*. Other plants with blue corollas and the banner hairy on the back cited from Wheatland County in Montana, collected by C. L. Hitchcock were noted by R. C. Barneby (1964).

353. Astragalus proimanthus Barneby, Mem. New York Bot. Gard. 13: 1153. 1964 • Precocious orophaca [C] [E]

Orophaca proimantha (Barneby) Isely

Plants tuft- or cushion-forming, 0.5–2(–3+) dm wide, acaulescent, silvery-hirsute; from branched caudex, branches with thatch of marcescent stipules and petioles. **Stems** obscured by stipules and marcescent leaf bases. **Leaves** unifoliolate or palmately trifoliolate, 1–3.5 cm; stipules sometimes ruptured in age, 7–12 mm, hyaline; leaflet blades spatulate to elliptic, (3–)5–9 mm, apex acute to subacute, surfaces silvery-pilosulous. **Peduncles** subobsolete. **Racemes** 1- or 2-flowered, capitate; axis obsolete or very short; bracts sometimes tridentate, 3–6 mm; bracteoles 2. **Pedicels** subobsolete. **Flowers** 12.3–17 mm; calyx 8.3–10.5 mm, loosely villous, tube 5.9–6.5 mm, lobes linear to narrowly subulate, 2.4–4.2 mm; corolla whitish to ochroleucous, petals glabrous abaxially; banner differentiated into blade and claw, with shoulderlike projections at middle; keel 11.1–12.8 mm. **Legumes** green, straight or slightly decurved, narrowly ellipsoid, 7–10 × 2.5–3 mm, fleshy becoming leathery, densely strigose-hirsutulous. **Seeds** 11–14.

Flowering late Apr–mid Jun. Barren, white shale hills, ridges of shale bluffs, with *Cryptantha* and wheatgrass; of conservation concern; 1900–2200 m; Wyo.

Astragalus proimanthus is restricted to the valley of Henry's Fork in southern Sweetwater County. Plants appear as miniature *A. gilviflorus*, being smaller in all parts.

354. Astragalus hyalinus M. E. Jones, Proc. Calif. Acad. Sci., ser. 2, 5: 648. 1895 • Summer orophaca [E]

Orophaca hyalina (M. E. Jones) Isely

Plants densely tuft- or mound-forming, 0.5–4+ dm wide, acaulescent or subcaulescent, to 2 cm, silvery-pilose; from branched caudex, branches obscured by marcescent petioles and stipules. **Stems** obscured by stipules. **Leaves** palmately trifoliolate, 0.7–3 cm; stipules 6–10 mm, hyaline; leaflet blades spatulate to obovate, 2.5–10 mm, apex subacute to obtuse, surfaces silvery-pilose. **Peduncles** ± obsolete. **Racemes** 1–3-flowered, subcapitate; axis obsolete; bracts sometimes tridentate, 3–6 mm; bracteoles 0. **Pedicels** ± subobsolete. **Flowers** 12.5–17.5 mm; calyx 7.3–10.7 mm, silvery-villous, tube 5.8–7.5 mm, lobes linear to narrowly subulate, 1.5–3.7 mm; corolla whitish to ochroleucous, petals villous abaxially; banner differentiated into blade and claw, with shoulderlike projections at middle; keel 10–13 mm. **Legumes** straight or slightly decurved, narrowly ellipsoid, 7–10 × 2.5–3.5 mm, fleshy becoming leathery, densely strigose-hirsutulous. **Seeds** 8 or 9.

Varieties 2 (2 in the flora): w c United States.

1. Petals white, conspicuously villose adaxially; ovules 8 or 9. . . . 354a. *Astragalus hyalinus* var. *hyalinus*
1. Petals white tinged or lined with lavender, glabrous adaxially or with short tuft of hair proximally; ovules 6–8 . . . . 354b. *Astragalus hyalinus* var. *glabratus*

354a. Astragalus hyalinus M. E. Jones var. **hyalinus** [E]

Flowers: petals usually white, conspicuously villose adaxially; ovules 8 or 9.

Flowering late Jun–early Aug. Hilltops, bluffs, badlands, on shale and limestone bedrock; 1000–2300 m; Colo., Kans., Mont., Nebr., N.Dak., S.Dak., Wyo.

Variety *hyalinus* occurs from southeastern Montana through eastern Wyoming to southwestern South Dakota, western Nebraska, northwestern Kansas, and northeastern Colorado. It was also reported for North Dakota by Ced. L. Porter (1951).

354b. Astragalus hyalinus M. E. Jones var. **glabratus** Evert ex Dorn, Phytologia 96: 26. 2014 • Smooth summer orophaca [C] [E]

Flowers: petals white, usually tinged or lined with lavender, glabrous adaxially or with short tuft of hair proximally; ovules 6–8.

Flowering late Jun–early Jul. Cushion plant communities in grassy areas associated with limestone outcrops; of conservation concern; 900–2300 m; Wyo.

Taxa Added After Completion of Manuscript

The following species were added to this treatment after *Astragalus* was finalized and do not appear in the key to species: 355. *A. tibetanus* (which will key to *A. agrestis* in sect. *Hypoglottidei*), 356. *A. asotinensis* (which will key to *A. sclerocarpus* in sect. *Podosclerocarpi*), and 357. *A. kelseyae* (a very distinctive species in sect. *Kelseyani*).

355. **Astragalus tibetanus** Bunge, Mém. Acad. Imp. Sci. Saint Pétersbourg, Sér. 7. 11(16): 52. 1868 • Tibet milkvetch [I]

Plants perennial, (4–)10–35 cm, strigulose; caudex usually subterranean, branched, rhizomatous, to 10 cm. **Stems** ascending to ± erect, usually strigulose, sometimes glabrescent. **Leaves** 3–13 cm; stipules connate throughout, 4–10 mm, scarious or subherbaceous; leaflets 15–29, blades narrowly elliptic, (3–)5–12(–18) mm, apex rounded or slightly retuse, surfaces strigulose. **Peduncles** 1–10 cm. **Racemes** 4–15-flowered, flowers ascending-erect; axis 0.5–2.5 cm in fruit; bracts 2–3 mm; bracteoles 0. **Pedicels** 1 mm. **Flowers** 16–22 mm; calyx cylindric, 7–10 mm, sparsely or densely strigulose, sometimes also pilosulous, tube 5–7.8 mm, lobes linear, 2.5–5.5 mm; corolla blue-violet, pale blue, or pale lilac, often drying yellowish; keel 12–15 mm. **Legumes** ascending to spreading or erect, straight or slightly incurved, narrowly oblong to narrowly ellipsoidal, 12–15 × 3 mm, widely keeled ventrally, sulcate dorsally, thin, densely hirsutulous with white hairs; stipe 0.5 mm. $2n = 16$.

Flowering Jul–Aug. Sandy-gravelly soils; ca. 2100 m; introduced; Wyo.; c Asia.

Astragalus tibetanus has been known for nearly two decades from a single collection in a more or less natural habitat in extreme northwestern Fremont County, originating from what is described as a sandy-gravelly bench above Wind River, in flowering and fruiting condition in late July 1991 (*Dorn 5274*, NY, RM). Dorn revisited the site in 2008, noting *A. tibetanus* to be abundant, and that it also occurred about 16 km downstream near Crowheart in highway rights-of-way.

Astragalus tibetanus, classified in sect. *Hypoglottidei*, will key to 180. *A. agrestis* in the key to species. Similar to *A. agrestis*, it has a subterranean crown and long, rhizomatous caudex branches, the stems and branches terminating in dense, subcapitate racemes, with ascending flowers and fruits. The fruits have stipes about 0.5 mm, and are approximately 3 mm wide, slender, straight or slightly incurved, 2-chambered, dorsally sulcate, to 18 mm, and hirsutulous with white hairs. A. G. Borissova et al. (1965) noted that there are two intergrading pubescence phases in *A. tibetanus*: one with white hairs on the fruits occurs at lower elevations in central Asia; the other, with black hairs, from montane regions.

356. **Astragalus asotinensis** Björk & Fishbein, Novon 16: 299, fig. 1. 2006 • Asotin milkvetch [C] [E]

Plants perennial, sparsely strigose, hairs basifixed. **Stems** decumbent to ascending, sparsely strigose. **Leaves** 5–8 cm; stipules distinct throughout, 1.7–3.3 mm; leaflets 15–23, blades obovate-cuneate or oblong-oblanceolate, 7–16 mm, apex mostly truncate-retuse to obtuse, surfaces sparsely pubescent abaxially, nearly glabrous adaxially. **Peduncles** 6–10 cm. **Racemes** 7–20-flowered, flowers ascending at anthesis; axis 1.5–4.5 cm in fruit; bracts 1.4–2.7 mm; bracteoles usually 2. **Pedicels** 2 mm. **Flowers** 14–19 mm; calyx campanulate to subcylindric, 7.5–8.8 mm, tube 6–7.3 mm, teeth 1.5 mm, acuminate; corolla creamy-white, often tinged rose or lavender, especially on keel tip; banner recurved through 40–50°. **Legumes** spreading or pendulous, falcately oblong, laterally compressed, 28–37 × 3–3.5 mm, bicarinate, unilocular, sparsely white-strigose; stipe 6–9 mm. **Seeds** unknown.

Flowering late Apr–early May. Dry limestone hillsides, among bunchgrasses and xeric shrubs; of conservation concern; 400–900 m; Idaho, Wash.

Astragalus asotinensis is restricted to Lime Hill at the northern extreme of Hells Canyon, divided by the Snake River, in Nez Perce County, Idaho, and Asotin County, Washington. It will key to 63. *A. sclerocarpus*, from which it differs in having sparse pubescence, trichomes shorter than 0.5 mm, 15–23 oblong to narrowly oblong leaflets, and a pod that is 3–3.5 mm and incurved 70–110°. It is also similar to *A. sinuatus*, from which it differs by its straight, appressed calyx pubescence and oblong to narrowly oblong leaflets.

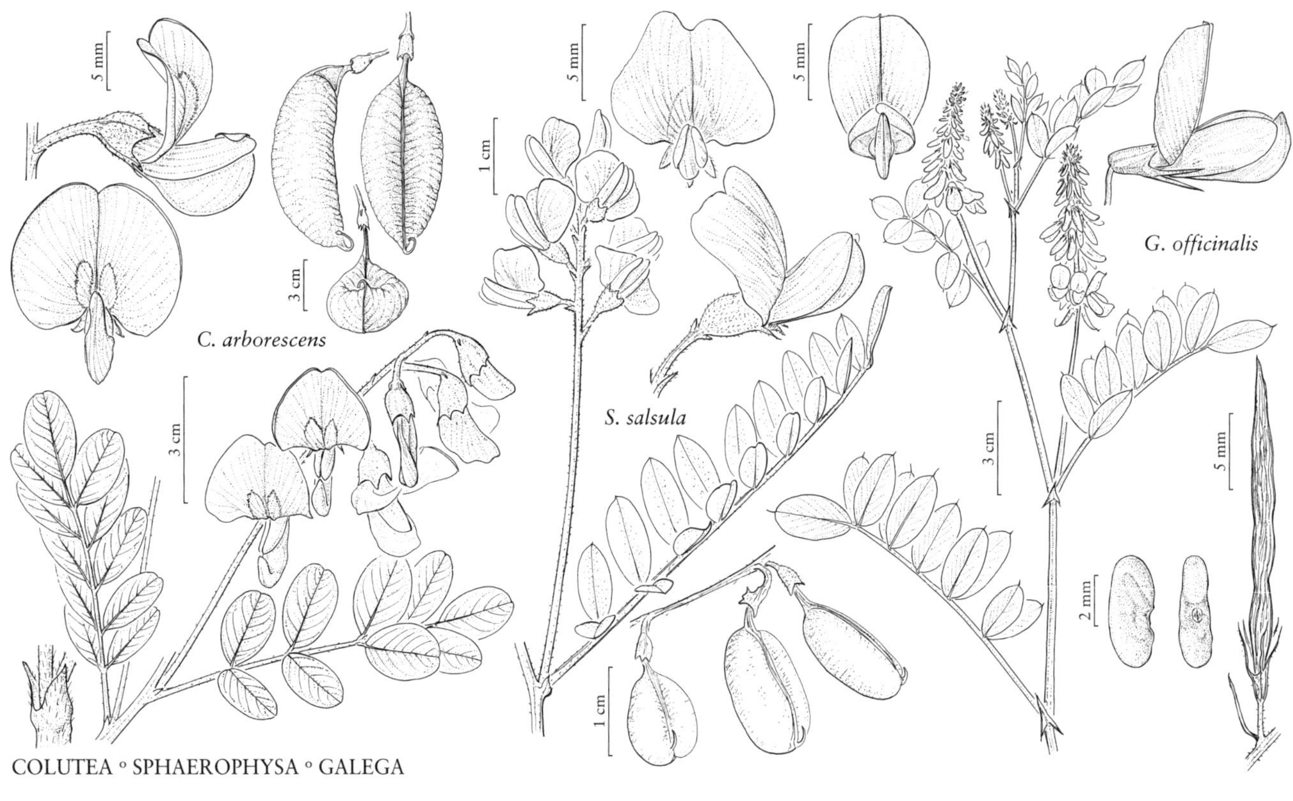

COLUTEA ∘ SPHAEROPHYSA ∘ GALEGA

135qqqq. ASTRAGALUS Linnaeus sect. KELSEYANI S. L. Welsh & B. L. Corbin in S. L. Welsh and N. D. Atwood, Pl. Endem. Geoendem. Areas Utah ed. 2, 86. 2012 [E]

Herbs perennial, low, shortly caulescent; caudex subterranean. **Hairs** malpighian. **Stems** few or several. **Stipules** distinct, at least on aerial stems. **Leaves** odd-pinnate, petiolate; leaflets (5 or)7–11(or 13). **Racemes** short, loosely few-flowered, flowers spreading. **Calyx tubes** cylindric. **Corollas** white tinged pinkish, banner recurved through 20–30°, keel apex blunt, rounded. **Legumes** deciduous, sessile, spreading, ovoid or ovoid-ellipsoid, bladdery-inflated (turgid), cartilaginous, bilocular except at short beak. **Seeds** ca. 26.

Species 1: Utah.

357. Astragalus kelseyae B. L. Corbin, Madroño 58: 185, figs. 1, 2. 2011 [C] [E]

Plants prostrate, 10–20 cm, from branched caudex, branches slender, subterranean for 2–10 cm+. **Stems** decumbent, with ascending tips, silvery green hairy. **Leaves** 3–5.2 cm; stipules triangular, 1–4.5 mm, papery; leaflets: terminal ones jointed, blades flat, oval to obovate, (5.7–)8–9.3(–15) × (4.5–)6–7.5(–12) mm, surfaces strigose. **Peduncles** prostrate, 1.3–2.5 cm, shorter than subtending leaf. **Racemes** 2–7-flowered; axis 0.5–1.2 cm in fruit; bracts 1.5–2.5 mm, hyaline; bracteoles 0. **Pedicels** 2.5–3 mm. **Flowers** 20–23 mm; calyx 11.4–12.7 mm, tube 8.7–9.7 mm, lobes subulate, 2.7–3.5 mm; corolla white tinged pinkish, fading cream. **Legumes** often red-mottled, 37–47 × 23–33 mm (when pressed), hairy; sessile on thickened gynophore 1.2–1.5 mm. **Seeds** 26.

Flowering May–Sep. Talus openings on slopes, Gambel oak and bigtooth maple shrublands; of conservation concern; 1600–1700 m; Utah.

This distinctive species is known only from the Wasatch Mountains in Weber County.

136. COLUTEA Linnaeus, Sp. Pl. 2: 723. 1753; Gen. Pl. ed. 5, 323. 1754 • Bladder-senna [Greek *koloutea*, ancient name of a leguminous plant, or *koluo*, amputate, probably alluding to branch lopping supposedly resulting in death of plants] [I]

Peter W. Ball

Shrubs, unarmed. **Stems** erect to somewhat spreading, glabrous or pubescent. **Leaves** alternate, odd-pinnate; stipules present; petiolate; leaflets 7–13, blade margins entire, surfaces pubescent. **Inflorescences** 3–8-flowered, axillary, racemes; bracts absent; bracteoles present. **Flowers** papilionaceous; calyx campanulate, lobes 5; corolla bright yellow [orange- or brownish red], banner sometimes with red markings; stamens 10, diadelphous; anthers basifixed, opening laterally. **Fruits** legumes, stipitate, bladdery-inflated, straight [curved adaxially], ellipsoid-orbicular, indehiscent [opening apically], glabrate. **Seeds** ca. 10, orbicular-reniform; hilum lateral. $x = 8$.

Species ca. 25 (1 in the flora): introduced; Europe, Asia, n Africa; introduced also in South America; temperate regions.

SELECTED REFERENCES Browicz, K. 1963. The genus *Colutea* L.: A monograph. Monogr. Bot. 14: 1–136. Browicz, K. 1967. A supplement to the monograph of the genus *Colutea* L. Arbor. Kórnickie 12: 33–43.

1. Colutea arborescens Linnaeus, Sp. Pl. 2: 723. 1753 [F] [I]

Shrubs to 6 m, much-branched. **Stems** appressed-puberulent when young. **Leaves** 5–15 × 2–6 cm; stipules distinct, relatively small; leaflet blades elliptic to obovate or ovate, 15–30 × 10–20 mm, base cuneate, apex usually emarginate, mucronate, surfaces appressed-pubescent abaxially, glabrate adaxially. **Peduncles** 2–4 cm. **Racemes** 4–6 × 3–4 cm; bracteoles linear, 2 mm. **Pedicels** 5–8 mm in flower, 10–12 mm in fruit. **Flowers:** calyx actinomorphic or slightly zygomorphic, 5–8 mm, lobes linear to deltate, 1–3 mm; banner 16–20 × 10–15 mm; wings equaling or shorter than keel; style pubescent apically. **Fruits** pale greenish brown, sometimes reddish proximally, 5–8 × 3 cm, papery. **Seeds** 3–5 mm. $2n = 16$ (Europe).

Flowering late spring–early summer. Roadside scrub, disturbed ground; 10–2500 m; introduced; Ont.; Calif., Colo., Conn., Kans., Mass., Mich., Nev., N.J., N.Mex., N.Y., Ohio, Okla., Pa., R.I., Utah, W.Va.; Europe; w Asia; n Africa (Algeria); introduced also in s South America (Argentina).

Colutea arborescens is cultivated as an ornamental for its flowers and large, conspicuous fruits. In addition to *C. arborescens*, *C.* ×*media* Willdenow (*C. arborescens* Linnaeus × *C. orientalis* Miller) also is cultivated and may occur as a relic. The hybrid has a brownish red or dark orange corolla and a fruit that is dehiscent apically.

137. SPHAEROPHYSA de Candolle in A. P. de Candolle and A. L. P. P. de Candolle, Prodr. 2: 270. 1825 • Austrian peaweed or field pea [Greek *sphaera*, sphere, and *physa*, bladder, alluding to shape of inflated fruit] I

Richard R. Halse

Herbs, perennial, unarmed; with creeping rhizomes. **Stems** erect, strigulose. **Leaves** alternate, odd-pinnate; stipules present; petiolate; leaflets (9–)15–25, opposite, stipels absent, blade margins entire, surfaces glabrous or pubescent. **Inflorescences** 5–17-flowered, axillary, racemes; bracts and bracteoles present. **Flowers** papilionaceous; calyx campanulate, lobes 5; corolla dull brick-red or orange-red [blue], 10–15 mm; stamens 10, diadelphous; anthers basifixed; style bearded distally. **Fruits** legumes, stipitate, bladdery-inflated, ovoid or globose, indehiscent, pubescent. **Seeds** 40, reniform. $x = 8$.

Species 2 (1 in the flora): introduced; se Europe (Turkey), c, e Asia; introduced also in South America (Argentina).

SELECTED REFERENCE Barneby, R. C. 1964. *Sphaerophysa*. Mem. New York Bot. Gard. 13: 1162–1164.

1. Sphaerophysa salsula (Pallas) de Candolle in A. P. de Candolle and A. L. P. P. de Candolle, Prodr. 2: 271. 1825 • Alkali swainsonpea, swainsona F I W

Phaca salsula Pallas, Reise Russ. Reich. 3: 747, plate Bb. 1776; *Astragalus iochrous* Barneby; *Swainsona salsula* (Pallas) Taubert

Rhizomes woody, vigorous, horizontal, creeping, developing new shoots. **Aerial stems** unbranched or sparsely branched, 4–10(–15) dm. **Leaves** (3–)4–11 cm; stipules 1–4 mm; petiole 3–20 mm; leaflet blades oblong-obovate, narrowly oblong, or narrowly elliptic, 3–18 × 3–9 mm, apex retuse to obtuse, apiculate, or acute, surfaces strigulose abaxially, glabrous adaxially. **Peduncles** (2.5–)3–7(–9) cm, 5–18 cm in fruit. **Racemes** ascending; bracts 1–4 mm; bracteoles immediately subtending calyx, 0.5–1 mm. **Pedicels** 2.5–5 mm, in fruit ± recurved, thickened, 3–8 mm. **Flowers:** calyx persistent, 5–6 mm, strigulose, lobes triangular, 1.2–2 mm, subequal, shorter than tube, becoming papery; corolla drying lavender or brownish, 10–15 mm. **Legumes** green to purplish, sulcate abaxially, 13–35 mm, 10–20 mm diam. pressed, papery, membranous, semitransparent, strigulose to glabrate; stipe 4–8(–12) mm. **Seeds** brown to greenish or reddish brown, dull, smooth.

Flowering May–Sep; fruiting Jul–Oct. Disturbed sites, floodplains, roadsides, sagebrush communities, salt flats; 100–2400 m; introduced; Sask.; Ariz., Colo., Idaho, Kans., Mont., Nev., N.Mex., Oreg., Tex., Utah, Wash., Wyo.; c Asia; introduced also in South America (Argentina).

Sphaerophysa salsula is a state-listed noxious weed in California, Nevada, Oregon, and Washington; it is considered eradicated in California (J. M. DiTomaso and E. A. Healy 2007). It can form extensive colonies by its wide-spreading rhizomes. Plants generally occur in saline, sandy, riverine, and lacustrine soils.

138. GALEGA Linnaeus, Sp. Pl. 2: 714. 1753; Gen. Pl. ed. 5, 320. 1754 • [Greek *gala*, milk, alluding to increased milk production in mammals fed with the plants] I

Leila M. Shultz

Herbs, perennial, unarmed, non-aromatic (slightly sulfur-scented); caudex woody. **Stems** erect or ascending, not glandular, glabrous or sparsely pubescent. **Leaves** alternate, odd-pinnate; stipules present, persistent, deeply lobed, base sagittate; petiolate; leaflets 9–17(or 19), blade margins entire, surfaces glabrous or glabrate. **Inflorescences** 15–30(–38)-flowered, axillary, racemes; bracts present, persistent after anthesis, subulate. **Flowers** papilionaceous; calyx campanulate, lobes 5; corolla bluish lilac, reddish purple, or white; stamens 10, monadelphous, dimorphic; anthers alternately basifixed and versatile, versatile anthers on shorter filaments; ovary 2-loculed. **Fruits** legumes, stipitate, terete, elongated, torulose, linear-cylindric, dehiscent, glabrous. **Seeds** 2–10, oblong. x = 8.

Species ca. 5 (1 in the flora): introduced; e Europe, w Asia, Africa; introduced also in s South America, Pacific Islands (New Zealand), Australia.

1. Galega officinalis Linnaeus, Sp. Pl. 2: 714. 1753 • Goat's-rue, professor weed, galéga officinal [F] [I] [W]

Stems clumped from caudex, 40–140 cm. **Leaves** (6–)8–20 × (3–)6–10 cm; stipules opposite petiole, base sagittate, margins toothed; leaflet blades linear-elliptic, (15–)30–50 × 25–18 mm, apex mucronate. **Pedicels** reflexed at anthesis, erect in fruit, 2–4.5 mm, glabrous. **Flowers:** calyx campanulate, subactinomorphic, tube 2–2.5 mm, 10-veined, glabrous, teeth subequal, puberulent or glabrous; banner shallowly lobed, wings equal or subequal to keel, keel 7–11 mm, apex blunt. **Legumes** ascending, light green, shallowly torulose with constrictions between seeds, sutures prominent, 25–45 × 2–3 mm. 2n = 16.

Flowering early spring–late summer. Disturbed sites; 10–1500 m; introduced; Ont., Que.; Colo., Conn., D.C., Fla., Idaho, Ind., Maine, Mass., Nebr., N.Y., Ohio, Oreg., Pa., Utah, Wash., W.Va.; Eurasia; introduced also in s South America, Pacific Islands (New Zealand), Australia.

Galega officinalis was introduced as a forage plant in northern Utah during the early twentieth century by a professor at the Utah Agricultural College. The species quickly became weedy in agricultural sites and it was given the local name professor weed; it has become a noxious weed in most of its range in North America. The plants contain toxic alkaloids.

139. CARAGANA Fabricius, Enum. ed. 2, 421. 1763 • Pea tree [Mongolian *qaraqan* or Turkic *karaghan*, name for *Caragana arborescens*, the type species] [I]

Richard R. Halse

Shrubs or subshrubs [trees], armed or unarmed, stipules sometimes spine-tipped or spinescent, rachis spine-tipped. **Stems** erect or decumbent, glabrous or pubescent. **Leaves** alternate, sometimes clustered on spurs, even-pinnate, subpinnate, or appearing palmate [digitate]; stipules present, membranous when young, some with thickened midribs becoming bristle- or spinelike, or spinescent, 1.5–9 mm; rachis, when present, usually persistent; petiolate; leaflets 2–12[–20], opposite, blade margins entire, surfaces villous, glabrate, or glabrous. **Inflorescences** 1–4(or 5)-flowered, axillary, fasciculate or solitary, each peduncle-pedicel 1-flowered; bracts present, membranous, at base of peduncle, bracteoles present or absent, linear, minute, at base of peduncle and pedicel. **Flowers** papilionaceous; calyx persistent, tubular or campanulate, subgibbous, lobes 5, distinct, subequal, much shorter than tube, adaxial 2 usually smaller; corolla yellow or orange-yellow [rarely white or pink]; stamens 10, diadelphous; anthers uniform, dorsifixed; style straight or slightly curved. **Fruits** legumes, sessile, flattened, oblong or linear, dehiscent, non-septate, valves twisting in dehiscence, glabrous. **Seeds** [2 or]3–8, monochrome or mottled and streaked, oblong, ovoid, 4-angled, or globose [ellipsoid, subglobose, or reniform], smooth. x = 8.

Species 70–80 (3 in the flora): introduced; e Europe, w, c Asia.

The number and persistence of spines on *Caragana* species is variable. The leaf rachises may persist after the leaflets fall, becoming woody and spinescent, and may last a few years. The stipules also may become spinescent and persist; plants under cultivation seem to produce relatively few or no spines, which may be relatively short or reduced to a bristle (W. J. Bean 1970–1988, vol. 1).

Some species of *Caragana* are cold- and drought-resistant. They are cultivated extensively in Canada and the northern United States as ornamentals, for hedges, windbreaks, shelterbelts, and erosion control, and may persist. In addition to the three species treated here, some additional species of *Caragana* are cultivated in North America, including *C. microphylla* Lamarck, *C. pygmaea* de Candolle, *C. sinica* (Buc'hoz) Rehder, and *C. spinosa* de Candolle. Some of these are found only in arboreta or in specialty collections; others are more common. The three species treated here are the only taxa known to have become naturalized in the flora area.

Caragana needs worldwide revision because species boundaries are uncertain in some taxa; names associated with some plants growing in cultivation are doubtful.

1. Leaves even-pinnate, leaflets 6–12(or 14) . . . . 1. *Caragana arborescens*
1. Leaves appearing palmate or subpinnate, leaflets 2–4.
    2. Leaflet blades oblanceolate to linear-oblanceolate, mostly curved or sickle-shaped, 0.1–0.3(–0.4) cm wide . . . . 2. *Caragana aurantiaca*
    2. Leaflet blades oblong-obovate to cuneate-obovate, not curved, 0.8–1.4 cm wide . . . . . 3. *Caragana frutex*

1. Caragana arborescens Lamarck in J. Lamarck et al., Encycl. 1: 615. 1785 • Siberian pea tree or shrub F I

Robinia caragana Linnaeus, Sp. Pl. 2: 722. 1753

Shrubs, to 7 m, unarmed or weakly spiny, glabrous or puberulent. **Stems** erect, branched from near base, branchlets pubescent; bark gray-brown. **Leaves** even-pinnate; stipules 5–9 mm, spine-tipped or not; petiole 1–10 cm; rachis present, deciduous, 3–9 cm, spinescent; leaflets 6–12(or 14), blades elliptic or obovate to broadly oblong, 1–4 × 0.5–1.5 cm, base rounded to cuneate, apex rounded or truncate, mucronate, surfaces villous or glabrescent. **Inflorescences** with (1 or) 2–4(or 5) flowers per fascicle; peduncle-pedicel 1–6 cm, usually pubescent (often glabrous in fruit). **Flowers:** calyx broadly campanulate, 4.5–8 mm, teeth broadly triangular, 1–1.5 mm, sometimes appearing unlobed, pubescent or glabrescent, orifice villous; corolla yellow, 1.5–2.3 cm. **Legumes** reddish brown to brown, linear to oblong, 2.5–6 × 0.4–0.7 cm. **Seeds** 3–8, grayish yellow to dark or reddish brown, oblong or ovoid to 4-angled, 4–6 mm. $2n = 16$.

Flowering May–Jul; fruiting Jun–Aug. Pastures, fields, roadsides, fencerows, woods; 100–2500 m; introduced; Alta., B.C., Man., N.B., N.W.T., Ont., Que., Sask., Yukon; Alaska, Colo., Idaho, Ill., Iowa, Maine, Mass., Mich., Minn., Mont., Nebr., N.Mex., N.Dak., Oreg., S.Dak., Utah, Vt., Wash., Wis., Wyo.; Asia (Manchuria, Mongolia, Siberia).

Caragana arborescens is the most commonly cultivated *Caragana* in North America. It is cultivated in almost every Canadian province and in the United States from Maine to Oregon, from Alaska to California, and from North Dakota to Oklahoma; it is naturalized somewhat more narrowly. Shrubs may persist in cultivation and be found in abandoned yards and gardens. The plants are valued for drought and cold resistance and are planted both as an ornamental and for windbreaks. The shoots have been used for cordage; the leaves contain a blue pigment used as a dye; the seeds can be used as food for birds; and the nectar of the flowers provide food for bees (A. I. Pojarkova 1971b). There are named cultivars or varieties of Siberian pea tree, which often are based on growth form or leaflet size and shape.

2. Caragana aurantiaca Koehne, Deut. Dendrol., 340. 1893 • Dwarf pea shrub I

Shrubs or subshrubs, 0.5–1.5 m, armed or unarmed, strigulose or glabrate. **Stems** erect or decumbent, often intricately branched; bark dark greenish gray to brownish gray. **Leaves** appearing palmate; stipules 2–6 mm, usually spinose; petiole 0.1–0.2 cm, sometimes spine-tipped; rachis absent; leaflets (3 or)4, blades oblanceolate to linear-oblanceolate, mostly curved or sickle-shaped, often folded or involute, 0.5–1.7(–2.3) × 0.1–0.3(–0.4) cm, base attenuate, apex acute or acuminate, apiculate, surfaces glabrous. **Inflorescences** with 1(or 2) flowers per fascicle; peduncle-pedicel 0.4–1.6 cm, glabrous. **Flowers:** calyx broadly campanulate, 5–8 mm, teeth 1.5–2 mm, glabrous, orifice ciliate; corolla orange-yellow, 1.5–2.2 cm. **Legumes** reddish brown, oblong, 1.5–4 × 0.3–0.4 cm. **Seeds** 4–8, greenish to reddish brown, ovoid to 4-angled, 3–4 mm. $2n = 16$.

Flowering Jun–Jul; fruiting Jun–Sep. Roadsides; 1700–2600 m; introduced; Colo., N.Dak.; c Asia.

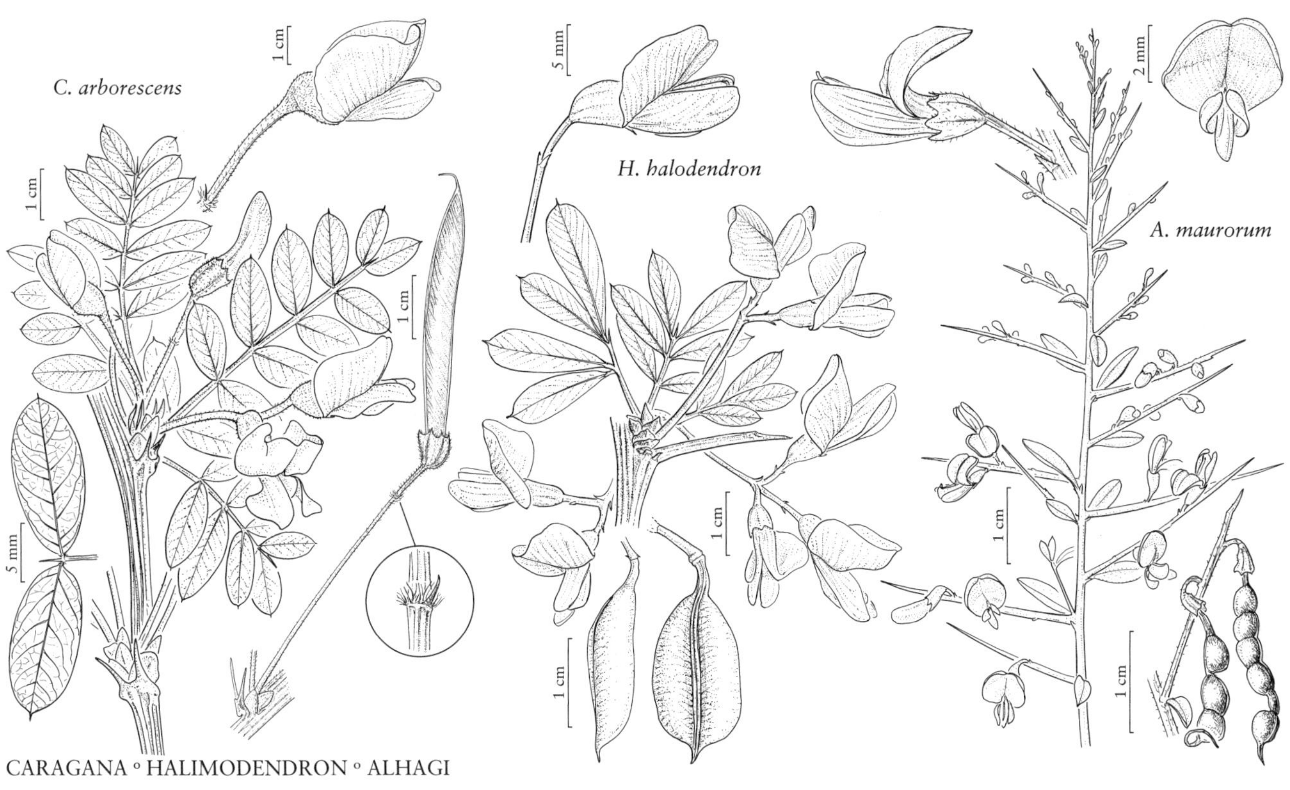

CARAGANA ◦ HALIMODENDRON ◦ ALHAGI

Caragana aurantiaca is known to be cultivated in Manitoba, Nova Scotia, Ontario, Saskatchewan, Colorado, Idaho, Iowa, Massachusetts, New York, Nevada, North Dakota, and South Dakota.

3. **Caragana frutex** (Linnaeus) K. Koch, Dendrologie 1: 48. 1869 • Russian pea shrub [I]

Robinia frutex Linnaeus, Sp. Pl. 2: 723. 1753; *Caragana frutescens* (Linnaeus) Medikus; *Robinia frutescens* Linnaeus

Shrubs, 1–3 m, unarmed to strongly spiny, glabrate. **Stems** erect, profusely branched; bark brown, glossy, striped. **Leaves** appearing palmate or subpinnate; stipules 1.5–5 mm, sometimes soft-spinose; petiole 0.2–2 cm, sometimes spine-tipped; rachis absent; leaflets 2–4, blades oblong-obovate to cuneate-obovate, 1–2.5 × 0.8–1.4 cm, base cuneate, apex obtuse to acute and apiculate, surfaces glaucous, glabrous. **Inflorescences** with 1–3 flowers per fascicle; peduncle-pedicel 1–3 cm, glabrous. **Flowers:** calyx tubular, 5–8 mm, teeth broadly triangular, 1–1.5 mm, glabrous, orifice ciliate; corolla bright yellow, 1.8–2.5 cm. **Legumes** dark reddish brown, narrowly oblong, 2–4.5 × 0.3–0.4 cm. **Seeds** 6, dark reddish brown, globose to 4-angled, 4–5 mm. $2n = 32$.

Flowering May; fruiting May–Oct. Slopes above creeks; 70–800 m; introduced; Ont.; e Europe; w, c Asia (Russia, Siberia).

Caragana frutex is known to be cultivated in Manitoba, Ontario, Prince Edward Island, Quebec, Saskatchewan, Colorado, Illinois, Indiana, Iowa, Massachusetts, Minnesota, Oklahoma, South Dakota, and Wisconsin. Some named cultivars or varieties of *C. frutex* are based on growth form, leaflet size, etc.; none are recognized here.

140. HALIMODENDRON Fischer ex de Candolle in A. P. de Candolle and A. L. P. P. de Candolle, Prodr. 2: 269. 1825 • Russian salt tree, Siberian sandthorn [Greek *halimos*, maritime, and *dendron*, tree, alluding to habitat] [I]

Richard R. Halse

Shrubs, 1–3 m, usually armed, leaf rachis spine-tipped, stipules sometimes spinescent. **Stems** sprawling or ascending, glabrous. **Leaves** alternate or clustered on spurs, even-pinnate; stipules present, 1–4 mm; petiolate; leaflets 2 or 4(–10), sessile, stipels absent, blade margins entire, surfaces glaucous, glabrous or sericeous. **Inflorescences** 1–5-flowered, axillary from spurs, racemes [umbels]; bracts and bracteoles present. **Flowers** papilionaceous; calyx broadly campanulate, lobes 5; corolla purple to lilac or white; stamens 10, diadelphous; anthers dorsifixed. **Fruits** legumes, stipitate, turgid, obovoid to ellipsoid or oblong, tardily dehiscent, indented along sutures, glabrous. **Seeds** 2–8, subreniform, smooth. $x = 8$.

Species 1: introduced; e Europe, w, c Asia.

1. Halimodendron halodendron (Pallas) Voss ex D. Fairchild, Invent. Seeds U.S.D.A. Bur. Pl. Industr. 34: 14. 1915 [F] [I]

Robinia halodendron Pallas, Reise Russ. Reich. 2: 741, plate W [left center]. 1773

Shrubs gray or bluish. **Roots** spreading, 1–3 m. **Bark** reddish brown. **Stems** with spine-tipped, persistent leaf rachises, 2–6 cm. **Leaves** 3–4 cm; stipules subulate; leaflet blade cuneate-obovate or oblanceolate, 5–35 × 2–11 mm, leathery, base tapered, apex cuspidate, mucro 0.5–1 mm. **Peduncles** 1–4 cm. **Racemes** 1–3 per spur, 3–4.5 cm; bracts 1–2 mm, membranous; bracteoles paired, from base of calyx or distal part of pedicel, 0.5–1 mm, membranous. **Pedicels** 3–10 mm. **Flowers:** calyx persistent, ± regular, often ± gibbous, 3–7 mm, finely hairy; lobes broadly triangular, 0.5–1 mm, margins ciliate; corolla 13–20 mm; ovary glabrous; style glabrous; stigma terminal. **Legumes** yellow-brown, unilocular, 10–30 × 7–12 mm, rugose, leathery to woody; stipe 2–5 mm.

Flowering Apr–Jul, fruiting Aug–Oct. Disturbed areas; 50–1800 m; introduced; Sask.; Utah; e Europe (Russia), w, c Asia (China, Iran, Mongolia, Siberia, Turkey).

Halimodendron halodendron is cultivated as an ornamental in British Columbia, California, Manitoba, Massachusetts, Michigan, New York, North Dakota, Oklahoma, Ontario, Pennsylvania, Saskatchewan, Utah, and Wyoming; it has been reported from Montana. It is sometimes used for erosion control. In some climates, it survives better if grafted onto root stocks of Siberian pea tree, *Caragana arborescens*.

California has listed *Halimodendron halodendron* a noxious weed; known naturalized populations there have been eradicated (J. M. DiTomaso and E. A. Healy 2007). The species does not appear to escape cultivation readily, and reports of it being naturalized in other states (D. Isely 1998) are unconfirmed.

141. ALHAGI Gagnebin, Acta Helv. Phys.-Math. 2: 59. 1755 • Camel-thorn [Arabic *al-haj*, pilgrim, or *al-agul*, thorn, alluding to plant's common occurrence along pilgrim's journey or thorny nature] [I]

Richard R. Halse

Subshrubs, [shrubs], armed. **Stems** erect, much-branched [sometimes simple], pubescent [glabrous]. **Leaves** alternate, unifoliolate; stipules present; shortly petiolate; leaflet blade margins entire, surfaces glabrous or pubescent. **Inflorescences** (1 or)2–7-flowered, axillary racemes; bracts present; bracteoles present. **Flowers** papilionaceous; calyx campanulate, lobes 5; corolla pink to reddish purple; stamens 10, diadelphous; anthers dorsifixed; style filiform, glabrous; stigma terminal. **Fruits** loments, shortly stipitate, exserted, moniliform to torulose, terete, linear to curved, indehiscent, glabrous [pubescent]. **Seeds** (1 or)2–8(–10), reniform to quadrangular. $x = 8$.

Species 1–5 (1 in the flora): introduced; se Europe, c Asia (China, India, Mongolia), ne Africa (Mediterranean Basin); introduced also in South Africa, Australia.

The number of species recognized in *Alhagi* is subject to interpretation based on robustness of growth, calyx lobe development, fruit shape, and indument of fruits, calyces, stems, and leaves. K. K. Shaperenko (1972) and K. H. Rechinger (1984b) recognized five species, while G. P. Yakovlev (1979) recognized one species with five subspecies.

Alhagi has served as fodder for camels and other animals in arid areas. In summer, some plants exude a sweet gummy material on the stems and branches that hardens into reddish brown lumps, which are collected by Arab nomads and are used as a food delicacy; this substance has also been used medicinally. The plants are sometimes grown in botanical gardens as a curiosity; they can be serious weeds in both their native and introduced habitats.

1. **Alhagi maurorum** Medikus, Vorles. Churpfälz. Phys.-Ökon. Ges. 2: 397. 1787 • Caspian or Persian manna [F] [I] [W]

Hedysarum alhagi Linnaeus, Sp. Pl. 2: 745. 1753; *Alhagi pseudalhagi* (M. Bieberstein) Desvaux ex B. Keller & Shaparenko

Subshrubs 0.3–2 m. **Roots** extensively creeping, to 2.5 m underground. **Stems** often intricately branched, greenish, strigose to glabrate; sterile branchlets thorn-tipped, these subtended by leaves or not, 1–5 cm. **Leaves:** stipules caducous, subulate to lanceolate-ovate, 0.5–3 mm; leaflet blade linear, elliptic, oblanceolate to narrowly obovate, or oblong, 3–35 × 1–12 mm, surfaces usually minutely red-dotted. **Racemes** simple; axis prolonged as a thorn; bracts subulate, 0.5–1 mm. **Pedicels** 1–2 mm. **Flowers:** calyx persistent, 2–3.2 mm, glabrous; lobes connate or distinct, subequal, 0.2–0.5 mm (shorter than tube), relatively broad, margins sometimes puberulent; petals distinct, 7–9.5 mm. **Loments** 0.5–3 cm, usually breaking between seeds; stipes nearly as long as calyx. **Seeds** yellowish to greenish brown or dark brown. $2n = 16$.

Flowering May–Sep; fruiting Jul–Oct. Roadsides, ditches, disturbed agricultural areas, sandy areas along rivers, alkaline meadows, playas, arid regions; 200–1600 m; introduced; Ariz., Calif., Colo., Idaho, Nev., N.Mex., Tex., Utah, Wash.; w Eurasia.

The stems and leaves of North American plants may be glabrous or pubescent, sometimes densely so. Young growth is almost always densely strigose; older stems and leaves may be essentially glabrous. The calyces and fruits are glabrous.

Alhagi maurorum is a state listed weed in Arizona, California, Colorado, Nevada, New Mexico, Oregon, Texas, and Washington. Eradication programs have eliminated most populations in California (J. M. DiTomaso and E. A. Healy 2007).

For a discussion of the choice of a specific epithet for the plants growing in North America see D. Isely (1998) and R. C. Barneby (1989). C. S. Awmack and J. M. Lock (2002) have divided *Alhagi maurorum* into two subspecies based in part on indument of the ovary and the shape of the calyx. These traits are variable. North American plants belong to subsp. *maurorum*.

Alhagi camelorum Fischer is an illegitimate name that pertains here.

142. HEDYSARUM Linnaeus, Sp. Pl. 2: 745. 1753; Gen. Pl. ed. 5, 332. 1754

• Sweetvetch, sainfoin [Greek *hedysma* or *hedys*, sweetness, and *aron*, ointment or fragrance, probably alluding to ancient use of *Trigonella foenum-graecum* seed oil, applied to the present taxon by Linnaeus]

Stanley L. Welsh

Herbs, perennial, unarmed; with ligneous taproot. **Stems** decumbent to erect or ascending, solid, terete, pubescent, hairs basifixed; from branching subterranean to superficial caudex. **Leaves** alternate, odd-pinnate; stipules present, slightly adnate to petiole base, ± connate-sheathing, often suffused with purple, lanceolate, simple or bidentate, scarious; petiolate, petiole much shorter than or subequal to blade; leaflets 5–27, opposite or alternate, petiolulate, blade margins entire, surfaces mostly pubescent, sometimes glabrous adaxially. **Inflorescences** 5–60-flowered, axillary, racemes, sometimes subcapitate; bracts present, 1 per flower; bracteoles usually 2. **Flowers** papilionaceous; calyx campanulate, lobes 5; corolla usually pink, pink-purple, lavender-pink, red-purple, lilac, lilac-purple, or yellow, rarely white, keel much exceeding wings, somewhat longer than banner, broadly truncate, apex prominent, oblique; stamens 10, diadelphous; anthers dorsifixed; ovary enclosed in staminal sheath; style glabrous. **Fruits** loments, stipitate, pendulous to spreading, compressed, straight, narrowly ellipsoid, indehiscent (breaking transversely), constricted into 1–8, 1-seeded segments, glabrous or pubescent, rarely with processes. **Seeds** 1 per segment, brown, flattened, reniform-ovoid, glossy. $x = 7$.

Species ca. 50 (4 in the flora): North America, Europe, Asia (Asia Minor).

SELECTED REFERENCES Northstrom, T. E. 1974. The Genus *Hedysarum* in North America. Ph.D. dissertation. Brigham Young University. Northstrom, T. E. and S. L. Welsh. 1970. Revision of the *Hedysarum boreale* complex. Great Basin Naturalist 30: 109–130. Rollins, R. C. 1940b. Studies in the genus *Hedysarum* in North America. Rhodora 42: 217–239.

1. Leaflet blade veins obscure; loment margins moderately or not winged; calyx lobes subequal to markedly unequal in size; wing auricles distinct, blunt, shorter than claw . . . . 1. *Hedysarum boreale*
1. Leaflet blade veins conspicuous; loment margins narrowly or conspicuously winged; calyx lobes equal or nearly so; wing auricles connate, linear, nearly equal or equal to claw.
   2. Flowers 10–19(–22) mm (when greater than 16 mm, then from north of 50th parallel), corollas usually lilac- to pink-purple, rarely white; loment segments 5.5–12 × 3.5–6 mm, margins narrowly winged; leaflet blades lanceolate to oblong, elliptic, or lanceolate-elliptic . . . . 2. *Hedysarum alpinum*
   2. Flowers (14–)16–25 mm, corollas usually yellow to pale yellow, or shades of pink or purple, rarely white; loment segments 7–14.5(–18) × 5.5–10.2(–11) mm, margins conspicuously winged; leaflet blades lanceolate to ovate, elliptic, oblong, or lanceolate-oblong.
      3. Corollas yellow to pale yellow, 14–20 mm; loment segments 5.5–9 mm wide, glabrous . . . . 3. *Hedysarum sulphurescens*
      3. Corollas usually lavender-pink or lilac- to pink-purple, rarely white, 16–25 mm; loment segments 5.6–10.2(–11) mm wide, pubescent or glabrous. . . . . 4. *Hedysarum occidentale*

1. Hedysarum boreale Nuttall, Gen. N. Amer. Pl. 2: 110. 1818 • Northern sweetvetch [E]

Stems decumbent to erect, usually much branched, 1.5–7 dm. **Leaves** 3–12(–14) cm; stipules pale brown, sometimes streaked, 2–10 mm; leaflets 5–15, blades usually oblong to elliptic, lanceolate-oblong, or ovate, rarely linear, 7–40 × 2–19 mm, veins obscure, surfaces strigose abaxially, strigose or glabrous adaxially. **Peduncles** 2.8–15 cm. **Racemes** 5–45-flowered, axis 5–28.5 cm in fruit; bracts 2–4 mm. **Pedicels** 0.8–4.5 mm. **Flowers** ascending at anthesis; calyx 4.5–8 mm; tube 2–3.5 mm, strigose; lobes subulate, 2–6 mm, subequal to markedly unequal; corolla usually red-purple, pink, magenta, or purple, rarely white, 10–22(–26) mm; wing auricles distinct, blunt, shorter than claw. **Loments:** segments 2–8, 4.5–9 × 4–6.2 mm, margins prickly or not, not winged to moderately winged, prominently reticulate, usually crisp-puberulent to minutely strigose, rarely glabrous.

Subspecies 2 (2 in the flora): North America.

1. Flowers 10–19 mm, usually pink to magenta or purple, rarely white; racemes 8–23 cm; loment segments 2–5. . . . 1a. *Hedysarum boreale* subsp. *boreale*
1. Flowers (14–)18–22(–26) mm, usually red-purple, sometimes pink, rarely white; racemes 2–10 (–15) cm; loment segments 3–8. . . . . 1b. *Hedysarum boreale* subsp. *mackenziei*

1a. Hedysarum boreale Nuttall subsp. **boreale** [E]

Hedysarum boreale var. *cinerascens* (Rydberg) Rollins; *H. boreale* var. *gremiale* (Rollins) Northstrom & S. L. Welsh; *H. boreale* var. *obovatum* Rollins; *H. boreale* var. *utahense* (Rydberg) Rollins; *H. carnosulum* Greene; *H. cinerascens* Rydberg; *H. gremiale* Rollins; *H. mackenziei* Richardson var. *canescens* B. Fedtschenko; *H. mackenziei* var. *fraseri* B. Boivin; *H. mackenziei* var. *pabulare* (A. Nelson) Kearney & Peebles; *H. pabulare* A. Nelson; *H. pabulare* var. *rivulare* L. O. Williams; *H. utahense* Rydberg

Stems usually branched distally, (1.7–)2.5–7 dm. **Leaves** 3–12 cm; stipules usually pale brown, sometimes brown-streaked; leaflets 5–15, blades 7–35 × 2–19 mm, surfaces pubescent abaxially, pubescent or glabrous adaxially. **Racemes** 13–45-flowered, elongated, 8–23 cm. **Flowers:** corolla usually pink to magenta (fading pink to lavender) or purple, rarely white, 10–19 mm. **Loments:** segments 2–5, rarely black-pigmented, 6.5–9 × 5.4–6.2 mm. **2*n*** = 16.

Flowering late spring–summer. Short-grass prairies, salt-desert shrub, sagebrush, pinyon-juniper, juniper, mountain brush, and aspen communities; 500–2500 m; Alta., B.C., Man., Sask.; Ariz., Colo., Idaho, Mont., Nev., N.Mex., N.Dak., Okla., Oreg., S.Dak., Tex., Utah, Wyo.

T. E. Northstrom (1974) attempted to recognize two taxa from among the materials included within the concept of subsp. *boreale*, based on degree and position of pubescence on the leaflets. The attempt resulted in a not very convincing segregation, which is not clearly geographically correlated. Consequently, all are treated here in subsp. *boreale*. Specimens from northeastern Utah in which the loment segments bear lateral prickles have been recognized as *Hedysarum boreale* var. *gremiale*.

1b. Hedysarum boreale Nuttall subsp. **mackenziei** (Richardson) S. L. Welsh, Great Basin Naturalist 28: 152. 1968 (as mackenzii) • Sainfoin de Mackenzie [E]

Hedysarum mackenziei Richardson in J. Franklin, Narr. Journey Polar Sea, 745. 1823 (as mackenzii); *H. americanum* (Michaux ex Pursh) Britton var. *mackenziei* (Richardson) Britton; *H. boreale* subsp. *dasycarpum* (Turczaninow) D. F. Murray & Elven; *H. boreale* var. *leucanthum* (Greene) M. E. Jones; *H. boreale* var. *mackenziei* (Richardson) C. L. Hitchcock; *H. dasycarpum* Turczaninow; *H. leucanthum* (Greene) Greene; *H. mackenziei* var. *leucanthum* Greene

Stems usually unbranched distally, 1.5–5(–6) dm. **Leaves** 3–12(–14) cm; stipules usually stramineous; leaflets 9–15, blades 10–40 × 3–14 mm, surfaces pubescent abaxially, glabrous adaxially. **Racemes** 5–20-flowered, 2–10(–15) cm. **Flowers:** corolla usually red-purple (fading dark purple), sometimes pink, rarely white, (14–)18–22(–26) mm. **Loments:** segments 3–8, margins and areolae often black-pigmented, 4.5–8 × 4–5.5 mm. **2*n*** = 16.

Flowering summer. Stream banks, gravel bars, sea beach ridges, terraces, mud flats, lacustrine deposits in willow, aspen, spruce, and along ridges in alpine tundra communities; 0–1900(–2200) m; Alta., B.C., Man., Nfld. and Labr. (Nfld.), N.W.T., Nunavut, Ont., Que., Sask., Yukon; Alaska, Oreg., Wash.

Subspecies *mackenziei* is the common phase of the species throughout northern North America; it is especially common on gravel bars where it serves as an ecological pioneer. In Alberta and southern British Columbia, it is somewhat transitional with subsp.

boreale. The plants at higher elevations in the mountains of northern British Columbia, Yukon, and Alaska are often very short, but maintain the large, dark flowers of the subspecies.

2. Hedysarum alpinum Linnaeus, Sp. Pl. 2: 750. 1753 • Alpine sweetvetch, sainfoin alpin

Hedysarum alpinum subsp. *americanum* (Michaux) B. Fedtschenko; *H. alpinum* [unranked] *americanum* Michaux; *H. alpinum* var. *americanum* (Michaux) Pursh; *H. alpinum* var. *grandiflorum* Rollins; *H. alpinum* subsp. *philoscia* (A. Nelson) Á. Löve & D. Löve; *H. alpinum* var. *philoscia* (A. Nelson) Rollins; *H. americanum* (Michaux) Britton; *H. philoscia* A. Nelson; *H. truncatum* Eastwood

Stems ascending to erect, 1–9(–11) dm. **Leaves** 4–16 cm; stipules 5–25 mm; leaflets 7–27, blades lanceolate to oblong, elliptic, or lanceolate-elliptic, 10–50 × 3–15 mm, veins conspicuous, surfaces sparsely strigose abaxially, especially along midvein, glabrous adaxially. **Peduncles** 6–17 cm. **Racemes** 5–50-flowered, axis 2–30 cm in fruit; bracts 1–4 mm. **Pedicels** 1–3.5 mm. **Flowers** ascending to declined at anthesis; calyx 3.5–7.5 mm; tube 2–5 mm, puberulent; lobes triangular, 1–2.5 mm, equal or nearly so; corolla usually lilac- to pink-purple, rarely white, 10–19(–22) mm; wing auricles connate, linear, nearly equal or equal to claw. **Loments:** segments (1 or)2–5, 5.5–12 × 3.5–6 mm, margins narrowly winged, prominently reticulate, glabrous or pubescent. $2n$ = 14 [16].

Flowering late spring–summer. Sand and gravel bars, stream banks, alder, aspen, birch, spruce, and tundra communities; 30–3400 m; Alta., B.C., Man., N.B., Nfld. and Labr., N.W.T., Nunavut, Ont., Que., Sask., Yukon; Alaska, Maine, Mich., Mont., N.H., N.Dak., R.I., S.Dak., Vt., Wyo.; n Eurasia.

Hedysarum alpinum has been regarded in the past as belonging to two or more species, or as a single species with at least three infraspecific taxa. T. E. Northstrom (1974) treated the North American materials of *H. alpinum* as indistinguishable from the Eurasian counterparts, thereby discounting the recognition of North American specimens as a separate taxon, but recognized three almost completely confluent taxa at varietal level among the American representatives. Variety *grandiflorum*, known from harsh habitats from western Alaska to Northwest Territories and east to Labrador and Newfoundland, consists of dwarf plants having compact inflorescences and flowers longer than 16 mm, and var. *philoscia*, known from southern Canada south to Wyoming and South Dakota, stands on the character of pubescent loments. However, the beadlike, uniformly sized loment segments are at least somewhat distinctive. The characters regarded by previous workers as diagnostic fail singly, and in combination, they are not correlated with other morphological characteristics, and the geographical correlation is tenuous at best. It has been determined that dwarf plants with compact inflorescences occur with or nearby the larger flowered dwarf specimens, and larger flowered specimens with elongate inflorescences are known, sometimes on tall plants as well. Glabrous loments occur within the supposed distribution of the variety with pubescent loments, and plants with pubescent loments occur sporadically through much of the range of the species northward. Therefore, it seems probable that the features are at least in part ecologically induced, and the better course is to treat all of the specimens as belonging within the variability of a single broadly distributed species.

Hedysarum alpinum differs in degree only from the closely allied *H. occidentale*, with which it is largely allopatric. Specimens assigned to *H. alpinum* var. *grandiflorum* closely simulate high elevation phases of *H. occidentale* in habit and flower size. A flowering specimen of unknown locality would be difficult to identify. Occasional specimens within the range of *H. occidentale* share the small floral size of *H. alpinum* and are essentially indistinguishable without mature or nearly mature fruit.

Hedysarum auriculatum Eastwood, not Link, is an illegitimate name that pertains here.

3. Hedysarum sulphurescens Rydberg, Bull. Torrey Bot. Club 24: 251. 1897 • Sulfur sweetvetch [E]

Hedysarum flavescens J. M. Coulter & Fisher, Bot. Gaz. 18: 300. 1893, not Regel & Schmalhausen 1882; *H. albiflorum* (Macoun) B. Fedtschenko; *H. boreale* Nuttall var. *flavescens* B. Fedtschenko

Stems ascending to erect, 1–6(–9) dm. **Leaves** (3–)7–12 cm; stipules 8–15 mm; leaflets (5–)9–17, blades elliptic or lanceolate-oblong, 9–40 × 4.5–15(–21) mm, veins conspicuous, surfaces strigose abaxially, glabrous adaxially. **Peduncles** 4.5–16 cm. **Racemes** (6–)10–60-flowered, axis 2.5–22 cm in fruit; bracts 2–6 mm. **Pedicels** 1–3.5(–4) mm. **Flowers** usually declined at anthesis; calyx 3–6 mm; tube 1.5–4 mm, puberulent; lobes triangular to subulate, 1–2.5(–3) mm, equal or nearly so; corolla yellow to pale yellow, 14–20 mm; wing auricles connate, linear, nearly equal or equal to claw. **Loments:** segments 1–4, 7–13 × 5.5–9 mm, margins conspicuously winged, prominently reticulate, glabrous.

Flowering late spring–summer. Fescue prairies, aspen parklands, pine or spruce woodlands; 700–2600 m; Alta., B.C.; Idaho, Mont., Oreg., Wash., Wyo.

Hedysarum sulphurescens is a near ally of *H. occidentale*, with which it shares a large portion of its range, and from which it differs mainly in flower color. The two taxa are apparently partitioned by subtle habitat differences and seldom occur closely juxtaposed. The morphological differences, though small and of little consequence in other plant groups, seem to support evolutionary processes that keep them separate.

4. Hedysarum occidentale Greene, Pittonia 3: 19. 1896 • Western sweetvetch E F

Stems decumbent to erect, (1.2–)2–9.5 dm. **Leaves** 3.5–23 cm; stipules 10–17 mm; leaflets 9–19, blades lanceolate to ovate, elliptic, or oblong, 5–40 × 3–16 mm, veins conspicuous, surfaces usually pubescent, rarely glabrous adaxially. **Peduncles** (3–)6–15 cm. **Racemes** 10–50-flowered, axis 4–25 cm in fruit; bracts 1–4 mm. **Pedicels** 1–3.5 mm. **Flowers** usually declined at anthesis; calyx 3.5–11 mm; tube 3–9 mm, puberulent; lobes subulate to triangular, 0.5–2 mm, equal or nearly so; corolla usually lavender-pink or lilac- to pink-purple, rarely white, 16–25 mm; wing auricles connate, linear, nearly equal or equal to claw. **Loments:** segments (1 or)2–5, 7–14.5(–18) × 5.6–10.2(–11) mm, margins conspicuously winged, prominently reticulate, pubescent or glabrous.

Varieties 2 (2 in the flora): w North America.

1. Leaflet blades usually 2–4 times longer than wide, not or rarely thickened, not especially deciduous; flowers 16–22 mm, usually lilac- to pink-purple, rarely white; widespread . . . . 4a. *Hedysarum occidentale* var. *occidentale*
1. Leaflet blades mostly 1–2 times longer than wide, becoming thickened, early deciduous; flowers (17–)20–25 mm, pale lavender-pink; w Colorado, e Utah . . . . .4b. *Hedysarum occidentale* var. *canone*

4a. Hedysarum occidentale Greene var. **occidentale** E F

Hedysarum lancifolium Rydberg; *H. marginatum* Greene; *H. uintahense* A. Nelson

Stems decumbent to erect, 1.2–9.5 dm. **Leaves** 3.5–15 cm; leaflets 11–19, blades 5–40 × 3–12 mm, usually 2–4 times longer than wide, not or rarely thickened, not especially deciduous. **Racemes:** axis 4–13 cm in fruit; peduncle (3–)6–15 cm. **Flowers:** corolla usually lilac- to pink-purple, rarely white, 16–22 mm.

Flowering late spring–summer. Sagebrush, aspen, lodgepole pine, spruce-fir, and alpine tundra communities; 900–3400 m; B.C.; Colo., Idaho, Mont., Utah, Wash., Wyo.

Variety *occidentale* is apparently more closely allied with *Hedysarum sulphurescens* than with *H. alpinum*. However, the three taxa could easily be accommodated within an expanded *H. alpinum*, which is not proposed herein. Similar sequences of large-flowered phases and dwarf versus tall plants occur in all three taxa, and in each the extremes are connected completely by intermediates.

4b. Hedysarum occidentale Greene var. **canone** S. L. Welsh, Great Basin Naturalist 38: 314. 1978 E

Stems usually erect, (3–)5–8.5 dm. **Leaves** 8–23 cm; leaflets 9–17, blades 12–29 × 9–16 mm, mostly 1–2 times longer than wide, becoming thickened, early deciduous. **Racemes:** axis 6–25 cm in fruit; peduncle 6–14 cm. **Flowers:** corolla pale lavender-pink, (17–)20–25 mm.

Flowering summer. Pinyon-juniper, sagebrush-grass, mountain brush communities on Cretaceous and Tertiary strata; 1900–2500 m; Colo., Utah.

Variety *canone* is a Colorado Plateau endemic; it is based on specimens from Carbon, Duchesne, and Emery counties, Utah, and from western Colorado, that have proportionally short, thick leaflets that tend to be early deciduous and pale lavender-pink, relatively large flowers. Plants with similarly proportioned leaflets are known from elsewhere in the range of the species, especially in southwestern Wyoming, but the flowers are more strongly colored and on average smaller. The plants in this variety form an apparent trend in morphological variation with marked, but not absolute, geographical correlation. The type of *Hedysarum uintahense* approaches but does not equal this entity.

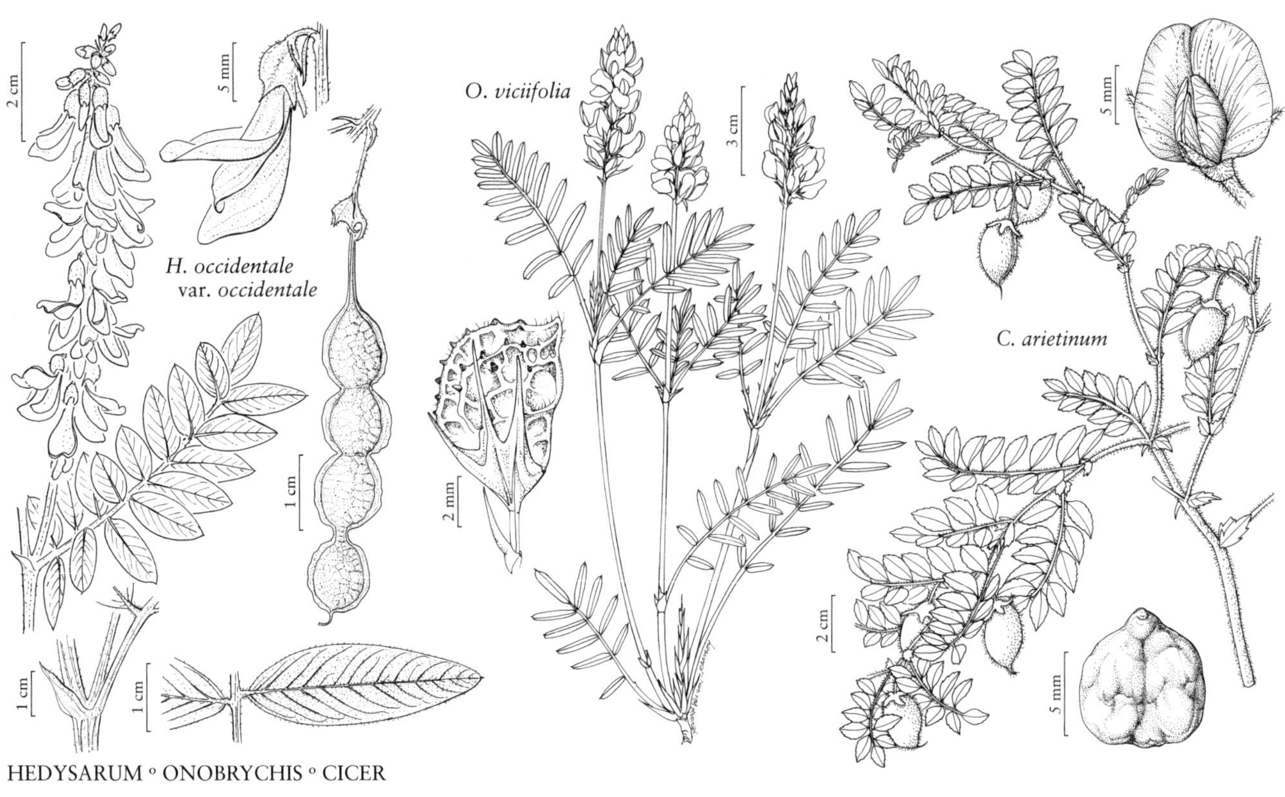

HEDYSARUM ◦ ONOBRYCHIS ◦ CICER

143. ONOBRYCHIS Miller, Gard. Dict. Abr. ed. 4, vol. 2. 1754 • Sainfoin [Greek *onos*, ass, and *brýkein*, devour, alluding to forage value of plants] I

Neil A. Harriman†

Herbs, perennial, [**annual**], unarmed. **Stems** erect, pubescent to glabrate. **Leaves** alternate, odd-pinnate; stipules present; petiolate; leaflets (7–)15–21, stipels absent, blade margins entire, surfaces pubescent abaxially, glabrous adaxially. **Inflorescences** 30+-flowered, axillary racemes; bracts and bracteoles present. **Flowers** sub-papilionaceous; calyx campanulate, lobes 5; corolla pink-purple, wings much shorter than other petals; stamens 10, monadelphous, adaxial filament distinct basally; anthers dorsifixed, equal. **Fruits** loments, sessile, flattened [to rounded], ovoid to obovoid, indehiscent, winged, edge prickly [to warty], coarsely reticulate, pubescent to glabrate. **Seed** 1, reniform. $x = 7$, [8].

Species ca. 130 (1 in the flora): introduced; Europe, Asia (China, Mongolia, Russia); introduced also in Australia.

1. Onobrychis viciifolia Scopoli, Fl. Carniol. ed. 2, 2: 76. 1772 (as viciaefolia) • Sainfoin, sainfoin cultivé [F] [I]

Hedysarum onobrychis Linnaeus, Sp. Pl. 2: 751. 1753

Herbs inconspicuously pubescent or glabrate. **Stems** clustered, 3–8 dm. **Leaves** 15–20 cm; stipules amplexicaul (or distinct), scarious; petiole 4–10 cm; leaflet blades obovate to narrowly elliptic, 10–25 × 3–6 mm, apiculate, surfaces appressed-pubescent abaxially, hairs 0.7 mm, these sometimes restricted to midrib, red-dotted adaxially. **Peduncles** 8–30 cm. **Racemes** (4–)5–12 × 1–1.5 cm; bracts 3 mm, longer than pedicels; bracteoles subulate, 0.5 mm, from pedicel apex. **Flowers:** calyx 5–7 mm, lobes subulate, longer than tube; corolla 8–15 mm, wings less than 1 mm. **Loments** exserted from persistent calyx, 5–7 × 4–6 mm, coarsely raised-reticulate, abaxial edge with prickly wing (surface reticulations sometimes also prickly), densely appressed-pubescent. **Seeds** dark olive to brown or black, 4–6 mm. $2n = 28$.

Flowering Jun–Sep. Waste places, grasslands, open forests, roadsides; 50–3000 m; introduced; Alta., B.C., N.W.T., Ont., Que., Sask., Yukon; Alaska, Calif., Colo., Idaho, Mont., Nebr., Nev., N.Mex., Oreg., S.Dak., Utah, Wash., Wyo.; Eurasia; introduced also in Australia.

Onobrychis viciifolia is widely introduced as a pasture plant, and the one-seeded fruits are regularly offered for sale; the species is to be expected almost anywhere in the flora area, especially northward. There are historical records from Newfoundland in Canada and from the north-central and northeastern United States. The attribution of *O. viciifolia* to Missouri (J. A. Steyermark 1963) is based on an incorrectly labeled specimen (*Schuette s.n.*, 16 Jul 1882, MO).

144. CICER Linnaeus, Sp. Pl. 2: 738. 1753; Gen. Pl. ed. 5, 327. 1754 • Chickpea [Latin *cicer*, Ciceronian name for pea] [I]

L. J. G. van der Maesen

Nochotta S. G. Gmelin

Herbs, annual [perennial], unarmed [armed], glandular- or/and eglandular-pubescent, except corolla. **Stems** semi-erect or erect to prostrate, straight or flexuous, pubescent, sometimes glandular-pubescent. **Leaves** alternate, odd-pinnate; stipules present, foliaceous, sometimes larger than proximalmost leaflets, toothed [spiny]; rachis apex with leaflet [tendril or spines]; petiolate; leaflets [3–]6–20[–36], blade margins dentate except at base, surfaces glandular-pubescent. **Inflorescences** 1(or 2)[–5]-flowered, axillary, racemes; bracts present, persistent; bracteoles absent. **Flowers** papilionaceous; calyx gibbous at base abaxially [subregular], lobes 5; corolla white to pink, purple, or blue; stamens 10, diadelphous; anthers basifixed; ovary pubescent; style glabrous; stigma relatively small. **Fruits** legumes, pedicellate, inflated, rhomboid-ellipsoid [ellipsoid to obovoid-rhomboid], late-dehiscent, densely pubescent, mostly glandular-pubescent. **Seeds** 1 or 2[–4], ovoid-globular or angular [bilobular to globular]. $x = 8$.

Species 44 (1 in the flora): introduced; s Europe (Greece, Turkey), c, s Asia (India), n Africa, Atlantic Islands (Canary Islands); introduced also in Mexico, South America (Argentina, Brazil, Chile).

Cicer is the only genus in tribe Cicereae. The range of closely related wild *Cicer* species points to a middle-eastern origin in Syria and Turkey for use of chickpea as a food plant. From there, the cultivated chickpea was distributed to circum-mediterranean areas and to central and southern Asia from Iran to India.

SELECTED REFERENCES Davies, A. M. R., N. Maxted, and L. J. G. van der Maesen. 2007. A natural infrageneric classification for *Cicer* (Leguminosae, Cicereae). Blumea 52: 379–400. van der Maesen, L. J. G. 1972. *Cicer* L., a monograph of the genus, with special reference to the chickpea (*Cicer arietinum* L.), its ecology and cultivation. Meded. Landbouwhogeschool 72-10. van der Maesen, L. J. G. 1987. Origin, history and taxonomy of chickpea. In: M. C. Saxena and K. B. Singh, eds. 1987. The Chickpea. Oxford. Pp. 11–34. van der Maesen, L. J. G. et al. 2007. Taxonomy of the genus *Cicer* revisited. In: S. S. Yadav et al., eds. 2007. Chickpea Breeding and Management. Wallingford and Cambridge, Mass. Pp. 14–46.

1. Cicer arietinum Linnaeus, Sp. Pl. 2: 738. 1753
• Garbanzo bean [F] [I]

Herbs (20–)25–60(–100) cm, ± branched from base, deep-rooted. **Leaves:** stipules ovate to oblique-triangular, 3–5(–11) × (1–)2–4(–6) mm, teeth 2–4(–6); petiole 5–10 mm; rachis green distally, with or without anthocyanins, or purple throughout, 25–60(–75) mm, grooved adaxially; leaflets opposite or alternate, subsessile, crowded or not, blades obovate-oblong to elliptic, (6–)10–15(–20) × (3–)4–12(–14) mm, base cuneate to rounded, margin teeth sometimes curved, to 1.5(–2) mm, apex rounded to acuminate, abaxial surface more prominently ribbed and more glandular-pubescent than adaxial. **Peduncles** (6–)13–17(–30) mm; bracts 0.5–1.5 mm. **Pedicels** straight in flower, recurved in fruit, 6–13 mm. **Flowers:** calyx green or purple, tube 3–4 mm, lobes lanceolate, 5–6 mm, midrib prominent; corolla 5–29 mm, veined; stamens 6–8 mm; ovary ovoid, 2–3 mm; style 3–4 mm. **Legumes** 14–25(–29) × 8–15(–20) mm. **Seeds** white, cream, brown, black, or dull green, (4–)7–10(–11) × 5–8 mm, beak conspicuous, coat rough or smooth (sometimes minute black dots or speckles present); hilum grayish, deep. $2n$ = (14), 16.

Flowering spring–summer. Fields, waste places; 0–900(–2400) m; introduced; Sask.; Calif., Idaho, N.Dak., Wash.; s Europe; Asia (India); introduced also in Mexico, South America (Argentina, Brazil, Chile), n Africa.

Cicer arietinum is cultivated in the United States in California, Idaho (particularly the Palouse region), North Dakota, and Washington, and in Canada in Alberta and Saskatchewan. The species occasionally escapes from cultivation but is not known to be invasive; it is the third most important pulse crop in the world, after beans and peas, and was introduced from the Mediterranean region and India. *Cicer arietinum* is widely cultivated as a cool-season crop in semi-arid, tropical areas of the world, or in summers in temperate zones. Mutants with phyllodes or unifoliolate leaves are known.

In North America, chickpeas are often canned; large- and cream-seeded Kabuli cultivars are used in salad bars. Hummus, mashed chickpeas with sesame oil and spices, is a popular appetizer in the Near East and has become popular in the West. The largest producer of *Cicer arietinum* is India, where it contributes protein to the vegetarian diet in a wide range of dishes.

145. TRIFOLIUM Linnaeus, Sp. Pl. 2: 764. 1753; Gen. Pl. ed. 5, 337. 1754 • Clover, trèfle [Greek *tris*, three, and *phyllon*, leaf, or Latin *tres*, three, and *folium*, leaf, alluding to occurrence of three-leafleted compound leaves in many species]

Michael A. Vincent

John M. Gillett†

Amoria C. Presl; *Chrysaspis* Desvaux; *Lupinaster* Fabricius

Herbs, annual or perennial, unarmed. **Stems** prostrate to erect, glabrous or pubescent. **Leaves** alternate, odd-pinnate or palmate; stipules present, persistent, adnate to petiole; petiolate or sessile; leaflets 3–9, stipels absent, blade margins usually entire or toothed, rarely lobed, surfaces glabrous or pubescent. **Inflorescences** (1–)25–100+-flowered, racemes, umbelliform, spicate, or headlike, axillary or terminal; bracts present or absent, connate or distinct; bracteoles present or absent. **Flowers** papilionaceous; calyx actinomorphic or zygomorphic, tubular or campanulate, sometimes inflated in fruit, lobes 5; corolla white, cream, pink, red, purple, or yellow, glabrous; stamens 10, diadelphous; anthers basifixed; pistil linear to lanceolate, style glabrous or pubescent, stigma terminal. **Fruits** legumes, sessile or stipitate, cylindric or laterally compressed, lanceolate to elliptic, dehiscent, usually longitudinally, rarely transversely or indehiscent, included in marcescent corolla or slightly exserted, papery, membranous, or leathery, glabrous or pubescent. **Seeds** 1–4[–9], globose, ovoid-oblong, mitten-shaped, or reniform, hilum lateral. x = 5, 6, 7, 8.

Species ca. 280 (98 in the flora): North America, Mexico, Central America, South America, Eurasia, Africa, Atlantic Islands; introduced in West Indies, Pacific Islands, Australia.

In the flora area, *Trifolium* is superficially similar to *Medicago*, *Melilotus*, and *Trigonella*. *Trifolium* differs from those genera by persistence of the corolla after anthesis, a legume that is included in or only slightly exserted from the persistent corolla, and distally dilated filaments (H. A. Gleason and A. Cronquist 1991; Wei Z. and M. A. Vincent 2010).

Trifolium has three major centers of diversity: the Mediterranean region of southern Europe, western Asia, and northern Africa; the California region in North America; and the eastern African highlands (M. Zohary and D. Heller 1984). In the New World, diversity is highest in the California region of the United States, the mountainous regions of western North America, and western South America. In North America, a suite of closely related species, centered in the southeastern United States, represents another locus of diversification.

Trifolium consists of subg. *Chronosemium* (Seringe) Reichenbach and subg. *Trifolium*; the latter is subdivided into eight sections (N. W. Ellison et al. 2006). Subgenus *Chronosemium* is represented in the flora area by the Old World species *T. aureum*, *T. campestre*, and *T. dubium*. All native New World species of subg. *Trifolium* represent a monophyletic lineage, sect. *Involucrarium* Hooker ex Lojacono. The introduced species of subg. *Trifolium* represent other sections: sect. *Lupinaster* (Fabricius) Seringe (*T. lupinaster*), sect. *Trichocephalum* W. D. J. Koch (*T. subterraneum*), sect. *Trifoliastrum* Gray (*T. cernuum*, *T. glomeratum*, *T. nigrescens*, *T. repens*, *T. retusum*, and *T. suffocatum*), sect. *Trifolium* (*T. alexandrinum*, *T. angustifolium*, *T. arvense*, *T. echinatum*, *T. hirtum*, *T. incarnatum*, *T. lappaceum*, *T. medium*, *T. pratense*, and *T. striatum*), and sect. *Vesicastrum* Seringe (*T. fragiferum*, *T. hybridum*, *T. ornithopodioides*, *T. resupinatum*, *T. tomentosum*, and *T. vesiculosum*). This differs dramatically from the phylogenetic arrangement of M. Zohary and D. Heller (1984), where the genus is subdivided into eight sections, and native New World species are placed in sects. *Involucrarium* and *Lotoidea* Crantz (in a narrow sense).

Species of *Trifolium* have been cultivated for centuries in parts of Europe as forage crops; some species were introduced into the flora area for that purpose. Of these, *T. repens* appears to have been the earliest introduction, perhaps as early as the mid 1600s (R. N. Mack 2003), and its spread across the continent was very rapid. Other commonly cultivated species include *T. hirtum*, *T. hybridum*, *T. incarnatum*, *T. pratense*, *T. subterraneum*, and *T. vesiculosum*; other species may also be cultivated in North America and may be important regionally (N. L. Taylor 1985; J. M. Gillett and Taylor 2001).

The following species have been mentioned as occurring in the flora area but are excluded as waifs or as only represented by cultivated material: *Trifolium ambiguum* M. Bieberstein, *T. dalmaticum* Visiani, *T. gemellum* Pourret ex Willdenow, *T. maritimum* Hudson, *T. michelianum* Savi, *T. occidentale* Coombe, *T. pannonicum* Jacquin, *T. purpureum* Loiseleur-Deslongchamps, *T. rubens* Linnaeus, *T. scabrum* Linnaeus, *T. spumosum* Linnaeus, *T. squamosum* Linnaeus, and *T. stellatum* Linnaeus.

Lojaconoa Bobrov 1967, which pertains here, is a later homonym of *Lojaconoa* Gandoger (Poaceae 1891).

SELECTED REFERENCES Ellison, N. W. et al. 2006. Molecular phylogenetics of the clover genus (*Trifolium* – Leguminosae). Molec. Phylogenet. Evol. 39: 688–705. Gillett, J. M. 1969. Taxonomy of *Trifolium* (Leguminosae). II. The *T. longipes* complex in North America. Canad. J. Bot. 47: 93–113. Gillett, J. M. 1972. Taxonomy of *Trifolium* (Leguminosae). IV. The American species of section *Lupinaster* (Adanson) Seringe. Canad. J. Bot. 50: 1975–2007. Gillett, J. M. 1980. Taxonomy of *Trifolium* (Leguminosae). V. The perennial species of section *Involucrarium*. Canad. J. Bot. 58: 1425–1448. Gillett, J. M. and N. L. Taylor. 2001. The World of Clovers. Ames. McDermott, L. F. 1910. An Illustrated Key to the North American Species of *Trifolium*. San Francisco. Zohary, M. and D. Heller. 1984. The Genus *Trifolium*. Jerusalem.

1. Involucres present, composed of free or fused bracts, surpassing pedicels; stipule margins usually dentate or lacerate, sometimes entire.
    2. Herbs perennial.
        3. Inflorescences 1–9-flowered; involucres incised nearly to base, lobes 2–8; keel petals usually purple-spotted. . . . . 46. *Trifolium monanthum*
        3. Inflorescences (8–)10–50-flowered; involucres incised to 3/4, lobes 10–12; keel petals not spotted.
            4. Calyx lobes subequal, abaxial rarely longer than tube; involucre: lobes sharply and acutely serrate; leaflet blades obovate to elliptic . . . . 33. *Trifolium wormskioldii*
            4. Calyx lobes ± equal, abaxial lobe longer than tube; involucre: lobes entire, irregular, bifurcate, or triaristate to lacerate; leaflet blades oblanceolate, obovate, linear, or elliptic.
                5. Involucral lobes linear-lanceolate, entire; stipule margins entire; roots stout, branched, rhizomes absent. . . . . .47. *Trifolium pinetorum*
                5. Involucre lobes triaristate to lacerate, or irregular to bifurcate; stipule margins entire, toothed, or lacerate; roots tuberous or taproots, rhizomes present or absent.
                    6. Roots tuberous, rhizomes present, elongate, slender; stipule margins entire or slightly lacerate; leaflet blades obovate, oblanceolate, or elliptic . . . . 34. *Trifolium siskiyouense*
                    6. Roots taproots, slender, rhizomes absent or short; stipule margins toothed or lacerate; leaflet blades linear, elliptic, or obovate. . . 35. *Trifolium mucronatum*
    2. Herbs annual or biennial.
        7. Calyx and/or banner inflated in fruit.
            8. Banner proximally inflated in fruit, distally twisted.
                9. Calyx lobes: apex unbranched, setaceous; calyx longer than corolla . . . . .43. *Trifolium barbigerum*
                9. Calyx lobes: apex of at least some branched, flattened or setaceous; calyx equaling or shorter than corolla.
                    10. Abaxial and lateral calyx lobes conspicuously 2- or 3-fid, segments glabrous, sometimes flattened . . . . 42. *Trifolium cyathiferum*
                    10. Calyx lobes unbranched or apex inconspicuously 3-fid, segments plumose, not flattened.
                        11. Corollas usually lavender or purple, sometimes purple with white tips; leaves and stems usually pubescent; seeds 1.6–2 mm. . . . . . .44. *Trifolium grayi*
                        11. Corollas yellow; leaves and stems glabrous; seeds 3.1–3.4 mm . . . . 45. *Trifolium jokerstii*
            8. Banner inflated entire length in fruit, not distally twisted.
                12. Flowers 10–27 mm; leaflet blades oblanceolate, obovate, orbiculate, or rhombic-obovate; involucral lobe apex acuminate, sometimes 2- or 3-fid or 3–5-fid.
                    13. Calyx tube 1.5–2.5 mm, abaxial lobe apex undivided or 2- or 3-fid; seed coat reticulate . . . . 40. *Trifolium fucatum*
                    13. Calyx tube 2.5–4 mm, abaxial lobe apex 3–5-fid; seed coat smooth . . . . 41. *Trifolium piorkowskii*
                12. Flowers 3–11 mm; leaflet blades lanceolate, linear, obovate, or oblanceolate; involucral lobe apex rounded to truncate, not split.
                    14. Involucres 3–13 mm, incised 1/2 their length; inflorescences 0.5–1 cm diam.; banners 4–7 mm; herbs 1–30 cm; stems erect or decumbent . . . . .48. *Trifolium depauperatum* (in part)
                    14. Involucres 3–4 mm, lobes incised less than 1/2 their length; inflorescences 1–1.8 × 1.3–1.5 cm; banners 7–9 mm; herbs 15–55 cm; stems erect . . . . .49. *Trifolium hydrophilum*
        7. Neither calyx nor banner inflated in fruit.

15. Involucres flattened or cup- or bowl-shaped, when compressed laterally, nearly completely hiding calyces.
    16. Involucral lobes entire or slightly toothed proximally; involucres conspicuously villous; corollas ± equal to calyces . . . . .54. *Trifolium microcephalum*
    16. Involucral lobes conspicuously toothed; involucres glabrous or sparsely hairy; corollas longer than calyces.
        17. Involucres flattened or shallowly bowl-shaped; inflorescences 0.5–0.8 cm; calyx lobes aristate, margins not membranous; early inflorescences hidden in stipules, subsessile, with 2–5 cleistogamous flowers. . . . . .36. *Trifolium buckwestiorum*
        17. Involucres cup-shaped; inflorescences 0.8–1.7 cm; calyx lobes not or minutely aristate, margins membranous; early inflorescences not hidden, without cleistogamous flowers . . . . 53. *Trifolium microdon*
15. Involucres rotate, bracts sometimes separate, or involucres flattened to bowl- or vase-shaped, when compressed laterally, not hiding flowers except proximally.
    18. Calyx tubes slit between adaxial lobes, lobes shorter than or equal to tube, 3-fid or shouldered below subulate apex (usually entire in *T. obtusiflorum*); leaflet blades linear, oblong, lanceolate, oblanceolate, elliptic, rhombic, or obovate.
        19. Flowers 11–16 mm; involucres 1–2 mm, incised $^{4}/_{5}$–$^{9}/_{10}$ their length, lobes not lacerate; inflorescences 0.3–0.8 cm diam., 3–15-flowered . . . . .56. *Trifolium oliganthum*
        19. Flowers 12–20 mm; involucres 3–9 mm, incised $^{1}/_{4}$–$^{1}/_{3}$ their length, lobes deeply lacerate; inflorescences 1–3 cm diam., 10–50-flowered.
            20. Peduncles and calyces glabrous; calyx lobes usually 3-fid or shouldered; leaflet margins serrate . . . . 51. *Trifolium willdenovii*
            20. Peduncles and calyces glandular; calyx lobes usually entire, rarely 3-fid or shouldered; leaflet margins coarsely spinulose-serrate . . . . .52. *Trifolium obtusiflorum*
    18. Calyx tubes not slit between adaxial lobes, lobes longer than tube, usually entire and without shoulders, rarely 3-fid or laciniate; leaflet blades obovate to oblanceolate, or elliptic.
        21. Calyces usually densely pubescent; involucres flattened or vase-shaped, 1–3 mm, incised $^{2}/_{3}$–$^{3}/_{4}$ their length; seeds 3–6(–9) . . . . 50. *Trifolium trichocalyx*
        21. Calyces glabrous; involucres flattened or bowl-shaped, 4–16 mm, incised $^{1}/_{2}$ their length; seeds 1 or 2.
            22. Calyx lobes 3-fid or laciniate; leaflet blades broadly elliptic to broadly obovate, apex rounded or truncate, often retuse; stems decumbent or ascending; Monterey Peninsula, California. . . 39. *Trifolium polyodon*
            22. Calyx lobes entire (rarely with a small, lateral tooth); leaflet blades elliptic, obovate, or oblanceolate, apex acute or retuse; stems usually erect or ascending, rarely decumbent; w North America.
                23. Banner petals 3.2–9.7 mm, included or exserted 0.1–5.7 mm beyond tips of calyx lobes, keel petals not beaked; mature seeds 1.1–1.6 mm; Alaska and British Columbia south to California, east to Arizona and Montana . . . . 37. *Trifolium variegatum*
                23. Banner petals 6.3–15.8 mm, exserted 1.5–8.4 mm beyond tips of calyx lobes, keel petals beaked or not; mature seeds 1.9–2.8 mm; California, s Oregon. . . . . 38. *Trifolium appendiculatum*

1. Involucres absent or vestigial, not exceeding pedicels, or if better developed, then formed of bracteoles, or with subtending leaves and stipules forming involucrelike structures; stipule margins usually entire, lobed, or toothed, sometimes serrate or denticulate.
    24. Calyces and/or corollas inflated in fruit; legumes usually shorter than calyces.
        25. Calyces not bilabiate in fruit, veins 5 or 20–36; involucres absent or vestigial.

26. Calyces inflated in fruit, corollas not inflated in fruit; tubes of fruiting calyces with interconnecting veins; involucres absent; bracteoles present, nearly equaling calyces; herbs 15–70 cm . . . . 18. *Trifolium vesiculosum*
26. Calyces not inflated in fruit, corollas inflated in fruit; tubes of fruiting calyces without interconnecting veins; involucres vestigial, reduced to narrow ring; bracteoles absent; herbs 1–30 cm . . . . 48. *Trifolium depauperatum* (in part)

25. Calyces markedly bilabiate in fruit, veins 5–10; involucres of bracteoles or a narrow rim.
27. Herbs perennial; stems prostrate or creeping; flowers not resupinate; involucres of bracteoles cup-shaped, 3–6 mm . . . . 19. *Trifolium fragiferum*
27. Herbs annual; stems prostrate, procumbent, ascending, or erect; flowers resupinate; involucres a narrow rim, 0.2 mm.
28. Inflorescences forming stellate-spreading clusters of calyces in fruit; calyces short-hairy or glabrescent in fruit, orifices open, lobes erect or divergent . . . . 20. *Trifolium resupinatum*
28. Inflorescences not forming stellate-spreading clusters in fruit; calyces densely white-woolly, orifices abruptly constricted in fruit, adaxial lobes spreading or curved . . . . 21. *Trifolium tomentosum*

[24. Shifted to left margin.—Ed.]

24. Calyces and corollas not inflated in fruit; legumes longer than or equal to calyces.
29. Calyx lobes: abaxial lobes longer, adaxial very short; banner spatulate, boat-shaped, or obovate; legumes stipitate, seeds 1 or 2.
30. Terminal leaflets sessile; stipules 0.9–1.5 cm; banners: apex emarginate . . . . 1. *Trifolium aureum*
30. Terminal leaflets obviously stalked; stipules 0.3–0.8 cm; banners: apex rounded or broadly acute.
31. Stipules 0.3–0.5 cm; flowers 2.8–3.5 mm; leaflet blades obovate to elliptic-lanceolate; corollas not or slightly ribbed . . . . 2. *Trifolium dubium*
31. Stipules 0.5–0.8 cm; flowers 4.3–5 mm; leaflet blades rhombic to obovate; corollas obviously ribbed . . . . 3. *Trifolium campestre*
29. Calyx lobes: abaxial ± equaling adaxial, or if lobes markedly unequal, then banner not spatulate or boat-shaped; legumes sessile or stipitate, seeds 1–9.
32. Inflorescences with 2–7 fertile flowers with corollas and 0–80 sterile flowers without corollas; inflorescences pedunculate, pushing into substrate in fruit, subterranean flowers chasmogamous . . . . 5. *Trifolium subterraneum*
32. Inflorescences with 1–100+ fertile flowers with corollas; inflorescences not pushing into substrate in fruit, if so (*T. amphianthum* only), subterranean inflorescences sessile and subterranean flowers cleistogamous.
33. Pedicels 0–1 mm; bracteoles usually absent (present in *T. arvense*); calyx orifices thickened or closed by callosity or ring of hairs; legumes leathery distally, transversely dehiscent; seeds 1 or 2.
34. Calyx veins 20.
35. Calyces pilose; peduncles 0 cm; inflorescences appearing involucrate (involucrelike structures formed by enlarging stipules), disarticulating in fruit . . . . 8. *Trifolium hirtum*
35. Calyces glabrous; peduncles 0.1–0.7 cm; inflorescences not involucrate, burlike, not disarticulating in fruit . . . . 9. *Trifolium lappaceum*
34. Calyx veins 10–20 or not distinguishable.
36. Flowers 5–8 mm.
37. Leaflet blades broadly ovate or obovate to oblong, lengths 1–1.5 (–2) times widths; calyx 3–4 mm . . . . 12. *Trifolium striatum*
37. Leaflet blades elliptic, oblong, linear-oblong, linear-lanceolate, or obovate, lengths usually (2.5–)3–7 times widths; calyx 5–8 mm . . . . 15. *Trifolium arvense*
36. Flowers 9–18 mm.

38. Herbs perennial.
    39. Peduncles ± 0 mm, hidden by stipules of distal leaves; calyx tubes hairy; stipules broadly triangular, apex mucronate or setaceous . . . . 6. *Trifolium pratense*
    39. Peduncles 1–3 cm, not hidden by subtending stipules; calyx tubes glabrous; stipules lanceolate-linear, apex subulate. . . 7. *Trifolium medium*
38. Herbs usually annual, rarely biennial.
    40. Leaflet blades broadly ovate or obovate to oblong, lengths 1–1.5(–2) times widths; corollas usually scarlet to red, rarely pink or white, banner oblong-elliptic, apex acute. . . . . 10. *Trifolium incarnatum*
    40. Leaflet blades elliptic, oblong, linear-oblong, linear-lanceolate, or obovate, lengths usually (2.5–)3–7 times widths; corollas usually whitish, pale pink, or purple, banner narrowly-spatulate, oblong-spatulate, or ovate-elliptic, apex acute, obtuse, or notched.
        41. Corollas shorter than or equaling calyx, usually pale pink or purple, rarely white; inflorescences 3–8 cm; calyx 8–13 mm, orifices closed by bilabiate callosities . . . . . 14. *Trifolium angustifolium*
        41. Corollas longer than calyx, whitish; inflorescences 1–2.5 cm; calyx 6–8 mm, orifices open or closed by bilabiate callosities.
            42. Calyx orifices closed by bilabiate callosities, lobes unequal, triangular-elliptic, stellate-spreading, tubes glabrescent; corollas 8–10 mm; banner apex acute; seeds 1.2–1.4 mm . . . . .11. *Trifolium echinatum*
            42. Calyx orifices open, hairy, lobes equal or abaxial 2 slightly longer, narrowly triangular, erect to slightly spreading, tubes appressed-hairy; corollas 13–16 mm; banner apex obtuse; seeds 2–2.2 mm. . . . . . 13. *Trifolium alexandrinum*

[33. Shifted to left margin.—Ed.]

33. Pedicels (0–)1–8(–12) mm; bracteoles usually present; calyx orifices open; legumes not leathery distally, longitudinally dehiscent; seeds 1–9.
    43. Calyces glabrous.
        44. Herbs perennial; stems creeping, rooting at nodes; peduncles erect, from prostrate stems; pedicels strongly reflexed in fruit; corollas equaling or 2 times calyces. . . .22. *Trifolium repens*
        44. Herbs annual or perennial; stems usually erect or ascending, rarely prostrate, not rooting at nodes; peduncles erect or not, from prostrate or upright stems; pedicels reflexed or not; corollas shorter to longer than calyces.
            45. Corollas 2+ times calyces.
                46. Pedicels erect or slightly reflexed, sometimes only those of proximal flowers reflexed.
                    47. Calyx lobes curved or twisted.
                        48. Herbs annual; stems procumbent, decumbent, or ascending; inflorescences 0.8–1 cm diam.; peduncles 0–0.1 cm . . . . 24. *Trifolium glomeratum*
                        48. Herbs perennial; stems erect; inflorescences 2–3.5 cm diam.; peduncles 3–12 cm . . . . .86. *Trifolium douglasii* (in part)
                    47. Calyx lobes straight.
                        49. Herbs 4–10 cm; stems mat-forming, cespitose; flowers 1–4; bracteoles membranous, connate, forming cuplike involucres . . . . . 76. *Trifolium nanum*
                        49. Herbs 10–20 cm; stems erect or ascending, loosely cespitose or rhizomatous; flowers 15–20; bracteoles purplish, scarious, sometimes connate, forming involucres. . . . . 77. *Trifolium parryi*
                46. Pedicels strongly reflexed.
                    50. Inflorescences: rachises not prolonged beyond flowers, without sterile flowers . . . . 16. *Trifolium hybridum* (in part)

50. Inflorescences: rachises prolonged beyond (fertile) flowers, often bearing a cluster of sterile flower buds distally.
51. Stems 30–100 cm, fistulose; leaflet blades 2.3–5 cm wide .... 78. *Trifolium howellii*
51. Stems 5–50 cm, not fistulose; leaflet blades 0.1–2 cm wide.
52. Calyx veins 5.
53. Peduncles thick, straight; banners straight, obovate to broadly elliptic.............................92. *Trifolium beckwithii*
53. Peduncles slender, bent distally just below flowers; banners curved, oblanceolate..................... 97. *Trifolium bolanderi*
52. Calyx veins 10 (5 sometimes faint).
54. Stems ± erect, loosely cespitose; leaves basal and cauline.
55. Leaflet blades lanceolate or elliptic; calyces 3–3.5 mm .... 80. *Trifolium productum*
55. Leaflet blades lanceolate to linear; calyces 6–8.5 mm .... 81. *Trifolium dedeckerae*
54. Stems ascending, cespitose; leaves mostly basal.
56. Inflorescences globose or subglobose; peduncles straight proximal to flowers; corollas salmon, buff-pink, or pink, with white or cream tips; calyx lobes equaling tubes........................... 90. *Trifolium haydenii*
56. Inflorescences hemispheric; peduncles curved distally, just below flowers, inflorescences appearing turned to one side; corollas purple, often white-tipped; calyx lobes shorter than tubes.....................96. *Trifolium rollinsii*

[45. Shifted to left margin.—Ed.]

45. Corollas less than 2 times calyces.
57. Pedicels straight or slightly reflexed in fruit.
58. Inflorescences loose, flowers 1–5, not overtopped by leafy stipules; calyx lobes straight in fruit... 17. *Trifolium ornithopodioides*
58. Inflorescences dense, flowers 10–20, overtopped by broad, membranous stipules; calyx lobes curved in fruit................................ 26. *Trifolium suffocatum* (in part)
57. Pedicels strongly reflexed or recurved in fruit.
59. Calyx lobes recurved in fruit.
60. Peduncles equaling or shorter than subtending leaves; stipule apex stramineous; corollas shorter than calyces.................................... 25. *Trifolium retusum*
60. Peduncles longer than subtending leaves; stipule apex dark purple or reddish; corollas longer than calyces ....27. *Trifolium nigrescens* (in part)
59. Calyx lobes not recurved (except *T. nigrescens*) in fruit.
61. Calyx lobe margins hyaline, dentate or pectinate, markedly ciliate......... .... 57. *Trifolium ciliolatum* (in part)
61. Calyx lobe margins green, purple, or pink, not dentate or pectinate, not ciliate.
62. Leaflet blades narrowly obcordate, obovate, oblanceolate, or linear, apex, at least some, retuse to deeply 2-fid ....55. *Trifolium bifidum* (in part)
62. Leaflet blades narrowly elliptic, lanceolate, obovate, obcordate, ovate, oblong, rhombic, or broadly elliptic, apex not 2-fid, sometimes shallowly retuse.
63. Leaflet blades narrowly elliptic or lanceolate, apex acute; calyx lobe margins membranous ....58. *Trifolium palmeri*
63. Leaflet blades obovate to obcordate or ovate, oblong, or rhombic, apex broadly rounded, broadly acute, truncate, emarginate, or retuse; calyx lobe margins not membranous.
64. Peduncles 0.6–1.5 cm, distal ones shorter; flowers 4–5.5 mm; banners: apex deeply emarginate ....23. *Trifolium cernuum*
64. Peduncles 1–9 cm; flowers 5–15 mm; banners: apex rounded, retuse, apiculate, erose-denticulate, or acute.

65. Calyx lobes (at least most) equaling to less than 2 times tube; stipule apex subulate, sharply recurved, dark purple or reddish . . . . 27. *Trifolium nigrescens* (in part)
65. Calyx lobes 2 times tube; stipule apex acute or acuminate, usually erect, green.
66. Inflorescences 0.5–2 cm diam.; calyx lobes unequal, long-triangular; stipules ovate-lanceolate, membranous; corollas 5–8 mm; bracteoles cuplike. . . . . 59. *Trifolium gracilentum*
66. Inflorescences 2–4 cm diam.; calyx lobes equal, narrowly triangular to subulate; stipules broadly ovate, foliaceous; corollas 9–14 mm; bracteoles broad-obovate, truncate to 2-fid . . . . 68. *Trifolium reflexum* (in part)

[43. Shifted to left margin.—Ed.]

43. Calyces entirely or partly pubescent.
67. Inflorescences 4–30(–50)-flowered.
68. Pedicels erect or only those of proximal flowers reflexed in fruit.
69. Peduncles ± 0 cm, inflorescences largely hidden by broad, membranous stipules; herbs 3–10 cm; pedicels 0.1 mm. . . . . 26. *Trifolium suffocatum* (in part)
69. Peduncles (0–)1–17 cm, usually not hidden by stipules (partially hidden in *T. macraei*); herbs 0.8–30 cm; pedicels (0–)0.5–4 mm.
70. Leaflets 3 or 5(–9); stipule margins entire, irregularly dentate, or serrate.
71. Stipule margins finely and sharply serrate; stems erect, unbranched or branched distally; Alaska. . . . . 4. *Trifolium lupinaster* (in part)
71. Stipule margins entire or irregularly dentate; stems cespitose, numerous, short, branched from woody crown; Oregon to Montana, southward to California and New Mexico. . . . . 89. *Trifolium gymnocarpon* (in part)
70. Leaflets 3; stipule margins entire.
72. Inflorescences usually in pairs, partially hidden by terminal leaves and stipules; peduncles 0–0.2 cm; pedicels 0 mm . . . . .60. *Trifolium macraei* (in part)
72. Inflorescences single, not hidden by terminal leaves and stipules; peduncles 1–17 cm; pedicels 0.5–3.5 mm.
73. Herbs canescent; leaflet blades oblanceolate to obovate, often folded, surfaces densely silvery-hairy; bracteoles absent; banners 8–10 mm, oblong, apex acute . . . . 75. *Trifolium friscanum*
73. Herbs glabrous or pubescent, not canescent; leaflet blades oblong-elliptic, oblanceolate, or obovate, sometimes folded, surfaces glabrous or hairy; bracteoles linear-lanceolate; banners 11–15 mm, broadly elliptic-ovate, apex rounded, apiculate. . . . . 30. *Trifolium dasyphyllum* (in part)
68. Pedicels curved or reflexed in fruit.
74. Peduncles ± geniculate distally.
75. Calyx tubular, lobes subequal, subulate . . . . .28. *Trifolium breweri* (in part)
75. Calyx campanulate, bilabiate, lobes markedly unequal, adaxial longer than abaxial, foliaceous.
76. Calyx lobes, except abaxial, obovate, veins reticulate, surfaces glabrous, sparsely pilose marginally. . . . . 70. *Trifolium bejariense* (in part)
76. Calyx lobes broadly triangular, veins slightly branched, surfaces villous . . . . 71. *Trifolium carolinianum* (in part)
74. Peduncles straight.
77. Stems creeping, rooting at nodes; inflorescences 2 kinds, one aerial, long-pedunculate, flowers chasmogamous, other subterranean, flowers cleistogamous . . . . .72. *Trifolium amphianthum* (in part)
77. Stems not creeping, not rooting at nodes; inflorescences aerial, flowers chasmogamous.

78. Herbs annual or biennial; stems not cespitose.
  79. Calyx lobe margins dentate or pectinate, ciliate . . . 57. *Trifolium ciliolatum* (in part)
  79. Calyx lobe margins entire.
    80. Leaflet blades narrowly obcordate, obovate, oblanceolate, or linear, at least some with apex retuse to deeply 2-fid; flowers 6–8 mm; banners elliptic to oblong, apex rounded, apiculate . . . . .55. *Trifolium bifidum* (in part)
    80. Leaflet blades ovate, obovate, oblong, rhombic, or orbiculate, apex acute, rounded, emarginate, or obcordate; flowers 9–15 mm; banners obovate-oblong or ovate-oblong, apex usually rounded or retuse, sometimes erose-denticulate.
      81. Stems erect or ascending; distalmost petioles 0.3–3.5 cm; calyx lobes 3–7 mm . . . . 68. *Trifolium reflexum* (in part)
      81. Stems decumbent; distalmost petioles 6–8 cm; calyx lobes 2–3.7 mm . . . . .69. *Trifolium kentuckiense*
78. Herbs perennial; stems mostly cespitose.
  82. Inflorescence rachises not surpassing distalmost flowers.
    83. Herbs pubescent, 5–30 cm; stems erect or ascending; stipules 1.8–2 cm; leaflet blades 1.5–6 cm, margins entire; flowers 15–22 mm; corollas red-purple. . . . . 31. *Trifolium attenuatum* (in part)
    83. Herbs mostly glabrous, 3–5 cm; stems densely matted; stipules 0.5–1 cm; leaflet blades 0.3–1.6 cm, margins sharply antrorsely serrate; flowers 8–13 mm; corollas creamy white . . . . 91. *Trifolium barnebyi*
  82. Inflorescence rachises surpassing distalmost flowers.
    84. Calyx 7–10 mm, lobes narrowly triangular, acuminate, length less than 2 times tube; corollas 15–18 mm; leaflet margins entire . . . . 32. *Trifolium brandegeei*
    84. Calyx 3.3–15 mm, lobes narrowly triangular, linear, or subulate, length 2+ times tube; corollas 5.3–20 mm; leaflet margins entire, serrate, or serrulate.
      85. Stems prostrate; stipule margins entire or finely serrulate; leaflet blades obovate to obcordate, largest to 1.6 × 1.2 cm; bracteoles linear-triangular, 0.5 mm; flowers 5.7–6.7 mm; banners obovate, apex broadly rounded or broadly acute . . . . 29. *Trifolium sonorense* (in part)
      85. Stems ascending; stipule margins entire proximally, 1–3-toothed distally; leaflet blades obovate or elliptic, largest to 4.2 × 2.5 cm; bracteoles scalelike, to 0.3 mm; flowers 13–17 mm; banners elliptic, apex tapered, sometimes retuse . . . . 93. *Trifolium latifolium* (in part)

[67. Shifted to left margin.—Ed.]

67. Inflorescences (5–)10–50(–80)-flowered.
  86. Petioles 0.5–0.7 cm; stipules adnate to petioles, sheathing; leaflets (3–)5(–9). . . . . 4. *Trifolium lupinaster* (in part)
  86. Petioles (0.3–)1–20(–25) cm; stipules not adnate to petioles, not sheathing; leaflets 3 or 5–9.
    87. Leaflets 5–9.
      88. Inflorescences 2.5–8 × 3–7 cm; calyx lobes 2–4 times tube.
        89. Leaflets 5–7, blades linear, linear-lanceolate, or linear-elliptic, 2–7 cm; inflorescences 3–5 × 3–4 cm; calyx lobes slightly pilose; corollas rose-pink to purple . . . . 82. *Trifolium thompsonii*
        89. Leaflets (5–)7–9, blades broadly to narrowly obovate, 1–2.7 cm; inflorescences 2.5–8 × 3–7 cm; calyx lobes plumose; corolla white, creamy white, or pinkish, keel petals deep pink . . . . 83. *Trifolium macrocephalum*
      88. Inflorescences 1–3 × 1–3 cm; calyx lobes shorter than or to 1.5 times tube.

90. Pedicels 0 mm; calyces 9–11 mm; leaflet margins entire; seeds 1.6–2 mm . . . . .74. *Trifolium andersonii*
90. Pedicels 1–4 mm; calyces 3–7.5 mm; leaflet margins dentate; seeds 2.5–4.5 mm.
    91. Flowers 6–15, 7.5–13 mm; peduncles 1–6.5 cm, ± surpassing leaves, not bent distally; inflorescences 1–2 cm. . . . . 89. *Trifolium gymnocarpon* (in part)
    91. Flowers 15–30, 11–13 mm; peduncles 5–15 cm, surpassing leaves, sharply bent distally, just below flowers; inflorescences 2–3 cm . . .98. *Trifolium lemmonii*

[87. Shifted to left margin.—Ed.]

87. Leaflets 3.
    92. Pedicels absent or not all reflexed in fruit.
        93. Leaflet blade lengths 3+ times widths.
            94. Bracteoles conspicuous, 2–6 mm, proximal ones sometimes connate, forming involucre; banners broadly elliptic-ovate, folded distally, apex rounded, apiculate; ovaries pubescent distally . . . . 30. *Trifolium dasyphyllum* (in part)
            94. Bracteoles inconspicuous, 0–0.5 mm, not forming involucre; banners oblong or ovate to oblanceolate, apex usually acute or obtuse, rarely rounded or truncate; ovaries glabrous or pubescent distally.
                95. Calyx veins 15–20; ovaries glabrous or pubescent distally.
                    96. Leaflet blades often folded, falcate; inflorescences spicate, ovoid to cylindric; calyx lobes subulate, straight . . . . 84. *Trifolium plumosum*
                    96. Leaflet blades flat, not falcate; inflorescences umbellate, globose to ovoid; calyx lobes triangular or subulate, lateral and adaxial tortuous, curved downwards and inwards around corollas, abaxial straight . . . . .86. *Trifolium douglasii* (in part)
                95. Calyx veins 5–10; ovaries pubescent distally.
                    97. Peduncles 0.1–1 cm; inflorescences usually formed of 2 sessile heads, subtended by distal stipules and leaves, forming involucrelike structure, or involucre absent; stipules oblanceolate, margins entire; calyx rough-hairy or glabrous, lobes subequal. . . . . .88. *Trifolium andinum*
                    97. Peduncles 1–30 cm; inflorescences: distal stipules not forming involucrelike structure; stipules ovate to lanceolate, margins usually entire, sometimes slightly serrate proximally; calyx hairy or glabrous, lobes unequal . . . . 94. *Trifolium longipes* (in part)
        93. Leaflet blade lengths to 2 times widths.
            98. Herbs perennial; stems erect or spreading, cespitose, little branched distally.
                99. Stipules fused at base, broadly obovate, margins slightly lobed; leaflets slightly overlapping, blades ovate, obovate, or orbiculate, apex emarginate. . . . . 87. *Trifolium owyheense*
                99. Stipules distinct at base, ovate to lanceolate, margins usually entire, sometimes slightly serrate proximally; leaflets not overlapping, blades linear, lanceolate to elliptic, or oblong, cauline sometimes ovate, apex acute . . . . 94. *Trifolium longipes* (in part)
            98. Herbs annual; stems erect, ascending, or prostrate, not cespitose, branched throughout or unbranched.
                100. Peduncles 0–0.2 cm; inflorescences usually paired, sometimes one head slightly stalked, partially hidden by terminal leaves and stipules . . . . .60. *Trifolium macraei* (in part)
                100. Peduncles 0.5–15 cm; inflorescences single, not hidden by terminal leaves or stipules.
                    101. Calyces campanulate, veins 10 (additional faint veins sometimes present), sinuses rounded, lobes divergent; corollas shorter than calyces. . . . . .61. *Trifolium albopurpureum*
                    101. Calyces tubular, veins 20–30, sinuses acute, lobes not divergent, appearing rigidly erect; corollas shorter or longer than calyces.

102. Corollas shorter than calyces or absent . . . . 64. *Trifolium columbinum*
102. Corollas longer than calyces.
103. Inflorescences bluntly conic, ellipsoid, globose, or subglobose, 1.5–3 × 1.5–2.5 cm; leaflet blades broadly obovate or elliptic, 1.7–3.3 × 1.1–2 cm; corollas 12–16 mm; calyces 9–12 mm. 62. *Trifolium amoenum*
103. Inflorescences ovoid-ellipsoid, 1.1–2.2 × 1–1.5 cm; leaflet blades obovate or oblanceolate, 0.5–1.5 × 0.2–1.1 cm; corollas 7–12 mm; calyces 4–8 mm. . . . . . . 63. *Trifolium dichotomum*

[92. Shifted to left margin.—Ed.]

92. Pedicels reflexed in fruit.
104. Herbs perennial; stems creeping, rooting at nodes.
105. Inflorescences of 2 kinds: one terminal, aerial, long-pedunculate, flowers chasmogamous, the other basal, subterranean, flowers cleistogamous. . . . . 72. *Trifolium amphianthum* (in part)
105. Inflorescences all aerial, flowers chasmogamous.
106. Peduncles 2–7 cm, single or paired at tips of erect stems, subtended by pair of opposite or subopposite, short-petiolate leaves; inflorescences 2–3.5 × 2–3.5 cm; flowers 15–30; leaflet blades broadly ovate or obcordate . . . . 65. *Trifolium stoloniferum*
106. Peduncles 10–12 cm, single, arising from stolons; inflorescences 1.8–2.2 × 1.8–2.2 cm; flowers 25–50; leaflet blades obovate, rhombic, or elliptic . . . . 66. *Trifolium calcaricum*
104. Herbs annual, biennial, or perennial; stems not creeping, not rooting at nodes.
107. Leaflet lengths 3+ times widths.
108. Herbs annual; leaflet blades narrowly obcordate, obovate, oblanceolate, or linear, apex rounded or truncate, shallowly to deeply retuse or deeply 2-fid. . . . . 55. *Trifolium bifidum* (in part)
108. Herbs perennial; leaflet blades elliptic, linear-elliptic, lanceolate, oblong, ovate, or linear, apex not deeply retuse to 2-fid.
109. Peduncles bent or curved proximal to flowers, inflorescences inverted or horizontal.
110. Ovaries pubescent distally; calyx curved in fruit, lobes unequal, lengths 2–3 times tube, plumose . . . . 85. *Trifolium eriocephalum*
110. Ovaries glabrous; calyx straight, lobes equal, lengths 1–1.5 times tube, sparsely pubescent or glabrate . . . . 95. *Trifolium kingii* (in part)
109. Peduncles straight, inflorescences erect.
111. Banners ovate to oblanceolate, apex tapering, acuminate or beaked . . . . 94. *Trifolium longipes* (in part)
111. Banners broadly oblong-elliptic or obovate-oblong, apex rounded, acute, or retuse, sometimes mucronate or apiculate.
112. Leaflet blade apex narrowly acute or acuminate, margins entire; proximal bracteoles forming involucres; flowers 10–20; calyces 8–15 mm; w United States . . . . 31. *Trifolium attenuatum* (in part)
112. Leaflet blade apex truncate to acute, margins entire or serrulate; bracteoles not forming involucres; flowers 20–40; calyces 4–7 mm; e United States. . . . . 67. *Trifolium virginicum*
107. Leaflet lengths usually to 2 times widths.

[113. Shifted to left margin.—Ed.]

113. Herbs annual or biennial.
 114. Calyces markedly bilabiate, lobes markedly unequal (adaxial longer than abaxial), oblong-ovate or broadly triangular, veins reticulate or branched.
  115. Calyx lobes, except abaxial, obovate, pubescent along margins, veins reticulate . . . . 70. *Trifolium bejariense* (in part)
  115. Calyx lobes broadly triangular, lanceolate, or linear, uniformly villous, veins slightly branched . . . . 71. *Trifolium carolinianum* (in part)
 114. Calyces not markedly bilabiate, lobes ± equal, triangular, lanceolate or linear, or subulate, veins unbranched.
  116. Inflorescence rachises not surpassing flowers; stipule apex recurved, dark purple or reddish; calyx lobes recurved in fruit . . . . 27. *Trifolium nigrescens* (in part)
  116. Inflorescence rachises sometimes surpassing flowers; stipule apex straight, green; calyx lobes straight in fruit.
   117. Calyx lobes unequal, margins dentate or pectinate, strongly ciliate, sinuses narrow; inflorescences 0.5–2 cm diam.; seeds 2.5–3 mm . . . . 57. *Trifolium ciliolatum* (in part)
   117. Calyx lobes equal, margins entire, sinuses broad; inflorescences 2–4 cm diam.; seeds 1.2–1.5 mm . . . . 68. *Trifolium reflexum* (in part)
113. Herbs perennial.
 118. Herbs canescent; margins of stipules and leaflets coarsely spinulose-dentate. . . . 73. *Trifolium leibergii*
 118. Herbs glabrous or pubescent, not canescent; margins of stipules and leaves entire or toothed, not spinulose.
  119. Inflorescence rachises not surpassing flowers; banners ovate-oblong, apex rounded-denticulate . . . . 16. *Trifolium hybridum* (in part)
  119. Inflorescence rachises sometimes surpassing flowers; banners elliptic, obovate, ovate-oblong, or lanceolate-ovate, apex not denticulate.
   120. Peduncles geniculate or bent proximal to flowers, inflorescences appearing inverted.
    121. Stipule apex long-acuminate, margins entire; corollas 6–10 mm; banners equaling wing and keel petals . . . . 28. *Trifolium breweri* (in part)
    121. Stipules apex acuminate or acute, margins entire proximally, 1–3-toothed distally; corollas 12–15 mm; banners longer than wing and keel petals . . . . 93. *Trifolium latifolium* (in part)
   120. Peduncles straight, inflorescences erect.
    122. Herbs pubescent; stems prostrate; leaflet blades obovate to obcordate, 0.9–1.6 cm; inflorescences 0.8–1.6 × 0.9–1.6 cm . . . . 29. *Trifolium sonorense* (in part)
    122. Herbs glabrous; stems erect, ascending, or decumbent; leaflet blades ovate, rhombic, elliptic, or lanceolate, 0.5–8 cm; inflorescences 1.5–4 × 1.4–3.5 cm.
     123. Inflorescences longer than wide, rachis internodes between floral whorls elongated; leaflet blades of basal leaves thin, margins setose to dentate . . . . .79. *Trifolium macilentum*
     123. Inflorescences ± as long as wide, rachis internodes not especially elongated; leaflet blades of basal leaves thick, margins sometimes shortly setose. . . . . 95. *Trifolium kingii* (in part)

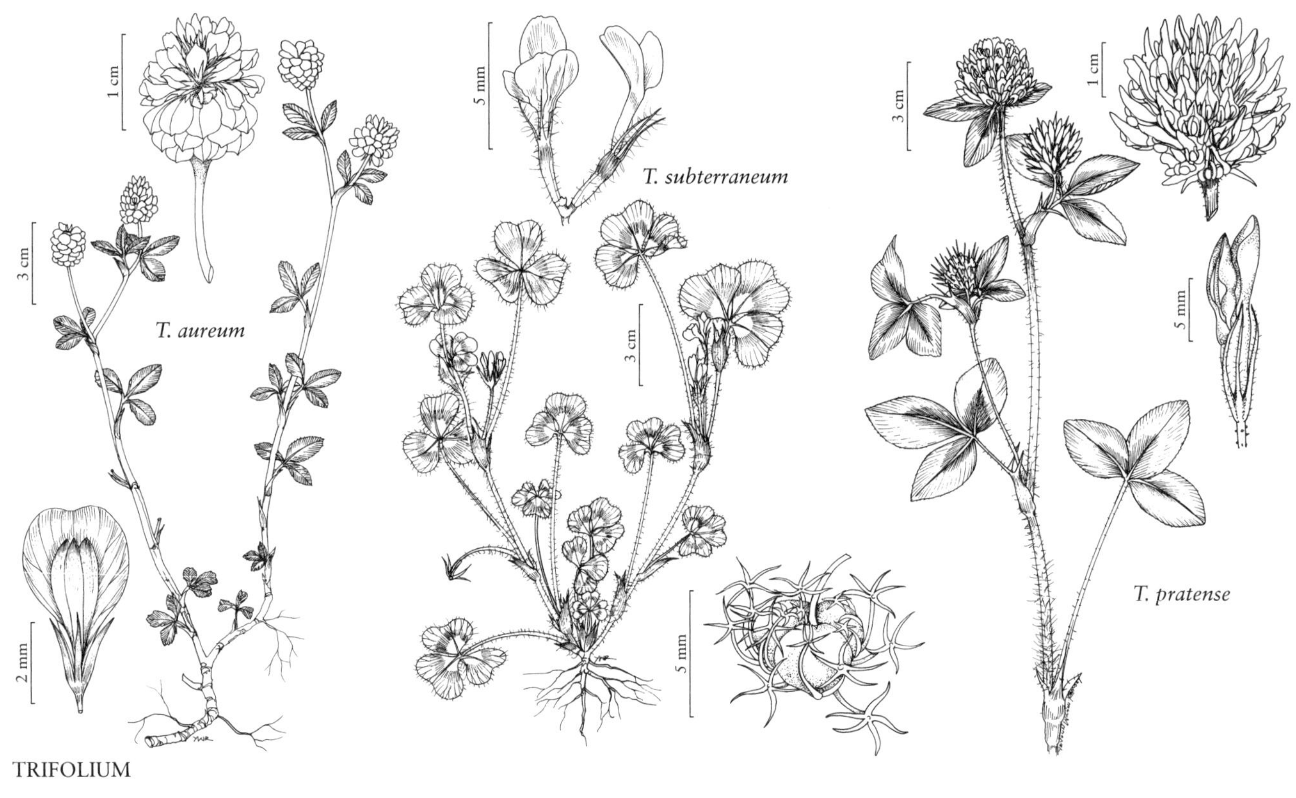

TRIFOLIUM

1. Trifolium aureum Pollich, Hist. Pl. Palat. 2: 344. 1777 • Golden hop clover, trèfle doré [F] [I] [W]

Chrysaspis aurea (Pollich) Greene

Herbs annual, 20–60 cm, glabrous or hirsute. **Stems** erect, unbranched or profusely branched. **Leaves** palmate; stipules oblanceolate, 0.9–1.5 cm, margins entire, apex acuminate or cuspidate; petiole 0.8–1 cm; petiolules 0–1 mm; leaflets 3, blades obovate to elliptic-lanceolate, 1–2.8 × 0.6–0.8 cm, base cuneate, lateral veins prominent, ± parallel, ascending, margins denticulate, apex acute, truncate, or retuse, mucronate, surfaces glabrous or sparsely hairy. **Peduncles** 2–5 cm. **Inflorescences** axillary or terminal, 20–80-flowered, usually ovoid-cylindric, sometimes globose, 1.2–2 × 1.3 cm; involucres absent. **Pedicels** reflexed, 0.3–0.6 mm; bracteoles a fringe of red setae. **Flowers** 7–8 mm; calyx campanulate, 2–2.5 mm, glabrous, veins 5, tube 0.8–1 mm, lobes unequal, adaxial deltate, 0.6–0.9 mm, 1/2 length of abaxial, abaxial linear, orifice open; corolla golden yellow becoming brown, 5–6 mm, banner persistent, obovate, boat-shaped, 4–4.5 × 2.4–2.6 mm, apex emarginate. **Legumes** stipitate, oblong, 3–3.5 mm, longer than calyx. **Seeds** 1, pale yellow-green, ovoid, 1–1.2 mm, smooth, glossy. $2n$ = 14, 16.

Flowering Jun–Aug. Roadsides, railroads, fields, disturbed woodland glades; 0–1700 m; introduced; St. Pierre and Miquelon; Alta., B.C., Man., N.B., Nfld. and Labr., N.S., Ont., P.E.I., Que., Sask.; Alaska, Calif., Conn., Del., D.C., Ga., Idaho, Ill., Ind., Iowa, Ky., Maine, Md., Mass., Mich., Minn., Mo., Mont., N.H., N.J., N.Y., N.C., Ohio, Oreg., Pa., R.I., S.C., Tenn., Vt., Va., Wash., W.Va., Wis., Wyo.; n, c Europe; w Asia; introduced also in s South America (Argentina, Chile), e Asia (e China), Pacific Islands (New Zealand), Australia.

Trifolium agrarium Linnaeus is a rejected name that has been used historically for *T. aureum* (J. E. Dandy 1958; N. J. Turland et al. 1996).

2. Trifolium dubium Sibthorp, Fl. Oxon., 231. 1794 • Little hop clover, petit trèfle jaune [I] [W]

Chrysaspis dubia (Sibthorp) Greene; *Trifolium minus* Smith

Herbs annual, 20–40 cm, glabrous or sparsely hairy. **Stems** erect to prostrate, branched from base. **Leaves** pinnate; stipules ovate, 0.3–0.5 cm, margins entire, apex acute; petiole to 1.5 cm; lateral leaflet petiolules to 0.5 mm, terminal leaflet stalk 1–1.5 mm; leaflets 3, blades obovate to elliptic-lanceolate, 1–2 × 0.5–1.5 cm, base cuneate, lateral veins prominent, ± parallel, ascending, margins dentate distally, apex rounded or retuse, surfaces glabrous or sparsely hairy. **Peduncles** 1–1.5 cm. **Inflorescences** axillary or terminal, 5–20-flowered, ovoid or globose, 0.5–0.9 × 0.6 cm; involucres absent. **Pedicels** reflexed, 0.2–0.5 mm; bracteoles a fringe of red setae. **Flowers** 2.8–3.5 mm; calyx campanulate, 1.5–2 mm, glabrous, veins 5, tube 0.8–1 mm, lobes unequal, longer than tube, adaxial 2 shorter, orifice open; corolla pale yellow becoming brown, 2.6–3.2 mm, not or slightly ribbed, banner persistent, spatulate, 2.6–3.2 × 2 mm, apex rounded to broadly acute. **Legumes** stipitate, ellipsoid, 1.5–2 mm, short beaked. **Seeds** 1, yellow or pale brown, ellipsoid, 0.9–1 mm, smooth, glossy. **2*n*** = 16, 28, 32.

Flowering May–Oct. Disturbed ground, fields; 0–2300 m; introduced; St. Pierre and Miquelon; B.C., N.B., N.S., Ont., P.E.I., Que.; Ala., Alaska, Ariz., Ark., Calif., Conn., Del., D.C., Fla., Ga., Idaho, Ill., Ind., Iowa, Kans., Ky., La., Maine, Md., Mass., Mich., Minn., Miss., Mo., Mont., Nebr., Nev., N.H., N.J., N.Mex., N.Y., N.C., N.Dak., Ohio, Okla., Oreg., Pa., R.I., S.C., Tenn., Tex., Vt., Va., Wash., W.Va., Wis., Wyo.; c, s Europe; w Asia; introduced also in s South America, e Asia (e China), n, s Africa, Pacific Islands (Hawaii, New Zealand), Australia.

Trifolium dubium is often confused with *Medicago lupulina* Linnaeus; the latter may be distinguished by its toothed stipules, deciduous corollas, and shiny, black fruits. Little hop clover may be the co-called shamrock of Irish folklore (E. C. Nelson 1991; P. S. Wyse Jackson 2014); other candidates include other species of *Trifolium* or species of *Medicago* or *Oxalis*.

3. Trifolium campestre Schreber in G. F. Hoffmann, Deutschl. Fl. 4: 16, plate 253. 1804 • Hop clover, trèfle couché [I] [W]

Chrysaspis campestris (Schreber) Desvaux

Herbs annual, 5–40 cm, slightly villous or glabrous. **Stems** erect to ascending, branched. **Leaves** pinnate; stipules ovate-lanceolate, 0.5–0.8 cm, margins entire, glandular, apex acuminate; petiole 0.3–2 cm; lateral leaflet petiolules 0.5–0.6 mm, terminal leaflet stalk 3–5 mm; leaflets 3, blades rhombic to obovate, 0.4–1.5 × 0.4–0.8 cm, base cuneate, lateral veins prominent, ± parallel, ascending, margins denticulate distally, apex truncate or retuse, surfaces strigose adaxially. **Peduncles** 1.5–3.5 cm. **Inflorescences** axillary, 30–60-flowered, globose or broadly ovoid, 0.8–1.5 × 0.7–1 cm; involucres absent. **Pedicels** reflexed, 0.7–1.2 mm; bracteoles a fringe of red setae. **Flowers** 4.3–5 mm; calyx campanulate, strongly bilabiate, 1.3–1.5 mm, glabrous, veins 5, tube 0.3–0.6 mm, lobes unequal, adaxial deltate, very short, lateral and abaxial linear-subulate, each tipped with 1 or 2 stiff hairs, orifice open; corolla yellow becoming brown, 3.5–6 mm, ribbed, banner persistent, obovate, enveloping other petals, boat-shaped, 4.3–5 × 2.8–3.2 mm, apex broad, acute. **Legumes** stipitate, oblong, 2–2.5 mm. **Seeds** 1 or 2, yellow, ellipsoid, 1–1.5 mm, smooth, lustrous. **2*n*** = 14.

Flowering Jun–Aug. Roadsides, fields; 0–1700 m; introduced; St. Pierre and Miquelon; B.C., N.B., Nfld. and Labr. (Nfld.), N.S., Ont., P.E.I., Que.; Ala., Alaska, Ariz., Ark., Calif., Conn., Del., D.C., Fla., Ga., Idaho, Ill., Ind., Iowa, Kans., Ky., La., Maine, Md., Mass., Mich., Minn., Miss., Mo., Mont., Nebr., N.H., N.J., N.Mex., N.Y., N.C., N.Dak., Ohio, Okla., Oreg., Pa., R.I., S.C., Tenn., Tex., Vt., Va., Wash., W.Va., Wis., Wyo.; Europe; w Asia; n Africa; introduced also in South America, e Asia (China), s Africa, Pacific Islands (Hawaii, New Zealand), Australia.

Trifolium filiforme Linnaeus and *T. procumbens* Linnaeus are rejected names that were used historically for *T. campestre* (J. E. Dandy 1958; N. J. Turland et al. 1996).

4. Trifolium lupinaster Linnaeus, Sp. Pl. 2: 766. 1753 • Lupine clover [I]

Lupinaster pentaphyllus Moench; *Pentaphyllon lupinaster* (Linnaeus) Persoon

Herbs perennial, 15–50 cm, glabrous or curly-pilose. **Stems** erect, unbranched or branched distally. **Leaves** palmate; stipules adnate entire length of petiole, sheathing, lanceolate-oblong, 0.8–1.3 cm, margins sharply and finely serrate, pilose, apex acute; petiole 0.5–0.7 cm; petiolules 0.5 mm; leaflets (3–)5(–9), blades elliptic to linear-elliptic, 1–4 × 0.3–1.4 cm, base cuneate, veins prominent, cartilagenous, ending in sharp, curved teeth, margins setaceous, apex acute to obtuse, surfaces glabrous except midrib abaxially. **Peduncles** 1–5 cm. **Inflorescences** terminal or axillary, 10–30-flowered, hemispheric or globose, 1.7–2.3 × 2.7–3.3 cm; involucres oblique, to 0.5 mm, wavy to toothed. **Pedicels** erect or horizontal, 1–3 mm; bracteoles broadly shell-shaped, sometimes connate into lobed ridge, to 0.5 mm. **Flowers** 11–17 mm; calyx campanulate, oblique, 6–9 mm, glabrous or sparsely hairy distally and along veins, veins 10, tube 3 mm, lobes subequal, pilose, abaxial slightly longer, subulate, orifice open; corolla white to rose-purple, 10–15 mm, banner rolled into open tube, arched upwards distally, 10–15 × 4–5 mm, apex broadly rounded or acute, apiculate. **Legumes** oblong, 6–8 mm. **Seeds** 3–6, dark brown or gray-brown, globose-reniform, 1.5–2 mm, slightly roughened, dull. **2*n*** = 16, 32, 40, 48.

Flowering Jun. Forest glades, meadows; 0–400 m; introduced; Alaska; Asia (n China, Russia).

Populations of *Trifolium lupinaster* in Alaska appear to have been introduced as a potential forage crop and spread from cultivation (D. F. Murray and H. F. Drury 1974).

5. **Trifolium subterraneum** Linnaeus, Sp. Pl. 2: 767. 1753 • Subterranean clover F I W

Herbs annual, 10–80 cm, glabrous or appressed-pubescent. **Stems** prostrate to ascending, branched. **Leaves** palmate; stipules ovate, 0.5–3 cm, margins entire or slightly toothed, ciliate, apex acute to acuminate; petiole 1–20 cm; petiolules 1 mm; leaflets 3, blades broadly obcordate, 0.8–2.8 × 1–3 cm, base cuneate, veins delicate, widely spaced, margins mostly entire, slightly dentate distally, apex emarginate, surfaces appressed-sericeous. **Peduncles** 2–6.5 cm. **Inflorescences** axillary, elongate and reflexed, pushing into substrate after anthesis, fertile flowers 2–7, sterile flowers 0–80, globose or cylindric, 0.5–1.5 × 0.8–1.5 cm; involucres absent. **Pedicels** reflexed after anthesis, 0.2–0.4 mm; bracteoles absent. **Flowers:** fertile ones 7–15 mm; calyx tubular, 5–6 mm, glabrous or hairy, veins indistinct, tube 3–4 mm, lobes subequal, pubescent or glabrous, spreading, orifice open; corolla white, pink, or pink-striped, 7–10 mm, banner ovate-elliptic, 7–10 × 1.5–2 mm, apex rounded; sterile flowers 4–7 mm; calyx teeth linear; corolla absent. **Legumes** subterranean, obovoid, 3–4 mm. **Seeds** 1, purplish black, ellipsoid, 2.6–3 mm, smooth, dull. **2*n*** = 16.

Flowering Mar–May. Open, disturbed sandy soils; 0–1000 m; introduced; B.C.; Calif., Ga., La., Mass., Miss., N.J., N.C., Oreg., S.C., Wash.; w Europe; w Asia; n Africa; introduced also in s South America, s Africa, Pacific Islands (Hawaii, New Zealand), Australia.

Trifolium subterraneum was first introduced by the USDA about 1921 as a pasture crop; it is utilized as such in the western and southern United States (W. S. McGuire 1985). Inflorescences of *T. subterraneum* consist of intermixed sterile and fertile flowers; after fetilization, the inflorescence is pushed underground, where the fruits develop.

6. **Trifolium pratense** Linnaeus, Sp. Pl. 2: 768. 1753 • Red clover, trèfle rouge F I W

Trifolium pensylvanicum Willdenow

Herbs perennial, 20–70 cm, pilose or glabrous. **Stems** erect, ascending, or decumbent, branched. **Leaves** palmate; stipules broadly triangular, 1–2 cm, margins entire, sometimes ciliate, apex mucronate or setaceous; petiole 1–9 cm; petiolules 1 mm; leaflets 3, blades elliptic to obovate, 1.5–5 × 0.7–1.5 cm, base cuneate, veins prominent, margins subentire, apex obtuse, acute, or retuse, surfaces appressed-pubescent. **Peduncles** ± 0 cm, subtended by stipules of distal leaves. **Inflorescences** terminal, solitary or paired, 75–100+-flowered, globose or ovoid, 1.2–7.7 × 0.7–2.2 cm; involucres absent, involucrelike structures formed of stipules of distalmost leaves. **Pedicels** straight, 0–1 mm; bracteoles absent. **Flowers** 15–18 mm; calyx tubular-campanulate, 8–11 mm, hairy, veins 10, tube 3–4 mm, lobes unequal, adaxial equaling tube, lateral and abaxial 2 times tube, orifice hairy, slightly closed; corolla usually rose-purple, rarely pink or white, 13–18 mm, banner elliptic-ovate, 10–13 × 3–5 mm, apex narrowly rounded. **Legumes** oblong, leathery distally, transversely dehiscent, 3 mm. **Seeds** 1 or 2, yellow, yellow-brown, or purple, ovoid, 1.6–2 mm, smooth, dull. **2*n*** = 14.

Flowering May–Sep. Fields, prairies, roadsides, disturbed areas; 0–3100 m; introduced; Greenland; St. Pierre and Miquelon; Alta., B.C., Man., N.B., Nfld. and Labr., N.W.T., N.S., Ont., P.E.I., Que., Sask., Yukon; Ala., Alaska, Ariz., Ark., Calif., Colo., Conn., Del., D.C., Fla., Ga., Idaho, Ill., Ind., Iowa, Kans., Ky., La., Maine, Md., Mass., Mich., Minn., Miss., Mo., Mont., Nebr., Nev., N.H., N.J., N.Mex., N.Y., N.C., N.Dak., Ohio, Okla., Oreg., Pa., R.I., S.C., S.Dak., Tenn., Tex., Utah, Vt., Va., Wash., W.Va., Wis., Wyo.; Eurasia; introduced also in s South America, s Africa, Pacific Islands (Hawaii, New Zealand), Australia.

Trifolium pratense is morphologically variable and numerous varieties have been recognized (M. Zohary and D. Heller 1984). Distinctions among these are slight and intergradation is common, perhaps due to the long-time cultivation of the species. In North America, the following varieties are sometimes recognized: var. *pratense* with stems decumbent to ascending, 20–40 cm, with dense, appressed, white hairs; var. *sativum* Schreber with stems mostly erect, 40–100 cm, sparsely hairy or glabrous; and var. *americanum* Harz with stems 30–100 cm, with dense, spreading hairs.

7. Trifolium medium Linnaeus, Amoen. Acad. 4: 105. 1759 • Zigzag clover, trèfle flexueux [I]

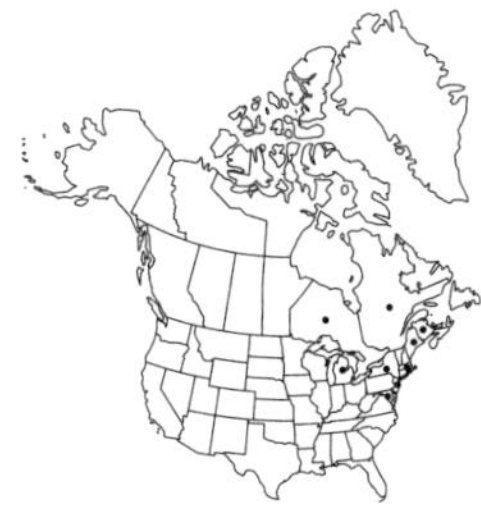

Herbs perennial, 20–70 cm, strigose. **Stems** erect-ascending, flexuous, often zigzag, branched. **Leaves** palmate; stipules lanceolate-linear, 1.8–2.8 cm, margins entire, ciliate, apex subulate; petiole 1–9 cm; petiolules 1 mm; leaflets 3, blades elliptic-oblong, obovate, or ovate, 1.5–5 × 0.8–3.5 cm, base cuneate, veins arcuate, forked, margins entire, finely ciliate, apex obtuse to acute, surfaces appressed-pubescent. **Peduncles** 1–3 cm. **Inflorescences** terminal or axillary, rarely paired, 20–50-flowered, globose or ovoid, 1.5–4 × 1.3–3.8 cm; involucres absent. **Pedicels** straight, 0.5 mm; bracteoles absent. **Flowers** 15–18 mm; calyx cylindric, 6–10 mm, glabrous, veins 10–15, tube 2.5–3.5 mm, lobes unequal, subulate-setaceous, orifice glabrous or hairy distally, closed; corolla usually reddish purple, rarely white, 12–20 mm, banner lanceolate-elliptic, 1.2–2 × 4–5 mm, apex acute. **Legumes** ovoid to globose, leathery distally, transversely dehiscent, 2–3 mm. **Seeds** 1 or 2, yellow-brown, mitten-shaped, 1–1.5 mm, smooth, lustrous. **2*n*** = 48, 64, 68, 70, 72, 80, ca. 126.

Flowering May–Aug. Fields, roadsides; 0–300 m; introduced; N.B., Ont., Que.; Maine, Md., Mass., Mich., N.J., N.Y., R.I.; Europe; w Asia; introduced also in e Asia (e China), Pacific Islands (New Zealand), Australia.

Trifolium medium was reported for Kentucky by H. Garman (1902); no non-cultivated specimens have been seen for that state (M. A. Vincent 2001). Reports of *T. medium* in Nova Scotia and Prince Edward Island are based on old reports and the species does not appear to be extant in those regions.

8. Trifolium hirtum Allioni, Auct. Fl. Pedem., 20. 1789 • Rose clover [I] [W]

Herbs annual, 10–35 cm, densely spreading-hairy. **Stems** curved-ascending, branched. **Leaves** palmate; stipules lanceolate-ovate, 0.8–1.8 cm, margins entire, apex long-setaceous; petiole 0.5–5 cm; petiolules 0.5 mm; leaflets 3, blades obovate to oblong, 0.8–2.5 × 0.5–1.3 cm, base cuneate, veins prominent, closely-spaced, margins denticulate distally, apex rounded, surfaces densely spreading-hairy. **Peduncles** absent. **Inflorescences** terminal on branches, 10–50-flowered, globose or ovoid, disarticulating in fruit, 1.5–2.5 × 1.5–2.5 cm; involucres absent, involucrelike structures formed by enlarged stipules. **Pedicels** absent; bracteoles absent. **Flowers** 10–17 mm; calyx campanulate, 7–11 mm, pilose, veins 20, tube 2–5 mm, lobes subequal, abaxial slightly longer, orifice hairy, open; corolla purplish red, 10–14 mm, banner lanceolate, 10–14 × 1–2 mm, apex acute-acuminate. **Legumes** ovoid, leathery distally, transversely dehiscent, 2–3 mm. **Seeds** 1, tan or brown, globose-ellipsoid, 1.5–2 mm, smooth, glossy. **2*n*** = 10.

Flowering Apr–Jun. Fields, roadsides; 0–2100 m; introduced; Ala., Calif., Fla., La., N.C., Oreg., Tenn., Va.; s Europe; w Asia; n Africa; introduced also in s Africa, Pacific Islands (New Zealand), Australia.

Trifolium hirtum was first cultivated in California in the 1940s as a forage plant and as a nitrogen source in roadside grass plantings (R. M. Love 1985); it is now widespread in that state. It was reported for Kentucky by D. Isely (1998); no non-cultivated specimens have been seen from that state (M. A. Vincent 2001).

9. Trifolium lappaceum Linnaeus, Sp. Pl. 2: 768. 1753 • Burdock clover [F] [I]

Herbs annual, 5–60 cm, hirsute or glabrous. **Stems** erect to decumbent, branched. **Leaves** palmate; stipules oblong, 0.5–1.9 cm, margins entire, apex lanceolate-subulate; petiole 0.3–5 cm; petiolules 1 mm; leaflets 3, blades ovate to obovate, 0.5–1.5 × 0.3–2 cm, base cuneate, veins fine, margins denticulate to dentate, apex rounded, truncate, or emarginate, surfaces hirsute. **Peduncles** 0.1–0.7 cm. **Inflorescences** terminal, 40–60-flowered, globose or ovoid, burlike, not disarticulating at maturity, 1–1.4 × 1.8–2 cm; involucres absent. **Pedicels** straight, 0.5 mm; bracteoles absent. **Flowers** 7–9 mm; calyx campanulate, 7–9 mm, glabrous, veins 20, tube 3 mm, lobes equal, longer than tube, setaceous becoming spinose, orifice hairy, open; corolla pinkish white, 6–10 mm, banner elliptic, 6–9 × 1.5–2 mm, apex emarginate. **Legumes** ovoid, leathery distally, transversely dehiscent, 1.5 mm, long-beaked. **Seeds** 1, light brown, reddish, or yellow with reddish spots, ovoid, 1 mm, smooth, shiny. **2*n*** = 16.

Flowering Mar–Jun. Fields, roadsides, grassy areas; 0–300 m; introduced; Ala., Fla., La., Miss., N.J., N.C., Pa., S.C., Tenn., Tex.; s Europe; w Asia; n Africa; Atlantic Islands (Canary Islands); introduced also in s South America (Uruguay), s Africa, Australia.

Trifolium lappaceum was introduced to the United States about 1903; it has been used as a winter annual pasture and hay crop (E. A. Hollowell 1939), as well as in roadside grass plantings as a nitrogen source.

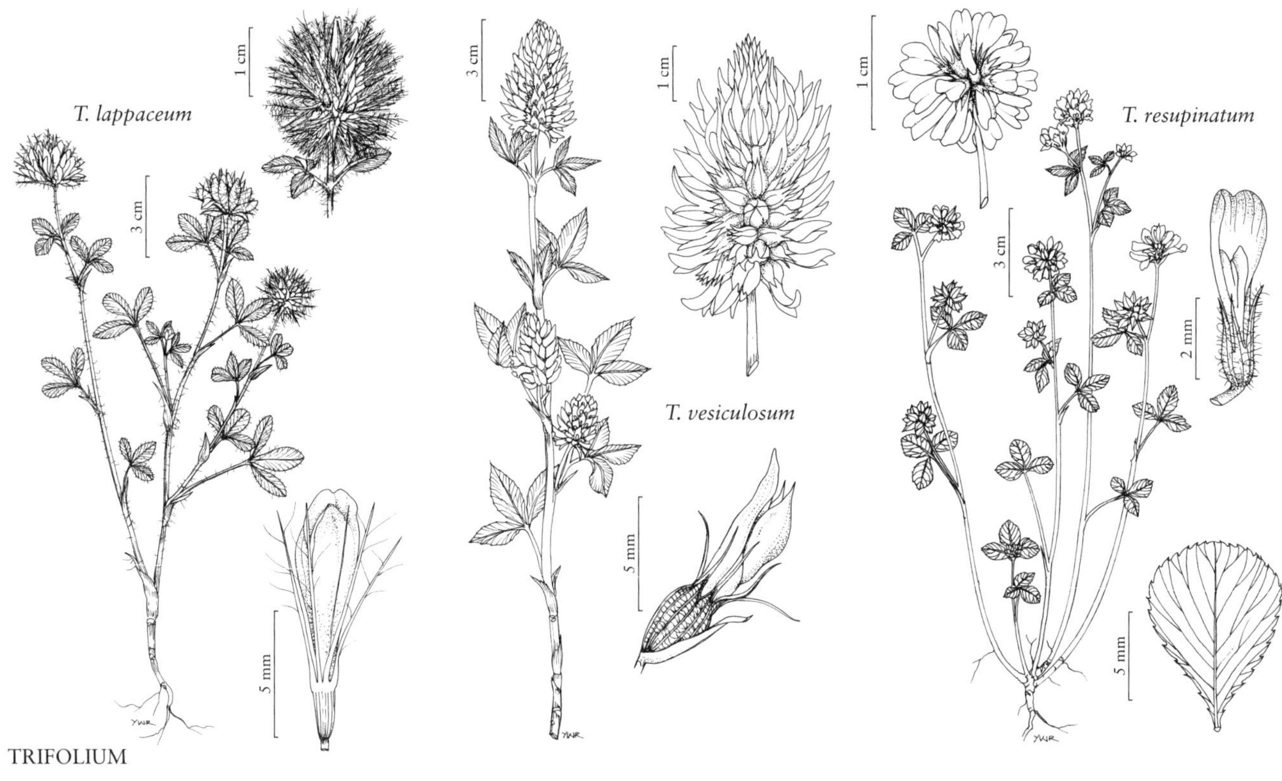

TRIFOLIUM

10. Trifolium incarnatum Linnaeus, Sp. Pl. 2: 769. 1753 • Crimson clover [I] [W]

Herbs usually annual, rarely biennial, 20–60 cm, short-villous. **Stems** erect, unbranched or sparsely branched. **Leaves** palmate; stipules ovate, 1–2 cm, margins wavy or toothed, apex blunt or ± tapering distally; petiole 1–8 cm; petiolules 1 mm; leaflets 3, blades broadly ovate, 1–3 × 1–1.5 cm, base cuneate, veins fine, margins denticulate, apex emarginate or retuse, surfaces with spreading, pustulate-based hairs. **Peduncles** 2–10 cm. **Inflorescences** terminal, 25–100-flowered, oblong, 2–7 × 1–2.5 cm; involucres absent. **Pedicels** straight, 0.5 mm; bracteoles absent. **Flowers** 10–15 mm; calyx tubular-campanulate, 10 mm, villous, veins 10, tube 3–4 mm, lobes equal, longer than tube, spreading in fruit, orifice narrowly opening; corolla usually scarlet to red, rarely pink or white, 11–17 mm, banner oblong-elliptic, much longer than wing and keel petals, 10–16 × 2 mm, apex acute. **Legumes** ovoid, leathery distally, transversely dehiscent, 2.5–3 mm. **Seeds** 1, reddish, ellipsoid, 2–2.5 mm, smooth, glossy. **2*n*** = 14.

Flowering May–Aug. Meadows, roadsides, especially in sandy soils; 0–1000 m; introduced; B.C.; Ala., Ark., Calif., Conn., Del., D.C., Fla., Ga., Idaho, Ill., Ind., Iowa, Kans., Ky., La., Maine, Md., Mass., Mich., Minn., Miss., Mo., Nebr., N.H., N.J., N.Mex., N.Y., N.C., N.Dak., Ohio, Okla., Oreg., Pa., R.I., S.C., S.Dak., Tenn., Tex., Vt., Va., Wash., W.Va., Wis.; Europe; introduced also in s South America (Chile), e Asia (e China), s Africa, Pacific Islands (Hawaii, New Zealand), Australia.

Trifolium incarnatum was introduced to the United States in 1818 as a forage crop and green manure crop; it is used commonly as a winter grazing crop and in roadside grass plantings as a nitrogen source, especially in the southeastern states (W. E. Knight 1985). Reports of *T. incarnatum* in Manitoba, Ontario, and Montana appear to have been based on cultivated specimens.

11. Trifolium echinatum M. Bieberstein, Fl. Taur.-Caucas. 2: 216. 1808 • Prickly clover [I]

Herbs annual, 10–50 cm, appressed-hairy. **Stems** erect or ascending, branched from base. **Leaves** palmate; stipules ovate-lanceolate, 0.4–0.8 cm, margins entire, apex acuminate, flared outward; petiole 0.5–6 cm; petiolules 1+ mm; leaflets 3, blades obovate, elliptic, or narrowly elliptic, 0.8–2.5 × 0.4–1.6 cm, base cuneate, veins prominent, thickened abaxially, margins denticulate or serrate, apex rounded, acute, or apiculate, surfaces sparsely hairy. **Peduncles** 0.8–2 cm. **Inflorescences** terminal and axillary, 15–50-flowered, obconic or obovoid, 1–2 ×

1–1.6 cm; involucres absent. **Pedicels** absent; bracteoles absent. **Flowers** 9–11 mm; calyx campanulate, 5–8 mm, glabrescent, veins 10, tube 2–3 mm, lobes unequal, triangular-elliptic, stellate-spreading, orifice closed by bilabiate callosities; corolla creamy white, 8–10 mm, banner oblong-spatulate, 8–10 × 2–3 mm, apex acute. **Legumes** obovoid, leathery distally, transversely dehiscent, 1.6–2 mm. **Seeds** 1, tan or brown, ovoid, 1.2–1.4 mm, smooth, glossy. **2*n*** = 16.

Flowering Mar–Jun. Disturbed roadsides, fields; 100–300 m; introduced; Ala., La.; c, s Europe; w Asia; n Africa.

Trifolium echinatum was recently discovered in Ouachita Parish in a disturbed construction area; an older record (1902) from ballast in Portland, Oregon, appears to have been a waif.

12. Trifolium striatum Linnaeus, Sp. Pl. 2: 770. 1753 • Knotted clover [I]

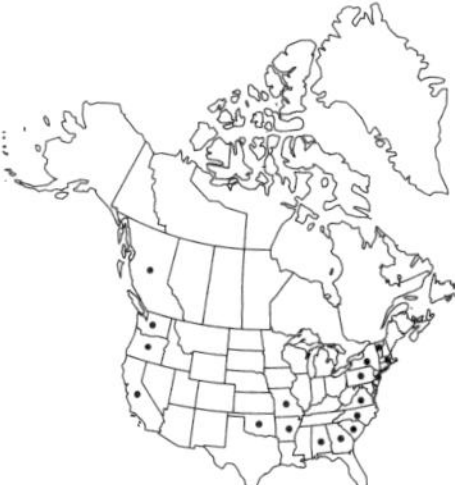

Herbs usually annual, rarely biennial, 10–50 cm, villous. **Stems** erect, ascending, or decumbent, branched from base. **Leaves** palmate; stipules lanceolate-ovate, 0.9–1.1 cm, margins entire, apex acute-acuminate, setaceous, ciliate; petiole 0.5–5 cm; petiolules 0.5 mm; leaflets 3, blades obovate to oblong, 0.9–1.6 × 0.4–1 cm, base cuneate, veins fine, margins denticulate, apex obtuse, obcordate, or emarginate, surfaces hairy. **Peduncles** 0–1 cm. **Inflorescences** axillary or terminal, solitary or paired, 20–60-flowered, ovoid or oblong, 0.8–1.6 × 0.6–1 cm; involucres absent. **Pedicels** absent; bracteoles absent. **Flowers** 5–7 mm; calyx ellipsoid to urceolate, 3–4 mm, hairy, veins 10, tube 2–3 mm, lobes erect or spreading, unequal, abaxial longest and equal to tube, subulate, orifice open; corolla pink, 25–35 mm, banner oblong, 2.5–3.5 × 1.5–2 mm, apex retuse. **Legumes** ovoid, leathery distally, transversely dehiscent, 2–2.5 mm. **Seeds** 1, tan or reddish brown, globose to ovoid, 1–1.5 mm, smooth, glossy. **2*n*** = 14.

Flowering May–Aug. Waste places; 0–500 m; introduced; B.C.; Ala., Ark., Calif., Ga., Mass., Mo., N.J., N.Y., N.C., Okla., Oreg., Pa., S.C., Vt., Va., Wash.; Europe; w Asia; nw Africa; introduced also in s South America (Chile), Pacific Islands (New Zealand), Australia.

Trifolium striatum has been recorded as an occasional weed in the flora area, having been first collected on ballast in New Jersey in 1880. It is found sporadically as a weed of disturbed habitats and appears to be spreading rapidly. It has been called Pitts's clover in the southern United States because it was discovered by J. D. Pitts in a field of crimson clover as a weed and he experimented with it as a forage plant (G. L. Fuller and B. H. Hendrickson 1928).

13. Trifolium alexandrinum Linnaeus, Cent. Pl. I, 25. 1755 • Egyptian clover [I]

Herbs annual, 20–60 cm, appressed-pubescent. **Stems** erect, branched. **Leaves** palmate; stipules lanceolate, 1–2 cm, margins denticulate distally, plumose-ciliate, apex caudate; petiole 1–8 cm; petiolules 1+ mm; leaflets 3, blades broadly elliptic to oblong, 1–5 × 0.5–1.5 cm, base cuneate, veins fine, margins denticulate, apex usually mucronate, sometimes retuse, surfaces hairy. **Peduncles** 0.5–9 cm. **Inflorescences** terminal, 25–100-flowered, ovoid, elongate in fruit, 1–2.5 × 1–1.5 cm; involucres minute or absent. **Pedicels** absent; bracteoles absent. **Flowers** 13–16 mm; calyx cylindric (campanulate in fruit), 6–8 mm, appressed-hairy, veins 10, tube 1–2 mm, lobes erect to slightly spreading, equal or abaxial 2 slightly longer, narrowly triangular, orifice open, hairy; corolla cream or yellowish white, 13–16 mm, banner narrowly spatulate, 13–16 × 3–4 mm, apex obtuse. **Legumes** ellipsoid, leathery distally, transversely dehiscent, 2.2–2.5 mm. **Seeds** 1, yellow, ovoid, 2–2.2 mm, smooth, glossy. **2*n*** = 16.

Flowering Apr–May. Disturbed areas, fields; 0–50 m; introduced; Calif.; w Asia (Syria); introduced also in e Asia (e China), n Africa, Australia.

Trifolium alexandrinum (known also as *berseem*, from its Arabic name) has been cultivated in the Mediterranean region for millennia and appears to have been introduced into Egypt in the sixth century (P. B. Kennedy and W. W. Mackie 1925). The origin of *T. alexandrinum* was long shrouded in mystery, because it appeared that the progenitors of the species were possibly extinct (W. E. Knight 1985b). Examination of similar species using molecular data gave indications that *T. berytheum* Boissier & C. I. Blanche and *T. salmoneum* Mouterde might be the primary ancestors from which domestication occurred through artificial selection in Syria (A. Badr et al. 2008).

14. Trifolium angustifolium Linnaeus, Sp. Pl. 2: 769. 1753 • Narrowleaf crimson clover [I] [W]

Herbs annual, 10–30 cm, appressed-pubescent. **Stems** erect, unbranched to sparsely branched. **Leaves** palmate; stipules lanceolate to linear, 0.5–2.2 cm, margins entire, apex lanceolate-linear; petiole 2–3 cm; petiolules 1+ mm; leaflets 3, blades linear-lanceolate, 3–5 × 0.2–0.4 cm, base cuneate, veins fine, margins entire, apex acute, surfaces hairy. **Peduncles** 1–2.2 cm.

Inflorescences terminal, 25–75-flowered, spicate, cylindric or conic, 3–8 × 1.5–2 cm; involucres absent. **Pedicels** erect, 0.5 mm; bracteoles absent. **Flowers** 10–13 mm; calyx tubular, 8–13 mm, tuberculate with appressed, stiff hairs, veins 10, tube 3–5 mm, lobes unequal, abaxial lobes longest, subulate-setaceous, spreading stellate in fruit, orifice closed by bilabiate callosities, hairy; corolla usually pale pink or purple, rarely white, 9–12 mm, banner ovate-elliptic, 9–12 × 2–2.5 mm, apex notched. **Legumes** ovoid, leathery distally, transversely dehiscent, 2.2–2.5 mm. **Seeds** 1, light brown or yellow, ovoid, 1.6–2 mm, smooth, glossy. $2n$ = 14, 16.

Flowering Mar–Apr. Waste places, fields, meadows; 0–1000 m; introduced; Ala., Calif., Oreg., S.C.; Europe; w Asia; n Africa; Atlantic Islands (Canary Islands); introduced also in s South America (Chile, Uruguay), s Africa, Pacific Islands (New Zealand), Australia.

Trifolium angustifolium is spreading rapidly in west-central California and is weedy in many regions globally (R. P. Randall 2002).

15. Trifolium arvense Linnaeus, Sp. Pl. 2: 769. 1753 • Rabbitfoot clover, trèfle pied-de-lièvre [I] [W]

Herbs annual, 5–30 cm, villous. **Stems** erect, branched distally. **Leaves** palmate; stipules linear-lanceolate to ovate-oblong, 0.5–0.8 cm, margins entire, apex filiform; petiole 0.4–4.5 cm; petiolules 1+ mm; leaflets 3, blades linear-oblong to narrowly elliptic, 1–2 × 0.2–0.5 cm, base cuneate, veins fine, margins denticulate distally, apex mucronate, surfaces hairy. **Peduncles** 0.5–2.5 cm. **Inflorescences** axillary or terminal, 30–100-flowered, ovoid or cylindric, elongate in fruit, 1–2.3 × 0.9–1.2 cm; involucres absent. **Pedicels** straight, to 0.5 mm; bracteoles obtuse, to 0.1 mm. **Flowers** 5–8 mm; calyx campanulate, 5–8 mm, villous, veins 10, tube 1.2–1.8 mm, lobes purple or pink, subequal, setacous, orifice open, hairy; corolla white to pink, 3–6 mm, much shorter than calyx, banner narrowly ovate-elliptic, 5–5.5 × 1–1.5 mm, apex obtuse. **Legumes** ovoid, leathery distally, transversely dehiscent, 1.5–2 mm. **Seeds** 1, yellow, globose, 1 mm, smooth, glossy. $2n$ = 14.

Flowering Mar–Jun. Waste places, roadsides, fields; 0–1300 m; introduced; St. Pierre and Miquelon; B.C., N.B., Nfld. and Labr. (Nfld.), N.S., Ont., P.E.I., Que.; Ala., Ariz., Ark., Calif., Conn., Del., D.C., Fla., Ga., Idaho, Ill., Ind., Iowa, Kans., Ky., La., Maine, Md., Mass., Mich., Minn., Miss., Mo., Mont., N.H., N.J., N.Mex., N.Y., N.C., N.Dak., Ohio, Okla., Oreg., Pa., R.I., S.C., Tenn., Tex., Utah, Vt., Va., Wash., W.Va., Wis.; s Europe; w Asia; n Africa; introduced also in s South America (Argentina, Chile, Uruguay), s Africa, Pacific Islands (New Zealand), Australia.

Trifolium arvense is widely distributed throughout the flora area. It was listed among cultivated clovers by F. J. Hermann (1953); J. M. Gillett (1985) expressed doubt that it had been cultivated.

16. Trifolium hybridum Linnaeus, Sp. Pl. 2: 766. 1753 • Alsike clover, trèfle alsike [I] [W]

Amoria hybrida (Linnaeus) C. Presl; *Trifolium elegans* Savi

Herbs perennial, 10–70 cm, glabrous or sparsely hairy. **Stems** erect or ascending, branched. **Leaves** palmate; stipules obovate or lanceolate, 1–2.5 cm, margins entire or toothed, apex long-acuminate; petiole 1–21 cm; petiolules 1 mm; leaflets 3, blades usually obovate or ovate, rarely rhombic, 1–4 × 1–2.5 cm, base cuneate, veins prominent, margins sharply serrate, apex broadly acute, obtuse, or emarginate, surfaces glabrous. **Peduncles** 2–10 cm. **Inflorescences** terminal or axillary, 10–70+-flowered, globose to subglobose, 1–2.5 × 1–2.5 cm, rachis not prolonged beyond flowers; involucres absent. **Pedicels** strongly reflexed, 2–3.5 mm; bracteoles lanceolate, 1 mm. **Flowers** 8–12 mm; calyx campanulate, 3.5–4 mm, glabrous or sparsely hairy, veins 10, tube 1.5–2 mm, lobes unequal, lanceolate-subulate, orifice open; corolla pale to dark pink, 7–10 mm, banner ovate-oblong, 6.5–10.5 × 4–6 mm, apex rounded-denticulate. **Legumes** stipitate, ellipsoid, 3–7 mm. **Seeds** 2–4, tan, brown, or red-brown, mitten-shaped, 1–1.4 mm, smooth, dull. $2n$ = 16.

Flowering May–Oct. Roadsides, open woods, edges, fields, meadows, waste places; 0–1800 m; introduced; Greenland; St. Pierre and Miquelon; Alta., B.C., Man., N.B., Nfld. and Labr., N.W.T., N.S., Ont., P.E.I., Que., Sask., Yukon; Ala., Alaska, Ariz., Ark., Calif., Colo., Conn., Del., D.C., Fla., Ga., Idaho, Ill., Ind., Iowa, Kans., Ky., La., Maine, Md., Mass., Mich., Minn., Miss., Mo., Mont., Nebr., Nev., N.H., N.J., N.Mex., N.Y., N.C., N.Dak., Ohio, Okla., Oreg., Pa., R.I., S.C., S.Dak., Tenn., Utah, Vt., Va., Wash., W.Va., Wis., Wyo.; Europe; w Asia; introduced also in South America, Europe, elsewhere in Asia, Africa, Pacific Islands, Australia.

Trifolium hybridum is widely cultivated as a forage crop. It may cause dermatitis in humans (J. W. Hardin and J. M. Arena 1974) and is implicated as a cause of dermatitis and biliary fibrosis in horses (C. Fisher 1995); the connection between the clover and the diseases is inconclusive (P. N. Nation 1989).

17. Trifolium ornithopodioides Linnaeus, Sp. Pl. 2: 766. 1753 (as M. ornithopodioides) • Bird clover [I]

Melilotus ornithopodioides (Linnaeus) Desrousseaux; *Trigonella ornithopodioides* (Linneaus) Lamarck & de Candolle

Herbs annual, 5–50 cm, glabrous or glabrescent. **Stems** procumbent, ascending, or erect, branched. **Leaves** palmate; stipules obovate-lanceolate, 0.5–0.8 cm, margins entire, apex subulate or cuspidate; petiole 4–10 cm; petiolules 0.5 mm; leaflets 3, blades obcordate or obovate, 0.6–1 × 0.4–0.6 cm, base cuneate, veins fine, margins finely serrate, apex truncate or emarginate, surfaces glabrous. **Peduncles** 0.5–2 cm. **Inflorescences** axillary, 1–5-flowered, loose, oblong, 0.5–1.2 × 0.1–0.5 cm; involucres absent or bracteoles shallow, cuplike, ± equaling pedicels. **Pedicels** straight or slightly reflexed, 1–3 mm; bracteoles lanceolate, 1 mm. **Flowers** 5–10 mm; calyx campanulate, 4–4.5 mm, glabrous, veins 10, tube 2.5–3 mm, lobes unequal, triangular, orifice open; corolla pink or white, 5–9 mm, banner oblong, 5–9 × 2–3 mm, apex rounded. **Legumes** stipitate, ellipsoid-oblong, 6–10 mm. **Seeds** 4–9, black or dark brown, ellipsoid-globose, 1–1.5 mm, smooth, glossy. **2*n*** = 16.

Flowering May–Jun. Coastal slopes, roadsides; 0–50 m; introduced; N.B.; Europe; n Africa; introduced also in Pacific Islands (New Zealand), Australia.

Trifolium ornithopodioides comprises small plants and has been considered a member of *Trigonella* by some authors; molecular studies by N. W. Ellison et al. (2006) showed that it is nested within *Trifolium.*

18. Trifolium vesiculosum Savi, Fl. Pis. 2: 165. 1798 (as vessiculosum) • Arrowleaf clover [F] [I]

Herbs annual, 15–70 cm, glabrous. **Stems** erect or ascending, branched. **Leaves** palmate; stipules linear-lanceolate, 1–3.5 cm, margins entire, apex subulate or setaceous; petiole 0.5–10 cm; petiolules 1 mm; leaflet 3, blades obovate to oblong, elliptic or lanceolate, 0.5–4 × 0.5–1.5 cm, base cuneate, veins prominent, thickened, margins spinulose-denticulate, apex apiculate, surfaces glabrous. **Peduncles** 1–12 cm. **Inflorescences** terminal or axillary, 50–100+-flowered, globose, ovoid, or oblong, 3–6 × 2–3.5 cm; involucres absent. **Pedicels** absent; bracteoles lanceolate, 6–7 mm, acuminate. **Flowers** 12–16 mm; calyx urceolate, not bilabiate, inflated in fruit, 6–10 mm, glabrous, veins 20–36, connected by transverse veins in fruit, tube 3–5 mm, lobes reflexed, subequal, subulate, as long as tube, orifice constricted; corolla white becoming pink, 12–15 mm, banner ovate, broadly clawed, striate, 12–15 × 2–4 mm, apex acute-acuminate. **Legumes** ellipsoid, 2.5–2.5 mm, shorter than calyx. **Seeds** 2 or 3, brown, ovoid, 1–1.5 mm, roughened. **2*n*** = 16.

Flowering Apr–Jul. Fields, roadsides, forest openings; 0–1000 m; introduced; Ala., Ark., Calif., Fla., Ga., La., Mass., Miss., Mo., Okla., Oreg., S.C., Tex., Va., Wash.; s, e Europe; w Asia.

Trifolium vesiculosum was first introduced into cultivation in the United States in 1963 and is grown in southern and western states (J. D. Miller and H. D. Wells 1985).

19. Trifolium fragiferum Linnaeus, Sp. Pl. 2: 772. 1753 • Strawberry clover [I] [W]

Amoria bonannii (C. Presl) Roskov; *Trifolium bonannii* C. Presl; *T. fragiferum* subsp. *bonannii* (C. Presl) Soják

Herbs perennial, 5–50 cm, pubescent or glabrous. **Stems** prostrate or creeping, branched, rooting at nodes. **Leaves** palmate; stipules linear or lanceolate, dilated proximally, 1.3–2 cm, margins entire, apex subulate or acuminate; petiole 1–9 cm; petiolules 1 mm; leaflets 3, blades ovate, obovate, or elliptic, 0.5–3 × 0.3–1.5 cm, base cuneate, veins prominent, thickened, curved, margins spinulose-denticulate, apex obtuse, often retuse, surfaces hairy abaxially, glabrous adaxially. **Peduncles** 3–17 cm. **Inflorescences** axillary, erect or ascending, 10–30-flowered, globose, 0.8–2 × 0.8–2 cm; involucres cup-shaped, composed of bracteoles, bracteoles lanceolate-oblong, 3–6 mm, distinct or connate proximally. **Pedicels** straight, to 0.5 mm; bracteoles linear or lanceolate, 2–3 mm, acuminate or 2-fid. **Flowers** 6–8 mm; calyx tubular, inflated in fruit, markedly asymmetric-bilabiate, 2.5–7 mm, usually pilose to woolly, sometimes glabrescent, veins 5–10, connected by reticulating lateral veins, tube 2–7 mm, lobes unequal, abaxial equal to or longer than tube, straight, adaxial spreading in fruit, shorter than tube, very unequal in fruit, orifice open; corolla white to pink, 5–8 mm, banner oblong-lancelate, 5–8 × 2 mm, apex emarginate to crenulate. **Legumes** ovoid, 2.5–3 mm, long-beaked. **Seeds** 1 or 2, tan or brown-spotted, globose-reniform, 1–1.4 mm, smooth, dull. **2*n*** = 16.

Flowering Apr–Nov. Meadows, fields, roadsides, sandy and saline soils; 0–2000 m; introduced; B.C., Ont.; Ariz., Calif., Colo., Ga., Idaho, Ill., Iowa, Kans.,

Mass., Minn., Mont., Nebr., Nev., N.J., N.Mex., N.Y., N.Dak., Ohio, Oreg., Pa., S.Dak., Utah, Wash., Wis., Wyo.; c, s Europe; w Asia; introduced also in s South America, Pacific Islands (New Zealand), Australia.

Trifolium fragiferum is cultivated for pastures and in mixtures with grass for hay and silage and, to a lesser extent, as groundcover in orchards and vineyards and as a green manure cover crop (L. St. John et al. 2010). It appears to have been introduced accidentally in the 1870s and as a crop around 1900 (E. A. Hollowell 1939).

20. Trifolium resupinatum Linnaeus, Sp. Pl. 2: 771. 1753 • Persian clover [F] [I]

Herbs annual, 20–60 cm, glabrous or glabrescent. **Stems** ascending, erect, or procumbent, branched. **Leaves** palmate; stipules lanceolate or ovate, 0.5–1.8 cm, margins entire, apex acuminate-filiform; petiole 0.5–20 cm; petiolules to 1 mm; leaflets 3, blades obovate, ovate, elliptic, or rhombic, 1–3 × 0.5–3 cm, base cuneate, veins moderately prominent, margins spinulose-dentate, apex rounded or broadly acute, surfaces hairy abaxially, glabrous adaxially. **Peduncles** 1–6 cm. **Inflorescences** axillary, 15–30-flowered, subglobose to globose, flowers resupinate, forming stellate-spreading clusters in fruit, 0.5–1.6 × 0.8–1.5 cm; involucres a narrow rim, 0.2 mm. **Pedicels** slightly reflexed, to 0.5 mm; bracteoles minute or absent. **Flowers** 5–6 mm; calyx tubular-campanulate, inflated in fruit, markedly asymmetric-bilabiate, slit between adaxial lobes, 2.5–3 mm, 8–11 mm in fruit, hairy, short-hairy or glabrescent in fruit, veins 10, connected by lateral veins, tube 2 mm, 7–9 mm in fruit, lobes green, erect, unequal, triangular, divergent, linear-lanceolate, unequal in fruit, orifice open; corolla pink to purple, 5–8 mm, banner oblong, 5–8 × 2 mm, apex emarginate to crenulate. **Legumes** lenticular, 1.8–2.2 mm. **Seeds** 1, ovoid, dark purple, olive green, yellow, or reddish brown, 1.5–1.9 mm, smooth, dull. $2n$ = 14, 16, 32.

Flowering Mar–May. Wet meadows, lawns, roadsides, fields, waste places; 0–700 m; introduced; Ont.; Ala., Ark., Calif., D.C., Fla., Ga., Ill., Ind., Iowa, Kans., Ky., La., Md., Mass., Miss., Mo., N.C., N.Dak., Ohio, Okla., Oreg., Pa., S.C., S.Dak., Tenn., Tex., Vt., Va., Wash., W.Va., Wis.; c, s Europe; sw Asia; n Africa; introduced also in s South America (Argentina, Uruguay), s Africa, Pacific Islands (Hawaii, New Zealand), Australia.

Widespread use of *Trifolium resupinatum* as a forage crop began in the late 1920s, after it began to flourish in Louisiana following a flood of the Mississippi River (E. A. Hollowell 1943). It is used in the southern United States as a pasture plant and for production of hay, and has spread widely from cultivation.

Reports of *Trifolium resupinatum* for New Brunswick and Quebec are based on old collections; since the species has not been recollected for many years in either province, they are excluded here.

21. Trifolium tomentosum Linnaeus, Sp. Pl. 2: 771. 1753 • Woolly clover [I]

Herbs annual, 10–20 cm, glabrous or sparsely hairy. **Stems** prostrate, ascending, or erect, branched. **Leaves** palmate; stipules ovate or triangular-lanceolate, 0.4–1.2 cm, margins entire, apex acute or acuminate; petiole 0.5–7 cm; petiolules to 1 mm; leaflets 3, blades obovate, obcordate, or elliptic, 0.4–1.5 × 0.3–1 cm, base cuneate, veins moderately prominent, margins denticulate, apex rounded or emarginate, surfaces sparsely hairy abaxially, glabrous adaxially. **Peduncles** 0.5–1.5 cm. **Inflorescences** axillary, 10–20-flowered, subglobose, soon becoming globose, flowers resupinate, calyces densely white-woolly, compacted, inflated, 0.5–1.5 × 0.5–1.5 cm; involucres a narrow rim, 0.2 mm. **Pedicels** slightly reflexed, to 0.5 mm; bracteoles cup-shaped, membranous, 0.2 mm. **Flowers** 3–7 mm; calyx tubular, inflated in fruit, markedly asymmetric-bilabiate, 2–6 mm, woolly adaxially, veins 5–10, connected by lateral veins, tube 1.5–2.5 mm, 4–5 mm in fruit, lobes unequal, subulate, shorter than tube, adaxial spreading or curved, orifice open, abruptly constricted in fruit; corolla pink, 3–6 mm, banner ovate, 3–6 × 3–6 mm, apex emarginate to crenulate. **Legumes** ovoid to globose, 2–3 mm. **Seeds** 1 or 2, yellow to brown, mottled, mitten-shaped, 0.9–1.1 mm, smooth, glossy. $2n$ = 16.

Flowering Feb–Apr. Sandy lawns, fields, meadows, roadsides, clay soils among vernal pools; 0–400 m; introduced; Calif., Fla., Mass., N.C., S.C.; s Europe (Mediterranean); sw Asia; n Africa; Atlantic Islands (Azores); introduced also in South America (Chile), s Africa, Pacific Islands (New Zealand), Australia.

Trifolium tomentosum is occasionally cultivated as a forage crop (F. J. Hermann 1953) and is becoming weedy in the flora area and in Australia (R. P. Randall 2002).

22. Trifolium repens Linnaeus, Sp. Pl. 2: 767. 1753 • White clover, trèfle blanc [I] [W]

Trifolium saxicola Small

Herbs perennial, 10–40 cm, glabrous or glabrescent. **Stems** creeping, branched, rooting at nodes. **Leaves** palmate; stipules lanceolate, 0.9–1.3 cm, margins entire, apex short-subulate; petiole 5–20 cm; petiolules to 1 mm; leaflets 3, blades obovate, obcordate, or orbiculate, 0.6–4 × 0.4–2.5 cm, base cuneate, veins moderately prominent, margins serrulate distally, apex rounded, emarginate, or retuse, surfaces glabrous. **Peduncles** erect, from prostrate stems, 1.5–30 cm. **Inflorescences** axillary, 20–40+-flowered, globose, 1.5–3.5 × 1.5–3.5 cm; involucres absent. **Pedicels** strongly reflexed in fruit, elongate, 3–5 mm; bracteoles white, lanceolate, 1–2 mm. **Flowers** 8–13 mm; calyx campanulate, 3–5 mm, glabrous, veins 6–10, tube 1.5–2.5 mm, lobes unequal to subequal, adaxial shorter than tube, triangular-lanceolate, orifice open; corolla white, often pinkish in age, 4–12 mm, banner ovate-lanceolate or oblong, 4–12 × 1–4 mm, apex rounded. **Legumes** linear-oblong, 4–5 mm. **Seeds** 3 or 4, yellow, reddish brown, or light brown, ovoid-reniform, 1 mm, smooth, glossy. $2n$ = 16, 28, 32, 48, 64.

Flowering Feb–Oct. Fields, lawns, roadsides, forest edges, waste places; 0–4000 m; introduced; Greenland; St. Pierre and Miquelon; Alta., B.C., Man., N.B., Nfld. and Labr., N.W.T., N.S., Ont., P.E.I., Que., Sask., Yukon; Ala., Alaska, Ariz., Ark., Calif., Colo., Conn., Del., D.C., Fla., Ga., Idaho, Ill., Ind., Iowa, Kans., Ky., La., Maine, Md., Mass., Mich., Minn., Miss., Mo., Mont., Nebr., Nev., N.H., N.J., N.Mex., N.Y., N.C., N.Dak., Ohio, Okla., Oreg., Pa., R.I., S.C., S.Dak., Tenn., Tex., Utah, Vt., Va., Wash., W.Va., Wis., Wyo.; Eurasia; introduced also in South America, Africa, Pacific Islands.

Trifolium repens may very well be the most important temperate pasture plant (M. J. Baker and W. M. Williams 1987) and has been considered the most important perennial pasture plant in North America (C. V. Piper 1924). It was introduced at least as early as the mid 1800s (R. N. Mack 2003) and spread so rapidly that it became known to Native Americans as White Man's Foot Grass (W. Strickland 1801). It is morphologically diverse; most material from the flora area represents var. *repens*, but some specimens fit within the circumscriptions given by M. Zohary and D. Heller (1984) of var. *giganteum* Lagrèze-Fossat, with inflorescences to 3.5 cm diameter and leaflets nearly 4 cm; others have smaller, pale-pink petals with hairy petioles and pedicels, and approach var. *biasolettii* (Steudel & Hochstetter) Ascherson & Graebner (*T. occidentale* Coombe).

23. Trifolium cernuum Brotero, Phytogr. Lusit. Select. 1: 150, plate 62. 1816 • Nodding clover [I]

Herbs annual, 5–40 cm, glabrous. **Stems** prostrate, ascending, or erect, branched. **Leaves** palmate; stipules triangular-lanceolate, 0.9–1 cm, margins entire, apex long-acuminate, reflexing; petiole 1–10 cm; petiolules to 1 mm; leaflets 3, blades obovate or obcordate, 0.4–1.5 × 0.4–1 cm, base cuneate, veins prominent, recurved, margins coarsely dentate, apex rounded, truncate, or emarginate, surfaces glabrous. **Peduncles** 0.6–1.5 cm, becoming shorter distally. **Inflorescences** axillary or terminal, 8–20-flowered, depressed-globose, 0.9–1.1 × 0.8–1 cm; involucres absent. **Pedicels** reflexed in fruit, 0.5–2 mm; bracteoles lanceolate, 1 mm. **Flowers** 4–5.5 mm; calyx tubular-campanulate, 4 mm, glabrous, veins 10, tube 2–2.2 mm, lobes subequal, triangular-subulate, margins green, pink, or purple, orifice open; corolla pink, 4–5 mm, banner obovate, 4–5 × 1–2 mm, apex deeply emarginate. **Legumes** ovoid-ellipsoid, 4 mm. **Seeds** 1–4, yellow, ovoid, 0.8–1 mm, minutely papillate. $2n$ = 16.

Flowering May–Jul. Roadsides, lawns; 0–150 m; introduced; Calif., Oreg., S.C.; Asia; n Africa; introduced also in s Africa, Pacific Islands (New Zealand), Australia.

Trifolium cernuum is a relatively recent introduction in the flora area. Other than a record from wool mill waste in North Carolina in 1932, the earliest records are from the 1990s in California.

24. Trifolium glomeratum Linnaeus, Sp. Pl. 2: 770. 1753 • Clustered clover [I] [W]

Herbs annual, 10–30 cm, glabrous. **Stems** procumbent, decumbent, or ascending, branched. **Leaves** palmate; stipules ovate, 1–1.5 cm, margins entire, apex subulate-setaceous; petiole 0–7 cm; petiolules to 0.5 mm; leaflets 3, blades obovate or obcordate, 0.6–1.5 × 0.4–1 cm, base cuneate, veins thickened distally, margins spinulose-serrate, apex retuse or rounded, surfaces glabrous. **Peduncles** absent or to 0.1 cm. **Inflorescences** axillary, 30+-flowered, globose, 0.8–1 × 0.8–1 cm; involucres absent. **Pedicels** straight, to 0.2 mm; bracteoles linear, to 0.5 mm. **Flowers** 6–8.5 mm; calyx tubular-obconic, 3–4 mm, glabrous, veins 10–12, tube 1.5–2 mm, lobes equal, triangular-ovate, spreading to recurved in fruit, orifice open; corolla pink, 6–8 mm, banner obovate, 6–8 × 1–2 mm, apex acute. **Legumes** obovoid, 2–3 mm. **Seeds** 2, brown, reniform, 1 mm, tuberculate. $2n$ = 14, 16.

Flowering May–Jun. Roadsides, lawns, thin grasslands; 0–500 m; introduced; B.C.; Ala., Calif., Oreg., S.C., Tex.; Europe; n Africa; introduced also in s South America, s Africa, Pacific Islands (New Zealand), Australia.

Trifolium glomeratum is cultivated occasionally as a forage crop (F. J. Hermann 1953) and sometimes spreads.

25. Trifolium retusum Linnaeus, Demonstr. Pl., 21. 1753 • Teasel clover [I]

Herbs annual, 15–40 cm, glabrous. **Stems** erect or ascending, branched. **Leaves** palmate; stipules triangular-lanceolate, 0.7–1.5 cm, margins entire, apex stramineous, subulate; petiole 1.5–5 cm; petiolules 1 mm; leaflets 3, blades obovate, oblong, or elliptic, 0.8–1.8 × 0.4–0.9 cm, base cuneate, veins prominent, margins dentate-spinulose, apex rounded to emarginate, surfaces glabrous. **Peduncles** 0.5–2 cm. **Inflorescences** axillary, 15–30-flowered, globose, 0.8–1 × 0.8–1 cm; involucres absent. **Pedicels** recurved in fruit, 1 mm; bracteoles folded, linear-subulate, 4–5 mm. **Flowers** 4–5 mm; calyx obconic, 4–5 mm, glabrous, veins 10, tube 1.3–2.1 mm, lobes unequal, longer than tube, subulate, recurved in fruit, orifice open; corolla white or pink, 3.2–4.5 mm, banner ovate, 3–4 × 1–2 mm, apex acute to rounded, entire to slightly erose distally. **Legumes** ovoid-oblong, 4.2–5.5 mm. **Seeds** 2, brown, ovoid-reniform, 1 mm, minutely granulose. $2n = 16$.

Flowering Apr–Jun. Roadsides, lawns; 100–800 m; introduced; Calif., Oreg., Wash.; s Europe; w Asia; introduced also in s Africa, Pacific Islands (New Zealand), Australia.

Trifolium retusum is a very recent introduction in the flora area; it is known from relatively few counties in the Pacific Coast states.

26. Trifolium suffocatum Linnaeus, Mant. Pl. 2: 276. 1771 • Small cluster clover [I]

Herbs annual, 3–10 cm, glabrous or sparsely hairy. **Stems** procumbent or erect, branched. **Leaves** palmate; stipules ovate, 0.3–0.5 cm, margins entire, apex acuminate-subulate; petiole 1–6 cm; petiolules to 0.5 mm; leaflets 3, blades obovate or obcordate, 0.3–0.8 × 0.2–0.6 cm, base cuneate, veins prominent adaxially, margins finely toothed, apex truncate or retuse, surfaces glabrous or sparsely hairy. **Peduncles** essentially absent. **Inflorescences** axillary, 10–20-flowered, dense, globose, 0.5–0.8 × 0.5–0.8 cm; involucres absent, stipules forming involucrelike structures, overtopping inflorescences. **Pedicels** straight, 0.1 mm; bracteoles triangular, membranous, 0.5–1.2 mm, apiculate. **Flowers** 3–5 mm; calyx tubular, 3–5 mm, slightly hairy or glabrous, veins 10, tube 2–3 mm, lobes subequal, lanceolate, curved in fruit, orifice open; corolla white, 2.5–3.5 mm, banner obovate, 2.5–3.5 × 1 mm, apex acute. **Legumes** ovoid-ellipsoid, 3–5 mm. **Seeds** 2, yellow, lenticular or reniform, 0.8–1 mm, minutely papillate. $2n = 16$.

Flowering Mar–Apr. Roadsides, gravelly lawns; 0–100 m; introduced; Calif., Oreg., Wash.; w Europe; n Africa; introduced also in s South America (Chile), w Asia, s Africa, Pacific Islands (New Zealand), Australia.

Trifolium suffocatum is known from Monterey and San Mateo counties in California, Benton and Coos counties in Oregon, and San Juan County in Washington.

27. Trifolium nigrescens Viviani, Fl. Ital. Fragm., 12, plate 13. 1808 • Small white clover [F] [I]

Herbs annual, 10–60 cm, glabrous or glabrescent. **Stems** usually erect or ascending, rarely prostrate, branched. **Leaves** palmate; stipules triangular-lanceolate, 0.4–0.8 cm, margins entire, apex dark purple or reddish, sharply recurved, subulate; petiole 0.5–10 cm; petiolules 0.5 mm; leaflets 3, blades obovate or obtriangular, 0.5–2.5 × 0.3–2.5 cm, base cuneate, veins fine, margins denticulate, apex rounded to emarginate, surfaces glabrous. **Peduncles** 1.5–4 cm. **Inflorescences** axillary or terminal, 15–50-flowered, globose, 1–1.8 × 1–1.8 cm; involucres a narrow rim, to 0.2 mm. **Pedicels** reflexed in fruit, 3–6 mm; bracteoles narrowly oblanceolate, 3–6.5 mm. **Flowers** 6.5–9 mm; calyx oblong, 3–5 mm, glabrous or pubescent, veins 5–10, tube 1–2.5 mm, lobes ± equal or unequal, triangular-lanceolate, recurved in fruit, margins green or purple, apex acute to acuminate, orifice open; corolla pink or white, 6–9 mm, banner obovate-oblong, 6–9 × 1–2 mm, apex acute to emarginate. **Legumes** linear-oblong, 3–4.5 mm. **Seeds** 1–5, yellow or pale or dark brown, oblong, 1 mm, smooth. $2n = 16$.

Flowering Mar–Oct. Roadsides, lawns, fields, waste places; 0–200 m; introduced; Ala., Fla., Ga., La., Miss., Tenn., Tex.; s Europe; w Asia; n Africa.

Trifolium nigrescens was shown, using molecular markers, to consist of three subspecies and to hybridize readily with *T. repens* (W. M. Williams et al. 2001). It was first introduced as a potential crop species in the early 1950s and is cultivated widely in the southeastern United States as a forage crop and as a nitrogen source in roadside grass plantings (C. S. Hoveland 1960).

28. Trifolium breweri S. Watson, Proc. Amer. Acad. Arts 11: 131. 1876 • Brewer's clover

Herbs perennial, 5–50 cm, glaucous, sparsely appressed-pubescent. **Stems** erect or ascending, branched. **Leaves** palmate; stipules lanceolate to narrowly ovate, 0.3–1 cm, margins entire, apex long-acuminate; petiole 0.3–4 cm; petiolules 0.5 mm; leaflets 3, blades obovate to obcordate, 0.3–1.5 × 0.3–1.2 cm, base cuneate, veins thickened, recurved, margins dentate, apex obtuse or emarginate, surfaces sparsely hairy abaxially, glabrous adaxially. **Peduncles** geniculate proximal to flowers, inflorescence appearing inverted, 3–5 cm. **Inflorescences** axillary, 5–25-flowered, globose, 1.3–1.5 × 1.3–1.5 cm; involucres absent. **Pedicels** strongly reflexed in fruit, 2–3 mm; bracteoles minute. **Flowers** 11–13 mm; calyx tubular, 6–8 mm, pilose or glabrous, veins 10, tube 1.5–2 mm, lobes subequal, subulate, orifice open; corolla rose-pink or creamy white, 6–10 mm, banner ovate-oblong, 6–10 × 3 mm, equaling wing and keel petals, apex rounded or emarginate. **Legumes** short-stipitate, ovoid-ellipsoid, 7–10 mm. **Seeds** 1 or 2, brown, ovoid-ellipsoid, 2.5–3 mm, smooth. **2*n*** = 16.

Flowering May–Aug. Wooded areas, roadsides, mixed evergreen or pine forests; 1000–2200 m; Calif., Oreg.; Mexico (Baja California).

Trifolium breweri, which ranges from Madera County, California, northward to Josephine County, Oregon, is also reported from Baja California, Mexico. It was considered by J. S. Martin (1943) to be remarkably morphologically uniform; F. E. Clements (1920) termed it a foundational species in the Sierran Montane Forest *Pinus* Association climax formation.

29. Trifolium sonorense T. K. Ahlquist & Vincent, Phytoneuron 2018-1: 1, fig. 1. 2018 • Sonoran clover

Herbs perennial, 25–38+ cm, pubescent. **Stems** prostrate, branched. **Leaves** palmate; stipules narrowly triangular, 0.7–1.7 cm, margins entire or finely serrulate, apex usually acute or acuminate, sometimes 2-fid; petiole 0.3–5 cm; petiolules to 1 mm; leaflets 3, blades obovate to obcordate, 0.9–1.6 × 0.7–1.2 cm, base cuneate, veins moderately thickened, margins serrate to weakly so, apex rounded or emarginate, mucronulate, surfaces slightly hairy abaxially, glabrous adaxially. **Peduncles** 2.8–5 cm. **Inflorescences** axillary, 10–20-flowered, depressed-globose or globose, 0.8–1.6 × 0.9–1.6 cm, rachis prolonged beyond flowers; involucres a narrow rim, or slightly proximally connate bracteoles of proximal flowers, 0.1–0.5 mm. **Pedicels** reflexed in fruit, 1–3 mm; bracteoles linear-triangular, 0.5 mm. **Flowers** 5.7–6.7 mm; calyx tubular, 3.3–6.5 mm, pubescent, veins 10, tube 0.8–1 mm, lobes subequal, narrowly triangular, orifice open; corolla white or pink, 5.3–6.5 mm, banner obovate, 5.3–6.5 × 2.8–3.8 mm, apex broadly rounded or broadly acute. **Legumes** obovoid, 4.3–4.4 mm. **Seeds** 2, brownish orange or olive-brown, globose or broadly reniform, 1.2–1.7 mm, smooth. **2*n*** = 16.

Flowering Aug–Oct. Dry stream banks, grassy places; 1500–1800 m; Ariz.; Mexico (Chihuahua, Jalisco, Sinaloa, Sonora).

Trifolium sonorense has long been equated with *T. amabile* Kunth, from which T. K. Ahlquist (2012) and also Ahlquist & M. A. Vincent have shown it to be distinct by longer sepal lobes (more than 3 mm), keel petal claws (more than 1.7 mm), and filament tubes (more than 3.6 mm). *Trifolium sonorense* is known from western Mexico and southernmost Arizona (Cochise County), largely in the Sonoran Desert region, and in mountainous Jalisco.

30. Trifolium dasyphyllum Torrey & A. Gray, Fl. N. Amer. 1: 315. 1838 • Alpine clover [E]

Trifolium anemophilum Greene; *T. dasyphyllum* subsp. *anemophilum* (Greene) J. M. Gillett; *T. dasyphyllum* subsp. *uintense* (Rydberg) J. M. Gillett; *T. dasyphyllum* var. *uintense* (Rydberg) S. L. Welsh; *T. lividum* Rydberg; *T. scariosum* A. Nelson; *T. uintense* Rydberg

Herbs perennial, 5–20 cm, appressed-pubescent. **Stems** cespitose, branched, numerous short stems. **Leaves** palmate; stipules lanceolate-linear, 1.5–2 cm, margins entire, apex acuminate; petiole 0.6–3.5 cm; petiolules to 0.5 mm; leaflets 3, blades oblong-elliptic, oblanceolate, or obovate, sometimes folded, 0.6–3.2 × 0.2–0.6 cm, base cuneate, veins obscure, margins entire, apex acute, surfaces glabrous or hairy. **Peduncles** 2–17 cm. **Inflorescences** axillary or terminal, 5–16-flowered, globose, 1.5–3.5 × 1.2–3.3 cm; involucres formed of proximal bracteoles, bases sometimes connate. **Pedicels** erect, 1.5–2 mm; bracteoles linear-lanceolate, scarious, 2–6 mm, or scalelike. **Flowers** 12–16 mm; calyx campanulate, 6–9 mm, pubescent, veins 10, tube 2–5 mm, lobes unequal, linear-subulate, orifice open; corolla often bicolored cream and violet, sometimes all red-purple or violet, 1.2–1.6 mm, banner broadly elliptic-ovate, 11–15 × 4–5 mm, folded distally, apex rounded, apiculate; ovaries pubescent distally. **Legumes** oblong, 4–6 mm. **Seeds** 1–3, dark brown, ovoid-reniform, 2–2.5 mm, smooth. **2*n*** = 16.

Flowering Jun–Aug. Alpine meadows, rocky slopes; 2100–4100 m; Colo., Mont., N.Mex., Utah, Wyo.

Three subspecies of *Trifolium dasyphyllum* were recognized by J. M. Gillett (1965), but he commented on the overlap in diagnostic characters of the subspecies. In their monograph of *Trifolium*, M. Zohary and D. Heller (1984) mirrored the treatment by Gillett, and also commented on intermediacy of characters in some specimens. The subspecies were not accepted by R. D. Dorn (1988), citing extensive intergradation, or by R. C. Barneby (1989), citing variability within *T. dasyphyllum* that is not linked with distribution or other morphological features.

Trifolium dasyphyllum is found from eastern Utah and from Santa Fe County in New Mexico northward through central Colorado to central and northwestern Wyoming and Cascade, Gallatin, and Madison counties in Montana.

31. Trifolium attenuatum Greene, Pittonia 4: 137. 1900 • Rocky Mountain clover [E]

Trifolium bracteolatum Rydberg; *T. petraeum* Greene; *T. stenolobum* Rydberg

Herbs perennial, 5–30 cm, pubescent. **Stems** erect or ascending, cespitose, branched from base, numerous short stems. **Leaves** palmate; stipules lanceolate, 1.8–2 cm, margins entire, apex acute-acuminate; petiole 2.5–10 cm; petiolules to 0.5 mm; leaflets 3, blades linear, lanceolate, or narrowly elliptic, 1.5–6 × 0.3–1 cm, base cuneate, veins moderately thickened, margins entire, apex acuminate or narrowly acute, surfaces glabrous or pubescent. **Peduncles** 2–28 cm. **Inflorescences** axillary or terminal, 10–20+-flowered, globose, 2.3–3.5 × 2.5–4 cm; involucres formed of proximal bracteoles, bases sometimes connate. **Pedicels** reflexed in fruit, 2–4 mm; bracteoles ovate, 2–4 mm, truncate or acuminate. **Flowers** 15–22 mm; calyx campanulate, 8–15 mm, pubescent, veins 10, tube 2.5–7 mm, lobes unequal, subulate, orifice open; corolla red-purple, 16–20 mm, banner broadly oblong-elliptic, 16–20 × 6–7 mm, apex acute, apiculate. **Legumes** oblong, 5–6 mm. **Seeds** 1–3, brown, ovoid-reniform, 2.5 mm, smooth. $2n$ = 16, 48.

Flowering Jun–Aug. Subalpine and alpine slopes, open montane forests; 3000–3800 m; Colo., N.Mex.

Trifolium attenuatum ranges from Park County in Colorado southward through southern and southwestern Colorado to northern and central New Mexico.

J. M. Gillett (1965) found both diploid and hexaploid populations of *Trifolium attenuatum* but was unable to find morphological distinctions between diploid and hexaploid individuals. Using flavonoid chemotaxonomy, E. V. Parups et al. (1966) found close associations between *T. attenuatum*, *T. brandegeei*, and *T. haydenii*.

Trifolium lilacinum Rydberg (1901), which pertains here, is a later homonym of *T. lilacinum* Greene (1896) and thus illegitimate.

32. Trifolium brandegeei S. Watson, Proc. Amer. Acad. Arts 11: 130. 1876 (as brandegei) • Brandegee's clover [E]

Herbs perennial, 5–15 cm, glabrous. **Stems** cespitose, short-branched. **Leaves** palmate; stipules broadly lanceolate, 1–1.5 cm, margins entire, apex acute-acuminate; petiole 0.6–1.2 cm; petiolules to 0.5 mm; leaflets 3, blades ovate, oblong-elliptic, or elliptic, 0.8–3 × 0.4–1.5 cm, base cuneate, veins moderately thickened, margins entire or faintly serrate, apex acute to rounded or minutely apiculate, surfaces glabrous. **Peduncles** 6–20 cm. **Inflorescences** terminal, 4–15-flowered, ovoid-ellipsoid, 2.5–4 × 2.2–3 cm, rachis prolonged ca. 10 mm beyond distalmost flower; involucres absent. **Pedicels** strongly reflexed, 1–2 mm; bracteoles linear, minute. **Flowers** 15–18 mm; calyx whitish, campanulate, 7–10 mm, sparsely pubescent, veins 10, tube 4–5 mm, lobes subequal, longer than tube, narrowly triangular, acuminate, orifice open; corolla purple to magenta, 15–18 mm, banner broadly ovate, 15–17 × 7–9 mm, apex obtuse or retuse. **Legumes** oblong, 6.5–7 mm. **Seeds** 1–3, yellow and red, flattened ovoid, 2–2.5 mm, smooth. $2n$ = 16.

Flowering Jul–Aug. Open montane forests and subalpine areas; 3500–3700 m; Colo., N.Mex.

A close relationship between *Trifolium brandegeei* and *T. parryi* was hypothesized by J. M. Gillett (1965); this has not been borne out by flavonoid chemosystematics (E. V. Parups et al. 1966) or DNA analyses (N. W. Ellison et al. 2006).

33. Trifolium wormskioldii Lehmann, Index Seminum (Hamburg) 1825: 17. 1825 • Cow clover [W]

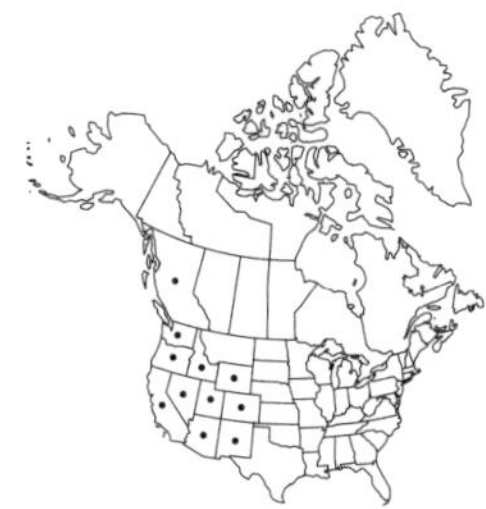

Lupinaster wormskioldii (Lehmann) C. Presl; *Trifolium fendleri* Greene; *T. fimbriatum* Lindley; *T. heterodon* Torrey & A. Gray; *T. spinulosum* Douglas

Herbs perennial, 10–40 cm, glabrous; rhizomes elongate. **Stems** erect, ascending, or decumbent, branched. **Leaves** palmate; stipules ovate to lanceolate, 1.5–2 cm, margins entire (proximal stipules) or lacerate (distal stipules), apex acute to acuminate; petiole 1–11 cm; petiolules 0.5 mm; leaflets 3, blades obovate to elliptic, 0.4–4.2 × 0.2–1.3 cm, base cuneate or rounded, veins fine or thickened distally, margins spinulose-serrate, apex usually acute to rounded, sometimes retuse or mucronate, surfaces glabrous. **Peduncles** 1.5–11 cm. **Inflorescences** axillary or terminal, 20–50-flowered, subglobose or globose, 1.8–2.5 × 2–2.5 cm; involucres broadly bowl-shaped, 12–20 mm, incised 1/3–1/2 their length, lobes 10+, sharply and acutely serrate, veins prominent. **Pedicels** straight, 1.5–2 mm; bracteoles linear or ovate, 1–2 mm. **Flowers** 12–14 mm, odor somewhat unpleasant; calyx whitish, tubular, 5–6 mm, glabrous, veins 10, tube 2–3 mm, lobes green to purple, subequal, abaxial rarely longer than tube, orifice open; corolla usually magenta to purple, rarely white or bicolored, 10–12 mm, banner ovate-oblong, 12–14 × 2–3 mm, apex truncate or rounded, slightly retuse. **Legumes** oblong, 2–4 mm. **Seeds** 3 or 4, brown, sometimes mottled, subglobose or mitten-shaped, 1.5 mm, smooth. $2n$ = 16, 32.

Flowering Mar–Sep. Saline flats, beaches, meadows, grassy areas, alluvial soils; 0–2700 m; B.C.; Ariz., Calif., Colo., Idaho, Nev., N.Mex., Oreg., Utah, Wash., Wyo.; Mexico (Baja California).

Trifolium wormskioldii is largely tetraploid and is widespread in western North America. Distinguishing *T. wormskioldii* from closely allied species (especially *T. mucronatum*) is sometimes difficult, which led R. C. Barneby (1989) to synonymize *T. mucronatum* and *T. pinetorum* under the former name. *Trifolium wormskioldii* produces long, white rhizomes; *T. mucronatum* produces only short rhizomes at most, often only small, fibrous roots or taproots (J. M. Gillett 1980). The distinction of *T. pinetorum* from *T. wormskioldii* was supported by N. W. Ellison et al. (2006); those authors did not include material of *T. mucronatum* in their DNA analyses.

Trifolium wormskioldii rhizomes may have been a food resource for Native American groups in the Pacific Northwest (N. J. Turner and H. V. Kuhnlein 1982).

34. Trifolium siskiyouense J. M. Gillett, Canad. J. Bot. 58: 1441. 1980 • Siskiyou clover [E]

Trifolium wormskioldii Lehmann var. *siskiyouense* (J. M. Gillett) Isely

Herbs perennial, 20–50 cm, glabrous; rhizomes elongate, slender, roots tuberous. **Stems** erect, sparsely branched. **Leaves** palmate; stipules lanceolate, 0.8–1.5 cm, margins entire or slightly lacerate, apex acuminate; petiole 1.6–2.4 cm; petiolules 0.5 mm; leaflets 3, blades obovate, oblanceolate, or elliptic, 0.8–3 × 0.5–0.7 cm, base cuneate, veins fine or thickened distally, margins finely serrulate, apex acute, mucronate, or retuse, surfaces glabrous. **Peduncles** 2.8–3.4 cm. **Inflorescences** usually terminal, sometimes axillary, 30–50-flowered, subglobose, 1.2–1.8 × 1.5–2 cm; involucres shallowly bowl-shaped, 18–22 mm, deeply incised, lobes slender, irregular or bifurcate. **Pedicels** straight, 0.5–0.8 mm; bracteoles linear, 1–2 mm. **Flowers** 10–13 mm; calyx tubular, 0.5–0.6 mm, glabrous, veins 10, tube 2 mm, lobes ± equal, 3–4 mm, orifice open; corolla white to purple, 9–12 mm, banner oblong, 7–12 × 2–3 mm, apex retuse. **Legumes** oblong, 2–4 mm. **Seeds** 2–4, brown, subglobose or mitten-shaped, 1.5 mm, smooth.

Flowering Jun–Jul. Wet meadows, grassy hillsides; 1000–1500 m; Calif., Oreg.

Trifolium siskiyouense is known from Shasta and Siskiyou counties, California, and Douglas, Jackson, and Josephine counties, Oregon. It is difficult to distinguish from *T. wormskioldii* without underground parts showing the tubers, but can be separated from the latter by deeply cut involucral segments, long-lobed, slender calyces, and the combination of long wing petals and short keel petals (J. M. Gillett 1980).

35. Trifolium mucronatum Willdenow ex Sprengel, Syst. Veg. 3: 208. 1826 • Cusp clover

Subspecies 3 (1 in the flora): w, sc United States, n Mexico.

The difficulty of distinguishing *Trifolium mucronatum* from *T. wormskioldii* is discussed under 33. *T. wormskioldii*. Populations in the United States represent *T. mucronatum* subsp. *lacerum*; in Mexico, subsp. *lacerum* is found in the north, subsp. *mucronatum* (petals pink or reddish, flowers 1.5–1.7 cm, inflorescences 2.5–3.5 cm diam.) is widespread, and subsp. *vaughanae* J. M. Gillett (petals lavender or white, flowers 1.2–1.4 cm, inflorescences 1.5–2 cm diam.) is restricted to central Mexico (Guanajuato, San Luis Potosí) (J. M. Gillett 1980).

Trifolium involucratum Ortega (1797), which pertains here, is a later homonym of *T. involucratum* Lamarck (1778, = *T. cherleri* Linnaeus).

35a. Trifolium mucronatum Willdenow ex Sprengel subsp. **lacerum** (Greene) J. M. Gillett, Canad. J. Bot. 58: 1444. 1980 • Spinytooth clover

Trifolium lacerum Greene, Erythea 2: 182. 1894; *T. arizonicum* Greene; *T. fistulosum* A. E. Vaughan; *T. involucratum* Ortega var. *arizonicum* (Greene) McDermott; *T. ortegae* Greene; *T. oxyodon* Greene ex Rydberg; *T. variegatum* Nuttall var. *parunuweapensis* S. L. Welsh; *T. wormskioldii* Lehmann var. *arizonicum* (Greene) Barneby; *T. wormskioldii* var. *ortegae* (Greene) Barneby

Herbs perennial, 10–65 cm, glabrous; rhizomes absent or relatively short, roots taproots, slender. **Stems** erect or decumbent, sparsely branched. **Leaves** palmate; stipules lanceolate to narrowly ovate, 1.5–2 cm, margins toothed or lacerate, apex acuminate; petiole 1–3.5 cm; petiolules to 0.5 mm; leaflet blades linear, elliptic, or obovate, 0.8–2.5 × 0.1–0.3 cm, base cuneate, veins thickened, margins entire or finely serrate to setose-spinulose, apex acute or apiculate, surfaces glabrous. **Peduncles** 4–6 cm. **Inflorescences** terminal or axillary, 8–20-flowered, subglobose to globose, 1.5–2 × 1.5–4 cm; involucres broadly campanulate, 10–22 mm, incised to 3/4 their length, lobes 10+, triaristate to lacerate. **Pedicels** straight, 0.5 mm; bracteoles subulate or broadly wavy-margined, 2–3 mm. **Flowers** 12–20 mm; calyx tubular-conic, 5–7 mm, glabrous, veins 10, tube 2–2.5 mm, lobes ± equal, 6–8 mm, abaxial lobe longer than tube, orifice open; corolla white, lavender, or purple, sometimes with different colors within inflorescence, 11–13 mm, banner narrowly oblong [broadly obovate-oblong], 11–13 × 4 mm, apex rounded. **Legumes** oblong, 3–6 mm. **Seeds** 2–4, olive, reniform, 1.3–1.5 mm, smooth. $2n = 16$.

Flowering Jun–Sep. Damp meadows, seeps, along streams in pine forests; 700–2500 m; Ariz., Calif., Colo., N.Mex., Tex.; Mexico (Chihuahua, Coahuila, Sonora).

The single California record for subsp. *lacerum* was collected in 1925 in Inyo County.

36. Trifolium buckwestiorum Isely, Madroño 39: 90, fig. 2. 1992 • Santa Cruz clover [C] [E]

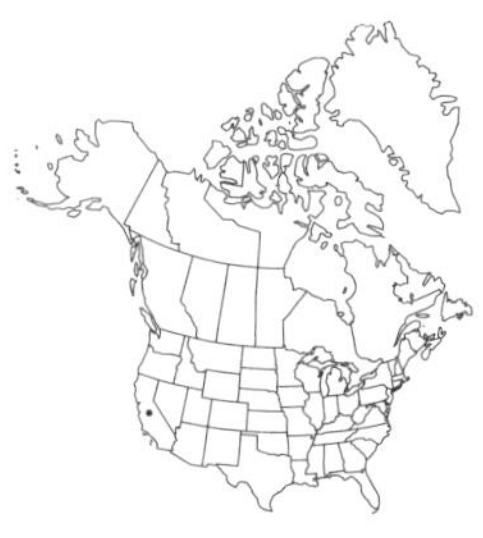

Herbs annual, 5–40 cm, glabrous. **Stems** decumbent to ascending or erect, slightly branched. **Leaves** palmate; stipules whitish with prominent green veins, ovate, 0.3–0.5 cm, margins lacerate, apex acute to acuminate; petiole 1–2.4 cm; petiolules to 0.5 mm; leaflets 3, blades obovate to elliptic, 0.6–1.5 × 0.3–0.8 cm, base cuneate, veins ± thickened distally, margins denticulate, sometimes entire proximally, apex rounded, acute, or retuse, surfaces glabrous. **Peduncles** 1–3.5 cm. **Inflorescences** terminal or axillary, 15–20-flowered (early inflorescences hidden in stipules, subsessile, 2–5-flowered, flowers cleistogamous), subglobose, 0.5–0.8 × 0.6–0.8 cm; involucres flattened or shallowly bowl-shaped, 6–8 mm, when folded, nearly hiding calyces, glabrous or sparsely hairy, lobes 4 or 5, ± parallel-sided, 3 or 4-toothed. **Pedicels** straight, to 0.5 mm; bracteoles absent. **Flowers** 7–8 mm; calyx tubular, 4–5 mm, glabrous, veins 10, tube 2–2.5 mm, lobes subequal, triangular, margins conspicuously 2 or 3-toothed, apex aristate, orifice open; corolla pale pink or white, 6–7 mm, banner oblong, 5–7 × 1 mm, apex emarginate or erose. **Legumes** ovoid, 2.5 mm. **Seeds** 1, dark brown, slightly mottled, ovoid, 2 mm, smooth.

Flowering May–Jun. Meadows, roadsides, grassy hillsides; of conservation concern; 0–300 m; Calif.

Trifolium buckwestiorum, which ranges from Mendocino to Monterey counties, is unique among clovers in North America because of its aboveground cleistogamous, axillary flowers. The only other clover in North America that produces cleistogamous flowers is *T. amphianthum*, which produces its cleistogamous flowers at ground level and then pushes them into the substrate.

37. Trifolium variegatum Nuttall in J. Torrey and A. Gray, Fl. N. Amer. 1: 317. 1838 • Whitetip clover

Trifolium dianthum Greene; *T. geminiflorum* Greene; *T. melananthum* Hooker & Arnott; *T. pusillum* Greene; *T. spinulosum* Douglas var. *triste* Torrey & A. Gray; *T. subsalinum* Greene; *T. tridentatum* Lindley var. *melananthum* (Hooker & Arnott) S. Watson; *T. ultramontanum* Greene; *T. variegatum* var. *geminiflorum* (Greene) Vincent; *T. variegatum* var. *melananthum* (Hooker & Arnott) Greene

Herbs annual, 1.5–48+ cm, glabrous. **Stems** usually erect, ascending, or prostrate, branched. **Leaves** palmate; stipules lanceolate or ovate, 0.3–1 cm, margins lacerate, apex acute to acuminate; petiole 1–9 cm; petiolules to 0.8 mm; leaflets 3, blades elliptic, obovate, oblanceolate, or obcordate, 0.2–5 × 0.1–1.2 cm, base cuneate, veins thickened, margins denticulate, apex acute or retuse, surfaces glabrous. **Peduncles** 0.5–5 cm. **Inflorescences** terminal or axillary, 1–20+-flowered, subglobose or globose, 0.5–1.3 × 0.1–1 cm; involucres flat, 2–6 mm, incised 1/2 their length, lobes 2–7, lacerate. **Pedicels** straight, to 0.5 mm; bracteoles absent. **Flowers** 5–11 mm; calyx campanulate, not slit between adaxial lobes, 1.9–2.4 mm, glabrous, veins 10–20, tube 1.5–4 mm, lobes subequal, narrowly triangular, margins usually entire, rarely with a small lateral tooth, orifice open; corolla purple, usually white-tipped, 3–10 mm, banner obovate, 3–10 × 0.6–2.6 mm, apex emarginate. **Legumes** oblong or ellipsoid, 2–4 mm. **Seeds** 2, blackish brown, sometimes mottled, ovoid or ellipsoid, 1–1.6 mm, smooth. **2*n*** = 16.

Flowering Mar–Sep. Wet places, coastal hills, meadows; 0–2500 m; B.C.; Alaska, Ariz., Calif., Idaho, Mont., Nev., Oreg., Utah, Wash., Wyo.; Mexico (Baja California).

Trifolium variegatum is widespread and morphologically variable (B. G. Foster and M. A. Vincent 2018). Because of this variability, *T. variegatum* and related species were treated as seven so-called phases by D. Isely (1998), who described these as ecotypic groups, some of which might deserve varietal or specific rank. C. S. Cooper (1957) considered *T. variegatum* a good choice for cultivation in wet areas for grazing and hay production.

38. Trifolium appendiculatum Lojacono, Nuovo Giorn. Bot. Ital. 15: 181. 1883 [E]

Trifolium appendiculatum var. *rostratum* (Greene) Jepson; *T. calophyllum* Greene; *T. morleyanum* Greene; *T. phaeocephalum* Greene; *T. rostratum* Greene; *T. splendens* A. Heller; *T. trilobatum* Jepson; *T. variegatum* var. *major* Lojacono; *T. variegatum* var. *rostratum* (Greene) C. L. Hitchcock; *T. variegatum* var. *trilobatum* (Jepson) Jepson

Herbs annual, 7–80+ cm, glabrous. **Stems** ascending or erect, branched. **Leaves** palmate; stipules lanceolate or ovate, 0.3–1.3 cm, margins lacerate, apex acute to acuminate; petiole 2–7.3 cm; petiolules to 0.9 mm; leaflets 3, blades obovate-obcordate, elliptic, or obovate, 0.3–2.6 × 0.2–1.1 cm, base cuneate, veins thickened, margins denticulate, apex acute or retuse, surfaces glabrous. **Peduncles** 1.7–7.5 cm. **Inflorescences** axillary, 4–25-flowered, subglobose or globose, 0.7–2 × 0.8–3 cm; involucres flat, 3.2–6.5 mm, incised 1/2 their length, lobes 4–7, lacerate. **Pedicels** straight, to 0.5 mm; bracteoles absent. **Flowers** 7–25 mm; calyx campanulate, not slit between adaxial lobes, 3.5–7.4 mm, glabrous, veins 10–20, tube 1.5–3.3 mm, lobes subequal, narrowly triangular, margins usually entire, orifice open; corolla deep purple, usually white-tipped, 6.5–17 mm, banner obovate, 6.3–16 × 1.5–4 mm, apex emarginate. **Legumes** oblong or ellipsoid, 3.6–3.8 mm. **Seeds** 2, blackish brown, mottled, ovoid or ellipsoid, 1.9–2.8 mm, smooth. **2*n*** = 16.

Flowering Mar–Jun. Coastal areas, foothills, mountain meadows, ditches, wet areas; 0–1400 m; Calif., Oreg.

Trifolium appendiculatum is found throughout California, although never east of the Sierra Nevada, and into southern Oregon.

39. Trifolium polyodon Greene, Pittonia 3: 215. 1897 • Woods or Pacific Grove clover [C] [E]

Trifolium tridentatum Lindley var. *polyodon* (Greene) Jepson

Herbs annual, 10–60 cm, glabrous. **Stems** decumbent or ascending, branched. **Leaves** palmate; stipules lanceolate to ovate, 0.4–1.8 cm, margins lacerate, apex acute to acuminate; petiole 0.5–6 cm; petiolules to 1 mm; leaflets 3, blades broadly elliptic to broadly obovate, 0.4–2.5 × 0.4–1.5 cm, base cuneate, veins moderately thickened, margins dentate-serrulate, apex rounded or truncate, often retuse, surfaces glabrous. **Peduncles** 1–2 cm. **Inflorescences** axillary, 10–25-flowered, subglobose or globose, 1–1.8 × 1–1.8 cm; involucres flattened or bowl-shaped, 4–7 mm, incised 1/2 their length, when folded, not hiding flowers except proximally, lobes 5–12, dentate-lacerate, spinulose. **Pedicels** straight, to 1 mm; bracteoles absent. **Flowers** 8–10 mm; calyx campanulate-tubular, not slit between adaxial lobes, 5–7 mm, glabrous, veins 20, tube 1.9–2.4 mm, lobes unequal, 3-fid or laciniate, often appearing 7+-lobed, orifice open; corolla pink or pale purple, 8–9 mm, banner elliptic, 8–9 × 2–3 mm, apex retuse. **Legumes** ellipsoid, 3.5–4 mm. **Seeds** 2, dark brown, mottled, ovoid or reniform, 1.7–1.9 mm, smooth.

Flowering Apr–Jun. Along streams, moist meadows; of conservation concern; 0–150 m; Calif.

The taxonomic status of *Trifolium polyodon*, known only from Monterey County, has long been debated. W. L. Jepson (1936) considered it a variety of *T. tridentatum* Lindley (= *T. willdenovii*). The first to consider it as a variety of *T. variegatum* was J. S. Martin (1943), who never formally published a new combination; an invalid combination was made by M. Zohary and D. Heller (1984). D. Isely (1998) included it in his interpretation of *T. variegatum* as phase 5 of that species; he speculated that *T. polyodon* might have originated as a hybrid of *T. variegatum* and *T. willdenovii*. Molecular studies (N. W. Ellison et al. 2006) showed that *T. polyodon* is closely related to *T. variegatum* but is distinct; it also appears to be related to *T. cyathiferum*.

40. Trifolium fucatum Lindley, Edwards's Bot. Reg. 22: plate 1883. 1836 • Bull clover [E] [F]

Trifolium flavulum Greene; *T. fucatum* var. *flavulum* (Greene) Jepson; *T. fucatum* var. *gambelii* (Nuttall) Jepson; *T. fucatum* var. *virescens* (Greene) Jepson; *T. gambelii* Nuttall; *T. physopetalum* Fischer & C. A. Meyer; *T. virescens* Greene

Herbs annual, 10–80 cm, glabrous or glabrescent. **Stems** erect or ascending, unbranched or densely dichotomously branched. **Leaves** palmate; stipules ovate or lanceolate, 1–3 cm, margins entire or toothed, apex usually acuminate, sometimes 2-fid; petiole 3–15 cm; petiolules 1–1.5 mm; leaflets 3, blades broadly obovate, orbiculate, or rhombic-obovate, 0.8–4 × 0.7–3 cm, base broadly cuneate, veins obscure, thickened near leaflet margin, margins remotely dentate to densely serrulate-dentate, apex rounded or slightly retuse, surfaces glabrous or glabrate. **Peduncles** 3–13 cm. **Inflorescences** terminal or axillary, 10–30-flowered, subglobose or globose, 1–4 × 1–4 cm; involucres broadly bowl-shaped, 4–15 mm, lobes 3–8, lanceolate, acuminate, undivided or 2- or 3-fid. **Pedicels** straight, 1 mm; bracteoles distinct or connate, broadly ovate, 1 mm. **Flowers** 10–27 mm; calyx campanulate, 3–8 mm, glabrous, veins 10, tube 1.5–2.5 mm, lobes 5–10, unequal, undivided or 3-fid, long-acuminate, orifice open; corolla creamy white to yellow, pink to purple in age, keel petals rarely dark purple, 10–27 mm, banner broadly ovate, inflated in fruit, not distally twisted, 10–27 × 6–15 mm, apex rounded, erose. **Legumes** stipitate, linear, 7–8 mm. **Seeds** 3–8, gray, mottled, globose, 1.6–2 mm, reticulate. $2n$ = 16.

Flowering Apr–Jun. Moist places, meadows, roadsides; 0–1000 m; Calif., Oreg., Wash.; introduced in Asia (China, Japan).

Trifolium fucatum is known as an invasive species in Japan (T. Mito and T. Uesugi 2004) and has also been introduced in China (specimen at BM). A single old collection exists from British Columbia, but the species has not been collected in that province again. The Michigan record of the species is an inadvertent waif.

41. Trifolium piorkowskii Rand. Morgan & A. L. Barber, Novon, 23: 65, plate 1. 2014 • Marshmallow clover [C] [E]

Herbs annual, 7–30 cm, glabrous. **Stems** erect or ascending, sparsely to much branched. **Leaves** palmate; stipules ovate-lanceolate, 1–1.5 cm, margins entire, apex acute-acuminate; petiole 8–12 cm; petiolules 1 mm; leaflets 3, blades oblanceolate or obovate, 2.8 × 1.9 cm, base cuneate, veins delicate, margins entire or shallowly dentate distally, lateral veins sometimes ending in a bristle, apex rounded to acute, surfaces glabrous. **Peduncles** 5–15 cm. **Inflorescences** axillary or terminal, 3–16-flowered, in 1–3 whorls, subglobose, 2–2.8 × 1.8–2.6 cm; involucres bowl-shaped, 6–15 mm, lobes 6–8, broadly lanceolate, margins entire, acuminate, apex 3–5-fid. **Pedicels** straight, 0.5–1 mm; bracteoles absent. **Flowers** 12–14 mm; calyx campanulate, 5–8 mm, glabrous, veins 10, tube 2.5–4 mm, lobes 11–15, unequal, abaxial 3–5 forked, adaxial unbranched, orifice open; corolla creamy white to pinkish, 11–13 mm, banner ovate, inflated entire length in fruit, not distally twisted, 11–13 × 5–7 mm, apex rounded. **Legumes** ellipsoid, 5–6 mm. **Seeds** 1 or 2, gray-brown, black-mottled, subglobose, 2.5 mm, smooth.

Flowering Apr–May. Shallow, vernally wet depressions on volcanic flats, banks of watercourses flowing through open rocky grassland, transitional habitats with scattered chaparral and conifers; of conservation concern; 300–800 m; Calif.

Trifolium piorkowskii is known only from Shasta County.

42. Trifolium cyathiferum Lindley, Bot. Reg. 13: sub plate 1070. 1827 • Cup clover [E]

Herbs annual, 5–50 cm, glabrous. **Stems** erect, branched. **Leaves** palmate; stipules ovate to lanceolate, 0.6–1.2 cm, margins entire, toothed, or lacerate, apex acute or aristate; petiole 1–10 cm; petiolules to 0.5 mm; leaflets 3, blades obovate, elliptic, or oblanceolate, 0.5–2.5 × 0.3–1.5 cm, base cuneate, veins prominent, green, margins finely toothed, apex rounded, blunt, or retuse, surfaces glabrous. **Peduncles** 1–8 cm. **Inflorescences** axillary or terminal, 1–35-flowered, subglobose or ovoid, 0.5–1.8 × 0.5–2 cm; involucres broadly bowl-shaped, 4–22 mm, shallowly incised, lobes 3–15, toothed, broad,

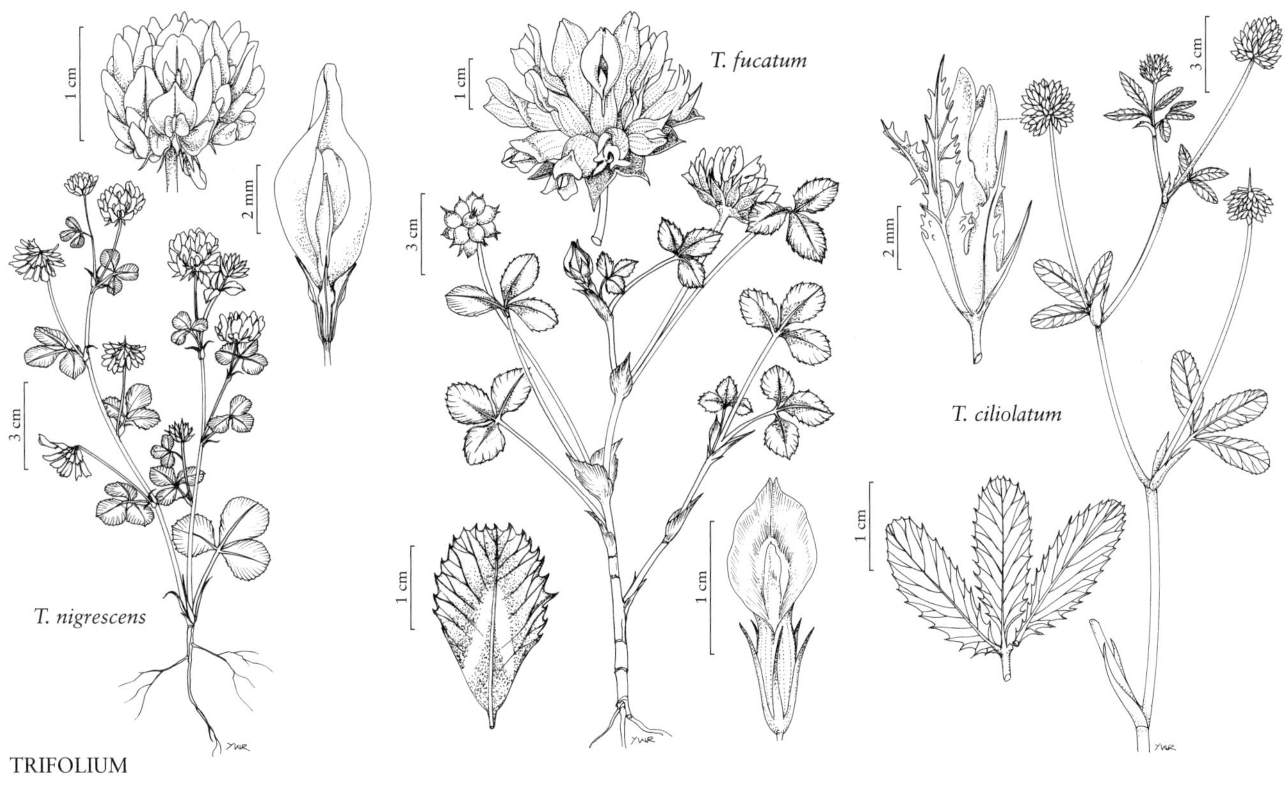

TRIFOLIUM

acute. **Pedicels** straight, 0.1–0.2 mm; bracteoles absent. **Flowers** 7–15 mm; calyx campanulate, inflated in fruit, 6–13 mm, glabrous, veins 13–20, tube 3–7 mm, lobes unequal, strongly oblique, broadly triangular, apex setaceous, adaxial unbranched, abaxial and lateral conspicuously 2- or 3-fid, segments glabrous, sometimes flattened, orifice open; corolla usually creamy white or rose to pink, sometimes whitish with pinkish tips, 6–13 mm, banner obovate or elliptic, proximally inflated in fruit, distally narrowed into twisted tip, 6–13 × 3–6 mm, apex rounded to broadly acute. **Legumes** ellipsoid, 2.5–3 mm. **Seeds** 1 or 2, yellow-brown, ovoid, 0.4–0.6 mm, smooth. **2*n*** = 16.

Flowering Apr–Oct. Wet meadows, roadsides, fields; 0–2700 m; B.C., Yukon; Alaska, Calif., Idaho, Mont., Nev., Oreg., Wash.; introduced in Asia (China, Japan).

Trifolium cyathiferum may be of hybrid origin; phylogenetic studies indicate it has the same *trn*L intron sequence as *T. buckwestiorum*, *T. polyodon*, and *T. variegatum* and *nr*DNA and combined analyses place it in a clade with other species (*T. barbigerum*, *T. fucatum*, *T. jokerstii*, and *T. physanthum* Hooker & Arnott) that have inflated fruiting corollas (N. W. Ellison et al. 2006).

The single record of *Trifolium cyathiferum* labeled as from Utah is likely mislabeled (S. L. Welsh et al. 2008). Populations in Yukon may be introductions.

43. Trifolium barbigerum Torrey in War Department [U.S.], Pacif. Railr. Rep. 4(5): 79. 1857 • Bearded clover [E]

Trifolium minutissimum D. Heller & Zohary

Herbs annual, 7–20 cm, puberulent or glabrous. **Stems** decumbent or erect, branched. **Leaves** palmate; stipules ovate-lanceolate, 0.5–1.1 cm, margins toothed or lacerate, apex acute-acuminate; petiole 1–10 cm; petiolules to 0.5 mm; leaflets 3, blades oblanceolate or obovate, 1.5–2.5 × 0.4–0.7 cm, base cuneate, veins fine, thickened distally, margins ± serrate or entire, apex rounded or retuse, surfaces pubescent or glabrous. **Peduncles** 5–10 cm. **Inflorescences** axillary or terminal, 5–20-flowered, subglobose or globose, 0.6–1.5 × 1–1.5 cm; involucres bowl-shaped, 5–15 mm, lobes 6–10, sharply setaceous-toothed, sinuses shallow. **Pedicels** straight, 0.2 mm; bracteoles absent. **Flowers** 4–6 mm; calyx campanulate, 5–9 mm, usually pubescent, rarely glabrous, veins 5, tube 2–3 mm, lobes ± equal, setaceous, often exceeding banner, orifice open; corolla usually lavender to purple, usually with white tips, rarely wholly white, 5–8 mm, banner broadly oblong, proximally inflated in fruit, distally narrowed into twisted tip,

6–8 × 6–8 mm, apex broadly acute. **Legumes** ovoid-ellipsoid, 2–3 mm. **Seeds** 1 or 2, brown, ellipsoid to subglobose, 1–1.5 mm, slightly roughened. **2*n*** = 16.

Flowering Apr–Jun. Vernal pools, stream banks, meadows, lawns; 0–1300 m; Calif., Oreg.

Trifolium barbigerum is relatively common and widespread in California, and extends northward into Coos, Curry, and Jackson counties in Oregon. It is morphologically similar to *T. physanthum* of Chile, to which it is a sister species in phylogenetic studies (N. W. Ellison et al. 2006).

44. Trifolium grayi Lojacono, Nuovo Giorn. Bot. Ital. 15: 189. 1883 • Gray's or Andrews's clover [E]

Trifolium barbigerum Torrey var. *andrewsii* A. Gray, Proc. Amer. Acad. Arts 7: 335. 1868; *T. barbigerum* var. *lilacinum* (Greene) Jepson; *T. lilacinum* Greene

Herbs annual, 10–40 cm, densely pubescent or glabrate. **Stems** erect, branched. **Leaves** palmate; stipules ovate, 0.5–1.5 cm, margins toothed or lacerate, apex acute-acuminate; petiole 1–15 cm; petiolules 1 mm; leaflets 3, blades elliptic, oblanceolate, or obovate, 2–2.5 × 1–1.5 cm, base cuneate, veins fine, margins dentate-serrate to crenulate, teeth shortly aristate, apex obtuse or broadly acute, surfaces pubescent or glabrate. **Peduncles** 2–15 cm. **Inflorescences** axillary or terminal, 5–30-flowered, subglobose or globose, 1.8–3 × 2–3 cm; involucres bowl-shaped, 10–25 mm, lobes 6–16, sharply setaceous-toothed, sinuses shallow. **Pedicels** straight, 0.5 mm; bracteoles absent. **Flowers** 10–17 mm; calyx campanulate, 6–13 mm, pubescent, veins 5, tube 3–5 mm, lobes unequal, setaceous, abaxial inconspicuously 2- or 3-fid, adaxial unbranched, segments plumose, orifice open; corolla usually lavender or purple, sometimes purple with white tips, 8–16 mm, banner oblong, proximally inflated in fruit, distally narrowed into twisted tip, 3–5 × 10–13 mm, apex obtuse, truncate, or emarginate. **Legumes** stipitate, ovoid-ellipsoid, 2.5–4 mm. **Seeds** 1 or 2, pale brown, mottled, ellipsoid to mitten-shaped, 1.6–2 mm, rugose.

Flowering Apr–Jun. Wet meadows, foothill slopes, pine woodlands; 0–600 m; Calif.

Trifolium grayi, which ranges from San Luis Obispo County in the south to Mendocino County in the north, and eastward into Amador, Sacramento, and Tuolumne counties, has long been considered a variety of *T. barbigerum* and some authors claim that intermediates between the two species are encountered (J. S. Martin 1943; D. Isely 1998); others state that the two taxa are distinct (L. F. McDermott 1910; M. A Vincent and R. Morgan 1998).

Trifolium andrewsii (A. Gray) A. Heller is an illegitimate superfluous name that pertains here.

45. Trifolium jokerstii Vincent & Rand. Morgan, Novon 8: 91, fig. 1. 1998 • Butte County golden clover [C] [E]

Herbs annual, 5–20 cm, glabrous. **Stems** erect-ascending, simple or cespitose, branched or unbranched. **Leaves** palmate; stipules ovate-lanceolate, 0.8–2 cm, margins toothed, apex rounded to acute; petiole 1–9 cm; petiolules 0.5 mm; leaflets 3, blades elliptic to obovate, 0.5–3.2 × 0.4–1.5 cm, base cuneate, veins fine to slightly thickened, margins usually serrulate, rarely nearly lobed, teeth shortly aristate, apex usually acute or obtuse, rarely emarginate, surfaces glabrous. **Peduncles** 2–15 cm. **Inflorescences** axillary or terminal, 10–30-flowered, subglobose, 1.2–3 × 1.2–3 cm; involucres widely campanulate to nearly flat, 6–11 mm. **Pedicels** straight, 0.5 mm; bracteoles absent. **Flowers** 10–16 mm; calyx campanulate, inflated in fruit, 7–9 mm, sparsely pubescent, veins 5, tube 3.5–4.5 mm, lobes unequal, abaxial and lateral 2- or 3-fid, adaxial unbranched, segments plumose, apex setaceous, orifice open; corolla yellow, 10–15 mm, banner broadly ovate, proximally inflated in fruit, distally narrowed into twisted tip, 10–15 × 3–5 mm, apex obtuse, truncate, or emarginate-apiculate. **Legumes** stipitate, ovoid, 3.3–3.5 mm. **Seeds** 1 or 2, dark brown, ellipsoid to mitten-shaped, 3.1–3.4 mm, rugose.

Flowering Mar–May. Wet meadows, streamsides; of conservation concern; 300–400 m; Calif.

Trifolium jokerstii is known only from Butte County, from Table Mountain and along a stream adjacent to it (M. A. Vincent and R. Morgan 1998).

46. Trifolium monanthum A. Gray, Proc. Amer. Acad. Arts 6: 523. 1865 • Mountain carpet clover

Herbs perennial, 3–22 cm, glabrous or hairy, often mat-forming. **Stems** decumbent to ascending, much-branched. **Leaves** palmate; stipules ovate to lanceolate, 0.3–1.2 cm, margins entire, serrate, or slightly lacerate, apex acute to acuminate; petiole 1–4.5 cm; petiolules 0.1–0.5 mm; leaflets 3, blades obovate, oblanceolate, or elliptic, 0.3–2 × 0.2–0.5 cm, base cuneate, veins prominent, margins ± dentate, serrate, or setose, apex acute, rounded, or retuse, surfaces glabrous or slightly villous. **Peduncles** 0.5–2 cm. **Inflorescences** axillary or terminal,

1–9-flowered, solitary or subglobose, 1–1.6 × 0.3–1.2 cm; involucres campanulate, 2–5 mm, incised nearly to base, lobes 2–8, lanceolate. **Pedicels** erect, 1 mm; bracteoles absent. **Flowers** 10–16 mm; calyx tubular, 2–10 mm, glabrous or pubescent, veins 10, tube 4–7 mm, lobes equal, triangular-subulate, orifice open; corolla white, pink, or lavender, keel petals usually purple-spotted, 8–16 mm, banner oblong, 8–13 × 2–5 mm, apex emarginate. **Legumes** oblong, 2–4 mm. **Seeds** 1 or 2, brown, mottled, mitten-shaped, 1–2 mm, dull. **2*n*** = 16.

Subspecies 4 (4 in the flora): w United States, nw Mexico.

Morphological intergradation among subspecies of *Trifolium monanthum* may be indicative of low genetic barriers to crossing. It might be just as plausible to divide *T. mononathum* into two species instead of four subspecies (J. M. Gillett 1980), with *T. monanthum* encompassing populations with white rhizomes, and *T. multicaule* encompassing populations with taproots.

Trifolium monanthum often forms dense mats.

1. Herbs glabrous or sparsely hairy, mat-forming; stems from thin to thick woody roots, rhizomes slender, white; peduncles straight or bent upwards at steep angle distally; flowers 1–5.
    2. Inflorescences (1 or)2–4-flowered; peduncles straight; leaflet blades obovate to oblanceolate, margins ± dentate, apex rounded or retuse . . . . 46a. *Trifolium monanthum* subsp. *monanthum*
    2. Inflorescences 1–5-flowered; peduncles bent upwards at steep angle distally; leaflet blades oblanceolate or elliptic, margins setose, apex acute . . . . 46b. *Trifolium monanthum* subsp. *grantianum*
1. Herbs densely hairy, decumbent to ascending; stems from thickened woody taproots, rhizomes absent; peduncles bent upwards at steep angle distally; flowers 1–9.
    3. Leaflet blade apex rounded, margins dentate . . . . 46c. *Trifolium monanthum* subsp. *parvum*
    3. Leaflet blade apex acute, margins serrate or setose. . . 46d. *Trifolium monanthum* subsp. *tenerum*

46a. Trifolium monanthum A. Gray subsp. **monanthum** [E]

Herbs mat-forming, ± glabrous or nearly so; stems from thin to thick woody roots, rhizomes slender, white. **Leaflet blades** obovate or oblanceolate, margins ± dentate, apex rounded or retuse. **Peduncles** straight. **Inflorescences** (1 or)2–4-flowered.

Flowering Jun–Sep. Wet meadows, stream banks, marshes, snowbelt areas; 1700–3900 m; Calif., Nev.

Subspecies *monanthum* ranges in eastern California from Lassen and Shasta counties in the north, southward to Inyo and Tulare counties, with scattered sites in Contra Costa, Los Angeles, San Bernardino, and Ventura counties; it is widespread in Nevada.

46b. Trifolium monanthum A. Gray subsp. **grantianum** (A. Heller) J. M. Gillett, Canad. J. Bot. 58: 1434. 1980

Trifolium grantianum A. Heller, Muhlenbergia 1: 136. 1906; *T. monanthum* var. *grantianum* (A. Heller) Parish; *T. simulans* House

Herbs mat-forming, glabrous or sparsely hairy; stems from thin to thick woody roots, rhizomes slender, white. **Leaflet blades** oblanceolate or elliptic, margins setose, apex acute. **Peduncles** bent upwards at steep angle distally. **Inflorescences** 1–5-flowered.

Flowering Jun–Sep. Wet meadows, stream banks, marshes, snowbelt areas; 1700–3100 m; Calif.; Mexico (Baja California).

Subspecies *grantianum* is found in Los Angeles, San Bernardino, and Tulare counties in California, and the Sierra de San Pedro Mártir in Baja California, Mexico.

46c. Trifolium monanthum A. Gray subsp. **parvum** (Kellogg) J. M. Gillett, Canad. J. Bot. 58: 1435. 1980 [E]

Trifolium pauciflorum Nuttall var. *parvum* Kellogg, Proc. Calif. Acad. Sci. 5: 54. 1873; *T. monanthum* var. *parvum* (Kellogg) McDermott; *T. multicaule* M. E. Jones; *T. parvum* (Kellogg) A. Heller

Herbs decumbent to ascending, densely hairy; stems from thickened woody taproots, rhizomes absent. **Leaflet blades** obovate or oblanceolate, margins dentate, apex rounded. **Peduncles** bent upwards at steep angle distally. **Inflorescences** 1–9-flowered.

Flowering Jun–Sep. Wet meadows, stream banks, marshes, snowbelt areas; 1500–2900 m; Calif.

Subspecies *parvum* is known from the Cascade Range and Sierra Nevada.

46d. Trifolium monanthum A. Gray subsp. **tenerum** (Eastwood) J. M. Gillett, Canad. J. Bot. 58: 1436. 1980 [E]

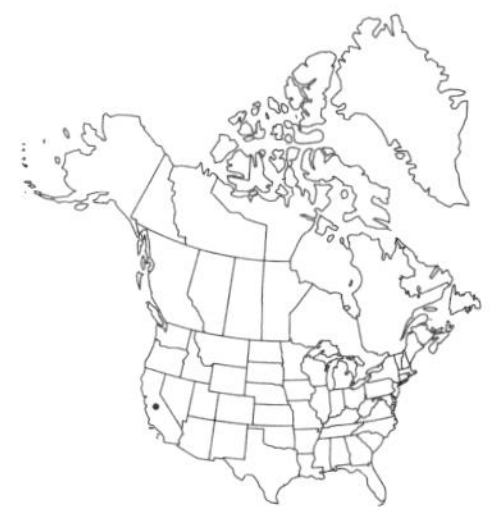

Trifolium tenerum Eastwood, Bull. Torrey Bot. Club 29: 81. 1902; *T. monanthum* var. *eastwoodianum* J. S. Martin

Herbs decumbent to ascending, densely hairy; stems from thickened woody taproots, rhizomes absent. **Leaflet blades** oblanceolate or elliptic, margins serrate or setose, apex acute. **Peduncles** bent upwards at steep angle distally. **Inflorescences** 1–7-flowered.

Flowering Jun–Sep. Wet meadows, stream banks, marshes, snowbelt areas; 1600–3300 m; Calif.

Subspecies *tenerum* is known from the Sierra Nevada.

47. Trifolium pinetorum Greene, Erythea 2: 182. 1894 • Pine clover

Trifolium longicaule Wooton & Standley; *T. willdenovii* Sprengel var. *longicaule* (Wooton & Standley) L. D. Benson; *T. wormskioldii* Lehmann var. *longicaule* (Wooton & Standley) L. D. Benson

Herbs perennial, 5–30 cm, glabrous or sparsely pilose; rhizomes absent, roots stout, branched. **Stems** prostrate to ascending, branched. **Leaves** palmate; stipules lanceolate-ovate, 0.7–1.3 cm, margins entire, apex acuminate; petiole 1–8.5 cm; petiolules 1–1.5 mm; leaflets 3, blades oblanceolate or obovate, 0.5–2.9 × 0.4–1.3 cm, base cuneate, veins prominent, margins denticulate to spinulose, apex usually rounded or truncate, sometimes retuse, surfaces glabrous. **Peduncles** 4–6 cm. **Inflorescences** axillary or terminal, 10–20-flowered, obconic, globose, or subglobose, 1.7–2.5 × 1.–1.5 cm; involucres broadly campanulate, 6–8 mm, incised ± 3/4 their length, lobes 15–20, linear-lanceolate, entire, acuminate. **Pedicels** erect to slightly reflexed, 1–2 mm; bracteoles ovate, 0.5 mm. **Flowers** 10–16 mm; calyx campanulate, 6–10 mm, glabrous, veins 10, tube 2–2.3 mm, lobes ± equal, subulate, 3–5 mm, orifice open; corolla white to pale purple, keel petals with dark purple-red tips, 11–13 mm, banner oblong, 11–13 × 4–5 mm, apex retuse. **Legumes** short-stipitate, oblong, 3.5–5 mm. **Seeds** 1 or 2, olive-brown, mottled purple, oblong, 1.5 mm, smooth, semiglossy. $2n = 16$.

Flowering Jun–Oct. Disturbed areas in pine, fir, or spruce forests; 2300–2800 m; Ariz., N.Mex.; Mexico (Chihuahua).

Trifolium pinetorum is found in Cochise, Coconino, Pima, and Santa Cruz counties in Arizona, and Catron, Grant, Lincoln, and Otero counties in New Mexico, as well as the Sierra Madre in Chihuahua, Mexico. It occupies disturbed areas in pine-fir-spruce forests, and has adapted well to anthropogenic disturbances, such as roadsides and other graded areas (J. M. Gillett 1980).

48. Trifolium depauperatum Desvaux, J. Bot. Agric. 4: 69, plate 32, fig. 2. 1814 • Cowbag clover

Lupinaster depauperatus (Desvaux) C. Presl

Herbs annual, 1–30 cm, glabrous. **Stems** erect or decumbent, branched. **Leaves** palmate; stipules sheathing proximally, ovate-oblong to lanceolate, 0.4–1.3 cm, margins entire or serrulate, apex short triangular-cuspidate; petiole 1–5 cm; petiolules to 1 mm; leaflets 3, blades lanceolate, linear, obovate, or oblanceolate, 0.4–2.5 × 0.1–0.7 cm, base cuneate, veins moderately thickened abaxially, margins entire, serrate, or pinnately lobed, apex rounded, truncate, acute, or retuse, surfaces glabrous. **Peduncles** 2–6 cm. **Inflorescences** axillary or terminal, 3–15-flowered, globose or depressed-globose, 0.5–1.5 × 0.5–1.5 cm; involucres flattened, 3–13 mm, ± distinct or incised 1/2 their length, lobes 5–7, linear to elliptic or irregular, or vestigial, reduced to narrow ring, apex rounded to broad and irregularly erose, not split. **Pedicels** straight, 0–0.5 mm; bracteoles absent. **Flowers** 3–10 mm; calyx campanulate, 2–5 mm, glabrous, veins 5, tube 1–2.5 mm, lobes unequal, triangular-lanceolate or subulate, orifice open; corolla white or pink, 3–11 mm, inflated in fruit, banner broadly ovate, 4–7 × 3–8 mm, apex rounded, broad, acute, or retuse. **Legumes** sessile or stipitate, ovoid, obovoid, or oblong, 2–4 mm. **Seeds** 1–6, gray or tan, mottled, mitten-shaped, 1.2–1.6 mm, irregularly bumpy. $2n = 16$.

Varieties 3 (3 in the flora): w, c North America, nw Mexico, South America (Chile, Peru).

The three varieties of *Trifolium depauperatum* are relatively easily distinguished by characteristics of the involucres and fruit stipes. Leaf morphology is not helpful in making the distinctions; in each variety, leaf margins can range from nearly entire or toothed or laciniate. In the phylogenetic treatment by N. W. Ellison et al. (2006), *T. depauperatum* is not allied with *T. fucatum* and other clovers with inflated corollas but rather with *T. obtusiflorum*, *T. trichocalyx*, and *T. willdenovii* (although with weak support).

1. Involucres reduced to narrow vestigial ring; inflorescences 1–1.5 cm diam.; flowers 7–10 mm; legumes ovoid, 3–4 mm, sessile . . . . 48a. *Trifolium depauperatum* var. *depauperatum*
1. Involucres with evident bracts; inflorescences 0.5–1 cm diam.; flowers 3–8 mm; legumes oblong, ovoid, or obovoid, 2–4 mm, sessile or stipes 0.5–1 mm.
   2. Involucral lobes broad, irregular, with broad, hyaline margins and reticulate veins; legumes oblong, 3–4 mm, ± sessile . . . . .48b. *Trifolium depauperatum* var. *amplectens*
   2. Involucral lobes oblong, often with narrow hyaline margins and raised, parallel veins; legumes ovoid or obovoid, 2–3 mm, stipes 0.5–1 mm . . . . 48c. *Trifolium depauperatum* var. *truncatum*

48a. Trifolium depauperatum Desvaux var. depauperatum

Trifolium depauperatum var. *angustatum* (Greene) Jepson; *T. depauperatum* var. *laciniatum* (Greene) Jepson; *T. laciniatum* Greene; *T. laciniatum* var. *angustatum* Greene

Inflorescences 1–1.5 cm diam. **Involucres** reduced to narrow vestigial ring. **Flowers** 7–10 mm. **Legumes** ovoid, 3–4 mm, sessile.

Flowering Mar–Jun. Meadows, grassy slopes, lawns; 0–1700 m; B.C.; Calif., Idaho, Oreg., Wash.; Mexico (Baja California); South America (Chile, Peru).

Variety *depauperatum* is known only as a waif in Michigan and South Carolina.

48b. Trifolium depauperatum Desvaux var. amplectens (Torrey & A. Gray) Rattan, Anal. Key West Coast Bot., 43. 1887 • Balloon sack clover [E]

Trifolium amplectens Torrey & A. Gray, Fl. N. Amer. 1: 319. 1838; *T. quercetorum* Greene

Inflorescences 0.5–1 cm diam. **Involucres:** lobes broad, equaling calyx, ± distinct or connate 1/2 their length, irregular, with broad, hyaline margins and reticulate veins. **Flowers** 3–8 mm. **Legumes** oblong, 3–4 mm, sessile.

Flowering Mar–Jun. Meadows, grassy slopes, lawns; 0–1700 m; Calif.

Variety *amplectens* is found in the Central Valley, San Francisco Bay Area, and South Coast Ranges.

48c. Trifolium depauperatum Desvaux var. truncatum (Greene) J. S. Martin ex Isely, Brittonia 32: 56. 1980 • Blunt sack clover

Trifolium franciscanum Greene var. *truncatum* Greene, Man. Bot. San Francisco, 100. 1894; *T. amplectens* Torrey & A. Gray var. *diversifolium* (Nuttall) Jepson; *T. amplectens* var. *stenophyllum* (Nuttall) Jepson; *T. amplectens* var. *truncatum* (Greene) Jepson; *T. anodon* Greene; *T. brachyodon* Greene; *T. decodon* Greene; *T. depauperatum* var. *diversifolium* (Nuttall) McDermott; *T. depauperatum* var. *stenophyllum* (Nuttall) McDermott; *T. diversifolium* Nuttall; *T. fransiscanum* Greene; *T. minutiflorum* Greene; *T. stenophyllum* Nuttall; *T. truncatum* (Greene) Greene

Inflorescences 0.5–1 cm diam. **Involucres:** lobes oblong, ± distinct, often with narrow hyaline margins and raised, parallel veins. **Flowers** 3–8 mm. **Legumes** ovoid or obovoid, 2–3 mm, stipes 0.5–1 mm.

Flowering Mar–Jun. Meadows, grassy slopes, lawns; 0–1600 m; Calif.; Mexico (Baja California).

In the flora area, var. *truncatum* is found in the North Coast Ranges through the Central Valley to southern California.

49. Trifolium hydrophilum Greene, Man. Bot. San Francisco, 100. 1894 • Water sack clover [C] [E]

Trifolium amplectens Torrey & A. Gray var. *hydrophilum* (Greene) Jepson; *T. depauperatum* Desvaux var. *hydrophilum* (Greene) J. S. Martin ex Isely

Herbs annual, 15–55 cm, glabrous. **Stems** erect, branched. **Leaves** palmate; stipules ovate-oblong to lanceolate, 0.4–1.3 cm, sheathing proximally, margins entire or serrate, apex acuminate; petiole 3–9 cm; petiolules 0.5 mm; leaflets 3, blades obovate to oblanceolate, 1.2–3 × 0.3–1.4 cm, base cuneate, veins fine, margins serrate, apex rounded or truncate, surfaces glabrous. **Peduncles** 3.5–6 cm. **Inflorescences** axillary or terminal, 5–15-flowered, ellipsoid, 1–1.8 × 1.3–1.5 cm; involucres flattened, 3–4 mm, shallowly incised, lobes 5–8, elliptic, apex rounded to truncate and irregularly erose, not split. **Pedicels** erect, 1 mm; bracteoles broadly ovate, to 0.5 mm. **Flowers** 7–11 mm; calyx campanulate-tubular, 2.5–5 mm, glabrous, veins 5, tube 1–2.5 mm, lobes unequal, lanceolate-subulate, orifice open; corolla reddish purple, 7–9 mm, inflated in fruit, banner oblong, 7–9 × 3–4 mm, apex rounded, retuse. **Legumes** stipitate, ovate-oblong, 4 mm. **Seeds** 1 or 2, red-brown, ovoid-ellipsoid, 2 mm, smooth or papillate.

Flowering Apr–May. Wet, alkaline soils, salt marshes; of conservation concern; 0–300 m; Calif.

Trifolium hydrophilum is closely allied to *T. depauperatum* and is restricted to the Sacramento Valley, northwestern San Joaquin Valley, and central-western California; it grows in moist areas, sometimes in standing water (M. A. Vincent and D. Isely 2012).

50. Trifolium trichocalyx A. Heller, Muhlenbergia 1: 55. 1904 • Monterey clover [C] [E]

Trifolium oliganthum Steudel var. *trichocalyx* (A. Heller) McDermott

Herbs annual, 5–45 cm, sparsely villous to glabrescent. **Stems** prostrate, decumbent, or erect, branched. **Leaves** palmate; stipules ovate, 0.4–1.2 cm, margins serrate-lacerate, apex acuminate; petiole 1–4 cm; petiolules 0.5 mm; leaflets 3, blades obovate, 0.5–1.5 × 0.4–1 cm, base cuneate, veins moderately prominent, margins denticulate, apex truncate, retuse, or mucronulate, surfaces glabrescent. **Peduncles** 1.5–4 cm. **Inflorescences** axillary or terminal, 2–15-flowered, subglobose, 1.5–1.8 × 0.5–1.5 cm; involucres flattened or vase-shaped, 1–3 mm, when folded, not hiding flowers except proximally, incised 2/3–3/4 their length, lobes 5–15, linear-lanceolate, entire, acuminate. **Pedicels** erect, 1.5 mm; bracteoles absent. **Flowers** 8–11 mm; calyx campanulate-tubular, not slit between adaxial lobes, 6–9 mm, usually densely pubescent, rarely sparsely so, veins 10, tube 2.5–4.5 mm, lobes unequal, lanceolate-subulate, orifice open; corolla light purple with darker purple keel petals, 6–10 mm, banner narrowly obovate, 4–5 × 1 mm, apex retuse. **Legumes** sessile, oblong, 5 mm. **Seeds** 3–6(–9), pale brown, mottled purple, globose to mitten-shaped, 0.8–1 mm, smooth to slightly roughened, semiglossy.

Flowering Apr–May. Sandy, rich soils in open Monterey pine forests, often after fire; of conservation concern; 0–50 m; Calif.

Trifolium trichocalyx is an extremely rare species known only from Mendocino and Monterey counties. D. I. Axelrod (1982) suggested that *T. trichocalyx* might have originated as a hybrid between *T. microcephalum* and *T. variegatum*, but this is not supported by molecular studies (N. W. Ellison et al. 2006). It appears to be fire-adapted and appeared in large numbers shortly after a fire in 1987 (U.S. Fish and Wildlife Service 2004).

51. Trifolium willdenovii Sprengel, Syst. Veg. 3: 208. 1826 • Thimble clover

Trifolium involucratum Willdenow, Sp. Pl. 3: 1372. 1802, not Lamarck 1778; *T. aciculare* Nuttall; *T. nuttallii* Steudel; *T. scabrellum* Greene; *T. segetum* Greene; *T. tridentatum* Lindley; *T. tridentatum* var. *aciculare* (Nuttall) McDermott; *T. tridentatum* var. *scabrellum* (Greene) Greene; *T. tridentatum* var. *segetum* (Greene) McDermott; *T. tridentatum* var. *watsonii* (Lojacono) Jepson; *T. trimorphum* Greene; *T. watsonii* Lojacono

Herbs annual, 10–60 cm, glabrous. **Stems** erect, branched. **Leaves** palmate; stipules lanceolate or ovate, 1–2 cm, margins dentate or lacerate, apex acuminate; petiole 1–8 cm; petiolules 0.5 mm; leaflets 3, blades linear, lanceolate, or elliptic, 1–5 × 0.2–1.5 cm, base cuneate, veins fine, margins serrate, apex acute, blunt, or retuse, surfaces glabrous. **Peduncles** 2–15 cm. **Inflorescences** axillary or terminal, 10–50-flowered, globose or ovoid, 1–3.5 × 1–3 cm; involucres flattened or bowl-shaped, 3–9 mm, when folded, not hiding flowers except proximally, incised 1/4–1/3 their length. **Pedicels** erect, 0.5 mm; bracteoles absent. **Flowers** 12–20 mm; calyx tubular-campanulate, slit between adaxial lobes, 6–9 mm, glabrous, veins 10–15, tube 3–7 mm, lobes unequal, triangular or subulate, usually 3-fid or shouldered below apex, orifice open; corolla usually white with purple spot, sometimes lavender or pink or all white, 10–18 mm, banner narrowly oblong, 12–20 × 3–4 mm, apex obtuse or retuse. **Legumes** ellipsoid, 3 mm. **Seeds** 1 or 2, yellow, mottled, globose-ellipsoid, 1.5–2.5 mm, smooth. $2n = 16$.

Flowering Mar–Jul. Roadsides, meadows, lawns, hillsides, stream margins, open oak chaparral; 0–2500 m; B.C.; Ariz., Calif., Idaho, Oreg., Wash.; Mexico (Baja California).

Trifolium willdenovii was described by M. Zohary and D. Heller (1984) as one of the most variable clover species in North America.

52. Trifolium obtusiflorum Hooker, Bot. Beechey Voy., 331. 1838 • Clammy clover

Trifolium majus Greene; *T. roscidum* Greene; *T. tridentatum* Lindley var. *obtusiflorum* (Hooker) S. Watson

Herbs annual, 2–100 cm, resinous stipitate-glandular. **Stems** erect or ascending, branched. **Leaves** palmate; stipules ovate, 1–1.5 cm, sheathing, margins deeply lacerate, apex acuminate; petiole 1.5–10 cm; petiolules to 0.5 mm; leaflets 3, blades elliptic, lanceolate, oblanceolate, rhombic, or obovate, 1.5–4 × 0.3–1.7 cm, base cuneate, veins thickened, margins coarsely spinulose-serrate, apex acute, mucronate, surfaces glandular. **Peduncles** 3–15 cm, glandular. **Inflorescences** axillary or terminal, 10–50-flowered, globose or ovoid, 1–3.5 × 1–3 cm; involucres flattened or bowl-shaped, 3–8 mm, when folded, not hiding flowers except proximally, incised 1/4–1/3 their length. **Pedicels** erect, 1 mm; bracteoles absent. **Flowers** 13–20 mm; calyx tubular-campanulate, slit between adaxial lobes, 10–13 mm, glandular, veins 20+, tube 5–7 mm, lobes unequal, narrowly triangular or lanceolate-subulate, usually entire, rarely 3-fid or shouldered below apex, orifice open; corolla white or pale pinkish with dark purple spot, 10–18 mm, banner broadly elliptic, 10–18 × 2–4 mm, apex blunt. **Legumes** obovoid, 3.5–4 mm. **Seeds** 1 or 2, brown, mottled, ellipsoid or mitten-shaped, 2.5 mm, smooth. $2n$ = 16.

Flowering Apr–Jul. Moist swales, creek bottoms; 0–1600 m; Calif., Oreg.; Mexico (Baja California, Sinaloa).

Trifolium obtusiflorum is much less common than the similar *T. willdenovii*, occurring in moist areas in cismontane California and north into Oregon (W. L. Jepson [1923–1925]). It is easy to distinguish from *T. willdenovii* by its glandularity, which causes fresh specimens to be sticky to the touch.

53. Trifolium microdon Hooker & Arnott, Bot. Misc. 3: 180. 1833 • Thimble clover

Trifolium microdon var. *pilosum* Eastwood

Herbs annual, 6–35 cm, villous or glabrous. **Stems** erect or ascending, branched. **Leaves** palmate; stipules obliquely ovate, 0.4–1.2 cm, margins entire, toothed, or lacerate, apex acuminate; petiole 1–8 cm; petiolules 0.5 mm; leaflets 3, blades obovate or obcordate, 0.4–1.4 × 0.3–1.2 cm, base cuneate, veins fine, thickened distally, margins serrate, apex rounded or emarginate, surfaces villous or glabrous. **Peduncles** 1.5–7.4 cm. **Inflorescences** axillary or terminal, 10–17-flowered, subglobose, 0.8–1.7 × 0.5–1.5 cm; involucres cup-shaped, 0.5–1.5 cm, glabrous or sparsely hairy, lobes 8–12, ovate, conspicuously sharply toothed. **Pedicels** absent; bracteoles absent. **Flowers** 6–7 mm; calyx tubular-campanulate, 3–4 mm, glabrous, veins 10, tube 2.5–3.5 mm, lobes ± equal, triangular, not or minutely aristate, conspicuously toothed, margins membranous, orifice open; corolla pale pink or white, 6–9 mm, banner oblong, 6–9 × 2–3 mm, apex narrowly rounded or emarginate-mucronate. **Legumes** ovoid, 2–3 mm. **Seeds** 1 or 2, greenish, sometimes mottled, oblong, 1.5–2 mm, smooth. $2n$ = 16.

Flowering Apr–Jul. Meadows, roadsides, dry slopes, fields, open oak or pine forests; 0–1500 m; B.C.; Calif., Idaho, Oreg., Wash.; Mexico (Baja California); South America (Chile).

Trifolium microdon is one of several clovers that have an apparently natural disjunct distribution between the western coast of South America (Chile) and western North America. Others include *T. depauperatum* var. *depauperatum* and *T. macraei.*

In herbarium specimens of *Trifolium microdon*, the folded involucre hides, or nearly hides, the calyces, whereas in herbarium specimens of similar *T. microcephalum*, the calyces are still visible.

54. Trifolium microcephalum Pursh, Fl. Amer. Sept. 2: 478. 1813 • Smallhead clover

Lojaconoa microcephala (Pursh) Bobrov; *Trifolium microcephalum* var. *bipedale* Hooker; *T. microcephalum* var. *lemmonii* Lojacono

Herbs annual, 3–55 cm, densely to sparsely pubescent. **Stems** erect to ascending, branched. **Leaves** palmate; stipules obliquely ovate, 0.4–1.2 cm, margins entire or slightly serrate, apex acuminate; petiole 1–5 cm; petiolules 0.5 mm; leaflets 3, blades oblanceolate, obovate, or obcordate, 0.4–1.7 × 0.3–1.1 cm, base cuneate, veins fine or slightly thickened, margins setose, often dentate distally, apex usually retuse, rarely rounded, surfaces villous. **Peduncles** 1–8 cm. **Inflorescences** axillary or terminal, 10–40-flowered, globose, 0.5–1.3 × 0.4–1.2 cm; involucres flattened or bowl-shaped, 0.4–1 cm, when folded, nearly completely hiding calyces, villous, incised 1/2 their length, lobes 5–12, lanceolate-ovate, entire or slightly toothed proximally, acuminate. **Pedicels** absent; bracteoles absent. **Flowers** 4–6 mm; calyx campanulate-tubular, 3–5.5 mm, pubescent, veins 10, tube 1.8–2.5 mm, lobes ± equal, triangular-aristate, margins hyaline, wavy, orifice open; corolla white or pink to lavender, 4–6 mm, banner oblong, 3–6 × 1–2 mm, apex emarginate. **Legumes** broadly ellipsoid, 1.5–2 mm. **Seeds** 1, yellow, reddish mottled, oblong, 1.5 mm, smooth. **2*n*** = 16.

Flowering Mar–Jul. Meadows, roadsides, stream banks, forest clearings, grassy slopes; 0–2500 m; B.C.; Alaska, Ariz., Calif., Idaho, Mont., Nev., Oreg., Wash.; Mexico (Baja California).

Trifolium microcephalum is common in much of its range in California and northward into Oregon, and is rare in much of the rest of its range. It is closely allied with the Chilean *T. vernum* Philippi (N. W. Ellison et al. 2006), which it resembles greatly, and from which it is distinguished by its shorter calyx lobes (M. Zohary and D. Heller 1984).

55. Trifolium bifidum A. Gray, Proc. Calif. Acad. Sci. 3: 102. 1864 • Notchleaf or pinole clover

Trifolium bifidum var. *decipiens* Greene; *T. greenei* House; *T. hallii* Howell

Herbs annual, 5–55 cm, sparsely pubescent or glabrous. **Stems** erect, branched. **Leaves** palmate; stipules ovate to lanceolate, 0.8–1.5 cm, margins entire or slightly serrate, apex acicular; petiole 1–7 cm; petiolules to 0.5 mm; leaflets 3, blades narrowly obcordate, obovate, oblanceolate, or linear, 1–2.5 × 0.3–0.7 cm, base cuneate, veins moderately thickened, margins serrate distally or entire, apex rounded, truncate, shallowly to deeply retuse, or deeply 2-fid, surfaces glabrous or hairy abaxially along midvein. **Peduncles** 3–8 cm. **Inflorescences** axillary or terminal, 5–30-flowered, globose to subglobose, 0.8–1.5 × 0.8–1.5 cm, rachis prolonged beyond flowers; involucres a very narrow rim, to 0.5 mm. **Pedicels** reflexed in fruit, 1–3 mm; bracteoles broadly triangular, membranous, to 0.5 mm. **Flowers** 6–8 mm; calyx campanulate, 3–3.6 mm, slightly hairy or glabrous, veins 10, tube 1–1.5 mm, lobes unequal, subulate, margins green or purple, orifice open; corolla pink or purple, 5–7 mm, banner elliptic to oblong, 5–7 × 3–4 mm, apex rounded, apiculate. **Legumes** stipitate, obovoid, 3–4 mm. **Seeds** 1 or 2, brown, mottled, oblong, 2–3 mm, smooth. **2*n*** = 16.

Flowering Apr–Jun. Open woodlands, fields, roadsides, slopes, stream margins, meadows; 0–1200 m; B.C.; Calif., Oreg., Wash.; Mexico (Baja California).

Trifolium bifidum ranges from Baja California, Mexico, northward through California to scattered sites in Oregon, Washington, and British Columbia.

Recent re-evaluation of *Trifolium bifidum* and related species showed complete overlap in characters for the two varieties that have been recognized previously, with no clear distinctions between them (L. Rogers, pers. comm.).

56. Trifolium oliganthum Steudel, Nomencl. Bot. ed. 2, 2: 707. 1841 • Few-flowered clover [E]

Trifolium pauciflorum Nuttall in J. Torrey and A. Gray, Fl. N. Amer. 1: 319. 1838, not d'Urville 1822; *T. filipes* Greene; *T. oliganthum* var. *sonomense* Greene; *T. triflorum* Greene

Herbs annual, 10–50 cm, glabrous. **Stems** erect, dichotomously branched. **Leaves** palmate; stipules lanceolate, 0.4–1.2 cm, margins lacerate, apex subulate; petiole 0.5–4 cm; petiolules to 0.5 mm; leaflets 3, blades linear, oblong, oblanceolate, or elliptic, 0.5–2.5 × 0.1–0.5 cm, base cuneate, veins fine or moderately thickened, margins entire, spinulose, or dentate, apex rounded or truncate, mucronate, surfaces glabrous. **Peduncles** 2.5–7.5 cm. **Inflorescences** axillary or terminal, 3–15-flowered, obconic, 0.3–1.2 × 0.3–0.8 cm; involucres flattened to bowl-shaped, 1–2 mm, when folded, not hiding flowers except proximally, incised 4/5–9/10 their length, lobes lanceolate-subulate. **Pedicels** erect, 0.5–2 mm; bracteoles absent. **Flowers** 11–16 mm; calyx campanulate, slit between adaxial lobes, 4–5 mm, glabrous, veins 10, tube 2.5–5.2 mm, lobes triangular-subulate, 3-fid or shouldered below apex, orifice open; corolla lavender with white tips, keel petals purple, 6–8 mm, banner narrowly ovate-oblong, 6–8 × 2 mm, apex narrowly rounded, erose. **Legumes** sessile, oblong, 2.1–3.2 mm. **Seeds** 1 or 2 (or 3), reddish brown, mottled, lenticular or reniform, 1.2–1.3 mm, smooth. **2*n*** = 16.

Flowering Mar–Jul. Stream banks, grassy, rocky slopes, meadows, fields; 0–1100 m; B.C.; Calif., Oreg., Wash.

Trifolium oliganthum is relatively common throughout much of its range in California; it is found in a few scattered sites northward into Oregon, Washington, and British Columbia. Even though it closely resembles *T. variegatum*, it is placed near *T. bifidum* in molecular studies (N. W. Ellison et al. 2006).

Trifolium hexanthum Greene ex A. Heller, which pertains here, is not a validly published name.

57. Trifolium ciliolatum Bentham, Pl. Hartw., 304. 1849 • Foothill clover [F]

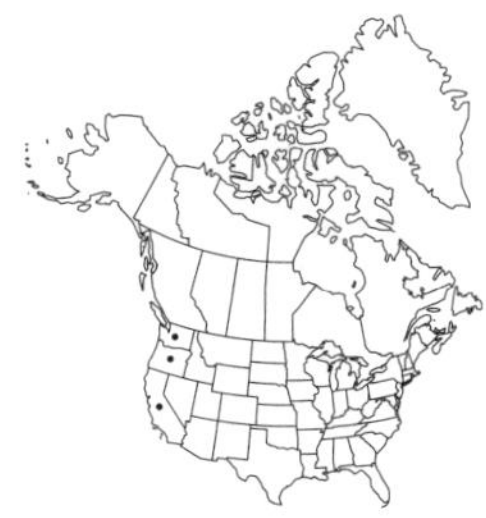

Trifolium ciliatum var. *discolor* Lojacono

Herbs annual, 5–50 cm, glabrous or sparsely hairy. **Stems** erect, branched. **Leaves** palmate; stipules ovate-lanceolate, 1–1.5 cm, margins entire, sometimes ciliate, apex acuminate; petiole 1–13 cm; petiolules 0.5 mm; leaflets 3, blades elliptic to oblong or obovate, 0.8–3.5 × 0.5–1.5 cm, base cuneate, veins thickened, margins serrate proximally, obscurely denticulate distally, apex usually rounded or retuse, rarely acute, surfaces glabrous. **Peduncles** 2.5–12 cm. **Inflorescences** axillary or terminal, 10–30-flowered, ovoid to subglobose, 0.7–2.2 × 0.5–2 cm; involucres a narrow rim, 0.5 mm, membranous, dentate. **Pedicels** erect becoming reflexed, 0.5–6 mm; bracteoles linear or cup-shaped, to 1 mm. **Flowers** 6–13 mm; calyx broadly campanulate, 5–11 mm, glabrous, veins 10, tube 1–5 mm, lobes unequal, elliptic to linear, margins hyaline, dentate or pectinate, ciliate, sinuses narrow, orifice open; corolla white, pink, or purple, 5–13 mm, banner broadly ovate, 6–13 × 4–7 mm, apex rounded, apiculate. **Legumes** short-stipitate, ovoid, 5–10 mm. **Seeds** 1 or 2, brown, mottled, ovoid, 2.5–3 mm, smooth. **2*n*** = 16.

Flowering Apr–Jun. Oak-pine chaparral, meadows, roadsides; 0–1500 m; Calif., Oreg., Wash.; Mexico (Baja California).

Trifolium ciliolatum is relatively widespread in California and is found in scattered sites in Baja California, Oregon, and Washington.

Trifolium ciliatum Nuttall (1848), which pertains here, is a later homonym of *T. ciliatum* E. D. Clarke (1813).

58. Trifolium palmeri S. Watson, Proc. Amer. Acad. Arts 11: 132. 1876 • Palmer's clover

Trifolium gracilentum Torrey & A. Gray var. *palmeri* (S. Watson) McDermott

Herbs annual, 4–40 cm, glabrous. **Stems** erect or ascending, branched. **Leaves** palmate; stipules lanceolate, 0.5–2.5 cm, margins entire or slightly serrate, apex acuminate; petiole 0.5–5 cm; petiolules to 1 mm; leaflets 3, blades narrowly elliptic or lanceolate, 0.8–3 × 0.3–0.8 cm, base cuneate, veins thickened, margins setose-serrulate, apex acute, surfaces glabrous. **Peduncles** 1–5 cm. **Inflorescences** axillary or terminal, 10–20-flowered, globose to subglobose, 0.5–2 × 0.5–2 cm, rachis prolonged beyond flowers; involucres absent. **Pedicels** becoming dramatically reflexed, 3–4 mm; bracteoles low, broadly triangular, membranous, to 0.5 mm. **Flowers** 5–9 mm; calyx narrowly campanulate, 5–6.5 mm, glabrous, veins 10, tube 2–3 mm, lobes unequal, narrowly triangular to acicular, margins green or purple, membranous, orifice open; corolla pink or purple, 5–9 mm, banner narrowly elliptic-oblong, 5–9 × 3–4 mm, apex narrowly rounded to acute. **Legumes** ovoid-ellipsoid, 4–6 mm. **Seeds** 1 or 2, yellow, purple-mottled, mitten-shaped, 2 mm, smooth. **2*n*** = 16.

Flowering Mar–Jun. Thin soils on slopes; 0–50 m; Calif.; Mexico (Baja California).

Trifolium palmeri is known from the islands off the coast of southern California and Baja California, Mexico. It was long considered a variety of *T. gracilentum* but molecular analyses support its recognition as distinct (N. W. Ellison et al. 2006).

59. Trifolium gracilentum Torrey & A. Gray, Fl. N. Amer. 1: 316. 1838 • Pinpoint clover [F]

Trifolium denudatum Nuttall; *T. exile* Greene; *T. gracilentum* var. *exile* (Greene) P. B. Kennedy; *T. gracilentum* var. *inconspicuum* Fernald; *T. gracilentum* var. *reductum* Parish; *T. inconspicuum* (Fernald) A. Heller

Herbs annual, 2–60 cm, glabrous. **Stems** erect or ascending, branched. **Leaves** palmate; stipules ovate-lanceolate, 0.5–2.5 cm, membranous, margins entire or slightly serrate, apex long-acuminate; petiole 0.5–9 cm; petiolules to 0.5 mm; leaflets 3, blades obovate to obcordate, 0.5–2.5 × 0.2–1.5 cm, base cuneate, veins moderately thickened, margins setose-serrulate, apex rounded, shallowly retuse, surfaces glabrous. **Peduncles** 1–9 cm. **Inflorescences** axillary or terminal, 10–25-flowered, globose to subglobose, 0.5–2 × 0.5–2 cm, rachis prolonged beyond flowers; involucres a narrow, membranous, dentate rim, to 0.5 mm. **Pedicels** becoming dramatically reflexed, 3–4 mm; bracteoles low, cuplike, membranous, to 0.5 mm. **Flowers** 5–7.5 mm; calyx narrowly campanulate, 4.5–6.5 mm, glabrous, veins 10, tube 2–2.5 mm, lobes unequal, long-triangular, margins green or purple, orifice open; corolla white, pink, or purple, 5–8 mm, banner ovate, 5–8 × 3–4 mm, apex broadly rounded, retuse or apiculate. **Legumes** ovoid-ellipsoid, 4–6 mm. **Seeds** 1 or 2, tan to brown, mitten-shaped, 1.1–1.5 mm, smooth. **2*n*** = 16.

Flowering Mar–Jun. Open, grassy areas, gravelly ridges, roadsides, adobe slopes, moist places; 50–1200 m; Ariz., Calif., Nev., Oreg., Wash.; Mexico (Baja California).

Abundance of *Trifolium gracilentum* increases in response to burns (J. M. DiTomaso et al. 1999).

The record of *Trifolium gracilentum* from South Carolina is a waif.

60. Trifolium macraei Hooker & Arnott, Bot. Misc. 3: 179. 1833 • Macrae's clover

Trifolium bicephalum Elmer; *T. catalinae* S. Watson; *T. mercedense* P. B. Kennedy; *T. traskiae* P. B. Kennedy

Herbs annual, 3–30 cm, pubescent. **Stems** erect, ascending, or prostrate, branched. **Leaves** palmate; stipules ovate to oblong, 0.6–1 cm, margins entire, apex acuminate to cuspidate; petiole 0.5–6 cm; petiolules to 0.5 mm; leaflets 3, blades obovate, oblanceolate, or elliptic, 0.6–1.6 × 0.3–1.2 cm, base cuneate, veins obscure or slightly thickened, margins subentire to serrate, apex rounded, retuse, surfaces pubescent. **Peduncles** 0–0.2 cm. **Inflorescences** terminal or subterminal, usually paired, sometimes one head slightly stalked, partially hidden by terminal leaves and stipules, 10–40-flowered, ovoid or subglobose, 0.8–2.5 × 0.5–2 cm; involucres absent, involucrelike structure formed from terminal leaves and stipules. **Pedicels** absent; bracteoles broadly ovate to linear, 1–2 mm. **Flowers** 5.5–7.5 mm; calyx tubular, 4–5 mm, pubescent, veins 5–10, tube 1.5–2 mm, lobes subequal, subulate, orifice open; corolla usually purple or pink, rarely white, 5–7 mm, banner obovate-oblong, 6–7 × 2–3 mm, apex rounded, slightly denticulate. **Legumes** oblong, 2.5–3 mm. **Seeds** 1, yellow, mottled, ellipsoid, 1.6–2 mm, smooth. **2*n*** = 16.

Flowering May–Jun. Grassy fields, sandy ocean bluffs; 0–800 m; Calif., Oreg.; South America (Chile).

Trifolium macraei was described from specimens collected in Chile; the South American plants have broader banners, smaller auricles on the wing petals, and styles that are barely curved upwards distally (D. Isely 1998). Further examination of the disjunct populations may reveal other differences and prompt reconsideration of the identity of North American specimens. The record from Massachusetts is a waif.

61. Trifolium albopurpureum Torrey & A. Gray, Fl. N. Amer. 1: 313. 1838 • Rancheria clover

Trifolium albopurpureum var. *neolagopus* (Lojacono) McDermott; *T. helleri* P. B. Kennedy; *T. macraei* Hooker & Arnott var. *albopurpureum* (Torrey & A. Gray) Greene; *T. neolagopus* Lojacono; *T. pseudoalbopurpureum* P. B. Kennedy

Herbs annual, 5–40 cm, pubescent. **Stems** erect, branched from base. **Leaves** palmate; stipules elliptic-ovate, 0.6–1 cm, margins entire, toothed, or remotely lobed, ciliate, apex acuminate; petiole 0.5–7 cm; petiolules 1 mm; leaflets 3, blades obovate or elliptic, 0.5–2 × 0.2–1 cm, base cuneate, veins obscure or slightly thickened, margins serrate, apex acute or obtuse, often retuse, surfaces pubescent. **Peduncles** 0.5–10 cm. **Inflorescences** axillary or terminal, 25–50-flowered, ovoid-ellipsoid, 1–1.8 × 0.8–1.5 cm; involucres absent. **Pedicels** absent; bracteoles absent. **Flowers** 6–9 mm; calyx campanulate, 6–8 mm, densely pubescent, veins 10 (additional faint veins sometimes present), tube 1–2 mm, lobes unequal, narrowly triangular, subulate, sinuses rounded, lobes divergent, orifice open; corolla white with purple tips, 4–6 mm, banner narrowly elliptic, 6–7 × 2 mm, apex acute, slightly erose. **Legumes** broadly ellipsoid, 2.8–3.2 mm. **Seeds** 1 (or 2), yellow or brown, often red-mottled, ellipsoid, 2–2.6 mm, smooth, glossy. **2*n*** = 16.

Flowering Apr–May. Grassy foothills and valleys; 0–2100 m; Ariz., Calif., Oreg., Wash.; Mexico (Baja California).

Trifolium albopurpureum is a widespread member of a closely allied group of species, including *T. amoenum*, *T. dichotomum*, and *T. columbinum*, that intergrade to varying degrees and may co-occur in some populations. The great similarity among these species has led to a maddening array of synonyms as new suites of species have been recognized and various new combinations have been made. In spite of the resultant confusion, these species are relatively distinct and are differentiated on the following characters: inflorescences generally greater than 3 cm diam. (*T. amoenum*) versus less than 2.5 cm diam. in the others; corollas usually 8–12 mm with calyx lobes 2–3 times the tube (*T. dichotomum*), versus corollas usually 5–8.5 mm with calyx lobes 3–6 times the tube; calyces 8–12+ mm with lobes exceeding the corollas by 3–6 mm (*T. columbinum*), versus calyces 4–9 mm with lobes equaling the corollas or exceeding them by 1.5–2 mm (D. Isely 1998; M. A. Vincent and Isely 2012).

Trifolium albopurpureum is widespread in California, northward through Oregon in coastal counties, and with scattered populations known from Washington and Arizona.

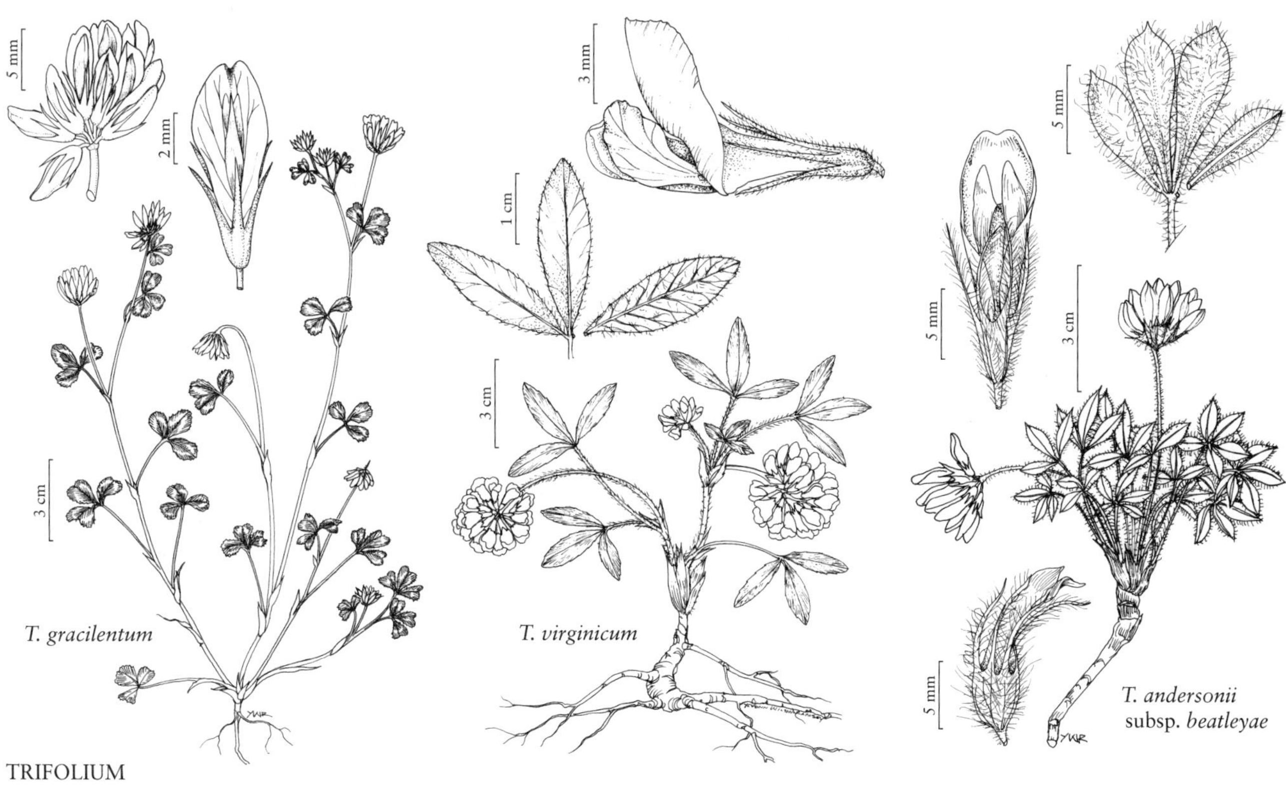

TRIFOLIUM

62. Trifolium amoenum Greene, Fl. Francisc., 27. 1891 • Showy Indian clover [C] [E]

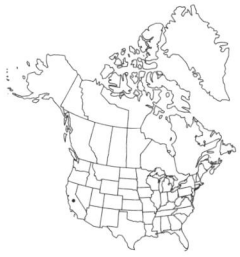

Herbs annual, 45–65 cm, canescent. **Stems** erect, branched from base and distally, or unbranched. **Leaves** palmate; stipules ovate-oblong, 0.5–1.8 cm, margins entire, toothed, or irregularly lobed, apex acuminate; petiole 0.5–10 cm; petiolules to 1 mm; leaflets 3, blades broadly obovate or elliptic, 1.7–3.3 × 1.1–2 cm, base cuneate, veins fine, margins entire or denticulate, apex rounded, obtuse, or retuse, surfaces pilose, abaxial less so. **Peduncles** 5–15 cm. **Inflorescences** terminal or axillary, 30–50-flowered, bluntly conic, ellipsoid, globose, or subglobose, 1.5–3 × 1.5–2.5 cm; involucres absent. **Pedicels** absent; bracteoles cuplike, to 0.5 mm. **Flowers** 13–16 mm; calyx tubular, 9–12 mm, pubescent, veins 20–30, tube 3 mm, lobes nearly equal, appearing rigidly erect, linear-setaceous, plumose, sinuses acute, orifice open; corolla white to pink with purple tips, 12–16 mm, banner ovate-oblong, 12–15 × 4 mm, apex broadly rounded, emarginate. **Legumes** obovoid, 4 mm. **Seeds** 1, dark brown, ellipsoid, 2–3 mm, smooth.

Flowering Apr–May. Grassy slopes, swales, clay soils; of conservation concern; 0–100 m; Calif.

Trifolium amoenum was considered extinct (J. P. Smith Jr. 1984) but was rediscovered in 1993 (P. G. Connors 1994). Specimens of *T. amoenum* are known from Marin, Napa, San Mateo, Solano, and Sonoma counties; it appears to be extant in only single populations in each of Marin and Solano counties. Allozyme studies of the two known populations revealed fixed genetic differences between them (E. E. Knapp and Connors 1999).

63. Trifolium dichotomum Hooker & Arnott, Bot. Beechey Voy., 330. 1838 • Branched Indian clover [E]

Trifolium albopurpureum Torrey & A. Gray var. *dichotomum* (Hooker & Arnott) Isely; *T. californicum* Jepson; *T. dichotomum* var. *turbinatum* Jepson; *T. insularum* P. B. Kennedy; *T. macraei* Hooker & Arnott var. *dichotomum* (Hooker & Arnott) Brewer ex S. Watson; *T. petrophilum* Greene ex A. Heller

Herbs annual, 15–30 cm, canescent. **Stems** erect, branched from base and distally, or unbranched. **Leaves** palmate; stipules ovate or elliptic, 0.3–1 cm, margins entire, ciliate, apex acuminate; petiole 0.5–6.5 cm; petiolules 0.5–0.7 mm; leaflets 3, blades obovate or oblanceolate, 0.5–1.5 × 0.2–1.1 cm, base cuneate, veins obscure or slightly thickened, margins dentate, apex rounded or emarginate, surfaces pilose or glabrescent. **Peduncles** 2.5–10 cm. **Inflorescences** terminal or axillary, 15–35-flowered, ovoid-ellipsoid, 1.1–2.2 × 1–1.5 cm; involucres absent. **Pedicels** absent; bracteoles cuplike, to 0.5 mm. **Flowers** 10–12 mm; calyx tubular, 4–8 mm, densely pubescent, veins 20–30, tube 2–4 mm, lobes nearly equal, appearing rigidly erect, linear-setaceous, plumose, sinuses acute, orifice open; corolla red-violet to pink, with pink or white tips, 7–12 mm, banner ovate-oblong, 9–11 × 3–4 mm, apex broadly rounded, emarginate. **Legumes** obovoid, 3–3.5 mm. **Seeds** 1, yellow-brown, ellipsoid, 2–2.5 mm, smooth.

Flowering Apr–May. Grassy slopes, meadows, adjacent to chaparral, serpentine soils, coastal dunes, open slopes, meadows, oak woodlands, disturbed areas; 0–1700 m; B.C.; Calif., Oreg., Wash.

Trifolium dichotomum is reportedly tetraploid (H. Wexelsen 1928) and closely related to the diploid *T. albopurpureum*. A so-called small form of *T. dichotomum* was named *T. dichotomum* var. *turbinatum* [*T. californicum* forma *turbinatum* (Jepson) McDermott].

64. Trifolium columbinum Greene, Pittonia 1: 4. 1887 • Olive clover [E]

Trifolium albopurpureum Torrey & A. Gray var. *columbinum* (Greene) D. J. Keil; *T. columbinum* var. *argillorum* Jepson; *T. olivaceum* Greene; *T. olivaceum* var. *columbinum* (Greene) Jepson; *T. olivaceum* var. *griseum* Jepson

Herbs annual, 8–30 cm, canescent. **Stems** erect, branched from base and distally, or unbranched. **Leaves** palmate; stipules ovate, 0.4–1.2 cm, margins entire, ciliate, apex often purple, acuminate, setaceous; petiole 0.5–8 cm; petiolules 0.5–1 mm; leaflets 3, blades obovate or elliptic, 0.5–3 × 0.3–1.2 cm, base cuneate, veins obscure or slightly thickened, margins dentate, apex rounded or emarginate, surfaces pilose. **Peduncles** 3–11 cm. **Inflorescences** terminal or axillary, 25–50-flowered, ovoid-ellipsoid, 1–2.5 × 1.2–2.5 cm; involucres absent. **Pedicels** absent; bracteoles cuplike, to 0.5 mm. **Flowers** 6–10 mm; calyx tubular, 8–14 mm, densely pubescent, veins 20–30, tube 1–2 mm, lobes nearly equal, appearing rigidly erect, linear-setaceous, plumose, sinuses acute, orifice open; corolla sometimes absent, red-violet, often with white tips, 4–6 mm, banner ovate-oblong, 7–8 × 2–3 mm, apex broadly rounded, apiculate. **Legumes** obovoid, 3–3.5 mm. **Seeds** 1, yellow-brown, ellipsoid, 2–2.5 mm, smooth.

Flowering Apr–May. Grassy slopes, meadows, heavy adobe/clay soils, oak woodland foothills; 0–1400 m; Calif.

D. Isely (1998) stated that Central Valley populations of *Trifolium columbinum* appeared to be extinct and populations outside that region (and here recognized as the same taxon) were similar in calyx and corolla proportions. It is rather widespread in California, ranging from Humboldt County southward to Santa Barbara County, and eastward into counties ranging from Shasta southward to Inyo, Kern, and Placer counties.

Trifolium albopurpureum var. *olivaceum* (Greene) Isely and *T. columbinum* var. *olivaceum* (Greene) Jepson are illegitimate names that pertain here (D. J. Keil 2019).

65. Trifolium stoloniferum Eaton, Man. Bot. ed. 2, 468. 1818 • Running buffalo clover [C] [E]

Herbs perennial, 10–20 cm, glabrous or sparsely pubescent. **Stems** creeping, branched, rooting at nodes. **Leaves** palmate, opposite or subopposite on erect stems; stipules lanceolate (on prostrate stems) or ovate (on erect stems), 1–2 cm, margins entire or shallowly serrate, apex acuminate; petioles 6–15 cm on prostrate stems, 0.5–4 cm on erect stems; petiolules 1 mm; leaflets 3, blades broadly ovate or obcordate, 1–2 × 0.5–2.5 cm, base broadly cuneate to rounded, veins fine, margins serrate, apex emarginate or rounded, surfaces glabrous. **Peduncles** 2–7 cm. **Inflorescences** terminal, single or paired at tip of upright stem, 15–30-flowered, globose, 2–3.5 × 2–3.5 cm; involucres absent. **Pedicels** elongated and strongly reflexed in fruit, 2–5 mm; bracteoles lanceolate, 2 mm. **Flowers** 9–15 mm; calyx campanulate, 4–7 mm, glabrous or sparsely pubescent, veins 10, tube 1.3–3.3 mm, lobes subequal, subulate, orifice open; corolla white, veins often pinkish, 8–14 mm, banner ovate or oblong, 8–14 × 4–5 mm, apex rounded or emarginate. **Legumes** oblong, 2.5–3 mm. **Seeds** 1 or 2, tan to brown, reniform, 1.3–2 mm, smooth. $2n = 16$.

Flowering Apr–Jun. Grassy openings in upland woods; of conservation concern; 150–900 m; Ind., Ky., Mo., Ohio, Pa., W.Va.

Trifolium stoloniferum was thought to be extinct but was rediscovered in the early 1980s (R. L. Bartgis 1985). It is now known from extant populations scattered throughout much of its original range, in five of the original eight states in which it was found historically (D. J. Crawford et al. 1998); it was discovered in Greene County, Pennsylvania, in 2017, but appears to be extirpated in Arkansas, Illinois, and Kansas. R. J. Hickey et al. (1991) examined genetic diversity of *T. stoloniferum* populations using allozymes and found low diversity, with some populations appearing genetically uniform. Molecular studies using RAPDs

(Crawford et al.) indicated somewhat higher genetic diversity, even in relatively small populations.

Trifolium stoloniferum is in the Center for Plant Conservation's National Collection of Endangered Plants.

66. Trifolium calcaricum J. L. Collins & Wieboldt, Castanea 57: 282, figs. 1, 2. 1992 • Running glade clover [C] [E]

Herbs perennial, 10–15 cm, glabrous or glabrate. **Stems** creeping, branched, rooting at nodes. **Leaves** palmate; stipules lanceolate or ovate, 0.5–1 cm, margins entire or shallowly lobed, apex acute to cuspidate; petiole 3–13(–25) cm; petiolules 1 mm; leaflets 3, blades obovate, rhombic, or elliptic, 1–1.9 × 0.8–1.2 cm, base cuneate, veins prominent, margins minutely denticulate or entire, apex rounded, emarginate, surfaces glabrous or sparsely hairy. **Peduncles** 1 or 2 from end of stolon at ground-level, 10–12 cm. **Inflorescences** terminal, 25–50-flowered, globose, 1.8–2.2 × 1.8–2.2 cm; involucres absent. **Pedicels** reflexed in fruit, 2–3 mm; bracteoles triangular-acuminate, 0.5–1.5 mm. **Flowers** 9–11 mm; calyx campanulate, 4.5–5.5 mm, sparsely puberulent, veins 10, tube 2 mm, lobes equal, narrowly triangular to subulate, orifice open; corolla white, veins often reddish, 8–9 mm, banner obovate-oblong, 9–11 × 5–6 mm, apex rounded, retuse. **Legumes** stipitate, ellipsoid, 2–3.5 mm. **Seeds** 1 or 2, light brown, mitten-shaped, 1.1–1.5 mm, smooth. $2n = 16$.

Flowering May–Jun. Shallow soils on limestone glades; of conservation concern; 100–500 m; Tenn., Va.

Trifolium calcaricum is endemic to xeric limestone prairies and in limestone cedar glades in western Virginia and eastern and central Tennessee (J. L. Collins and T. F. Wieboldt 1992; P. J. Lawless et al. 2006).

67. Trifolium virginicum Small, Mem. Torrey Bot. Club 4: 112, plate 75. 1894 • Kates Mountain clover [C] [E] [F]

Herbs perennial, 3–10 cm, pilose. **Stems** cespitose, prostrate, branched from crown. **Leaves** palmate; stipules oblanceolate to ovate, 1–1.5 cm, margins entire, apex acute-acuminate; petiole 5–10 cm; petiolules to 1 mm; leaflets 3, blades linear-elliptic, elliptic, narrowly oblong, or lanceolate, 1–7 × 0.4–1 cm, base cuneate, veins fine or thickened, margins entire or serrulate, apex truncate to acute, surfaces pubescent abaxially, glabrous adaxially. **Peduncles** 2–6 cm. **Inflorescences** terminal or axillary, 20–40-flowered, becoming supine in fruit, globose, 1.5–3.5 × 1.5–3 cm; involucres absent. **Pedicels** reflexed in fruit, 3–8 mm; bracteoles ovate or lanceolate-linear, to 1 mm. **Flowers** 10–12 mm; calyx campanulate, 4–7 mm, pilose, veins 10, tube 1.5–3 mm, lobes equal, subulate, orifice open; corolla white, sometimes becoming pink to red, 10–12 mm, banner obovate-oblong, 10–12 × 4–5 mm, apex rounded, retuse or mucronate. **Legumes** stipitate, obovoid, 4–7.5 mm. **Seeds** 1, yellow-brown, mitten-shaped, 1.8–2.1 mm, rugose. $2n = 16$.

Flowering May–Jun. Shale barren slopes; of conservation concern; 400–1200 m; Md., Pa., Va., W.Va.

Trifolium virginicum is an endemic species of shale barrens in the Appalachian Mountains, from Bedford, Franklin, and Fulton counties in Pennsylvania, southward through eastern West Virginia and western Maryland, to northwestern Virginia.

Genetic similarity is high among populations of *Trifolium virginicum*, and gene flow appears to be low (T. M. Linscott 1994).

68. Trifolium reflexum Linnaeus, Sp. Pl. 2: 766. 1753 • Buffalo clover [E] [W]

Amoria reflexa (Linnaeus) C. Presl; *Trifolium adscendens* Hornemann; *T. comosum* Linnaeus; *T. platycephalum* Bischoff

Herbs annual or biennial, 10–60 cm, villous or glabrate. **Stems** erect or ascending, unbranched or branched. **Leaves** palmate; stipules broadly ovate, 1–2.5 cm, margins entire or denticulate, apex acute or acuminate; petiole 1–10 cm (distalmost 0.3–3.5 cm); petiolules 0.5–1.5 mm; leaflets 3, blades ovate, obovate, oblong, or rhombic, 1–4.5 × 0.7–2 cm, base cuneate, veins fine, margins dentate to denticulate, apex broadly acute, rounded, or emarginate, surfaces pubescent or glabrous. **Peduncles** 2–8 cm. **Inflorescences** terminal or axillary, 10–50-flowered, globose to subglobose, 1.5–4 × 2–4 cm; bracteoles forming shallow, membranous cups, to 0.5 mm. **Pedicels** reflexed in fruit, 5–12 mm; bracteoles broad-obovate, membranous, 0.5–1 mm, truncate to 2-fid. **Flowers** 10–15 mm; calyx campanulate, 6–9 mm, pilose or glabrous, veins 10, tube 1–1.5 mm, lobes equal, narrowly triangular to subulate, 3–7 mm, margins green, sinuses broad, orifice open; corolla usually pink, magenta, or creamy white, sometimes bicolored, 9–14 mm, banner obovate-oblong, 9–14 × 5–8 mm, apex rounded or retuse, often erose-denticulate. **Legumes** oblong, 4–5 mm. **Seeds** 1–6, yellow to brown, purple-mottled, globose, 1.2–1.5 mm, slightly rugose. $2n = 16$.

Flowering Apr–Jun. Clearings in forests, open woods, meadows, especially after fires; 200–500 m; Ont.; Ala., Ark., D.C., Fla., Ga., Ill., Ind., Iowa, Kans., Ky., La., Md., Miss., Mo., Nebr., N.J., N.C., Ohio, Okla., Pa., S.C., Tenn., Tex., Va., W.Va.

Nearly glabrous plants of *Trifolium reflexum* have been called var. *glabrum* Lojacono; var. *reflexum* is described as densely pubescent. The distinctions between these two varieties is inconsistent and may be based in part on age (M. A. Vincent 1991).

69. Trifolium kentuckiense Chapel & Vincent, Phytoneuron 2013-63: 4, figs. 3, 4. 2013 • Kentucky clover [C] [E]

Herbs annual or biennial, 10–30 cm, glabrous. **Stems** decumbent, branched. **Leaves** palmate; stipules broadly ovate, 1.3–1.7 cm, margins entire or faintly denticulate, apex acuminate; petiole 7–17 cm (distalmost 6–8 cm); petiolules 1–1.5 mm; leaflets 3, blades ovate or orbiculate, 0.8–3.5 × 0.5–1.9 cm, base cuneate, veins fine, margins dentate to denticulate, apex rounded or obcordate, surfaces glabrous. **Peduncles** 2.2–2.5 cm. **Inflorescences** terminal, 20–50-flowered, globose becoming subglobose or hemispheric, 1.2–2.5 × 1.8–2.7 cm; involucres a narrow rim. **Pedicels** reflexed in fruit, 5–7 mm; bracteoles broadly ovate, membranous, to 0.5 mm, truncate. **Flowers** 9–11 mm; calyx campanulate, 3–5 mm, sparsely pubescent or glabrous, veins 10, tube 1–2 mm, lobes equal, narrowly triangular to subulate, 2–3.7 mm, orifice open; corolla white, 9–10 mm, banner ovate-oblong, 9–10 × 6–8 mm, apex rounded or retuse. **Legumes** oblong, 3–4 mm. **Seeds** 2–4, yellow to brown, purple-mottled, globose, 1.2–1.5 mm, slightly rugose.

Flowering Apr–May. Cedar glades; of conservation concern; 150–300 m; Ky.

According to Chapel and Vincent, *Trifolium kentuckiense*, endemic to the Bluegrass region, has been found in only one population in each of Fayette and Franklin counties.

70. Trifolium bejariense Moricand, Pl. Nouv. Amér., 2, plate 2. 1834 • Bejar clover [E]

Trifolium macrocalyx Hooker

Herbs annual, 5–25 cm, pilose. **Stems** erect or ascending, branched. **Leaves** palmate; stipules oblong to ovate, 0.8–1 cm, margins slightly denticulate or entire, apex acute to acuminate; petiole 1–5 cm; petiolules to 1 mm; leaflets 3, blades obovate, 0.7–1.4 × 0.3–0.8 cm, base broadly cuneate, veins thickened, recurved, margins slightly denticulate, apex rounded or retuse, surfaces pubescent abaxially, glabrous adaxially. **Peduncles** geniculate proximal to flowers, inflorescence appearing inverted, 2.5–11 cm. **Inflorescences** axillary or terminal, 5–15-flowered, globose or subglobose, 1–2 × 1.5–2 cm; involucres floral bracts forming a small, scarious involucre. **Pedicels** curved, 3–4 mm; bracteoles broadly rhombic, membranous, to 0.5 mm, margins dentate. **Flowers** 7–9 mm; calyx campanulate, markedly bilabiate, venation strongly reticulate, 5–6 mm, sparsely pilose marginally, veins 5, reticulate in lobes, tube 0.7–1 mm, lobes unequal, abaxial 3 triangular-ovate, 2–3 mm, central abaxial lobe nearly linear, pubescent only along margins, adaxial 2 obovate, 5 mm, orifice open; corolla white, tinged with pink or lavender, darkening in age, 6–8 mm, banner broadly ovate, 6–8 × 5–6 mm, apex rounded, denticulate. **Legumes** oblong-ovoid, 3–4 mm. **Seeds** 2–6, yellow, globose to mitten-shaped, 1.1–1.6 mm, rugose. $2n = 16$.

Flowering Mar–May. Sandy prairies, open woods; 0–100 m; Ark., La., Tex.

Trifolium bejariense ranges in east-central Texas from Hunt and Lamar counties in the north, southward to Fort Bend and Harris counties, and westward to Travis and Wilson counties; the species is also known from Acadia and Rapides parishes in Louisiana, and Nevada County in Arkansas.

L. F. McDermott reduced *Trifolium bejariense* to *T. carolinianum* forma *bejariense* (Moricand) McDermott.

71. Trifolium carolinianum Michaux, Fl. Bor.-Amer. 2: 58. 1803 • Carolina clover [E]

Amoria caroliniana (Michaux) C. Presl; *Trifolium oxypetalum* Fischer & C. A. Meyer; *T. umbellatum* Seringe

Herbs annual, 5–30 cm, pilose. **Stems** prostrate, ascending, or erect, branched. **Leaves** palmate; stipules ovate, 0.6–1 cm, margins entire or serrate, apex acuminate; petiole 2–5 cm; petiolules 1 mm; leaflets 3, blades obovate, 0.6–1.4 × 0.3–1.1 cm, base cuneate, veins moderately thickened, margins denticulate, apex rounded, sometimes retuse, surfaces glabrous except on veins abaxially. **Peduncles** ± geniculate proximal to flowers, inflorescence appearing sideways or inverted, 3.5–10 cm. **Inflorescences** axillary or terminal, 5–40-flowered, globose, 1–2 × 1–2 cm; involucres minute. **Pedicels** reflexed, 2–3 mm; bracteoles ovate or lanceolate, 0.5 mm. **Flowers** 4.5–7 mm; calyx usually pink to magenta, campanulate, bilabiate, 3–4 mm, pilose, veins 5, slightly branched in lobes, tube 0.8–1 mm, lobes unequal, abaxial 3 lanceolate or linear, 0.8–1 mm, villous, adaxial 2 broadly triangular, 2.5–3 mm, orifice open; corolla creamy white, often pink-tinged, darkening in age, 4–4.5 mm, banner broadly ovate-rhombic, 4–4.5 × 3.8–4 mm, apex rounded, slightly erose. **Legumes** oblong, 3–4 mm. **Seeds** 2–4, yellow-brown to brown, globose to mitten-shaped, 1.1–1.6 mm, rugose. $2n = 16$.

Flowering Apr–Jun. Sandy soils in dry fields, lawns, open woods, disturbed ground, rocky slopes; 0–400 m; Ala., Ark., Del., Fla., Ga., Kans., La., Miss., Mo., N.C., Okla., Pa., S.C., Tex., Va.

Trifolium arvense Walter (1788), a later homonym of *T. arvense* Linnaeus (1753), was considered a synonym of *T. carolinianum* by M. Zohary and D. Heller (1984). *Trifolium repens* Walter (1788, not Linnaeus 1753) is likely also a synonym of *T. carolinianum*. The record of the species from Vermont is a waif.

72. Trifolium amphianthum Torrey & A. Gray, Fl. N. Amer. 1: 316. 1838 • Peanut clover [E]

Trifolium roemerianum Scheele

Herbs perennial, 10–25 cm, glabrous or glabrate. **Stems** creeping, branched, rooting at nodes. **Leaves** palmate; stipules ovate-lanceolate, 0.5–1 cm, margins entire, apex acute to acuminate; petiole 3–10 cm; petiolules 0.5–1 mm; leaflets 3, blades obcordate, 0.5–1.8 × 0.5–1.5 cm, base cuneate, veins thickened, margins entire or denticulate distally, apex usually deeply emarginate, rarely rounded, surfaces glabrous. **Peduncles:** chasmogamous 6–8 cm, cleistogamous ± sessile. **Inflorescences** axillary, 5–20-flowered, globose, 1–2.2 × 1–20 cm, chasmogamous erect, cleistogamous becoming subterranean; involucres formed of distinct, narrowly lanceolate bracts, 2.5–3.5 mm. **Pedicels** reflexed in fruit, cleistogamous pushing fruit underground, chasmogamous 1–8 mm, cleistogamous 4–20 mm; bracteoles lanceolate, 2–4 mm. **Flowers:** chasmogamous 8–11 mm, cleistogamous 4–5 mm; calyx campanulate, 3–5 mm, slightly pilose, veins 10, tube 1.5–2 mm, lobes subequal, adaxial pair connate proximally, sometimes nearly entire length, narrowly triangular-subulate, orifice open; corolla magenta or pink, 7.5–11 mm, banner broadly obovate-elliptic, 5–10 × 5–8 mm, apex rounded, emarginate. **Legumes** stipitate, chasmogamous ellipsoid, cleistogamous ovoid-globose, chasmogamous longitudinally dehiscent, 3–6 mm, cleistogamous indehiscent, 3–6 mm. **Seeds** 2–6 (chasmogamous), 1–3 (cleistogamous), tan, mitten-shaped, 1.2–1.5 mm, smooth. $2n = 16, 32$.

Flowering Mar–Jun. Sandy soils, prairies; 0–200 m; La., Tex.

Trifolium amphianthum ranges in east-central Texas from Aransas County northward to Denton County, and eastward to San Augustine and Shelby counties; it is also recorded from Natchitoches and Rapides parishes in Louisiana. *Trifolium amphianthum* was collected once in Arkansas, but the specimen may have been from cultivation.

The name *Trifolium polymorphum* Poiret applies to plants found in Argentina, Brazil, Paraguay, and Uruguay and has been misapplied to this North American endemic, as was done by M. Zohary and D. Heller (1984). *Trifolium amphianthum* is distinguished from *T. polymorphum* by its much larger leaves and flowers and essentially glabrous leaves and peduncles.

73. Trifolium leibergii A. Nelson & J. F. Macbride, Bot. Gaz. 65: 58. 1918 • Leiberg's clover [C] [E]

Herbs perennial, 10–15 cm, canescent. **Stems** erect, aerial stems sparsely branched. **Leaves** palmate; stipules lanceolate, 0.7–1.5 cm, margins coarsely spinulose-dentate, apex acuminate; petiole 1–3 cm; petiolules to 0.5 mm; leaflets 3, blades obovate, rhombic, or elliptic, sometimes folded, 0.9–1.5 × 0.5–1.3 cm, base cuneate, veins very thick, margins coarsely spinulose-dentate, apex rounded, long-apiculate, surfaces canescent. **Peduncles** 2–4.5 cm. **Inflorescences** axillary, 5–25-flowered, globose, 2.2–2.5 × 2.3–2.7 cm; involucres a narrow, papery, irregular rim, to 0.5 mm. **Pedicels** reflexed in fruit, 1.5–4 mm; bracteoles triangular, to 0.2 mm. **Flowers** 11–15 mm; calyx campanulate, 5–11 mm, pilose, veins 10, tube 1.8–2.2 mm, lobes subequal, lanceolate-setiform, orifice open; corolla creamy white with purplish veins, becoming pinkish purple-tinged, 10.5–13 mm, banner broadly rhombic-ovate or obovate, 10.5–13 × 5–7 mm, apex rounded, slightly emarginate. **Legumes** ovoid, 3–4 mm. **Seeds** 1 or 2, brown, mitten-shaped, 1.5–2 mm, smooth.

Flowering Jun–Jul. Open, rocky slopes and crests, ash-flows; of conservation concern; 1900–2400 m; Nev., Oreg.

Trifolium leibergii is known from only a few populations from Harney County, Oregon, and Elko County, Nevada. It is in the Center for Plant Conservation's National Collection of Endangered Plants.

74. Trifolium andersonii A. Gray, Proc. Amer. Acad. Arts 6: 522. 1865 • Anderson's clover [E] [F]

Herbs perennial, 5–12 cm, canescent. **Stems** erect-ascending, cespitose, mat-forming, branched; from deep taproot-like crown. **Leaves** palmate; stipules ovate or lanceolate, 0.5–1.5 cm, margins entire, apex long-acuminate; petiole 1–5 cm; petiolules to 0.5 mm; leaflets (3–)5, blades obovate, 0.5–2.2 × 0.2–1.2 cm, base cuneate, veins obscured by pubescence, margins entire, apex rounded or acute, apiculate, surfaces canescent. **Peduncles** 1–14 cm. **Inflorescences** axillary, 10–20-flowered, depressed-globose, 1–2 × 1–2.3 cm; involucres formed of connate, narrow, membranous bracts, to 0.5 mm. **Pedicels** absent; bracteoles absent. **Flowers** 10–17 mm; calyx campanulate, 9–11 mm, pilose, veins 10, tube 4–5 mm, lobes equal, subulate, plumose, orifice open; corolla white or pink, 10–17 mm, banner ovate-oblong, 12–19 × 3–5 mm, apex rounded, retuse. **Legumes** ellipsoid, 4–5 mm. **Seeds** 1 (or 2), tan or brown, irregularly ovoid, 1.6–2 mm, smooth, glossy.

Subspecies 3 (3 in the flora): w United States.

Trifolium andersonii encompasses three moderately well separable subspecies, with subsp. *andersonii* the more northern form in the range of the species, subsp. *monoense* in the southwestern portion of the range, and subsp. *beatleyae* in the eastern portion of the range (J. M. Gillett 1972). Intermediates between the latter two (and overlap in their ranges) make differentiation between them somewhat problematic, which prompted R. C. Barneby (1989) to combine them as var. *beatleyae*.

1. Leaflet blades 0.5–1.1 cm, surfaces with appressed hairs to 1 mm; 3000–4000 m. . . . . 74c. *Trifolium andersonii* subsp. *monoense*
1. Leaflet blades 0.9–2.2 cm, surfaces with spreading hairs 1.5–2 mm; 800–2500 m.
    2. Peduncles 1–3 cm, not overtopping leaves . . . . 74a. *Trifolium andersonii* subsp. *andersonii*
    2. Peduncles 4–14 cm, overtopping leaves . . . . 74b. *Trifolium andersonii* subsp. *beatleyae*

74a. Trifolium andersonii A. Gray subsp. **andersonii** [E]

Leaflet blades 0.9–2.2 cm, surfaces with spreading hairs 1.5–2 mm. **Peduncles** 1–3 cm, not overtopping leaves. **2*n*** = 16.

Flowering Apr–Jul. Dry ridges, grassy plains, sage-pinyon or juniper areas, sage flats; 800–2500 m; Calif., Idaho, Nev.

Subspecies *andersonii* ranges from eastern and northeastern California eastward into western Nevada (Washoe to Douglas counties), and is also known from Owyhee County in Idaho.

74b. Trifolium andersonii A. Gray subsp. **beatleyae** J. M. Gillett, Canad. J. Bot. 50: 1997. 1972 • Beatley's clover [E] [F]

Trifolium andersonii var. *beatleyae* (J. M. Gillett) Isely

Leaflet blades 0.9–2.2 cm, surfaces with spreading hairs 1.5–2 mm. **Peduncles** 4–14 cm, overtopping leaves.

Flowering Apr–Jul. Dry ridges, grassy plains, sage-pinyon or juniper areas, sage flats; 800–2500 m; Calif., Nev.

Subspecies *beatleyae* is known from Inyo and Mono counties in California, and from Douglas, Humboldt, Nye, and Washoe counties in Nevada.

74c. Trifolium andersonii A. Gray subsp. **monoense** (Greene) J. M. Gillett, Canad. J. Bot. 50: 1997. 1972 • Mono clover [E]

Trifolium monoense Greene, Erythea 2: 181. 1894; *T. andersonii* var. *monoense* (Greene) Isely

Leaflet blades 0.5–1.1 cm, surfaces with appressed hairs 1 mm. **Peduncles** 4–9 cm, overtopping leaves. **2*n*** = 16.

Flowering Apr–Jul. Plateaus; 3000–4000 m; Calif., Nev.

Subspecies *monoense* is restricted to Inyo and Mono counties in California, and Esmeralda County in Nevada.

75. Trifolium friscanum (S. L. Welsh) S. L. Welsh, Rhodora 95: 407. 1993 • Frisco clover [C] [E]

Trifolium andersonii A. Gray var. *friscanum* S. L. Welsh, Great Basin Naturalist 38: 355. 1978

Herbs perennial, mat-forming, 0.8–3 cm, canescent. **Stems** cespitose, acaulescent. **Leaves** palmate; stipules broadly lanceolate, 0.5–0.9 cm, margins entire, apex acute; petiole 0.3–1.5 cm; petiolules to 0.2 mm; leaflets 3, blades oblanceolate to obovate, often folded, 0.3–0.8 × 0.1–0.4 cm, base cuneate, veins thickened, obscured by pubescence, margins entire or toothed distally, apex acute, surfaces densely silvery-hairy. **Peduncles** 1–3 cm. **Inflorescences** terminal, 4–9-flowered, globose or depressed-globose, 1–1.5 × 1–2 cm; involucres absent. **Pedicels** erect, 0.5 mm; bracteoles absent. **Flowers** 9–11 mm; calyx campanulate, 8.5–9.5 mm, canescent, veins 5–10 (obscured by hairs), tube 2.5–3 mm, lobes subequal, subulate, orifice open; corolla with magenta banner, pale pink wing and keel petals, 8–10 mm, banner oblong, 8–10 × 2–3 mm, apex acute. **Legumes** depressed-ellipsoid, 3–4 mm. **Seeds** 1, brown, reniform, 2–2.5 mm, smooth. $2n = 16$.

Flowering Jun–Jul. Volcanic gravel and limestone in pinyon-juniper woodlands; of conservation concern; 2100–2300 m; Utah.

Trifolium friscanum is a rare species endemic to the Great Basin and is known from only five populations occupying nine sites in Beaver and Millard counties (D. Tilley 2012).

76. Trifolium nanum Torrey, Ann. Lyceum Nat. Hist. New York 1: 35, plate 3, fig. 4. 1824 • Dwarf clover [E]

Herbs perennial, 4–10 cm, glabrous. **Stems** cespitose, matted, acaulescent. **Leaves** palmate; stipules ovate-lanceolate, 1–2 cm, margins entire, apex acuminate, sometimes forked; petiole 0.3–2.5 cm; petiolules to 0.2 mm; leaflets 3, blades oblanceolate or obovate, 0.3–1.2 × 0.1–0.5 cm, base cuneate, veins ± thickened, margins toothed, apex acute or acuminate, surfaces glabrous. **Peduncles** 0.5–3 cm. **Inflorescences** terminal or axillary, 1–4-flowered, umbellate, 1.5–2 × 0.5–1 cm, rachis not prolonged beyond flowers; involucres a narrow, membranous, dentate rim, 1 mm. **Pedicels** erect, 1 mm; bracteoles cuplike, membranous, 0.5–1 mm. **Flowers** 15–20 mm; calyx campanulate, 4–7 mm, glabrous, veins 5–10, tube 3–4 mm, lobes equal, triangular-acuminate, orifice open; corolla purple or violet, 15–20 mm, banner oblong, 15–20 × 7–9 mm, apex rounded, slightly retuse. **Legumes** oblanceoloid, 9–11 mm. **Seeds** 4–6, tan or brown, mitten-shaped, 2–2.2 mm, smooth, dull. $2n = 16$.

Flowering Jun–Aug. Alpine slopes, tundra; 2600–4500 m; Colo., Mont., N.Mex., Utah, Wyo.

Trifolium nanum is abundant in alpine tundra areas from Montana through Wyoming and Utah into Colorado (where it is most common) and northern New Mexico; populations are morphologically variable with regard to leaf size and petiole length, and this variability appears to be related to water availability (J. M. Gillett 1965).

77. Trifolium parryi A. Gray, Amer. J. Sci. Arts, ser. 2, 33: 409. 1862 • Parry's clover [E]

Herbs perennial, 10–20 cm, glabrous. **Stems** erect or ascending, loosely cespitose, sometimes rhizomatous, sparsely branched. **Leaves** palmate; stipules oblong, 0.5–2 cm, margins entire, apex acute to short-acuminate; petiole 2–10 cm; petiolules 0.5 mm; leaflets 3, blades elliptic to obovate, 1–4.1 × 0.5–1.6 cm, base cuneate, veins fine, margins entire, serrulate, or dentate, apex usually acute or obtuse, rarely retuse or apiculate, surfaces glabrous. **Peduncles** 2.5–15 cm. **Inflorescences** terminal, 15–20-flowered, globose, ovoid, or ellipsoid, 1.4–3.7 × 1.8–3 cm; involucres formed of distinct or connate bracteoles, apex acute or obtuse. **Pedicels** erect, reflexed slightly, or only those of proximal flowers reflexed, 1 mm; bracteoles purplish, oblong, 3–6 mm, scarious. **Flowers** 12–22 mm; calyx campanulate, slightly gibbous, 6–9 mm, glabrous, veins 10, tube 3–4 mm, lobes unequal, subulate to narrowly triangular, orifice open; corolla pale purplish violet, keel petals darker purple, 10–22 mm, banner broadly elliptic or obovate, 10–22 × 8–10 mm, apex rounded, acute, or retuse. **Legumes** stipitate, oblong, 6–7 mm. **Seeds** 1–4, tan or brown, mitten-shaped, 1.5–2 mm, smooth, dull.

Subspecies 3 (3 in the flora): w United States.

Subdivision of *Trifolium parryi* into three subspecies (J. M. Gillett 1965) or two varieties (D. Isely 1998) was rejected by R. C. Barneby (1989).

1. Inflorescences ellipsoid, 3–3.7 cm; leaflet blades thick; stipules 1.5–2 cm; peduncles thickened . . . . 77c. *Trifolium parryi* subsp. *salictorum*
1. Inflorescences globose or ovoid, 1.4–2.9 cm; leaflet blades thin; stipules 0.5–1 cm; peduncles slender or slightly thickened.
   2. Involucres: bracteoles relatively large, acute; inflorescences 2.1–2.9 cm; flowers 14–22 mm; Colorado, New Mexico, s Wyoming . . . . 77a. *Trifolium parryi* subsp. *parryi*
   2. Involucres: bracteoles relatively short, obtuse; inflorescences 1.4–2.4 cm; flowers 12–17 mm; s Idaho, Montana, e Utah, n Wyoming . . . . 77b. *Trifolium parryi* subsp. *montanense*

77a. Trifolium parryi A. Gray subsp. **parryi** [E]

Stipules 0.5–1 cm. **Leaflet blades** thin. **Peduncles** slender or slightly thickened. **Inflorescences** globose or ovoid, 2.1–2.9 cm. **Involucres:** bracteoles relatively large, acute. **Flowers** 14–22 mm. **2*n*** = 16.

Flowering Jun–Aug. Alpine tundra, meadows, grassy slopes, open areas of forests; 2700–4100 m; Colo., N.Mex., Wyo.

Subspecies *parryi* is widespread in Colorado; in Wyoming, it is known from Albany and Carbon counties; in New Mexico, it is known only from the Sangre de Cristo Mountains.

77b. Trifolium parryi A. Gray subsp. **montanense** (Rydberg) J. M. Gillett, Brittonia 17: 132. 1965 [E]

Trifolium montanense Rydberg, Mem. New York Bot. Gard. 1: 236. 1900; *T. inaequale* Rydberg; *T. parryi* var. *montanense* (Rydberg) S. L. Welsh

Stipules 0.5–1 cm. **Leaflet blades** thin. **Peduncles** slender or slightly thickened. **Inflorescences** globose or ovoid, 1.4–2.4 cm. **Involucres:** bracteoles relatively short, obtuse. **Flowers** 12–17 mm. **2*n*** = 16.

Flowering Jun–Aug. Alpine tundra, meadows, grassy slopes, open areas of forests; 2700–4100 m; Idaho, Mont., Utah, Wyo.

Subspecies *montanense* is known from Fremont County in Idaho; Carbon, Gallatin, Madison, and Park counties in Montana; Daggett, Duchesne, Grand, Rich, San Juan, Summit, Uintah, and Wasatch counties in Utah; and Hot Springs and Park counties in Wyoming.

77c. Trifolium parryi A. Gray subsp. **salictorum** (Greene ex Rydberg) J. M. Gillett, Brittonia 17: 132. 1965 [E]

Trifolium salictorum Greene ex Rydberg, Fl. Colorado, 201, 202. 1906

Stipules 1.5–2 cm. **Leaflet blades** thick. **Peduncles** thickened. **Inflorescences** ellipsoid, 3–3.7 cm. **Involucres:** bracteoles relatively large, acute. **Flowers** 14–22 mm. **2*n*** = 32.

Flowering Jun–Aug. Alpine tundra, meadows, grassy slopes, open areas of forests; 2700–4100 m; Colo.

Subspecies *salictorum* is known from Grand, Lake, La Plata, Mineral, Ouray, Park, Pitkin, and Summit counties.

78. Trifolium howellii S. Watson, Proc. Amer. Acad. Arts 23: 262. 1888 • Howell's clover [E]

Herbs perennial, 30–100 cm, glabrous. **Stems** erect, fistulose, unbranched or branched distally. **Leaves** palmate; stipules ovate, 1.5–4.5 cm, margins usually entire, sometimes lobed, apex acuminate; petiole 0.5–20 cm; petiolules 1–1.5 mm; leaflets 3, blades ovate, elliptic, or rhombic, 3.5–9.5 × 2.3–5 cm, base cuneate, veins obscure, margins ± serrate, apex acute, rounded, or obtuse, surfaces glabrous. **Peduncles** 3–11 cm. **Inflorescences** terminal or axillary, 20–70-flowered, globose or ellipsoid, 2.5–4 × 2–2.5 cm, rachis prolonged beyond flowers, undivided or forked, often bearing sterile flower buds distally; involucres absent. **Pedicels** strongly reflexed in fruit, 1 mm; bracteoles minute, blunt or acute, membranous. **Flowers** 10–14 mm; calyx campanulate, gibbous, 4–5.5 mm, glabrous, veins 10, tube 2–2.5 mm, lobes subequal, linear-lanceolate, orifice open; corolla white, lemon yellow, or greenish yellow, 11–12 mm, banner elliptic-oblong, 11–12 × 4–5 mm, apex obtuse. **Legumes** oblong or clavate, 4–5 mm. **Seeds** 1–3, reddish black or brown, angular, mitten-shaped, 2.5 mm, smooth or slightly roughened, dull.

Flowering Jun–Jul. Wet stream banks, wet meadows, flood plains, shady woodlands, springs, thickets; 800–2000 m; Calif., Oreg.

Trifolium howellii is known from Del Norte, Humboldt, Siskiyou, and Trinity counties in California, and Clackamas, Douglas, Jackson, Josephine, Klamath, Lane, and Linn counties in Oregon (J. M. Gillett 1972). It has some of the largest leaves of any species of *Trifolium* in North America.

79. Trifolium macilentum Greene, Pittonia 3: 223. 1897 • Lean clover [E]

Herbs perennial, 12–38 cm, glabrous. **Stems** erect, ascending, or decumbent, unbranched or branched distally. **Leaves** palmate; stipules lanceolate-elliptic on basal leaves, triangular-ovate on distal leaves, 0.8–3 cm, margins entire, apex acute or acuminate; petiole 1–15 cm; petiolules 1 mm; leaflets 3, blades ovate, rhombic, or lanceolate, 1–4.5 × 0.3–2.5 cm, thin, base cuneate, veins prominent, margins serrate, those of basal leaves setose and/or dentate, apex rounded or acute, surfaces glabrous. **Peduncles** 4–15 cm. **Inflorescences** terminal or axillary, 20–40-flowered, ovoid or obovoid, 2–4 × 1.4–3.5 cm, rachis internodes between floral whorls elongated; involucres absent. **Pedicels** reflexed, to 1 mm; bracteoles minute, blunt. **Flowers** 14–17 mm; calyx campanulate, 4–5.7 mm, sparsely hairy, veins 10, tube 2–3.5 mm, lobes unequal, shorter than tube, narrowly triangular, orifice open; corolla violet or deep purple, 14–17 mm, banner ovate-oblong, 14–16 × 8–10 mm, apex rounded or slightly emarginate. **Legumes** oblong or clavate, 4–5 mm. **Seeds** 1–3, brown, flattened ovoid, 2 mm, smooth or slightly roughened, dull.

Flowering May–Jun. Dry hillsides; 1200–2800 m; Nev., Utah.

Trifolium macilentum and morphologically similar species (*T. dedeckerae*, *T. kingii*, *T. productum*, and *T. rollinsii*) have been treated in diverse ways. J. M. Gillett (1972) recognized the latter four as distinct and considered *T. macilentum* a subspecies of *T. kingii*. D. Isely (1998) recognized *T. kingii*, *T. macilentum*, and *T. productum*, and considered *T. dedeckerae* and *T. rollinsii* to be varieties of *T. macilentum*. R. C. Barneby (1989) treated these as two species, *T. kingii* (with *T. productum* in synonymy) and *T. macilentum* (with *T. dedeckerae* and *T. rollinsii* as varieties). M. Zohary and D. Heller (1984) recognized *T. kingii*, with the other four taxa considered subspecies. As treated here, *T. macilentum* is known from extreme southwestern Utah and adjacent Nevada.

80. Trifolium productum Greene, Erythea 2: 181. 1894 • Shasta clover [E]

Trifolium kingii S. Watson subsp. *productum* (Greene) D. Heller; *T. kingii* var. *productum* (Greene) Jepson

Herbs perennial, 15–45 cm, glabrous. **Stems** ± erect, loosely cespitose, branched. **Leaves** basal and cauline, palmate; stipules ovate-lanceolate, 0.5–2 cm, margins usually entire, sometimes lobed, apex acute to acuminate; petiole 0.5–12 cm; petiolules 1 mm; leaflets 3, blades lanceolate or elliptic, 0.5–2 × 0.3–1.3 cm, base cuneate, veins prominent, margins serrate, apex acute, apiculate, surfaces glabrous. **Peduncles** 2–13 cm, slightly twisted apically. **Inflorescences** terminal or axillary, 15–30-flowered, ellipsoid or conic, 1.5–2 × 1–3 cm, rachis prolonged beyond flowers, undivided or forked, often bearing sterile flower buds distally; involucres absent. **Pedicels** strongly reflexed in fruit, 0.5 mm; bracteoles minute, lanceolate. **Flowers** 12–14 mm; calyx pink to purple, campanulate, 3–3.5 mm, glabrous, veins 10 (5 sometimes faint), tube 1.5–1.7 mm, lobes subequal, triangular-subulate, orifice open; corolla pink to deep purple, 12–14 mm, banner oblong, 12–14 × 4–5 mm, apex rounded or retuse. **Legumes** obliquely ellipsoid, 5 mm. **Seeds** 1 or 2, brown, often purple-mottled, flattened ovoid, 2–3 mm, smooth. $2n = 16$.

Flowering May–Sep. Open coniferous woods, rocky places, stream banks, grassy meadows, near springs; 1100–2800 m; Calif., Nev., Oreg.

Trifolium productum is morphologically most similar to *T. kingii*, from which it differs by its glabrous calyces and inflorescence rachises surpassing the flowers to 1.5 cm and apically forked (M. Zohary and D. Heller 1984). *Trifolium productum* is geographically isolated from *T. kingii*; the former is restricted to northern California, western Oregon, and western Nevada, while the latter is restricted to Utah and easternmost Nevada (J. M. Gillett 1972).

81. Trifolium dedeckerae J. M. Gillett, Madroño 21: 451, fig. 1. 1972 • Dedecker's clover [C] [E]

Trifolium kingii S. Watson subsp. *dedeckerae* (J. M. Gillett) D. Heller; *T. macilentum* Greene var. *dedeckerae* (J. M. Gillett) Barneby

Herbs perennial, 20–25 cm, glabrous. **Stems** ± erect, loosely cespitose, branched. **Leaves** basal and cauline, palmate; stipules ovate, 1.1–1.5 cm, margins entire, apex acuminate-subulate; petiole 5–15 cm; petiolules absent; leaflets

3, blades lanceolate to linear, 2–4 × 0.1–0.6 cm, base cuneate, veins prominent, margins remotely serrate, apex acute, surfaces glabrous. **Peduncles** 7–16 cm, slightly twisted apically. **Inflorescences** terminal or axillary, 10–18-flowered, ellipsoid to subglobose, 1.8–2.2 × 2.3–2.5 cm, rachis prolonged beyond flowers, undivided or forked, often bearing sterile flower buds distally; involucres absent. **Pedicels** strongly reflexed in fruit, 0.5 mm; bracteoles minute. **Flowers** 13–15 mm; calyx tubular-campanulate, 6–8.5 mm, glabrous, veins 10, tube 2–2.5 mm, lobes unequal, triangular-subulate, orifice open; corolla pink to purple, 15 mm, banner oblong, 14–16 × 6–7 mm, apex acute or apiculate. **Legumes** ellipsoid, 5 mm. **Seeds** 1 or 2, brown, flattened ovoid, 2 mm, smooth.

Flowering May–Jun. Rock crevices, dry slopes; of conservation concern; 2100–3400 m; Calif.

Trifolium dedeckerae is known from Inyo, Kern, Mono, and Tulare counties. It is similar to *T. macilentum* and *T. productum*, from which it differs by its much narrower leaflets (J. M. Gillett 1972).

82. Trifolium thompsonii C. V. Morton, J. Wash. Acad. Sci. 23: 270. 1933 • Thompson's clover [C] [E]

Lupinaster thompsonii (C. V. Morton) Latschaschvili

Herbs perennial, 35–50 cm, antrorse-strigose. **Stems** erect, branched. **Leaves** palmate; stipules lanceolate, 3–4 cm, margins entire, apex acuminate; petiole 5–20 cm; petiolules to 1 mm; leaflets 5–7, blades linear, linear-elliptic, linear-lanceolate, often folded, falcate, 2–7 × 0.2–0.6 cm, base cuneate, veins thickened, margins setose, apex acute-setiform, surfaces pubescent. **Peduncles** 10–15 cm. **Inflorescences** terminal, 60-flowered, in 10–12 whorls, globose or ovoid to subglobose, 3–5 × 3–4 cm; involucres absent. **Pedicels** reflexed in fruit, 1–1.5 mm; bracteoles minute. **Flowers** 20–23 mm; calyx campanulate, 6–8 mm, slightly pilose, veins 10–15, tube 2.5–3 mm, lobes equal, subulate, slightly pilose, orifice open; corolla rose-pink to purple, 18–22 mm, banner oblong, folded, 18–22 × 11–13 mm, apex rounded. **Legumes** flattened, lanceoloid-oblong, 6 mm. **Seeds** 1 or 2, yellow, often mottled, mitten-shaped, 2.8–3 mm, smooth, glossy. $2n$ = 16.

Flowering May–Jun. Dry talus fans at base of slopes; of conservation concern; 100–300 m; Wash.

Trifolium thompsonii is known from Chelan and Douglas counties (J. E. Canfield 1977). It is in the Center for Plant Conservation's National Collection of Endangered Plants.

83. Trifolium macrocephalum (Pursh) Poiret in J. Lamarck et al., Encycl., suppl. 5: 336. 1817 • Largehead clover [E] [F]

Lupinaster macrocephalum Pursh, Fl. Amer. Sept. 2: 479, plate 23. 1813

Herbs perennial, 5–25 cm, villous. **Stems** erect or ascending, branched. **Leaves** palmate; stipules ovate, obovate, or oblong, 1–3 cm, margins entire, irregularly lobed, or serrate, apex acute or acuminate; petiole 1–14 cm; petiolules 0.9–1.2 mm; leaflets (5–)7–9, blades broadly to narrowly obovate, often folded, 1–2.7 × 0.4–1.1 cm, base cuneate, veins thickened, especially distally, margins serrulate, apex rounded or truncate, apiculate, surfaces villous abaxially, sparsely villous to glabrate adaxially. **Peduncles** 2–8 cm. **Inflorescences** terminal, 20–32-flowered, globose or ovoid-ellipsoid, 2.5–8 × 3–7 cm; involucres absent. **Pedicels** erect, 1–1.5 mm; bracteoles broadly ovate, membranous, to 0.5 mm, truncate. **Flowers** 20–30 mm; calyx campanulate, 10–22 mm, villous, veins 10–15, tube 2.5–4 mm, lobes subequal, subulate, plumose, orifice open; corolla white, creamy white, or pinkish, keel petals deep pink, 20–28 mm, banner ovate or oblong, 20–28 × 10–13 mm, apex rounded or slightly emarginate. **Legumes** ovoid, 4–5 mm. **Seeds** 1 or 2, yellow or reddish, mitten-shaped to ellipsoid, 2.5–3 mm, smooth. $2n$ = 32, 48.

Flowering Apr–Jun. Rocky places, hard, compacted clay-gumbo, lava beds, sage-covered slopes, full sun; 80–2500 m; Calif., Idaho, Nev., Oreg., Wash.

Trifolium macrocephalum has the largest inflorescences of any clover. *Trifolium megacephalum* Nuttall (1818) is an illegitimate replacement name for *Lupinaster macrocephalum* Pursh.

84. Trifolium plumosum Douglas in W. J. Hooker, Fl. Bor.-Amer. 1: 130, plate 49. 1831 • Plumed clover [E]

Herbs perennial, 10–60 cm, villous. **Stems** erect, branched or unbranched. **Leaves** palmate; stipules linear, oblong, or ovate, 1.5–2.5 cm, margins entire or slightly serrulate, apex acute to acuminate; petiole 1–20 cm; petiolules to 0.5 mm; leaflets 3, blades linear, elliptic, oblong, or lanceolate-elliptic, often folded, falcate, 4–11 × 0.1–1.6 cm, base cuneate, veins thickened, margins denticulate, apex acute or acuminate, surfaces villous. **Peduncles**

TRIFOLIUM

2–6 cm. **Inflorescences** terminal, 70–80-flowered, spicate, ovoid to cylindric, 3–6 × 2.5–3 cm; involucres absent. **Pedicels** erect or absent, 0–0.5 mm; bracteoles absent. **Flowers** 17–18 mm; calyx campanulate, 5 mm, villous, veins 20, tube 2.5 mm, lobes subequal, subulate, straight, orifice open; corolla creamy white, keel petals crimson, 12–22 mm, banner oblong, 12–22 × 3–5 mm, apex acute; ovaries glabrous or pubescent distally. **Legumes** obovoid, 4–5 mm. **Seeds** 1–3, reddish brown or tan, ellipsoid, 1.8–2 mm, smooth, glossy. **2*n*** = 32.

Subspecies 2 (2 in the flora): nw United States.

J. M. Gillett (1972) stated that the leaflet width in the basal leaves is the best distinction between the two subspecies, which are geographically isolated.

1. Leaflet blades of basal leaves 0.2–0.5(–0.7) cm wide, apex acuminate; herbs 20–35 cm. . . . . 84a. *Trifolium plumosum* subsp. *plumosum*
1. Leaflet blades of basal leaves (0.8–)0.9–1.6 cm wide, apex acute; herbs 10–60 cm. 84b. *Trifolium plumosum* subsp. *amplifolium*

84a. Trifolium plumosum Douglas subsp. **plumosum** [E]

Herbs 20–35 cm. **Leaflet blades** linear, 0.1–0.7 cm wide, those of basal leaves 0.2–0.5(–0.7) cm wide, apex acuminate.

Flowering May–Jul. Dry rocky hillsides, clay roadsides, fields, open pine forests; 500–1500 m; Oreg., Wash.

Subspecies *plumosum* is restricted to northeastern Oregon and southeastern Washington.

84b. Trifolium plumosum Douglas subsp. **amplifolium** (J. S. Martin) J. M. Gillett, Canad. J. Bot. 50: 1981. 1972 • Bigleaf clover [C] [E]

Trifolium plumosum var. *amplifolium* J. S. Martin, Bull. Torrey Bot. Club 73: 369. 1946

Herbs 10–60 cm. **Leaflet blades** elliptic, oblong, or lanceolate-elliptic, 0.8–1.6 cm wide, those of basal leaves (0.8–)0.9–1.6 cm wide, apex acute.

Flowering May–Jul. Dry, rocky hillsides, clay roadsides, fields, open pine forests; of conservation concern; 500–1500 m; Idaho.

Subspecies *amplifolium* is restricted to Idaho, Lewis, Nez Perce, and Washington counties.

85. Trifolium eriocephalum Nuttall in J. Torrey and A. Gray, Fl. N. Amer. 1: 313. 1838 • Woolly-headed clover [E] [F]

Herbs perennial, 12–46 cm, sparsely hairy to densely villous, appressed-pubescent, or glabrate. **Stems** erect or decumbent, branched. **Leaves** palmate; stipules lanceolate or ovate, 1–5 cm, margins entire or denticulate, apex acuminate or acute; petiole 1–15 cm; petiolules 1 mm; leaflets 3, blades linear, linear-elliptic, elliptic, lanceolate, lanceolate-oblong, or obovate, 1–5 × 0.4–1.2 cm, base cuneate, veins fine or ± thickened, margins denticulate or serrulate, apex acuminate or acute, surfaces appressed-pubescent abaxially, glabrous, densely villous, or sparsely or densely pilose adaxially. **Peduncles** bent distally, proximal to flowers, 3–18 cm. **Inflorescences** terminal or axillary, 25–70-flowered, inverted or horizontal, ellipsoid or globose to subglobose, 2–3 × 1–3 cm, rachis prolonged beyond flowers; involucres absent. **Pedicels** reflexed, to 0.3 mm; bracteoles absent. **Flowers** 9–18 mm; calyx campanulate, curved in fruit, 4–11 mm, villous, veins 10, tube 1.5–2.5 mm, lobes unequal, 2–3 times tube, subulate, often strongly curved and twisted, plumose, orifice open; corolla white, cream, or purple, 8–16 mm, banner oblanceolate, 8–16 × 3–5 mm, apex rounded or retuse, recurved; ovaries pubescent distally. **Legumes** ovoid, 2–3.5 mm. **Seeds** (1 or)2–4, yellow-brown to brown, mitten-shaped or subglobose, 1.2–2 mm, smooth.

Subspecies 6 (6 in the flora): w United States.

Trifolium eriocephalum was revised by J. M. Gillett (1971). The subspecies exhibit unusually complex distributional patterns, and overlapping morphological features sometimes make identifications problematic (M. Zohary and D. Heller 1984).

SELECTED REFERENCE Gillett, J. M. 1971. Taxonomy of *Trifolium* (Leguminosae). III. *T. eriocephalum*. Canad. J. Bot. 49: 395–405.

1. Ovules usually 2, rarely 1 or 3; calyx lobes usually green, rarely purple, straight, subequal, 3–4 times tube.
    2. Herbs densely villous; leaflet blades of basal and median leaves elliptic or lanceolate-oblong; roots cylindric, thickened . . . . 85a. *Trifolium eriocephalum* subsp. *eriocephalum*
    2. Herbs slightly villous, appressed-pubescent, or glabrate; leaflet blades of basal and median leaves usually narrowly lanceolate or linear, rarely narrowly elliptic; roots fusiform-tuberous. . . . . 85b. *Trifolium eriocephalum* subsp. *cascadense*
1. Ovules 3 or 4; calyx lobes usually purple, contorted, abaxial lobes longer, lateral lobes 1–1.5 times tube.
    3. Leaflet blades of basal leaves linear or linear-elliptic, apex acute, surfaces sparsely or densely hairy adaxially; roots cylindric, thickened, branched, often rhizomelike.
        4. Blades of leaflets of median leaves linear or linear-elliptic; herbs slightly villous . . . 85c. *Trifolium eriocephalum* subsp. *cusickii*
        4. Blades of leaflets of median leaves broadly elliptic; herbs densely villous . . . . 84d. *Trifolium eriocephalum* subsp. *villiferum*
    3. Leaflet blades of basal leaves obovate, apex rounded to retuse, surfaces usually glabrous adaxially, sometimes sparsely hairy; roots fusiform-tuberous.
        5. Inflorescences 2.5 cm diam., significantly overtopping distal leaves; leaflet blades of median leaves broadly lanceolate, surfaces sparsely hairy or glabrous adaxially. . . . . 85e. *Trifolium eriocephalum* subsp. *arcuatum*
        5. Inflorescences 1 cm diam., scarcely overtopping distal leaves; leaflet blades of median leaves narrowly lanceolate or linear, surfaces densely villous adaxially . . . 85f. *Trifolium eriocephalum* subsp. *martinii*

85a. Trifolium eriocephalum Nuttall subsp. **eriocephalum** [E] [F]

Trifolium scorpioides Blasdale

Herbs densely villous; roots cylindric, thickened. **Leaflet blades** of basal and median leaves elliptic or lanceolate-oblong, surfaces densely villous adaxially. **Flowers:** calyx lobes usually green, rarely purple, straight, subequal, 3–4 times tube; corolla white; ovules usually 2, rarely 1 or 3. $2n = 16$.

Flowering May–Jul. Open pine forests, riverbanks, clearings, wet meadows; 100–2300 m; Calif., Oreg.

Subspecies *eriocephalum* occurs in northern California and in southwestern, west-central, and northeastern Oregon.

85b. Trifolium eriocephalum Nuttall subsp. **cascadense** J. M. Gillett, Canad. J. Bot. 49: 400. 1971 • Cascade clover E

Herbs slightly villous, appressed-pubescent, or glabrate; roots fusiform-tuberous. **Leaflet blades** of basal and median leaves usually narrowly lanceolate or linear, rarely narrowly elliptic, surfaces sparsely hairy adaxially. **Flowers:** calyx lobes green, straight, subequal, 3–4 times tube length; corolla white; ovules usually 2, rarely 1 or 3. $2n = 16$.

Flowering May–Jul. Open pine forests, riverbanks, clearings, wet meadows; 500–1500 m; Oreg.

Subspecies *cascadense* occurs in north-central and southwestern Oregon.

85c. Trifolium eriocephalum Nuttall subsp. **cusickii** (Piper) J. M. Gillett, Canad. J. Bot. 49: 402. 1971 • Cusick's clover E

Trifolium arcuatum Piper var. *cusickii* Piper, Bull. Torrey Bot. Club 29: 642. 1902; *T. eriocephalum* var. *cusickii* (Piper) J. S. Martin; *T. eriocephalum* var. *harneyense* (Howell) McDermott; *T. harneyensis* Howell; *T. tropicum* A. Nelson

Herbs slightly villous; roots cylindric, thickened, branched, often rhizomelike. **Leaflet blades** of basal and median leaves linear or linear-elliptic, apex acute, surfaces sparsely hairy adaxially. **Flowers:** calyx lobes usually purple, contorted, abaxial lobes longer, lateral lobes 1–1.5 times tube; corolla white, cream, or purple; ovules 3 or 4. $2n = 16$.

Flowering May–Jul. Open pine forests, riverbanks, clearings, wet meadows; 1200–2300 m; Idaho, Nev., Oreg.

Subspecies *cusickii* ranges from central and northern Nevada into eastern Oregon and southwestern Idaho.

85d. Trifolium eriocephalum Nuttall subsp. **villiferum** (House) J. M. Gillett, Canad. J. Bot. 49: 403. 1971 • Fuzzyleaf clover E

Trifolium villiferum House, Bot. Gaz. 41: 335, fig. 3. 1906; *T. eriocephalum* var. *villiferum* (House) J. S. Martin

Herbs densely villous, especially calyces; roots cylindric, thickened, branched, often rhizomelike, not predominantly fusiform-tuberous. **Leaflet blades** of basal leaves linear or linear-elliptic, of median leaves broadly elliptic, apex acute, surfaces densely hairy adaxially. **Flowers:** calyx lobes usually purple, contorted, abaxial lobes longer, lateral lobes 1–1.5 times tube; corolla white, cream, or purple; ovules 3 or 4.

Flowering May–Jul. Open pine forests, riverbanks, clearings, wet meadows; 1800–2300 m; Nev., Utah.

Subspecies *villiferum* ranges from west-central Utah to east-central Nevada.

85e. Trifolium eriocephalum Nuttall subsp. **arcuatum** (Piper) J. M. Gillett, Canad. J. Bot. 49: 400. 1971 • Arched clover E

Trifolium arcuatum Piper, Bull. Torrey Bot. Club 28: 39. 1901; *T. eriocephalum* var. *piperi* J. S. Martin

Herbs sparsely hairy or glabrous; roots fusiform-tuberous, not rhizomelike, except by burial of crown. **Leaflet blades** of basal leaves obovate, of median leaves broadly lanceolate, apex rounded to retuse, surfaces sparsely hairy or glabrous adaxially. **Inflorescences** significantly overtopping distal leaves, 2.5 cm diam. **Flowers:** calyx lobes usually purple, contorted, abaxial lobes longer, lateral lobes 1–1.5 times tube; corolla white, cream, or purple; ovules 3 or 4. $2n = 16$.

Flowering May–Jul. Open pine forests, riverbanks, clearings, wet meadows; 300–2000 m; Idaho, Mont., Oreg., Wash.

Subspecies *arcuatum* ranges from west-central Montana through north-central Idaho to northeastern Oregon and southeastern Washington.

85f. Trifolium eriocephalum Nuttall subsp. **martinii** J. M. Gillett, Canad. J. Bot. 49: 401. 1971 • Martin's clover [E]

Herbs densely villous; roots fusiform-tuberous, not rhizome-like, except by burial of the crown. **Leaflet blades** of basal leaves obovate, surfaces glabrous adaxially, of median leaves narrowly lanceolate or linear, surfaces densely villous adaxially, apex rounded to retuse. **Inflorescences** scarcely overtopping distal leaves, 1 cm wide. **Flowers:** calyx lobes usually purple, contorted, abaxial lobes longer, lateral lobes 1–1.5 times tube; corolla white, cream, or purple; ovules 3 or 4.

Flowering May–Jul. Open pine forests, riverbanks, clearings, wet meadows; 1200–2100 m; Idaho, Oreg.

Subspecies *martinii* occurs in west-central Idaho and northeastern Oregon.

86. Trifolium douglasii House, Bot. Gaz. 41: 335. 1906 • Douglas's clover [C] [E]

Trifolium altissimum Douglas in W. J. Hooker, Fl. Bor.-Amer. 1: 130, plate 48. 1831, not Loiseleur-Deslongchamps 1807

Herbs perennial, 20–75 cm, glabrous or slightly pilose. **Stems** erect, unbranched or sparsely branched. **Leaves** palmate; stipules lanceolate to ovate, 1.5–6.5 cm, margins setose-serrulate or entire, apex acuminate; petiole 1.5–15 cm; petiolules 1 mm; leaflets 3, blades elliptic-oblanceolate to linear-elliptic, 3–9.5 × 0.5–1.6 cm, base cuneate, lateral veins prominent, recurved, dichotomously forked near margin, margins setose-denticulate to serrate, apex rounded or acute, surfaces glaucous, glabrous, sometimes sparsely pubescent abaxially. **Peduncles** 3–12 cm. **Inflorescences** terminal or axillary, 30–50+-flowered, umbellate, globose to ovoid, 1.5–5 × 2–3.5 cm; involucres absent. **Pedicels** erect or slightly reflexed, to 0.2 mm; bracteoles minute. **Flowers** 14–16 mm; calyx campanulate, 6–9 mm, pilose, veins 15–20, tube 1.5–3 mm, lobes unequal, narrow, triangular or subulate, abaxial lobe straight, lateral and adaxial tortuous, recurved inwards around corolla, orifice open; corolla magenta, 12–16 mm, banner oblong, 12–16 × 4–6 mm, apex flared, acute or obtuse; ovaries glabrous or pubescent distally. **Legumes** ovoid, 3–4.5 mm. **Seeds** 1 or 2, tan to brown, ovoid, 1–1.5 mm, slightly roughened. $2n = 16$.

Flowering Jun–Jul. Moist meadows, rich soils in prairies, stream bottoms and banks, openings in pine forests; of conservation concern; 600–1500 m; Idaho, Oreg., Wash.

Trifolium douglasii is rare throughout its range and has been impacted by agricultural practices (P. Camp et al. 2011).

87. Trifolium owyheense Gilkey, Madroño 13: 169, fig. 1. 1956 • Owyhee clover [C] [E]

Herbs perennial, 10–20 cm, glaucous, glabrous. **Stems** cespitose, spreading, branched proximally, sparsely branched distally. **Leaves** palmate; stipules broadly obovate, 1–2 cm, fused at base, margins slightly lobed, apex acute; petiole 2–6 cm; petiolules 1–1.5 mm; leaflets 3, blades ovate, obovate, or orbiculate, slightly overlapping, 1–2 × 0.7–2.3 cm, base truncate to rounded, veins prominent, margins sparsely dentate, apex rounded, emarginate, surfaces glabrous. **Peduncles** 3–7 cm, surpassing subtending leaves. **Inflorescences** terminal, 20–30-flowered, globose, usually formed of 2 sessile heads, 2.5–5 × 2.5–5 cm; involucres absent. **Pedicels** erect, reflexed in proximalmost flowers, 1 mm; bracteoles cuplike, 0.5 mm. **Flowers** 15–21 mm; calyx tubular-campanulate, 9–12 mm, pilose, veins 10, tube 4.5–6 mm, lobes subequal, abaxialmost longest, subulate, orifice open; corolla deep pink or magenta, 20–23 mm, banner tubular for most their length, 18–22 × 5–7 mm, apex flared. **Legumes** ellipsoid, 4–5 mm. **Seeds** 1 or 2, yellow-mottled, mitten-shaped, 2–3 mm, smooth.

Flowering May–Jun. Dry shale hillsides on diatomaceous earth; of conservation concern; 1000–2000 m; Idaho, Oreg.

Trifolium owyheense is known from about 40 populations in a small portion of east-central Malheur County in Oregon, and immediately adjacent Owyhee County in Idaho (M. Mancuso 2001).

88. Trifolium andinum Nuttall in J. Torrey and A. Gray, Fl. N. Amer. 1: 314. 1838 • Intermountain clover [E]

Trifolium andinum var. *canone* S. L. Welsh & N. D. Atwood; *T. andinum* var. *navajoense* S. L. Welsh & N. D. Atwood; *T. andinum* var. *podocephalum* Barneby; *T. andinum* var. *wahwahense* S. L. Welsh & N. D. Atwood

Herbs perennial, 5–15 cm, pubescent. **Stems** erect or ascending, cespitose, much-branched. **Leaves** palmate; stipules oblanceolate, 0.5–1.4 cm, margins entire, apex acute-acuminate; petiole 0.5–4 cm; petiolules to 0.1 mm; leaflets 3, blades oblanceolate, often folded, 0.4–1.5 × 0.2–0.4 cm, base cuneate, veins obscure, margins subentire to denticulate distally, apex acute, mucronulate, surfaces villous. **Peduncles** between distal leaves or involucrelike structure and inflorescences 0.5–6 cm. **Inflorescences** terminal, usually formed of 2 sessile heads, 15–25-flowered, globose, 0.8–2 × 0.6–1.5 cm; involucres absent, distal stipules and leaves sometimes forming involucrelike structure. **Pedicels** straight, (0–)1–2 mm; bracteoles broadly ovate, truncate, membranous, to 0.5 mm. **Flowers** 10–15 mm; calyx tubular-campanulate, 6–9 mm, rough-hairy or glabrous, veins 10, tube 3–6 mm, lobes subequal, subulate, orifice open; corolla light purple, 10–15 mm, banner oblong, 9–13 × 3–4 mm, apex rounded or truncate; ovaries pubescent distally. **Legumes** ellipsoid, 4–5 mm. **Seeds** 1 or 2, brown, ovoid, 1.5–2 mm, smooth.

Flowering May–Jun. Shale or clay bluffs and hilltops, crevices of volcanic or limestone rock, pinyon-juniper belt; 1600–2300 m; Ariz., Colo., Nev., N.Mex., Utah, Wyo.

Trifolium andinum ranges from central and southern Nevada into west-central Utah, north-central Arizona to southeastern Utah, north-central New Mexico, and northeastern Utah into southwestern Wyoming. Differentiation of *T. andinum* into subspecific taxa proved impossible, since no consistent gaps in morphological traits could be found.

89. Trifolium gymnocarpon Nuttall in J. Torrey and A. Gray, Fl. N. Amer. 1: 320. 1838 • Nuttall's clover [E] [F]

Trifolium gymnocarpon var. *plummerae* (S. Watson) J. S. Martin; *T. gymnocarpon* var. *subcaulescens* (A. Gray) A. Nelson; *T. nemorale* Greene; *T. plummerae* S. Watson; *T. subcaulescens* A. Gray

Herbs perennial, 2–15 cm, pubescent. **Stems** cespitose, numerous, short, branched from woody crown. **Leaves** palmate; stipules ovate to lanceolate, 0.5–1.5 cm, margins entire or irregularly dentate, apex acute to acuminate; petiole 1.5–10 cm; petiolules to 0.5 mm; leaflets 3–5, blades ovate, obovate, oblong, or elliptic, 0.8–3 × 0.2–1.8 cm, base cuneate, veins thickened distally, margins spinose-dentate, apex rounded or acute, surfaces usually pubescent, sometimes glabrous adaxially. **Peduncles** 1–6.5 cm, ± surpassing leaves, not bent distally. **Inflorescences** terminal, 6–15-flowered, subglobose, 1–2 × 1.3–2.4 cm; involucres a narrow, membranous, dentate rim, 0.5 mm. **Pedicels** erect, those of proximal flowers sometimes reflexed, 1–4 mm; bracteoles ovate-triangular, to 0.8 mm. **Flowers** 7.5–13 mm; calyx tubular-campanulate, 4–7.5 mm, strigose, veins 10, tube 2–3 mm, lobes subequal, narrowly triangular, orifice open; corolla pink-purple, often with whitish tips, sometimes nearly wholly whitish, 7–12 mm, banner oblong, 7–14 × 5–7 mm, apex rounded, usually retuse. **Legumes** ovoid, 4–5 mm. **Seeds** 1, tan to brown, mitten-shaped, 3–4.5 mm, roughened.

Flowering Apr–Jun. Rocky slopes, clay or gumbo soils on plains; 1500–3500 m; Ariz., Calif., Colo., Idaho, Mont., Nev., N.Mex., Oreg., Utah, Wyo.

Two loosely differentiated varieties or subspecies of *Trifolium gymnocarpon* have sometimes been recognized: var. *plummerae* with three to five adaxially pilose leaflets, and var. *gymnocarpon* with three adaxially glabrous leaflets (J. M. Gillett 1972; D. Isely 1998). There is considerable overlap among characters, and other authors have rejected the distinction (M. Zohary and D. Heller 1984; R. C. Barneby 1989).

90. Trifolium haydenii Porter in F. V. Hayden, Prelim. Rep. U.S. Geol. Surv. Montana, 480. 1872 (as haydeni) • Hayden's clover [E] [F]

Trifolium idahoense L. F. Henderson

Herbs perennial, 5–10 cm, glabrous. **Stems** ascending, cespitose, short-branched. **Leaves** mostly basal, palmate; stipules lanceolate, 0.4–0.8 cm, margins entire or lobed, apex acute or acuminate; petiole 1–6 cm; petiolules to 0.5 mm; leaflets 3, blades broadly ovate, 0.4–2 × 0.3–1.5 cm, base cuneate, veins thickened distally, ± straight, sometimes arching distally, 0.5+ mm apart, 5–10 pairs of primary veins, margins sharply antrorse-serrate, apex acute, short-apiculate, surfaces glabrous. **Peduncles** straight distally, proximal to inflorescence, 5–8 cm. **Inflorescences** terminal, 5–20-flowered, erect, globose or subglobose, 0.5–1.5 × 0.8–2.5 cm, rachis prolonged beyond flowers, undivided or forked, often bearing sterile flower buds distally; involucres a narrow, membranous, dentate rim, 0.5 mm. **Pedicels** strongly reflexed, 1.5 mm; bracteoles broadly ovate, truncate, membranous, to 0.5 mm. **Flowers** 13–17 mm; calyx campanulate, 4.5–6.5 mm, glabrous, veins 10 (5 sometimes faint), tube 2–3 mm, lobes subequal, narrowly triangular-subulate, equaling tube, orifice open; corolla salmon, buff-pink, or pink, with white or cream tips, 13–17 mm, banner broadly elliptic-oblong, 13–17 × 6–8 mm, apex rounded, retuse or slightly apiculate. **Legumes** stipitate, obovoid-oblong, 6–7 mm. **Seeds** 1–4, brown, lenticular-ovoid, 2.5–3 mm, smooth. 2*n* = 16.

Flowering Jun–Aug. Alpine and subalpine slopes; 2200–3800 m; Idaho, Mont., Wyo.

Trifolium haydenii, which is found in east-central Idaho, southwestern Montana, and northwestern Wyoming, appears related to *T. kingii*, *T. productum*, and similar species (J. M. Gillett 1972) and is sometimes confused with *T. latifolium* (Gillett 1969), from which it differs by the absence of hairs.

91. Trifolium barnebyi (Isely) Dorn & Lichvar, Madroño 28: 189. 1981 • Barneby's clover [C] [E]

Trifolium haydenii Porter var. *barnebyi* Isely, Brittonia 32: 56. 1980

Herbs perennial, 3–5 cm, mostly glabrous. **Stems** densely mat-forming, short-branched. **Leaves** palmate; stipules ovate or lanceolate, 0.5–1 cm, margins entire or lobed, apex acute or acuminate; petiole 0.3–30 cm, pubescent; petiolules 0.2 mm; leaflets 3, blades oblanceolate, 0.3–1.6 × 0.1–0.7 cm, base cuneate, veins close-set, 12–18 pairs of primary veins, 0.5 mm apart, margins sharply antrorsely serrate, apex acute, long-apiculate, surfaces usually glabrous, rarely midvein pubescent abaxially. **Peduncles** 0.5–3.5 cm, pubescent. **Inflorescences** terminal, 8–18-flowered, globose or subglobose, 1.2–2.5 × 2–3 cm; involucres absent. **Pedicels** reflexed, 2–3.5 mm, pubescent; bracteoles broad, membranous, to 0.2 mm. **Flowers** 8–13 mm; calyx campanulate, 4–6 mm, pubescent, veins 5–10, tube 1.5–2.5 mm, lobes subequal, narrowly triangular-subulate, orifice open; corolla creamy white, 8–13 mm, banner broadly elliptic-oblong, 10–13 × 6–8 mm, apex rounded, slightly apiculate. **Legumes** stipitate, flattened, ovoid, 2–3.5 mm. **Seeds** 1, yellow, mottled, flattened-ovoid, 2 mm, smooth.

Flowering Jun. Sandstone ledges and outcrops; of conservation concern; 1700–2100 m; Wyo.

Trifolium barnebyi is known from central Wyoming. It was originally described as a variety of *T. haydenii*, but was elevated to species rank based on its pubescent petioles, pedicels, and peduncles, closely spaced leaflet veins, and more elongate leaflets that are two times as long as wide.

92. Trifolium beckwithii Brewer ex S. Watson, Proc. Amer. Acad. Arts 11: 128. 1876 • Beckwith's clover [E]

Herbs perennial, 5–50 cm, glabrous. **Stems** erect or ascending, unbranched or several stems clumped from crown. **Leaves** palmate; stipules narrowly ovate, lanceolate, or linear-lanceolate, 1–2 cm, margins entire or toothed, apex acute; petiole 0.5–20 cm; petiolules 1 mm; leaflets 3, blades usually rhombic, oblong, or elliptic, sometimes ovate, 2.5–5 × 0.6–2 cm, base cuneate, veins slightly thickened, margins setose-serrulate, apex obtuse or retuse, surfaces glaucous abaxially, glabrous. **Peduncles** straight, thick, 5–25 cm. **Inflorescences** terminal or axillary, 30–70+-flowered, globose or ovoid becoming subglobose, 1.5–4 × 1.8–3.3 cm, rachis prolonged beyond flowers, undivided or forked, often bearing sterile flower buds distally; involucres absent. **Pedicels** strongly reflexed in fruit, 1–1.5 mm; bracteoles minute. **Flowers** 11–14 mm, sweetly fragrant; calyx campanulate, gibbous, 4–6 mm, glabrous, veins 5, tube 2–3 mm, lobes unequal, narrowly triangular or subulate, orifice open; corolla light purplish, sometimes with pink tips, 10–13 mm, banner straight, obovate to broadly elliptic, 13–18 × 6–8 mm, apex rounded or retuse, apiculate. **Legumes** oblong, 5 mm. **Seeds** 2–4, reddish brown, flattened globose, 1.5–2 mm, smooth. **2*n*** = 48.

Flowering May–Jul. Moist, grassy meadows along streams; 1200–2000 m; Calif., Idaho, Mont., Nev., Oreg., S.Dak., Utah, Wash.

Disjunct populations of *Trifolium beckwithii* found in South Dakota are over 1200 km east of the nearest populations in Montana. The South Dakota populations appear to have been long-distance introductions from populations in northern California, based on molecular data (M. R. Duvall et al. 1999).

93. Trifolium latifolium (Hooker) Greene, Pittonia 3: 223. 1897 • Broad-leaved clover [F]

Trifolium longipes Nuttall var. *latifolium* Hooker, London J. Bot. 6: 209. 1847; *T. aitonii* Rydberg; *T. orbiculatum* P. B. Kennedy & McDermott

Herbs perennial, 4–40 cm, appressed-pubescent. **Stems** ascending, branched from slender, rhizomatous crown. **Leaves** palmate; stipules ovate or lanceolate, 0.5–2 cm, margins entire proximally, 1–3-toothed distally, apex acuminate or acute; petiole 1.5–10 cm; petiolules to 1 mm; leaflets 3, blades obovate or elliptic, 0.5–4.2 × 0.3–2.5 cm, base cuneate, veins fine or slightly thickened, margins serrulate, apex acute, rounded, or retuse, apiculate, surfaces appressed-pubescent. **Peduncles** bent proximal to flowers, inflorescence appearing inverted, 2.5–12 cm. **Inflorescences** terminal, 6–30-flowered, globose, 2.3–3.1 × 2–3 cm, rachis prolonged beyond flowers; involucres absent. **Pedicels** reflexed in fruit, 1.5–2 mm; bracteoles minute, scalelike, membranous, to 0.3 mm. **Flowers** 13–17 mm, sweetly fragrant; calyx campanulate, 4.5–5 mm, appressed-pubescent, veins 5, tube 2 mm, lobes subequal, linear, orifice open; corolla white, sometimes with purplish or buff-pink veins, 12–15 mm, banner elliptic, 12–15 × 4 mm, longer than

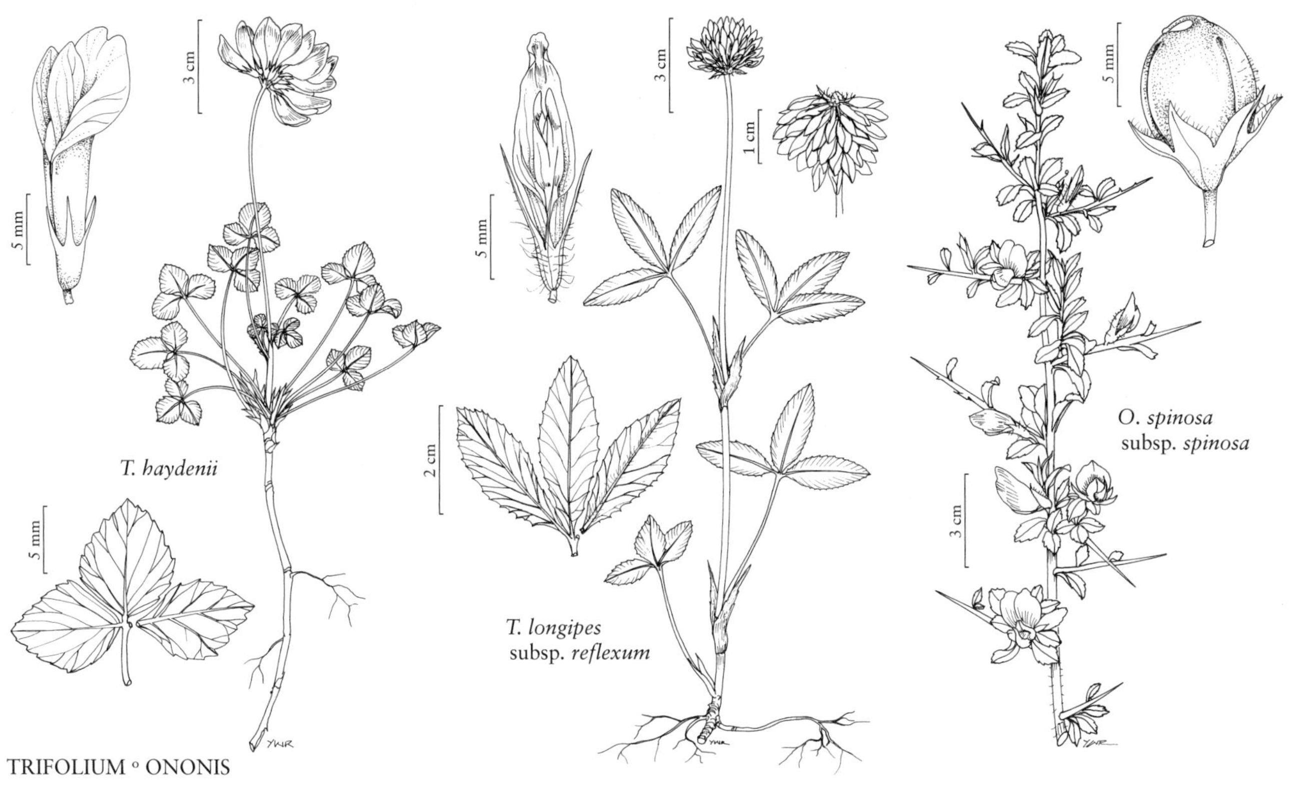

TRIFOLIUM ◦ ONONIS

wing and keel petals, apex tapered, sometimes retuse. **Legumes** oblong to subglobose, 5 mm. **Seeds** 1 or 2, dark brown, ± globose, 1.2 mm, smooth. $2n$ = 16, 32.

Flowering May–Jul. Clearings in conifer forests, moist gravelly, rocky, or clay soils, grassy hillsides and gullies, prairies; 800–1500 m; Idaho, Mont., Oreg., Wash.

Trifolium latifolium, which is found in northwestern Montana, northern Idaho, northeastern Oregon, and southeastern Washington, is morphologically allied to *T. longipes* (J. M. Gillett 1969) and molecular phylogenetic studies place it as sister to *T. longipes* (N. W. Ellison et al. 2006).

94. Trifolium longipes Nuttall in J. Torrey and A. Gray, Fl. N. Amer. 1: 314. 1838 • Longstalk clover [E] [F]

Herbs perennial, 5–46 cm, slightly pilose. **Stems** erect or ascending, cespitose, unbranched to sparsely branched distally. **Leaves** palmate; stipules ovate to lanceolate, 1–5 cm, margins usually entire, sometimes slightly serrate proximally, apex acute or acuminate; petiole 1–13 cm; petiolules to 1 mm; leaflets 3, blades linear, lanceolate to elliptic, or oblong, cauline sometimes ovate, 0.8–6 × 0.2–1.6 cm, base cuneate, veins slightly to very thickened, arching, margins entire or serrate, apex acute, surfaces glabrous abaxially, usually appressed-pubescent adaxially. **Peduncles** 1–30 cm. **Inflorescences** terminal, 10–40-flowered, globose, ellipsoid, obconic, or subglobose, 1–3.5 × 1–3.2 cm; involucres absent. **Pedicels** erect or reflexed in fruit, 0.5–2 mm; bracteoles scalelike, 0.5 mm. **Flowers** 10–19 mm; calyx tubular, 4–10 mm, hairy or glabrous, veins 5–10, tube 2.5–3 mm, lobes unequal, linear, shorter than or to 6 times tube, orifice open; corolla white, cream, pink, lavender, or purple, sometimes pale with purple tips, 10–18 mm, petals not beaked except subsp. *multipedunculatum*, banner ovate to oblanceolate, 10–18 × 3–4 mm, apex usually not beaked, usually obtuse, acute, or acuminate, rarely emarginate; ovaries pubescent distally. **Legumes** oblong to ellipsoid, 4–5 mm. **Seeds** 1–4, dark brown, flattened globose, 2–3 mm, smooth.

Subspecies 12 (12 in the flora): w United States.

Trifolium longipes encompasses a morphologically diverse and taxonomically difficult suite of populations. J. M. Gillett (1969) united *T. longipes* with *T. rusbyi* and differentiated ten subspecies, with *T. neurophyllum* recognized as distinct. M. Zohary and D. Heller (1984) maintained *T. rusbyi* (with seven subspecies, including subsp. *neurophyllum*) as distinct from *T. longipes* (with five subspecies). Analyses of molecular data support the union of *T. longipes* and *T. rusbyi* (N. W. Ellison et al. 2006).

1. Banner, wing, and, often, keel petals beaked . . . . 94l. *Trifolium longipes* subsp. *multipedunculatum*
1. Banner, wing, and keel petals without beaks, banner apex acute to attenuate.
    2. Pedicels erect or proximalmost horizontal or slightly reflexed in fruit.
        3. Herbs rhizomatous; roots not fusiform, sometimes thickened.
            4. Calyx lobes lax, usually slightly longer than tube length, tube veins not prominent; leaflet blades lanceolate, elliptic to oblong, or ovate . . . . 94d. *Trifolium longipes* subsp. *hansenii*
            4. Calyx lobes often ± rigid, 6 times tube length, tube veins usually prominent; leaflet blades linear to elliptic-linear or broadly elliptic . . . . . . 94e. *Trifolium longipes* subsp. *elmeri*
        3. Herbs not rhizomatous (stems ascending from crowns); roots thickened, often fusiform.
            5. Banner and wing apices slender-acuminate . . . . 94a. *Trifolium longipes* subsp. *longipes*
            5. Banner and wing apices usually acute or obtuse, rarely emarginate.
                6. Calyces and distal ends of peduncles densely pilose; banner apex acute . . . . 94b. *Trifolium longipes* subsp. *atrorubens*
                6. Calyces and distal ends of peduncles sparsely pilose or glabrous; banner apex usually broad, acute or obtuse, rarely emarginate. . .94c. *Trifolium longipes* subsp. *pedunculatum*
    2. Pedicels (at least proximal ones, usually all), strongly reflexed in fruit.
        7. Herbs with thickened roots, often fusiform, with crown of buried stems . . . . 94f. *Trifolium longipes* subsp. *pygmaeum*
        7. Herbs usually rhizomatous, if rarely with roots ± thickened, then with crown of rhizomes above thickened portion, or with slender taproots bearing a crown of wiry, pilose stems.
            8. Pedicels slender, 1.5–2 mm; herbs with slender taproots, bearing crown of wiry, pilose stems . . . . 94g. *Trifolium longipes* subsp. *oreganum*
            8. Pedicels stout, to 1 mm; herbs rhizomatous.

[9. Shifted to left margin.—Ed.]

9. Inflorescences globose or ellipsoid; proximal pedicels more strongly reflexed than distal ones.
    10. Inflorescences 18–22-flowered, globose, 2.2–2.5 cm diam.; flowers 10–13 mm, corollas purple, sometimes tips white . . . . .94h. *Trifolium longipes* subsp. *shastense*
    10. Inflorescences 28–32-flowered, ellipsoid, 3–3.2 cm diam.; flowers 14–16 mm, corollas lavender. . . 94i. *Trifolium longipes* subsp. *caurinum*
9. Inflorescences hemispheric, obconic, or subglobose; all pedicels strongly reflexed.
    11. Calyces sparsely pilose or curly-pilose at sinuses, often glabrous proximally; corollas white, cream, or violet. . . . . 94j. *Trifolium longipes* subsp. *reflexum*
    11. Calyces white-villous, veins and lobes green; corollas purple-violet or lavender. . . . . 94k. *Trifolium longipes* subsp. *neurophyllum*

94a. Trifolium longipes Nuttall subsp. **longipes** [E]

Herbs 15–30 cm; not rhizomatous; roots thickened, often fusiform. **Inflorescences** 15–40-flowered, subglobose, 1–2 cm diam. **Pedicels** erect or proximalmost horizontal or slightly reflexed in fruit, stout, to 1 mm. **Flowers** 10–12 mm; calyx sparsely hairy or glabrous; corolla white, banner and wing apices slender-acuminate. $2n = 16$.

Flowering May–Aug. Boggy meadows; 1000–2000 m; Oreg., Wash.

Subspecies *longipes* occurs in west-central Oregon and central Washington.

94b. Trifolium longipes Nuttall subsp. **atrorubens** (Greene) J. M. Gillett, Canad. J. Bot. 47: 108. 1969 • Reddish longstalk clover [E]

Trifolium rusbyi Greene var. *atrorubens* Greene, Erythea 4: 66. 1896; *T. atrorubens* (Greene) House; *T. longipes* var. *atrorubens* (Greene) Jepson

Herbs 15–40 cm; not rhizomatous; roots thickened, often fusiform. **Inflorescences** 15–40-flowered, subglobose, 1.5–2 cm diam.; peduncles densely pilose distally. **Pedicels** erect or proximalmost horizontal or slightly reflexed in fruit, stout, to 1 mm. **Flowers** 11–13 mm; calyx densely pilose; corolla lavender or purple, sometimes tips darker, banner and wing apices acute. $2n = 48$.

Flowering May–Jul. Meadows; 1100–3000 m; Calif.

Subspecies *atrorubens* is known from Fresno, Riverside, San Bernardino, and Tulare counties.

94c. Trifolium longipes Nuttall subsp. **pedunculatum** (Rydberg) J. M. Gillett, Canad. J. Bot. 47: 109. 1969 • Longstalk clover [E]

Trifolium pedunculatum Rydberg, Bull. Torrey Bot. Club 30: 254. 1903; *T. longipes* Nuttall var. *pedunculatum* (Rydberg) C. L. Hitchcock

Herbs 5–15 cm; not rhizomatous; roots thickened, often fusiform. **Inflorescences** 15–25-flowered, subglobose, 1–2 cm diam.; peduncles sparsely pilose or glabrous distally. **Pedicels** erect or proximalmost horizontal or slightly reflexed in fruit, stout, to 1 mm. **Flowers** 11–13 mm; calyx sparsely pilose or glabrous; corolla white, lavender, or purple, banner and wing apices usually broad, acute or obtuse, rarely emarginate. $2n$ = 16, 48.

Flowering Jun–Jul. Meadows, pine forests; 2100–2300 m; Idaho.

Subspecies *pedunculatum* is found only in central Idaho.

94d. Trifolium longipes Nuttall subsp. **hansenii** (Greene) J. M. Gillett, Canad. J. Bot. 47: 109. 1969 • Hansen's clover [E]

Trifolium hansenii Greene, Erythea 3: 17. 1895

Herbs 15–40 cm; rhizomatous; roots not fusiform, sometimes thickened. **Leaflet blades** lanceolate, elliptic to oblong, or ovate. **Inflorescences** 15–25-flowered, subglobose, 1.5–3 cm diam. **Pedicels** erect or proximalmost horizontal or slightly reflexed in fruit, stout, to 1 mm. **Flowers** 13–15 mm; calyx sparsely hairy, lobes lax, usually only slightly longer than tubes, tube veins not prominent; corolla white, lavender, or pink, banner and wing apices acute or acuminate. $2n$ = 48.

Flowering Jun–Aug. Moist meadows, pine forests; 300–3200 m; Calif., Nev., Oreg.

Subspecies *hansenii* ranges from Tulare County, California, northward through eastern and northern California to southern, central, and northeastern Oregon, with scattered populations in Nevada, from Eureka, Mineral, Nye, Ormsby, Storey, and Washoe counties.

94e. Trifolium longipes Nuttall subsp. **elmeri** (Greene) J. M. Gillett, Canad. J. Bot. 47: 111. 1969 • Elmer's clover [E]

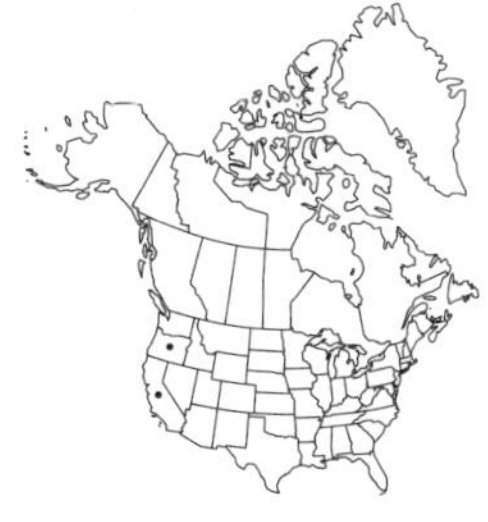

Trifolium elmeri Greene, Pittonia 3: 223. 1897; *T. longipes* var. *elmeri* (Greene) McDermott

Herbs 20–40 cm; rhizomatous; roots not fusiform, sometimes thickened. **Leaflet blades** linear to elliptic-linear to broadly elliptic. **Inflorescences** 10–30-flowered, subglobose, 1.5–2 cm diam. **Pedicels** erect or proximalmost horizontal or slightly reflexed in fruit, stout, to 1 mm. **Flowers** 10–14 mm; calyx sparsely hairy, lobes often ± rigid, 6 times tube, tube veins usually prominent; corolla white, lavender, or pink, banner apex acute or acuminate. $2n$ = 16.

Flowering May–Aug. Meadows; 50–2500 m; Calif., Oreg.

Subspecies *elmeri* occurs in northwestern California and southwestern Oregon.

94f. Trifolium longipes Nuttall subsp. **pygmaeum** (A. Gray) J. M. Gillett, Canad. J. Bot. 47: 102. 1969 • Pygmy clover [E]

Trifolium longipes var. *pygmaeum* A. Gray in J. C. Ives, Rep. Colorado R. 4: 9. 1861; *T. brachypus* (S. Watson) Blankinship; *T. confusum* Rydberg; *T. rusbyi* Greene

Herbs 5–30 cm; not rhizomatous; roots thickened, often fusiform, with a crown of buried stems. **Inflorescences** 10–25-flowered, globose, 1.5–2.5 cm diam. **Pedicels** (at least proximal, usually all) strongly reflexed in fruit, slender, 1.5–2 mm. **Flowers** 11–12 mm; calyx curly-pubescent throughout or at sinuses; corolla purple or pink, banner apex acute or acuminate. $2n$ = 16.

Flowering Apr–Aug. Ponderosa pine or Engelmann spruce forests, aspen groves, open meadows; 700–3500 m; Ariz., Colo., N.Mex., Utah.

Subspecies *pygmaeum* occurs in northeastern Arizona, southwestern and north-central Colorado, northwestern New Mexico, and southern Utah.

94g. Trifolium longipes Nuttall subsp. **oreganum** (Howell) J. M. Gillett, Canad. J. Bot. 47: 103. 1969 • Oregon clover [E]

Trifolium oreganum Howell, Erythea 1: 110. 1893; *T. longipes* var. *oreganum* (Howell) Isely; *T. rusbyi* Greene subsp. *oreganum* (Howell) D. Heller & Zohary

Herbs 7–25 cm; not rhizomatous; taproots slender, bearing a crown of pilose wiry stems. **Inflorescences** 10–25-flowered, globose or obconic, 2–2.8 cm diam. **Pedicels** (at least proximal, usually all) strongly reflexed in fruit, slender, 1.5–2 mm. **Flowers** 11–13 mm; calyx sparsely hairy; corolla pink or white, often bicolored, banner apex acute or acuminate.

Flowering May–Jun. Forested slopes; 1200–1900 m; Calif., Oreg.

Subspecies *oreganum* is found in northwestern California and southwestern Oregon.

94h. Trifolium longipes Nuttall subsp. **shastense** (House) J. M. Gillett, Canad. J. Bot. 47: 104. 1969 • Shasta longstalk clover [E]

Trifolium shastense House, Bot. Gaz. 41: 336, fig. 4. 1906; *T. longipes* var. *shastense* (House) Jepson; *T. rusbyi* Greene subsp. *shastense* (House) D. Heller & Zohary

Herbs 10–17 cm; rhizomatous; roots usually not thickened, if so, then crown of rhizomes above thickened portion. **Inflorescences** 18–22-flowered, globose, 2.2–2.5 cm diam. **Pedicels** (at least proximal, usually all) strongly reflexed in fruit, proximal more strongly reflexed than distal, stout, to 1 mm. **Flowers** 10–13 mm; calyx sparsely hairy; corolla purple, sometimes tips white, banner apex acute or acuminate.

Flowering May–Jun. Open gravelly places to upper limit of *Pinus monticola*; 1200–2800 m; Calif.

Subspecies *shastense* occurs in Shasta, Siskiyou, and Trinity counties.

94i. Trifolium longipes Nuttall subsp. **caurinum** (Piper) J. M. Gillett, Canad. J. Bot. 47: 104. 1969 • Beaked longstalk clover [E]

Trifolium caurinum Piper, Erythea 6: 29. 1898; *T. covillei* House

Herbs 10–20 cm; rhizomatous; roots usually not thickened, if so, then crown of rhizomes above thickened portion. **Inflorescences** 28–32-flowered, ellipsoid, 3–3.2 cm diam. **Pedicels** (at least proximal, usually all) strongly reflexed in fruit, proximal more strongly reflexed than distal, stout, to 1 mm. **Flowers** 14–16 mm; calyx usually glabrous, rarely very sparsely hairy; corolla lavender, banner apex acute or acuminate. 2*n* = 48.

Flowering May–Jun. Montane forests; 400–2300 m; Oreg., Wash.

Subspecies *caurinum* is found in central and western Washington, with populations in Oregon in the northeast and northwest, as well as in scattered sites elsewhere.

94j. Trifolium longipes Nuttall subsp. **reflexum** (A. Nelson) J. M. Gillett, Canad. J. Bot. 47: 105. 1969 • Reflexed longstalk clover [E] [F]

Trifolium longipes var. *reflexum* A. Nelson, Wyoming Agric. Exp. Sta. Bull. 28: 94. 1896; *T. rydbergii* Greene

Herbs 15–37 cm; rhizomatous; roots usually not thickened, if so, then crown of rhizomes above thickened portion. **Inflorescences** 10–20-flowered, hemispheric, obconic, or subglobose, 2–3 cm diam. **Pedicels** strongly reflexed in fruit, stout, to 1 mm. **Flowers** 13–15 mm; calyx sparsely pilose or curly-pilose at sinuses, often glabrous proximally; corolla white, cream, or violet, banner apex acute or acuminate. 2*n* = 24, 48.

Flowering May–Jul. Moist meadows; 1000–3600 m; Ariz., Colo., Idaho, Mont., N.Mex., Oreg., Utah, Wash., Wyo.

94k. Trifolium longipes Nuttall subsp. **neurophyllum** (Greene) J. M. Gillett in J. Maschinski et al., S.W. Rare Endang. Pl. 1995, 262. 1996 • White Mountain clover [C] [E]

Trifolium neurophyllum Greene, Leafl. Bot. Observ. Crit. 1: 154. 1905; *T. longipes* var. *neurophyllum* (Greene) J. S. Martin ex Isely; *T. rusbyi* Greene subsp. *neurophyllum* (Greene) D. Heller & Zohary

Herbs 10–46 cm; short-rhizomatous; roots becoming thickened, woody. **Inflorescences** 35–40-flowered, hemispheric or subglobose, 2–3 cm diam. **Pedicels** strongly reflexed in fruit, stout, to 1 mm. **Flowers** 11–14 mm; calyx white-villous, veins and lobes green; corolla purple-violet or lavender, banner apex obtuse. **2*n*** = 16.

Flowering Jul–Aug. Open meadows, pine forests; of conservation concern; 2300–3000 m; Ariz., N.Mex.

Subspecies *neurophyllum*, as *Trifolium neurophyllum*, is listed in NatureServe as a G2 plant of conservation concern. It is found in Apache and Greenlee counties in Arizona, and Catron and Socorro counties in New Mexico.

94l. Trifolium longipes Nuttall subsp. **multipedunculatum** (P. B. Kennedy) J. M. Gillett, Canad. J. Bot. 47: 101. 1969 • Multistalk clover [E]

Trifolium multipedunculatum P. B. Kennedy, Muhlenbergia 5: 59, plate 2. 1909; *T. longipes* var. *multipedunculatum* (P. B. Kennedy) J. S. Martin ex Isely; *T. rusbyi* Greene subsp. *multipedunculatum* (P. B. Kennedy) D. Heller & Zohary

Herbs 10–17 cm; usually not rhizomatous; roots slender, or taproots bearing a cluster of rhizomes. **Inflorescences** 10–25-flowered, globose, 2–3 cm diam. **Pedicels** (at least proximal, often all) strongly reflexed in fruit, slender, 1.5–2 mm. **Flowers** 12–14 mm; calyx curly-pubescent at sinuses; corolla purple, sometimes keel petals white, banner, wing, and, often, keel apices beaked. **2*n*** = 32, 48.

Flowering Jun–Aug. Open pine or spruce-fir forest to alpine, on talus, rocky places, meadows; 2000–3000 m; Calif., Oreg., Wash.

Subspecies *multipedunculatum* is found in Modoc County in California, Crook, Grant, Harney, Lake, Union, and Wallowa counties in Oregon, and in Kittitas County in Washington.

95. Trifolium kingii S. Watson, Botany (Fortieth Parallel), 59. 1871 • King's clover [E]

Herbs perennial, 2–40 cm, glabrous. **Stems** erect or ascending, branched from root stock. **Leaves** palmate; stipules lanceolate, 0.8–3 cm, margins entire, apex acuminate; petiole 0.8–15 cm; petiolules 1 mm; leaflets 3, blades ovate, elliptic, or lanceolate, 0.5–8 × 0.4–2.6 cm, basal blades thick, base cuneate, veins prominent, margins sharply serrate, those of basal leaves entire, sometimes shortly setose, apex acute, obtuse, or obcordate, surfaces glabrous. **Peduncles** curved apically, 3–14 cm. **Inflorescences** terminal or axillary, 20–35-flowered, inverted or horizontal, depressed-globose or obovoid, 1.5–3.2 × 1.5–3 cm, rachis internodes not especially elongated; involucres absent. **Pedicels** reflexed, 0.5 mm; bracteoles broadly ovate, blunt, minute. **Flowers** 12–16 mm; calyx campanulate, 5–6 mm, usually sparsely pubescent, sometimes glabrate, veins 5, tube 2–3.5 mm, lobes equal, 1–1.5 times tube, subulate, curved, orifice open; corolla usually pink-purple, rarely white, 13–15 mm, banner lanceolate-ovate, 15–18 × 4–5 mm, apex rounded; ovaries glabrous. **Legumes** flattened, ellipsoid, 3–4 mm. **Seeds** 1–3, brown, flattened ovoid, 2–2.2 mm, smooth. **2*n*** = 16.

Flowering Jul–Aug. Alpine meadows, stream banks, open aspen and spruce-fir woods; 2200–3300 m; Colo., Nev., Utah.

Trifolium kingii is widely distributed throughout Utah (S. L. Welsh et al. 2008), is found in Mesa County southward to Dolores County in Colorado, and is found rarely in eastern Nevada.

96. Trifolium rollinsii J. M. Gillett, Madroño 21: 453, fig. 2. 1972 • Rollins's clover [E]

Trifolium kingii S. Watson subsp. *rollinsii* (J. M. Gillett) D. Heller; *T. macilentum* Greene var. *rollinsii* (J. M. Gillett) Barneby

Herbs perennial, 5–20 cm, glabrous. **Stems** ascending, cespitose, branched. **Leaves** mostly basal, palmate; stipules ovate, 1 cm, margins entire, apex blunt; petiole 2–6 cm; petiolules to 1 mm; leaflets 3, blades obovate or rhombic, 0.6–1.3 × 0.6–1 cm, base cuneate, veins prominent, margins denticulate, apex rounded or retuse, apiculate, surfaces pale abaxially, glabrous. **Peduncles** curved distally proximal to flowers, 3–9 cm. **Inflorescences** terminal or axillary, 8–15-flowered, appearing turned to one side, obconic, 1.3–1.8 × 1.1–2.5 cm, rachis prolonged beyond flowers, undivided or forked, often bearing sterile flower buds distally; involucres absent. **Pedicels** reflexed, 1–1.2 mm; bracteoles minute. **Flowers** 10–13 mm; calyx purple, campanulate, 5–6 mm, glabrous, veins 10, tube 3.5 mm, lobes equal, subulate, 2 mm, orifice open; corolla purple, often with white tips, 15 mm, banner obovate, 11–13 × 5–6 mm, apex flared. **Legumes** not seen. **Seeds** not seen.

Flowering Jun–Aug. Wind-swept alpine areas; 3000–3100 m; Nev.

Trifolium rollinsii is known from the Toiyabe Range in Lander and Nye counties in central Nevada.

97. Trifolium bolanderi A. Gray, Proc. Amer. Acad. Arts 7: 335. 1868 • Bolander's clover [C] [E]

Herbs perennial, 15–30 cm, glabrous. **Stems** ascending, cespitose, branched. **Leaves** palmate; stipules ovate or lanceolate, 0.6–1.5 cm, margins entire, apex acute; petiole 1–7 cm; petiolules to 1 mm; leaflets 3, blades obcordate, obovate, or elliptic, 1–1.9 × 0.5–1.1 cm, base cuneate, veins fine to slightly thickened, margins setose, apex obtuse, rounded, or emarginate, apiculate, surfaces glabrous. **Peduncles** slender, bent distally, just below flowers, 5–20 cm. **Inflorescences** terminal, 12–30-flowered, ovoid, 1–2 × 1.5–3 cm, rachis prolonged beyond flowers, undivided or forked, often bearing sterile flower buds distally; involucres absent. **Pedicels** strongly reflexed, 1–1.2 mm; bracteoles minute, cuplike. **Flowers** 12–14 mm; calyx deep violet, campanulate, gibbous, 3–5 mm, glabrous, veins 5, tube 1.5–2 mm, lobes unequal, triangular-subulate, orifice open; corolla lavender to purplish, 11–12 mm, banner curved, oblanceolate, 10–12 × 3–4 mm, apex narrow, rounded, slightly emarginate. **Legumes** ellipsoid, 3–4 mm. **Seeds** 1 or 2, brown, ellipsoid, 1.2–1.5 mm, smooth.

Flowering Jun–Aug. Meadows; of conservation concern; 2000–2300 m; Calif.

Trifolium bolanderi is known from the Sierra Nevada in California and may be vulnerable to shifts in climate patterns. Genetic diversity of populations of the species (based on allozyme patterns) was found to be relatively high; two genetically distinct groups of populations are known (R. G. Denton 2002).

98. Trifolium lemmonii S. Watson, Proc. Amer. Acad. Arts 11: 127. 1876 (as lemmoni) • Lemmon's clover [E]

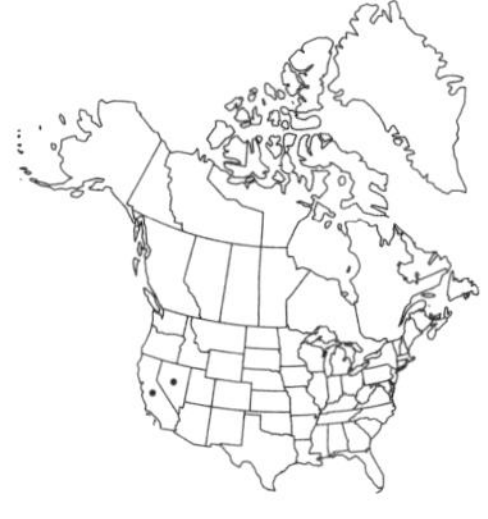

Lupinaster lemmonii (S. Watson) Latschaschvili

Herbs perennial, subcaulescent, 10–20 cm, appressed-pubescent. **Stems** cespitose, branched. **Leaves** palmate; stipules ovate to lanceolate, 0.8–1 cm, margins irregularly lobed, apex acuminate; petiole 1–16.5 cm; petiolules 0.5 mm; leaflets 3–7, blades obovate or elliptic, 0.9–1.9 × 0.5–0.8 cm, base cuneate, veins prominent abaxially, margins coarsely dentate, apex rounded, acute, or mucronate, surfaces strigose. **Peduncles** sharply bent distally, just below flowers, 5–15 cm, surpassing leaves. **Inflorescences** terminal or axillary, 15–30-flowered, globose to subglobose, 2–3 × 2–3 cm; involucres a narrow membranous, dentate rim, to 0.2 mm. **Pedicels** reflexed in fruit, 2–3 mm; bracteoles minute, cuplike, membranous, minute. **Flowers** 11–13 mm; calyx purple, campanulate, 3–5 mm, slightly pilose, veins 5 (obscure), tube 2–2.5 mm, lobes subequal, subulate, orifice open; corolla white to pink, 10–12 mm, banner oblong-obovate, 10–12 × 4–5 mm, apex rounded, emarginate. **Legumes** oblong, 3.2–3.5 mm. **Seeds** 1, dark brown, ellipsoid, 2.5–3 mm, smooth.

Flowering Jul–Aug. Dry, rocky soils, roadsides; 1500–2500 m; Calif., Nev.

Populations of *Trifolium lemmonii* studied by S. J. Sommer (1999) fall into two groups, east (in Sierra County, California, and Washoe County, Nevada) and west (in Plumas County, California) of a gap where no suitable habitat is known; gene flow between these two regions appears to be limited.

146. ONONIS Linnaeus, Sp. Pl. 2: 716. 1753; Gen. Pl. ed. 5, 321. 1754 • Restharrow [Greek *onos*, donkey, and *onemos*, pleasing, alluding to use as fodder] [I]

Ernest Small

Herbs, annual [perennial], or shrubs, armed or unarmed. **Stems** ascending, erect, procumbent, or decumbent, ± pubescent throughout [rarely glabrescent], hairs simple, glandular. **Leaves** alternate, odd-pinnate; stipules present, often leafy, adnate to petiole much of their lengths [rarely stipules fused]; petiolate; leaflets 1 or 3[or 5], blade margins usually serrulate, at least distally, rarely entire, surfaces pubescent; terminal blade larger than laterals. **Inflorescences** 1–3-flowered, terminal, leafy, racemes [spikes or panicles]; bracts present. **Flowers** papilionaceous; calyx campanulate or tubular, lobes 5, ± subequal; corolla usually pink or purple, sometimes white [variegated or yellow]; stamens 10, monadelphous (at least basally); anthers dimorphic, alternately basifixed and dorsifixed. **Fruits** legumes, tan to light brown, subsessile or stipitate, turgid, straight, ovoid or oblong-rhomboid [linear], usually not exceeding calyx, dehiscent, pubescent. **Seeds** 1–4[+], spherical or ovoid [reniform, suborbicular], smooth or tuberculate. $x = 8$.

Species ca. 80 (2 in the flora): introduced; Europe, Asia, n Africa; introduced also in Pacific Islands, Australia.

Ononis has been considered to be marginally related to *Medicago*, *Melilotus*, *Trifolium*, and *Trigonella*, which have been interpreted as constituting tribe Trifolieae, sometimes with the addition of *Parochetus* Buchanan-Hamilton ex D. Don (C. C. Heyn 1981). *Ononis* is often considered to constitute its own tribe, Ononideae Hutchinson. Molecular (plastid nucleic acid) phylogenetic analyses (M. F. Wojciechowski et al. 2000; K. P. Steele and Wojciechowski 2003; Wojciechowski 2003) have confirmed the close relationship of *Medicago*, *Melilotus*, and *Trigonella*, and also the rather distant relationship of *Parochetus* from the other genera. These analyses also indicate that *Ononis* is much closer to this group than hitherto appreciated, and that *Trifolium* is more closely related to genera of tribe Vicieae. This interpretation of generic relationships suggests that a redefinition of tribal composition is required, and that nomenclaturally the tribal name Trifolieae may need to be abandoned. Before such actions are taken, it is advisable to await additional studies of generic relationships.

Ononis is of limited economic significance, although some species are grown as ornamentals, some are weeds, and some are employed for medicinal purposes. Species of *Ononis* are sparsely introduced and rarely collected in the flora area.

SELECTED REFERENCE Širjaev, G. I. 1932. Generis *Ononis* L. revisio critica. Beih. Bot. Centralbl. 49: 381–665.

1. Shrubs (woody basally); stems with or without thorns; seeds tuberculate . . . . 1. *Ononis spinosa*
1. Herbs; stems without thorns; seeds smooth . . . . 2. *Ononis alopecuroides*

1. Ononis spinosa Linnaeus, Sp. Pl. 2: 716. 1753, name conserved [F] [I]

Shrubs, 10–100[–160] cm, woody basally; rhizomes present or absent. **Stems** ascending, erect, or procumbent [prostrate]; thorns present or absent. **Leaflets** 1 or 3, blades ovate, elliptic, or oblong to narrowly oblong, 3–40 × 2–23 mm. **Racemes** dense or lax. **Flowers** 1 or 2 per node, pedicellate, (6–)10–20 mm; corolla usually pink or purple [white]. **Fruits** ovoid or oblong-rhomboid, 5–10 mm. **Seeds** 1–4, spherical to ovoid, 2–3 mm, tuberculate [smooth].

Subspecies ca. 4 (3 in the flora): introduced; Eurasia, n Africa.

R. B. Ivimey-Cook (1968) stated that, with regard to *Ononis spinosa*, a pair of chromosomes possess a long constriction such that it may appear to be two pairs, which probably accounts for the records of $2n = 32$ (for subsp. *spinosa*) and for records of $2n = 32$ and 64 (for subsp. *maritima*).

The taxonomy of what is treated here as *Ononis spinosa* in the broad sense is controversial and unsettled, with the three subspecies recognized here alternatively delimited as separate species (circumscribed as done here, more broadly, or more narrowly). Moreover, additional taxa have been recognized in Eurasia and circumscribed differently by various authors. The present treatment of all of the North American perennial *Ononis* as subspecies of *O. spinosa* is consistent with the circumscriptions and rankings in ILDIS (International Legume Database & Information Service), but use of the name *O. spinosa* subsp. *maritima* follows J. A. Davesa (2000).

1. Flowers borne in pairs at nodes; thorns absent . . . . 1c. *Ononis spinosa* subsp. *hircina*
1. Flowers usually borne singly at nodes; thorns present or absent.
    2. Stems ascending or erect; thorns present; rhizomes absent. . . 1a. *Ononis spinosa* subsp. *spinosa*
    2. Stems procumbent or ascending; thorns often absent (when present, usually relatively soft); rhizomes often present. . . . . 1b. *Ononis spinosa* subsp. *maritima*

1a. Ononis spinosa Linnaeus subsp. **spinosa** • Spiny or thorny restharrow F I

Shrubs 10–90 cm; rhizomes absent. **Stems** ascending or erect; thorns present, rigid, terminating branchlets. **Leaflets** usually 3. **Racemes** lax. **Flowers** usually borne singly at nodes, (6–)10–20 mm; corolla pink or purple. **Fruits** 1–4-seeded, 6–10 mm. $2n$ = 30, 32 (Europe).

Flowering early–late summer. Ruderal habitats (mostly on ballast, some apparently as escapes); 0–200 m; introduced; Ill., Md., N.J., N.Y., Pa.; Eurasia; n Africa; introduced also in Pacific Islands (New Zealand), Australia.

C. A. Stace (1997) distinguished subspp. *spinosa* and *maritima* by the former having leaflet lengths more than three times widths, the latter having leaflet lengths less than three times widths. This characteristic has some validity, but is not dependable.

1b. Ononis spinosa Linnaeus subsp. **maritima** (Dumortier) P. Fournier, Quatre Fl. France, 540. 1936 • Common restharrow I

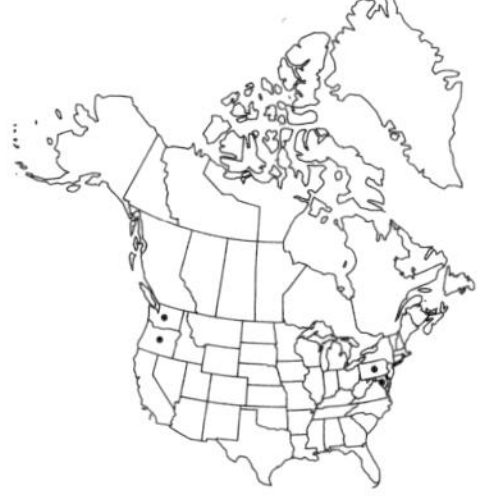

Ononis maritima Dumortier, Bull. Soc. Roy. Bot. Belgique 1: 113. 1862; *O. repens* Linnaeus

Shrubs 30–70 cm; rhizomes often present. **Stems** procumbent or ascending; thorns often absent, when present, usually relatively soft. **Leaflets** 1 or 3. **Racemes** lax. **Flowers** usually borne singly at nodes, (7–)10–20 mm; corolla pink or purple. **Fruits** 1 or 2(–4)-seeded, 5–8 mm. $2n$ = 30, 32, 60, 64 (Europe).

Flowering early–late summer. Ruderal habitats, sandy seashores; 0–400 m; introduced; Md., Oreg., Pa., Wash.; Eurasia; n Africa; introduced also in Pacific Islands (New Zealand), Australia.

Until the early twentieth century, ballast for stabilizing ships was usually soil taken from near berthing areas and discharged at ports where cargo was taken on. Subspecies *maritima* furnishes the principal seashore ecotypes of the species, which accordingly have most often been taken up in ballast, collected for the most part on ballast deposits, and found growing as introductions in or near seashores.

1c. Ononis spinosa Linnaeus subsp. **hircina** (Jacquin) Gams in G. Hegi, Ill. Fl. Mitt.-Eur. 4: 1224. 1923 • Field restharrow I

Ononis hircina Jacquin, Hort. Bot. Vindob. 1: 40, plate 93. 1771; *O. arvensis* Linnaeus

Shrubs 30–100 cm; rhizomes absent. **Stems** ascending or erect; thorns absent. **Leaflets** mostly 3. **Racemes** dense. **Flowers** borne in pairs at nodes, 10–20 mm; corolla pink. **Fruits** 1–3-seeded, 6–9 mm. $2n$ = 30 (Europe).

Flowering mid–late summer. Ruderal habitats; 0–400 m; introduced; Alta.; N.Y., Oreg.; Eurasia.

A note on an Alberta specimen of subsp. *hircina* (*G. W. Wheeler* NY) states that the plants were brought to Canada about 1940 for medicinal purposes and subsequently became established in the Thorsby area along a stream bank and in roadside ditches.

2. Ononis alopecuroides Linnaeus, Sp. Pl. 2: 717. 1753 • Foxtail restharrow [I]

Herbs, 10–65(–100) cm; rhizomes absent. **Stems** decumbent, ascending, or erect; thorns absent. **Leaflets** usually 1 (sometimes 3 distally and in inflorescences), blades elliptic, oblong-elliptic, or elliptic-orbiculate, (10–)20–50 × 5–30 mm. **Racemes** dense. **Flowers** 1 per node, subsessile, (9–)13–16 mm; corolla often pink, sometimes white. **Fruits** ovoid, 6–10 mm. **Seeds** 2 or 3, ovoid, 2–3 mm, smooth. $2n$ = 30 (Europe).

Flowering spring. Open, grazed oak woodlands, savannas, dry arroyos; 300–400 m; introduced; Calif.; s Europe; w Asia; n Africa; introduced also in n Europe, Australia.

The first and only report of *Ononis alopecuroides* in North America is based on a colony discovered in San Luis Obispo county in 1998. Because *O. alopecuroides* is considered weedy in northern Europe (where it is introduced) and is a potential invasive weed in California, state officials eradicated all plants located in subsequent years, and have maintained an alert for any reoccurrence.

147. MELILOTUS (Linnaeus) Miller, Gard. Dict. Abr. ed. 4, vol. 2. 1754 • Sweet-clover, melilot [Greek *mel*, honey, alluding to sweet fragrance of foliage or plants being favorite resort of bees, and *lotos*, alluding to similarity to *Lotus*] [I]

Ernest Small

Trifolium [unranked] *Melilotus* Linnaeus, Sp. Pl. 2: 764. 1753 (as Meliloti)

Herbs, annual, biennial, or short-lived perennial, unarmed. **Stems** usually erect or ascending, sometimes decumbent, glabrous or glabrescent. **Leaves** alternate, odd-pinnate; stipules present, adnate to petiole; petiolate; leaflets 3, blade margins usually dentate, rarely entire or subentire, surfaces glabrous or pubescent. **Inflorescences** pedunculate, (5–)8–80(–120)-flowered, axillary, racemes, usually elongating in fruit; bracts present or absent. **Flowers** papilionaceous, usually pendulous, sometimes upright; calyx campanulate, lobes 5, ± subequal; corolla yellow or white; stamens 10, diadelphous; anthers basifixed. **Fruits** legumes, stipitate, usually ± compressed, usually globose, subglobose, obovoid, or ovoid, sometimes lanceolate-rhomboid or elongated-elliptic, indehiscent or tardily dehiscent, reticulately or concentrically patterned with raised venation, thickly leathery, usually glabrous (pubescent in *M. altissimus*). **Seeds** 1 or 2 (or 3) [–5], usually ovoid, obovoid, oblong to subglobose, or ellipsoid, smooth or slightly tuberculate. x = 8.

Species ca. 18 (6 in the flora): introduced; Europe, Asia, n Africa; introduced also in temperate areas nearly worldwide.

Trigonella and *Melilotus* may merit amalgamation (P. Coulot and P. Rabaute 2013), and *Melilotus* has been subdivided in various ways (reviewed by G. A. Stevenson 1969). Most species of *Melilotus* have a characteristic vanillalike odor and a bitter taste, due to the presence of coumarins.

Some species of *Melilotus* are cultivated as forage crops, for soil improvement, erosion control, revegetation and reclamation plantings, and as honey plants. Some are significant weeds, including the cultivated species.

Some *Melilotus* specimens at GH and NY were collected from ballast sites and have been identified as *M. neapolitanus* Tenore ex Gussone or *M. gracilis* de Candolle; these are correctly identified as *M. neapolitanus*, according to the key written by G. A. Stevenson (1969). However,

F. Sales and I. C. Hedge (1993) concluded that the name *M. neapolitanus* Tenore is confused, applied in the past to *M. sulcatus* Desfontaines and incorrectly applied by most authors to *M. spicatus* (Smith) Breistroffer. Regardless of the correct name, the species is not naturalized in the flora area.

SELECTED REFERENCES Isely, D. 1954. Keys to sweet clovers (*Melilotus*). Proc. Iowa Acad. Sci. 61: 119–131. Schulz, O. E. 1901. Monographie der Gattung *Melilotus*. Bot. Jahrb. Syst. 29: 660–735. Stevenson, G. A. 1969. An agronomic and taxonomic review of the genus *Melilotus* Mill. Canad. J. Pl. Sci. 49: 1–20. Turkington, R. A., P. B. Cavers, and E. Rempel. 1978. The biology of Canadian weeds. 29. *Melilotus alba* Desr. and *M. officinalis* (L.) Lam. Canad. J. Pl. Sci. 58: 523–537.

1. Corollas white.
    2. Flowers 3.5–5(–6) mm; pedicels 1–1.5(–2) mm; widespread, including Manitoba and Saskatchewan . . . . . 1. *Melilotus albus*
    2. Flowers 3–3.5 mm; pedicels 2–4 mm; Manitoba, Saskatchewan . . . . . 6. *Melilotus wolgicus*
1. Corollas yellow.
    3. Stipule margins dentate (mostly at base); legumes concentrically striated-veined . . . . . 5. *Melilotus sulcatus*
    3. Stipule margins entire or subentire; legumes reticulate-veined, transversely rugose, or sigmoid-veined.
        4. Flowers 1.5–3 mm . . . . . 3. *Melilotus indicus*
        4. Flowers 4–7 mm.
            5. Ovaries and young fruits appressed-pubescent . . . . . 2. *Melilotus altissimus*
            5. Ovaries and young fruits glabrous . . . . . 4. *Melilotus officinalis*

1. **Melilotus albus** Medikus, Vorles. Churpfälz. Phys.-Ökon. Ges. 2: 382. 1787 (as alba) • White sweet-clover or melilot, honey-clover, mélilot blanc [F] [I] [W]

Herbs usually biennial, rarely annual, 30–150(–260) cm. **Stems** erect or ascending. **Leaves:** stipules lanceolate-subulate to setaceous, 4–6(–10) mm, margins usually entire, sometimes toothed at base; leaflet blades narrowly oblong-obovate to suborbiculate-oblong, 10–24(–50) × 5–12(–15) mm, margins dentate. **Racemes** 40–80(–120)-flowered. **Pedicels** 1–1.5(–2) mm. **Flowers** 3.5–5(–6) mm; corolla white; ovary glabrous. **Legumes** obovoid, subglobose, or globose-ovoid, 3–5 mm, reticulate-veined, glabrous. **Seeds** 1 or 2(or 3), ovoid, (1.7–)2–2.5(–3.5) mm. 2*n* = 16.

Flowering spring–fall. Grasslands, mixed forests, canyons, streamsides, riverbeds, lakeshores, waste places, roadsides; 0–2700 m; introduced; Greenland; St. Pierre and Miquelon; Alta., B.C., Man., N.B., Nfld. and Labr., N.W.T., N.S., Nunavut, Ont., P.E.I., Que., Sask., Yukon; Ala., Alaska, Ariz., Ark., Calif., Colo., Conn., Del., D.C., Fla., Ga., Idaho, Ill., Ind., Iowa, Kans., Ky., La., Maine, Md., Mass., Mich., Minn., Miss., Mo., Mont., Nebr., Nev., N.H., N.J., N.Mex., N.Y., N.C., N.Dak., Ohio, Okla., Oreg., Pa., R.I., S.C., S.Dak., Tenn., Tex., Utah, Vt., Va., Wash., W.Va., Wis., Wyo.; Eurasia; introduced also in Mexico, West Indies, South America, Australia.

Melilotus albus is extremely variable in Eurasia, and has been divided into many infraspecific taxa. It is the most important economic species in *Melilotus*, often grown as a crop, green manure, and honey plant, and posing a widespread weed problem.

Essentially all white-petaled *Melilotus* plants growing outside of cultivation in North America are *M. albus*; herbarium specimens often do not show the color well, sometimes resulting in misidentification, particularly between *M. albus* and *M. officinalis*. Aside from petal color, the species are quite similar. The venation areolae on the mature pods tend to differ: the raised venation ridges tend to form an irregular reticulation on the mature fruits of *M. albus*; they tend to form transverse areolae on the fruits of *M. officinalis* (S. J. Darbyshire and E. Small 2018). Although *M. albus* and *M. officinalis* are sometimes merged, there are very strong barriers to interbreeding between the two (G. T. Webster 1955; M. Maekawa et al. 1991), in addition to geographical and ecological differences, which justify their continued recognition as separate species.

P. Coulot and P. Rabaute (2013) included *Melilotus albus* in *Trigonella sulcata* (Desfontaines) Coulot & Rabaute (treated here as *M. sulcatus*). Most botanical literature incorrectly lists the authority for *Melilotus albus* as Desrousseaux in Lamarck instead of Medikus.

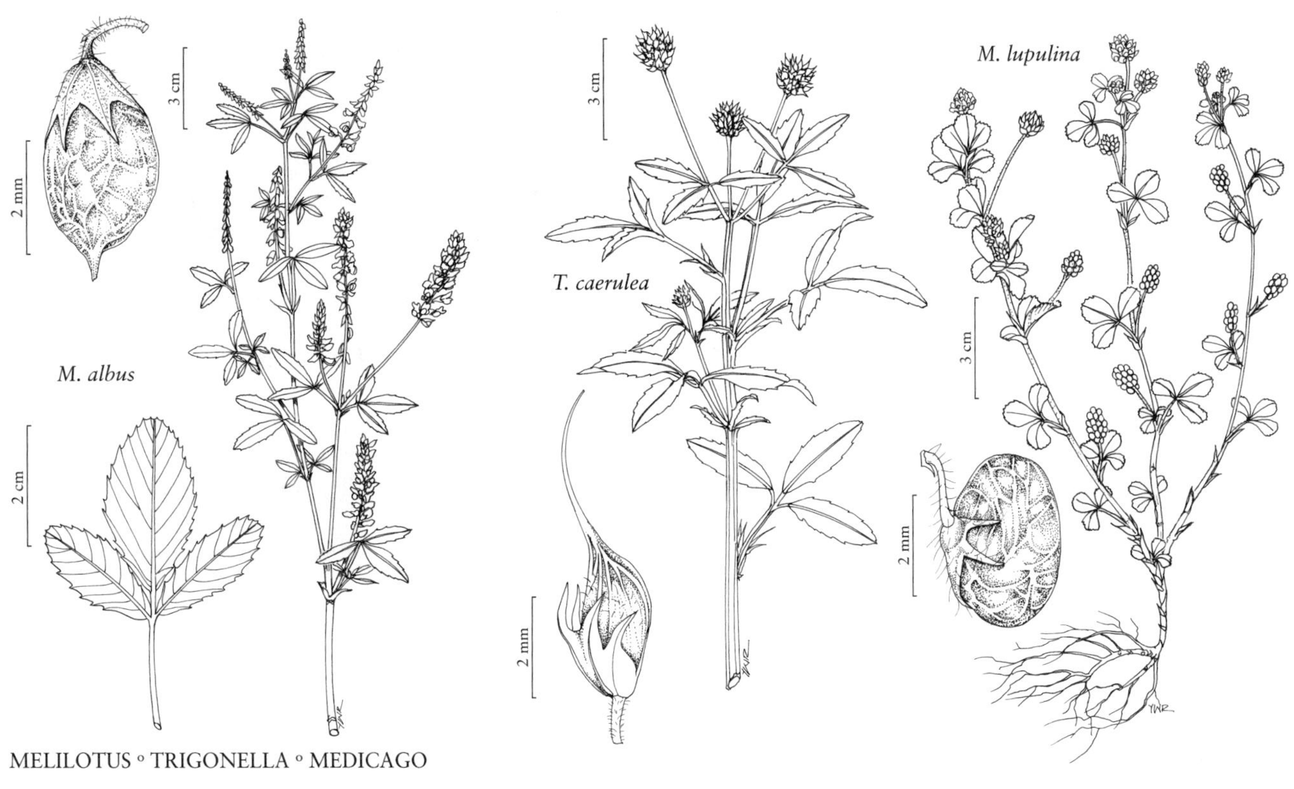

MELILOTUS ◦ TRIGONELLA ◦ MEDICAGO

2. Melilotus altissimus Thuillier, Fl. Env. Paris ed. 2, 378. 1799 (as altissima) • Tall melilot or yellow sweet-clover, grand mélilot [I] [W]

Trigonella altissima (Thuillier) Coulot & Rabaute

Herbs biennial or short-lived perennial, 60–160 cm. **Stems** erect. **Leaves:** stipules subulate-setaceous, 5–8 mm, margins entire; leaflet blades linear to lanceolate-oblong, oblong-ovate, or cuneate, 20–40 × 4–10 mm, margins subentire or dentate. **Racemes** 15–50-flowered. **Pedicels** 2 mm. **Flowers** 5–7 mm; corolla yellow; ovary appressed-pubescent. **Legumes** obovoid or elongated-ellipsoid, 3.5–5(–6) mm, reticulate-veined, areoles not notably elongated transversely, appressed-pubescent. **Seeds** usually 2, ovoid or ellipsoid, 2–2.5 mm. **2*n*** = 16 (Eurasia).

Flowering early summer–fall. Waste places, roadsides; 0–1000 m; introduced; Greenland; N.B., N.S., Ont.; Ill., Maine, Mich., N.J., N.Y., Ohio, Pa., Wis.; Europe; introduced also in South America, Asia.

3. Melilotus indicus (Linnaeus) Allioni, Fl. Pedem. 1: 308. 1785 (as indica) • Annual yellow or Indian or small-flowered sweet-clover, Indian or small melilot, sour-clover [I] [W]

Trifolium indicum Linnaeus, Sp. Pl. 2: 765. 1753 (as indica); *Trigonella smallii* Coulot & Rabaute

Herbs annual, (10–)15–60 cm. **Stems** erect or ascending. **Leaves:** stipules lanceolate-subulate to setaceous, (3–)4–6 (–8) mm, margins subentire (entire or toothed at base); leaflet blades lanceolate-oblong, oblanceolate, or obovate, (8–)12–25 × (2–)7–10 mm, margins dentate. **Racemes** 10–50-flowered. **Pedicels** 1 mm. **Flowers** 1.5–3 mm; corolla yellow; ovary glabrous. **Legumes** subglobose, 1.5–3(–4) mm, strongly reticulate-veined, glabrous. **Seeds** 1 (or 2), ovoid, 1.8–2.3 mm. **2*n*** = 16 [18 (Asia)].

Flowering spring–fall. Waste places, roadsides, grasslands; 0–2000 m; introduced; Greenland; N.S.; Ala., Ariz., Ark., Calif., Del., Fla., Ga., Idaho, Ky., La., Maine, Mass., Mich., Minn., Miss., Nev., N.H., N.J., N.Mex., N.Y., N.C., N.Dak., Okla., Oreg., Pa., S.C., Tex., Utah, Vt., Va., Wash., Wis.; Europe; Asia; Africa; introduced also in Mexico, Central America (Honduras), South America (Argentina, Bolivia, Chile), Pacific Islands (New Zealand).

Melilotus indicus occasionally has been grown as a forage crop in the southern United States; it is generally considered to be an undesirable weed.

4. **Melilotus officinalis** (Linnaeus) Lamarck, Fl. Franç. 2: 594. 1779 • Yellow sweet-clover, field or ribbed or yellow melilot, mélilot jaune, trèfle d'odeur jaune [I] [W]

Trifolium officinale Linnaeus, Sp. Pl. 2: 765. 1753 (as officinalis); *Trigonella officinalis* (Linnaeus) Coulot & Rabaute

Herbs usually biennial, sometimes annual, (15–)30–280 cm. **Stems** decumbent to erect. **Leaves:** stipules lanceolate or subulate, 3–6(–12) mm, margins entire; leaflet blades obovate, obovate-oblong, ovate, or ovate-lanceolate, 8–25 × 4–15 mm, margins dentate. **Racemes** 30–70(–80)-flowered. **Pedicels** (1.5–)2–2.5 mm. **Flowers** 4–7 mm; corolla yellow; ovary glabrous. **Legumes** ovoid, 2.5–5 mm, transversely rugose, areoles notably elongated, glabrous. **Seeds** 1 (or 2), ovoid, obovoid, or ellipsoid, (1.5–)1.8–2(–2.5) mm. **2*n*** = 16.

Flowering spring–fall. Grasslands, slopes, plains, hillsides, waste places, roadsides, cultivated fields; 0–3100 m; introduced; Alta., B.C., Man., N.B., Nfld. and Labr., N.W.T., N.S., Ont., P.E.I., Que., Sask., Yukon; Ala., Alaska, Ariz., Ark., Calif., Colo., Conn., Del., D.C., Fla., Ga., Idaho, Ill., Ind., Iowa, Kans., Ky., La., Maine, Md., Mass., Mich., Minn., Miss., Mo., Mont., Nebr., Nev., N.H., N.J., N.Mex., N.Y., N.C., N.Dak., Ohio, Okla., Oreg., Pa., R.I., S.C., S.Dak., Tenn., Tex., Utah, Vt., Va., Wash., W.Va., Wis., Wyo.; Eurasia; introduced also in Mexico, South America, Africa, Australia.

Melilotus officinalis is occasionally grown as a forage crop, but it is generally considered to be an undesirable weed.

5. **Melilotus sulcatus** Desfontaines, Fl. Atlant. 2: 193. 1799 (as sulcata) • Furrowed or grooved melilot, Mediterranean sweet-clover [I]

Trigonella sulcata (Desfontaines) Coulot & Rabaute

Herbs annual, 10–70 cm. **Stems** erect or ascending. **Leaves:** stipules ovate-acuminate or subulate, 5–10 mm, margins dentate (mostly at base); leaflet blades obovate, oblanceolate, or oblong-cuneate, 10–25 × 5–12 mm, margins dentate. **Racemes** (5–)8–20(–50)-flowered. **Pedicels** 1–2 mm. **Flowers** (2.5–)3–4(–8) mm; corolla yellow; ovary glabrous. **Legumes** globose or ovoid, (2–)3–4(–5.5) mm, concentrically striate-veined, glabrous. **Seeds** 1(or 2), oblong-subglobose or ovoid, (2–)2.5–3(–3.5) mm. **2*n*** = 16 [Eurasia].

Flowering spring–summer. Ruderal areas; 0–200 m; introduced; Ala., N.J., Pa.; Europe; Asia; Africa.

In Europe, *Melilotus sulcatus* appears to intergrade or at least hybridize with *M. infestus* Gussone [*M. sulcatus* subsp. *infestus* (Gussone) Bonnier & Layens] and *M. segetalis* (Brotero) Seringe [*M. sulcatus* subsp. *segetalis* (Brotero) P. Fournier].

6. **Melilotus wolgicus** Poiret in J. Lamarck et al., Encycl., suppl. 3: 648. 1814 (as wolgica) • Volga sweet-clover [I]

Herbs biennial, 40–120(–150) cm. **Stems** erect. **Leaves:** stipules linear-setaceous or subulate, 6–8(–10) mm, margins entire; leaflet blades rhombic-ovate to oblong-lanceolate, or linear, 10–30 × 2–8 mm, margins dentate or entire. **Racemes** 25–60-flowered. **Pedicels** 2–4 mm. **Flowers** 3–3.5 mm; corolla white; ovary glabrous. **Legumes** obovoid, 4–5 mm, distinctly reticulate-veined, glabrous. **Seeds** usually 1 (or 2), oblong-ovoid, 2.5 mm. **2*n*** = 16 [Eurasia].

Flowering spring–summer. Gravel pits, wasteland, drainage ditches, sandy banks; 200–500 m; introduced; Man., Sask.; Eurasia.

The Manitoba vouchers of *Melilotus wolgicus* are mostly G. A. Stevenson collections at DAO from the Brandon area and are almost certainly established escapes from the extensive experimental cultivation of *Melilotus* species by Stevenson; it has also been observed persisting in the forage plot area of the Research Station, Saskatoon, Saskatchewan, but does not appear to have spread elsewhere.

148. TRIGONELLA Linnaeus, Sp. Pl. 2: 776. 1753; Gen. Pl. ed. 5, 338. 1754 • Fenugreek

[Latin *tries*, three, *gonu*, angle, and *-ella*, diminutive, alluding to corolla appearance] I

Ernest Small

Herbs, annual [perennial], unarmed, [sometimes base woody]. **Stems** erect to procumbent or decumbent, glabrous or glabrate to pubescent. **Leaves** alternate, odd-pinnate; stipules present; petiolate; leaflets 3, blade margins dentate or denticulate, [entire, toothed at base, dissected, or laciniate], surfaces glabrous or sparsely pubescent. **Inflorescences** pedunculate or subsessile, 1–30-flowered, axillary, racemes or flowers subsolitary, [heads or umbels]; bracts absent. **Flowers** papilionaceous; calyx campanulate, symmetric or with 2 larger lobes, lobes 5; corolla yellow to white, sometimes tinged violet, or pale to lilac-blue, 5.5–18 mm; stamens 10, diadelphous; anthers dorsifixed; style usually relatively long. **Fruits** legumes, yellow to light brown, stipitate, sometimes compressed, linear and subterete, ovoid, or rhomboid-obovoid [reniform, lunate, semicircular, moniliform], not coiled, often curved [or prickly], [margins rarely winged or fimbriate], usually beaked, dehiscent, sometimes tardily so, thickly leathery, glabrous or sparsely pubescent. **Seeds** 1–20[–40], oblong or ovoid, usually tuberculate or verrucose, sometimes smooth. $x = 8$.

Species ca. 50 (4 in the flora): introduced; Eurasia, n Africa, Australia.

Several *Trigonella* species are known in the flora area only from ballast collections or as waifs. *Trigonella monspeliaca* Linnaeus and *T. polycarpa* Boissier & Heldreich were reported as waifs on chrome ore piles in Maryland by C. F. Reed (1964). Reports of *T. laciniata* Linnaeus, *T. noeana* Boissier, and *T. hamosa* Linnaeus (as "*T. ramosa*") by C. H. Knowlton and W. Deane (1918) in Massachusetts could not be substantiated.

Trigonella has been an umbrella genus. More than two dozen species were transferred recently to *Medicago*. Molecular analyses (G. Bena et al. 1998; M. F. Wojciechowski et al. 2000; K. P. Steele and Wojciechowski 2003; Wojciechowski 2003) have suggested that at least some of the species of *Trigonella* and *Melilotus* belong to the same clade, and, accordingly, the two genera need to be combined. More extensive analysis is desirable to support their amalgamation.

SELECTED REFERENCES Širjaev, G. 1928–1934. Generis *Trigonella* L. revisio critica. Spisy Prir. Fak. Masarykovy Univ. 102, 110, 128, 136, 148, 170, 192. Vassilczenko, I. T. 1953. A review of the species of the genus *Trigonella* L. Trudy Bot. Inst. Akad. Nauk S.S.S.R., Ser. 1, Fl. Sist. Vyssh. Rast. 14: 124–269.

1. Inflorescences 1- or 2-flowered (in axils), subsessile; peduncles not evident .... 1. *Trigonella foenum-graecum*
1. Inflorescences 10–30-flowered; peduncles 1.5–6 cm.
    2. Legumes (including beaks) 10+ mm; seeds 4–8; corollas yellow .... 2. *Trigonella corniculata*
    2. Legumes (including beaks) less than 10 mm; seeds 1–3; corollas blue, pale blue, lilac-blue, or white.
        3. Inflorescences globose racemes, slightly elongated in fruit; leaflet blades ovate to oblong ....3. *Trigonella caerulea*
        3. Inflorescences globose or subglobose to ovoid racemes, elongated in fruit; leaflet blades oblong to linear-oblong or linear-lanceolate.......................4. *Trigonella procumbens*

1. Trigonella foenum-graecum Linnaeus, Sp. Pl. 2: 777. 1753 • Fenugreek, Greek hay or clover, fenugrec [I]

Herbs 10–50 cm, glabrous or sparsely pubescent. **Stems** single or several, usually erect, sometimes ascending, unbranched or several-branched. **Leaves:** stipules triangular-lanceolate, margins entire, apex acuminate; leaflet blades obovate or oblong to oblanceolate, 10–30 × 5–15 mm, margins usually dentate, rarely incised, distal portion denticulate. **Peduncles** not evident. **Inflorescences** 1- or 2-flowered (in axils), subsessile. **Flowers** 12–18 mm; calyx lobes nearly equal to tube; corolla yellowish white or white, sometimes tinged violet. **Legumes** erect or patent, seed-bearing (proximal) part linear, somewhat flattened, 50–110(–150) × 3–6 mm, gradually tapering into beak (10–)20–40(–50) mm. **Seeds** 10–20, usually yellow- or pale brown, rarely rose-yellow, white, bluish, or olive green, oblong or ovoid, 3–5 × 2–3 mm. **2*n*** = 16.

Flowering early–late summer. Roadsides, waste areas, fields; 0–1000 m; introduced; Calif., Md.; Eurasia.

Trigonella foenum-graecum probably originated in southwestern Asia; its present widespread distribution in Eurasia is due to escapes from cultivation.

Trigonella foenum-graecum is the most economically important species in the genus, used mostly in Asia. All plant parts are consumed by livestock; the seeds are an important source of artificial maple flavorings. Humans, also, consume the seeds, and, to a lesser extent, the leaves are used as a potherb. The plants are also employed to some extent medicinally and for various pharmaceutical extracts.

2. Trigonella corniculata (Linnaeus) Linnaeus, Syst. Nat. ed. 10, 2: 1180. 1759 • Sickle-fruited or sicklefruit fenugreek [I]

Trifolium corniculatum Linnaeus, Sp. Pl. 2: 766. 1753 (as corniculata)

Herbs 10–40(–60) cm, glabrous or sparsely pubescent. **Stems** erect or procumbent, diffusely branched. **Leaves:** stipules lanceolate-subulate, margins dentate or incised; leaflet blades obovate to oblong-obovate or oblong-cuneate, (5–)10–30(–40) × (3–)8–20(–35) mm, margins dentate. **Peduncles** 1.5–6 cm. **Inflorescences** 10–20-flowered, spicate, ovate racemes, elongated in fruit. **Flowers** 6–7(–10) mm; calyx lobes 1/2 to as long as tube; corolla yellow. **Legumes** pendent, linear, flattened-compressed, ± curved-falcate, 10–20(–30) × (1.5–)2–2.5(–3) mm, tapering-acuminate into beak 0.5–1.5 mm. **Seeds** 4–8, yellow- to light brown, oblong, 1–2 × 1.3 mm. **2*n*** = 16.

Flowering early–late summer. Roadsides, waste areas, fields; 0–1000 m; introduced; Calif., Mass., Utah; Eurasia.

Trigonella corniculata may be extirpated from California. The Massachusetts record is from 1979 at a single ballast site.

Trigonella corniculata is a minor, cultivated food herb in Asia, where the young leaves and stem tips are consumed as a potherb, and the seeds are used as a flavoring agent.

3. Trigonella caerulea (Linnaeus) Seringe in A. P. de Candolle and A. L. P. P. de Candolle, Prodr. 2: 181. 1825 (as coerulea) • Sweet trefoil, blue fenugreek [F] [I]

Trifolium caeruleum Linnaeus, Sp. Pl. 2: 764. 1753 (as caerulea)

Herbs 20–60(–100) cm, sparsely pubescent. **Stems** erect, densely branched. **Leaves:** stipules triangular-lanceolate, margins dentate; leaflet blades ovate to oblong, (10–)20–40(–50) × (5–)10–20(–35) mm, margins denticulate. **Peduncles** 2–5 cm. **Inflorescences** 20–30-flowered, globose racemes, slightly elongated in fruit. **Flowers** 5.5–6.5 mm; calyx lobes nearly equal to tube; corolla blue, pale blue, or white. **Legumes** erect-spreading, rhomboid-obovate, flattened, 4–5 × 3 mm, with short, abrupt beak 2–3 mm. **Seeds** 1 or 2(or 3), brownish, ovoid, 2 mm. **2*n*** = 16.

Flowering early–late summer. Roadsides, waste areas, fields; 0–1000 m; introduced; Alta., Man., Sask.; Fla., Md., N.Y.; Eurasia; introduced also in n Africa.

A specimen of *Trigonella caerulea* from Ontario (in DAO) is a garden escape.

Trigonella caerulea, a cultigen believed to have been derived from *T. procumbens*, is not thought to have an indigenous range; it is widely grown and naturalized or casual in Europe, present in North Africa, and only occasionally collected as a ruderal in North America.

Trigonella caerulea is a minor culinary herb; the dried, powdered leaves and flowers are used as a condiment in breads, soups, and teas, and especially to flavor cheeses.

4. **Trigonella procumbens** (Besser) Reichenbach, Iconogr. Bot. Pl. Crit. 4: 35. 1826 • Trailing fenugreek [I]

Melilotus procumbens Besser, Enum. Pl., 30. 1821

Herbs 20–50(–80) cm, sparsely pubescent. **Stems** decumbent, ascending, or suberect, usually branched from base. **Leaves:** stipules lanceolate, margins dentate; leaflet blades oblong to linear-oblong or -lanceolate, 10–30(–40) × 3–10(–20) mm, margins denticulate. **Peduncles** 2–6 cm. **Inflorescences** 20–30-flowered, globose or subglobose to ovoid racemes, densely flowered but elongated to ± lax in fruit. **Flowers** 5.5–7 mm; calyx ca. 1/2 as long as corolla, lobes nearly equal to tube; corolla pale blue or lilac-blue. **Legumes** erect-spreading, ovoid, flattened, seed-bearing part 4.5–6 × 2–3 mm, tapering into subulate beak 2–3 mm. **Seeds** 1–3, brownish, oblong, 2.5 × 1 mm. **2*n*** = 16.

Flowering early–late summer. Waste ground, ballast; 0–1000 m; introduced; Pa.; Eurasia.

Trigonella caerulea (see discussion under that species) is thought to be a domesticated phase of *T. procumbens*. Although the two are generally recognized as different species, they could be combined into one species [as indicated by the combination *T. caerulea* subsp. *procumbens* (Besser) Thellung].

149. MEDICAGO Linnaeus, Sp. Pl. 2: 778. 1753; Gen. Pl. ed. 5, 339. 1754 • Alfalfa, lucerne, medic [Latin *medica*, from Medes (Media), and *ago*, connection, alluding to a kind of cultivated forage clover supposedly native to Media] [I]

Ernest Small

Herbs [shrubs], annual, biennial, or perennial, unarmed, sometimes base woody; roots fibrous or branched taproots; rhizomes sometimes present. **Stems** prostrate, procumbent, decumbent, ascending, or erect, branched or unbranched, especially when small or crowded by vegetation, usually slightly to moderately pubescent, hairs eglandular or sometimes gland-tipped, sometimes septate. **Leaves** alternate, odd-pinnate; stipules present, margins entire, toothed, or lobed, glabrous or pubescent, hairs eglandular and/or gland-tipped; epulvinate; petiolate; leaflets 3(5 or 7), pulvinate, blade margins partly serrate, sometimes laciniate or incised, surfaces glabrous or pubescent, hairs eglandular and/or gland-tipped, especially abaxially. **Inflorescences** 1–50-flowered, axillary or terminal, usually racemes or heads, sometimes umbels or flowers subsolitary; bracts present or absent. **Flowers** papilionaceous; calyx funnelform to campanulate, lobes 5, triangular to lanceolate, equal or subequal (adaxial pair longer); corolla usually yellow or orange-yellow, rarely purple, violet, variegated violet-yellow, or white; banner subequal to or longer than wings and keel; wings strongly adherent to keel by wing spur in keel invagination; keel rounded, not strongly incurved, hooding stamens; stamens 10, diadelphous; anthers dorsifixed, uniform, distinct portion of alternating filaments often thick. **Fruits** legumes, tan to brown or black, sessile or short-stipitate, terete, compressed, or flat [moniliform, plicate], straight, curved, or coiled, indehiscent or dehiscent at sutures; dorsal sutures prickly, tuberculate, or smooth [winged and fimbriate], faces papery, soft, or thickly leathery, sometimes with proliferative alveolar, spongy tissue, glabrous or pubescent, hairs eglandular and/or glandular, intersuture venation obscure to prominent, often anastomosing in species-specific patterns, sometimes a submarginal vein present, parallel to dorsal suture but somewhat remote from it. **Seeds** 1–30, usually reniform, sometimes oval, triangular, or rhomboid-ovoid, smooth, rugose, or tuberculate. x = 7, 8, 9.

Species ca. 85 (13 in the flora): introduced; Europe, Asia, n Africa; introduced also nearly worldwide in temperate and tropical areas.

Several species of *Medicago* not treated here have been recorded very rarely in the flora area, particularly as coastal, ballast waifs. These include *Medicago disciformis* de Candolle, collected in 1949 from Worcester County, Massachusetts (*Johnson s.n.*, DINH, now transferred to CONN); *M. monantha* (C. A. Meyer) Trautvetter collected in 1884 from Middlesex County, Massachusetts (*Swan s.n.*, NEBC); and *M. sphaerocarpa* Bertoloni, collected in 2016 from Santa Catalina Island, California, by C. M. Guilliams (SBBG). Several annual species are present in parts of the flora area because they escape from experimental or commercial forage cultivation; additional introduced species will likely be discovered, and because the majority are of Mediterranean origin, it will likely be in California and the southern states. All of the species treated here have shown weedy tendencies in some areas outside of the flora area, while some are weeds in the flora area. None is significantly troublesome.

Medicago sativa is arguably the most important temperate region forage plant in the world. Several other perennial species, and, more commonly, annual species, which are commonly called medics or medicks, are cultivated for forage, but infrequently in the flora area.

Species in sect. *Spirocarpos*, all with coiled fruits, normally have two rows of prickles on the dorsal suture, but in some plants these are reduced to tubercles or the dorsal sutures are without ornamentation. Cultivars often have been selected for lack of fruit prickles, as this prevents entanglement in fur and makes the nutritious fruits easier for livestock consumption. Cultivars have been grown in the flora area, increasing the likelihood that prickleless-fruited forms will be encountered. The prickles protect the fruit, serve to adhere to fur for distribution, and perhaps also to facilitate burial of the indehiscent fruits in soil. In their native area, prickly and prickleless forms occur randomly on a geographic basis. The literature is replete with extensive infraspecific classifications of the species on the basis of presence and length of prickles.

In the nineteenth and twentieth centuries, *Medicago* was controversially separated from *Trigonella*, less controversially from *Melilotus*, with given species assigned to these and many other genera depending on taxonomic treatment. Recent morphological, chemical, and molecular evidence has made it clear that *Medicago* is well demarcated from its nearest allies, including *Trigonella*, *Melilotus*, and *Trifolium*. *Medicago* flowers have an irreversible explosively tripping pollination mechanism, which is degenerate in the annual species, but evident by a syndrome of floral characteristics. Although fruits of *Medicago* are usually indispensable for species identification, flowers suffice for distinguishing *Medicago* from allied genera. Contrasting characters possessed by *Medicago* but not related genera include: banner, except when very small, with major basal vein usually with more than three branches near base; horn of wing petal large, about one-third of wing limb; keel very strongly adherent to wing by a wing spur in a keel invagination; androecium with apex of fused portion of anther column arched, alternating distinct portions of filaments often relatively thick; stigma fungiliform; style always short.

Several character states are unique to one or just a few species in the flora range. *Medicago arabica* is the only species in which the fruit has a dorsal suture with a pattern of four ridges separated by three grooves. *Medicago lupulina* is the only species that has one-seeded fruits. *Medicago monspeliaca* is the only species that has deflexed fruit and a stellate inflorescence; *M. monspeliaca* and *M. orbicularis* are the only species with rough-surfaced seeds. *Medicago orbicularis* is the only species with papery pod edges (although *M. scutellata* fruits are somewhat reminiscent). *Medicago sativa* is the only species that has violet or purple flowers. *Medicago scutellata* is the only species that has fruit resembling a stack of bowls. *Medicago rigidula*, *M. truncatula*, *M. turbinata*, and sometimes *M. polymorpha* have fruits that are extremely hard-walled at maturity, while the remaining species have fruit walls that are flexible or relatively easily bent.

Several forage species have a number of widely used common names, some often more or less confined to Europe, Australia, or different areas of the United States. Only vernacular names that have been used repeatedly in the literature are reported here.

Perennial species of *Medicago* are slightly to substantially outbreeding, while annual species are mostly strongly inbreeding.

SELECTED REFERENCES Bena, G. 2001. Molecular phylogeny supports the morphologically based taxonomic transfer of the "medicagoid" *Trigonella* species to the genus *Medicago* L. Pl. Syst. Evol. 229: 217–236. Heyn, C. C. 1963. The Annual Species of *Medicago*. Jerusalem. Lesins, K. A. and I. Lesins. 1979. Genus *Medicago* (Leguminosae). A Taxogenetic Study. The Hague. Small, E. 1987. Generic changes in Trifolieae subtribe Trigonellinae. In: C. H. Stirton, ed. 1987. Advances Legume Systematics. Part 3. Kew. Pp. 159–181. Small, E. 2011. Alfalfa and Relatives: Evolution and Classification of *Medicago*. Ottawa and Wallingford. Small, E. and M. Jomphe. 1989. A synopsis of the genus *Medicago* (Leguminosae). Canad. J. Bot. 67: 3260–3294. Small, E., P. Lassen, and B. S. Brookes. 1987. An expanded circumscription of *Medicago* (Leguminosae, Trifolieae) based on explosive flower tripping. Willdenowia 16: 415–437.

1. Corollas usually uniformly purple or variegated yellow-violet, sometimes violet or greenish . . . . 1. *Medicago sativa* (in part)
1. Corollas yellow, rarely orange-yellow.
   2. Legumes 1-seeded, nutletlike . . . . 2. *Medicago lupulina*
   2. Legumes 2–30-seeded.
      3. Legumes not coiled (often falcate), prickleless.
         4. Flowers not stellate in inflorescences; legumes not deflexed . . . . 1. *Medicago sativa* (in part)
         4. Flowers stellate in inflorescences; legumes deflexed . . . . 13. *Medicago monspeliaca*
      3. Legumes coiled, prickly, prickleless, or tuberculate.
         5. Legume coils conspicuously imbricate, concave (convex surface facing fruit base) . . . . 4. *Medicago scutellata*
         5. Legume coils ± flat.
            6. Legume coils papery at margins, prickleless; seeds tuberculate . . . . . . 3. *Medicago orbicularis*
            6. Legume coils not papery at margins, prickly or prickleless; seeds smooth.
               7. Mature legumes extremely hard-walled (prickly and prickleless forms occur, coils of prickly forms cannot be separated by hand without probability of injury); prickles, when present, very stocky and difficult to bend; base of prickles often round, 2 roots often apparent at maturity; venation pattern often obscure on coil face of mature fruit because of proliferation of alveolar tissue.
                  8. Legumes: coil face with radial veins entering veinless margin in distal 1/4 or 1/3 of coil, prickles absent or reduced to tubercles, no more than 5 mm, sometimes inclined opposite to direction of fruit coiling (giving fruit appearance of rapidly spinning top) . . . . . 5. *Medicago turbinata*
                  8. Legumes: coil face with slightly branching and/or anastomosing veins, prickles or tubercles usually present, shorter to longer than 5 mm, not inclined opposite to direction of fruit coiling.
                     9. Young legumes with glandular hairs, evident only in young pods, often producing velvety appearance; calyx with eglandular and/or glandular hairs . . . . 6. *Medicago rigidula* (in part)
                     9. Young legumes with eglandular hairs, if glandular hairs present, without velvety appearance; calyx usually with eglandular hairs only.
                        10. Legumes usually ovoid, sometimes discoid, cylindrical, or spherical, prickles, when present, at various angles to plane of coil; coils weakly to strongly adpressed, radial veins of coil face very strongly curved, veins in peripheral 1/3 of coil face slightly to moderately anastomosing, evident only in young pods . . . . 6. *Medicago rigidula* (in part)

10. Legumes usually cylindrical, prickles usually present, often at 90° to plane of coil, pointed towards ends of pod; coils often strongly adpressed; radial veins of fruit coil face weakly to moderately curved, veins in peripheral 1/3 of coil face weakly if at all anastomosing . . . . 7. *Medicago truncatula*

[7. Shifted to left margin.—Ed.]

7. Mature legumes soft-walled (sometimes hard in *M. polymorpha*); prickles usually present, often relatively thin and flexible, base of prickles 2-rooted, one root arising in dorsal suture, other in submarginal vein; venation discernible on coil face of mature fruit.
    11. Legume coil edges with 4 ridges separated by 3 grooves; leaflet blades often with conspicuous, central, purple-red (anthocyanin) blotch adaxially . . . . 8. *Medicago arabica*
    11. Legume coil edges with fewer than 4 ridges, if any; leaflet blades very rarely with central purple-red blotch.
        12. Outer periphery of legume coil faces with distinct veinless margin, venation not extending to dorsal suture.
            13. Stipule margins entire or minutely dentate at base; legumes: veinless margin from 1/3 of coil face radius away from dorsal suture; leaflet blades not laciniate . . . . 9. *Medicago minima*
            13. Stipule margins deeply dentate to laciniate; legumes: coil face with veinless area from 1/5 of coil face radius away from dorsal suture; leaflet blades often laciniate . . . . 10. *Medicago laciniata*
        12. Outer periphery of legume coil faces without distinct veinless margin, venation extending to dorsal suture.
            14. Flowers 3.5–6 mm; legumes 4–10 mm wide . . . . 11. *Medicago polymorpha*
            14. Flowers 2–4 mm; legumes 2–3 mm wide . . . . 12. *Medicago praecox*

149a. MEDICAGO Linnaeus sect. MEDICAGO [I]

Herbs perennial. **Legumes** curved or coiled [straight], prickleless [prickly], coil edges not paper-thin, multi-seeded. **Seeds** smooth; radicle 1/2–2/3 seed length, usually slightly longer than 1/2. **Cotyledons** epulvinate.

Species 12 (1 in the flora): introduced; n Mexico, Europe, Asia, n Africa; introduced also in West Indies, Central America, South America, Pacific Islands, Australia.

1. Medicago sativa Linnaeus, Sp. Pl. 2: 778. 1753 • Alfalfa, lucerne [I] [W]

Herbs: shoots glabrescent to pubescent, hairs eglandular [glandular]. **Stems** prostrate to erect. **Stipules:** margins entire or basally toothed. **Leaflets:** blades obovate to linear or oblanceolate, 5–35 × 2–15 mm, margins serrate distally. **Inflorescences** 3–30(–50)-flowered, racemes. **Flowers** 5–15 mm; calyx glabrous or pubescent, hairs eglandular or glandular, lobes equal to tube; corolla usually purple, yellow, or variegated yellow-violet, rarely violet, green, or white, [yellow-orange, pink], 2 times length of calyx. **Legumes** curved or with 1.5–6 coils, falcate when curved, lenticular, ovoid, or cylindrical when coiled, 7–15 × 1.5–3 mm when falcate, 4–14 × 3–9 mm when coiled, glabrescent or pubescent with eglandular and/or glandular hairs; face veins (when coiled) oblique from ventral suture, slightly branched, fusing towards dorsal suture. **Seeds** 2–12, yellow, brownish, greenish yellow, or violet-brown, reniform, 1–2.5 × 1–1.5 mm. 2*n* = 16, 32.

Subspecies 6 (3, including 1 hybrid, in the flora): introduced; n Mexico, Eurasia; introduced also in West Indies, Central America, South America (Argentina, Brazil, Chile, Uruguay), Pacific Islands, Australia.

Medicago sativa is the most widely grown of the temperate forage legumes. Wherever it is cultivated, escapes are likely to be found in the vicinity, and the species has become established in most countries. This polymorphic Old World species is complicated by polyploidy, hybridization, and domestication and has been divided by some (E. Small 2011) into several species (dozens, by some Russian taxonomists) and innumerable infraspecific taxa. The natural habitats of the wild progenitors of *M. sativa* in Asia (mostly in the former U.S.S.R.) are rapidly being decimated, and there is considerable danger that valuable genetic diversity is being lost.

According to the literature cited below, the three subspecies in the flora region should be expected in all provinces and territories of Canada, and in all states.

SELECTED REFERENCES Small, E. 1985. Morphological differentiation in *Medicago sativa* s.l. in relation to ploidy. Canad. J. Bot. 63: 1747–1752. Small, E. and B. S. Brookes. 1984. Taxonomic circumscription and identification in the *Medicago sativa-falcata* (alfalfa) continuum. Econ. Bot. 38: 83–96.

1. Flowers usually purple, sometimes violet, not bicolored, very rarely white; legumes with at least 1.5 coils, usually 2–6. . . . . 1a. *Medicago sativa* subsp. *sativa*
1. Flowers yellow or variegated yellow-violet, rarely green or violet; legumes falcate or with fewer than 1.5 coils.
   2. Flowers yellow; legumes falcate, less than 0.5 coil. . . . . 1b. *Medicago sativa* subsp. *falcata*
   2. Flowers usually variegated yellow-violet, sometimes green, yellow, or violet; legumes with 0.8–1.4 coils . . . . 1c. *Medicago sativa* subsp. ×*varia*

1a. Medicago sativa Linnaeus subsp. **sativa** • Purple alfalfa or lucerne, luzerne cultivée [I]

Flowers usually purple, sometimes violet, very rarely white. **Legumes** with 1.5–6 coils. **2*n*** = 32.

Flowering spring–fall. Prairies, rocky and grassy slopes, thickets, meadows, sand dunes, fallow fields, roadsides; 0–3000 m; introduced; Alta., B.C., Man., N.B., Nfld. and Labr., N.W.T., N.S., Nunavut, Ont., P.E.I., Que., Sask., Yukon; Ala., Alaska, Ariz., Ark., Calif., Colo., Conn., Del., D.C., Fla., Ga., Idaho, Ill., Ind., Iowa, Kans., Ky., La., Maine, Md., Mass., Mich., Minn., Miss., Mo., Mont., Nebr., Nev., N.H., N.J., N.Mex., N.Y., N.C., N.Dak., Ohio, Okla., Oreg., Pa., R.I., S.C., S.Dak., Tenn., Tex., Utah, Vt., Va., Wash., W.Va., Wis., Wyo.; Mexico (Baja California, Baja California Sur, México, Nuevo León, Puebla, Sonora); Eurasia; introduced also in West Indies, Central America, South America (Argentina, Brazil, Chile, Uruguay), Pacific Islands, Australia.

Subspecies *sativa* includes most cultivated forms of alfalfa (including most of the thousands of cultivars) and escapes from cultivation, and is the most common subspecies in the flora area. Many of the plants assignable here have been introgressed from subsp. *falcata*, but not sufficiently to warrant recognition as the hybrid taxon subsp. ×*varia*, discussed here. Domesticated forms often escape from cultivation but are not aggressive weeds.

1b. Medicago sativa Linnaeus subsp. **falcata** (Linnaeus) Arcangeli, Comp. Fl. Ital., 160. 1882 • Yellow-flowered or Siberian or sickle-podded alfalfa, sickle-podded medic, luzerne en faux [I]

Medicago falcata Linnaeus, Sp. Pl. 2: 779. 1753

Flowers yellow. **Legumes** falcate. **2*n*** = 16, 32.

Flowering spring–fall. Prairies, rocky and grassy slopes, thickets, meadows, sand dunes, fallow fields, roadsides; 0–3000 m; introduced; Alta., B.C., Man., N.B., N.W.T., N.S., Nunavut, Ont., P.E.I., Que., Sask., Yukon; Ala., Alaska, Ariz., Ark., Colo., Del., D.C., Fla., Ga., Idaho, Ill., Ind., Iowa, Ky., La., Md., Mass., Mich., Minn., Miss., Mo., Mont., Nebr., Nev., N.J., N.Mex., N.Y., N.C., N.Dak., Ohio, Oreg., Pa., S.C., S.Dak., Tenn., Tex., Utah, Va., Wash., W.Va., Wis., Wyo.; n Eurasia; introduced also in South America (Argentina), Australia.

Subspecies *falcata* is very widespread in northern Eurasia. It has given rise to a few domesticated forms, but there are only a few cultivars. Although not often cultivated for forage, subsp. *falcata* has been sown in wild areas of the northern United States and Canada to promote wildlife. It is much used for breeding alfalfa resistant to cold, acid soils, and disease, and is able to thrive in many colder areas of North America. In Eurasia, it is both diploid (2*n* = 16) and tetraploid (2*n* = 32).

1c. Medicago sativa Linnaeus nothosubsp. **×varia** (Martyn) Arcangeli, Comp. Fl. Ital., 160. 1882, as subspecies • Bastard or hybrid or sand or variegated alfalfa, bastard or hybrid or sand or variegated lucerne, luzerne bigarrée [I]

Medicago ×*varia* Martyn, Fl. Rust. 3: 87. 1793, as species

Flowers usually variegated yellow-violet, sometimes green, yellow, or violet. **Legumes** often with 1.5 coils, sometimes falcate or with 0.8–1.4 coils. **2*n*** = 32 [also 16 in Eurasia].

Flowering spring–fall. Prairies, rocky and grassy slopes, thickets, meadows, sand dunes, fallow fields, roadsides; 0–3000 m; introduced; Alta., B.C., Man., N.B., N.W.T., N.S., Ont., P.E.I., Que., Sask., Yukon; Ala., Alaska, Ariz., Ark., Calif., Colo., Conn., Del., D.C., Fla., Ga., Idaho, Ill., Ind., Iowa, Kans., Ky., La., Maine, Md., Mass., Mich., Minn., Miss., Mo., Mont., Nebr., Nev., N.H., N.J., N.Mex., N.Y., N.C., N.Dak., Ohio, Okla., Oreg., Pa., R.I., S.C.,

S.Dak., Tenn., Tex., Utah, Vt., Va., Wash., W.Va., Wis., Wyo.; Eurasia; introduced also in Central America, South America, Pacific Islands, Australia.

Subspecies ×*varia* is the result of hybridization of subspp. *falcata* and *sativa*. Most plants are not F1 hybrids, but the result of local backcrossing that has produced introgressants showing intermediacy in fruit characters (neither notably coiled nor more or less straight) and flower color (neither completely yellow nor completely violet, but usually a mixture or variegation of these colors). F1 hybrid plants are generally recognizable by the presence of greenish flowers, the result of a blending of the yellow pigment of subsp. *falcata* and the violet color pigments of subsp. *sativa*. Since several of the diagnostic characters segregate and combine more or less independently, precise delimitation from the parental species can be difficult. Subspecies ×*varia* is extensively cultivated, especially in more northern areas of the world, and has a greater tendency to weediness than the other subspecies, and so it is also very widely distributed.

149b. MEDICAGO Linnaeus sect. LUPULARIA Seringe in A. P. de Candolle and A. L. P. P. de Candolle, Prodr. 2: 172. 1825 [I]

Herbs usually annual, sometimes biennial or short-lived perennial. **Legumes** curved, tip twisted in small coil, prickleless, coil edges not paper-thin, nutletlike. **Seeds** smooth; radicle 1/2–2/3 seed length. **Cotyledons** epulvinate.

Species 2 (1 in the flora): introduced; Mexico, Europe, Asia, n Africa; introduced also worldwide in temperate and tropical regions.

2. Medicago lupulina Linnaeus, Sp. Pl. 2: 779. 1753
• Black medic, yellow trefoil, luzerne lupuline

Herbs: shoots glabrescent to densely pubescent, hairs eglandular, appressed, sometimes glandular. **Stems** prostrate, decumbent, or semi-erect. **Stipules:** margins entire or irregularly toothed. **Leaflets:** blades elliptic, ovate, or obovate, 10–20 × 6–15 mm, margins serrate on distal 1/2. **Inflorescences** (5–)15–50-flowered, cylindrical heads. **Flowers** 2–4 mm; calyx pubescent, hairs eglandular or glandular, lobes equal to tube; corolla yellow, 2 times length of calyx. **Legumes** ± ovoid, 2–3.5 × 1 mm, covered with eglandular hairs, sometimes also gland-tipped hairs when young; face with somewhat fusing, prominent veins sometimes appearing as ridges from ventral suture obliquely to dorsal suture. **Seeds** 1, yellow to olive green, oval to reniform, 1.5–2 × 1–1.15 mm. $2n$ = 16, 32.

Flowering spring–fall. Lawns, riverbanks, disturbed areas, roadsides, often on slopes and meadows, railway embankments, wastelands; 0–3000 m; introduced; Greenland; St. Pierre and Miquelon; Alta., B.C., Man., N.B., Nfld. and Labr. (Nfld.), N.W.T., N.S., Ont., P.E.I., Que., Sask., Yukon; Ala., Alaska, Ariz., Ark., Calif., Colo., Conn., Del., D.C., Fla., Ga., Idaho, Ill., Ind., Iowa, Kans., Ky., La., Maine, Md., Mass., Mich., Minn., Miss., Mo., Mont., Nebr., Nev., N.H., N.J., N.Mex., N.Y., N.C., N.Dak., Ohio, Okla., Oreg., Pa., R.I., S.C., S.Dak., Tenn., Tex., Utah, Vt., Va., Wash., W.Va., Wis., Wyo.; Mexico; Europe; Asia; n Africa; introduced also nearly worldwide in temperate and tropical regions.

Medicago lupulina is valued as a pasture plant (there are several cultivars), cover crop, and as a green manure plant; it is typically plowed under in the fall as part of a crop rotation. Although *M. lupulina* is often considered a lawn weed, nitrogen fixation associated with this plant contributes to lawn health.

Medicago lupulina is a variable species, but the variation is not structured in ways that can reasonably be classified formally. Of the many criteria that have been used to delimit infraspecific groups, presence of gland-tipped hairs and whether annual/biennial or perennial have been most frequently employed. Density of glandular trichomes is highly variable in the species (L. R. Goertzen and E. Small 1993), and taxa such as *M. lupulina* var. *glandulosa* Neilreich have no merit.

SELECTED REFERENCES Goertzen, L. R. and E. Small. 1993. The defensive role of trichomes in black medick (*Medicago lupulina* L.). Pl. Syst. Evol. 184: 101–111. Turkington, R. A. and P. B. Cavers. 1979. The biology of Canadian weeds. 33. *Medicago lupulina* L. Canad. J. Pl. Sci. 59: 99–110.

149c. MEDICAGO Linnaeus sect. ORBICULARES Urban, Verh. Bot. Vereins Prov. Brandenburg 15: 48. 1873 [I]

Herbs annual. **Legumes** coiled, prickleless, coil edges paper-thin, multi-seeded. **Seeds** tuberculate; radicle equal to seed length. **Cotyledons** epulvinate.

Species 1: introduced; s Europe, w Asia, n Africa; introduced also in South America, s Africa, Pacific Islands, Australia.

3. Medicago orbicularis (Linnaeus) Bartalini, Cat. Piante Siena, 60. 1776 • Black-disc medic, button-clover, button or large-disc (disk) medic [I]

Medicago polymorpha Linnaeus var. *orbicularis* Linnaeus, Sp. Pl. 2: 779. 1753

Herbs: shoots usually glabrous or glabrescent, hairs usally eglandular, sparse, rarely gland-tipped. **Stems** usually procumbent, sometimes ascending. **Stipules:** margins laciniate. **Leaflets:** blades obovate to cuneate, 7–13 × 5–10 mm, margins serrate on distal 1/3–2/3. **Inflorescences** 1- or 2(–5)-flowered, racemes, usually 1 pod developing on each peduncle. **Flowers** 3–4(–6) mm; calyx glabrous or sparsely hairy, hairs eglandular, lobes equal to tube; corolla yellow, to 2 times length of calyx. **Legumes** with (2–)3–7 coils, lenticular or discoid, 5–10 × 8–20(–24) mm, coil edges papery at margins, glabrous, glabrescent, sometimes hairs gland-tipped; coil face with fusing radial veins, often thickened at coil margin. **Seeds** 9–30, yellow, brownish yellow or reddish brown, triangular, 2.5–3 × 2.5–3 mm. 2*n* = 16.

Flowering spring–summer. Ruderal and fallow habitats, hilly slopes; 0–600 m; introduced; Ala., Calif., Fla., Ga., Ill., Ky., La., Md., Miss., N.J., N.C., Okla., Pa., Tenn., Tex.; s Europe; w Asia; n Africa; introduced also in South America (Argentina), s Africa, Pacific Islands (Hawaii), Australia.

Medicago orbicularis is cultivated to a minor degree as a forage plant, and there is at least one cultivar; it is uncertain if it is native or introduced in Europe and central Asia.

149d. MEDICAGO Linnaeus sect. SPIROCARPOS Seringe in A. P. de Candolle and A. L. P. P. de Candolle, Prodr. 2: 174. 1825 [I]

Herbs annual. **Legumes** coiled, dorsal suture prickly, tuberculate, or smooth, coils rarely paper-thin at dorsal suture. **Seeds** smooth; radicle mostly 1/2(–2/3) seed length. **Cotyledons** epulvinate.

Species ca. 35 (9 in the flora): introduced; Europe, Asia, Africa; introduced also in South America, Pacific Islands (New Zealand), Australia.

4. Medicago scutellata (Linnaeus) Miller, Gard. Dict. ed. 8, Medicago no. 2. 1768 • Shield medic, snail alfalfa or clover or medic [I]

Medicago polymorpha Linnaeus var. *scutellata* Linnaeus, Sp. Pl. 2: 779. 1753

Herbs: shoots usually pubescent, hairs eglandular and glandular. **Stems** usually ascending, sometimes prostrate or decumbent. **Stipules:** margins dentate, incised, or laciniate. **Leaflets:** blades obovate, ovate, ovate-lanceolate, or oblanceolate, 10–25 × 5–12 mm, margins serrate on distal 2/3 or less. **Inflorescences** 1–3(or 4)-flowered, racemes or heads. **Flowers** 6–9 mm; calyx pubescent, hairs glandular, sometimes also eglandular, lobes equal to or longer than tube; corolla yellow to orange-yellow, less than 2 times length of calyx. **Legumes** with (4–)5–7(–8) coils, coils concave ("bowl-like") and imbricated, stacked within each other, convex surface facing pod base, 7–20 × 7–15(–19) mm, with glandular hairs, margin prickleless; coil face with dense net of veins. **Seeds** 5–15, light yellow to brown, reniform, 4–7 × 2.5–4 mm; radicle less than 1/2 seed length. 2*n* = 16, 28, 30, 32.

Flowering spring–summer. Meadows, fallow fields, margins of woods; 0–300 m; introduced; Calif., Md.; s Europe; w Asia; n Africa; introduced also in South America (Argentina, Uruguay), Pacific Islands (New Zealand), Australia.

Medicago scutellata is one of the principal annual species of the genus from which forage cultivars have been developed, mainly in Australia during the latter half of the twentieth century. In Victorian times, the plant was popular in gardens, and the species is occasionally used as an ornamental cover for dry, sunny banks. In the flora area, it has been found in California (E. Dean et al. 2008) and Maryland (C. F. Reed 1964).

Most chromosome counts are 2*n* = 32; however, G. R. Bauchan and J. H. Elgin (1984) found only 2*n* = 30 in numerous plants, and pointed out that the large chromosomal satellites present in this species may have led to the erroneous chromosome counts of 2*n* = 32.

SELECTED REFERENCE Small, E. et al. 1993. A systematic comparison of morphology and seed proteins of early- and late-flowering forms of *Medicago scutellata*. Canad. J. Bot. 71: 183–192.

5. Medicago turbinata (Linnaeus) Allioni, Fl. Pedem. 1: 315. 1785 • Tubercled medic [I]

Medicago polymorpha Linnaeus var. *turbinata* Linnaeus, Sp. Pl. 2: 780. 1753; *M. tuberculata* (Retzius) Willdenow

Herbs: shoots pubescent, often densely so, hairs eglandular. **Stems** procumbent or ascending. **Stipules:** margins entire or dentate. **Leaflets:** blades obovate, ovate, or oblanceolate, 12–16 × 6–8 mm, margins serrate or doubly serrate on distal 3/4 or less. **Inflorescences** (1–)3–8(–10)-flowered, racemes. **Flowers** (3–)5–8 mm; calyx pubescent or glabrescent, hairs eglandular, sometimes also glandular, lobes equal to or slightly longer than tube; corolla yellow or orange-yellow, less than 2 times length of calyx. **Legumes** with (4–)5–7(–9) coils, spherical to ovoid, 6–12(–15) × 5–8 mm, apex truncate, glabrous, margin usually prickly or tuberculate, sometimes smooth, prickles or tubercles, when present, sometimes inclined opposite to direction of fruit coiling, giving appearance of rapidly spinning top, very stocky and difficult to bend, base often round, 2 roots often apparent at maturity; faces very hard at maturity, coil face with radial veins entering veinless margin in distal 1/4–1/3 of coil, veins obscure at maturity from developing spongy tissue. **Seeds** yellow to light brown, reniform, 4–5 × 2–2.5 mm; radicle less than 1/2 seed length. **2*n*** = 16, 18.

Flowering spring–summer. Fallow fields, waste ground, edges of woods, open woods; 0–1000 m; introduced; N.J., Oreg.; s Europe; w Asia; n Africa.

Medicago turbinata is rarely sown for forage. No cultivars have been developed.

The widely used combination *Medicago turbinata* (Linnaeus) Allioni is adopted here, although it is considered to be a confused name (W. Greuter et al. 1981+, vol. 4). The species treated here is not *M. turbinata* in the sense of Willdenow (= *M. doliata* Carmignani).

6. Medicago rigidula (Linnaeus) Allioni, Fl. Pedem. 1: 316. 1785 • Rigid or Tifton bur (burr) medic, Tifton bur-clover or medic [I]

Medicago polymorpha Linnaeus var. *rigidula* Linnaeus, Sp. Pl. 2: 780. 1753

Herbs: shoots ± pubescent, hairs eglandular, sometimes also glandular. **Stems** procumbent to ascending. **Stipules:** margins dentate to laciniate. **Leaflets:** blades cuneate to obovate, (4–)6–12 × (3–)4–8 mm, margins serrate on distal 1/2. **Inflorescences** 1–3(–6)-flowered, racemes. **Flowers** (3–)4–6(–8) mm; calyx pubescent, hairs eglandular and/or glandular, lobes shorter to longer than calyx length; corolla yellow, less than 2 times length of calyx. **Legumes** with (4–)5–6.5(–7.5) coils, coils weakly to strongly adpressed, usually ovoid, sometimes cylindrical, discoid, or spherical, 5–10(–12) × 5–10(–15) mm, usually pubescent with eglandular and gland-tipped hairs, evident only when young, when glandular, often producing velvety appearance, rarely glabrous, margin prickly, tuberculate, or prickleless, prickles, when present, at different angles to plane of coil, very stocky and difficult to bend, base often round, 2 roots often apparent at maturity; faces very hard at maturity, coil face with strongly curved radial veins anastomosing somewhat towards coil periphery, veins obscure at maturity from developing spongy tissue. **Seeds** yellow to yellow-brown, reniform, (2.5–)3–4(–4.5) × (1.3–)1.5–2(–2.5) mm; radicle 1/2, or slightly less, seed length. **2*n*** = 14, 16.

Flowering spring–summer. Roadsides, fallow ground, open woodlands, shrublands; 0–400 m; introduced; Calif., Mass.; w Asia; introduced also in Australia.

Medicago rigidula has been sown for forage only to a limited extent. There are a few forage cultivars, including 'Laramie', a self-regenerating pasture species for the Central High Plains of the United States.

The European and African populations of this species complex have been segregated as *Medicago rigiduloides* E. Small, based particularly on pollen morphology and fruit characters (E. Small et al. 1990). Additional studies confirming separation of these taxa are needed (D. C. Heft and R. W. Groose, http://www.naaic.org/Publications/1996Proc/poster_session.htm), before determining their applicability to the plants in the flora area.

SELECTED REFERENCE Small, E., B. S. Brookes, and E. J. Crawford. 1990. Inter-continental differentiation in *Medicago rigidula*. Canad. J. Bot. 68: 2607–2613.

7. Medicago truncatula Gaertner, Fruct. Sem. Pl. 2: 350, plate 155, fig. [7]. 1791 • Barrel clover or medic [I]

Medicago tribuloides Desrousseaux

Herbs: shoots ± pubescent, hairs eglandular. **Stems** procumbent to ascending. **Stipules:** margins deeply dentate to laciniate. **Leaflets:** blades cuneate to obovate, 8–15 × 7–12 mm, margins serrate on distal 1/2, rarely incised or laciniate. **Inflorescences** 1–3(–5)-flowered, racemes. **Flowers** 6–8 mm; calyx pubescent, hairs eglandular, lobes longer than tube; corolla yellow, less than 2 times length of calyx. **Legumes** with 2.5–8 coils, coils often strongly adpressed, usually cylindrical, 6–12 × 7–12 mm, often pubescent, sometimes glabrescent, hairs eglandular, margin usually prickly, rarely prickleless, prickles often at 90° to plane of coil, pointed to ends of pod, very stocky and difficult to bend, base often round, 2 roots often apparent at maturity; faces very hard at maturity, coil face with slightly branched and anastomosing veins, veins weakly to moderately curved. **Seeds** 2–25, yellow or brownish yellow, reniform, 2.5–4.5 × 1.3–2.5 mm; radicle less than 1/2 seed length. $2n$ = (14) 16.

Flowering spring–summer. Roadsides, fallow ground, open woodlands, shrublands; 0–800 m; introduced; Calif.; Europe; w Asia; n Africa; introduced also in South America (Argentina, Uruguay), Pacific Islands (New Zealand), Australia.

Medicago truncatula is the most important annual forage species of the genus, next in agricultural importance only to *M. sativa* (alfalfa). It is grown in Australia and other Mediterranean climate regions around the world. The species is also being developed as a model legume plant in both classical and molecular genetic studies to elucidate the functions of its genes and to exploit its genome to improve seed quality and production of specific secondary metabolites.

SELECTED REFERENCES Mathesius, U., E. P. Journet, and L. W. Sumner, eds. 2006. The *Medicago truncatula* Handbook. Ardmore, Okla. Small, E. and B. S. Brookes. 1990. A numerical taxonomic analysis of the *Medicago littoralis* – *M. truncatula* complex. Canad. J. Bot. 68: 1667–1674.

8. Medicago arabica (Linnaeus) Hudson, Fl. Angl., 288. 1762 • Southern bur-clover, spotted bur medic or bur-clover or medic [I] [W]

Medicago polymorpha Linnaeus var. *arabica* Linnaeus, Sp. Pl. 2: 780. 1753

Herbs: shoots sparsely to moderately pubescent, hairs eglandular and glandular. **Stems** procumbent to ascending. **Stipules:** margins deeply dentate to lobed. **Leaflets:** blades cuneate, obovate, or obcordate, 8–25 × 7–20 mm, margins serrate on distal 1/3, often with conspicuous central, purple-red (anthocyanin) blotch adaxially. **Inflorescences** (1 or)2–5(–8)-flowered, racemes. **Flowers** 4–5(–6) mm; calyx pubescent, hairs eglandular, sometimes multicellular and gland-tipped, lobes equal to or longer than tube; corolla yellow, 2 times length of calyx. **Legumes** with 3–5(–7) coils, shortly ellipsoid to subglobose (ends rounded), or discoid to cylindriform (ends flattened), (4–)5–9 × (4–)5–7(–8) mm, glabrous, margin usually prickly, sometimes tuberculate, prickles, when present, often relatively thin and flexible, base 2-rooted, 1 root arising in dorsal suture, other in submarginal vein; faces soft, coil face with venation anastomosing considerably on outer 1/3, coil edge in end view shows central groove flanked by lateral grooves to form pattern of 3 grooves separating 4 ridges, not visible in side view of coil. **Seeds** 2+, yellow or yellow-brown, reniform, 2–3.5 × 1.2–1.5 mm; radicle usually slightly more than 1/2 seed length. $2n$ = 16.

Flowering spring–summer. Edges of woods, shrub thickets, meadows, cleared or disturbed areas; 0–1000 m; introduced; B.C., N.B.; Ala., Ariz., Ark., Calif., Conn., D.C., Fla., Ga., Ill., La., Maine, Mass., Miss., Mo., N.J., N.Y., N.C., Okla., Oreg., Pa., R.I., S.C., Tenn., Tex., Vt., Va., Wash.; Europe; w Asia; n Africa; introduced also in Central America, South America (Argentina, Brazil, Chile, Uruguay), Pacific Islands (New Zealand), Australia.

Medicago arabica is sown for forage only to a small extent.

Although the majority of *Medicago* plants cannot be identified to species with much certainty without fruits, in most cases vegetative plants with purplish blotches on the centers of the leaflets will be this species. However, these markings occur occasionally on other annual species of *Medicago* and are absent from some plants of *M. arabica*.

Medicago maculata Sibthorp and *M. maculata* Willdenow are illegitimate names that pertain here.

9. Medicago minima (Linnaeus) Bartalini, Cat. Piante Siena, 61. 1776 • Goldfields or Kaalgoorlie or least or little medic, lesser bur medic, little bur or small bur-clover, small bur or small woolly bur or woolly bur medic [I] [W]

Medicago polymorpha Linnaeus var. *minima* Linnaeus, Sp. Pl. 2: 780. 1753

Herbs: shoot pubescent, hairs eglandular and/or gland-tipped. **Stems** ascending or procumbent. **Stipules:** margins entire or minutely dentate at base. **Leaflets:** blades usually obovate, rarely oblanceolate, 5–8(–12) × 2–7 mm, margins serrate on distal 1/3. **Inflorescences** 2–5(–8)-flowered, racemes. **Flowers** 2–4.5(–6) mm; calyx pubescent, hairs eglandular and/or glandular, lobes equal to tube; corolla yellow, less than 2 times length of calyx. **Legumes** with 3–5 coils, discoid, cylindrical, or ovoid, 3–5 × 2.5–6 mm, hairs glandular and/or eglandular, margin usually prickly, sometimes tuberculate, prickles, when present, often relatively thin and flexible, base 2-rooted, 1 root arising in dorsal suture, other in submarginal vein; faces soft, coil face with strongly curved, unbranched radial veins entering broad, veinless margin that occupies 1/3 outer radius of coil face. **Seeds** 3–10, yellow to light brown, somewhat reniform, 1.5–2.5 × 0.9–1.3 mm; radicle 1/2 seed length. $2n = 16$.

Flowering spring–summer. Hillsides, fields, sand dunes, forest edges, rural sites; 0–1400 m; introduced; Ala., Ariz., Calif., Conn., Fla., Idaho, Kans., La., Md., Mass., Mich., Miss., Mo., N.J., N.Mex., N.Y., N.C., Okla., Oreg., Pa., R.I., S.C., Tenn., Tex., Va., Wash.; Eurasia; Africa; introduced also in South America (Argentina, Uruguay), Pacific Islands (Hawaii, New Zealand), Australia.

Medicago minima has been only slightly developed to date for agricultural purposes, although in areas where it grows it is considered to be good forage. In Argentina and Australia, *M. minima* is an extremely important component of the rangelands used for livestock grazing. The first cultivar of *M. minima* to be registered (as 'Devine') was released in 2005 by the Texas Agricultural Experiment Station.

Medicago minima is most frequently confused with *M. laciniata*, but *M. minima* has much hairier foliage and much less dissected stipules.

10. Medicago laciniata (Linnaeus) Miller, Gard. Dict. ed. 8, Medicago no. 5. 1768 • Cutleaf medic [I]

Medicago polymorpha Linnaeus var. *laciniata* Linnaeus, Sp. Pl. 781. 1753; *M. aschersoniana* Urban

Herbs: shoots pubescent, hairs eglandular. **Stems** procumbent to ascending. **Stipules:** margins deeply dentate to laciniate. **Leaflets:** blades obovate to oblong-cuneate, 5–10 × 2–5 mm, margins laciniate, incised-dentate, incised-pinnatifid, or serrate to deeply serrate on distal 1/2, laciniate and non-laciniate leaves often on same plant. **Inflorescences** 1- or 2(or 3)-flowered, racemes. **Flowers** 3–6(–8) mm; calyx pubescent, hairs eglandular, lobes shorter than tube; corolla pale to dark yellow, less than 2 times length of calyx. **Legumes** with 3–7(–9) coils, short-cylindrical, spherical, or ovoid, 3–8(–10) × 2.5–6 mm, usually glabrous or glabrescent, rarely pubescent with eglandular hairs, very rarely with glandular hairs, margin prickly, prickles often relatively thin and flexible, base 2-rooted, 1 root arising in dorsal suture, other in submarginal vein; faces soft, coil face with S-shaped (sigmoid) radial veins, some branched, that enter broad lateral vein near dorsal suture, veinless area occupying outer 1/5 of coil face. **Seeds** 3–14, yellow to yellow-brown, reniform, 2–3 × 1–1.5 mm; radicle 1/2–2/3 seed length. $2n = 16$.

Flowering spring–early summer. Dry habitats, woodlands, grasslands, fallow fields; 0–300 m; introduced; Ont.; La., Maine, Mass., N.Y., S.C.; Asia; Africa; introduced also in Australia.

Laciniate leaves occur sporadically in several annual species of *Medicago*, most frequently in *M. laciniata*.

Medicago laciniata is an exceptionally drought-tolerant species and in its natural habitat occurs particularly in dry, stony deserts and less commonly in woodlands and grasslands.

11. Medicago polymorpha Linnaeus, Sp. Pl. 2: 779. 1753 • Bur-clover or medic, luzerne polymorphe [F] [I] [W]

Medicago denticulata Willdenow; *M. hispida* Gaertner; *M. nigra* (Linnaeus) Krocker

Herbs: shoots glabrescent, hairs eglandular. **Stems** procumbent, decumbent, or ascending. **Stipules:** margins laciniate. **Leaflets:** blades obovate, obcordate, or cuneate, 8–20 × 7–18(–20) mm, margins usually serrate, rarely laciniate, on distal 1/3–1/2. **Inflorescences** (1 or)2–6(–10)-flowered, racemes. **Flowers** 3.5–6 mm; calyx sparsely pubescent, hairs eglandular, lobes equal to tube; corolla yellow, usually

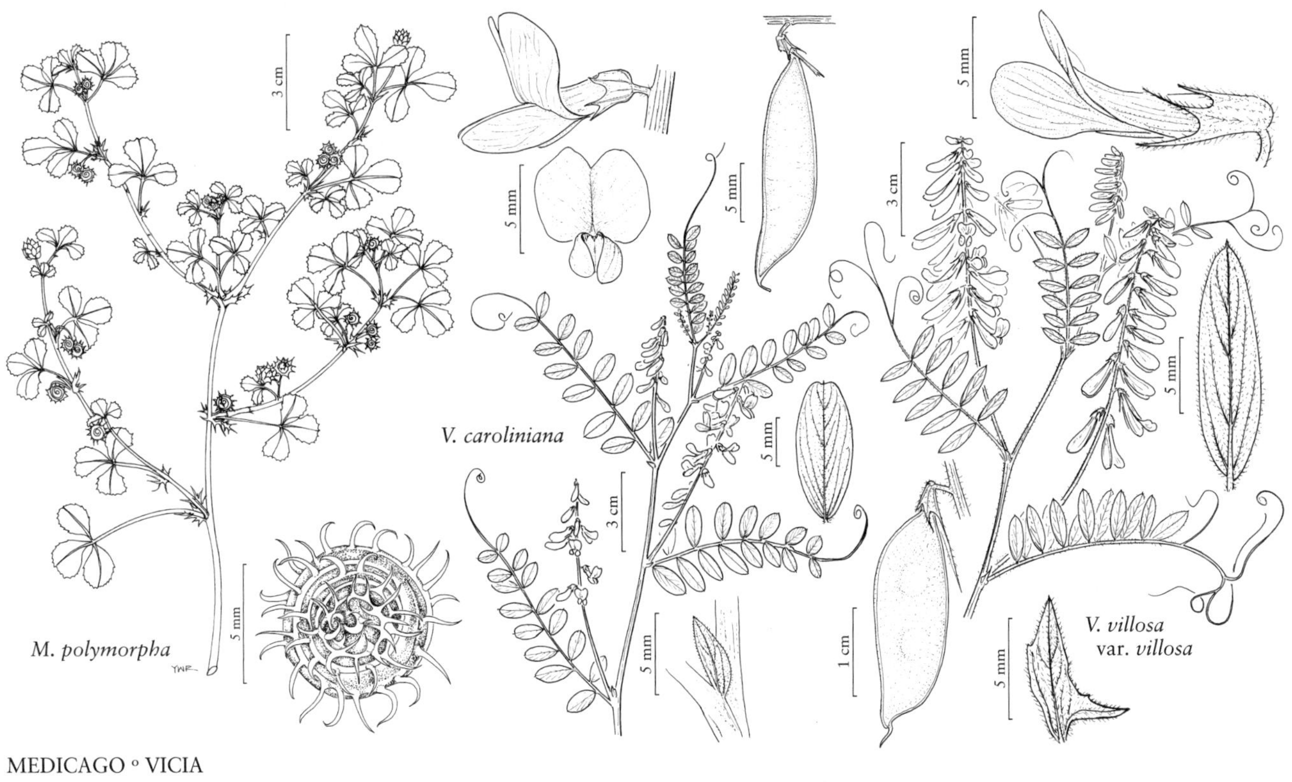

MEDICAGO ◦ VICIA

less than 2 times length of calyx. **Legumes** with 1.5–7 coils, discoid, short to long cylindrical, or conical-truncate, 2–12 × 4–10 mm, usually glabrous, margin usually prickly, sometimes tuberculate or prickleless, prickles, when present, often relatively thin and flexible, base 2-rooted, 1 root arising in dorsal suture, other in submarginal vein; faces moderately soft, sometimes very hard at maturity, coil face with transverse veins anastomosing in outer part of coil before entering lateral vein near coil edge. **Seeds** 2–12, light yellow to brownish, reniform, 2–4 × 1.5–2.2 mm; radicle $^{1}/_{2}$ seed length. 2*n* = 14, 16.

Flowering spring–early summer. Fallow fields, waste places; 0–2200 m; introduced; B.C., N.B., Ont., Que., Sask.; Ala., Alaska, Ariz., Ark., Calif., Conn., Fla., Ga., Idaho, La., Maine, Mass., Mich., Miss., Mo., Mont., Nev., N.J., N.Mex., N.Y., N.C., Ohio, Okla., Oreg., Pa., R.I., S.C., Tenn., Tex., Utah, Vt., Va., Wash., Wyo.; Mexico (Baja California, Hidalgo, México, Morelos, Nuevo León, Puebla, San Luis Potosí, Sonora, Zacatecas); Eurasia; Africa; introduced also in Central America, South America (Argentina, Brazil, Chile, Uruguay), Pacific Islands (New Zealand), Australia.

Medicago polymorpha is one of the more important annual medics that have been developed for use as pasture forage for dry, hot environments. About a dozen cultivars have been bred.

Medicago polymorpha is the most likely species of the genus to be confused with other species. The fruits are easily misidentified as one of the hard-fruited *Medicago* (*M. rigidula*, *M. truncatula*, *M. turbinata*), but are fairly similar to those of certain of the soft-fruited taxa, particularly *M. laciniata and M. minima*, two species that are also quite common as weeds. The fruit coil faces of both of the latter species have distal veinless areas. The coil face of *M. polymorpha* has quite reticulate venation, whereas that of *M. laciniata* has notably S-shaped radial veins that anastomose little. *Medicago minima* is a quite hairy plant, whereas *M. polymorpha* is almost always glabrous.

12. Medicago praecox de Candolle, Cat. Pl. Hort. Monsp., 123. 1813 • Early medic, small-leaf bur, small-leaved bur medic [I]

Herbs: shoots sparsely pubescent, hairs eglandular. **Stems** usually procumbent, sometimes ascending. **Stipules:** margins dentate, incised, or lacerate. **Leaflets:** blades obovate to obcordate, 2–7(–12) × 2–5(–10) mm, margin serrate on distal $^{1}/_{3}$. **Inflorescences** 1- or 2-flowered, usually 1 ripe pod remaining on peduncle, umbels or racemes. **Flowers** 2–4 mm; calyx pubescent, hairs eglandular, lobes mostly equal to tube; corolla yellow, slightly longer than calyx. **Legumes** with 2.5–4(–5) coils, short-cylindrical, 2–4(–5) × 2–3 mm, usually pubescent with eglandular hairs, rarely glabrescent, margin prickly, prickles often relatively thin and flexible, base 2-rooted, 1 root arising in dorsal suture, other in submarginal vein; faces soft, coil face with very strongly curving radial veins that branch slightly and enter broad lateral vein near dorsal suture. **Seeds** yellow or brownish yellow, reniform, 1.7–2.4 × 0.9–1.3 mm; radicle usually slightly less than 1/2 seed length. **2*n*** = 14.

Flowering early summer. Rangelands, scrublands, waste places; 0–1000 m; introduced; Calif., Mass., Oreg.; s Europe; w Asia; introduced also in Asia (China), Pacific Islands (New Zealand), Australia.

149e. MEDICAGO Linnaeus sect. BUCERAS (Seringe) E. Small in C. H. Stirton, Advances Legume Syst. 3, 180. 1987 [I]

Trigonella Linnaeus sect. *Buceras* Seringe in A. P. de Candolle and A. L. P. P. de Candolle, Prodr. 2: 182. 1825

Herbs annual. **Legumes** curved, mostly subterete, [conspicuously strangulate between seeds], prickleless, coil edges not paper-thin. **Seeds** finely tuberculate [rugose, smooth]; radicle usually more than 1/2 to equal seed length. **Cotyledons** pulvinate.

Species 19 (1 in the flora): introduced; Europe, Asia, Africa; introduced also in South America, Australia.

13. Medicago monspeliaca (Linnaeus) Trautvetter, Bull. Acad. Imp. Sci. Saint-Pétersbourg 8: 272. 1841 • Hairy medic [I]

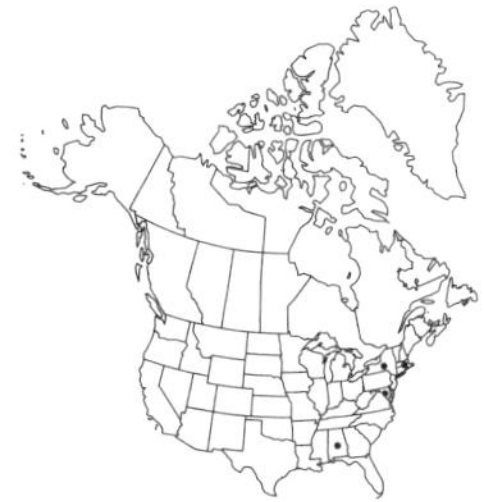

Trigonella monspeliaca Linnaeus, Sp. Pl. 2: 777. 1753

Herbs: shoots pubescent, hairs eglandular. **Stems** prostrate to ascending. **Stipules:** margins dentate to incised. **Leaflets:** blades obovate, obovate-cuneate, oval, ovate, or globose, (3–)4–10(–13) × (2.5–)3–7(–10) mm, margins usually serrate, sometimes laciniate or incised, on distal 1/2–3/4. **Inflorescences** 4–18-flowered, capitate or subumbellate, with stellate flowers, deflexed fruits. **Flowers** 3.5–5 mm; calyx pubescent, hairs eglandular, lobes longer than tube; corolla yellow, slightly longer than calyx. **Legumes** linear, slightly compressed, 7–15(–25) × 1–2 mm, pubescent or glabrous, margin prickleless; faces with obliquely transverse, anastomosing, prominent veins. **Seeds** 4–10, yellow or yellow-brown, rhomboid-ovoid, 1–1.6 × 0.7–1.1 mm. **2*n*** = 16.

Flowering spring–summer. Fallow fields, roadsides; 0–1000 m; introduced; Ala., Md., Mass., N.Y.; s Europe; c Asia; n Africa; introduced also in South America (Argentina, Chile), Australia.

150. VICIA Linnaeus, Sp. Pl. 2: 734. 1753; Gen. Pl. ed. 5, 327. 1754 • Vetch [Latin *vicis*, curve, or *vincio*, bind, probably alluding to climbing habit]

Steven L. Broich

Herbs, annual, biennial, or perennial, unarmed. **Stems** erect, sprawling, or climbing, angled, not winged, glabrous or pubescent, hairs unicellular, eglandular. **Leaves** alternate, even-pinnate; stipules present, persistent, inconspicuous or foliose, with or without nectariferous patch; rachis not winged, usually terminating in a simple or branched, sometimes mucronate, tendril; petiolate; leaflets 2–30, usually scattered, ptyxis conduplicate (except in some *V. faba*), blade margins entire or serrate, surfaces glabrous or pubescent. **Inflorescences** 2–50-flowered, axillary, racemes, flowers solitary, erect or lax; bracts and bracteoles absent. **Flowers** papilionaceous, chasmogamous or cleistogamous; calyx campanulate, symmetric or oblique, 2-lipped, base sometimes gibbous, lobes 5, equal or unequal, some or all lobes at least 1/2 as long as tube; corolla white, cream, yellow, rose, lilac, blue, purple, lavender, or violet, wings and keel often lighter than banner, 2–35 mm; stamens 10, diadelphous; anthers dorsifixed, uniform; ovary glabrous or pubescent; style terete or compressed abaxially or adaxially, not twisted, usually encircled with short hairs just proximal to stigma and/or apically tufted abaxially. **Fruits** legumes, sessile or stipitate, terete or flattened, oblong, oblong-falcate, linear, or elliptic, dehiscent, valves twisted after dehiscence, non-septate, margins usually obscure, splitting along both margins, glabrous, glabrate, or pubescent. **Seeds** 2–15, usually brown or black, often spherical, sometimes angular. $x = 6, 7$.

Species ca. 140 (25 in the flora): North America, Mexico, s South America, Europe, Asia, n Africa, Mediterranean region; introduced in temperate regions worldwide.

F. K. Kupicha (1976) partitioned *Vicia* into two subgenera (subg. *Vicia* and subg. *Vicilla*) and 22 sections. *Vicia* species native to North America belong to subg. *Vicilla* (Schur) Rouy, which includes about 75% of all *Vicia*; nine of the 12 native *Vicia* are included in sect. *Cracca* Dumortier, which contains about 30% of all *Vicia*. Of the remaining native species, two [*V. americana* (sect. *Americanae* Kupicha), and *V. leucophaea* (sect. *Mediocinctae* Kupicha)] belong to monospecific sections; the third (*V. nigricans*) has been placed in sect. *Cassubicae* Radzhi, which includes another eight perennial European and Asian species. *Vicia* is predominantly diploid with $2n = 12$ or 14. Chromosome counts have been reported for five of the 12 species native to the flora area. There has been no worldwide treatment of the genus at the species level. *Vicia* in North America was last reviewed by F. J. Hermann (1960) and summarized by D. Isely (1998).

Recent phylogenetic studies (M. F. Wojciechowski et al. 2004) have placed *Vicia* consistently within the Vicieae as delimited by F. K. Kupicha (1981). The nearest sister group to the Vicieae appears to be *Trifolium*, but not directly other Trifolieae. Infra-generic relationships within *Vicia* continue to be explored (M. Leht 2005; Choi B. et al. 2006; Y. Endo et al. 2008; H. Schaefer et al. 2012).

Of the 13 *Vicia* species introduced to North America, seven probably arrived as agricultural crops and have become locally established to widely naturalized. Agricultural interest in *Vicia* species has stimulated extensive work on seeds and seedling morphology (F. J. Hermann 1960; C. R. Gunn 1970b; C. N. Nozzolillo 1977; J. S. Lassetter 1978). Seed descriptions reported here are (mostly) from Hermann.

Banner blade and styler morphology have become important indicators of intrageneric relationships within *Vicia* (F. K. Kupicha 1976; Choi B. et al. 2006; Y. Endo et al. 2008). Banner petals can be oblong (blade and claw of nearly equal width), pandurate (blade and claw of nearly equal width and with constriction between), or stenonychioid (blade notably wider than the claw).

Styles can be terete in cross section, compressed abaxially (perpendicular to the axis of the ovary) or compressed adaxially (parallel to the axis of the ovary). Abaxially compressed styles can be uniformly pubescent near the stigma or tufted with longer hairs adaxially. Descriptions reported here are from F. K. Kupicha 1976, Choi B. et al. 2006, or personal observation.

Unless otherwise noted, the length of leaves listed herein includes petiole and rachis but not tendrils; inflorescence length includes peduncle and raceme at mid flowering; and flower length includes distance from base of calyx to distal margins of wing petals.

SELECTED REFERENCES Hermann, F. J. 1960. Vetches of the U.S.—Native, Naturalized and Introduced. Washington. U.S.D.A., Agric. Handb. 168. Kupicha, F. K. 1976. The infrageneric structure of *Vicia*. Notes Roy. Bot. Gard. Edinburgh 34: 287–326.

1. Stipules with nectariferous patch abaxially; inflorescences 2–7-flowered, to 1 cm or flowers solitary, shorter than subtending leaf rachis [subg. *Vicia*].
    2. Stipules much smaller than leaflets . . . . 18. *Vicia sepium*
    2. Stipules foliose, approaching leaflets in size.
        3. Calyx lobes equal or subequal.
            4. Flowers 5–8 mm. . . . . 21. *Vicia lathyroides*
            4. Flowers 10–35 mm.
                5. Calyx lobes ± equal to tube; corollas violet-purple, lavender, or whitish . . . . . 19. *Vicia sativa*
                5. Calyx lobes shorter than tube; corollas yellow suffused with violet . . . . . 20. *Vicia grandiflora*
        3. Calyx lobes unequal.
            6. Herbs stout; calyx lobes longer than tube.
                7. Leaflet surfaces glabrous; tendrils absent . . . . 22. *Vicia faba*
                7. Leaflet surfaces sparsely pubescent; tendrils simple or branched . . . . . . 23. *Vicia narbonensis*
            6. Herbs usually slender or robust; abaxial calyx lobes subequal to tube.
                8. Banners glabrous; corollas pale to bright yellow . . . . 24. *Vicia lutea*
                8. Banners pubescent adaxially; corollas cream, sometimes with purplish tinge. . . . . 25. *Vicia pannonica*
1. Stipules without nectariferous patch; inflorescences 2–50-flowered, 1–25 cm, or flowers solitary, somewhat shorter, equaling, or exceeding subtending leaf rachis [subg. *Vicilla*].
    9. Leaflets 16–30; flowers 15–25 mm, banners oblong . . . . 1. *Vicia nigricans*
    9. Leaflets (2–)4–18(–24); flowers 2–18(–25) mm, banners oblong, pandurate, or stenonychioid.
        10. Banners oblong or stenonychioid; calyx base symmetric; styles terete or compressed abaxially.
            11. Herbs annual; flowers 2–6 mm.
                12. Legumes hirsute, tip oblique . . . . 10. *Vicia hirsuta*
                12. Legumes glabrous, tip rounded, style attached to center of curve. . . . . . 16. *Vicia tetrasperma*
            11. Herbs perennial; flowers 7–25 mm.
                13. Leaflets 8–18, blade surfaces glabrous or finely pubescent; inflorescences 3–9-flowered; flowers 12–25 mm, styles abaxially compressed . . . . 15. *Vicia americana*
                13. Leaflets 6–8, blade surfaces long-villous abaxially, glabrous adaxially; inflorescences 2-flowered or flowers solitary; flowers 7–9 mm, styles terete . . . . 17. *Vicia leucophaea*
        10. Banners pandurate; calyx base symmetric or gibbous; styles compressed adaxially.
            14. Flowers 8–18 mm.
                15. Leaflets (2 or)4(or 6); inflorescences 5–10-flowered; flowers 8–12 mm . . . . 7. *Vicia ocalensis* (in part)
                15. Leaflets 10–24; inflorescences (2–)7–50-flowered; flowers 8–18 mm.
                    16. Herbs perennial; calyx base symmetric or slightly gibbous; banners equal to or longer than claws; legumes 4–8 mm diam.
                        17. Stipules semisagittate; corollas usually blue-violet or purple, sometimes lilac or whitish; calyx lobes unequal . . . . 2. *Vicia cracca*
                        17. Stipules ligulate; corollas white with blue tip; calyx lobes subequal . . . . 4. *Vicia caroliniana* (in part)
                    16. Herbs annual or biennial; calyx base gibbous; banners 1/2 length or equal to claws; legumes 6–12 mm diam.
                        18. Legumes glabrous; widely distributed . . . . 8. *Vicia villosa*
                        18. Legumes densely villous; California . . . . 9. *Vicia benghalensis*
            14. Flowers 2–12 mm.
                19. Proximal leaves with 2–8 leaflets; longest calyx lobes usually shorter than tube.
                    20. Herbs annual; inflorescences 1- or 2-flowered.
                        21. Legumes reddish brown, narrowly oblong-falcate, 15–30 × 4–5 mm, apiculate, glabrous; stipe absent . . . . 12. *Vicia minutiflora*
                        21. Legumes tawny, oblong, 22–38 × 5–7 mm, oblique-tipped, strongly reticulate-veined, glabrous or finely pubescent; stipe to 2–3 mm. . . . . 14. *Vicia hassei*
                    20. Herbs perennial; inflorescences 2–10-flowered.

22. Legumes 8–15 mm; flowers 2–5 mm; leaflets 7–18 mm . . . . 6. *Vicia floridana*
22. Legumes 20–45 mm; flowers 6–12 mm; leaflets 15–40 mm.
23. Legumes 20–25 mm; flowers 6–8 mm; leaflets 15–30 mm . . . . 3. *Vicia acutifolia*
23. Legumes 40–45 mm; flowers 8–12 mm; leaflets 30–40 mm . . . . 7. *Vicia ocalensis* (in part)

[19. Shifted to left margin.—Ed.]

19. Proximal leaves with 7–24 leaflets; longest calyx lobes equal to or longer than tube.
24. Herbs annual; stipules semisagittate; corollas blue to bluish purple or pinkish white to light lavender.
25. Legumes 12–16 mm; banner blade 2 times length of claw; leaflets 12–20. . . . . 11. *Vicia disperma*
25. Legumes 15–38 mm; banner blade equal to or less than 2 times longer than claw; leaflets 7–14 . . . . 13. *Vicia ludoviciana*
24. Herbs perennial; stipules ligulate; corollas white to cream-white with blue to purple tip.
26. Flowers 8–12 mm; e Texas to Atlantic coast and Great Lakes . . . . .4. *Vicia caroliniana* (in part)
26. Flowers 4–7 mm; Arizona, New Mexico. . . . . 5. *Vicia pulchella*

1. Vicia nigricans Hooker & Arnott, Bot. Beechey Voy., 20. 1830 • Giant vetch

Varieties 2 (1 in the flora): w North America, s South America (Argentina, Chile).

Variety *nigricans* is known from Pacific coastal areas of southern South America.

1a. Vicia nigricans Hooker & Arnott var. **gigantea** (Hooker) Broich, Madroño 54: 70. 2007 [E]

Vicia gigantea Hooker, Fl. Bor.-Amer. 1: 157. 1831; *V. nigricans* subsp. *gigantea* (Hooker) Lassetter & C. R. Gunn

Herbs perennial. **Stems** climbing, robust, 6–20 dm. **Leaves** 9–23 cm; tendrils usually branched; stipules foliose, semisagittate, without nectariferous patch; leaflets 16–30, blades ovate to lanceolate, 15–75 × 4–20 mm, apex obtuse, surfaces sparsely appressed-pubescent. **Inflorescences** 6–25-flowered, 5–25 cm, somewhat shorter than subtending leaf rachis. **Flowers** 15–25 mm; calyx base symmetric, lobes unequal, longest one equal to tube; corolla reddish purple to yellowish, banner oblong, blade equal to claw, glabrous; style compressed abaxially, evenly pubescent throughout. **Legumes** black, oblong, 33–55 × 10–20 mm, oblique-tipped, glabrous; stipe to 4 mm. **Seeds** 3 or 4, purplish black, subglobose, 5–6 mm diam.; hilum encircling 3/4+ circumference of seed. **2*n*** = 14.

Flowering May–Jul. Upper margins of beaches, meadows, clearings, stream banks, thickets, mesic forests, open, coniferous forests, roadsides, forest edges; 0–100 m; B.C.; Alaska, Calif., Oreg., Wash.

J. S. Lassetter and C. R. Gunn (1979) made a case for combining the common North American Pacific Coast taxon *Vicia gigantea* with *V. nigricans* of the South American Pacific Coast.

2. Vicia cracca Linnaeus, Sp. Pl. 2: 735. 1753 • Bird or tufted vetch, vesce jargeau [W]

Herbs perennial. **Stems** sprawling or climbing, slender to robust, to 20 dm. **Leaves** 2–8 cm; tendrils usually branched; stipules foliose, semisagittate, without nectariferous patch; leaflets 10–28, blades narrowly oblong or elliptic to linear, 10–25 × 2–8 mm, apex obtuse to acute, surfaces glabrate to pilose. **Inflorescences** 10–50-flowered, 4–20 cm, equal to or longer than subtending leaf rachis. **Flowers** 8–16 mm; calyx base symmetric to slightly gibbous, lobes unequal, pilose, lateral ones equal to tube; corolla usually blue-violet or purple, sometimes lilac or whitish, banner pandurate, blade equal to or longer than claw, glabrous; style compressed adaxially, pubescent apically. **Legumes** tawny, broadly oblong, 15–30 × 6–8 mm, oblique-tipped, glabrous; stipe to 1.5 mm. **Seeds** 4–8, dark grayish to purplish brown, sometimes mottled purple, globose to ellipsoid-ovoid, 2.5–4 mm diam.; hilum encircling 1/5–1/3 circumference of seed. **2*n*** = 12, 14, 21, 22, 28.

Varieties ca. 5 (2 in the flora): North America, Eurasia; introduced in South America, Australia.

Vicia cracca is part of a European species complex (P. W. Ball 1968) and may or may not be native to North America (F. J. Hermann 1960); it is distinguished from the similar *V. villosa* by a symmetric calyx base and banner blade length equal to claw.

1. Leaflet blades elliptic to oblong; inflorescences 20–50-flowered, 1–1.5 times length of subtending leaf rachis; flowers 8–12 mm, banner blades ca. equal to claw. . . . . 2a. *Vicia cracca* var. *cracca*
1. Leaflet blades linear; inflorescences 10–25-flowered, to 2 times length of subtending leaf rachis; flowers 12–16 mm, banner blade 2 times length of claw . . . . 2b. *Vicia cracca* var. *angustissima*

2a. Vicia cracca Linnaeus var. **cracca** [W]

Vicia semicincta Greene

Leaflet blades elliptic to oblong. **Inflorescences** 20–50-flowered, 1–1.5 times length of subtending leaf rachis. **Flowers** 8–12 mm, banner blades ca. equal to claw. **Seeds** dark grayish brown, sometimes mottled purple, globose, 2.5–3 mm diam.; hilum encircling 1/4–1/3 circumference of seed.

Flowering Jun–Aug. Open woodlands, old fields, thickets, roadsides; 0–1000 m; Alta., B.C., Man., N.B., Nfld. and Labr., N.W.T., N.S., Ont., P.E.I., Que., Sask., Yukon; Alaska, Calif., Conn., Ill., Iowa, Maine, Mass., Mich., Mo., N.H., N.Y., Oreg., R.I., Vt., Va., Wash., Wis., Wyo.; Eurasia; introduced in South America, Australia.

2b. Vicia cracca Linnaeus var. **angustissima** Neilreich, Fl. Nied.-Oesterr., 959. 1859 [I]

Vicia cracca subsp. *tenuifolia* (Roth) Corbière; *V. tenuifolia* Roth

Leaflet blades linear. **Inflorescences** 10–25-flowered, to 2 times length of subtending leaf rachis. **Flowers** 12–16 mm, banner blade 2 times length of claw. **Seeds** purplish brown, subglobose to ellipsoid-ovoid, to 4 mm; hilum encircling 1/5–1/4 circumference of seed.

Flowering Jun–Aug. Disturbed areas; 0–100 m; introduced; Ont.; Wis.; Europe.

3. Vicia acutifolia Elliott, Sketch Bot. S. Carolina 2: 225. 1823 • Sand vetch [E] [W]

Herbs perennial. **Stems** few, sprawling or climbing, slender, 2–15 dm. **Leaves** 2–6 cm; tendrils simple or branched; stipules much smaller than leaflets, semisagittate, without nectariferous patch; leaflets (2 or)4(or 6), blades narrowly lanceolate to linear, 15–30 × 1–5 mm, apex obtuse, surfaces glabrous or sparsely long-pubescent. **Inflorescences** 4–10-flowered, 2–7 cm, longer than subtending leaf rachis. **Flowers** 6–8 mm; calyx base symmetric, lobes unequal, longest one shorter than tube; corolla pale blue or lavender to white, banner pandurate, blade subequal to claw, glabrous; style compressed adaxially, evenly pubescent apically. **Legumes** brown to black, linear-oblong, 20–25 × 4–6 mm, oblique-tipped, sparsely long-pubescent; stipe to 1–2 mm. **Seeds** 4–8, purplish black, compressed-globose, 2–2.5 mm diam.; hilum encircling 2/3 circumference of seed.

Flowering Apr–May. Wet woodlands, margins of swamps, wet ditches, sandy soils; 0–100 m; Fla., Ga., S.C.

Typical *Vicia acutifolia* has four leaflets. Populations in the northern part of its range in Georgia and South Carolina sometimes have six somewhat broader leaflets, which may indicate intergradation with *V. caroliniana* (D. Isely 1990). *Vicia acutifolia* differs from *V. floridana* in its longer fruits, flowers, leaflets, and inflorescences.

4. Vicia caroliniana Walter, Fl. Carol., 182. 1788 • Carolina or pale or wood vetch [E] [F]

Vicia hugeri Small

Herbs perennial. **Stems** sprawling or climbing, slender, 3–15 dm. **Leaves** 2–8 cm; tendrils mucronate on proximal leaves, simple or branched on distal leaves; stipules much smaller than leaflets, ligulate, without nectariferous patch; leaflets 10–24, blades elliptic-oblong or oblanceolate to linear, 10–30 × 2–6 mm, apex obtuse, surfaces glabrous or abaxial puberulent. **Inflorescences** 7–20-flowered, 3–10 cm, shorter to longer than subtending leaf rachis. **Flowers** 8–12 mm; calyx base symmetric, lobes subequal, shorter than tube; corolla white with blue tip, banner pandurate, blade equal to or longer than claw, glabrous; style compressed adaxially, pubescent apically, tufted abaxially. **Legumes** reddish brown, narrowly oblong, 15–30 × 4–5 mm, obliquely long-tipped, glabrous; stipe to 2 mm. **Seeds** 5–8 violet brown to black, compressed-subglobose or subglobose, 2–4 mm diam.; hilum encircling 3/4 circumference of seed.

Flowering Mar–May. Rich alluvial woodlands, woodland borders, roadsides, old fields; 0–1000 m; Ont.; Ala., Ark., Del., D.C., Fla., Ga., Ill., Ind., Ky., La., Md., Mich., Miss., Mo., N.J., N.Y., N.C., Ohio, Pa., S.C., Tenn., Tex., Va., W.Va., Wis.

Vicia caroliniana possibly intergrades with *V. acutifolia* where their ranges overlap in Georgia and South Carolina (D. Isely 1990); *V. caroliniana* and *V. pulchella*, native to the American Southwest, are almost certainly related.

5. Vicia pulchella Kunth in A. von Humboldt et al., Nov. Gen. Sp. 6(fol.): 390; 6(qto.): 499; plate 583. 1824 • Beautiful or showy vetch

Vicia melilotoides Wooton & Standley

Herbs perennial. **Stems** sprawling or climbing, slender, 2–15 dm. **Leaves** 4–11 cm; tendrils branched; stipules much smaller than leaflets, ligulate, without nectariferous patch; leaflets 10–16, blades elliptic-oblong to linear, 7–30 × 1–11 mm, apex obtuse, abaxial surface glabrous, adaxial often sparsely long-pubescent. **Inflorescences** 8–25-flowered, 2–15 cm, shorter to longer than subtending leaf rachis. **Flowers** 4–7 mm; calyx base symmetric, lobes equal, usually shorter than tube; corolla cream-white with purple-tipped keel, banner pandurate, blade equal to claw, glabrous; style compressed adaxially, pubescent evenly for some length along style. **Legumes** reddish brown, oblong, 20–35 × 5–8 mm, acute-tipped, glabrous; stipe 1–2 mm. **Seeds** 5–9, purplish black, compressed-subglobose, 2–3 mm diam.; hilum encircling 1/4 circumference of seed.

Flowering Jul–Sep. Pine woods, juniper grasslands, moist meadows, open stony hillsides; 1500–3000 m; Ariz., N.Mex.; Mexico.

6. Vicia floridana S. Watson, Proc. Amer. Acad. Arts 14: 292. 1879 • Florida vetch [E]

Herbs perennial. **Stems** sprawling or climbing, filiform, 3–8 dm. **Leaves** 3–5 cm; tendrils simple; stipules much smaller than leaflets, semisagittate, without nectariferous patch; leaflets 2–6, blades usually broadly elliptic to oblong or oblanceolate, sometimes linear, 7–18 × 2–8 mm, apex obtuse, surfaces glabrous. **Inflorescences** 2–8-flowered, 2–5 cm, shorter to longer than subtending leaf rachis. **Flowers** 5–6 mm; calyx base symmetric, lobes equal, much shorter than tube; corolla white to bluish, banner pandurate, blade equal to claw, glabrous; style compressed adaxially, pubescent apically. **Legumes** brown to black, broadly oblong, 8–15 × 3–5 mm, oblique-tipped, glabrous; stipe to 1–2 mm. **Seeds** 1 or 2, purplish black, compressed-globose, 3 mm diam.; hilum encircling 1/2–3/4 circumference of seed.

Flowering Apr–May. Moist soils, ditches, roadsides; 0–100 m; Fla., Ga.

Vicia floridana is distinguished from *V. acutifolia* by the broader leaflets (elliptic to lanceolate versus linear) and shorter (8–15 mm versus 20–25 mm) fruits.

7. Vicia ocalensis R. K. Godfrey & Kral, Rhodora 60: 256, figs. 4, 5. 1958 • Ocala vetch [C] [E]

Herbs perennial. **Stems** sprawling or climbing, slender, 5–15 dm. **Leaves** 4–8 cm; tendrils simple; stipules much smaller than leaflets, semisagittate, without nectariferous patch; leaflets (2 or)4(or 6), blades narrowly oblong to linear, 30–50 × 3–6 mm, apex obtuse, surfaces glabrous. **Inflorescences** 5–10-flowered, 3–15 cm, longer than subtending leaf rachis. **Flowers** 8–12 mm; calyx base symmetric, lobes equal, shorter than or equal to tube; corolla blue or lavender and white, banner pandurate, blade equal to claw, glabrous; style compressed adaxially, pubescent apically. **Legumes** brown, oblong, 40–45 × 7–8 mm, oblique-tipped, glabrous; stipe 1–2 mm. **Seeds** 8–12, purplish black, compressed-globose, 3–3.5 mm diam.; hilum encircling 2/3 circumference of seed.

Flowering Apr–May. Thickets, open moist areas; of conservation concern; 0–70 m; Fla.

Vicia ocalensis is known only from Lake and Marion counties; it is similar to *V. acutifolia* but differs in its more robust stature and larger leaflets, flowers, and fruits.

8. Vicia villosa Roth, Tent. Fl. Germ. 2(2): 182. 1793 • Hairy or winter or woolly vetch, vesce velue [F] [I] [W]

Herbs annual or biennial. **Stems** erect, sprawling, or climbing, slender, 2–13 dm. **Leaves** 4–9 cm; tendrils branched; stipules much smaller than leaflets, semisagittate, without nectariferous patch; leaflets 10–18, blades narrowly oblong to linear, 10–35 × 1–10 mm, apex obtuse to acute or apiculate, surfaces glabrate to villous. **Inflorescences** 10–20+-flowered, 3–19 cm, longer than subtending leaf rachis. **Flowers** 12–18 mm; calyx base gibbous, lobes unequal, usually longer than tube; corolla violet to rose and white, banner pandurate, blade 1/2 length of claw, glabrous; style compressed adaxially, pubescent apically. **Legumes** tawny, oblong, 15–40 × 6–11 mm, oblique-tipped, glabrous; stipe to 2–3 mm. **Seeds** 2–8, black to blackish brown, globose to ovoid-oblong, 3–5 mm diam.; hilum encircling 1/7 circumference of seed.

Varieties 5 (2 in the flora): introduced; Europe, c, sw Asia, n Africa; introduced also in South America, Australia.

Vicia villosa was introduced as a forage crop and has become widely established in North America. It can be distinguished from the similar *V. cracca* by its distinctly asymmetric (gibbous) calyx base and banner blade half the length of the claw.

1. Herbs villous, hairs conspicuous, 1–2 mm; inflorescences 20+-flowered, flowers crowded on rachis; adaxial calyx lobe acicular, 2–4 mm . . . . 8a. *Vicia villosa* var. *villosa*
1. Herbs glabrate, hairs inconspicuous, subappressed to spreading, 1 mm; inflorescences 10–20-flowered, flowers loosely arranged on rachis; adaxial calyx lobe lanceolate to narrowly lanceolate, 1–2(–2.4) mm . . . . 8b. *Vicia villosa* var. *glabrescens*

8a. Vicia villosa Roth var. **villosa** [F] [I]

Herbs villous, hairs conspicuous, 1–2 mm. **Inflorescences** 20+-flowered, flowers crowded on rachis. **Flowers** 14–18 mm; adaxial calyx lobe acicular, 2–4 mm. $2n$ = 14.

Flowering Apr–Jul. Fields, foothill woodlands, roadsides, waste areas; 0–2000 m; introduced; B.C., Man., N.S., Ont., Que., Yukon; Ala., Alaska, Ark., Calif., Conn., D.C., Idaho, Ill., Ind., Iowa, Kans., Ky., La., Maine, Md., Mass., Mich., Minn., Miss., Mo., Mont., Nebr., Nev., N.H., N.J., N.Mex., N.Y., N.C., N.Dak., Ohio, Okla., Oreg., Pa., R.I., S.C., S.Dak., Tenn., Tex., Vt., Va., Wash., W.Va., Wis.; Europe; introduced also in South America (Argentina, Chile)

8b. Vicia villosa Roth var. **glabrescens** W. D. J. Koch, Syn. Fl. Germ. Helv., 194. 1835 [I] [W]

Vicia dasycarpa Tenore; *V. varia* Host; *V. villosa* subsp. *varia* (Host) Corbière

Herbs glabrate, hairs inconspicuous, subappressed to spreading, 1 mm. **Inflorescences** 10–20-flowered, flowers loosely arranged on rachis. **Flowers** 12–16 mm; adaxial calyx lobe lanceolate to narrowly lanceolate, 1–2(–2.4) mm. $2n$ = 14.

Flowering Apr–Jun. Fields, roadsides, waste areas; 0–2000 m; introduced; B.C., N.S.; Ala., Ark., Calif., Fla., Ga., Ill., Ind., Iowa, Kans., Ky., La., Maine, Md., Mass., Mich., Minn., Miss., Mo., Nebr., N.J., N.Y., N.C., N.Dak., Ohio, Okla., Oreg., Pa., S.C., S.Dak., Tenn., Tex., Va., Wash., W.Va., Wis.; Europe.

9. Vicia benghalensis Linnaeus, Sp. Pl. 2: 736. 1753 • Purple vetch [I] [W]

Vicia atropurpurea Desfontaines

Herbs annual or biennial. **Stems** sprawling or climbing, slender, 10–20 dm. **Leaves** 3–6 cm; tendrils branched; stipules much smaller than leaflets, semisagittate, without nectariferous patch; leaflets 10–16, blades ovate-oblong to linear, 10–30 × 4–9 mm, apex obtuse, surfaces villous. **Inflorescences** 2–12-flowered, 3–12 cm, equal to subtending leaf rachis. **Flowers** 13–18 mm; calyx base gibbous, lobes unequal, usually equal to tube; corolla white at base, purple apically, banner pandurate, blade shorter than or equal to claw, glabrous; style compressed adaxially, pubescent apically. **Legumes** tawny, narrowly oblong, 25–35 × 8–12 mm, oblique-tipped, densely villous; stipe to 1–2 mm. **Seeds** 4 or 5, velvety black with prominent white hilum, compressed-subglobose, 4–5 mm diam.; hilum encircling 1/5 circumference of seed. $2n$ = 14.

Flowering Apr–May. Disturbed areas; 0–200 m; introduced; Calif; s Asia; introduced also in s South America.

Vicia benghalensis is cultivated as a cover crop along the Pacific Coast; it has become established in California. It can be distinguished from *V. villosa* by its pubescent fruits.

10. Vicia hirsuta (Linnaeus) Gray, Nat. Arr. Brit. Pl. 2: 614. 1822 • Hairy or tiny vetch, vesce hérissée [I] [W]

Ervum hirsutum Linnaeus, Sp. Pl. 2: 738. 1753

Herbs annual. **Stems** sprawling or climbing, filiform, 2–8 dm. **Leaves** 2–8 cm; tendrils simple or branched; stipules much smaller than leaflets, semisagittate, tips purple, without nectariferous patch; leaflets 8–16, blades narrowly oblong-elliptic to linear, 5–23 × 1–6 mm, apex truncate to emarginate, surfaces glabrous. **Inflorescences** 2–7-flowered, 1–5 cm, ± shorter than subtending leaf rachis. **Flowers** 2–4 mm; calyx base symmetric, lobes subequal, equal to or longer than tube; corolla whitish blue to purplish blue, banner stenonychioid, blade equal to claw, glabrous; style terete, sparsely pubescent apically. **Legumes** black, oblong, 6–10 × 3–4 m, oblique at both ends, hirsute; stipe absent. **Seeds** 2, greenish ochroleucous to pale reddish brown or chestnut, usually ± mottled purple, subglobose to compressed-globose, 1–3 mm diam.; hilum encircling 1/2 circumference of seed. $2n$ = 14.

Flowering Apr–Jun. Roadsides, fields, waste areas, open woodlands, maritime bluffs and dunes, streamsides; 0–2000 m; introduced; Greenland; St. Pierre and Miquelon; B.C., N.B., N.S., Ont., P.E.I., Que.; Ala., Alaska, Ark., Calif., Conn., Del., D.C., Fla., Ga., La., Maine, Mass., Mich., Miss., N.H., N.J., N.Y., N.C., Ohio, Okla., Oreg., Pa., R.I., S.C., Tex., Va., Wash., Wis.; Europe; introduced also in South America (Argentina, Brazil, Chile).

11. Vicia disperma de Candolle, Cat. Hort. Monsp., 154. 1813 • Two-seeded vetch [I]

Herbs annual. **Stems** sprawling, 2–6 dm. **Leaves** 3–6 cm; tendrils usually branched; stipules much smaller than leaflets, semisagittate; leaflets 12–20, blades narrowly elliptic to linear, 7–12 × 1–5 mm, apex blunt to acute and mucronulate, surfaces glabrous or puberulent. **Inflorescences** 2–5-flowered, 2–5 cm, somewhat shorter than subtending leaf rachis. **Flowers** 4–5 mm; calyx base symmetric, lobes unequal, lateral lobes equal to tube; corolla blue, banner pandurate, blade 2 times length of claw, glabrous; style compressed adaxially, pubescent apically. **Legumes** tawny, oblong-subrhomboidal, 12–16 × 5–7 mm, glabrous; short-stipitate. **Seeds** 2, purplish black, compressed-globose, 4–5 mm diam.; hilum encircling 1/6 circumference of seed.

Flowering Apr–May. Disturbed areas; 0–100 m; introduced; Calif.; Europe.

12. Vicia minutiflora D. Dietrich, Syn. Pl. 4: 1107. 1847 • Small-flowered vetch [E]

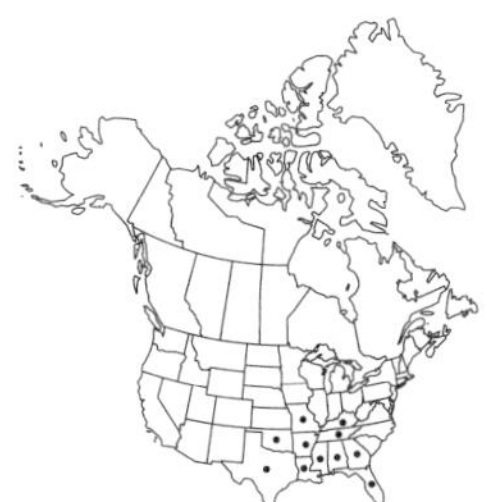

Vicia micrantha Nuttall ex Torrey & A. Gray, Fl. N. Amer. 1: 271. 1838, not Lowe 1831; *V. reverchonii* S. Watson

Herbs winter annual. **Stems** sprawling or climbing, slender, 2–8 dm. **Leaves** 2–6 cm; tendrils simple or branched (absent on proximal leaves); stipules foliose, semisagittate, without nectariferous patch; leaflets 2 or 4 proximally, 4–8 distally, blades ovate proximally, linear distally, 5–30 × 1–5 mm, apex obtuse to acute, surfaces glabrous. **Inflorescences** 1- or 2-flowered, 1–5 cm, ± shorter than subtending leaf rachis. **Flowers** 5–8 mm; calyx base symmetric, lobes unequal, shorter than tube; corolla pale blue to lavender, banner pandurate, blade equal to claw, glabrous; style compressed adaxially, pubescent apically. **Legumes** reddish brown, narrowly oblong-falcate, 15–30 × 4–5 mm, apiculate, glabrous; stipe absent. **Seeds** 6–8, blackish purple, subglobose, 2 mm diam.; hilum encircling 5/8 circumference of seed.

Flowering Apr–May. Mesic woodlands, limestone soils, disturbed sites; 0–500 m; Ala., Ark., Fla., Ga., Ky., La., Miss., Mo., Okla., Tenn., Tex.

13. Vicia ludoviciana Nuttall ex Torrey & A. Gray, Fl. N. Amer. 1: 271. 1838 • Deerpea or Louisiana vetch

Herbs annual or winter annual. **Stems** sprawling or climbing, slender to robust, 2–20 dm. **Leaves** 2–10 cm; tendrils branched; stipules much smaller than leaflets, semisagittate, without nectariferous patch; leaflets 7–14, blades ovate to linear, 5–25 × 1–11 mm, apex acute to emarginate, surfaces glabrous or puberulent. **Inflorescences** 2–19-flowered, 1–15 cm, or flowers 1, ± shorter than subtending leaf rachis. **Flowers** 4–7 mm; calyx base symmetric, lobes subequal, shorter than or equal to tube; corolla deep blue to bluish purple or pinkish white to light lavender, banner pandurate, blade equal to or longer than claw, glabrous; style compressed adaxially, pubescent apically. **Legumes** yellow to brown, flat, rhombic-oblong, 16–30 × 4–6 mm, oblique-tipped, glabrous; stipe to 1 mm. **Seeds** 4–8, brownish gray, mottled dark purple, subglobose to compressed-subglobose, 2.2–2.5 mm diam.; hilum encircling 1/4–1/3 circumference of seed.

Varieties 2 (2 in the flora): North America, n Mexico.

J. S. Lassetter (1984) showed that the taxa traditionally treated as *Vicia exigua*, *V. leavenworthii*, *V. ludoviciana*, and *V. producta* are morphologically confluent and part of one evolving species complex. Within the complex, there is a strong tendency toward cleistogamy in populations traditionally delimited as *V. leavenworthii*: styles and anthers are shorter and pollination takes place before flowers open and peduncles fully elongate. Lassetter treated cleistogamous populations as var. *leavenworthii* and all other populations as var. *ludoviciana*.

J. S. Lassetter (1984), D. Isely (1998), and S. L. Broich (2007) presented more detailed treatments of vars. *leavenworthii* and *ludoviciana*, delimiting two races within var. *leavenworthii* and five races within var. *ludoviciana*.

1. Leaflets 7–10(–14); flowers opening after peduncle and internode elongation, without young fruit when first open . . . . 13a. *Vicia ludoviciana* var. *ludoviciana*
1. Leaflets 11–14; flowers opening before peduncle and internode elongation, usually with young fruit when first open . . . . 13b. *Vicia ludoviciana* var. *leavenworthii*

13a. Vicia ludoviciana Nuttall ex Torrey & A. Gray var. **ludoviciana**

Vicia exigua Nuttall; *V. leavenworthii* Torrey & A. Gray var. *occidentalis* Shinners; *V. ludoviciana* var. *laxiflora* Shinners; *V. ludoviciana* var. *texana* (Torrey & A. Gray) Shinners; *V. producta* Rydberg; *V. texana* (Torrey & A. Gray) Small

Leaflets 7–10(–14). **Inflorescences** 1–19-flowered. **Flowers** opening after peduncle and internode elongation, fruits not present when first open; corolla deep blue to bluish purple. **2*n*** = 14.

Flowering Mar–May. Sandy soils, dense to open woodlands, chaparral, thickets, grasslands, rocky slopes and hillsides, pastures, roadsides, waste areas; 0–2500 m; Ala., Ariz., Ark., Calif., Colo., La., Miss., Nev., N.Mex., Okla., Tex., Utah, Wyo.; Mexico (Baja California, Baja California Sur, Nuevo León).

13b. Vicia ludoviciana Nuttall ex Torrey & A. Gray var. **leavenworthii** (Nuttall ex Torrey & A. Gray) Broich, Madroño 54: 70. 2007 [E]

Vicia leavenworthii Torrey & A. Gray, Fl. N. Amer. 1: 271. 1838; *V. ludoviciana* subsp. *leavenworthii* (Torrey & A. Gray) Lassetter & C. R. Gunn

Leaflets 11–14. **Inflorescences** 1–6-flowered. **Flowers** opening before peduncle and internode elongation, usually containing young fruit when first open; corolla pinkish white to light lavender. **2*n*** = 14.

Flowering Mar–May. Sandy or clay soils, limestone hills, cedar breaks, deciduous woodlands, bottomlands, wooded streamsides; 0–1000 m; Ark., La., Miss., Mo., Okla., Tex.

14. Vicia hassei S. Watson, Proc. Amer. Acad. Arts 25: 129. 1890 • Hasse's or slender vetch

Vicia exigua Nuttall var. *hassei* (S. Watson) Jepson

Herbs annual. **Stems** sprawling or climbing, somewhat robust, to 10 dm. **Leaves** 2–4 cm; tendrils simple or branched; stipules much smaller than leaflets, semisagittate, without nectariferous patch; leaflets 4–8, blades elliptic to lanceolate-linear, 8–40 × 1–9 mm, apex acute to truncate, surfaces glabrous or sparsely pubescent. **Inflorescences** 1- or 2-flowered, 1–3 cm, ± shorter than subtending leaf rachis. **Flowers** 6–9 mm; calyx base symmetric, lobes subequal, 1/2 length of tube; corolla white to faint bluish or lavender, banner pandurate, blade equal to claw, glabrous; style compressed adaxially, pubescent along style. **Legumes** tawny, oblong, 22–38 × 5–7 mm, oblique-tipped, strongly reticulate-veined, glabrous or finely pubescent; stipe to 2–3 mm. **Seeds** 4–7, purplish black, compressed-subglobose, 2.5–3 mm diam.; hilum encircling 1/5 circumference of seed. **2*n*** = 14.

Flowering Mar–Apr. Sandy or rocky soils, understory of grass- or brush-covered slopes, streamsides, floodplains, forest margins; 0–1200 m; Calif., Oreg.; Mexico (Baja California).

Vicia hassei was reduced to a variety of *V. exigua* (= *V. ludoviciana* var. *ludoviciana*) by Jepson in 1901. J. S. Lassetter (1975) made a case for retaining *V. hassei* as a separate species. Chromosomes of *V. hassei* are much larger than those of *V. ludoviciana*. Ovaries of *V. hassei* are pubescent; those of *V. ludoviciana* are glabrous. Arrangement of hairs on the stylar apices differs, with *V. hassei* having a pronounced inequilateral stylar brush, and *V. ludoviciana* having hairs distributed evenly around the tip of the style.

15. Vicia americana Muhlenburg ex Willdenow, Sp. Pl. 3: 1096. 1802 • American vetch, vesce d'Amérique [F]

Herbs perennial. **Stems** erect, trailing, or climbing, slender to stout, to 20 dm. **Leaves** 2–8 cm; tendrils simple or branched; stipules much smaller than leaflets, semisagittate, without nectariferous patch; leaflets 8–18, blades ovate or elliptic to linear, 3–44 × 1–19 mm, apex obtuse to truncate-emarginate, or apiculate, surfaces glabrous or finely pubescent. **Inflorescences** 3–9-flowered, 2–8 cm, shorter than or equal to subtending leaf rachis. **Flowers** 12–25 mm; calyx base symmetric, lobes subequal, shorter than tube; corolla usually bluish purple, rarely white, banner oblong, blade equal to claw, glabrous; style compressed abaxially, pubescent apically, tufted abaxially. **Legumes** tawny to brown, oblong, 25–39 × 5–9 mm, oblique-tipped, glabrous or pubescent; stipe to 4–5 mm. **Seeds:** number not known, olive-brown to deep violet-brown, subglobose, 3–4 mm diam.; hilum encircling 1/4–1/3 circumference of seed.

Varieties 3 (2 in the flora): North America, n Mexico, e Asia.

Vicia americana consists of a polymorphic assemblage of populations among which leaflet size, shape, and vestiture is variable. Intergradation is widespread. C. R. Gunn (1968) described two relatively distinct entities which may represent the extremes of a continuum of variation in some regions. Variety *sinensis* C. R. Gunn occurs in eastern Asia.

1. Stems usually 4–20 dm, trailing or climbing; leaves with branched tendrils; inflorescences (3–)4–9-flowered . . . 15a. *Vicia americana* var. *americana*
1. Stems usually to 4 dm, erect; leaves often with simple tendrils; inflorescences 3–4(–5)-flowered . . . . 15b. *Vicia americana* var. *minor*

15a. Vicia americana Muhlenberg ex Willdenow var. **americana** [F]

Vicia americana subsp. *oregana* (Nuttall) Abrams; *V. americana* var. *truncata* (Nuttall) W. H. Brewer; *V. americana* var. *villosa* (Kellogg) F. J. Hermann; *V. californica* Greene; *V. californica* var. *madrensis* Jepson; *V. oregana* Nuttall

Stems trailing or climbing, usually 4–20 dm. **Leaves** with branched tendrils; leaflet blades 3–44 × 1–19 mm. **Inflorescences** (3–)4–9-flowered. $2n$ = 14, 28.

Flowering May–Aug. Open, moist woods, thickets, meadows, tallgrass prairies, sagebrush steppes, roadsides, waste areas; 0–3000 m; Alta., B.C., Man., N.W.T., Ont., Que., Sask., Yukon; Alaska, Ariz., Calif., Colo., Idaho, Ill., Ind., Iowa, Kans., Mich., Minn., Mo., Mont., Nebr., Nev., N.Mex., N.Y., N.Dak., Okla., Oreg., Pa., S.Dak., Tex., Utah, Wash., Wis., Wyo.; Mexico (Chihuahua, Coahuila, México)

15b. Vicia americana Muhlenberg ex Willdenow var. **minor** Hooker, Fl. Bor.-Amer. 1: 157. 1831 [E]

Vicia americana var. *angustifolia* Nees; *V. americana* var. *linearis* (Nuttall) S. Watson; *V. americana* subsp. *minor* (Hooker) Piper & Beattie

Stems erect, usually to 4 dm. **Leaves** often with simple tendrils; leaflet blades 20–40 × 2–5 mm. **Inflorescences** 3–4(–5)-flowered. $2n$ = 14, 28.

Flowering May–Jul. Sandy plains, dry prairies, pinyon-juniper woodlands; 500–2000 m; Alta., B.C., Man., N.W.T., Sask.; Ariz., Colo., Iowa, Kans., Mont., Nebr., Nev., N.Mex., N.Dak., Okla., S.Dak., Utah, Wyo.

Vicia sparsifolia Nuttall ex Torrey & A. Gray 1838, not Tenore 1835, is an illegitimate name that pertains here.

16. Vicia tetrasperma (Linnaeus) Schreber, Spic. Fl. Lips., 26. 1771 • Lentil tare, slender or sparrow vetch, vesce à quatre graines [I] [W]

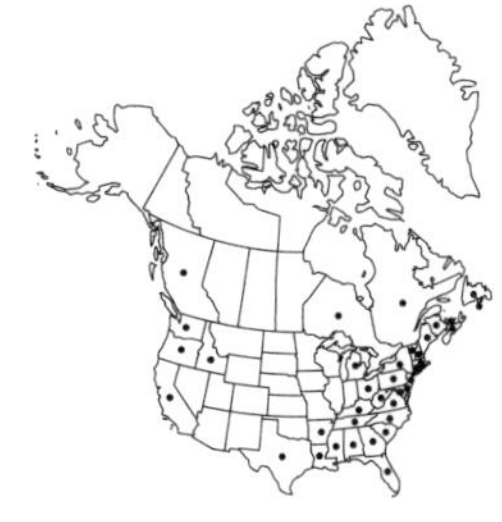

Ervum tetraspermum Linnaeus, Sp. Pl. 2: 738. 1753

Herbs annual, sparsely pubescent. **Stems** sprawling or climbing, filiform, 1–5 dm. **Leaves** 1–4 cm; tendrils simple or branched; stipules much smaller than leaflets, semisagittate, without nectariferous patch; leaflets 4–12, blades oblanceolate or elliptic to linear, 6–20 × 1–5 mm, apex acute to apiculate, surfaces glabrous or sparsely villous. **Inflorescences** 1–3-flowered, 1–3 cm, equal to or longer than subtending leaf rachis. **Flowers** 3–6 mm; calyx base symmetric, lobes unequal, longer than or equal to tube; corolla light purple to pale lavender, banner stenonychioid, blade equal to claw, glabrous; style compressed abaxially, sparsely pubescent apically. **Legumes** yellow to light brown, oblong, 10–15 × 3–4 mm, tip rounded, stigma attached to center of curve, glabrous; stipe to 1 mm. **Seeds** 4, greenish gray to purplish black, subglobose, 1.5–2 mm diam.; hilum encircling 1/5–1/4 circumference of seed. $2n$ = 14.

Flowering Apr–Jun. Fields, roadsides, waste areas, woodlands; 0–2000 m; introduced; St. Pierre and Miquelon; B.C., N.B., Nfld. and Labr. (Nfld.), N.S., Ont., P.E.I., Que.; Ala., Ark., Calif., Conn., Del., D.C., Fla., Ga., Idaho, Ky., La., Maine, Md., Mass., Mich., Miss., N.H., N.J., N.Y., N.C., Ohio, Oreg., Pa., R.I., S.C., Tenn., Tex., Vt., Va., Wash., W.Va.; Europe; introduced also in s South America (Chile).

Vicia tetrasperma var. *tenuissima* Druce in the sense of M. L. Fernald (1950), and listed as a separate variety of *V. tetrasperma*, is considered here and by D. Isely (1990) as a synonym of *V. tetrasperma*.

17. Vicia leucophaea Greene, Bot. Gaz. 6: 217. 1881 (as leucophoea) • Mogollon vetch [F]

Herbs perennial. **Stems** erect, sprawling, or climbing, slender to robust, 1–8 dm. **Leaves** 1–4 cm; tendrils simple or branched; stipules foliose, sometimes wider than leaflets, semisagittate, without nectariferous patch; leaflets 6 or 8, blades oblong-elliptic to linear, 7–25 × 1–6 mm, apex obtuse, surfaces long-villous abaxially, glabrous adaxially. **Inflorescences** 1- or 2-flowered, 1–3 cm, equal to subtending leaf rachis. **Flowers** 7–9 mm; calyx base symmetric, lobes subequal, longer than tube; corolla cream to white with purple keel tip, banner stenonychioid, blade shorter than or equal to claw,

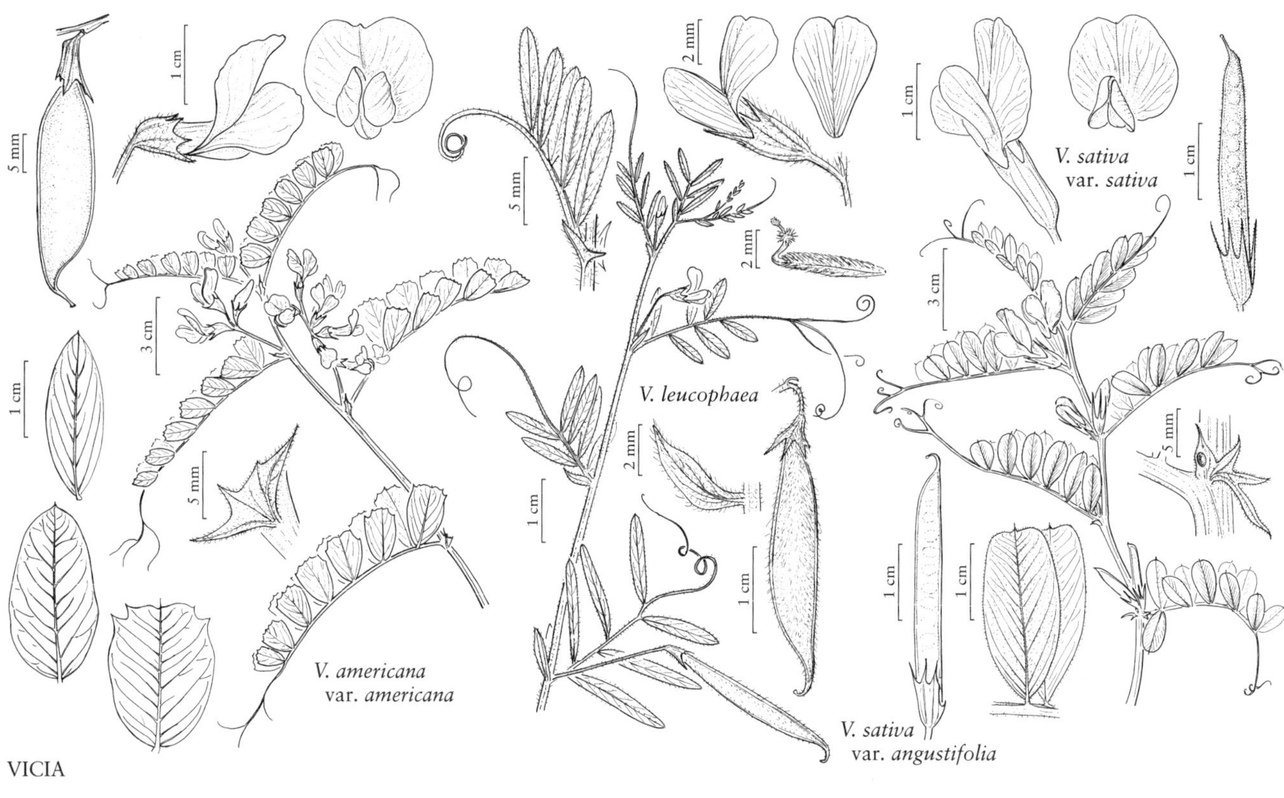

VICIA

glabrous; style terete, hairs in dense ring between stigma and ovary. **Legumes** pale brown, oblong, 25–40 × 4–6 mm, oblique-tipped, appressed-pubescent; stipe to 1 mm. **Seeds** 6–9, reddish brown, compressed-globose, 2.5 mm diam.; hilum encircling $1/4$ circumference of seed.

Flowering Jul–Sep. Pine forests; 1600–2500 m; Ariz., N.Mex.; Mexico (Chihuahua, Coahuila, Durango, Sonora).

Vicia leucophaea is found in eastern and southern Arizona and in southwestern New Mexico.

18. Vicia sepium Linnaeus, Sp. Pl. 2: 737. 1753 • Hedge vetch, vesce des haies 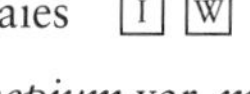

Vicia sepium var. *montana* W. D. J. Koch

Herbs perennial. **Stems** erect or climbing, slender, 3–10 dm. **Leaves** 6–10 cm; tendrils branched; stipules much smaller than leaflets, semisagittate, with nectariferous patch abaxially; leaflets 8–16, blades ovate or elliptic to lanceolate, 20–35 × 5–15 mm, apex obtuse to truncate-emarginate, abaxial surface sparsely pubescent, adaxial glabrous. **Inflorescences** 2–7-flowered, to 1 cm, shorter than subtending leaf rachis. **Flowers** 8–15 mm; calyx base symmetric, lobes equal, shorter than tube; corolla blue-violet and white, banner oblong, blade equal to claw, glabrous; style compressed abaxially, pubescent apically, tufted abaxially. **Legumes** black, elliptic, 20–35 × 5–8 mm, tip up-curved, glabrate; stipe to 2 mm. **Seeds** 3–6, yellowish, reddish, gray or greenish gray with blackish spots or entirely black, globose, 3–4 mm diam.; hilum encircling $1/2$–$3/4$ circumference of seed. $2n$ = 12, 14.

Flowering May–Jun. Roadsides, old fields; 0–1000 m; introduced; Greenland; N.B., Nfld. and Labr. (Nfld.), N.S., Ont., P.E.I., Que.; Maine, Mass., Mich., N.H., N.Y., Pa., Vt., W.Va.; Europe; Asia.

19. Vicia sativa Linnaeus, Sp. Pl. 2: 736. 1753 • Common or spring vetch, tare, vesce cultivée F I W

Herbs annual. **Stems** erect-ascending or climbing, slender to robust, 3–10 dm. **Leaves** 3–8 cm; tendrils simple or branched; stipules foliose, approaching leaflets in size, semisagittate, with nectariferous patch abaxially; leaflets 8–14, blades ovate-oblong, narrowly elliptic, or linear [obovate], 15–30 × 5–15 mm, apex obtuse to truncate-emarginate, distinctly apiculate, surfaces hirsute. **Inflorescences** usually (1 or)2(–4)-flowered, 0–1 cm.

Flowers 10–30 mm; calyx base symmetric, lobes subequal, ± equal to tube; corolla violet-purple, lavender, or whitish, banner stenonychioid, blade shorter than or equal to claw, glabrous; style compressed abaxially, pubescent apically, tufted abaxially. **Legumes** yellow to brown, or reddish brown to black, linear, 25–60 × 3–11 mm, oblique-tipped, glabrous or pubescent; stipe absent. **Seeds** 4–12, usually greenish gray to maroon or black, rarely yellowish white, globose or ± compressed, 3–5 mm diam.; hilum encircling $1/6$–$1/5$ circumference of seed.

Varieties 7 (2 in the flora): introduced; Europe, w Asia; introduced also in Mexico, South America, elsewhere in Asia, Africa, Australia.

D. Zohary and U. Plitmann (1979) provided a detailed description of the morphological and genetic variation found within the *Vicia sativa* complex. Of the seven infraspecific taxa they described, two (vars. *angustifolia* and *sativa*) are cultivated as forage crops and widely introduced in the flora area. Variety *angustifolia* is an aggressive colonizer of cultivated and disturbed habitats.

1. Flowers 18–30 mm; calyx lobes usually equal to tube; legumes yellow to brown, pubescent . . . . 19a. *Vicia sativa* var. *sativa*
1. Flowers 10–18(–20) mm; calyx lobes usually slightly shorter than tube; legumes reddish brown to black, glabrous . . . . 19b. *Vicia sativa* var. *angustifolia*

19a. Vicia sativa Linnaeus var. **sativa** [F] [I]

Vicia sativa var. *linearis* Lange

Leaflet blades usually ovate-oblong to narrowly elliptic, sometimes linear. **Flowers** 18–30 mm; calyx lobes usually equal to tube. **Legumes** yellow to brown, pubescent. **2*n*** = 12.

Flowering May–Aug. Fields, roadsides, waste areas; 0–1000 m; introduced; Greenland; B.C., N.B., Nfld. and Labr. (Nfld.), N.S., Ont., Que.; Ala., Ark., Calif., Conn., Del., Fla., Ga., Idaho, Ill., Ind., Iowa, Ky., La., Maine, Md., Mass., Minn., Miss., N.H., N.J., N.Y., N.C., Ohio, Oreg., Pa., R.I., S.C., Tenn., Tex., Vt., Va., Wash., Wis.; Europe; introduced also in Mexico (Hidalgo, México), South America, Asia, Africa, Australia.

19b. Vicia sativa Linnaeus var. **angustifolia** Linnaeus, Fl. Suec. ed. 2, 255. 1755 • Narrow-leaved vetch, vesce à folioles étroites [F] [I] [W]

Vicia angustifolia Linnaeus; *V. angustifolia* var. *segetalis* (Thuillier) W. D. J. Koch; *V. angustifolia* var. *uncinata* (Desvaux) Rouy; *V. sativa* subsp. *nigra* (Linnaeus) Ehrhart; *V. sativa* var. *nigra* Linnaeus

Leaflet blades narrowly elliptic to linear. **Flowers** 10–18(–20) mm; calyx lobes usually slightly shorter than tube. **Legumes** reddish brown to black, glabrous. **2*n*** = 12.

Flowering May–Aug. Fields, roadsides, waste areas; 0–2000 m; introduced; Greenland; St. Pierre and Miquelon; B.C., N.B., Nfld. and Labr. (Nfld.), N.S., Ont., P.E.I., Que., Sask., Yukon; Ala., Alaska, Ariz., Ark., Calif., Colo., Conn., Del., D.C., Fla., Ga., Idaho, Ill., Ind., Iowa, Kans., Ky., La., Maine, Md., Mass., Mich., Minn., Miss., Mo., Mont., Nebr., N.H., N.J., N.Mex., N.Y., N.C., Ohio, Okla., Oreg., Pa., R.I., S.C., S.Dak., Tenn., Tex., Vt., Va., Wash., W.Va., Wis.; Europe.

20. Vicia grandiflora Scopoli, Fl. Carniol. ed. 2, 2: 65, plate 42. 1772 • Big-flowered vetch [I]

Herbs annual. **Stems** sprawling or climbing, slender to robust, 3–6 dm. **Leaves** 1–4 cm; tendrils branched; stipules foliose, approaching leaflets in size, semisagittate, with nectariferous patch abaxially; leaflets 6–14, blades oblong to linear, 10–25 × 1–5 mm, apex obtuse to truncate-emarginate, surfaces finely pubescent. **Inflorescences** 1–3-flowered, 0–1 cm. **Flowers** 25–35 mm; calyx base symmetric, lobes equal, $1/2$–$2/3$ length of tube; corolla yellow suffused with violet, banner stenonychioid, blade equal to claw, glabrous; style compressed abaxially, pubescent apically, tufted abaxially. **Legumes** black, linear, 25–45 × 7–10 mm, oblique-tipped, glabrate; stipe absent. **Seeds** ca. 15, brown with indistinct black spots, compressed-globose, 3–3.5 mm diam.; hilum raised, white, encircling $3/4$ circumference of seed. **2*n*** = 12, 14.

Flowering Apr–May. Roadsides, open woods, cultivated fields; 0–1000 m; introduced; Ala., Ark., Del., Fla., Ga., Ky., La., Md., Mass., Mich., Miss., N.J., N.Y., N.C., S.C., Tenn., Tex., Va., W.Va.; c, se Europe.

21. Vicia lathyroides Linnaeus, Sp. Pl. 2: 736. 1753 • Spring vetch [I]

Herbs annual or winter annual. **Stems** erect or sprawling, slender, 0.5–3 dm. **Leaves** 1–2 cm; tendrils simple; stipules foliose, approaching leaflets in size, hastate, with nectariferous patch abaxially; leaflets 4–8, blades ovate-obovate to elliptic-linear, 8–16 × 1–3 mm, apex acute to truncate-emarginate, apiculate, surfaces glabrous or sparsely pubescent, hairs long. **Inflorescences** undeveloped, 1(or 2)-flowered, 0–1 cm. **Flowers** 5–8 mm; calyx base symmetric, lobes equal, subequal to tube; corolla violet, fading white, banner stenonychioid, blade longer than claw, glabrous; style compressed abaxially, pubescent apically, tufted abaxially. **Legumes** dark brown to black, linear, 15–25 × 3–4 mm, oblique-tipped, glabrous; stipe absent. **Seeds** 6 or 7, reddish maroon, grayish brown, or blackish, quadrate, 1.5–2 mm diam.; hilum minute. $2n$ = 10, 12.

Flowering Apr–Jun. Sandy grasslands, field edges, lawns, waste areas; 0–500 m; introduced; B.C.; Ala., Calif., Ga., Mass., Miss., N.H., N.C., S.C., Va., Wash.; Europe.

22. Vicia faba Linnaeus, Sp. Pl. 2: 737. 1753 • Broad or fava or horse bean [I]

Herbs annual. **Stems** erect, stout, 5–20 dm. **Leaves** 1–7 cm; tendrils absent; stipules foliose, approaching leaflets in size, broadly semisagittate, with nectariferous patch abaxially; leaflets 2–6, blades elliptic to ovate-lanceolate, 40–100 × 10–30 mm, apex obtuse, surfaces glabrous. **Inflorescences** 2–4-flowered, to 1 cm, much shorter than subtending leaf rachis. **Flowers** 20–30 mm; calyx base symmetric, lobes unequal, longer than tube; corolla white with purple mottling, banner stenonychioid, blade longer than claw, glabrous; style compressed abaxially, pubescent apically, tufted abaxially. **Legumes** dark brown to black, linear, 80–200 × 10–30 mm, oblique-tipped, sparsely pubescent; stipe 1–2 mm. **Seeds** 2–4, purplish, greenish, or black, sometimes spotted gray, globose and 7–9 mm diam., or strongly compressed and 12–35 mm diam.; hilum large, terminal, blackish, encircling 1/6–1/5 circumference of seed. $2n$ = 12, 14.

Flowering Jun–Aug. Roadsides, waste areas; 0–800 m; introduced; Calif., Conn., D.C., Maine, Md., Mass., N.Y., Oreg., Pa., Vt., Wash.; sw Asia; n Africa.

Vicia faba has been domesticated and is grown as a vegetable crop and for forage in temperate and subtropical areas worldwide.

23. Vicia narbonensis Linnaeus, Sp. Pl. 2: 737. 1753 • Narbonne vetch [I]

Herbs annual. **Stems** erect, stout, 3–7 dm. **Leaves** 3–8 cm; tendrils simple on proximal leaves, branched on distal leaves; stipules foliose, approaching leaflets in size, semicordate, with nectariferous patch abaxially; leaflets 2–6, blades obovate to elliptic, 30–60 × 20–35 mm, margins rarely serrate, apex obtuse, surfaces sparsely pubescent. **Inflorescences** 1–4-flowered, to 1 cm, much shorter than subtending leaf rachis. **Flowers** 15–30 mm; calyx base symmetric, lobes unequal, to 2 times as long as tube; corolla purple, drying black, banner stenonychioid, blade subequal to claw, glabrous; style compressed abaxially, pubescent apically, tufted abaxially. **Legumes** black, linear, 30–70 × 10–15 mm, oblique-tipped, glabrous, sutures with pustulate-based bristles; stipe absent. **Seeds** 4–6, purplish violet to black, subglobose or compressed-globose, 5–6 mm diam.; hilum whitish, short, oblong, encircling 1/8 circumference of seed. $2n$ = 14.

Flowering Apr–May. Disturbed areas; 0–500 m; introduced; D.C., Md., N.Y.; Europe; introduced also in Africa.

Vicia narbonensis is cultivated as a forage crop and is locally established in the flora area.

24. Vicia lutea Linnaeus, Sp. Pl. 2: 736. 1753 • Yellow vetch [I]

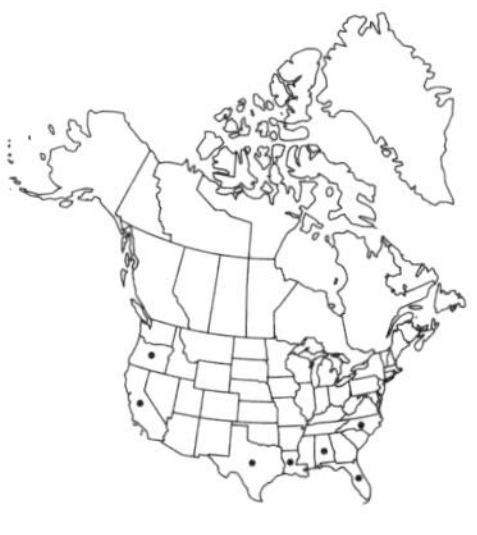

Herbs annual. **Stems** erect, sprawling, or climbing, slender to robust, 2–6 dm. **Leaves** 2–6 cm; tendrils simple or branched; stipules foliose, approaching leaflets in size, semisagittate, with nectariferous patch abaxially; leaflets 6–16, blades oblong to lanceolate-linear, 8–20 × 1–5 mm, apex obtuse to truncate-emarginate, abaxial surface sparsely pubescent, hairs long, pustulose-based, adaxial glabrous. **Inflorescences** 1–3-flowered, 0 cm. **Flowers** 18–25 mm; calyx base symmetric, lobes unequal, abaxial lobe subequal to tube; corolla pale to bright yellow, banner stenonychioid, blade much longer than claw, glabrous; style compressed abaxially, pubescent apically, tufted abaxially. **Legumes** reddish black, elliptic, 25–35 × 7–14 mm, oblique-tipped, pilose, hairs tuberculate-based; stipe to 3–4 mm. **Seeds** 3–9, blackish and ± mottled, or velvety to entirely black, compressed-globose, 3 mm diam.; hilum whitish, linear, encircling 1/6–1/5 circumference of seed. $2n = 14$.

Flowering Apr–May. Roadsides, fields; 0–500 m; introduced; Ala., Calif., Fla., La., N.C., Oreg., Tex.; c, s Europe; w Asia; n Africa.

25. Vicia pannonica Crantz, Stirp. Austr. Fasc. ed. 2, 2: 393. 1769 • Hungarian vetch [I]

Herbs annual. **Stems** erect, sprawling, or climbing, robust, 3–8 dm. **Leaves** 4–8 cm; tendrils rudimentary or branched; stipules foliose, approaching leaflets in size, semisagittate, with nectariferous patch abaxially; leaflets 10–20, blades obovate or oblong-elliptic to linear, 5–20 × 2–6 mm, apex obtuse to truncate-emarginate, surfaces pilose. **Inflorescences** 2–4-flowered, 0–1 cm. **Flowers** 14–20 mm; calyx base symmetric, lobes unequal, abaxial lobe subequal to tube; corolla cream, sometimes with purplish tinge, banner oblong, blade subequal to claw, pubescent adaxially; style compressed abaxially, pubescent apically, tufted abaxially. **Legumes** purple to black, elliptic, 20–30 × 7–11 mm, oblique-tipped, villous; stipe to 1–2 mm. **Seeds** 2–8, purplish, sometimes spotted black, globose to strongly flatted, 3–5 mm diam.; hilum whitish, linear, encircling 1/6–1/4 circumference of seed. $2n = 12$.

Flowering Apr–Jun. Pastures, meadows, roadsides; 0–500 m; introduced; Ark., Calif., Conn., Ga., Idaho, N.C., Oreg., Wash.; c Europe.

Vicia pannonica is cultivated for forage and as a seed crop and has become locally established, particularly in Pacific Coast states.

151. LENS Miller, Gard. Dict. Abr. ed. 4, vol. 2. 1754, name conserved • Lentil [Latin *lens*, lentil] [I]

Steven L. Broich

Herbs, annual, unarmed, hairs unicellular. **Stems** erect, angled, pilose. **Leaves** alternate, even-pinnate; stipules present, foliose, semisagittate; rachis with tendril or bristle, not winged; petiolate; leaflets [4–]10–14[–16], stipels absent, blade margins entire or dentate, surfaces pilose. **Inflorescences** 1–3-flowered, axillary racemes; bracts and bracteoles absent. **Flowers** papilionaceous; calyx campanulate, lobes 5, 2–4 times longer than tube; corolla white to bluish [pale lavender], 10–15 mm; stamens 10, diadelphous; anthers basifixed; ovary glabrous; style abaxially flattened, laterally pubescent. **Fruits** legumes, sessile, flattened, rhomboidal, dehiscent, glabrous. **Seeds** 1 or 2, lenticular. $x = 7$.

Species 6 (1 in the flora): introduced; s Europe, w Asia, n Africa.

Lens comprises species of varying degrees of genetic isolation (G. Ladizinsky et al. 1984) and includes the cultivated lentil, *L. culinaris*. The wild species of *Lens* are native to the Mediterranean region and western Asia.

Phylogenetic studies have placed *Lens* consistently within the Vicieae (M. F. Wojciechowski et al. 2004; H. Schaefer et al. 2012).

SELECTED REFERENCES Durán, Y. and M. Pérez de la Vega. 2004. Assessment of genetic variation and species relationships in a collection of *Lens* using RAPD and ISSR. Span. J. Agric. Res. 2: 538–544. Ladizinsky, G. et al. 1984. The biological species of the genus *Lens* L. Bot. Gaz. 145: 253–261. Mayer, M. S. and S. K. Bagga. 2002. The phylogeny of *Lens* (Leguminosae): New insight from ITS sequence analysis. Pl. Syst. Evol. 232: 145–154. Sonnante, G., I. Galasso, and D. Pignone. 2003. ITS sequence analysis and phylogenetic inference in the genus *Lens* Mill. Ann. Bot. (Oxford), n. s. 91: 49–54.

1. Lens culinaris Medikus, Vorles. Churpfälz. Phys.-Ökon. Ges. 2: 361. 1787 • Cultivated lentil, lentille cultivée [F] [I]

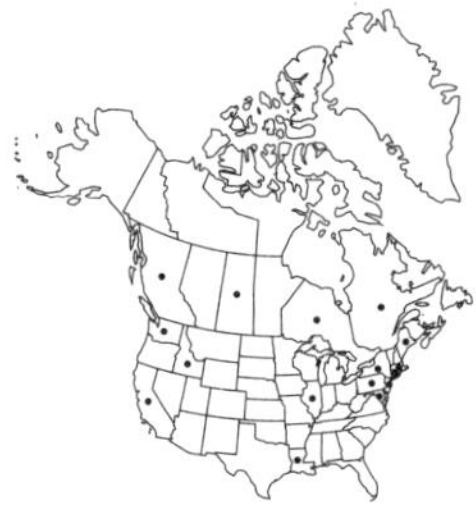

Ervum lens Linnaeus, Sp. Pl. 2: 738. 1753

Stems 2–7 dm. **Leaves** 5–10 cm; stipules without nectariferous patch; rachis with mucronate tendrils on proximal leaves, well-developed tendrils on distal leaves; leaflet blades ovate to narrowly oblong, 7–15 × 3–6 mm. **Racemes** erect or lax. **Flowers** chasmogamous, 10–15 mm; calyx symmetrical, equal; corolla wings and keel often lighter than banner; anthers uniform; ovary glabrous. **Legumes** not septate, 10–14 × 5–9 mm, margins usually obscure; valves splitting along both margins, twisted after dehiscence. **Seeds** usually dull brown, black, tan, or dark green, 4–8 mm diam., often mottled. $2n$ = 14 [extralimital].

Flowering May–Jul. Waste places; 0–500 m; introduced; B.C., Ont., Que., Sask.; Calif., Conn., Idaho, Ill., La., Maine, Md., Mass., N.J., N.Y., Pa., Wash.; s Europe; w Asia; n Africa; introduced also widely in temperate areas.

Lens culinaris is cultivated for human consumption and is a major farm crop in parts of eastern Washington and adjacent Idaho (V. E. Youngman 1968), as well as in Saskatchewan (Saskatchewan Agriculture and Food 2006). In some parts of the flora area, the species is observed recurrently but may not persist.

152. LATHYRUS Linnaeus, Sp. Pl. 2: 729. 1753; Gen. Pl. ed. 5, 326. 1754 • Sweet pea, vetchling [Derivation uncertain; perhaps Greek *la*, enhance, and *thouros*, stimulant, alluding to ancient use of seeds of *Lathyrus sativus* or similar species in *farina ervi*, a flour used as a purgative]

Steven L. Broich

Herbs, annual or perennial, unarmed, trichomes unicellular and eglandular, and/or multicellular and glandular; from rhizomes (rarely tuberous), rootstock, or taproots. **Stems** erect, sprawling, or climbing, angled and/or winged, glabrous or pubescent. **Leaves** alternate, even-pinnate (phyllodic in *L. nissolia*); stipules present, foliose, base usually semisagittate, rarely sagittate or hastate; rachis sometimes winged, usually terminated in simple or branched, prehensile tendril, sometimes reduced to bristle or absent; petiolate; leaflets (0 or)2–18, paired or unpaired, usually decreasing in size distally, stipels absent, blades 5–150 mm, margins entire, usually with several longitudinal veins in addition to midrib, surfaces glabrous or sparsely to densely pubescent. **Inflorescences** 1–20-flowered, axillary (terminal in *L. pusillus*), racemes or flowers solitary, erect or lax; bracts absent; bracteoles absent. **Flowers** papilionaceous; calyx symmetric or obliquely campanulate, without gibbous base, 5–12 mm, lobes 5, equal or unequal, when unequal, abaxial lobes short and triangular, lateral and keel lobes longer and lanceolate or linear; corolla white, cream, yellow, pink, lavender, lilac, rose, red, reddish orange, crimson, blue to purple, violet, magenta, or bicolored, wings and keel often lighter than banner, 6–30 mm; petal clawed, distinct from blade; stamens 10, diadelphous; anthers dorsifixed, uniform; style abaxially compressed, sometimes twisted, laterally pubescent. **Fruits** legumes, usually sessile, rarely stipitate, flattened or terete, linear, dehiscent, non-septate, usually with obscure margins, splitting along both margins, glabrous or sparsely pubescent; valves twisted after dehiscence. **Seeds** 3–15, usually dull brown, black, tan, or dark green, often mottled, spherical, sometimes angular. x = 7 (polyploidy rare).

Species ca. 150 (41 in the flora): North America, Mexico, South America, Europe, Asia, n Africa; introduced widely in temperate regions.

F. K. Kupicha (1983) separated *Lathyrus* into 13 sections worldwide; about three-fourths of the members are perennials and one-fourth are annuals. All perennial North American species

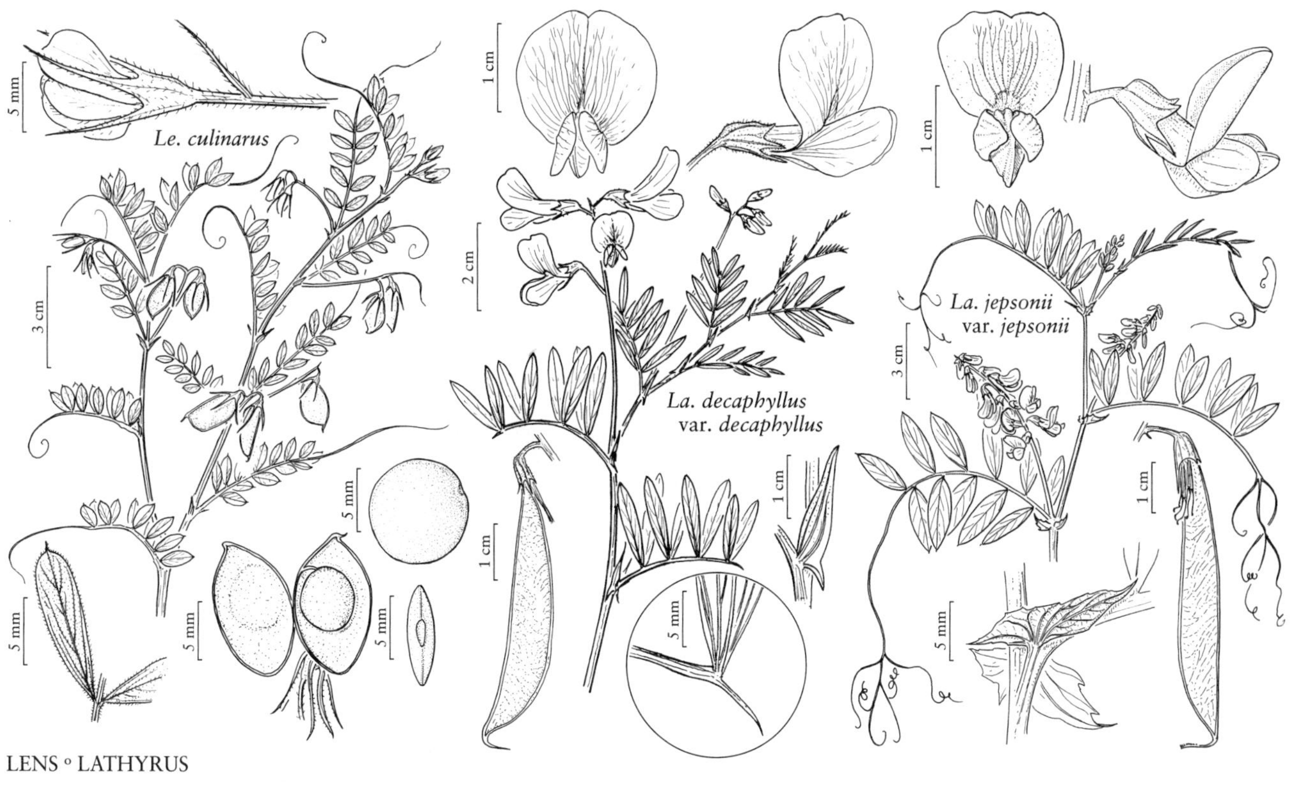

LENS ◦ LATHYRUS

are included in sect. *Orobus* (Linnaeus) Godron, which contains about one-third of all *Lathyrus* species. The single native annual species, *L. pusillus*, has been assigned to sect. *Notolathyrus* Kupicha, a section perhaps closely allied to *Orobus* species in North America (C. B. Amussen and A. Liston 1998). *Lathyrus* is predominantly diploid with $2n = 14$. Chromosome counts have been reported for 20 of the 29 species native to North America (S. L. Broich 1989). There has been no worldwide treatment of the genus at the species level. *Lathyrus* in North America was last revised by C. L. Hitchcock (1952) and summarized by D. Isely (1998).

Recent phylogenetic studies have placed *Lathyrus* consistently within the Vicieae (M. F. Wojciechowski et al. 2004); subgeneric relationships have yet to be resolved (C. B. Amussen and A. Liston 1998; G. J. Kenicer et al. 2005; H. Schaefer et al. 2012).

Twelve of the 41 *Lathyrus* species treated herein have been introduced to North America and have become locally established to widely naturalized. Deliberate introductions include species used as ornamentals, cover, and green manure and cover crops. One native species, *L. pusillus*, has been developed as a winter cover crop; a second native species, *L. splendens*, has been cultivated as an ornamental.

A number of native *Lathyrus* are polymorphic and include one or more of the following: glabrous and pubescent races, variation in stature and habit from short-stemmed and erect to long-stemmed and sprawling or climbing, variation in tendril morphology from bristles to well developed and branched, variable leaflet number, ovate and linear leafleted races, and variation in flower color and size. Within some polymorphic species, morphological variation is such that distinct varieties can be delimited. Within other species, however distinctive some populations may be, intergradation among forms is such that well-marked taxa cannot be reliably described.

Although probably cultivated where possible in North America and occasionally escaping, *Lathyrus sativus* Linnaeus and *L. niger* (Linnaeus) Bernhardi are not treated here.

Diets that include large quantities of flour made from seed of several *Lathyrus* species (primarily *L. sativus*, *L. cicera* Linnaeus, and *L. clymenum* Linnaeus) are known to produce lathyrism, a paralytic syndrome in humans and livestock (A. D. Kaul and D. Combes 1986). In humans, lathyrism has been associated historically with poverty or drought that force populations to rely on *Lathyrus* seed for consumption.

Unless otherwise noted in the taxon description: stipules are semisagittate; leaf rachises are not winged; styles are flattened perpendicular to the ovary axis and not rotated; legumes are sessile, without winged abaxial sutures, and are not prominently veined; vestiture, if reported present, consists of unicellular, eglandular trichomes; the number of leaflets and tendril morphology are for distal stem leaves bearing inflorescences; leaflet dimensions given are for basal leaflets on the rachis of leaves subtending inflorescences; flower lengths reported are the distance from the base of the calyx tube to the distal keel petal margin; references to the relationship between calyx lobe length and calyx tube length always take into account the longest lobe present; wing and keel petals are almost always lighter in color than the banner petal and colors given in descriptions are for the most pigmented part of the corolla. Distributions of introduced species are approximate.

SELECTED REFERENCES Hitchcock, C. L. 1952. A revision of the North American species of *Lathyrus*. Univ. Wash. Publ. Biol. 15: 1–104. Kaul, A. D. and D. Combes, eds. 1986. *Lathyrus* and Lathyrism. New York. Kupicha, F. K. 1983. The infrageneric structure of *Lathyrus*. Notes Roy. Bot. Gard. Edinburgh 41: 209–244.

1. Leaflets 0 or 2.
    2. Leaflets 0.
        3. Stipules ovate, base hastate; leaf rachises reduced to branched or unbranched tendrils; corollas yellow . . . . . 38. *Lathyrus aphaca*
        3. Stipules filiform-linear, base semisagittate; tendrils absent, leaves phyllodic, grasslike; corollas crimson . . . . . 41. *Lathyrus nissolia*
    2. Leaflets 2.
        4. Herbs perennial; inflorescences 4–15-flowered.
            5. Corollas yellow . . . . . 37. *Lathyrus pratensis*
            5. Corollas reddish, purple, magenta, pink, or white.
                6. Stems not winged; ovaries glabrous . . . . . 30. *Lathyrus tuberosus*
                6. Stems broadly winged; ovaries glandular-pubescent.
                    7. Stipules 7–15 mm wide, at least 1/2 width of stem . . . . . 31. *Lathyrus latifolius*
                    7. Stipules 1–3 mm wide, less than 1/2 width of stem . . . . . 32. *Lathyrus sylvestris*
        4. Herbs annual; inflorescences 1–3(or 4)-flowered.
            8. Stems not winged; inflorescences extending beyond terminal flower in a bristle.
                9. Inflorescences 2–7 cm; legumes with indistinct reticulate venation. . . . 39. *Lathyrus angulatus*
                9. Inflorescences 1–2 cm; legumes with prominent longitudinal venation. . . . . 40. *Lathyrus sphaericus*
            8. Stems narrowly to broadly winged; inflorescences with a terminal flower.
                10. Ovaries densely pustulose-based pubescent.
                    11. Flowers 20–25 mm . . . . . 34. *Lathyrus odoratus*
                    11. Flowers 8–10 mm . . . . . 35. *Lathyrus hirsutus*
                10. Ovaries glabrous.
                    12. Leaf rachis not winged; flowers 7–10 mm . . . . . 29. *Lathyrus pusillus*
                    12. Leaf rachis winged (as the stem); flowers 10–30 mm.
                        13. Flowers 20–30 mm; lateral calyx lobes deltate, usually shorter than tube . . . . . 33. *Lathyrus tingitanus*
                        13. Flowers 10–12 mm; lateral calyx lobes linear-triangular, much longer than tube . . . . . 36. *Lathyrus cicera*

1. Leaflets (2–)4–18.
    14. Tendrils often absent or reduced to bristles, not well developed.
        15. Leaflet blades obovate to oblanceolate, surfaces densely villous; corollas dark purple; coastal sand dunes, deflation plains along Pacific Coast from c California northward to British Columbia . . . . 28. *Lathyrus littoralis*
        15. Leaflet blades usually linear, lanceolate, or ovate, rarely obovate, surfaces not densely villous; corollas blue-purple, lilac, pinkish, violet, magenta, or cream to white; not coastal.
            16. Corollas white or cream.
                17. Inflorescences 5–15-flowered; n California . . . . 22. *Lathyrus tracyi* (in part)
                17. Inflorescences 1–6-flowered; w North America.
                    18. Stipules much smaller than distal leaflets.
                        19. Flowers 7–15 mm; inflorescences 2–5 cm; Arizona, California, Colorado, Nevada, New Mexico, c Oregon, Utah, c Washington, Wyoming . . . . 7. *Lathyrus lanszwertii* (in part)
                        19. Flowers 18–22 mm; inflorescences 3–15 cm; ne Oregon, se Washington, adjacent Idaho . . . . 16. *Lathyrus nevadensis* (in part)
                    18. Stipules equal to distal leaflets.
                        20. Flowers 7–8 mm; leaflet blades finely villous; Humboldt County, California . . . . 10. *Lathyrus biflorus*
                        20. Flowers 12–18 mm; leaflet blades glabrous; California, Nevada, Oregon, adjacent Idaho . . . . 20. *Lathyrus rigidus* (in part)
            16. Corollas usually blue-purple, sometimes violet to magenta, lavender, or pinkish.
                21. Flowers 8–12 mm.
                    22. Leaflets 2–4, blades 20–50 mm; British Columbia, n Idaho, w Montana, e Washington . . . . 7. *Lathyrus lanszwertii* (in part)
                    22. Leaflets 8–16, blades 5–15 mm; coastal forests of California, Oregon, Washington . . . . 27. *Lathyrus torreyi*
                21. Flowers 13–20 mm.
                    23. Leaflets usually scattered; legumes sessile.
                        24. Leaflets 6–12; n Arizona, sw Colorado, s Idaho, Nevada, nw New Mexico, Utah . . . . 4. *Lathyrus brachycalyx* (in part)
                        24. Leaflets 4 or 6; n California, Oregon, Washington . . . . 16. *Lathyrus nevadensis* (in part)
                    23. Leaflets usually paired; legumes stipitate.
                        25. Leaflets 8–12; flowers 16–22 mm; Great Plains and e slopes of Rocky Mountains . . . . 2. *Lathyrus decaphyllus*
                        25. Leaflets 4–8; flowers 12–18 mm; California, Idaho, Nevada, Oregon.
                            26. Stipules much smaller than distal leaflets; Elko County, Nevada . . . . 5. *Lathyrus grimesii*
                            26. Stipules equal to distal leaflets; e Oregon, adjacent w Idaho, ne California, nw Nevada . . . . 20. *Lathyrus rigidus* (in part)
    14. Tendrils well developed, often branched.
        27. Stipules sagittate; lake and ocean shores in North America, ca. 38–70° N latitude . . . . 1. *Lathyrus japonicus*
        27. Stipules semisagittate; not of coastal shores, sometimes coastal wetlands.
            28. Corollas usually white, cream-white, or yellow-cream, rarely light pink or lavender.
                29. Corollas orange to yellow-cream, banner blade shorter than claw; California Central Valley and adjacent foothills, northward to sw Oregon . . . . 23. *Lathyrus sulphureus*
                29. Corollas white or cream-white (sometimes light pink or lavender in *L. laetivirens*); banner blade equal to or longer than claw; distribution widespread.

[30. Shifted to left margin.—Ed.]

30. Leaflets usually paired.
 31. Leaflets (5 or)6(–8), stipules somewhat foliose, sometimes equal to distal leaflets; n North America (sw Alaska to Washington, eastward to Atlantic coast) . . . . . . 15. *Lathyrus ochroleucus*
 31. Leaflets 4–10, stipules much smaller than leaflets; nw California southeastward to New Mexico.
  32. Tendrils well developed, often branched; Arizona, Colorado, Nevada, New Mexico, Utah . . . . 17. *Lathyrus laetivirens*
  32. Tendrils 0–3 cm, usually not branched; n California . . . . 22. *Lathyrus tracyi* (in part)
30. Leaflets usually scattered (paired in *L. hitchcockianus*, *L. palustris*).
 33. Stems narrowly winged.
  34. Stipules sometimes equal to distal leaflets; nw California, adjacent Oregon . . . 9. *Lathyrus delnorticus*
  34. Stipules much smaller than distal leaflets; w California, Oregon, Washington.
   35. Lateral calyx lobes lanceolate, (wider distal to base); stems basally branched; coastal ranges of n California, w Oregon, Washington. . . . . 13. *Lathyrus vestitus* (in part)
   35. Lateral calyx lobes linear-triangular; stems often branched mid stem (at or just proximal to flowering nodes); Willamette Valley, Oregon, Washington . . . . 21. *Lathyrus holochlorus* (in part)
 33. Stems angled but not winged.
  36. Inflorescences 2–6-flowered; Colorado, Utah, Wyoming. . . . . 7. *Lathyrus lanszwertii* (in part)
  36. Inflorescences (2–)5–20-flowered; Arizona, California, Idaho, New Mexico, Oregon, Texas, Washington.
   37. Lateral calyx lobes lanceolate (wider distal to base); coastal ranges of n California, Oregon, Washington . . . . 13. *Lathyrus vestitus* (in part)
   37. Lateral calyx lobes deltate or linear-triangular; Arizona, Idaho, New Mexico, Oregon, Texas, Washington.
    38. Leaflet blades usually linear, rarely lanceolate; Arizona, New Mexico, w Texas . . . . 24. *Lathyrus graminifolius* (in part)
    38. Leaflet blades ovate to lanceolate; Idaho, Oregon, Washington.
     39. Stems branched from base or unbranched; Idaho . . . . . 16. *Lathyrus nevadensis* (in part)
     39. Stems often branched mid stem (at or just proximal to flowering nodes); Oregon, Washington . . . . 21. *Lathyrus holochlorus* (in part)

[28. Shifted to left margin.—Ed.]

28. Corollas pink, lavender, rose, blue to purple, or deep red.
 40. Stems narrowly to broadly winged.
  41. Leaflets 14–18, blade surfaces: both with eglandular trichomes, glandular-pubescent abaxially; Humboldt and n Mendocino counties, California. . . . . 26. *Lathyrus glandulosus*
  41. Leaflets 4–12, blade surfaces glabrous, glabrate, or eglandular-pubescent; ne North America, coastal marshes along Pacific Coast of Oregon northward, or coastal mountains of w California from Humboldt County southward to Monterey County.
   42. Leaflets 4–8, paired; ovaries glandular-pubescent; ne, e, midwestern North America and coastal marshes along Pacific Coast from California northward . . . . 6. *Lathyrus palustris*
   42. Leaflets 8–12, scattered; ovaries glabrous; c, n California from Monterey County northward to Humboldt County eastward through Central Valley . . . . 8. *Lathyrus jepsonii*
 40. Stems angled but not winged.
  43. Leaflets 4 or 6, paired; flowers 8–10 mm; Grapevine Mountains of Inyo County, California and adjacent Nye County, Nevada. 11. *Lathyrus hitchcockianus*
  43. Leaflets (2–)6–16, scattered; flowers (7–)10–30 mm; distribution widespread.
   44. Flowers 16–30 mm, corollas deep wine red, banners reflexed toward calyx tube; sw California.
    45. Flowers 16–25 mm . . . . 13. *Lathyrus vestitus* (in part)
    45. Flowers 25–30 mm . . . . 14. *Lathyrus splendens*

[44. Shifted to left margin.—Ed.]

44. Flowers (7–)10–20(–25) mm, corollas lavender, pink, or blue to purple, banners erect; distribution widespread.
    46. Leaflets 10–16; stipules nearly equal to distal leaflets . . . . 25. *Lathyrus polyphyllus*
    46. Leaflets 4–10(–14); stipules much smaller than leaflets.
        47. Wings longer than keel (by 1–4 mm).
            48. Inflorescences 3–4 cm, 2–4-flowered; ne California, adjacent Nevada and Oregon. . . . . 18. *Lathyrus brownii*
            48. Inflorescences 5–18 cm, 4–13-flowered; sw Colorado, Idaho, ne Oregon, Utah, e Washington . . . . 19. *Lathyrus pauciflorus*
        47. Wings equal to keel.
            49. Corollas white to blue-orchid; leaflet blades usually linear, rarely lanceolate; stems sometimes branched at flowering nodes; inflorescences 10–18 cm; Arizona, New Mexico, w Texas . . . . 24. *Lathyrus graminifolius* (in part)
            49. Corollas rose, lavender, or blue-purple; leaflet blades usually ovate to lanceolate or elliptic, rarely linear; stems usually basally branched; inflorescences 2–10 (–25) cm; distribution widespread.
                50. Legumes short-stipitate; inflorescences 2–4-flowered; flowers 18–20 mm; Arizona, Colorado, New Mexico, w Texas, se Utah, Wyoming . . . . . . .3. *Lathyrus eucosmus*
                50. Legumes sessile; inflorescences 2–20-flowered; flowers (7–)10–18(–20) mm; distribution north and west or eastern United States.
                    51. Inflorescences 5–20-flowered.
                        52. Stipules of distal leaves usually less than 1/4 width of distal leaflets; central and eastern North America . . . . 12. *Lathyrus venosus*
                        52. Stipules on distal leaves usually more than 1/4 width of distal leaflets; coastal mountains of California into sw Oregon . . . . 13. *Lathyrus vestitus* (in part)
                    51. Inflorescences 2–6-flowered.
                        53. Banner deeply cordate; n Arizona, sw Colorado, e Nevada, nw New Mexico, w, se Utah . . . . 4. *Lathyrus brachycalyx* (in part)
                        53. Banner retuse to shallowly cordate; coastal ranges of California, northward to British Columbia, Great Basin.
                            54. Flowers 10–15 mm; leaflet blades usually lanceolate, rarely linear; ne California, w Nevada, c Idaho, e Oregon, ne Utah, se Washington . . . . .7. *Lathyrus lanszwertii* (in part)
                            54. Flowers 13–18 mm; leaflet blades ovate to lanceolate; coastal ranges of California northward to British Columbia . . . . 16. *Lathyrus nevadensis* (in part)

1. Lathyrus japonicus Willdenow, Sp. Pl. 3: 1092. 1802 • Beach or maritime or sand pea, pois de mer, gesse maritime

Herbs perennial, from rhizome, glabrous or sparsely pubescent. **Stems** angled to narrowly winged, erect, sprawling, or climbing, basally branched 0–4 times, 1–10 dm. **Leaves** 3–15 cm; tendrils usually well developed, branched or unbranched; stipules sagittate-ovate, 7–35 × 7–30 mm, as large as basal leaflets; leaflets 6–12, usually scattered, blades ovate to lanceolate, 15–55 × 5–35 mm, surfaces glabrous throughout or pubescent abaxially. **Inflorescences** 4–9-flowered, 4–15 cm. **Flowers** 12–29 mm; calyx lobes unequal, lateral lobes linear-triangular, longer than tube; corolla blue to purple, banner erect, blade longer than claw, wings equal to keel; ovary eglandular and glandular-pubescent. **Legumes** 35–65 × 6–12 mm.

Varieties 3 (3 in the flora): North America, Eurasia; introduced in s South America.

Within *Lathyrus japonicus*, in the narrow sense, there is a south to north reduction in plant size, including plant height, robustness, and leaflet size, but not flower size, flower number, or fruit size. On the east coast of North America this shift seems fairly abrupt, giving the appearance of a clear distinction between var. *maritimus* and var. *pellitus* in the south, and var. *japonicus* to the north in Labrador and Greenland. However, on the West Coast, there are few truly pubescent forms (var. *pellitus*), and there seem to be many more intermediates between var. *maritimus* in the south and var. *japonicus* to the north.

1. Stems 1–3.5 dm; leaflet blades 15–35 mm; tendrils unbranched, less than 3 cm. . . . . 1a. *Lathyrus japonicus* var. *japonicus*
1. Stems 3–10 dm; leaflet blades 30–50(–55) mm; tendrils branched, 3+ cm.
   2. Leaflet blades glabrous. . . . . 1b. *Lathyrus japonicus* var. *maritimus*
   2. Leaflet blades pubescent abaxially (especially new growth) . . . 1c. *Lathyrus japonicus* var. *pellitus*

1a. Lathyrus japonicus Willdenow var. **japonicus**

Lathyrus japonicus var. *aleuticus* (Greene ex T. G. White) Fernald; *L. japonicus* var. *parviflorus* Fassett

Stems 1–3.5 dm. **Leaves** 3–7 cm; tendrils unbranched, less than 3 cm; leaflets 6–8, blades 15–35 × 5–15 mm, surfaces glabrous. **2*n*** = 14.

Flowering Apr–Sep. Sandy or gravelly ocean shores, lakeshores; 0–50 m; Greenland; St. Pierre and Miquelon; Man., N.B., Nfld. and Labr., N.W.T., Nunavut, Ont., P.E.I., Que., Yukon; Alaska, Mich.; Eurasia; introduced in South America (Chile).

Variety *japonicus* is a diminutive, low-growing form found most often on sandy or rocky beaches in arctic and subarctic regions.

1b. Lathyrus japonicus Willdenow var. **maritimus** (Linnaeus) Kartesz & Gandhi, Phytologia 71: 277. 1991 [E]

Pisum maritimum Linnaeus, Sp. Pl. 2: 727. 1753; *Lathyrus japonicus* var. *glaber* (Seringe) Fernald; *L. japonicus* subsp. *maritimus* (Linnaeus) P. W. Ball; *L. maritimus* Bigelow; *P. maritimum* var. *glabrum* Seringe

Stems 3–10 dm. **Leaves** 6–15 cm; tendrils branched, 3+ cm; leaflets 6–12, blades 30–50 × 15–30 mm, surfaces glabrous. **2*n*** = 14.

Flowering Apr–Sep. Sandy or gravelly ocean shores, lakeshores; 0–50 m; B.C., N.B., Nfld. and Labr. (Nfld.), N.S., Ont., P.E.I., Que.; Alaska, Calif., Conn., Ill., Ind., Maine, Mass., Mich., Minn., N.H., N.J., N.Y., Ohio, Oreg., R.I., Vt., Wash., Wis.

1c. Lathyrus japonicus Willdenow var. **pellitus** Fernald, Rhodora 34: 183. 1932 [E]

Lathyrus maritimus Bigelow subsp. *pubescens* (Hartman) C. Regel

Stems 3–10 dm. **Leaves** 6–15 cm; tendrils branched, 3+ cm; leaflets 6–12, blades 30–55 × 15–35 mm, surfaces pubescent abaxially, especially new growth. **2*n*** = 14.

Flowering Apr–Sep. Sandy or gravelly ocean shores, lakeshores; 0–50 m; St. Pierre and Miquelon; N.B., Nfld. and Labr. (Nfld.), N.S., Ont., Que.; Conn., Maine, Mass., Mich., N.H., N.J., N.Y., R.I., Vt., Wis.

2. Lathyrus decaphyllus Pursh, Fl. Amer. Sept. 2: 471. 1813 [E] [F]

Herbs perennial, from rhizome. **Stems** angled, erect or sprawling, basally branched 0–2 times, 1.5–3 dm. **Leaves** 1–4 cm; tendrils bristlelike, usually less than 1 cm; stipules linear to lanceolate, 10–30 × 1–5 mm, nearly equal to leaflets; leaflets 8–12, often paired, blades lanceolate to linear, 10–35 × 1–5 mm, surfaces glabrous or pubescent. **Inflorescences** 2–6-flowered, 4–11 cm. **Flowers** 16–22 mm; calyx lobes subequal, lateral lobes deltate, shorter than tube; corolla usually violet to magenta, sometimes white, banner erect, blade longer than claw, wings 4–5 mm longer than keel; ovary glabrous. **Legumes** 35–50 × 8–12 mm, stipitate.

Varieties 2 (2 in the flora): wc United States.

1. Herbs mostly glabrous . . . . 2a. *Lathyrus decaphyllus* var. *decaphyllus*
1. Herbs sparsely to densely villous. . . . . 2b. *Lathyrus decaphyllus* var. *incanus*

2a. Lathyrus decaphyllus Pursh var. **decaphyllus** [E] [F]

Lathyrus hapemanii A. Nelson; *L. polymorphus* var. *hapemanii* (A. Nelson) C. L. Hitchcock

Herbs mostly glabrous.

Flowering May–Jul. Grasslands, open wooded areas, sand dunes, stream valleys; 1000–2000 m; Kans., Nebr., Okla., S.Dak., Tex., Wyo.

Lathyrus polymorphus Nuttall is a superfluous illegitimate name that pertains here.

2b. Lathyrus decaphyllus Pursh var. **incanus** (J. G. Smith & Rydberg) Broich, Phytologia 91: 566. 2009 • Hoary vetchling [E]

Lathyrus ornatus Nuttall var. *incanus* J. G. Smith & Rydberg in University of Nebraska, Fl. Nebr., Rosales, 64. 1895; *L. incanus* (J. G. Smith & Rydberg) Rydberg; *L. polymorphus* Nuttall subsp. *incanus* (J. G. Smith & Rydberg) C. L. Hitchcock; *L. polymorphus* var. *incanus* (J. G. Smith & Rydberg) Dorn; *L. stipulaceus* (Pursh) Butters & H. St. John var. *incanus* (J. G. Smith & Rydberg) Butters & H. St. John

Herbs sparsely to densely villous.

Flowering May–Jul. Sandy soils, grasslands, open woodlands; 1200–2200 m; Colo., Kans., Nebr., N.Mex., Okla., Tex., Wyo.

3. Lathyrus eucosmus Butters & H. St. John, Rhodora 19: 160. 1917

Lathyrus brachycalyx Rydberg subsp. *eucosmus* (Butters & H. St. John) S. L. Welsh; *L. brachycalyx* var. *eucosmus* (Butters & H. St. John) S. L. Welsh

Herbs perennial, from rhizome, glabrous or puberulent. **Stems** angled, erect, basally branched 0–2 times, 2–5 dm. **Leaves** 2–4 cm; tendrils simple or branched, sometimes prehensile; stipules linear, 5–15 × 1–2 mm, much smaller than leaflets; leaflets 6 or 8, scattered, blades ovate to lanceolate, 15–45 × 4–10 mm, surfaces glabrous throughout or puberulent abaxially. **Inflorescences** 2–4-flowered, 7–12 cm. **Flowers** 18–20 mm; calyx lobes unequal, lateral lobes deltate, shorter than tube; corolla blue-purple, banner erect, blade longer than claw, wings equal to keel (held above keel); ovary glabrous. **Legumes** 40–50 × 8–10 mm, short-stipitate. $2n = 14$.

Flowering Apr–Jun. Dry soils in washes, pinyon-juniper woodlands, oak-brush, ponderosa pine forests, open prairies, grasslands; 1200–2500 m; Ariz., Colo., N.Mex., Tex., Utah, Wyo.; Mexico (Coahuila).

Lathyrus eucosmus is known from the northern two-thirds of Arizona northward to southeastern Utah, and eastward in southeastern Wyoming, Colorado, New Mexico, and Texas to the edge of the Great Plains.

4. Lathyrus brachycalyx Rydberg, Bull. Torrey Bot. Club 34: 425. 1907 • Bonneville vetchling, Rydberg's sweet pea [E]

Herbs perennial, from rhizome, glabrous or villous. **Stems** angled, erect, sprawling, or climbing, basally branched 0–3 times, 1–5 dm. **Leaves** 2–9 cm; tendrils usually well developed, sometimes reduced to a single bristle; stipules lanceolate, 5–12 × 1–3 mm, much smaller than leaflets; leaflets 6–12, scattered, blades elliptic to narrowly so, 8–70 × 3–8 mm, surfaces glabrous or villous. **Inflorescences** 2–5-flowered, 5–15 cm. **Flowers** 13–20 mm; calyx lobes unequal, lateral lobes deltate, shorter than tube; corolla pinkish to deep blue-purple, banner erect, blade nearly 2 times as long as claw, wings equal to keel; ovary glabrous. **Legumes** 30–40 × 6–8 mm.

Varieties 2 (2 in the flora): w United States.

1. Stems 1–3 dm, erect; herbs mostly villous throughout; banners shallowly cordate . . . . 4a. *Lathyrus brachycalyx* var. *brachycalyx*
1. Stems 3–5 dm, sprawling or climbing; herbs glabrous or sparsely villous; banners deeply cordate . . . . 4b. *Lathyrus brachycalyx* var. *zionis*

4a. Lathyrus brachycalyx Rydberg var. **brachycalyx** [E]

Herbs mostly villous throughout. **Stems** erect, 1–3 dm. **Leaves** 2–5 cm; leaflets 6–12, blades 8–25(–30) × 3–6 mm. **Flowers** 15–20 mm, banner shallowly cordate. $2n = 14$.

Flowering Apr–Jun. Sagebrush, juniper, and pinyon pine communities; 1500–2300 m; Idaho, Nev., Utah.

4b. Lathyrus brachycalyx Rydberg var. **zionis** (C. L. Hitchcock) S. L. Welsh, Great Basin Naturalist 38: 317. 1978 [E]

Lathyrus zionis C. L. Hitchcock, Revis. N. Amer. Lathyrus, 36, fig. 27. 1952; *L. brachycalyx* subsp. *zionis* (C. L. Hitchcock) S. L. Welsh

Herbs glabrous or sparsely villous. **Stems** sprawling or climbing, 3–5 dm. **Leaves** 5–9 cm; leaflets 6–10, blades 18–70 × 3–8 mm. **Flowers** 13–16 mm, banner deeply cordate. $2n = 14$.

Flowering Apr–Jun. Sagebrush, juniper, and pinyon pine communities; 1300–2300 m; Ariz., Colo., N.Mex., Utah.

Variety *zionis* is found in northern Arizona, southwestern Colorado, northwestern New Mexico, and western and southeastern Utah.

5. **Lathyrus grimesii** Barneby in A. Cronquist et al., Intermount. Fl. 3(B): 208, plate [p. 211], fig. s.n. [center right]. 1989 • Grimes's vetchling [C] [E]

Herbs perennial, from rhizome-like rootstock, glabrous. **Stems** angled, erect, branched 0–2 times basally or from proximal nodes, 0.5–2 dm. **Leaves** 1–2 cm; tendrils reduced to bristles; stipules lanceolate to linear, 5–15 × 1–5 mm, much smaller than leaflets; leaflets 4 or 6, paired, blades ovate to obovate, 10–25 × 5–10 mm, surfaces glabrous. **Inflorescences** 2–4-flowered, 4–6 cm. **Flowers** 14–17 mm; calyx lobes unequal, lateral lobes deltate, shorter than tube; corolla bicolored lavender and white, banner erect, blade longer than claw, wings longer than keel, 1–3 mm; ovary glabrous. **Legumes** 25–30 × 8–10 mm, stipitate.

Flowering Jun–Jul. Talus slopes in sagebrush communities; of conservation concern; 1800–2600 m; Nev.

Lathyrus grimesii is known only from the northern Independence Range and southern Bull Run Mountains in Elko County.

6. **Lathyrus palustris** Linnaeus, Sp. Pl. 2: 733. 1753 • Marsh pea, gesse des marais [E] [W]

Lathyrus myrtifolius Muhlenberg ex Willdenow; *L. palustris* var. *linearifolius* Seringe; *L. palustris* var. *macranthus* (T. G. White) Fernald; *L. palustris* var. *myrtifolius* (Muhlenberg ex Willdenow) A. Gray; *L. palustris* subsp. *pilosus* (Chamisso) Hultén; *L. palustris* var. *pilosus* (Chamisso) Ledebour; *L. palustris* var. *retusus* Fernald & H. St. John

Herbs perennial, from rhizome, glabrous or pubescent. **Stems** narrowly to broadly winged, sprawling or climbing, basally branched 0–4 times, 2–10 dm. **Leaves** 1–6 cm; tendrils well developed; stipules ovate-lanceolate to linear, 5–25 × 1–10 mm, much smaller than leaflets; leaflets 4–8, paired, blades lanceolate to linear, 15–75 × 2–20 mm, surfaces glabrous, glabrate, or pubescent. **Inflorescences** 2–7-flowered, 3–15 cm. **Flowers** 10–15 mm; calyx lobes unequal, lateral lobes deltate, shorter than tube; corolla blue-purple, banner erect, blade equal to claw, wings equal to keel; ovary glandular-pubescent. **Legumes** 25–60 × 4–8 mm. **2*n*** = 14.

Flowering Apr–Aug. Coastal and inland wetlands; 0–1800 m; St. Pierre and Miquelon; B.C., Man., N.B., Nfld. and Labr., N.S., Nunavut, Ont., P.E.I., Que., Sask.; Ala., Alaska, Ark., Calif., Colo., Conn., Del., D.C., Ill., Ind., Iowa, Ky., Maine, Md., Mass., Mich., Minn., Mo., Nebr., N.H., N.J., N.Y., N.C., N.Dak., Ohio, Oreg., Pa., R.I., S.Dak., Tenn., Vt., Va., Wash., W.Va., Wis.

Morphological variation within *Lathyrus palustris* is extensive. Although the most distinctive forms (see synonyms) have been accorded formal nomenclatural recognition (M. L. Fernald 1911; C. L. Hitchcock 1952), intergradation among these mostly sympatric ecotypes is widespread (D. Isely 1998). In Nunavut, it is known only from Akimiski Island in James Bay.

7. **Lathyrus lanszwertii** Kellogg, Proc. Calif. Acad. Sci. 2: 150, fig. 44. 1863 • Lanszwert's vetchling, mountain or Nevada sweet or thick-leaved pea [E]

Herbs perennial, from rhizome, glabrous or sparsely pubescent. **Stems** angled, erect, sprawling, or climbing, basally branched 0–4 times, 1–8 dm. **Leaves** (0.5–)1–8 cm; tendrils mucronate to well developed; stipules linear to lanceolate, 5–25 × 1–6 mm, much smaller than leaflets; leaflets 2–10, scattered, blades lanceolate or linear, 20–70 × 2–20 mm, surfaces glabrous or sparsely pubescent. **Inflorescences** 2–6-flowered, 2–10 cm. **Flowers** 7–15 mm; calyx lobes unequal, lateral lobes deltate, shorter than tube; corolla white or blue-purple, banner erect, blade equal to claw, wings equal to keel; ovary glabrous. **Legumes** 25–45 × 6–10 mm.

Varieties 5 (5 in the flora): w North America.

1. Stems (2–)3–8 dm, usually climbing, sometimes sprawling or erect; tendrils well developed, usually branched.
   2. Leaflets 8–10; corollas blue-purple; California northward to Washington, eastward to Colorado and Wyoming. . . . . 7a. *Lathyrus lanszwertii* var. *lanszwertii*
   2. Leaflets 6–8; corollas white; w Colorado, c Utah, Wyoming. . . . . .7b. *Lathyrus lanszwertii* var. *pallescens*
1. Stems 1–3(–4) dm, usually erect (sometimes var. *bijugatus* sprawling or climbing); tendrils reduced to simple bristles less than 1 cm.
   3. Leaflets 2–4; e Washington, adjacent Idaho, Montana, British Columbia . . . . 7c. *Lathyrus lanszwertii* var. *bijugatus*
   3. Leaflets 4–8; California northward to sc Washington and eastward to New Mexico, Colorado, and Wyoming.

4. Flowers 7–10 mm; California, Nevada, Oregon, Washington. . . . . 7d. *Lathyrus lanszwertii* var. *aridus*
4. Flowers 10–15 mm; Arizona, Colorado, New Mexico, Utah, Wyoming . . . . 7e. *Lathyrus lanszwertii* var. *leucanthus*

7a. Lathyrus lanszwertii Kellogg var. **lanszwertii** [E]

Stems sprawling or climbing, 4–8 dm. **Leaves** 5–8 cm, terminating in well-developed, usually branched tendril; leaflets 8–10, blades usually lanceolate, rarely linear, 30–70 × 5–20 mm. **Inflorescences** 3–9 cm. **Flowers** 10–15 mm, corolla blue-purple, banner retuse to shallowly cordate. **2*n*** = 14, 28.

Flowering Mar–Jun. Parkland, thickets, sagebrush, juniper, pine, and aspen woodlands; 900–3100 m; Calif., Colo., Idaho, Nev., Oreg., Utah, Wash., Wyo.

Variety *lanszwertii* is found in northern California, western Colorado, central Idaho, western Nevada, eastern Oregon, the Wasatch Mountains of northeastern Utah, southeastern Washington, and north-central Wyoming.

7b. Lathyrus lanszwertii Kellogg var. **pallescens** Barneby in A. Cronquist et al., Intermount. Fl. 3(B): 206. 1989 [E]

Stems erect to climbing, 2–6 dm. **Leaves** 3–6 cm, usually terminating in well-developed, usually branched tendril; leaflets 6–8, blades lanceolate, 20–50 × 7–16 mm. **Inflorescences** 5–10 cm. **Flowers** 10–15 mm, corolla white.

Flowering Apr–Jun. Parkland, thickets, sagebrush, oak, pine, aspen, and mixed conifer woodlands; 1500–3200 m; Colo., Utah, Wyo.

Variety *pallescens* is sometimes confused with *Lathyrus laetivirens* from which it differs in having smaller flowers (10–15 mm versus 15–20 mm in *L. laetivirens*), and 6–8 lanceolate versus 8–10 ovate leaflets.

7c. Lathyrus lanszwertii Kellogg var. **bijugatus** (T. G. White) Broich, Madroño 54: 371. 2008 • Sandberg's vetchling [E]

Lathyrus bijugatus T. G. White, Bull. Torrey Bot. Club 21: 457. 1894; *L. bijugatus* var. *sandbergii* T. G. White

Stems erect, sprawling, or climbing, 2–4 dm. **Leaves** 0.5–2 cm, terminating in simple bristle less than 1 cm; leaflets 2–4, blades lanceolate or linear, 20–50 × 4–15 mm or 30–90 × 2–5 mm. **Inflorescences** 2–3 cm. **Flowers** 8–10 mm, corolla pink or blue.

Flowering Apr–Jun. Edges and openings of coniferous woodlands; 600–1600 m; B.C.; Idaho, Mont., Wash.

Variety *bijugatus*, which is found from southern British Columbia to eastern Washington, northern Idaho, and western Montana, includes two distinct sympatric races: one with lanceolate leaflets (= *L. bijugatus* var. *bijugatus* in the sense of White), and one with linear leaflets (= *L. bijugatus* var. *sandbergii*).

7d. Lathyrus lanszwertii Kellogg var. **aridus** (Piper) Jepson, Fl. Calif. 2: 389. 1936 [E]

Lathyrus coriaceus T. G. White subsp. *aridus* Piper, Proc. Biol. Soc. Wash. 31: 190. 1918; *L. lanszwertii* subsp. *aridus* (Piper) Bradshaw

Stems erect, 1–3 dm. **Leaves** 2–4 cm, terminating in simple bristle, usually less than 1 cm; leaflets 4–8, blades linear, 20–40 × 2–5 mm. **Inflorescences** 2–4 cm. **Flowers** 7–10 mm, corolla white. **2*n*** = 14.

Flowering Apr–Jun. Open ponderosa pine woodlands, adjacent sagebrush steppes; 800–2000 m; Calif., Nev., Oreg., Wash.

Variety *aridus* is known from the eastern flanks of the Sierra Nevada in California and western Nevada and in the Cascade Range north to south-central Washington. It appears to intergrade with var. *lanszwertii* in central Washington and Oregon.

7e. Lathyrus lanszwertii Kellogg var. **leucanthus** (Rydberg) Dorn, Vasc. Pl. Wyoming, 171, 297. 1988 [E]

Lathyrus leucanthus Rydberg, Bull. Torrey Bot. Club 28: 37. 1901; *L. arizonicus* Britton; *L. lanszwertii* var. *arizonicus* (Britton) S. L. Welsh

Stems erect, 1–3 dm. **Leaves** 2–3 cm, terminating in simple bristle, less than 1 cm; leaflets 4–6, blades lanceolate and 25–50 × 5–15 mm, or linear and 35–70 × 2–5 mm. **Inflorescences** 3–5 cm. **Flowers** 10–15 mm, corolla white. **2*n*** = 28.

Flowering Apr–Jun. In sagebrush, openings in pine, oak, and aspen woodlands; 2000–3200 m; Ariz., Colo., N.Mex., Utah, Wyo.

Variety *leucanthus* includes two distinct sympatric races: one with lanceolate leaflets (= *L. leucanthus*), and one with linear leaflets (= *L. arizonicus* Britton).

8. Lathyrus jepsonii Greene, Pittonia 2: 158. 1890 (as jepsoni) • Jepson's sweet pea [E] [F]

Herbs perennial, from rhizome, glabrous or pubescent. **Stems** winged, sprawling or climbing, basally branched 0–3 times, 4–25 dm. **Leaves** 5–15 cm; tendrils well developed; stipules narrowly lanceolate to linear, 10–25 × 2–6 mm, much smaller than leaflets; leaflets 8–12, scattered, blades lanceolate, 20–60 × 4–20 mm, surfaces glabrous or pubescent. **Inflorescences** 5–15-flowered, 6–16 cm. **Flowers** 14–17 mm; calyx lobes unequal, lateral lobes linear-triangular, equal to tube; corolla pale pink to rose-purple, banner erect, blade longer than claw, wings equal to keel; ovary glabrous. **Legumes** 50–90 × 6–9 mm.

Varieties 2 (2 in the flora): California.

1. Herbs glabrous; of marshes and wetlands . . . . 8a. *Lathyrus jepsonii* var. *jepsonii*
1. Herbs pubescent; of drier upland sites. . . . . 8b. *Lathyrus jepsonii* var. *californicus*

8a. Lathyrus jepsonii Greene var. **jepsonii** • Delta tule or tule pea [C] [E] [F]

Herbs glabrous. **Stems** often longer than 10 dm. **2*n*** = 14.

Flowering May–Aug. Tidal marshes, sloughs, wetlands; of conservation concern; 0–20 m; Calif.

Variety *jepsonii* is largely restricted to the Suisun Marshes and the Sacramento River delta region above San Pablo Bay and at the southern end of San Francisco Bay. Sparsely pubescent populations in drier areas of this region suggest intergradation between vars. *californicus* and *jepsonii*.

8b. Lathyrus jepsonii Greene var. **californicus** (S. Watson) Hoover, Leafl. W. Bot. 10: 349. 1966 [E]

Lathyrus venosus Muhlenberg ex Willdenow var. *californicus* S. Watson, Proc. Amer. Acad. Arts 11: 133. 1876; *L. jepsonii* subsp. *californicus* (S. Watson) C. L. Hitchcock; *L. watsonii* T. G. White

Herbs pubescent. **Stems** usually less than 10 dm. **2*n*** = 14.

Flowering May–Jun. Meadows, wooded streams; 0–2000 m; Calif.

Lathyrus californicus (S. Watson) S. Watson, not Douglas, is an illegitimate name that pertains here.

9. Lathyrus delnorticus C. L. Hitchcock, Revis. N. Amer. Lathyrus, 30, fig. 21. 1952 • Del Norte pea [E]

Herbs perennial, from rhizome, glabrous. **Stems** narrowly winged, erect to climbing, basally branched 0–several times, 2–8 dm. **Leaves** 9–13 cm; tendrils well developed; stipules lanceolate, 10–30 × 3–15 mm, sometimes equal to distal leaflets; leaflets 9–12, scattered, blades lanceolate, 30–50 × 5–15 mm, surfaces glabrous. **Inflorescences** 8–12-flowered, 7–10 cm. **Flowers** 9–12 mm; calyx lobes unequal, lateral lobes deltate, shorter than tube; corolla cream-white, banner erect, blade longer than claw, wings equal to keel; ovary glabrous. **Legumes** 30–40 × 3–5 mm. **2*n*** = 14.

Flowering May–Jun. Serpentine areas along rivers and creeks in coniferous and mixed evergreen forests; 0–1000 m; Calif., Oreg.

Lathyrus delnorticus is restricted to Del Norte and western Siskiyou counties in California, and Curry and Josephine counties in Oregon.

10. Lathyrus biflorus T. W. Nelson & J. P. Nelson, Brittonia 35: 183, fig. 2. 1983 • Two-flowered sweet pea [C] [E]

Herbs perennial, from rhizome, villous. **Stems** angled, erect or sprawling, basally branched 1–3 times, 0.5–1 dm. **Leaves** 0.5–1 cm; tendrils absent or reduced to flattened bristles; stipules linear, 4–5 × 1–2 mm, ca. 1/2 length of leaflets; leaflets (3 or)4(or 5), paired, blades lanceolate, 6–12 × 2–3 mm, surfaces finely villous. **Inflorescences** 1- or 2-flowered, 1 cm. **Flowers** 7–8 mm; calyx lobes subequal, lateral lobes deltate, shorter than tube; corolla cream, banner erect, blade equal to claw, wings equal to keel; ovary glabrous. **Legumes** 13–15 × 3–5 mm.

Flowering Jun. Serpentine outcrops and Jeffrey pine woodlands; of conservation concern; 1300–1400 m; Calif.

Lathyrus biflorus is known only from southeastern Humboldt County.

11. Lathyrus hitchcockianus Barneby & Reveal, Aliso 7: 362. 1971 • Hitchcock's sweet pea [C] [E]

Herbs perennial, from rhizome, sparsely pubescent. **Stems** angled, erect or sprawling, basally branched 3–5 times, 1–3 dm. **Leaves** 3–4 cm; tendrils well developed; stipules linear, 5–10 × 1–2 mm, much smaller than leaflets; leaflets 4 or 6, paired, blades linear, 15–50 × 1–5 mm, surfaces sparsely pubescent. **Inflorescences** 2 or 3-flowered, 3–6 cm. **Flowers** 8–10 mm; calyx lobes unequal, lateral lobes deltate, shorter than tube; corolla lilac to purple, banner erect, blade longer than claw, wings equal to keel; ovary glabrous. **Legumes** 40–70 × 4–9 mm.

Flowering Apr–May. Washes in sagebrush or pinyon-juniper woodlands; of conservation concern; 1200–2100 m; Calif., Nev.

Lathyrus hitchcockianus is known only from the Bullfrog Hills and Yucca Mountain in Nye County, Nevada, and the Grapevine Mountains of adjacent Inyo County, California.

12. Lathyrus venosus Muhlenberg ex Willdenow, Sp. Pl. 3: 1092. 1802 • Bushy vetchling, gesse veinée [E] [F]

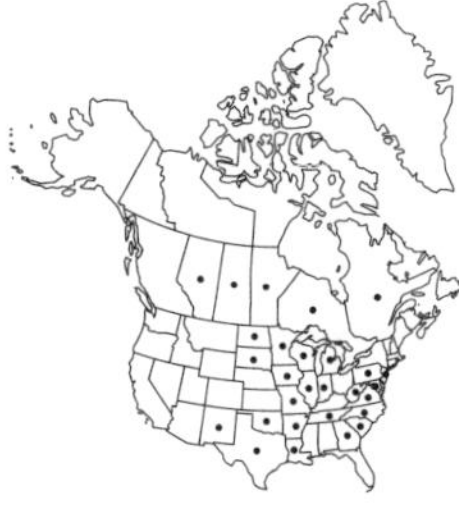

Herbs perennial, from rhizome, glabrous or pubescent. **Stems** angled, sprawling or climbing, basally branched 0–3 times, 4–10 dm. **Leaves** 6–18 cm; tendrils well developed; stipules lanceolate to linear, 10–20 × 2–10 mm, much smaller than distal leaflets (less than 1/4 width of distal leaflets); leaflets 8–14, scattered, blades ovate to lanceolate, 25–70 × 10–35 mm, surfaces glabrous or pubescent. **Inflorescences** 5–20-flowered, 6–20 cm. **Flowers** 10–15 mm; calyx lobes unequal, lateral lobes linear-triangular or lanceolate, shorter to longer than tube; corolla blue-purple to rose, banner erect, blade equal to claw, wings equal to keel; ovary glabrous or pubescent. **Legumes** 20–50 × 3–7 mm.

Varieties 3 (3 in the flora): North America.

1. Herbs sparsely to densely pubescent . . . . 12c. *Lathyrus venosus* var. *intonsus*
1. Herbs glabrous.
   2. Calyces: lateral lobes linear-triangular, equal to or shorter than tubes . . . . .12a. *Lathyrus venosus* var. *venosus*
   2. Calyces: lateral lobes lanceolate, longer than tubes . . . . 12b. *Lathyrus venosus* var. *arkansanus*

12a. Lathyrus venosus Muhlenberg ex Willdenow var. **venosus** [E]

Lathyrus oreophilus Wooton & Standley

Herbs glabrous; tendrils sometimes unbranched. **Calyces:** lateral lobes linear-triangular, equal to or shorter than tube. $2n = 28$.

Flowering May–Jul. Woodlands, stream banks; 0–500 m; D.C., Ga., Md., N.J., N.C., Pa., S.C., Va., W.Va.

12b. Lathyrus venosus Muhlenberg ex Willdenow var. **arkansanus** Fassett, Rhodora 39: 377. 1937 [E]

Herbs glabrous; tendrils branched. **Calyces:** lateral lobes lanceolate, longer than tube. $2n = 28$.

Flowering Apr–Jun. Woodlands; 0–500 m; Ark., La., Okla., Tex.

Lateral calyx lobes in var. *arkansanus* are somewhat polymorphic. It is found in the extreme southwestern corner of the distribution of the species.

12c. Lathyrus venosus Muhlenberg ex Willdenow var. **intonsus** Butters & H. St. John, Rhodora 19: 158. 1917 [E] [F]

Lathyrus venosus var. *meridionalis* Butters & St. John

Herbs sparsely to densely pubescent; tendrils sometimes unbranched. **Calyces:** lateral lobes linear-triangular, usually shorter than tube. **2*n*** = 28.

Flowering May–Jul. Woodlands, stream banks; 0–1000 m; Alta., Man., Ont., Que., Sask.; Ill., Ind., Iowa, Mich., Minn., Mo., N.Mex., N.Dak., Okla., S.Dak., Tenn., Tex., Va., W.Va., Wis.

13. Lathyrus vestitus Nuttall in J. Torrey and A. Gray, Fl. N. Amer. 1: 276. 1838 • Pacific vetchling

Herbs perennial, from rhizome, glabrous or sparsely to densely pubescent. **Stems** angled to narrowly winged, sprawling or climbing, basally branched 0–4 times, 2–20 dm. **Leaves** 4–14 cm; tendrils well developed; stipules lanceolate to linear, 5–25 × 1–10 mm, much smaller than leaflets (more than 1/4 width of distal leaflets); leaflets 6–12, scattered, blades ovate to linear, 12–50 × 5–25 mm, surfaces glabrous or pubescent. **Inflorescences** 5–20-flowered, 5–25 cm. **Flowers** 12–25 mm; calyx lobes unequal, lateral lobes deltate, linear-triangular, or lanceolate and wider distal to base, shorter to longer than tube; corolla cream-white, rose, lavender, blue-purple, or deep wine red, banner erect or reflexed toward calyx tube, blade equal to or longer than claw, wings equal to keel; ovary glabrous or pubescent. **Legumes** 40–60 × 4–7 mm.

Varieties 3 (3 in the flora): w United States, nw Mexico.

1. Flowers 16–25 mm, corollas dark wine red, banners reflexed against calyx tube . . . . 13c. *Lathyrus vestitus* var. *alefeldii*
1. Flowers 12–17 mm, corollas cream-white, rose, lavender, or blue-purple, banners erect.
    2. Leaflet blades often sparsely to densely pubescent throughout, sometimes pubescent abaxially, glabrous adaxially; flowers rose, lavender, or blue-purple; California, sw Oregon . . . . 13a. *Lathyrus vestitus* var. *vestitus*
    2. Leaflet blades glabrous; flowers cream-white; Puget Sound area to sw Oregon and nw California . . . . 13b. *Lathyrus vestitus* var. *ochropetalus*

13a. Lathyrus vestitus Nuttall var. **vestitus**

Lathyrus bolanderi S. Watson; *L. laetiflorus* Greene; *L. laetiflorus* subsp. *barbarae* (T. G. White) C. L. Hitchcock; *L. vestitus* subsp. *bolanderi* (S. Watson) C. L. Hitchcock; *L. vestitus* subsp. *laetiflorus* (Greene) Broich; *L. vestitus* subsp. *laevicarpus* Broich; *L. vestitus* subsp. *puberulus* (T. G. White ex Greene) C. L. Hitchcock; *L. vestitus* subsp. *violaceus* (Greene) Abrams; *L. violaceus* Greene; *L. violaceus* Greene var. *barbarae* T. G. White

Leaflets: blade surfaces often sparsely to densely pubescent throughout, sometimes pubescent abaxially, glabrous adaxially. **Flowers** 14–17 mm; lateral calyx lobes lanceolate or linear-triangular and equal to tube, or deltate and shorter than tube; corolla rose, lavender, or blue-purple, banner erect, blade equal to or somewhat longer than claw. **2*n*** = 14.

Flowering Apr–May. Roadside fencerows, grasslands, oak or conifer woodlands along creeks, chaparral; 0–2000 m; Calif., Oreg.; Mexico (Baja California).

As delimited here, var. *vestitus* includes populations found in habitats from moist coastal coniferous forests to chaparral, from California to southwestern Oregon. Numerous attempts to describe distinctive taxa within this series of populations (R. V. Bradshaw 1925; C. L. Hitchcock 1952; S. L. Broich 1987; D. Isely 1992) have been undermined by extensive intergradation among them.

13b. Lathyrus vestitus Nuttall var. **ochropetalus** (Piper) Isely, Madroño 39: 96. 1992 [E]

Lathyrus ochropetalus Piper, Proc. Biol. Soc. Wash. 31: 189. 1918; *L. peckii* Piper; *L. vestitus* subsp. *ochropetalus* (Piper) C. L. Hitchcock

Leaflets: blade surfaces glabrous. **Flowers** 12–15 mm; lateral calyx lobes lanceolate, longer than tube; corolla cream-white, banner erect, blade equal to claw. **2*n*** = 14.

Flowering Apr–May. Roadside fencerows, grasslands, openings in coastal coniferous forests; 0–800 m; Calif., Oreg., Wash.

Variety *ochropetalus* is known from the Puget Sound area southward to northwestern California.

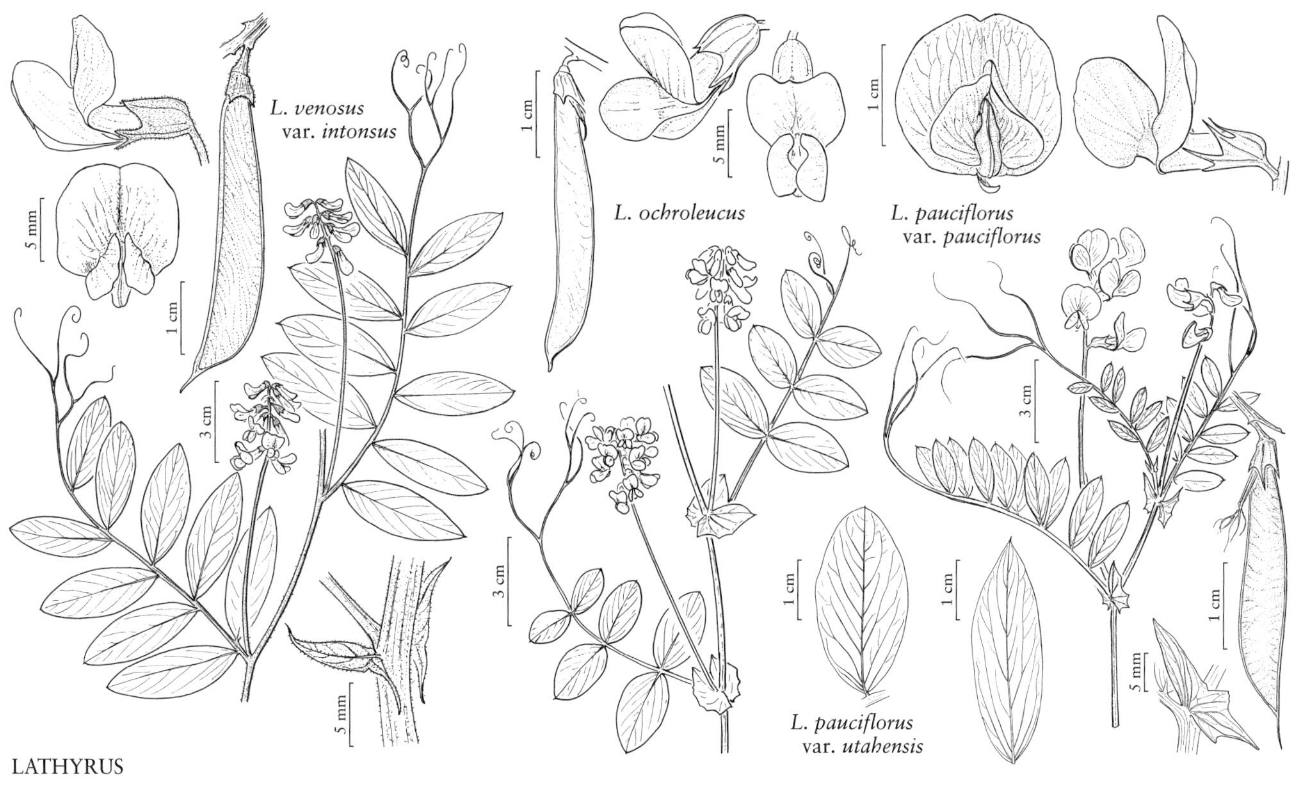

LATHYRUS

13c. Lathyrus vestitus Nuttall var. **alefeldii** (T. G. White) Isely, Madroño 39: 96. 1992

Lathyrus alefeldii T. G. White, Bull. Torrey Bot. Club 21: 449. 1894 (as alefeldi); *L. laetiflorus* Greene subsp. *alefeldii* (T. G. White) Bradshaw; *L. laetiflorus* var. *alefeldii* (T. G. White) Jepson; *L. vestitus* subsp. *alefeldii* (T. G. White) Broich

Leaflets: blade surfaces often pubescent abaxially, glabrous adaxially. **Flowers** 16–25 mm; lateral calyx lobes deltate, shorter than tube; corolla deep wine red, banner reflexed toward calyx tube, blade much longer than claw. $2n$ = 14.

Flowering Feb–May. Chaparral; 0–2000 m; Calif.; Mexico (Baja California).

Variety *alefeldii* is known from the South Coast, Channel Islands, and Peninsular Ranges.

14. Lathyrus splendens Kellogg, Proc. Calif. Acad. Sci. 7: 90. 1877 • Campo pea, pride-of-California

Herbs perennial, from rhizome, glabrate. **Stems** angled, sprawling, basally branched 0–3 times, 4–30 dm. **Leaves** 5–8 cm; tendrils well developed; stipules lanceolate to linear, 10–20 × 2–8 mm, much smaller than leaflets; leaflets 6–10, scattered, blades ovate to linear, 20–40 × 3–15 mm, surfaces glabrous throughout or sparsely pubescent abaxially. **Inflorescences** 6–10-flowered, 4–16 cm. **Flowers** 25–30 mm; calyx lobes unequal, lateral lobes deltate, shorter than tube; corolla deep wine red, banner reflexed against calyx tube, blade much longer than claw, wings equal to keel; ovary glandular-pubescent. **Legumes** 50–80 × 5–9 mm. $2n$ = 14.

Flowering Mar–May. Chaparral; 50–1500 m; Calif.; Mexico (Baja California).

Morphological similarities between *Lathyrus splendens* and *L. vestitus* var. *alefeldii* (R. V. Bradshaw 1925; C. L. Hitchcock 1952) are such that these two taxa might be considered a parent-offspring species pair worthy of an evolutionary study of factors involved in their origin. *Lathyrus splendens* is known from the South Coast and Peninsular Ranges.

15. Lathyrus ochroleucus Hooker, Fl. Bor.-Amer. 1: 159. 1831 • Cream-flowered sweet pea, yellow vetchling, peavine, gesse jaunâtre [E] [F]

Lathyrus nevadensis S. Watson subsp. *stipulaceus* (T. G. White) Bradshaw

Herbs perennial, from rhizome, glabrous except calyx ciliate. **Stems** angled, sprawling or climbing, basally branched 0–3 times, 3–8 dm. **Leaves** (2–)3–10 cm; tendrils well developed; stipules somewhat foliose, ovate-lanceolate, 15–35 × 5–20 mm, sometimes equal to distal leaflets; leaflets (5 or)6(–8), usually paired, blades broadly ovate to lanceolate, (20–)25–65 × 10–35(–42) mm, surfaces glabrous. **Inflorescences** 4–10(–13)-flowered, 3–12 cm. **Flowers** 10–15 mm; calyx lobes unequal, lateral lobes lanceolate, usually longer than tube; corolla cream-white, banner erect, blade longer than claw, wings equal to keel; ovary glabrous. **Legumes** 30–70 × 4–7 mm. $2n = 14$.

Flowering Apr–Jul. Moist woodlands, clearings, thickets, glades, meadows; 0–1500 m; Alta., B.C., Man., N.W.T., Nunavut, Ont., Que., Sask., Yukon; Alaska, Idaho, Ill., Ind., Iowa, Mich., Minn., Mont., Nebr., N.J., N.Y., N.Dak., Ohio, Pa., S.Dak., Vt., Wash., W.Va., Wis., Wyo.

16. Lathyrus nevadensis S. Watson, Proc. Amer. Acad. Arts 11: 133. 1876 • Sierra Nevada sweet pea [E]

Herbs perennial, from rhizome, pubescent except glabrous on legumes and leaflets adaxially. **Stems** angled, erect, sprawling, or climbing, basally branched 0–several times, 1–6 dm. **Leaves** 2–10 cm; tendrils mucronate (less than 1 cm) to well developed; stipules linear, 5–25 × 1–8 mm, much smaller than leaflets; leaflets 4–12, usually scattered, blades broadly ovate to lanceolate or linear, (17–)20–110 × 2–30(–37) mm, surfaces usually glabrous, rarely finely pubescent. **Inflorescences** 2–10-flowered, 3–15 cm. **Flowers** 12–22 mm; calyx lobes unequal, lateral lobes deltate, usually shorter than tube; corolla blue-purple to pink-purple or white, banner erect, blade longer than claw, wings equal to keel; ovary glabrous. **Legumes** 20–30(–45) × 5–10 mm.

Varieties 3 (3 in the flora): w North America.

1. Corollas blue-purple to pink-purple; British Columbia, California, w Oregon, w, c Washington .... 16a. *Lathyrus nevadensis* var. *nevadensis*
1. Corollas white; ne Oregon, e Washington, adjacent Idaho.
   2. Leaves 4–10 cm; leaflets 6–10; tendrils well developed; flowers 5–10, 12–18 mm .... 16b. *Lathyrus nevadensis* var. *parkeri*
   2. Leaves 2–5 cm; leaflets 4 or 6; tendrils reduced to bristles, (usually less than 1 cm); flowers 2–4, 18–22 mm .... 16c. *Lathyrus nevadensis* var. *cusickii*

16a. Lathyrus nevadensis S. Watson var. **nevadensis** • Peavine [E]

Lathyrus lanceolatus Howell; *L. nevadensis* subsp. *lanceolatus* (Howell) C. L. Hitchcock; *L. nevadensis* var. *pilosellus* (M. Peck) C. L. Hitchcock; *L. nevadensis* var. *puniceus* C. L. Hitchcock; *L. nuttallii* S. Watson

Stems erect to climbing, 1–6 dm. **Leaves** 2–10 cm; tendrils bristlelike to well developed; leaflets 4–12, blades ovate to lanceolate. **Inflorescences** 2–6-flowered. **Flowers** 13–18 mm; corolla blue-purple to pink-purple, banner retuse to shallowly cordate. $2n = 28$.

Flowering Apr–Jul. Open, coniferous and mixed forests, thickets, meadows, wetland margins; 0–1600 m; B.C.; Calif., Oreg., Wash.

Variety *nevadensis* includes two races (S. L. Broich 2007). One race consists of short (less than 3 dm), erect plants bearing four or six leaflets, with leaf rachises ending in, at most, short (less than 1 cm) bristles rather than tendrils, and with 2–4(–6)-flowered racemes of rather large (15–20 mm) flowers (*Lathyrus nevadensis* in the strict sense). A second race consists of sprawling or clambering plants to 6 dm bearing leaves of 6 or 8(or 10) leaflets, with rachises ending in long (more than 2 cm), often branched and prehensile tendrils, and with racemes of 4–8 smaller (10–17 mm) flowers (*L. lanceolatus* Howell). The *nevadensis* race is more common in the southwestern part of the range; the *lanceolatus* race is found throughout the range of the variety but is more common to the north and in the eastern foothills of the Cascade Range in central Washington. Although the extremes are well marked, intermediate populations are common enough in some areas that D. Isely (1992) recognized both forms as one variety.

Variety *nevadensis* is found from the coastal ranges of California northward to British Columbia.

16b. Lathyrus nevadensis S. Watson var. **parkeri** (H. St. John) C. L. Hitchcock, Revis. N. Amer. Lathyrus, 45. 1952 • Parker's sweet pea [E]

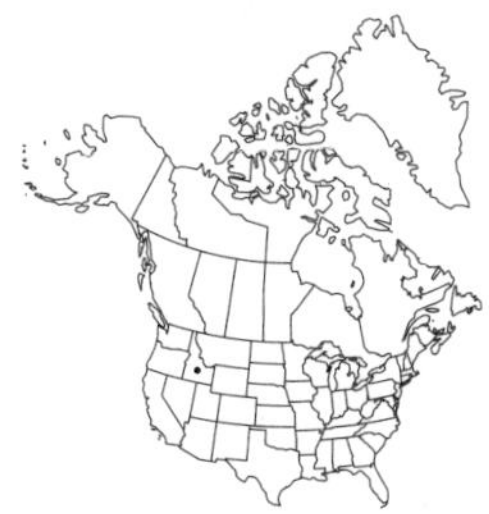

Lathyrus parkeri H. St. John, Fl. S.E. Washington, 223. 1937

Stems erect to climbing, 2–6 dm. **Leaves** 4–10 cm; tendrils well developed; leaflets 6–10, blades ovate to lanceolate. **Inflorescences** 5–10-flowered. **Flowers** 12–18 mm; corolla white.

Flowering Apr–Jun. Open, moist coniferous forests; 500–1800 m; Idaho.

A few pink- to blue-purple-flowered populations of what would otherwise be var. *nevadensis* occur on the east slopes of the Cascade Range in central Washington (Chelan County). In morphology, these populations are similar to var. *parkeri* and clearly indicate a connection between var. *parkeri* to the east and the *lanceolatus* race of var. *nevadensis* to the west.

16c. Lathyrus nevadensis S. Watson var. **cusickii** (S. Watson) Broich, Madroño 54: 64. 2007 • Cusick's sweet pea [E]

Lathyrus cusickii S. Watson, Proc. Amer. Acad. Arts Sci. 17: 371. 1882; *L. nevadensis* subsp. *cusickii* (S. Watson) C. L. Hitchcock

Stems erect to sprawling, 2–4 dm. **Leaves** 2–5 cm; tendrils reduced to bristles, usually less than 1 cm; leaflets (2 or)4 or 6, blades ovate-lanceolate or linear. **Inflorescences** 2–4-flowered. **Flowers** 18–22 mm; corolla white.

Flowering Apr–Jun. Open, coniferous forests; 100–1800 m; Idaho, Oreg., Wash.

Variety *cusickii* includes two distinct races: one with ovate to lanceolate leaflets and the other with linear leaflets. Plants from an intermediate population have been collected in Umatilla County, Oregon.

17. Lathyrus laetivirens Greene ex Rydberg, Fl. Colorado, 217. 1906 • Plateau vetchling [E]

Lathyrus lanszwertii Kellogg var. *laetivirens* (Greene ex Rydberg) S. L. Welsh; *L. leucanthus* Rydberg var. *laetivirens* (Greene ex Rydberg) C. L. Hitchcock

Herbs perennial, from rhizome, glabrous. **Stems** angled, sprawling to erect, basally branched 0–3 times, 2–8 dm. **Leaves** 3–8 cm; tendrils well developed, often branched; stipules lanceolate, 8–12 × 2–5 mm, much smaller than leaflets; leaflets 6–10, usually paired, blades ovate, 20–40 × 10–20 mm, surfaces glabrous. **Inflorescences** 2–5-flowered, 4–7 cm. **Flowers** 15–20 mm; calyx lobes unequal, lateral lobes deltate, shorter than tube; corolla white to slightly pink or lavender, banner erect, blade longer than claw, wings equal to keel; ovary glabrous. **Legumes** 30–50 × 5–15 mm.

Flowering Apr–Jul. Flats, hillsides, sagebrush communities, pinyon-juniper, oak, pine, aspen and Douglas-fir forests; 1200–3200 m; Ariz., Colo., Nev., N.Mex., Utah.

C. L. Hitchcock (1952), S. L. Welsh et al. (1987), and D. Isely (1998) placed *Lathyrus laetivirens* within the *L. lanszwertii* complex, whereas R. C. Barneby (1989) treated it as a separate species.

18. Lathyrus brownii Eastwood, Bull. Torrey Bot. Club 30: 491. 1903 • Brown's sweet pea [E]

Lathyrus lanszwertii Kellogg var. *brownii* (Eastwood) Jepson; *L. pauciflorus* Fernald subsp. *brownii* (Eastwood) Piper

Herbs perennial, from rhizome, glabrous. **Stems** angled, sprawling, basally branched 0–3 times, 2–5 dm. **Leaves** 4–6 cm; tendrils well developed; stipules linear, 5–15 × 1–5 mm, much smaller than leaflets; leaflets 6–10, scattered, blades ovate to linear, 15–40 × 1–10 mm, surfaces glabrous. **Inflorescences** 2–4-flowered, 3–4 cm. **Flowers** 12–16 mm; calyx lobes unequal, lateral lobes deltate, shorter than tube; corolla purple, banner erect, blade longer than claw, wings longer than keel (by 1–3 mm); ovary glabrous. **Legumes** 30–40 × 5–8 mm.

Flowering May–Jul. Stream banks, open ponderosa pine forests; 800–1800 m; Calif., Nev., Oreg.

Lathyrus brownii has been variously allied with *L. pauciflorus* (C. L. Hitchcock 1952) or with *L. lanszwertii* (R. C. Barneby 1989). It is distinct from *L. pauciflorus* by its smaller leaflets and flowers and by its range (northeastern California and adjacent Nevada and Oregon versus Colorado and Utah to Idaho, northeastern Oregon, and eastern Washington), and from *L. lanszwertii* by its larger flowers, smaller leaflets, general absence of pubescence, and its more typical prostrate, sprawling habit.

C. L. Hitchcock (1952) considered *Lathyrus schaffneri* Rydberg as described by L. Abrams and R. S. Ferris (1923–1960, vol. 2) to be referable to *L. brownii*.

19. Lathyrus pauciflorus Fernald, Bot. Gaz. 19: 335. 1894 • Few-flowered vetchling [E] [F]

Herbs perennial, from rhizome or thickened rootstock, glabrous. **Stems** angled, erect, sprawling, or climbing, basally branched 1–3 times, 3–8 dm. **Leaves** 6–9 cm; tendrils well developed; stipules ovate to lanceolate, 15–25 × 5–11 mm, much smaller than leaflets; leafets 6–10, scattered, blades lanceolate to linear or ovate, 20–80 × 2–35 mm, surfaces glabrous. **Inflorescences** 4–13-flowered, 5–18 cm. **Flowers** 12–20 mm; calyx lobes unequal, lateral lobes deltate, shorter than tube; corolla pale blue-lavender to purple, banner erect, blade longer than claw, wings longer than keel, (by 1–4 mm); ovary glabrous. **Legumes** 30–50 × 5–10 mm.

Varieties 2 (2 in the flora): w United States.

1. Leaflet blades lanceolate to linear, width less than 1/2 length . . . . . 19a. *Lathyrus pauciflorus* var. *pauciflorus*
1. Leaflet blades ovate, width equal to or greater than 1/2 length . . . 19b. *Lathyrus pauciflorus* var. *utahensis*

19a. Lathyrus pauciflorus Fernald var. **pauciflorus** [E] [F]

Lathyrus pauciflorus var. *tenuior* (Piper) H. St. John

Leaflets: blades lanceolate to linear, 20–80 × 2–25 mm, width less than 1/2 length. **Inflorescences** 4–6-flowered.

Flowering Apr–Jun. Sagebrush steppes, pine and pine-juniper woodlands; 500–2000 m; Idaho, Oreg., Wash.

While the range of leaflet shape (lanceolate to extreme linear) in var. *pauciflorus* is striking, there is a complete series of intermediate forms making recognition of var. *tenuior*, with linear leaflets, as separate from var. *pauciflorus*, with broader leaflets, unreliable.

19b. Lathyrus pauciflorus Fernald var. **utahensis** (M. E. Jones) R. J. Davis, Madroño 11: 144. 1951 • Utah sweet pea [E] [F]

Lathyrus utahensis M. E. Jones, Proc. Calif. Acad. Sci., ser. 2, 5: 678. 1895; *L. pauciflorus* subsp. *utahensis* (M. E. Jones) Piper

Leaflets: blades ovate, 25–50 × 15–35 mm, width equal to or greater than 1/2 length. **Inflorescences** 5–13-flowered.

Flowering May–Jul. Sagebrush, oak, aspen, aspen-fir, and pinyon-juniper woodlands; 1300–2900 m; Colo., Idaho, Oreg., Utah.

20. Lathyrus rigidus T. G. White, Bull. Torrey Bot. Club 21: 455. 1894 • Bushy or modoc pea, stiff vetchling [E]

Lathyrus albus S. Watson in W. H. Brewer et al., Bot. California 2: 442. 1880, not Garcke 1858

Herbs perennial, from rootstock, glabrous. **Stems** angled, erect, basally branched 5–10 times, 1–3 dm. **Leaves** 1–3 cm; tendrils bristlelike, less than 1 cm; stipules lanceolate, 10–15 × 1–8 mm, equal to distal leaflets; leaflets 4–8, paired, blades lanceolate, 15–30 × 5–10 mm, surfaces glabrous. **Inflorescences** 2- or 3-flowered, 4–9 cm. **Flowers** 12–18 mm; calyx lobes ± unequal, lateral lobes deltate, shorter than tube; corolla white to lilac, banner erect, blade longer than claw, wings longer than keel; ovary glabrous. **Legumes** 20–40 × 5–10 mm, stipitate. $2n = 14$.

Flowering Apr–Jun. Basalt scablands with sagebrush; 800–1700 m; Calif., Idaho, Nev., Oreg.

21. Lathyrus holochlorus (Piper) C. L. Hitchcock, Revis. N. Amer. Lathyrus, 31. 1952 • Thin-leaved pea [C] [E]

Lathyrus ochropetalus Piper subsp. *holochlorus* Piper, Proc. Biol. Soc. Wash. 31: 190. 1918

Herbs perennial, from rhizome, glabrous. **Stems** angled to narrowly winged, sprawling, often branched mid stem (at or just proximal to flowering nodes), 3–10 dm. **Leaves** 6–10 cm; tendrils well developed; stipules lanceolate to linear, 10–20 × 1–8 mm, much smaller than leaflets; leaflets 8–12, usually paired, sometimes scattered, ovate to lanceolate, 20–45 × 15–25 mm, glabrous. **Inflorescences** 7–15-flowered, 5–15 cm. **Flowers** 12–14 mm; calyx lobes unequal, lateral lobes linear-triangular, shorter than or equal to tube; corolla cream-white, banner erect, blade longer than claw, wings equal to keel; ovary glabrous. **Legumes** 40–70 × 4–9 mm. **2*n*** = 14.

Flowering Apr–Jun. Roadside fencerows, stream banks, grasslands, open oak woodlands; of conservation concern; 50–500 m; Oreg., Wash.

Lathyrus holochlorus is restricted to the Willamette Valley of western Oregon and at least one site in southwestern Washington.

22. Lathyrus tracyi Bradshaw, Bot. Gaz. 80: 245. 1925 • Tracy's sweet pea [E]

Lathyrus bolanderi S. Watson var. *tracyi* (Bradshaw) Jepson; *L. lanszwertii* Kellogg var. *tracyi* (Bradshaw) Isely

Herbs perennial, from rhizome, glabrous or pubescent. **Stems** angled, erect, sprawling, or climbing, often branched mid stem 1–4 times, 2–6 dm. **Leaves** 2–6 cm; tendrils absent to well developed, 0–3 cm, usually not branched; stipules linear, 5–15 × 1–5 mm, much smaller than leaflets; leaflets 4–8, often paired, blades ovate, 15–30 × 5–20 mm, surfaces glabrous, or linear, 30–70 × 1–10 mm, surfaces glabrous or pubescent. **Inflorescences** 5–15-flowered, 2–7 cm. **Flowers** 7–13 mm; calyx lobes unequal, lateral lobes often linear-triangular, sometimes lanceolate, shorter than tube; corolla white, banner erect, blade equal to claw, wings equal to keel; ovary glabrous. **Legumes** 40–60 × 4–7 mm. **2*n*** = 14.

Flowering Apr–Jun. Roadsides, open coniferous and mixed evergreen forests; 300–1300 m; Calif.

Although W. L. Jepson (1909–1943, vol. 2) treated *Lathyrus tracyi* of northwestern California as a variety of *L. bolanderi* S. Watson (= *L. vestitus*), D. Isely (1992, 1998) considered *L. tracyi* a variety of *L. lanszwertii*. *Lathyrus tracyi* includes both ovate- and linear-leaflet forms. Linear-leaflet populations certainly suggest a relationship to *L. lanszwertii*, but ovate-leaflet forms, the presence of mid stem branching, and differences in floral structures suggest that *L. tracyi* may be better allied to *L. holochlorus* found to the north in the Willamette Valley of western Oregon and southwestern Washington. *Lathyrus tracyi* has been reported from Jackson County, Oregon, but specimens could not be examined.

23. Lathyrus sulphureus W. H. Brewer ex A. Gray, Proc. Amer. Acad. Arts 7: 399. 1868 • Brewer's sweet or snub or sulfur pea [E]

Herbs perennial, from rhizome, usually glabrous, rarely pubescent. **Stems** angled, climbing, basally branched 0–3 times, 5–15 dm. **Leaves** 9–12 cm; tendrils well developed; stipules lanceolate, 15–25 × 4–10 mm, sometimes equal to distal leaflets; leaflets 6–12, scattered, blades ovate to lanceolate, 25–50 × 10–20 mm, surfaces glabrous or pubescent. **Inflorescences** 9–15-flowered, 6–10 cm. **Flowers** 11–13 mm; calyx lobes unequal, lateral lobes deltate to lanceolate, shorter than tube; corolla orange to yellow-cream, banner erect, blade shorter than claw, wings equal to keel; ovary glabrous. **Legumes** 40–70 × 4–6 mm.

Varieties 2 (2 in the flora): w United States.

1. Herbs glabrous . . . . 23a. *Lathyrus sulphureus* var. *sulphureus*
1. Herbs densely villous . . . . 23b. *Lathyrus sulphureus* var. *argillaceus*

23a. Lathyrus sulphureus W. H. Brewer ex A. Gray var. **sulphureus** [E]

Herbs glabrous. **2*n*** = 14.

Flowering Apr–Jun. Oak woodlands; 100–2700 m; Calif., Oreg.

Variety *sulphureus* is known from California's Central Valley and adjacent foothills northward to southwestern Oregon.

23b. Lathyrus sulphureus W. H. Brewer ex A. Gray var. **argillaceus** Jepson, Fl. Calif. 2: 393. 1936 [C] [E]

Herbs densely villous.

Flowering Apr–Jun. Oak woodlands; of conservation concern; 100–800 m; Calif.

Variety *argillaceus* is a rare, pubescent form that is known only from five older collections (1899–1936) from Calaveras, Nevada, Placer, Shasta, and Tehama counties.

24. Lathyrus graminifolius (S. Watson) T. G. White, Bull. Torrey Bot. Club 21: 454. 1894 • Grass-leaved pea [F]

Lathyrus palustris Linnaeus var. *graminifolius* S. Watson, Proc. Amer. Acad. Arts 23: 263. 1888

Herbs perennial, from rhizome or woody rootstock, glabrous. **Stems** angled, sprawling or climbing, sometimes branched at flowering nodes, 2–6 dm. **Leaves** 5–9 cm; tendrils usually well developed; stipules lanceolate to linear, 8–12 × 1–5 mm, much smaller than leaflets; leaflets 4–8, scattered, blades usually linear, rarely lanceolate, 30–80 × 1–20 mm, surfaces glabrous. **Inflorescences** 5–8-flowered, 10–18 cm. **Flowers** 8–15 mm; calyx lobes subequal, lateral lobes deltate, shorter than tube; corolla white to blue-orchid, banner erect, blade equal to claw, wings equal to keel; ovary glabrous. **Legumes** 30–50 × 4–8 mm. **2*n*** = 14.

Flowering Apr–Aug. Slopes of ponderosa pine, mixed conifer, spruce-fir and oak-juniper forests; 1000–2800 m; Ariz., N.Mex., Tex.; Mexico (Chihuahua, Sonora).

Lathyrus graminifolius is known from the eastern half of Arizona to the western two-thirds of New Mexico and in trans-Pecos Texas.

25. Lathyrus polyphyllus Nuttall in J. Torrey and A. Gray, Fl. N. Amer. 1: 274. 1838 • Leafy or Oregon pea [E]

Herbs perennial, from rhizome, glabrous. **Stems** angled, erect, sprawling, or climbing, basally branched 0–2 times, 4–8 dm. **Leaves** 11–16 cm; tendrils well developed; stipules ovate to lanceolate, 20–30 × 10–30 mm, nearly equal to distal leaflets; leaflets 10–16, scattered, blades ovate to lanceolate, 30–50 × 10–30 mm, surfaces glabrous. **Inflorescences** 8–12-flowered, 9–14 cm. **Flowers** 15–18 mm; calyx lobes unequal, lateral lobes linear-triangular, equal to or longer than tube; corolla blue-purple, banner erect, blade longer than claw, wings equal to keel; ovary glabrous. **Legumes** 40–70 × 4–9 mm. **2*n*** = 14.

Flowering Apr–Jul. Openings in coniferous forests; 0–1800 m; Calif., Oreg., Wash.

Lathyrus polyphyllus is known from in and west of the Cascade Range. *Lathyrus ecirrhosus* A. Heller (1904), not Philippi (1892), is an illegitimate name that pertains here.

26. Lathyrus glandulosus Broich, Madroño 33: 136, figs. 1, 2. 1986 • Sticky pea [E]

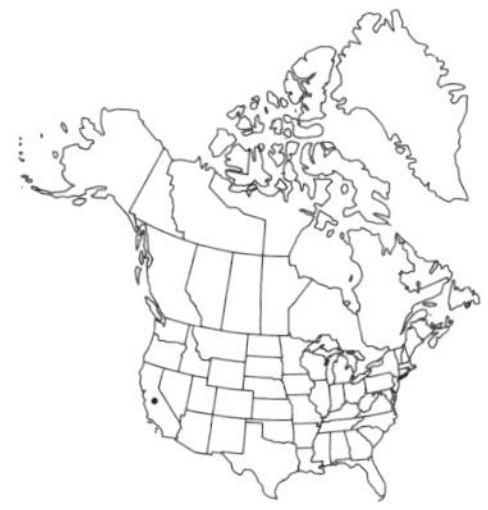

Herbs perennial, from rhizome, sparsely puberulent. **Stems** narrowly winged, erect, sprawling, or climbing, basally branched 0–2 times, 2–6 dm. **Leaves** 14–18 cm; tendrils well developed; stipules lanceolate, 10–20 × 1–5 mm, much smaller than leaflets; leaflets 14–18, scattered, blades ovate to lanceolate, 30–50 × 10–20 mm, surfaces pubescent with eglandular trichomes, glandular-pubescent abaxially. **Inflorescences** 7–12-flowered, 10–16 cm. **Flowers** 10–14 mm; calyx lobes unequal, lateral lobes linear-triangular, longer than tube; corolla blue-purple, banner erect, blade longer than claw, wings equal to keel; ovary densely glandular-pubescent. **Legumes** 30–50 × 6–8 mm. **2*n*** = 14.

Flowering May–Jun. Roadsides, talus slopes, oak woodlands; 0–800 m; Calif.

Lathyrus glandulosus is known only from Humboldt and northern Mendocino counties.

27. Lathyrus torreyi A. Gray, Proc. Amer. Acad. Arts 7: 337. 1868 • Redwood or Torrey's pea [E]

Herbs perennial, from rhizome, finely villous. **Stems** angled, erect to sprawling, basally branched 0–3 times, 1–4 dm. **Leaves** 2–7 cm; tendrils absent or mucronate; stipules lanceolate, 7–12 × 2–5 mm, much smaller than leaflets; leaflets 8–16, scattered, blades ovate to lanceolate, 5–15 × 3–10 mm, surfaces villous. **Inflorescences** 1- or 2-flowered, 0.5–3 cm. **Flowers** 8–12 mm; calyx lobes unequal, lateral lobes linear-triangular, longer than tube; corolla blue-purple, banner erect, blade equal to claw, wings longer than keel; ovary densely pubescent. **Legumes** 15–20 × 4–5 mm. **2*n*** = 14.

Flowering Apr–Jul. Open coniferous forests; 50–1500 m; Calif., Oreg., Wash.

Lathyrus torreyi is known from in and west of the Cascade Range; it is very rare in Washington.

28. Lathyrus littoralis (Nuttall) Endlicher in W. G. Walpers, Repert. Bot. Syst. 1: 722. 1842 • Gray beach or silky beach pea [E]

Astrophia littoralis Nuttall in J. Torrey and A. Gray, Fl. N. Amer. 1: 278. 1838

Herbs perennial, from rhizome, cinereous and densely villous throughout. **Stems** angled, sprawling, basally branched 0–4 times, 1–4 dm. **Leaves** 1–3 cm; tendrils flattened bristles; stipules ovate to lanceolate, 10–27 × 5–12 mm, often larger than leaflets; leaflets 4 or 6, paired, blades obovate to oblanceolate, 10–20 × 4–8 mm, surfaces densely villous. **Inflorescences** 4–8-flowered, 3–10 cm. **Flowers** 13–15 mm; calyx lobes equal, lateral lobes deltate, equal to or shorter than tube; corolla dark purple, banner erect, blade longer than claw, wings longer than keel; ovary densely pubescent. **Legumes** 20–30 × 9–13 mm. **2*n*** = 28.

Flowering Apr–Jun. Coastal sand dunes, deflation plain interdune areas; 0–15 m; B.C.; Calif., Oreg., Wash.

29. Lathyrus pusillus Elliott, Sketch Bot. S. Carolina 2: 223. 1823 • Singletary vetchling, tiny pea

Herbs annual, glabrate. **Stems** narrowly winged, sprawling or climbing, basally branched 0–4 times, 3–6 dm. **Leaves** 1–3 cm; tendrils well developed; stipules linear, 10–20 × 2–5 mm, equal to smaller leaflets; leaflets 2, blades linear, 15–60 × 2–8 mm, surfaces glabrous. **Inflorescences** terminal, 1- or 2-flowered, 2–4 cm. **Flowers** 7–10 mm; calyx lobes subequal, linear-triangular, usually longer than tube; corolla blue, banner erect, blade equal to claw, wings equal to keel; ovary glabrous. **Legumes** 30–50 × 2–4 mm. **2*n*** = 14.

Flowering Mar–May. Roadsides, pastures, prairies, open habitats; 0–800 m; Ala., Ark., Fla., Kans., La., Miss., Mo., N.C., Okla., Tex., Va.; South America (Argentina, Brazil, Chile, Ecuador, Paraguay, Peru, Uruguay).

Lathyrus pusillus, the only North American member of section *Notolathyrus*, a section centered in South America, is also the only annual species of *Lathyrus* native to North America. It is native to the southeastern United States; it has been cultivated as a forage crop in Oregon and occasionally escapes, but it has not become naturalized there.

30. Lathyrus tuberosus Linnaeus, Sp. Pl. 2: 732. 1753 • Earth-nut pea, tuberous vetchling, gesse tubéreuse [I] [W]

Herbs perennial, from tuber-bearing rhizome, glabrous. **Stems** not winged, sprawling, branched along trailing stems several times, 2–6 dm. **Leaves** 0.5–2 cm; tendrils well developed; stipules filiform-linear, 5–10 × 1–3 mm, much smaller than leaflets; leaflets 2, blades lanceolate, 10–40 × 5–15 mm, surfaces glabrous. **Inflorescences** 4–6-flowered, 6–15 cm. **Flowers** 8–12 mm; calyx lobes unequal, lateral lobes linear-triangular, equal to tube; corolla reddish, banner erect, blade longer than claw, wings equal to keel; ovary glabrous, style rotated 90° from ovary axis. **Legumes** 20–30(–40) × 3–6 mm. **2*n*** = 14.

Flowering Apr–Jun. Roadsides, meadows, fields; 50–100 m; introduced; Man., Ont., Que., Sask.; Conn., Ill., Ind., Iowa, Ky., Maine, Mass., Mich., Minn., Mo., Mont., Nebr., N.H., N.J., N.Y., Ohio, Pa., Tenn., Vt., Wash., W.Va., Wis.; Europe, w Asia; introduced also in Pacific Islands (New Zealand), Australia.

31. Lathyrus latifolius Linnaeus, Sp. Pl. 2: 733. 1753 • Everlasting or perennial sweet pea, gesse à feuilles larges [I] [W]

Herbs perennial, from rhizome, glabrous. **Stems** broadly winged, sprawling or climbing, basally branched 1–5 times, 8–20 dm. **Leaves** 2–5 cm, rachises broadly winged; tendrils well developed, branched; stipules lanceolate, 30–40 × 7–15 mm, at least 1/2 width of stem, much smaller than leaflets; leaflets 2, blades lanceolate-elliptic, 30–120 × 7–50 mm, surfaces glabrous. **Inflorescences** 5–15-flowered, 10–33 cm. **Flowers** 15–20 mm; calyx lobes unequal, lateral lobes linear-triangular, shorter than tube; corolla purple, magenta, pink, or white, banner erect, blade longer than claw, wings equal to keel; ovary densely glandular-pubescent, style rotated 90° from ovary axis. **Legumes** 50–110 × 5–10 mm. **2*n*** = 14.

Flowering May–Sep. Roadsides, disturbed areas; 50–2100 m; introduced; B.C., N.B., N.S., Ont., P.E.I., Que.; Ala., Ariz., Ark., Calif., Colo., Conn., Del., D.C., Ga., Idaho, Ill., Ind., Iowa, Kans., Ky., La., Maine, Md., Mass., Mich., Minn., Miss., Mo., Mont., Nebr., Nev., N.H., N.J., N.Mex., N.Y., N.C., Ohio, Okla., Oreg., Pa., R.I., S.C., Tenn., Tex., Utah, Vt., Va., Wash., W.Va., Wis., Wyo.; Europe; introduced also in Mexico, South

America (Argentina, Chile, Uruguay), Asia (China, Japan), n, e, s Africa, Pacific Islands (Hawaii, New Zealand), Australia.

Lathyrus latifolius is widely naturalized in North America and forms large thickets along roadsides, especially in the Pacific Coast states. M. J. W. Godt and J. L. Hamrick (1991) explored genetic variation within the species as it occurs in North America.

32. Lathyrus sylvestris Linnaeus, Sp. Pl. 2: 733. 1753
• Flat or narrow leaved everlasting or sweet pea, gesse des bois [I] [W]

Herbs perennial, from rhizome, glabrous. **Stems** broadly winged, sprawling or climbing, basally branched 1–3 times, 6–20 dm. **Leaves** 2–4 cm, rachises winged; tendrils well developed, branched; stipules linear, 10–30 × 1–3 mm, less than 1/2 width of stem, much smaller than leaflets; leaflets 2, blades linear, 20–150 × 4–24 mm, surfaces glabrous. **Inflorescences** 3–10-flowered, 9–27 cm. **Flowers** 12–17 mm; calyx lobes equal, lateral lobes deltate, usually shorter than tube; corolla red-purple, banner erect, blade longer than claw, wings equal to keel; ovary glandular-pubescent, style rotated 90° from ovary axis. **Legumes** 30–75 × 5–10 mm. **2*n*** = 14.

Flowering May–Aug. Roadsides, fencerows, waste ground; 0–1000 m; introduced; B.C., N.B., N.S., Ont., P.E.I., Que.; Ala., Ark., Calif., Colo., Conn., Ga., Idaho, Ind., Ky., Mass., Mich., Minn., Miss., Mo., Mont., N.H., N.Y., Oreg., Pa., R.I., S.C., Utah, Vt., Va., Wash., W.Va., Wis., Wyo.; Europe; introduced also in Mexico (Nuevo León), Pacific Islands (New Zealand).

Lathyrus sylvestris is similar to *L. latifolius* and intermediate populations are known to occur in Europe (M. Valero 1991). In North America, *L. sylvestris* is distinguished by its distinctly narrower stipules.

33. Lathyrus tingitanus Linnaeus, Sp. Pl. 2: 732. 1753
• Tangier pea [I] [W]

Herbs annual, glabrous. **Stems** broadly winged, climbing, basally branched 1–3 times, 8–20 dm. **Leaves** 2–4 cm, rachises winged as the stem; tendrils well developed; stipules lanceolate, 15–25 × 5–10 mm, smaller than leaflets; leaflets 2, blades ovate or obovate to lanceolate, 25–60 × 5–35 mm, surfaces glabrous. **Inflorescences** 1–3-flowered, 4–20 cm. **Flowers** 20–30 mm; calyx lobes equal, lateral lobes deltate, usually shorter than tube; corolla rose-purple, banner erect, blade longer than claw, wings longer than keel; ovary glabrous, style rotated 90° from ovary axis. **Legumes** 70–100 × 8–12 mm, narrowly winged on abaxial suture. **2*n*** = 14.

Flowering Apr–May. Disturbed areas; 0–1200 m; introduced; B.C.; Calif., Idaho, Oreg.; Europe; introduced also in Mexico (Oaxaca), nw Africa, Pacific Islands (Hawaii, New Zealand), Australia.

34. Lathyrus odoratus Linnaeus, Sp. Pl. 2: 732. 1753
• Sweet pea, gesse odorante [I] [W]

Herbs annual, glabrous or sparsely pubescent. **Stems** broadly winged, climbing, basally branched 1–3 times, 8–30 dm. **Leaves** 2–6 cm, rachises winged; tendrils well developed; stipules lanceolate, 10–25 × 2–6 mm, smaller than leaflets; leaflets 2, blades ovate or obovate, 15–50 × 10–40 mm, surfaces glabrous or sparsely pustulose-hirsute. **Inflorescences** 2–4-flowered, 10–20 cm. **Flowers** 20–25 mm; calyx lobes equal, lateral lobes linear-triangular to lanceolate, equal to tube; corolla white, pink, purple, violet, or blue, banner erect, blade much longer than claw, wings longer than keel; ovary densely pustulose-hirsute, style rotated 90° from ovary axis. **Legumes** 50–70 × 8–15 mm. **2*n*** = 14.

Flowering Apr–May. Disturbed areas; 50–400 m; introduced; Man., Nfld. and Labr. (Nfld.), Ont., Que.; Ariz., Calif., Conn., Ill., Ind., Ky., Maine, Mich., Ohio, Okla., S.C., Tenn., Tex., Va., W.Va.; Europe; introduced also in Mexico (México), Asia (China, India), n, e Africa, Pacific Islands (New Zealand), Australia.

Lathyrus odoratus is cultivated as an ornamental and is an occasional escape.

35. Lathyrus hirsutus Linnaeus, Sp. Pl. 2: 732. 1753
• Caley or rough pea, hairy vetchling [I] [W]

Herbs annual, glabrous, except legumes. **Stems** winged, sprawling, basally branched 0–several times, 2–10 dm. **Leaves** 0.8–3 cm, rachises narrowly winged; tendrils well developed; stipules linear, 5–10 × 1–3 mm, much smaller than leaflets; leaflets 2, blades lanceolate to linear, 25–75 × 5–12 mm, surfaces glabrous. **Inflorescences** 1- or 2-flowered, 4–15 cm. **Flowers** 8–10 mm; calyx lobes subequal, lateral lobes linear-triangular, longer than tube; corolla blue to red, banner erect, blade 2 times as long as claw, wings equal to keel; ovary densely pustulose-based pubescent, style rotated 90° from ovary axis. **Legumes** 25–40 × 5–10 mm. **2*n*** = 14.

Flowering Apr–Jul. Roadsides, pastures, railroad rights-of-way, disturbed areas; 0–1500 m; introduced;

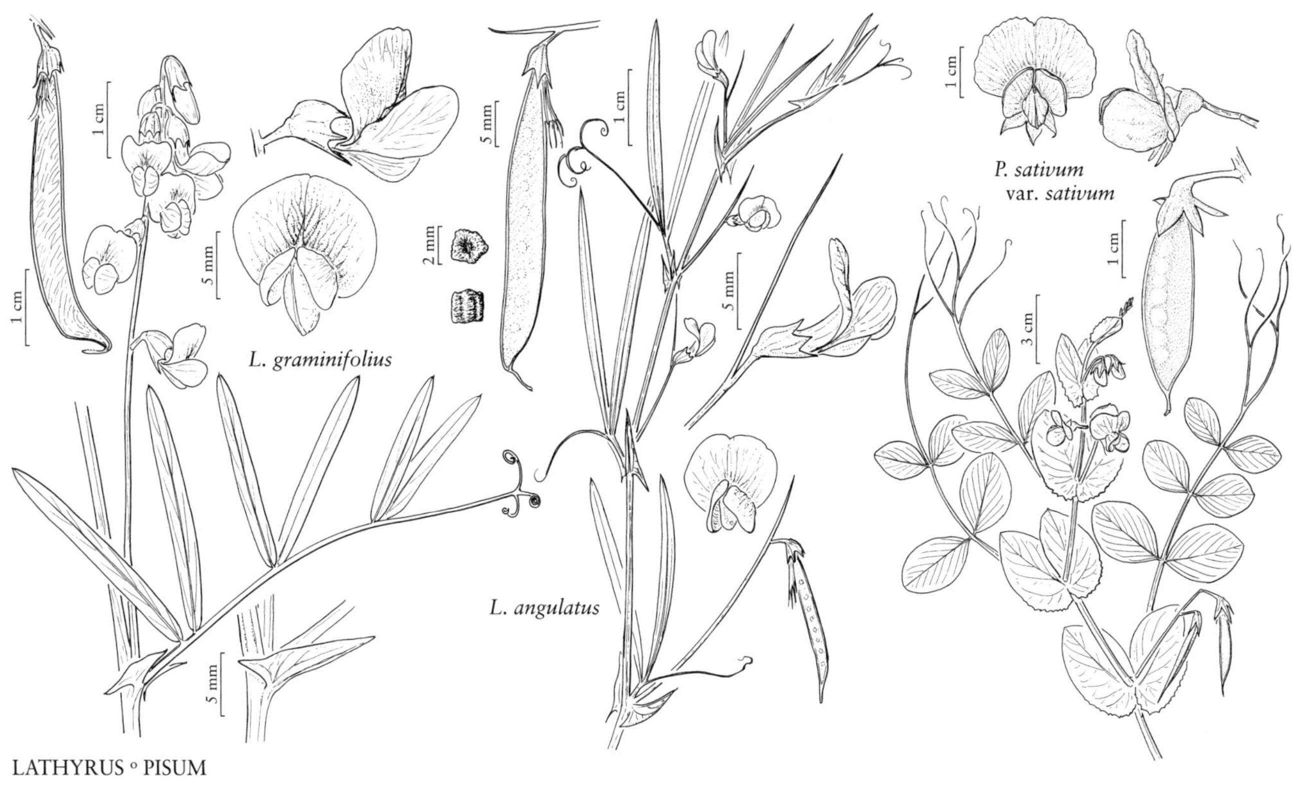

LATHYRUS ◦ PISUM

Ala., Ark., Calif., Fla., Ga., Ill., Ind., Ky., La., Md., Mich., Miss., Mo., N.Mex., N.C., Okla., Oreg., S.C., Tenn., Tex., Va.; Europe; introduced also in South America (Argentina, Chile, Uruguay), n, e Africa.

Lathyrus hirsutus is cultivated as a forage crop.

36. Lathyrus cicera Linnaeus, Sp. Pl. 2: 730. 1753
• Red vetch or pea [I] [W]

Herbs annual, glabrous. **Stems** winged, sprawling or climbing, basally branched 0–3 times, 2–10 dm. **Leaves** 0.5–2 cm, rachises winged as the stem; tendrils well developed; stipules lanceolate, 10–20 × 2–6 mm, sometimes as wide as leaflets; leaflets 2, blades linear, 20–50 × 1–6 mm, surfaces glabrous. **Inflorescences** usually 1-flowered, 1–4 cm. **Flowers** 10–12 mm; calyx lobes equal, lateral lobes linear-triangular, 2–3 times longer than tube; corolla reddish purple, banner erect, blade equal to claw, wings equal to keel; ovary glabrous, style rotated 90° from ovary axis. **Legumes** 20–40 × 5–10 mm, broadly winged on abaxial suture. **2*n*** = 14.

Flowering Apr–May. Disturbed areas; 50–600 m; introduced; Calif.; Europe; introduced also in South America (Argentina, Uruguay).

Lathyrus cicera is cultivated as an ornamental and occasionally escapes.

37. Lathyrus pratensis Linnaeus, Sp. Pl. 2: 733. 1753
• Meadow pea, gesse des prés [I] [W]

Herbs perennial, from rhizome, pubescent. **Stems** not winged, sprawling or climbing, branched along trailing stems several times, 4–10 dm. **Leaves** 1–4 cm; tendrils bristlelike to well developed; stipules ovate-lanceolate, 5–38 × 3–15 mm, sometimes equal to leaflets; leaflets 2, blades lanceolate, 5–40 × 1–10 mm, surfaces glabrous or pubescent. **Inflorescences** 5–10-flowered, 4–16 cm. **Flowers** 8–12 mm; calyx lobes unequal, lateral lobes linear-triangular, longer than tube; corolla yellow, banner erect, blade equal to claw, wings equal to keel; ovary glabrous or pubescent. **Legumes** 15–35 × 5–7 mm. **2*n*** = 9, 14, 16, 21, 28, 42.

Flowering Apr–Jul. Roadsides, fencerows, meadows; 50–150 m; introduced; Greenland; B.C., N.B., Nfld. and Labr. (Nfld.), N.S., Ont., P.E.I., Que.; Alaska, Conn., Ill., Maine, Mass., Mich., N.H., N.J., N.Y., Ohio, Vt., Wash., Wis.; Europe; introduced also in Asia (China, India, Japan), Pacific Islands (New Zealand), Australia.

Lathyrus pratensis is common throughout Europe where it is a variable and taxonomically difficult group (P. W. Ball 1968b; K. Brunsberg 1977).

38. Lathyrus aphaca Linnaeus, Sp. Pl. 2: 729. 1753 • Yellow pea [I]

Herbs annual, glabrous. **Stems** not winged, erect or climbing, basally branched 1–several times, 2–6 dm. **Leaves** reduced to tendrils, unbranched or branched, 1–4 cm; stipules ovate, 10–35 × 10–25 mm, base hastate, margins entire; leaflets 0. **Inflorescences** 1-flowered, 2–4 cm. **Flowers** 6–10 mm; calyx lobes equal, lateral lobes broadly lanceolate, longer than tube; corolla yellow, banner erect, blade equal to claw, wings equal to keel; ovary glabrous. **Legumes** 15–30 × 5–7 mm. **2*n*** = 14.

Flowering May–Jun. Roadsides, waste areas; 0–700 m; introduced; Ala., Ark., Calif., Ky., La., Md., Nebr., Oreg., Pa., Tenn., Tex., Wash.; Eurasia; introduced also in n, e Africa.

39. Lathyrus angulatus Linnaeus, Sp. Pl. 2: 731. 1753 • Angled pea [F] [I] [W]

Herbs annual, glabrous. **Stems** angled, erect, sprawling, or climbing, basally branched 1–several times, 1–5 dm. **Leaves** 0.3–1 cm; tendrils reduced to bristles on proximal leaves, well developed distally; stipules lanceolate, 10–20 × 2–4 mm, as wide as leaflets; leaflets 2, blades linear, 20–70 × 1–4 mm, surfaces glabrous. **Inflorescences** 1-flowered, 2–7 cm, prolonged beyond flower into tendril-like structure. **Flowers** 8–10 mm; calyx lobes equal, lateral lobes deltate, shorter than tube; corolla blue-purple, banner erect, blade equal to claw, wings equal to keel; ovary glabrous. **Legumes** 20–40 × 3–5 mm, with indistinct reticulate venation. **2*n*** = 14.

Flowering Mar–Jun. Disturbed areas, waste ground; 0–1000 m; introduced; Calif., Oreg., Wash.; Europe; introduced also in Australia.

40. Lathyrus sphaericus Retzius, Observ. Bot. 3: 39. 1783 • Grass pea [I]

Herbs annual, glabrous. **Stems** not winged, erect, sprawling or climbing, basally branched 1–several times, 2–5 dm. **Leaves** 0.5–1.5 cm; tendrils bristlelike to 4 cm, often unbranched; stipules linear, 10–15 × 2–10 mm, much smaller than leaflets; leaflets 2, blades linear, 20–90 × 2–10 mm, surfaces glabrous. **Inflorescences** 1-flowered, 1–2 cm, prolonged beyond flower into a bristle. **Flowers** 6–10 mm; calyx lobes subequal, lateral lobes lanceolate, longer than tube; corolla reddish orange, banner erect, blade longer than or equal to claw, wings equal to keel; ovary glabrous. **Legumes** 40–60 × 4–6 mm, longitudinal venation prominent. **2*n*** = 14.

Flowering Apr–Jul. Roadsides, pastures, waste areas; 0–500 m; introduced; B.C.; Calif., Oreg., Wash.; Europe; introduced also in Mexico, Asia, Pacific Islands (New Zealand), Australia.

41. Lathyrus nissolia Linnaeus, Sp. Pl. 2: 729. 1753 • Grass pea [I]

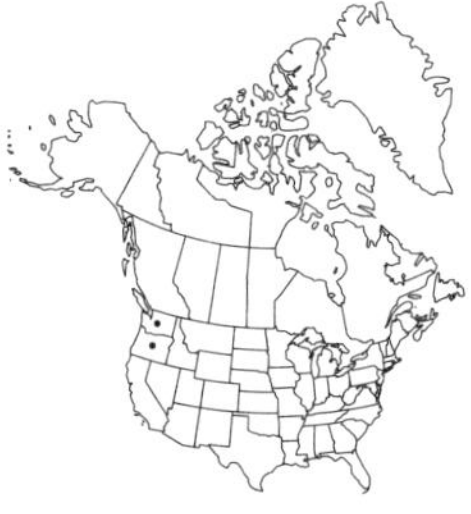

Herbs annual, glabrous. **Stems** not winged, erect or sprawling, basally branched 1–several times, 1–8 dm. **Leaves** phyllodic; tendrils absent; stipules filiform-linear, 1–2 × 1 mm, much smaller than phyllode, base semisaggitate; leaflets 0; phyllodes flattened, linear, and grass-like, 80–140 × 4–10 mm, glabrous. **Inflorescences** 1- or 2-flowered, 6–10 cm. **Flowers** 8–10 mm; calyx lobes equal, lateral lobes deltate, equal to tube; corolla crimson, banner erect, blade equal to claw, wings equal to keel; ovary glabrous or pubescent. **Legumes** 30–60 × 2–4 mm. **2*n*** = 14.

Flowering Apr–May. Disturbed areas, grassy meadows; 50–150 m; introduced; Oreg., Wash.; Europe; introduced also in n Africa.

153. PISUM Linnaeus, Sp. Pl. 2: 727. 1753; Gen. Pl. ed. 5, 324. 1754 • Pea [Latin *pisum* or Greek *pison*, pea] [I]

Steven L. Broich

Herbs, annual, unarmed. **Stems** erect or sprawling, ribbed, branched, glabrous. **Leaves** alternate, even-pinnate; stipules present, foliose, usually larger than leaflets, without nectariferous patch; rachis winged, usually terminating in branched tendril; petiolate; leaflets [2 or]4 or 6[or 8], opposite, folded in bud, stipels absent, blades usually becoming smaller from base of rachis, margins entire or dentate, surfaces glabrous. **Inflorescences** 1–3[or 4]-flowered, axillary, racemes, erect or lax; bracts present, caducous, bracteoles absent. **Flowers** papilionaceous; calyx campanulate, base symmetric, lobes 5, equal, lanceolate, exceeding tube; corolla white or bicolored (banner lilac, wings reddish purple), 15–30 mm; stamens 10, diadelphous; anthers basifixed; ovary glabrous or pubescent; style abaxially compressed, folded longitudinally, laterally pubescent. **Fruits** legumes, sessile, terete, oblong-linear, dehiscent, non-septate, margins usually obscure, splitting, glabrous; valves twisted after dehiscence. **Seeds** 3–10, globose or angular, smooth or papillose, sometimes wrinkled. x = 7.

Species 3 (1 in the flora): introduced; s Europe, sw Asia, n Africa; introduced also in n Europe, n, c Asia.

Pisum consists of three closely related species (O. E. Kosterin and V. S. Bogdanova 2008; P. Smýkal et al. 2011). *Pisum sativum* includes both culinary and forage varieties, which are widely cultivated in North America.

Recent phylogenetic studies have placed *Pisum* consistently within the Vicieae (M. F. Wojciechowski et al. 2004; H. Schaefer et al. 2012).

SELECTED REFERENCES Kosterin, O. E. and V. S. Bogdanova. 2008. Relationship of wild and cultivated forms of *Pisum* L. as inferred from an analysis of three markers, of the plastid, mitochondrial and nuclear genomes. Genet. Resources Crop Evol. 55: 735–755. Smýkal, P. et al. 2011. Phylogeny, phylogeography and genetic diversity of the *Pisum* genus. Pl. Genet. Resources Charact. Utiliz. 9: 4–18.

1. Pisum sativum Linnaeus, Sp. Pl. 2: 727. 1753 F I

Subspecies 3 (1 in the flora): introduced; s Europe, c, s, w Asia (Middle East), n Africa.

1a. Pisum sativum Linnaeus subsp. **sativum** • Common or sugar pea F I

Stems 1–20 dm, branched basally 1–4 times. **Leaves** 5–10 cm, flattened, tendrils well developed; stipules ovate to lanceolate, semisagittate, 15–80 × 10–40 mm, usually larger than leaflets; leaflet blades ovate to lanceolate, 20–50 × 15–30 mm. **Racemes** 3–10 cm. **Flowers** 15–30 mm; corollas white or bicolored. **Legumes** 50–90 × 15–20 mm. **Seeds** usually yellow or green, sometimes mottled, 4–12 mm diam.

Varieties 2 (2 in the flora): introduced; s Europe, c, s, w Asia (Middle East), n Africa.

1. Corollas white; seeds 8–12 mm, globose, not mottled . . . . 1a.1. *Pisum sativum* var. *sativum*
1. Corollas bicolored (banner lilac, wings darker reddish purple); seeds 4–8 mm, angular, sometimes mottled . . . . 1a.2. *Pisum sativum* var. *arvense*

1a.1. Pisum sativum Linnaeus var. **sativum** • Garden pea, pois cultivé F I

Corollas white. **Seeds** not mottled, globose, 6–12 mm. **2*n*** = 14.

Flowering May–Jul. Disturbed areas; 0–500 m; introduced; Greenland; Man., Ont., Que.; Calif., Conn., Fla., Ill., Ky., La., Maine, Mich., Mo., N.H., N.Y., N.C., Okla., Pa., S.C., Utah, Va., Wash.; c, s Asia (Middle East); nw Africa.

Variety *sativum* is cultivated as a cool-season garden vegetable crop.

1a.2. Pisum sativum Linnaeus var. **arvense** (Linnaeus) Poiret in J. Lamarck et al., Encycl. 5: 456. 1804 • Field pea I

Pisum arvense Linnaeus, Sp. Pl. 2: 727. 1753

Corollas bicolored (banner lilac, wings darker reddish purple). **Seeds** sometimes mottled, angular, 4–8 mm. **2*n*** = 14.

Flowering Apr–Jul. Ruderal habitats; 0–500 m; introduced; Alta., Man., Sask.; Idaho, Kans., Mont., N.Dak., Oreg., S.Dak., Wash., Wis.; c, s, w Asia; nw Africa.

Variety *arvense* is cultivated for soil improvement or as a seed crop for export.

Literature Cited

Robert W. Kiger, Editor

This is a consolidated list of all works cited in volume 11, whether as selected references, in text, or in nomenclatural contexts. In citations of articles, both here and in the taxonomic treatments, and also in nomenclatural citations, the titles of serials are rendered in the forms recommended in G. D. R. Bridson and E. R. Smith (1991). When those forms are abbreviated, as most are, cross references to the corresponding full serial titles are interpolated here alphabetically by abbreviated form. In nomenclatural citations (only), book titles are rendered in the abbreviated forms recommended in F. A. Stafleu and R. S. Cowan (1976–1988) and Stafleu et al. (1992–2009). Here, those abbreviated forms are indicated parenthetically following the full citations of the corresponding works, and cross references to the full citations are interpolated in the list alphabetically by abbreviated form. Two or more works published in the same year by the same author or group of coauthors will be distinguished uniquely and consistently throughout all volumes of *Flora of North America* by lower-case letters (b, c, d, ...) suffixed to the date for the second and subsequent works in the set. The suffixes are assigned in order of editorial encounter and do not reflect chronological sequence of publication. The first work by any particular author or group from any given year carries the implicit date suffix "a"; thus, the sequence of explicit suffixes begins with "b". There may be citations in this list that have dates suffixed "b," "c," "d," etc. but that are not preceded by citations of "[a]," "b," and/or "c," etc. works for that year. In such cases, the missing "[a]," "b," and/or "c," etc. works are ones cited (and encountered first from) elsewhere in the *Flora* that are not pertinent in this volume.

Abbott, J. R. and W. S. Judd. 2000. Floristic inventory of the Waccasassa Bay State Preserve, Levy County, Florida. Rhodora 102: 439–513.

Abh. Königl. Ges. Wiss. Göttingen = Abhandlungen der Königlichen Gesellschaft der Wissenschaften zu Göttingen.

Abh. Königl. Ges. Wiss. Göttingen, Math.-Phys. Kl. = Abhandlungen der Königlichen Gesellschaft der Wissenschaften zu Göttingen. Mathematisch-physikalische Klasse.

Abh. Math.-Phys. Cl. Königl. Bayer. Akad. Wiss. = Abhandlungen der Mathematisch-physikalischen Classe der Königlich bayerischen Akademie der Wissenschaften.

Abrams, L. 1904. Flora of Los Angeles and Vicinity. Stanford. (Fl. Los Angeles)

Abrams, L. 1917. Flora of Los Angeles and Vicinity, ed. 3. Stanford. (Fl. Los Angeles ed. 3)

Abrams, L. 1944b. *Astragalus.* In: L. Abrams and R. S. Ferris. 1923–1960. Illustrated Flora of the Pacific States: Washington, Oregon, and California. 4 vols. Stanford. Vol. 2, pp. 562–611.

Abrams, L. and R. S. Ferris. 1923–1960. Illustrated Flora of the Pacific States: Washington, Oregon, and California. 4 vols. Stanford. (Ill. Fl. Pacific States)

Acta Acad. Sci. Imp. Petrop. = Acta Academiae Scientiarum Imperialis Petropolitanae.

Acta Helv. Phys.-Math. = Acta Helvetica, Physico-mathematico-anatomico-botanico-medica.

Adanson, M. 1763[–1764]. Familles des Plantes. 2 vols. Paris. [Vol. 1, 1764; vol. 2, 1763.] (Fam. Pl.)

Adema, F. 2003. Notes on Malesian Fabaceae (Leguminosae-Papilionoideae): 10. The genus *Alysicarpus*. Blumea 48: 145–152.

Advances Legume Syst. 3—See: C. H. Stirton 1987

Agardh, J. G. 1835. Synopsis Generis *Lupini*.... 3 parts. Lund. [3 dissertations paged consecutively.] (Syn. Lupini)

Agric. Res. (Washington, DC) = Agricultural Research.

Agron. J. = Agronomy Journal.

Ahlquist, T. K. 2012. A Morphological Analysis of the *Trifolium amabile* Kunth Species Complex in North America. M.S. thesis. Miami University.

Aiken, S. G. et al. 2007. Flora of the Canadian Arctic Archipelago.... Ottawa. [CD-ROM.]

Aiton, W. 1789. Hortus Kewensis; or, a Catalogue of the Plants Cultivated in the Royal Botanic Garden at Kew. 3 vols. London. (Hort. Kew.)

Aiton, W. and W. T. Aiton. 1810–1813. Hortus Kewensis; or a Catalogue of the Plants Cultivated in the Royal Botanic Garden at Kew. 5 vols. London. (Hortus Kew.)

Akulova, Z. V., T. V. Kuznetsova, and D. D. Sokoloff. 2000. On inflorescence structure in the genus *Anthyllis* (Papilionaceae, Loteae). Bot. Zhurn. (Moscow & Leningrad) 85: 12–25.

Alexander, J. A. 2005. The taxonomic status of *Astragalus mokiacensis* (Fabaceae), a species endemic to the southwestern United States. Brittonia 57: 320–323.

Ali, S. I. 1958. Revision of the genus *Indigofera* L. from W. Pakistan and N. W. Himalayas. Bot. Not. 3: 543–577.

Ali, S. I. 1977. Papilionaceae. In: E. Nasir and S. I. Ali, eds. 1970+. Flora of West Pakistan. 219+ nos. Karachi and Islamabad. No. 100.

Allan, G. J. et al. 2003. Molecular phylogenetic analyses of tribe Loteae (Leguminosae): Implications for classification and biogeography. In: B. B. Klitgaard and A. Bruneau, eds. 2003. Advances in Legume Systematics. Part 10. Kew. Pp. 371–393.

Allan, G. J. and J. M. Porter. 2000. Tribal delimitation and phylogenetic relationships of Loteae and Coronilleae (Faboideae: Fabaceae) with special reference to *Lotus:* Evidence from nuclear ribosomal ITS sequences. Amer. J. Bot. 87: 1871–1881.

Allan, H. H. et al. 1961–2000. Flora of New Zealand. 5 vols. Wellington, Christchurch, and Lincoln.

Allen, O. N. and E. K. Allen. 1981. The Leguminosae: A Source Book of Characteristics, Uses, and Nodulation. Madison.

Allioni, C. 1785. Flora Pedemontana sive Enumeratio Methodica Stirpium Indigenarum Pedemontii. 3 vols. Turin. (Fl. Pedem.)

Allioni, C. 1789. Auctuarium ad Floram Pedemontanum.... Turin. (Auct. Fl. Pedem.)

Allison, C. D. 1984. Locoweeds and Livestock Poisoning. Las Cruces.

Allred, K. W. and R. D. Ivey. 2012. Flora Neomexicana III: An Illustrated Identification Manual. Raleigh.

Alston, R. E. and B. L. Turner. 1962.. New techniques in analysis of complex natural hybridization. Proc. Natl. Acad. Sci. U.S.A. 48: 130–137.

Amer. Hort. (Alexandria) = American Horticulturalist.

Amer. J. Bot. = American Journal of Botany.

Amer. J. Sci. Arts = American Journal of Science, and Arts.

Amer. Midl. Naturalist = American Midland Naturalist; Devoted to Natural History, Primarily That of the Prairie States.

Amer. Naturalist = American Naturalist....

American Peanut Research and Education Association, eds. 1973. Peanuts—Culture and Uses. Stillwater.

Amoen. Acad.—See: C. Linnaeus 1749[–1769]

Amussen, C. B. and A. Liston. 1998. Chloroplast DNA characters, phylogeny, and classification of *Lathyrus* (Fabaceae). Amer. J. Bot. 85: 387–401.

Anal. Key West Coast Bot.—See: V. Rattan 1887

Anales Inst. Biol. Univ. Nac. Autón. México, Bot. = Anales del Instituto de Biológia de la Universidad Nacional Autónoma de México. Série Botánica.

Anales Jard. Bot. Madrid = Anales del Jardín Botánico de Madrid.

Anales Univ. Chile, I, Mem. Ci. Lit. = Anales de la Universidad de Chile. I. Memorias Cientificas i Literarias.

Anderson, L. C. 1988. Noteworthy plants from north Florida. III. Sida 13: 93–100.

Andrews, M. and M. E. Andrews. 2017. Specificity in legume-rhizobia symbioses. Int. J. Molec. Sci. 18(705): 1–39.

Angiosperm Phylogeny Group. 2016. An update of the Angiosperm Phylogeny Group classification for the orders and families of flowering plants: APG IV. Bot. J. Linn. Soc. 181: 1–20.

Ann. Bot. Fenn. = Annales Botanici Fennici.

Ann. Bot. (Oxford) = Annals of Botany. (Oxford.)

Ann. Lyceum Nat. Hist. New York = Annals of the Lyceum of Natural History of New York.

Ann. Missouri Bot. Gard. = Annals of the Missouri Botanical Garden.

Ann. Mus. Bot. Lugduno-Batavi = Annales Musei Botanici Lugduno-Batavi.

Ann. New York Acad. Sci. = Annals of the New York Academy of Sciences.

Ann. Sci. Nat., Bot. = Annales des Sciences Naturelles. Botanique.

Ann. Sci. Nat. (Paris) = Annales des Sciences Naturelles. (Paris.)

Ann. Soc. Linn. Lyon = Annales de la Société Linnéenne de Lyon.

Anonymous. 2000. Proceedings of the 2000 Conference on Hazardous Waste Research. Manhattan, Kans.

Aplaca, J. 2012. Non-native species new to Texas with comments on other species. Phytoneuron 2012-95: 1–6.

App. Parry J. Sec. Voy.—See: W. E. Parry 1825

Appl. Engin. Agric. = Applied Engineering in Agriculture.

Arambarri, A. M. 2000. A cladistic analysis of the New World species of *Lotus* L. (Fabaceae, Loteae). Cladistics 16: 283–297.

Arbor. Kórnickie = Arboretum Kórnickie.

Arbust. Amer.—See: H. Marshall 1785

Arcangeli, G. 1882. Compendio della Flora Italiana.... Turin. (Comp. Fl. Ital.)

Ark. Bot. = Arkiv för Botanik.

Arnoldia (Jamaica Plain) = Arnoldia; a Continuation of the Bulletin of Popular Information.

Ashe, W. W. 1922. The eastern shrubby species of *Robinia.* J. Elisha Mitchell Sci. Soc. 37: 175–177

Astragalogia—See: A. P. de Candolle 1802

Atlantic J. = Atlantic Journal, and Friend of Knowledge.

Auct. Fl. Pedem.—See: C. Allioni 1789

Austral. J. Bot. = Australian Journal of Botany.

Austral. Syst. Bot. = Australian Systematic Botany.

Awmack, C. S. and J. M. Lock. 2002. The genus *Alhagi* (Leguminosae: Papilionoideae) in the Middle East. Kew Bull. 57: 435–443.

Axelrod, D. I. 1982. Age and origin of the Monterey endemic area. Madroño 29: 127–147.

B. M. C. Biol. = B M C Biology.

B. M. C. Evol. Biol. = B M C Evolutionary Biology.

Backer, C. A. and D. F. van Slooten. 1924. Geillustreerd Handboek der Javaansche Theeonkruiden.... Batavia. (Geill. Handb. Jav. Theeonkr.)

Badr, A., H. H. El-Shazly, and L. E. Watson. 2008. Origin and ancestry of Egyptian clover (*Trifolium alexandrinum* L.) as revealed by AFLP markers. Genet. Resources Crop Evol. 55: 21–31.

Baileya = Baileya; a Quarterly Journal of Horticultural Taxonomy. Baker, E. G. 1926–1930. The Leguminosae of Tropical Africa. 3 parts in 1 vol. Ghent. [Parts paged consecutively.]

Baker, M. J. and W. M. Williams. 1987. White Clover. Wallingford.

Ball, P. W. 1968. *Vicia.* In: T. G. Tutin et al., eds. 1964–1980. Flora Europaea. 5 vols. Cambridge. Vol. 2, pp. 129–136.

Ball, P. W. 1968b. *Lathyrus.* In: T. G. Tutin et al., eds. 1964–1980. Flora Europaea. 5 vols. Cambridge. Vol. 2, pp. 136–143.

Ballenger, J. A. 1992. A Biosystematic Revision of the Genus *Cercis* (Leguminosae) in North America. Ph.D. dissertation. Miami University.

Barlow, R. et al. 2000. Lead hyperaccumulation by *Sesbania drummondii.* In: Anonymous. 2000. Proceedings of the 2000 Conference on Hazardous Waste Research. Manhattan, Kans. Pp. 112–114.

Barneby, R. C. 1944. Pugillus *Astragalorum* alter. Proc. Calif. Acad. Sci., ser. 4, 25: 147–169.

Barneby, R. C. 1945. Pugillus *Astragalorum* IV. The section *Diplocystium.* Leafl. W. Bot. 4: 65–147.

Barneby, R. C. 1947. Pugillus *Astragalorum* VI. Notes on section *Drabellae.* Leafl. W. Bot. 5: 1–9.

Barneby, R. C. 1947b. Pugillus *Astragalorum* VII. A revision of the *Argophylli.* Amer. Midl. Naturalist 37: 421–516.

Barneby, R. C. 1947c. Pugillus *Astragalorum* VIII. Notes on the section *Genistoidei.* Leafl. W. Bot. 5: 25–35.

Barneby, R. C. 1949. Pugillus *Astragalorum* X. New species, varieties, and combinations. Amer. Midl. Naturalist 41: 496–502.

Barneby, R. C. 1952. Pugillus *Astragalorum* XIV. Notes on sect. *Lonchocarpi.* Leafl. W. Bot. 6: 172–177.

Barneby, R. C. 1952b. A revision of the North American species of *Oxytropis* DC. Proc. Calif. Acad. Sci., ser. 4, 27: 177–312.

Barneby, R. C. 1957. Pugillus *Astragalorum* XX. Notes on *A. mulfordiae* and some close relatives. Leafl. W. Bot. 8: 120–125.

Barneby, R. C. 1964. Atlas of North American *Astragalus.* Mem. New York Bot. Gard. 13.

Barneby, R. C. 1977. *Errazurizia.* Mem. New York Bot. Gard. 27: 13–21.

Barneby, R. C. 1977b. *Marina.* Mem. New York Bot. Gard. 27: 55–135.

Barneby, R. C. 1977c. *Dalea.* Mem. New York Bot. Gard. 27: 135–592.

Barneby, R. C. 1977d. *Psorothamnus.* Mem. New York Bot. Gard. 27: 21–54.

Barneby, R. C. 1977e. Dragma hippomanicum III. Novitates Californicae. Brittonia 29: 376–381.

Barneby, R. C. 1984. Dragma hippomanicum X. *Astragali* (Leguminosae) Nevadenses novi criticive, singulo Peruviano adjecto. Brittonia 36: 167–173.

Barneby, R. C. 1989. Fabales. In: A. Cronquist et al. 1972–2017. Intermountain Flora. Vascular Plants of the Intermountain West, U.S.A. 7 vols. in 9. New York and London. Vol. 3, part B.

Barneby, R. C. 1991. Sensitivae censitae. A description of the genus *Mimosa* L. (Mimosaceae) in the New World. Mem. New York Bot. Gard. 65: 1–835.

Barneby, R. C. 1998. Silk tree, guanacaste, monkey's earring. A generic system for the synandrous Mimosaceae of the Americas. Part III. *Calliandra.* Mem. New York Bot. Gard. 74(3): 1–223.

Barneby, R. C. and J. W. Grimes. 1996. Silk tree, guanacaste, monkey's earring: A generic system for the synandrous Mimosaceae of the Americas. Part I. *Abarema, Albizia,* and allies. Mem. New York Bot. Gard. 74(1): 1–292.

Barneby, R. C. and J. W. Grimes. 1997. Silk tree, guanacaste, monkey's earring: A generic system for the synandrous Mimosaceae of the Americas. Part II. *Pithecellobium.* Mem. New York Bot. Gard. 74(2): 2–36.

Barneby, R. C. and S. L. Welsh. 1996. *Astragalus laxmannii* Jacquin (Leguminosae) in North America. Great Basin Naturalist 56: 85–86.

Bartalini, B. 1776. Catalogo delle Piante...di Siena. Siena. (Cat. Piante Siena)

Bartgis, R. L. 1985. Rediscovery of *Trifolium stoloniferum* Muhl. ex A. Eaton. Rhodora 87: 425–429.

Barton, W. P. C. 1818. Compendium Florae Philadelphicae.... 2 vols. Philadelphia. (Comp. Fl. Philadelph.)

Bartonia = Bartonia; a Botanical Annual.

Basic Appl. Ecol. = Basic and Applied Ecology.

Baskin, J. M. et al. 1998. Effect of salinity on germination and viability of nondormant seeds of the federal-threatened species *Aeschynomene virginica* (Fabaceae). J. Torrey Bot. Soc. 125: 246–248.

Baskin, J. M. and C. C. Baskin. 2005. Ecology of two geographically restricted *Astragalus* species (Fabaceae), *A. bibullatus* and *A. tennesseensis*, of the eastern United States. Brittonia 57: 345–353.

Baskin, J. M., C. C. Baskin, and R. W. Tyndall. 2005. Studies on dormancy, germination, and survival of seeds buried in soil of a rare plant species *Aeschynomene virginica* (Fabaceae). Nat. Areas J. 25: 147–155.

Basurto-Peña, F. et al. 1999. Use and nutritive value of talet beans, *Amphicarpaea bracteata* (Linnaeus) Fernald (Fabaceae: Phaseoleae) as human food in Puebla, Mexico. Econ. Bot. 53: 427–434.

Batlle, I. and J. Tous. 1997. Carob Tree, *Ceratonia siliqua* L. Gatersleben and Rome.

Battandier, J. A. et al. 1888–1897. Flore de l'Algérie.... 3 vols. Algiers and Paris. (Fl. Algérie)

Bauchan, G. R. and J. H. Elgin. 1984. A new chromosome number for the genus *Medicago*. Crop Sci. (Madison) 24: 193–195.

Beck, L. C. 1833. Botany of the Northern and Middle States; or, a Description of the Plants found in the United States, North of Virginia.... Albany. (Bot. North. Middle States)

Beih. Bot. Centralbl. = Beihefte zum Botanischen Centralblatt. Original Arbeiten.

Bena, G. 2001. Molecular phylogeny supports the morphologically based taxonomic transfer of the "medicagoid" *Trigonella* species to the genus *Medicago* L. Pl. Syst. Evol. 229: 217–236.

Bena, G. et al. 1998. Molecular phylogenetic approach for studying life-history evolution: The ambiguous example of the genus *Medicago* L. Proc. Roy. Soc. Biol. Sci. Ser. B 265: 1141–1151.

Benson, L. D. 1940. Taxonomic contributions. Amer. J. Bot. 27: 186–190.

Bentham, G. 1837. Commentationes de Leguminosarum Generibus. Vienna. (Comm. Legum. Gen.)

Bentham, G. 1839[–1857]. Plantas Hartwegianas Imprimis Mexicanas.... London. [Issued by gatherings with consecutive signatures and pagination.] (Pl. Hartw.)

Bentham, G. 1842. Notes on Mimoseae, with a short synopsis of species. Hooker's J. Bot. Kew Gard. Misc. 4: 323–416.

Bentham, G. 1844[–1846]. The Botany of the Voyage of H.M.S. Sulphur, under the Command of Captain Sir Edward Belcher...during the Years 1836–1842. 6 parts. London. [Parts paged consecutively.] (Bot. Voy. Sulphur)

Bentham, G. 1846. Notes on Mimoseae, with a synopsis of species. Tribe III. Acacieae. London J. Bot. 5: 75–108.

Bentham, G. 1863–1878. Flora Australiensis.... 7 vols. London.

Bentham, G. 1875. Revision of the suborder Mimoseae. Trans. Linn. Soc. London 30: 335–664.

Bentham, G. and J. D. Hooker. 1862–1883. Genera Plantarum ad Exemplaria Imprimis in Herbariis Kewensibus Servata Definita. 3 vols. London. (Gen. Pl.)

Berger, C. A. et al. 1958. Cytotaxonomic studies in the Leguminosae. Bull. Torrey Bot. Club 85: 405–414.

Beskr. Guin. Pl.—See: H. C. F. Schumacher 1827

Besser, W. S. J. G. von. 1821. Enumeratio Plantarum.... Vilna. (Enum. Pl.)

Bigelow, J. 1824. Florula Bostoniensis. A Collection of Plants of Boston and Its Vicinity..., ed. 2. Boston. (Fl. Boston. ed. 2)

Biltmore Bot. Stud. = Biltmore Botanical Studies; a Journal of Botany Embracing Papers by the Director and Associates of the Biltmore Herbarium.

Biochem. Syst. & Ecol. = Biochemical Systematics and Ecology.

Biol. Invasions = Biological Invasions.

Biol. Skr. = Biologiske Skrifter.

Blair, M. W., W. Pantoja, and L. C. Muñoz. 2012. First use of microsatellite markers in a large collection of cultivated and wild accessions of tepary bean (*Phaseolus acutifolius* A. Gray). Theor. Appl. Genet. 125: 1137–1147.

Blumea = Blumea; Tidjschrift voor die Systematiek en die Geografie der Planten (A Journal of Plant Taxonomy and Plant Geography).

Boe, A. and R. Wynia. 1985. Seed predation, seedling emergence, and rhizome characteristics of American licorice. J. Range Managem. 38: 400–402.

Boissier, P. E. 1839–1845. Voyage Botanique dans le Midi de l'Espagne pendant l'Année 1837. Paris. (Voy. Bot. Espagne)

Bol. Soc. Argent. Bot. = Boletín de la Sociedad Argentina de Botánica.

Bol. Soc. Brot. = Boletim da Sociedade Broteriana.

Bol. Soc. Venez. Ci. Nat. = Boletín de la Sociedad Venezolana de Ciencias Naturales.

Bongarten, B. C. 1992. Genetic variation in black locust within its native range. In: J. W. Hanover et al., eds. 1992. Black Locust: Biology, Culture, & Utilization. East Lansing. Pp. 78–97.

Boonkerd, T., S. Pechsri, and B. R. Baum. 2005. A phenetic study of *Cassia* sensu lato (Leguminosae-Caesalpinioideae: Cassieae: Cassiinae) in Thailand. Pl. Syst. Evol. 252: 153–165.

Borissova, A. G. et al. 1965. Leguminosae: *Astragalus*. In: V. L. Komarov et al., eds. 1963+. Flora of the U.S.S.R. (Flora SSSR). Translated from Russian. 30+ vols. Jerusalem etc. Vol. 12.

Bosch, C. H. 2008. *Cassia fistula* Linn. In: G. H. Schmelzer and A. Gurib-Fakim, eds. 2008. Medicinal Plants. Wageningen. [Incl. CD-ROM database.]

Boschin, G. and D. Resta. 2013. Alkaloids derived from lysine: Quinolizidine (a focus on lupine alkaloids). In: K. G. Ramawat and J.-M. Mérillon, eds. 2013. Natural Products: Phytochemistry, Botany and Metabolism of Alkaloids, Phenolics and Terpenes. 5 vols. Berlin. Vol. 1, pp. 381–403.

Bossard, C. C. 1991. The role of habitat disturbance, seed predation, and ant dispersal on establishment of the exotic shrub *Cytisus scoparius* in California. Amer. Midl. Naturalist 126: 1–13.

Bossard, C. C. 1993. Seed germination in the exotic shrub *Cytisus scoparius* (Scotch broom) in California. Madroño 40: 47–61.

Bossard, C. C. 1996. *Cytisus scoparius*. In: J. M. Randall and J. Marinelli, eds. 1996. Invasive Plants: Weeds of the Global Garden. New York. P. 52.

Bossard, C. C., J. M. Randall, and M. C. Hoshovsky, eds. 2000. Invasive Plants of California's Wildlands. Berkeley.

Boston J. Nat. Hist. = Boston Journal of Natural History.

Bot. Acta = Botanica Acta; Berichte der Deutschen botanischen Gesellschaft.

Bot. Beechey Voy.—See: W. J. Hooker and G. A. W. Arnott [1830–]1841

Bot. Bull. Acad. Sin. = Botanical Bulletin of Academia Sinica; a Quarterly Journal Containing Scientific Contributions from the Institute of Botany, Academia Sinica. [Kuo Li Chung Yang Yen Chiu Yuan Chih Wu Hsüeh Hui Pao.]

Bot. California—See: W. H. Brewer et al. 1876–1880

Bot. Cult. ed. 2—See: G. L. M. Dumont de Courset 1811–1814

Bot. Explor. = The Botanical Explorer.

Bot. Gaz. = Botanical Gazette; Paper of Botanical Notes.

Bot. Handb.—See: C. Schkuhr [1787–]1791–1803

Bot. J. Linn. Soc. = Botanical Journal of the Linnean Society.

Bot. Mag. = Botanical Magazine; or, Flower-garden Displayed.... [Edited by Wm. Curtis.] [With vol. 15, 1801, title became Curtis's Botanical Magazine; or....]

Bot. Mag. (Tokyo) = Botanical Magazine. [Shokubutsu-gaku Zasshi.] (Tokyo.)

Bot. Misc. = Botanical Miscellany.

Bot. North. Middle States—See: L. C. Beck 1833

Bot. Not. = Botaniska Notiser.

Bot. Reg. = Botanical Register....

Bot. Repos. = Botanists' Repository, for New, and Rare Plants.

Bot. Voy. Sulphur—See: G. Bentham 1844[–1846]

Bot. Zeitung (Berlin) = Botanische Zeitung. (Berlin.)

Bot. Zhurn. (Moscow & Leningrad) = Botanicheskii Zhurnal. (Moscow and Leningrad.)

Botany (Fortieth Parallel)—See: S. Watson 1871

Bothalia = Bothalia; a Record of Contributions from the National Herbarium, Union of South Africa.

Braam, J. 2005. In touch: Plant responses to mechanical stimuli. New Phytol. 165: 373–389.

Bradshaw, R. V. 1925. Pacific Coast species of *Lathyrus*. Bot. Gaz. 80: 233–261.

Brenan, J. P. M. 1959. *Mimosa*. In: W. B. Turrill et al., eds. 1952+. Flora of Tropical East Africa. 152+ vols. London and Rotterdam. Leguminosae subfam. Mimosoideae, pp. 42–47.

Brenan, J. P. M. 1963. Notes on African Caesalpinioideae: The genus *Pentophoropsis* Chiov. and its relationship. Bull. Misc. Inform. Kew 17: 203–209.

Brenan, J. P. M. and R. K. Brummitt. 1965. The variation of *Dichrostachys cinerea* (L.) Wight & Arn. Bol. Soc. Brot. 39: 61–115.

Breteler, F. J. 1960. Revision of *Abrus* Adanson (Papilionoideae) with special reference to Africa. Blumea 10: 607–624.

Brett, C. H. 1946. Insecticidal properties of the indigobush *(Amorpha fruticosa)*. J. Agric. Res. 73: 81–96.

Brett, C. H. 1946b. Repellant properties of extract of *Amorpha fruticosa*. J. Econ. Entomol. 39: 810.

Brewer, W. H. et al. 1876–1880. Geological Survey of California.... Botany.... 2 vols. Cambridge, Mass. (Bot. California)

Bridson, G. D. R. 2004. BPH-2: Periodicals with Botanical Content. 2 vols. Pittsburgh.

Bridson, G. D. R. and E. R. Smith. 1991. B-P-H/S. Botanico-Periodicum-Huntianum/Supplementum. Pittsburgh.

Britton, N. L. et al., eds. 1905+. North American Flora.... 47+ vols. New York. [Vols. 1–34, 1905–1957; ser. 2, parts 1–13+, 1954+.] (N. Amer. Fl.)

Britton, N. L. and A. Brown. 1896–1898. An Illustrated Flora of the Northern United States, Canada and the British Possessions from Newfoundland to the Parallel of the Southern Boundary of Virginia, and from the Atlantic Ocean Westward to the 102d Meridian.... 3 vols. New York. (Ill. Fl. N. U.S.)

Britton, N. L. and J. N. Rose. 1928. Mimosaceae. In: N. L. Britton et al., eds. 1905+. North American Flora.... 47+ vols. New York. Vol. 23, pp. 1–194..

Britton, N. L., E. E. Sterns, J. F. Poggenburg, et al. 1888. Preliminary Catalogue of Anthophyta and Pteridophyta Reported As Growing Spontaneously within One Hundred Miles of New York City. New York. [Authorship often attributed as B.S.P. in nomenclatural contexts.] (Prelim. Cat.)

Brittonia = Brittonia; a Journal of Systematic Botany....

Broich, S. L. 1987. Revision of the *Lathyrus vestitus-laetiflorus* complex (Fabaceae). Syst. Bot. 12: 139–153.

Broich, S. L. 1989. Chromosome numbers of North American *Lathyrus* (Fabaceae). Madroño 36: 41–48.

Broich, S. L. 2007. New combinations in North American *Lathyrus* and *Vicia* (Fabaceae: Faboideae: Fabeae). Madroño 54: 63–71.

Brotero, F. 1804[–1805]. Flora Lusitanica.... 2 vols. Lisbon. (Fl. Lusit.)

Brotero, F. 1816–1827. Phytographia Lusitaniae Selectior.... 2 vols. Lisbon. (Phytogr. Lusit. Select.)

Browicz, K. 1963. The genus *Colutea* L.: A monograph. Monogr. Bot. 14: 1–136.

Browicz, K. 1967. A supplement to the monograph of the genus *Colutea* L. Arbor. Kórnickie 12: 33–43.

Brown, Gill. K. et al. 2008. *Acacia* s.s. and its relationship among tropical legumes, tribe Ingeae (Leguminosae: Mimosoideae). Syst. Bot. 33: 739–751.

Brown, R. 1823. Chloris Melvilliana. A List of Plants Collected in Melville Island...in the Year 1820.... London. [Preprint with independent pagination from W. E. Parry. 1824. A Supplement to the Appendix of Captain Parry's Voyage.... London.] (Chlor. Melvill.)

Browne, P. 1756. The Civil and Natural History of Jamaica.... London. (Civ. Nat. Hist. Jamaica)

Brummitt, R. K. 2004. Report of the Committee for Spermatophyta: 54. Taxon 53: 813–825.

Brummitt, R. K. and C. E. Powell, eds. 1992. Authors of Plant Names. A List of Authors of Scientific Names of Plants, with Recommended Standard Forms of Their Names, Including Abbreviations. Kew.

Bruneau, A. et al. 2001. Phylogenetic relationships in the Caesalpinioideae (Leguminosae) as inferred from chloroplast *trn*L intron sequences. Syst. Bot. 26: 487–514.

Bruneau, A. et al. 2008. Phylogenetic patterns and diversification in the caesalpinioid legumes. Botany (Ottawa) 86: 697–718.

Bruneau, A. and G. J. Anderson. 1988. Reproductive biology of diploid and triploid *Apios americana* (Leguminosae). Amer. J. Bot. 75: 1876–1883.

Bruneau, A. and G. J. Anderson. 1994. To bee or not to bee?: The pollination biology of *Apios americana* (Leguminosae). Pl. Syst. Evol. 192: 147–149.

Brunsberg, K. 1977. Biosystematics of the *Lathyrus pratensis* complex. Opera Bot. 41: 1–78.

Buchmann, S. L. 1974. Buzz pollination of *Cassia quiedondilla* (Leguminosae) by bees of the genera *Centris* and *Melipona*. Bull. S. Calif. Acad. Sci. 73: 171–173.

Bull. Acad. Imp. Sci. Saint-Pétersbourg = Bulletin de l'Académie Impériale des Sciences de Saint Pétersbourg.

Bull. Acad. Roy. Sci. Bruxelles = Bulletins de l'Académie Royale des Sciences et Belles-lettres de Bruxelles.

Bull. Bot. Lab. N. E. Forest. Inst., Harbin = Bulletin of Botanical Laboratory of North-eastern Forestry Institute. [Chih Wu Yen Chiu Shih Hui Kan.]

Bull. Calif. Acad. Sci. = Bulletin of the California Academy of Sciences.

Bull. Calif. Agric. Exp. Sta. = Bulletin of the California Agricultural Experiment Station.

Bull. Cl. Phys.-Math. Acad. Imp. Sci. Saint-Pétersbourg = Bulletin de la Classe Physico-mathématique de l'Académie Impériale des Sciences de Saint-Pétersbourg.

Bull. Forest Exp. Sta., Chosen = Bulletin, Forest Experiment Station, Government General of Chosen.

Bull. Herb. Boissier = Bulletin de l'Herbier Boissier.

Bull. Jard. Bot. État Bruxelles = Bulletin du Jardin Botanique de l'État à Bruxelles.

Bull. Kentucky Agric. Exp. Sta. = Bulletin of the Kentucky Agricultural Experiment Station.

Bull. Misc. Inform. Kew = Bulletin of Miscellaneous Information, Royal Gardens, Kew.

Bull. Mus. Natl. Hist. Nat., B, Adansonia = Bulletin du Muséum National d'Histoire Naturelle. Section B, Adansonia: Botanique Phytochimie.

Bull. Natl. Mus. Canada = Bulletin of the National Museum of Canada.

Bull. New York Bot. Gard. = Bulletin of the New York Botanical Garden.

Bull. New York State Mus. Sci. Serv. = Bulletin of the New York State Museum and Science Service.

Bull. Public Mus. Milwaukee = Bulletin of the Public Museum of Milwaukee.

Bull. S. Calif. Acad. Sci. = Bulletin of the Southern California Academy of Sciences.

Bull. Sci. Soc. Philom. Paris = Bulletin des Sciences, par la Société Philomatique (de Paris).

Bull. Soc. Bot. France = Bulletin de la Société Botanique de France.

Bull. Soc. Imp. Naturalistes Moscou = Bulletin de la Société Impériale des Naturalistes de Moscou.

Bull. Soc. Roy. Bot. Belgique = Bulletin de la Société Royale de Botanique de Belgique.

Bull. Tall Timbers Res. Sta. = Bulletin of Tall Timbers Research Station.

Bull. Torrey Bot. Club = Bulletin of the Torrey Botanical Club.

Bull. U.S. Geol. Geogr. Surv. Territ. = Bulletin of the United States Geological and Geographical Survey of the Territories.

Burkart, A. 1971. El género *Galactia* (Legum.-Phaseoleae) en Sudamérica con especial referencia a la Argentina y países vecinos. Darwiniana 16: 663–796.

Burkart, A. 1976. A monograph of the genus *Prosopis* (Leguminosae subfam. Mimosoideae). J. Arnold Arbor. 57: 219–249.

Burkart, A. 1976b. A monograph of the genus *Prosopis* (Leguminosae subfam. Mimosoideae): Catalogue of the recognized species of *Prosopis*. J. Arnold Arbor. 57: 450–524.

Burman, N. L. 1768. Flora Indica ... Nec Non Prodromus Florae Capensis. Leiden and Amsterdam. (Fl. Indica)

Burrows, G. E. and R. J. Tyrl. 2013. Toxic Plants of North America, ed. 2. Oxford.

Callahan, H. S. 1997. Infraspecific differentiation in the *Amphicarpaea bracteata* (Fabaceae) species complex: Varieties and ecotypes. Rhodora 99: 64–82.

Callihan, R. H., S. L. Carson, and R. T. Dobbins. 1995. NAWEEDS, Computer-aided Weed Identification for North America. Illustrated User's Guide plus Computer Floppy Disk. Moscow, Idaho.

Calvillo Canadell, L. and S. R. S. Cevallos-Ferriz. 2005. Diverse assemblage of Eocene and Oligocene Leguminosae from Mexico. Int. J. Pl. Sci. 166: 671–692.

Camp, P., J. Gamon, and J. Arnett. 2011. Field Guide to the Rare Plants of Washington. Seattle.

Canad. Field-Naturalist = Canadian Field-Naturalist.

Canad. J. Bot. = Canadian Journal of Botany.

Canad. J. Genet. Cytol. = Canadian Journal of Genetics and Cytology.

Canad. J. Pl. Sci. = Canadian Journal of Plant Science.

Canad. Rec. Sci. = The Canadian Record of Science; Including the Proceedings of the Natural History Society of Montreal [etc.].

Canad. Veterin. J. = Canadian Veterinary Journal.

Candolle, A. P. de. 1802. Astragalogia.... Paris. (Astragalogia)

Candolle, A. P. de. 1813b. Catalogus Plantarum Horti Botanici Monspeliensis.... Montpellier, Paris, and Strasbourg. (Cat. Pl. Hort. Monsp.)

Candolle, A. P. de and A. L. P. P. de Candolle, eds. 1823–1873. Prodromus Systematis Naturalis Regni Vegetabilis.... 17 vols. Paris etc. [Vols. 1–7 edited by A. P. de Candolle, vols. 8–17 by A. L. P. P. de Candolle.] (Prodr.)

Candollea = Candollea; Organe du Conservatoire et du Jardin Botaniques de la Ville de Genève.

Canfield, J. E. 1977. The Ecological Life History of *Trifolium thompsonii* Morton, with Reference to Its Distribution. M.S. thesis. University of Washington.

Carter, A. M. 1974. Pollen studies in relation to hybridization in *Cercidium* and *Parkinsonia* (Leguminosae: Caesalpinioideae). Madroño 22: 301–311.

Carter, A. M. 1974b. The genus *Cercidium* (Leguminosae: Caesalpinioideae) in the Sonoran Desert of Mexico and the United States. Proc. Calif. Acad. Sci., ser. 4, 40: 17–57.

Carulli, J. P. and D. E. Fairbrothers. 1988. Allozyme variation in three eastern United States species of *Aeschynomene* (Fabaceae), including the rare *A. virginica*. Syst. Bot. 13: 559–566.

Carulli, J. P., A. O. Tucker, and N. H. Dill. 1988. *Aeschynomene rudis* Benth. (Fabaceae) in the United States. Bartonia 54: 18–20.

Castanea = Castanea; Journal of the Southern Appalachian Botanical Club.

Castroviejo, S. et al., eds. 1986+. Flora Ibérica: Plantas Vasculares de la Peninsula Ibérica e Islas Baleares. 17+ vols. Madrid.

Cat. N. Amer. Pl. ed. 2—See: A. A. Heller 1900

Cat. Piante Siena—See: B. Bartalini 1776

Cat. Pl. Cub.—See: A. H. R. Grisebach 1866

Cat. Pl. Hort. Monsp.—See: A. P. de Candolle 1813b

Cat. Pl. Upper Louisiana—See: T. Nuttall 1813

Catholic Univ. Amer., Biol. Ser. = Catholic University of America. Biological Series.

Cavanilles, A. J. 1791–1801. Icones et Descriptiones Plantarum, Quae aut Sponte in Hispania Crescunt, aut in Hortis Hospitantur. 6 vols. Madrid. (Icon.)

Cent. Pl. I—See: C. Linnaeus 1755

Ceolin, G. B. 2011. O Gênero *Galactia* P. Browne (Leguminosae, Papilionoideae) no Brasil. Ph.D. thesis. Universidad Federal do Rio Grande do Sul.

Chapman, A. W. 1860. Flora of the Southern United States.... New York. (Fl. South. U.S.)

Chapman, A. W. 1883. Flora of the Southern United States..., ed. 2. New York. (Fl. South. U.S. ed. 2)

Chapman, A. W. 1892. Flora of the Southern United States..., ed. 2 reprint 2. New York, Cincinnati, and Chicago. (Fl. South. U.S. ed. 2 repr. 2)

Chapman, A. W. 1897. Flora of the Southern United States..., ed. 3. Cambridge, Mass. (Fl. South. U.S. ed. 3)

Chen, C. J., M. G. Mendenhall, and B. L. Turner. 1994. Taxonomy of *Thermopsis* (Fabaceae) in North America. Ann. Missouri Bot. Gard. 81: 714–742.

Chevallier, A. 1996. The Encyclopedia of Medicinal Plants. New York.

Chlor. Melvill.—See: R. Brown 1823

Cho, J. Y. et al. 2000. Inhibitor of tumor necrosis factor-production in lipopolysaccharide-stimulated RAX264.7 cells from *Amorpha fruticosa*. J. Ethnopharmacol. 70: 127–133.

Choi, B. et al. 2006. Phylogenetic significance of stylar features in genus *Vicia* (Leguminosae): An analysis with molecular phylogeny. J. Pl. Res. 119: 513–523.

Chow, L. M. C. et al. 2003. *Gleditsia sinensis* fruit extract is a potential chemotherapeutic agent in chronic and acute myelogenous leukemia. Oncology Rep. 10: 1601–1607.

Christenhusz, M. J. M., M. F. Fay, and M. W. Chase. 2017. Plants of the World. Kew.

Chudnoff, M. 1984. Tropical Timbers of the World. Washington.

Cincinnati Lit. Gaz. = The Cincinnati Literary Gazette.

Civ. Nat. Hist. Jamaica—See: P. Browne 1756

Cladistics = Cladistics; the International Journal of the Willi Hennig Society.

Clarke, H. D., D. S. Seigler, and J. E. Ebinger. 1989. *Acacia farnesiana* (Fabaceae: Mimosoideae) and related species from Mexico, the southwestern U.S., and the Caribbean. Syst. Bot. 14: 549–564.

Clarke, H. D., D. S. Seigler, and J. E. Ebinger. 1990. *Acacia constricta* (Fabaceae: Mimosoideae) and related species from the southwestern U.S. and Mexico. Amer. J. Bot. 77: 305–315.

Clements, F. E. 1920. Plant indicators: The relation of plant communities to process and practice. Publ. Carnegie Inst. Wash. 290.

Clewell, A. F. 1964. The biology of the common native lespedezas in southern Indiana. Brittonia 16: 208–220.

Clewell, A. F. 1964b. An appraisal of *Lespedeza hirta* on the Atlantic coastal plain. Brittonia 16: 74–76.

Clewell, A. F. 1966. Native North American species of *Lespedeza* (Leguminosae). Rhodora 68: 359–405.

Clewell, A. F. 1966b. Identification of the lespedezas of North America. II. Selected Bibliography of *Lespedeza*. Bull. Tall Timbers Res. Sta. 7.

Clewell, A. F. 1966c. Natural history, cytology, and isolating mechanisms of the native American lespedezas. Bull. Tall Timbers Res. Sta. 6.

Clewell, A. F. and W. H. Stickell. 1990. Establishment of *Lespedeza virgata* (Leguminosae) in the southeastern United States. J. Elisha Mitchell Sci. Soc. 106(2): 32–37.

Colladon, L. T. F. 1816. Histoire Naturelle et Médicale des Casses, et particulièrement de la Casse et des Sénés Employés en Médicine. Montpellier. (Hist. Nat. Méd. Casses)

Collectanea—See: N. J. Jacquin 1786[1787]–1796[1797]

Collins, J. L. and T. F. Wieboldt. 1992. *Trifolium calcaricum* (Fabaceae), a new clover from limestone barrens of eastern United States. Castanea 57: 282–286.

Comm. Acac. Aphyll.—See: H. L. Wendland 1820

Comm. Legum. Gen.—See: G. Bentham 1837

Comm. Pl. Afr. Austr.—See: E. Meyer and J. F. Drège 1836–1838

Commonw. Forest. Rev. = Commonwealth Forestry Review.

Comp. Fl. Ital.—See: G. Arcangeli 1882

Comp. Fl. Philadelph.—See: W. P. C. Barton 1818

Compan. Bot. Mag. = Companion to the Botanical Magazine....

Conceição, A. et al. 2009. Phylogeny of *Chamaecrista* Moench (Leguminosae-Caesalpinioideae) based on nuclear and chloroplast DNA regions. Taxon 58: 1168–1180.

Connors, P. G. 1994. Rediscovery of showy Indian clover. Fremontia 22: 3–7.

Conrad, M. 1980. Monograph of *Lupinus albicaulis*-*L. formosus* Complex. Ph.D. dissertation. University of Missouri.

Conservation Biol. = Conservation Biology; Journal of the Society for Conservation Biology.

Conservation Genet. = Conservation Genetics.

Contr. Dudley Herb. = Contributions from the Dudley Herbarium of Stanford University.

Contr. Gray Herb. = Contributions from the Gray Herbarium of Harvard University. [Some numbers reprinted from (or in?) other periodicals, e.g. Rhodora.]

Contr. Lab. Bot. Univ. Montréal = Contributions du Laboratoire de Botanique de l'Université de Montréal.

Contr. New South Wales Natl. Herb. = Contributions from the New South Wales National Herbarium.

Contr. Ocas. Mus. Hist. Nat. Colegio "De La Salle" = Contribuciones Ocasionales del Museo de Historia Natural del Colegio "De La Salle".

Contr. U.S. Natl. Herb. = Contributions from the United States National Herbarium.

Contr. W. Bot. = Contributions to Western Botany.

Cooper, C. S. 1957. A legume for native flood meadows: 1. Establishment and maintenance of stands of white-tip clover *(T. variegatum)* in native flood meadows and its effect upon yields, vegetative and chemical composition of hay. Agron. J. 49: 473–477.

Corby, H. D. L. 1988. Types of rhizobial nodules and their distribution among Leguminosae. Kirkia 13: 53–123.

Correll, D. S. and M. C. Johnston. 1970. Manual of the Vascular Plants of Texas. Renner, Tex.

Coulot, P. and P. Rabaute. 2013. Monographie des Leguminosae de France. Tome 3, Tribu des Trifolieae. Arnac.

Cox, B. J. 1972. Biosystematics of *Lupinus lepidus-Lupinus caespitosus* Complex. Ph.D. thesis. University of Missouri.

Crantz, H. J. N. von. 1769. Stirpium Austriarum Fasciculus I [-VI]. 2 vols. in 6 fascs. Vienna. [Vols. paged consecutively.] (Stirp. Austr. Fasc. ed. 2)

Crawford, D. J. et al. 1998. Genetic variation in running buffalo clover (*Trifolium stoloniferum:* Fabaceae) using random amplified polymorphic DNA markers (RAPDs), Ann. Missouri Bot. Gard. 85: 81–89.

Cronquist, A. 1981. An Integrated System of Classification of Flowering Plants. New York.

Cronquist, A. et al. 1972–2017. Intermountain Flora. Vascular Plants of the Intermountain West, U.S.A. 7 vols. in 9. New York and London. (Intermount. Fl.)

Crop Sci. (Madison) = Crop Science. (Madison, Wisc.)

Crotalaria Afr. Madag.—See: R. M. Polhill 1982

Crowder, C. A. 1978. The Ecology and Reproduction of *Sophora leachiana* (Fabaceae). M.S. thesis. Oregon State University.

Crowder, C. A. 1982. Systematics and Phylogeny of the Herbaceous North American and Inland Argentine Sophoras (Fabaceae). Ph.D. thesis. Texax Tech University.

Cruden, R. W. and S. M. Hermann-Parker. 1979. Butterfly pollination of *Caesalpinia pulcherrima,* with observations on a psychophilous syndrome. J. Ecol. 67: 155–168.

Cubas, P., C. Pardo, and H. Tahir. 2002. Molecular approach to the phylogeny and systematics of *Cytisus* (Leguminosae) and related genera based on nucleotide sequences of nrDNA (ITS region) and cpDNA (*trn*L-*trn*F intergenic spacer). Pl. Syst. Evol. 233: 223–242.

Cullina, M. D. et al. 2011. The Vascular Plants of Massachusetts: A County Checklist, rev. 1. Westborough.

Cuvier, F., ed. 1816–1845. Dictionnaire des Sciences Naturelles..., ed. 2. 61 vols. Strasbourg and Paris. (Dict. Sci. Nat. ed. 2)

Cycl.—See: A. Rees [1802–]1819–1820

Cytologia = Cytologia; International Journal of Cytology.

Dandy, J. E. 1958. List of British Vascular Plants. London.

Daniels, M. 2006. Medicinal Plants: Chemistry and Properties. Enfield, N.H.

Darbyshire, S. J. and E. Small. 2018. Are *Melilotus albus* and *M. officinalis* conspecific? Genet. Resources Crop Evol. 65: 1571–1580.

Dart, R. C., ed. 2004. Medical Toxicology, ed. 3. Philadelphia.

Darwiniana = Darwiniana; Carpeta del "Darwinion."

Davesa, J. A. 2000. *Ononis.* In: S. Castroviejo et al., eds. 1986+. Flora Ibérica: Plantas Vasculares de la Peninsula Ibérica e Islas Baleares. 17+ vols. Madrid. Vol. 7(2), pp. 590–646.

Davidson, V. E. 1940. Shrubs for Wildlife on Farms in the Southeast. Washington. [U.S.D.A. Leafl. 200.]

Davies, A. M., N. Maxted, and L. J. G. van der Maesen. 2007. A natural infrageneric classification for *Cicer* (Leguminosae, Cicereae). Blumea 52: 379–400.

Davis, A. M. 1982. The occurrence of anagyrine in a collection of western American lupines. J. Range Managem. 35: 81–84.

de Moura, T. M. et al. 2018. A new circumscription of *Nissolia* (Leguminosae-Papilionoideae-Dalbergieae), with *Chaetocalyx* as a new generic synonym. Novon 26: 193–213.

de Queiroz, L. P. et al. 2015. A multilocus phylogenetic analysis reveals the monophyly of a recurcumscribed papilionoid legume tribe Diocleae with well-supported generic relationships. Molec. Phylogen. Evol. 90: 1–19.

de Queiroz, L. P. et al. 2017. A molecular phylogeny reveals the Cuban enigmatic genus *Behaimia* as a new piece in the Brongniartieae puzzle of papilionoid legumes. Molec. Phylogen. Evol. 109: 191–202.

de Queiroz, L. P., R. H. Fortunato, and A. M. Giulietti. 2003. Phylogeny of the Diocleinae (Papilionoideae: Phaseoleae) based on morphological characters. In: B. B. Klitgaard and A. Bruneau, eds. 2003. Advances in Legume Systematics. Part 10. Kew. Pp. 303–324.

de Queiroz, L. P. and M. Lavin. 2011. *Coursetia* (Leguminosae) from eastern Brasil: Nuclear ribosomal and chloroplast DNA sequence analysis reveal the monophyly of three caatinga-inhabiting species. Syst. Bot. 36: 69–79.

De Wildeman, É. A. J. 1921–1929. Plantae Bequaertianae.... 6 vols. Ghent and Paris. (Pl. Bequaert.)

Dean, E. et al. 2008. Catalogue of nonnative vascular plants occurring spontaneously in California beyond those addressed in the Jepson Manual—Part II. Madroño 55: 93–112.

Dec. Gen. Nov.—See: É. P. Ventenat 1808

Dec. Pl. Horti Upsal.—See: C. Linnaeus f. 1762[–1763]

Degtjareva, G. V. et al. 2008. New data on nrITS phylogeny of *Lotus* (Leguminosae, Loteae). Wulfenia 15: 35–49.

DeHann, L. R. et al. 2006. Evaluation of diversity among North Americana accessions of false indigo (*Amorpha fruticosa* L.) for forage and biomass. Genet. Resources Crop Evol. 53: 1463–1476.

DeLaney, K. R. 2010b. *Tephrosia mysteriosa* (Fabaceae; Millettieae), a new species from central Florida. Bot. Explor. 4: 99–126.

Delgado-Salinas, A. et al. 2011. *Vigna* (Leguminosae) sensu lato: The names and identities of the American segregate genera. Amer. J. Bot. 98: 1694–1715.

Delgado-Salinas, A., R. Bibler, and M. Lavin. 2006. Phylogeny of the genus *Phaseolus* (Leguminosae): A recent diversification in an ancient landscape. Syst. Bot. 31: 779–791.

Delgado-Salinas, A. and W. R. Carr. 2007. *Phaseolus texensis* (Leguminosae: Phaseolinae): A new species from the Edwards Plateau of central Texas. Lundellia 10: 11–17.

Delgado-Salinas, A. and E. Estrada-Castillón. 2010. A new combination in the genus *Oxyrhynchus* (Leguminosae: Phaseolinae). Brittonia 62: 239–242.

Delgado-Salinas, A. and M. Lavin. 2004 Proposals to change the conserved type of *Phaseolus helvolus,* nom. cons. and to conserve the name *Glycine umbellata* with a conserved type (Fabaceae). Taxon 53: 839–841.

Delgado-Salinas, A. and L. Torres-Colín. 1995. Una nueva combinación en el género *Macroptilium* (Fabaceae: Phaseolinae). Anales Inst. Biol. Univ. Nac. Autón. México, Bot. 66: 189–192.

Delgado-Salinas, A. and N. J. Turland. 2008. Proposal to reject the name *Phaseolus alatus* (Leguminosae). Taxon 57: 310–311.

Demonstr. Pl.—See: C. Linnaeus [1753]

Dendrologie—See: K. H. E. Koch 1869–1873

Denton, R. G. 2002. Isozyme Variation in *Trifolium bolanderi* A. Gray: A Narrow Endemic, Compared with *Trifolium longipes* Nutt., a Sympatric, Native Congener. M.S. thesis. California State University, Fresno.

Derickx, L. and P. M. Antunes. 2013. A Guide to the Identification and Control of Exotic Invasive Species in Ontario's Hardwood Forests. Sault Ste. Marie.

Descr. Pl. Nouv.—See: É. P. Ventenat [1800–1803]

Desert Pl. = Desert Plants; a Quarterly Journal Devoted to Broadening Our Knowledge of Plants Indigenous or Adaptable to Arid and Sub-arid Regions.

Desfontaines, R. L. [1798–1799.] Flora Atlantica sive Historia Plantarum, Quae in Atlante, Agro Tunetano et Algeriensi Crescunt. 2 vols. in 9 parts. Paris. (Fl. Atlant.)

Deut. Dendrol.—See: B. A. E. Koehne 1893

Deutschl. Fl.—See: G. F. Hoffmann [1791–1804]

Dexter, D. F., K. Martin, and L. Travis. 2014. Prehistoric plant use at Beaver Creek Rock Shelter, southwestern Montana, USA. Ethnobot. Res. Applic. 12: 355–384.

Diamond, A. R. 2015. Two species rediscovered in Alabama after 100 years. Phytoneuron 2015-47: 1–3.

Diamond, A. R. 2016. New vascular plant county records from Alabama. Phytoneuron 2016-70: 1–6.

Dict. Sci. Nat. ed. 2—See: F. Cuvier 1816–1845

Diego-Pérez, N. et al., eds. 1989+. Flora de Guerrero. 34+ nos. Mexico City. (Fl. Guerrero)

Dietrich, D. N. F. 1839–1852. Synopsis Plantarum.... 5 vols. Weimar. (Syn. Pl.)

Dietrich, F. G. 1815–1824. Nachtrag zum vollstândigen Lexicon der Gärtneri und Botanik.... 10 vols. Berlin. (Nachtr. Vollst. Lex. Gärtn.)

Dippel, L. 1889–1893. Handbuch der Laubholzkunde. 3 vols. Berlin. (Handb. Laubholzk.)

Dirr, M. A. 2011. Dirr's Encyclopedia of Trees and Shrubs. Portland.

DiTomaso, J. M. and E. A. Healy. 2007. Weeds of California and Other Western States. 2 vols. Oakland, Calif.

DiTomaso, J. M., G. B. Kyser, and M. S. Hastings. 1999. Prescribed burning for control of yellow starthistle *(Centaurea solstitialis)* and enhanced native plant diversity. Weed Sci. 47: 233–242.

Don, G. 1831–1838. A General History of the Dichlamydeous Plants.... 4 vols. London. (Gen. Hist.)

Donovan, M. 2006. Conservation evaluation of the bog bird's-foot trefoil, *Lotus pinnatus,* in Canada. Canad. Field-Naturalist 120: 157–162.

Dorado, Ó. 1988. A Morphological Revision of the *Podalyrioides* Group of *Brongniartia* (Fabaceae: Faboideae). M.S. thesis. Claremont Graduate School.

Dorn, R. D. 1988. Vascular Plants of Wyoming. Cheyenne. (Vasc. Pl. Wyoming)

Douglas, G. W. and M. Ryan. 2006. Conservation evaluation of the seaside birds-foot trefoil, *Lotus formosissimus,* in Canada. Canad. Field-Naturalist 120: 153–156.

Doyle, J. J. et al. 1996. The distribution and phylogenetic significance of a 50-kb chloroplast DNA inversion in the flowering plant family Leguminosae. Molec. Phylogen. Evol. 5: 429–438.

Drummond, C. S. et al. 2012. Multiple continental radiations and correlates of diversification in *Lupinus* (Leguminosae): Testing for key innovation with incomplete taxon sampling. Syst. Biol. 61: 443–460.

Du Puy, D. J. et al., eds. 2002. The Leguminosae of Madagascar. Kew.

Du Puy, D. J., J. N. Labat, and B. D. Schrire. 1993. The separation of two previously confused species in the *Indigofera spicata* complex (Leguminosae: Papilionoideae). Kew Bull. 48: 727–733.

Duke, J. A. 1981. Handbook of Legumes of World Economic Importance. New York.

Duley, M. L. and M. A. Vincent. 2003. A synopsis of the genus *Cladrastis* (Leguminosae). Rhodora 105: 205–239.

Dumont de Courset, G. L. M. 1811–1814. Le Botaniste Cultivateur..., ed. 2. Paris. (Bot. Cult. ed. 2)

Duncan, W. H. 1979b. Changes in *Galactia* (Fabaceae) of the southeastern United States. Sida 8: 170–180.

Dunn, D. B. 1955. Taxonomy of Lupinus, group *Micranthi* (Leguminosae) of the Pacific Coast. Aliso 3: 135–171.

Dunn, D. B. 1959. *Lupinus pusillus* and its relationship. Amer. Midl. Naturalist 62: 500–510.

Dunn, D. B. and J. M. Gillett. 1966. The Lupines of Canada and Alaska. Ottawa.

Dunn, S. T. 1912. A revision of the genus *Millettia* Wight et Arn. J. Linn. Soc., Bot. 41: 123–243.

Duno de Stefano, R. et al. 2010. The morphological and phylogenetic distinctions of *Coursetia greenmanii* (Leguminosae): Taxonomic and ecological implications. Syst. Bot. 35: 289–295.

Durán, Y. and M. Pérez de la Vega. 2004. Assessment of genetic variation and species relationships in a collection of *Lens* using RAPD and ISSR. Span. J. Agric. Res. 2: 538–544.

Durand, E. M. and T. C. Hilgard. 1854. Plantae Heermannianae.... Philadelphia. [Preprinted from J. Acad. Nat. Sci. Philadelphia, n. s. 3: 37–46. 1855.] (Pl. Heermann.)

Duvall, M. R., J. D. Noll, and G. E. Larson. 1999. Disjunct populations of *Trifolium beckwithii* (Fabaceae) in eastern South Dakota: Vicariance or recent long-distance dispersal?—a preliminary analysis. Madroño 46: 199–204.

Eaton, A. 1818. A Manual of Botany for the Northern States, ed. 2. Albany. (Man. Bot. ed. 2)

Eaton, A. 1829. A Manual of Botany for the Northern States, ed. 5. Albany. (Man. Bot. ed. 5)

Eaton, A. and J. Wright. 1840. North American Botany..., ed. 8. Troy, N.Y. (Man. Bot. ed. 8)

Ebinger, J. E., D. S. Seigler, and H. D. Clarke. 2002. Notes on the segregates of *Acacia farnesiana* (Linnaeus) Willdenow (Fabaceae: Mimosoideae) and related species in North America. SouthW. Naturalist 47: 86–91.

Ecol. & Evol. = Ecology and Evolution.

Ecol. Appl. = Ecological Applications; a Publication of the Ecological Society of America.

Ecology = Ecology, a Quarterly Journal Devoted to All Phases of Ecological Biology.

Econ. Bot. = Economic Botany; Devoted to Applied Botany and Plant Utilization.

Edinburgh J. Bot. = Edinburgh Journal of Botany.

Edwards's Bot. Reg. = Edwards's Botanical Register....

Egan, A. N. 2015. Species delimitation and recognition in the *Pediomelum megalanthum* complex (Fabaceae) via multivariate morphometrics. PhytoKeys 44: 65–87.

Egan, A. N. and K. A. Crandall. 2008. Incorporating gaps as phylogenetic characters across eight DNA regions: Ramifications for North American Psoraleeae (Leguminosae). Molec. Phylogen. Evol. 46: 532–546.

Egan, A. N. and K. A. Crandall. 2008b. Divergence and diversification in North American Psoraleeae due to climate change. B. M. C. Biol. 6(15).

Egan, A. N. and Pan B. 2015. Resolution of polyphyly in *Pueraria* (Leguminosae: Papilionoideae): The creation of two new genera, *Haymondia* and *Toxicopueraria,* the resurrection of *Neustanthus,* and a new combination in *Teyleria.* Phytotaxa 218: 201–226.

Egan, A. N., M. Vatanparast, and W. Cagle. 2016. Parsing polyphyletic *Pueraria:* Delimiting distinct lineages through phylogeny. Molec. Phylogen. Evol. 104: 44–59.

Eisa, M. M. et al. 2000. Antibacterial activity of *Dichrostachys cinerea.* Fitoterapia 71: 324–327.

Elias, T. S. 1980. The Complete Trees of North America: Field Guide and Natural History. New York.

Elliott, S. [1816–]1821–1824. A Sketch of the Botany of South-Carolina and Georgia. 2 vols. in 13 parts. Charleston. (Sketch Bot. S. Carolina)

Ellison, N. W. et al. 2006. Molecular phylogenetics of the clover genus (*Trifolium* - Leguminosae). Molec. Phylogen. Evol. 39: 688–705.

Elmore, F. H. 1943. Ethnobotany of the Navajo. Albuquerque. [Reprinted 1978, New York.]

Emory, W. H. 1848. Notes of a Military Reconnoissance, from Fort Leavenworth, in Missouri, to San Diego, in California, Including Part of the Arkansas, Del Norte, and Gila Rivers.... Made in 1846–7, with the Advanced Guard of the "Army of the West." Washington. (Not. Milit. Reconn.)

Emory, W. H. 1857–1859. Report on the United States and Mexican Boundary Survey, Made under the Direction of the Secretary of the Interior. 2 vols. in parts. Washington. (Rep. U.S. Mex. Bound.)

Encycl.—See: J. Lamarck et al. 1783–1817

Endo, Y. et al. 2008. Phylogenetic relationships of New World *Vicia* (Leguminosae) inferred from nrDNA internal transcribed spacer sequences and floral characters. Syst. Bot. 33: 356–363.

Endo, Y. and H. Ohashi. 1990. New distinctions between *Alysicarpus vaginalis* and *A. ovalifolius* (Leguminosae). Nat. Hist. Res. 1: 43–48.

Endo, Y. and H. Ohashi. 1997. Cladistic analysis of phylogenetic relationships among tribes Cicereae, Trifolieae, and Vicieae (Leguminosae). Amer. J. Bot. 84: 523–529.

Engelmann, G. and A. Gray. 1845. Plantae Lindheimerianae I. Boston J. Nat. Hist. 5: 210–264.

Engler, H. G. A. and K. Prantl, eds. 1887–1915. Die natürlichen Pflanzenfamilien.... 254 fascs. Leipzig. [Sequence of fasc. (Lieferung) numbers (order of publication) is independent of the sequence of division (Teil) and subdivision (Abteilung) numbers (taxonomic order).] (Nat. Pflanzenfam.)

Enquist, M. 1995. *Desmodium lindheimeri* (Leguminosae) in Mexico and Texas. Sida 16: 781–786.

Enum.—See: P. C. Fabricius 1759

Enum. ed. 2—See: P. C. Fabricius 1763

Enum. Hort. Berol. Alt.—See: J. H. F. Link 1821–1822

Enum. Pl.—See: W. S. J. G. von Besser 1821; C. L. Willdenow 1809–1813[–1814]

Enum. Syst. Pl.—See: N. J. Jacquin 1760

Erickson, R. O. 1943. Taxonomy of *Clematis* section *Viorna.* Ann. Missouri Bot. Gard. 30: 1–62, plate 1.

Erythea = Erythea; a Journal of Botany, West American and General.

Espert, S. M. et al. 2007. Phylogeny of *Macroptilium* (Leguminosae): Morphological, biochemical and molecular evidece. Cladistics 23: 119–129.

Ethnobot. Res. Applic. = Ethnobotany Research and Applications. [Electronic journal.]

Etterson, J. R. 2004. Evolutionary potential of *Chamaecrista fasciculata* in relation to climate change. I. Clinal patterns of selection along an envioromnemtal gradient in the Great Plains. Evolution 58: 1446–1458.

Euphytica = Euphytica. Netherlands Journal of Plant Breeding.

Evans, D. O. 1990. What is *Sesbania?* Botany, taxonomy, plant geography and natural history of the perennial members of the genus. In: B. Macklin and D. O. Evans, eds. 1990. Perennial *Sesbania* Species in Agroforestry Systems. Waimanalo. Pp. 5–18.

Evolution = Evolution; International Journal of Organic Evolution.

Exell, A. W. and H. Wild, eds. 1960+. Flora Zambesiaca: Mozambique, Federation of Rhodesia and Nyasaland, Bechuanaland Protectorate. 12+ vols. in parts. London.

Exped. Great Salt Lake—See: H. Stansbury 1852

Fabricius, P. C. 1759. Enumeratio Methodica Plantarum Horti Medici Helmstadiensis.... Helmstedt. (Enum.)

Fabricius, P. C. 1763. Enumeratio Methodica Plantarum Horti Medici Helmstadiensis..., ed. 2. Helmstedt. (Enum. ed. 2)

Fam. Pl.—See: M. Adanson 1763[–1764]

Fant, J. B. et al. 2010. Hybridization between the threatened plant, *Lespedeza leptostachya* Engelm. and its co-occurring congener *Lespedeza capitata* Michx.: Morphological and molecular evidence. Conservation Genet. 11: 2195–2205.

Fantz, P. R. 1991. Ethnobotany of *Clitoria* (Leguminosae). Econ. Bot. 45: 511–520.

Fantz, P. R. 1993. Revision of cultivated *Centrosema* and *Clitoria* in the United States. HortScience 28: 674–676.

Fantz, P. R. 2002. Distribution of *Centrosema* (Leguminosae: Phaseoleae: Clitoriinae) for the Flora of North America project. Vulpia 1: 41–81.

Farris, B. M. 2007. Assessment of Black Locust on the Black Kettle National Grasslands. M.S. thesis. Oklahoma State University.

Farruggia, F. T. 2009. Phylogenetic and Monographic Studies of the Pantropical Genus *Sesbania*. Ph.D. dissertation. Arizona State University.

Fassett, N. C. 1939b. The leguminous plants of Wisconsin. Madison.

Fawcett, W. and A. B. Rendle. 1910–1936. Flora of Jamaica.... 5 vols. London. (Fl. Jamaica)

Fearing, O. S. 1959. A Cytotaxonomic Study of the Genus *Cologania* and its Relationship to *Amphicarpaea* (Leguminosae-Papilionoideae). Ph.D. dissertation. University of Texas.

Feddes Repert. Spec. Nov. Regni Veg. = Feddes Repertorium Specierum Novarum Regni Vegetabilis.

Felger, R. S., M. B. Johnson, and M. F. Wilson. 2001. The Trees of Sonora, Mexico. Oxford and New York.

Felger, R. S. and M. B. Moser. 1985. People of the Desert and Sea: Ethnobotany of the Seri Indians. Tucson.

Fenster, C. B. 1995. Mirror image flowers and their effect on outcrossing rate in *Chamaecrista fasciculata* (Leguminosae). Amer. J. Bot. 82: 46–50.

Fernald, M. L. 1911. The variations of *Lathyrus palustris* in eastern America. Rhodora 13: 47–52.

Fernald, M. L. 1950. Gray's Manual of Botany, ed. 8. New York.

Fery, R. L. 2002. New opportunities in *Vigna*. In: J. Janick and A. Whipkey, eds. 2002. Trends in New Crops and New Uses. Alexandria. Pp. 424–428.

Field & Lab. = Field & Laboratory.

Fieldiana, Bot. = Fieldiana: Botany.

Fisher, C. 1995. Horse care: Perilous pasture plants. Rural Herit. 20: 44–45.

Fisher, E. M. 1892. Revision of North American species of *Hoffmannseggia*. Contr. U.S. Natl. Herb. 1: 143–150.

Fitoterapia = Fitoterapia; Rivista di Studi ed Applicazioni delle Piante Medicinali.

Fl. Aegypt.-Arab.—See: P. Forsskål 1775

Fl. Alaska Yukon—See: E. Hultén 1941–1950

Fl. Algérie—See: J. A. Battandier et al. 1888–1897

Fl. Amer. Sept.—See: F. Pursh [1813]1814

Fl. Angl.—See: W. Hudson 1762

Fl. Arct. URSS—See: A. I. Tolmatchew 1960–1987

Fl. Atlant.—See: R. L. Desfontaines [1798–1799]

Fl. Bilaspur Dist.—See: G. Panigrahi and S. K. Murti 1989

Fl. Bor.-Amer.—See: W. J. Hooker [1829–]1833–1840; A. Michaux 1803

Fl. Boston. ed. 2—See: J. Bigelow 1824

Fl. Bras.—See: C. F. P. von Martius et al. 1840–1906

Fl. Calif.—See: W. L. Jepson 1909–1943

Fl. Cap.—See: W. H. Harvey et al. 1860–1933

Fl. Carniol. ed. 2—See: J. A. Scopoli 1771–1772

Fl. Carol.—See: T. Walter 1788

Fl. Cochinch.—See: J. de Loureiro 1790

Fl. Colorado—See: P. A. Rydberg 1906

Fl. Congo Belge—See: W. Robyns 1948+

Fl. Env. Paris ed. 2—See: J. L. Thuillier 1799

Fl. Flumin.—See: J. M. Vellozo 1825–1827[1829–1831]

Fl. Franç.—See: J. Lamarck 1778[1779]

Fl. Franç. ed. 3—See: J. Lamarck and A. P. de Candolle 1805–1815

Fl. Francisc.—See: E. L. Greene 1891–1897

Fl. Guerrero—See: N. Diego-Pérez et al. 1989+

Fl. Ind. ed. 1832—See: W. Roxburgh 1832

Fl. Indica—See: N. L. Burman 1768

Fl. Ital. Fragm.—See: D. Viviani 1808

Fl. Jamaica—See: W. Fawcett and A. B. Rendle 1910–1936

Fl. Los Angeles—See: L. Abrams 1904

Fl. Los Angeles ed. 3—See: L. Abrams 1917

Fl. Ludov.—See: C. S. Rafinesque 1817

Fl. Lusit.—See: F. Brotero 1804[–1805]

Fl. Miami—See: J. K. Small 1913b

Fl. N. Amer.—See: J. Torrey and A. Gray 1838–1843

Fl. Nebr., Rosales—See: University of Nebraska 1895

Fl. Nied-Oesterr.—See: A. Neilreich [1857–]1859

Fl. Novo-Galiciana—See: R. McVaugh and W. R. Anderson 1974+

Fl. Oxon.—See: J. Sibthorp 1794

Fl. Pedem.—See: C. Allioni 1785

Fl. Pis.—See: G. Savi 1798

Fl. Rocky Mts.—See: P. A. Rydberg 1917

Fl. Rust.—See: T. Martyn 1792–1794[–1795]

Fl. S.E. U.S.—See: J. K. Small 1903

Fl. S.E. Washington—See: H. St. John 1937

Fl. South. U.S.—See: A. W. Chapman 1860

Fl. South. U.S. ed. 2—See: A. W. Chapman 1883

Fl. South. U.S. ed. 2 repr. 2—See: A. W. Chapman 1892

Fl. South. U.S. ed. 3—See: A. W. Chapman 1897

Fl. Suec. ed. 2—See: C. Linnaeus 1755b

Fl. Taur.-Caucas.—See: F. A. Marschall von Bieberstein 1808–1819

Fl. Tellur.—See: C. S. Rafinesque 1836[1837–1838]

Fl. Terr. Tschukt.—See: E. R. von Trautvetter 1878

Fl. URSS—See: V. L. Komarov et al. 1934–1964

Fl. Yosemite Sierra—See: D. W. Taylor 2010

Fleet, R. R. and B. L. Young. 2000. Facultative mutualism between imported fire ants *(Solenopsis invicta)* and a legume *(Senna occidentalis)*. SouthW. Naturalist 45: 289–298.

Flexner, S. B. and L. C. Hauck, eds. 1987. The Random House Dictionary of the English Language, ed. 2 unabridged. New York.

Flora = Flora; oder (allgemeine) botanische Zeitung. [Vols. 1–16, 1818–1833, include "Beilage" and "Ergänzungsblätter"; vols. 17–25, 1834–1842, include "Beiblatt" and "Intelligenzblatt."]

Flora Zambesiaca Managing Committee. 1960+. Flora Zambesiaca.... 12+ vols. some in parts. London.

Flores, A. 2008. Perennial peanut for quality pasturage and hay. Agric. Res. (Washington, DC) 56(Mar.): 16–17.

Flores-Franco, G. 2013. Análisis Taxonómico del Género *Cologania* (Leguminosae). M.Ci.(Biol.) tesis. Universidad Nacional Autónoma de México.

Food Sci. Technol. Res. = Food Science and Technology Research.

Forsskål, P. 1775. Flora Aegyptiaco-Arabica. Copenhagen. (Fl. Aegypt.-Arab.)

Fortunato, R. H., L. P. de Queiroz, and G. P. Lewis. 1996. *Lackeya*, a new genus in tribe Phaseoleae subtribe Diocleinae (Leguminosae: Papilionoideae) from North America. Kew Bull. 51: 365–370.

Foster, B. G. and M. A. Vincent. 2018. A new taxonomy for *Trifolium variegatum* and its relatives. Madroño 65: 141–150.

Fournier, P. V. [1934–]1940. Les Quatre Flores de la France. Poinson-les-Grancey.

Fox, W. E., K. W. Allred, and E. H. Roalson. 1998. A Guide to Common Locoweeds and Milkvetches of New Mexico. Las Cruces.

Fragm. Bot.—See: N. J. Jacquin [1800–]1809

Frahm-Leliveld, J. A. 1966. Cytotaxonomic notes on the genera *Indigofera* L. and *Cyamopsis* DC. Genetica 37: 403–426.

Franchet, A. R. 1889[–1890]. Plantae Delavayanae; Plantes de Chine Recueillis au Yun-nan par l'Abbé Delavay.... 3 parts. Paris. [Parts paged consecutively.] (Pl. Delavay.)

Franck, A. R. 2017. Notes on trifoliolate species of *Galactia* (Fabaceae) in Florida. Phytologia 99: 139–185.

Frankel, E. 1989. Distribution of *Pueraria lobata* in and around New York City. Bull. Torrey Bot. Club 116: 390–394.

Franklin, J. et al. 1823. Narrative of a Journey to the Shores of the Polar Sea, in the Years 1819, 20, 21 and 22. London. [Richardson: Appendix VII. Botanical appendix, pp. [729]–768, incl. bryophytes by Schwägrichen, algae and lichens by Hooker.] (Narr. Journey Polar Sea)

Freeman, G. 1918. The purple hyacinth bean. Bot. Gaz. 66: 512–523.

Fremontia = Fremontia; Journal of the California Native Plant Society.

French, E. C. et al. 1994. Regional experience with forage *Arachis* in the United States. In: P. C. Kerridge and B. Hardy, eds. 1994. Biology and Agronomy of Forage *Arachis*. Cali. Pp. 169–186.

Freytag, G. F. and D. G. Debouck. 2002. Taxonomy, Distribution, and Ecology of the Genus *Phaseolus* (Leguminosae - Papilionoideae) in North America, Mexico and Central America. Fort Worth. [Sida Bot. Misc. 23.]

Fritsch, P. W. and B. C. Cruz. 2012. Phylogeny of *Cercis* based on DNA sequences of nuclear ITS and four plastid regions: Implications for transatlantic historical biogeography. Molec. Phylogen. Evol. 62: 816–825.

Frodin, D. G. 2004. History and concepts of big plant genera. Taxon 53: 753–776.

Frohne, D. and H. J. Pfander. 2004. Poisonous Plants: A Handbook for Doctors, Pharmacists, Toxicologists, Biologists, and Veterinarians, ed. 2. London.

Fruct. Sem. Pl.—See: J. Gaertner 1788–1791[–1792]

Fuller, G. L. and B. H. Hendrickson. 1928. Soil Survey of Elbert County, Georgia. Washington.

Funk, V. A. et al. 2007. Checklist of the plants of the Guyana Shield (Venezuela: Amazonas, Bolivar, Delta Amacuro; Guyana, Surinam, French Guiana). Contr. U.S. Natl. Herb. 55.

Gaertner, J. 1788–1791[–1792]. De Fructibus et Seminibus Plantarum.... 2 vols. Stuttgart and Tübingen. [Vol. 1 in 1 part only, 1788. Vol. 2 in 4 parts paged consecutively: pp. 1–184, 1790; pp. 185–352, 353–504, 1791; pp. 505–520, 1792.] (Fruct. Sem. Pl.)

Gagnon, E. et al. 2016. A new generic system for the pantropical *Caesalpinia* group (Leguminosae). PhytoKeys 71: 1–160.

Gandhi, K. N. 2015. Validation of *Pediomelum palmeri* (Fabaceae). Harvard Pap. Bot. 20: 213.

Gandhi, K. N., M. A. Vincent, and J. L. Reveal. 2011. *Dermatophyllum*, the correct name for *Calia* (Fabaceae). Phytoneuron 2011-57: 1–4.

Gard. & Forest = Garden and Forest; a Journal of Horticulture, Landscape Art and Forestry.

Gard. Dict. ed. 8—See: P. Miller 1768

Gard. Dict. Abr. ed. 4—See: P. Miller 1754

Garman, H. 1902. Kentucky forage plants—The clovers and their allies. Bull. Kentucky Agric. Exp. Sta. 98: 3–46.

Geesink, R. 1984. Scala *Millettiearum*. Leiden Bot. Ser. 8: 1–131.

Geill. Handb. Jav. Theeonkr.—See: C. A. Backer and D. F. van Slooten 1924

Gen. Cass. Syn.—See: T. Vogel 1837

Gen. Hist.—See: G. Don 1831–1838

Gen. N. Amer. Pl.—See: T. Nuttall 1818

Gen. Pl.—See: G. Bentham and J. D. Hooker 1862–1883

Gen. Pl. ed. 5—See: C. Linnaeus 1754

Genet. Resources Crop Evol. = Genetic Resources and Crop Evolution; an International Journal.

Genetics = Genetics; a Periodical Record of Investigations Bearing on Heredity and Variation.

Genoways, H. H. and R. J. Baker, eds. 1979. Biological Investigations in the Guadalupe Mountains National Park, Texas. Washington.

Gepts, P. 1988. Genetic Resources of *Phaseolus* Beans.... Dordrecht and Boston.

Gholami, A. et al. 2017. Molecular systematics of Indian *Alysicarpus* (Fabaceae) based on analyses of nuclear ribosomal DNA sequences. J. Genet. 96: 353–363.

Gibbs, P. E. 1966. A revision of the genus *Genista* L. Notes Roy. Bot. Gard. Edinburgh 27: 11–99.

Gibson, M. R. 1978. *Glycyrrhiza* in old and new perspectives. Lloydia 41: 348–354.

Gillett, J. B. 1963. *Sesbania* in Africa (excluding Madagascar) and southern Arabia. Kew Bull. 17: 91–159.

Gillett, J. M. 1965. Taxonomy of *Trifolium:* Five American species of section *Lupinaster* (Leguminosae). Brittonia 17: 121–136.

Gillett, J. M. 1969. Taxonomy of *Trifolium* (Leguminosae). II. The *T. longipes* complex in North America. Canad. J. Bot. 47: 93–113.

Gillett, J. M. 1971. Taxonomy of *Trifolium* (Leguminosae). III. *T. eriocephalum*. Canad. J. Bot. 49: 395–405.

Gillett, J. M. 1972. Taxonomy of *Trifolium* (Leguminosae). IV. The American species of section *Lupinaster* (Adanson) Seringe. Canad. J. Bot. 50: 1975–2007.

Gillett, J. M. 1980. Taxonomy of *Trifolium* (Leguminosae). V. The perennial species of section *Involucrarium*. Canad. J. Bot. 58: 1425–1448.

Gillett, J. M. 1985. Taxonomy and morphology. In: N. L. Taylor, ed. 1985. Clover Science and Technology. Madison. Pp. 7–69.

Gillett, J. M. et al. 2007. Fabaceae. In: S. G. Aiken et al. 2007. Flora of the Canadian Arctic Archipelago.... Ottawa. [CD-ROM.]

Gillett, J. M. and N. L. Taylor. 2001. The World of Clovers. Ames.

Gilman, E. F. 1997. Trees for Urban and Suburban Landscapes. New York.

Gilmore, M. R. 1909. A Study in the Ethnobotany of the Omaha Indians. Ph.D. dissertation. University of Nebraska.

Gilmore, M. R. 1919. Uses of plants by the Indians of the Missouri River region. Rep. (Annual) Bur. Amer. Ethnol. 33: 1–126.

Glad, J. B. and R. R. Halse. 1993. Invasion of *Amorpha fruticosa* L. (Leguminosae) along the Columbia and Snake rivers in Oregon and Washington. Madroño 40: 62–63.

Gleason, H. A. 1952. The New Britton and Brown Illustrated Flora of the Northeastern United States and Adjacent Canada. 3 vols. New York. (Ill. Fl. N.E. U.S.)

Gleason, H. A. and A. Cronquist. 1963. Manual of Vascular Plants of Northeastern United States and Adjacent Canada. Princeton.

Gleason, H. A. and A. Cronquist. 1991. Manual of Vascular Plants of Northeastern United States and Adjacent Canada, ed. 2. Bronx.

Global Envioronm. Res. = Global Environmental Research.

Gmelin, J. F. 1791[–1792]. Caroli à Linné...Systema Naturae per Regna Tria Naturae.... Tomus II. Editio Decima Tertia, Aucta, Reformata. 2 parts. Leipzig. (Syst. Nat.)

Godt, M. J. W. and J. L. Hamrick. 1991. Genetic variation in *Lathyrus latifolius* (Leguminosae). Amer. J. Bot. 78: 1163–1171.

Goertzen, L. R. 1993. The defensive role of trichomes in black medic (*Medicago lupulina* L.). Pl. Syst. Evol. 184: 101–111.

Gómez-Acevedo, S. et al. 2010. Neotropical mutualism between *Acacia* and *Pseudomyrmex*. Phylogeny and divergence times. Molec. Phylogen. Evol. 56: 393–408.

Gottsberger, G. and I. Silberbauer-Gottsberger. 1988. Evolution of flower structures and pollination in neotropical Cassiinae (Caesalpiniaceae) species. Phyton (Horn) 28: 293–320.

Graham, E. H. 1941. Legumes for Erosion Control and Wildlife. Washington. [U.S.D.A., Misc. Publ. 412.]

Graham, P. H. and C. P. Vance. 2003. Legumes: Importance and constraints to greater use. Pl. Physiol. (Lancaster) 131: 872–877.

Gray, A. 1854. Plantae Novae Thurberianae.... Cambridge, Mass. [Preprinted from Mem. Amer. Acad. Arts, n. s. 5: 297–328. 1855.] (Pl. Nov. Thurb.)

Gray, A. 1856. A Manual of the Botany of the Northern United States..., ed. 2. New York. (Manual ed. 2)

Gray, A. 1864. A revision and arrangement (mainly by the fruit) of the North American species of *Astragalus* and *Oxytropis*. Proc. Amer. Acad. Arts 6: 188–236.

Gray, A. 1884b. A revision of the North American species of *Oxytropis* DC. Proc. Amer. Acad. Arts 20: 1–7.

Gray, S. F. 1821[–1822]. A Natural Arrangement of British Plants.... 2 vols. London. (Nat. Arr. Brit. Pl.)

Grear, J. W. 1978. A revision of the New World species of *Rhynchosia* (Leguminosae-Faboideae). Mem. New York Bot. Gard. 31(1): 1–168.

Great Basin Naturalist Mem. = Great Basin Naturalist Memoirs.

Greene, E. L. 1891–1897. Flora Franciscana. An Attempt to Classify and Describe the Vascular Plants of Middle California. 4 parts. San Francisco. [Parts paged consecutively.] (Fl. Francisc.)

Greene, E. L. 1894. Manual of the Botany of the Region of San Francisco Bay.... San Francisco. (Man. Bot. San Francisco)

Greene, E. L. [1901.] Plantae Bakerianae. 3 vols. [Washington.] (Pl. Baker.)

Greuter, W., H. M. Burdet, and G. Long. 1981+. Med-checklist: A Critical Inventory of Vascular Plants of the Circum-Mediterranean Countries. 4+ vols Geneva and Berlin.

Griffith, A. B. and I. N. Forseth. 2002. Primary and secondary seed dispersal of a rare, tidal wetland annual, *Aeschynomene virginica*. Wetlands 22: 696–704.

Griffith, A. B. and I. N. Forseth. 2003. Establishment and reproduction of *Aeschynomene virginica* (L.) Britton, Sterns & Poggenb. (Fabaceae) a rare, annual, wetland species in relation to vegetation removal and water level. Pl. Ecol. 167: 117–125.

Griffith, A. B. and I. N. Forseth. 2005. Population matrix models of *Aeschynomene virginica*, a rare annual plant: Implications for conservation. Ecol. Appl. 15: 222–233.

Griffiths, M. 1994. Index of Garden Plants. Portland.

Grimes, J. W. 1990. A revision of the New World species of Psoraleeae (Leguminosae: Papilionoideae). Mem. New York Bot. Gard. 61: 1–114.

Grisebach, A. H. R. 1866. Catalogus Plantarum Cubensium Exhibens Collectionem Wrightianam Aliasque Minores ex Insula Cuba Missas. Leipzig. (Cat. Pl. Cub.)

Guernsey, W. J. 1970. Sericea lespedeza, its use and management. U.S.D.A. Farmers Bull. 2245.

Guinet, P. and H. M. Hernández. 1989. Pollen characters in the genera *Zapoteca* and *Calliandra* (Leguminosae, Mimosoideae): Their systematic and phylogenetic relevance. Pollen & Spores 31: 5–22.

Gunn, C. R. 1968. The *Vicia americana* complex (Leguminosae). Iowa State J. Sci. 42: 171–214.

Gunn, C. R. 1970b. A key and diagrams for the seeds of one hundred species of *Vicia* (Leguminosae). Proc. Int. Seed Testing Assoc. 35: 773–790.

Gunn, C. R. 1984. Fruits and Seeds of Genera in the Subfamily Mimosoideae (Fabaceae). Washington. [U.S.D.A. Agric. Res. Serv., Techn. Bull. 1681.]

Gunn, C. R. 1991. Fruits and Seeds of Genera in the Subfamily Caesalpinioideae (Fabaceae). Washington. [U.S.D.A. Agric. Res. Serv., Techn. Bull. 1755.]

Gunn, C. R., E. M. Norman, and J. S. Lassetter. 1980. *Chapmannia floridana* Torrey & Gray (Fabaceae). Brittonia 32: 178–185.

Gupta, P. K. and K. Agarwal. 1982. Cytological studies in the genus *Indigofera* L. Cytologia 47: 665–681.

Hammons, R. O. 1973. Early history and origin of the peanut. In: American Peanut Research and Education Association, eds. 1973. Peanuts—Culture and Uses. Stillwater. Pp. 17–45.

Han, J. E. et al. 2010. Phylogenetic analysis of eastern Asian and eastern North American disjunct *Lespedeza* (Fabaceae) inferred from nuclear ribosomal ITS and plastid region sequences. Bot. J. Linn. Soc. 164: 221–235.

Handb. Laubholzk.—See: L. Dippel 1889–1893

Handbuch—See: J. H. F. Link 1829–1833

Hanover, J. W., K. Miller, and S. Plesko, eds. 1992. Black Locust: Biology, Culture, & Utilization. East Lansing.

Hao, G. et al. 2003. Phylogenetics of *Bauhinia* subgenus *Phanera* (Leguminosae: Caesalpinioideae) based on ITS sequences of nuclear ribosomal DNA. Bot. Bull. Acad. Sin. 44: 223–228.

Hardin, J. W. and J. M. Arena. 1974. Human Poisoning from Native and Cultivated Plants. Durham, N.C.

Harvard Pap. Bot. = Harvard Papers in Botany.

Harvey, W. H. et al., eds. 1860–1933. Flora Capensis.... 7 vols., some in parts. Dublin etc. (Fl. Cap.)

Haston, E. M., G. P. Lewis, and J. A. Hawkins. 2005. A phylo°°genetic reappraisal of the *Peltophorum* group (Caesalpinieae: Leguminosae) based on the chloroplast *trn*L-F, *rbc*L and *rps*16 sequence data. Amer. J. Bot. 92: 1359–1371.

Hawkins, J. A. 1996. Systematics of *Parkinsonia* L. and *Cercidium* Tul. (Leguminosae: Caesalpinioideae). Ph.D. dissertation. University of Oxford.

Hawkins, J. A. et al. 2007. Intercontinental dispersal prior to human translocation revealed in a cryptogenic invasive tree. New Phytol. 175: 575–587.

Hayden, F. V. 1872. Preliminary Report of the United States Geological Survey of Montana and Portions of Adjacent Territories; Being a Fifth Annual Report of Progress. Washington. (Prelim. Rep. U.S. Geol. Surv. Montana)

Heenan, P. B., M. I. Dawson, and S. J. Wagstaff. 2004. The relationship of *Sophora* sect. *Edwardsia* (Fabaceae) to *Sophora tomentosa,* the type species of the genus *Sophora,* observed from DNA sequence data and morphological characters. Bot. J. Linn. Soc. 146: 439–446.

Hegi, G. et al. [1906–1931.] Illustrierte Flora von Mittel-Europa. 7 vols. in 13. Munich. (Ill. Fl. Mitt.-Eur.)

Heil, K. D. and S. L. O'Kane. 2007. Plant distribution reports. New Mexico Bot. Newslett. 41: 7.

Heim, J. 1990. Illinois Nature Preserves Commission Vegetation Management Guidelines on Black Locust. Springfield, Ill.

Heller, A. A. 1900. Catalogue of North American Plants North of Mexico, Exclusive of the Lower Cryptogams, ed. 2. [Lancaster, Pa.] (Cat. N. Amer. Pl. ed. 2)

Henslow, G. 1867. Note on the structure of *Indigofera,* as apparently offering facilities for the intercrossing of distinct flowers. J. Linn. Soc., Bot. 9: 355–358.

Herb. Amb.—See: C. Linnaeus 1754b

Herendeen, P. S. 1992. The fossil record of the Leguminosae from the Eocene of southeastern North America. In: P. S. Herendeen and D. L. Dilcher, eds. 1992. Advances in Legume Systematics. Part 4. The Fossil Record. Kew. Pp. 85–160.

Herendeen, P. S. and A. Bruneau, eds. 2000. Advances in Legume Systematics. Part 9. Kew.

Herendeen, P. S. and D. L. Dilcher. 1992. Advances in Legume Systematics. Part 4. The Fossil Record. Kew.

Hermann, F. J. 1953. A Botanical Synopsis of the Cultivated Clovers *(Trifolium).* Washington. [U.S.D.A., Agric. Monogr. 22.]

Hermann, F. J. 1954. A Synopsis of the Genus *Arachis.* Washington. [U.S.D.A., Agric. Monogr. 19.]

Hermann, F. J. 1960. Vetches of the U.S.—Native, Naturalized and Introduced. Washington. [U.S.D.A., Agric. Handb. 168.]

Hernández, H. M. 1986. *Zapoteca,* a new genus of neotropical Mimosoideae. Ann. Missouri Bot. Gard. 73: 755–763.

Hernández, H. M. 1989. Systematics of *Zapoteca* (Leguminosae). Ann. Missouri Bot. Gard. 76: 781–862.

Hershey, D. R. 1977. The American yellowwood. Amer. Hort. (Alexandria) 56: 42–43.

Heyn, C. C. 1963. The Annual Species of *Medicago.* Jerusalem.

Heyn, C. C. 1981. Trifolieae. In: R. M. Polhill and P. H. Raven, eds. 1981. Advances in Legume Systematics. Parts 1 and 2. 2 vols. Kew. Vol. 1, pp. 383–385.

Heyne, K. 1927. De Nuttige Planten van Nederlandsch-Indie..., ed. 2. 3 vols. Batavia. (Nutt. Pl. Ned.-Ind. ed. 2)

Hickey, R. J., M. A. Vincent, and S. I. Guttman. 1991. Genetic variation in running buffalo clover (*Trifolium stoloniferum,* Fabaceae). Conservation Biol. 5: 309–316.

Hickman, J. C. , ed. 1993. The Jepson Manual. Higher Plants of California. Berkeley, Los Angeles, and London.

Hildebrand, F. H. G. 1866. Uber die Vorrichgtungen an einigen Bluthen zur Befruchtung durch Insektenhulfe. Bot. Zeitung (Berlin) 24: 73–78.

Hill, J. 1759–1775. The Vegetable System.... 26 vols. London. (Veg. Syst.)

Hines, D. A. and K. Eckman. 1993. Indigenous Multipurpose Trees of Tanzania: Uses and Economic Benefits for People. Ottawa.

Hist. Nat. Îles Canaries—See: P. B. Webb and S. Berthelot [1835–]1836–1850

Hist. Nat. Méd. Casses—See: L. T. F. Colladon 1816

Hist. Pl. Palat.—See: J. A. Pollich 1776–1777

Hitchcock, C. L. 1952. A Revision of the North American Species of *Lathyrus.* Seattle. [Univ. Wash. Publ. Biol. 15.] (Revis. N. Amer. Lathyrus)

Hitchcock, C. L. 1961b. *Astragalus.* In: C. L. Hitchcock et al. 1955–1969. Vascular Plants of the Pacific Northwest. 5 vols. Seattle. Vol. 3, pp. 197–273.

Hitchcock, C. L. et al. 1955–1969. Vascular Plants of the Pacific Northwest. 5 vols. Seattle. [Univ. Wash. Publ. Biol. 17.] (Vasc. Pl. Pacif. N.W.)

Hoffman, W. J. 1891. The Midewiwin or "Grand Medicine Society" of the Ojibwa. Rep. (Annual) Bur. Amer. Ethnol. 7: 143–300.

Hoffmann, G. F. [1791–1804.] Deutschland Flora oder botanisches Taschenbuch.... 4 vols. Erlangen. (Deutschl. Fl.)

Hollowell, E. A. 1939. Strawberry Clover. Washington. [U.S.D.A. Leafl. 176.]

Hollowell, E. A. 1943. Persian clover. U.S.D.A. Farmers Bull. 1929.

Hooker, W. J. [1829–]1833–1840. Flora Boreali-Americana; or, the Botany of the Northern Parts of British America.... 2 vols. in 12 parts. London, Paris, and Strasbourg. (Fl. Bor.-Amer.)

Hooker, W. J. and G. A. W. Arnott. [1830–]1841. The Botany of Captain Beechey's Voyage; Comprising an Account of the Plants Collected by Messrs Lay and Collie, and Other Officers of the Expedition, during the Voyage to the Pacific and Bering's Strait, Performed in His Majesty's Ship Blossom, under the Command of Captain F. W. Beechey...in the Years 1825, 26, 27, and 28. 10 parts. London. [Parts paged and plates numbered consecutively.] (Bot. Beechey Voy.)

Hooker's J. Bot. Kew Gard. Misc. = Hooker's Journal of Botany and Kew Garden Miscellany.

Hopkins, M. 1942. *Cercis* in North America. Rhodora 44: 193–211.

Hornemann, J. W. 1813–1815. Hortus Regius Botanicus Hafniensis.... 2 vols. Copenhagen. (Hort. Bot. Hafn.)

Hort. Berol.—See: C. L. Willdenow 1803–1816

Hort. Bot. Hafn.—See: J. W. Hornemann 1813–1815

Hort. Bot. Vindob.—See: N. J. Jacquin 1770–1776

Hort. Brit.—See: J. C. Loudon 1830; R. Sweet 1826

Hort. Kew.—See: W. Aiton 1789

Hortus Kew.—See: W. Aiton and W. T. Aiton 1810–1813

Hoveland, C. S. 1960. Ball clover. Leafl. Alabama Agric. Exp. Sta. 64: 1–4.

Howard, R. A. 1974–1989. Flora of the Lesser Antilles: Leeward and Windward Islands. 6 vols. Jamaica Plain.

Hu, J. M. et al. 2000. Phylogenetic systematics of the tribe Millettieae (Leguminosae) based on chloroplast *trn*K/*mat*K sequences and its implications for evolutionary patterns in Papilionoideae. Amer. J. Bot. 87: 418–430.

Huang, D. I. and E. A. Friar. 2011. Relationships in the *Lupinus albifrons* species complex (Fabaceae) based on two highly variable chloroplast regions. Syst. Bot. 36: 362–370.

Hudson, W. 1762. Flora Anglica.... London. (Fl. Angl.)

Huffman, H. H. 1986. Field survey of the yellowwood, *Cladrastis lutea,* in Brown County, Indiana. Proc. Indiana Acad. Sci. 95: 433–442.

Hughes, C. E. 1987. Biological considerations in designing a seed collection strategy for *Gliricidia sepium* (Jacquin) Steudel (Leguminosae). Commonw. Forest. Rev. 66: 31–45.

Hughes, C. E. 1998. Monograph of *Leucaena* (Leguminosae-Mimosoideae). Syst. Bot. Monogr. 55: 1–244.

Hughes, C. E. et al. 2003. Relationships among genera of the informal *Dichrostachys* and *Leucaena* groups (Mimosoideae) inferred from nuclear ribosomal ITS sequences. In: B. B. Klitgaard and A. Bruneau, eds. 2003. Advances in Legume Systematics. Part 10. Kew. Pp. 221–238.

Hughes, C. E., C. D. Bailey, and S. A. Harris. 2002. Divergent and reticulate species relationships in *Leucaena* (Fabaceae) inferred from multiple data sources: Insights into polyploidy origins and nrDNA polymorphism. Amer. J. Bot. 89: 1057–1073.

Hultén, E. 1941–1950. Flora of Alaska and Yukon. 10 vols. Lund and Leipzig. [Vols. paged consecutively and designated as simultaneous numbers of Lunds Univ. Årsskr. (= Acta Univ. Lund.) and Kungl. Fysiogr. Sällsk. Handl.] (Fl. Alaska Yukon)

Hultén, E. 1968. Flora of Alaska and Neighboring Territories: A Manual of the Vascular Plants. Stanford.

Humboldt, A. von, A. J. Bonpland, and C. S. Kunth. 1815[1816]–1825. Nova Genera et Species Plantarum Quas in Peregrinatione Orbis Novi Collegerunt, Descripserunt.... 7 vols. in 36 parts. Paris. (Nov. Gen. Sp.)

Ibeawuchi, I. I. 2007. Landrace legumes: Synopsis of the culture, importance, potentials, and roles in agricultural production systems. J. Biol. Sci. (Faisalabad) 7: 464–474.

Icon.—See: A. J. Cavanilles 1791–1801

Icon. Pl. Rar.—See: N. J. Jacquin 1781–1793[–1795]; J. H. F. Link et al. 1841–1844

Iconogr. Bot. Pl. Crit.—See: H. G. L. Reichenbach 1823–1832

Ill. Fl. Mitt.-Eur.—See: G. Hegi et al. [1906–1931]

Ill. Fl. N. U.S.—See: N. L. Britton and A. Brown 1896–1898

Ill. Fl. N.E. U.S.—See: H. A. Gleason 1952

Ill. Fl. Pacific States—See: L. Abrams and R. S. Ferris 1923–1960

Ill. Handb. Laubholzk.—See: C. K. Schneider [1904–]1906–1912

Index Seminum (Hamburg) = Semina in Horto Botanico Hamburgensi...Collecta Quae pro Mutua Commutatione Offeruntur. [1823–1840 for years 1822–1840. Title after 1829: Delectus Seminum Quae in Horto Hamburgensium Botanico e Collectioni Anni... Mutuae Commutatione Offeruntur.]

Index Seminum (St. Petersburg) = Index Seminum, Quae Hortus Botanicus Imperialis Petropolitanus pro Mutua Commutatione Offert.

Instituto Nacional de Investigaciones sobre Recursos Bióticas. 1978+. Flora de Veracruz. 162+ fascs. Xalapa.

Int. J. Molec. Sci. = International Journal of Molecular Sciences.

Int. J. Pl. Sci. = International Journal of Plant Sciences.

Intermount. Fl.—See: A. Cronquist et al. 1972–2017

Interpr. Herb. Amboin.—See: E. D. Merrill 1917

Invent. Seeds U.S.D.A. Bur. Pl. Industr. = Inventory of Seeds and Plants Imported by the Office of Foreign Seed and Plant Introduction, United States Department of Agriculture.

Iowa State J. Res. = Iowa State Journal of Research.

Iowa State J. Sci. = Iowa State Journal of Science.

Irié-N'guessan, G. et al. 2011. Tracheal relaxation of five Ivorian anti-asthmatic plants: Role of epithelium and K^+ channels in the effect of the aqueous-alcoholic extract of *Dichrostachys cinerea* root bark. J. Ethnopharmacol. 138: 432–438.

Irwin, H. S. and R. C. Barneby. 1977. Monographic studies in *Cassia* (Leguminosae Caesalpinioideae). III. Sections *Absus* and *Grimaldia*. Mem. New York Bot. Gard. 30: 1–300.

Irwin, H. S. and R. C. Barneby. 1981. Cassieae. In: R. M. Polhill and P. H. Raven, eds. 1981. Advances in Legume Systematics. Parts 1 and 2. 2 vols. Kew. Vol. 1, pp. 97–106.

Irwin, H. S. and R. C. Barneby. 1982. The American Cassiinae. Mem. New York Bot. Gard. 35: 1–918.

Irwin, H. S. and B. L. Turner. 1960. Chromosomal relationships and taxonomic considerations in the genus *Cassia*. Amer. J. Bot. 47: 309–318.

Isely, D. 1948. *Lespedeza striata* and *L. stipulacea*. Rhodora 50: 21–27.

Isely, D. 1951. *Desmodium* section *Podocarpium* Benth. Brittonia 7: 185–224.

Isely, D. 1953. *Desmodium paniculatum* (L.) DC. and *D. viridiflorum* (L.) DC. Amer. Midl. Naturalist 49: 920–933.

Isely, D. 1954. Keys to sweet clovers. Proc. Iowa Acad. Sci. 61: 119–131.

Isely, D. 1969. Legumes of the United States. I. Native *Acacia*. Sida 3: 365–386.

Isely, D. 1972. Legumes of the U.S. VI. *Calliandra, Pithecellobium, Prosopis*. Madroño 21: 273–298.

Isely, D. 1973. Leguminosae of the United States: I. Subfamily Mimosoideae. Mem. New York Bot. Gard. 25(1): 1–152.

Isely, D. 1975. Leguminosae of the United States. II. Subfamily Caesalpinioideae. Mem. New York Bot. Gard. 25(2): 1–228.

Isely, D. 1981. Leguminosae of the United States. III. Subfamily Papilionoideae: Tribes Sophoreae, Podalyrieae, Loteae. Mem. New York Bot. Gard. 25(3).

Isely, D. 1981b. Leguminosae of the United States. III. *Baptisia*. Mem. New York Bot. Gard. 25(3): 49–89.

Isely, D. 1982. New combinations and one new variety among the genera *Indigofera, Robinia*, and *Tephrosia* (Leguminosae). Brittonia 34: 339–341.

Isely, D. 1983. New combinations and two new varieties in *Astragalus, Orophaca*, and *Oxytropis* (Leguminosae). Syst. Bot. 8: 420–426.

Isely, D. 1983b. The *Desmodium paniculatum* (Linnaeus) de Candolle (Fabaceae) complex revisited. Sida 10: 142–158.

Isely, D. 1984. *Astragalus* Linnaeus (Leguminosae: Papilionoideae) II. Species summary A–E. Iowa State J. Res. 59: 99–209.

Isely, D. 1986. Notes on Mimosoideae (Leguminosae). Castanea 51: 202–206.

Isely, D. 1990. Leguminosae. In: A. E. Radford et al., eds. 1980+. Vascular Flora of the Southeastern United States. 2+ vols. Chapel Hill. Vol. 3, part 2.

Isely, D. 1992. Innovations in California *Trifolium* and *Lathyrus*. Madroño 39: 90–97.

Isely, D. 1993. *Lotus*. In: J. C. Hickman, ed. 1993. The Jepson Manual. Higher Plants of California. Berkeley, Los Angeles, and London. Pp. 616–622.

Isely, D. 1998. Native and Naturalized Leguminosae (Fabaceae) of the United States (Exclusive of Alaska and Hawaii). Provo. (Native Natural. Legum. U.S.)

Isely, D. and F. J. Peabody. 1984. *Robinia* (Leguminosae-Papilionoideae). Castanea 49: 187–202.

Iselya = Iselya; Botanical Journal of the X Club.

Ives, J. C. 1861. Report upon the Colorado River of the West, Explored in 1857 and 1858 by Lieutenant Joseph C. Ives.... 5 parts, appendices. Washington. (Rep. Colorado R.)

Ivimey-Cook, R. B. 1968. *Ononis*. In: T. G. Tutin et al., eds. 1964–1980. Flora Europaea. 5 vols. Cambridge. Vol. 2, pp. 143–148.

Izaddoost, M. 1975. Alkaloid chemistry of the genus *Sophora*. Phytochemistry 14: 203–204.

J. Acad. Nat. Sci. Philadelphia = Journal of the Academy of Natural Sciences of Philadelphia.

J. Adelaide Bot. Gard. = Journal of the Adelaide Botanic Gardens.

J. Agric. Res. = Journal of Agricultural Research.

J. Arnold Arbor. = Journal of the Arnold Arboretum.

J. Asiat. Soc. Bengal, Pt. 2, Nat. Hist. = Journal of the Asiatic Society of Bengal. Part 2, Natural History.

J. Biol. Sci. (Faisalabad) = Journal of Biological Sciences (Faisalabad)

J. Bot. = Journal of Botany, British and Foreign.

J. Bot. Agric. = Journal de Botanique, Appliquée à l'Agriculture, à la Pharmacie, à la Médecine et aux Arts.

J. Bot. (Hooker) = Journal of Botany, (Being a Second Series of the Botanical Miscellany), Containing Figures and Descriptions....

J. Bot. Res. Inst. Texas = Journal of the Botanical Research Institute of Texas.

J. Chem. Educ. = Journal of Chemical Education.

J. Coastal Res. = Journal of Coastal Research.

J. Ecol. = Journal of Ecology.

J. Econ. Entomol. = Journal of Economic Entomology.

J. Econ. Taxon. Bot. = Journal of Economic and Taxonomic Botany.

J. Elisha Mitchell Sci. Soc. = Journal of the Elisha Mitchell Scientific Society.

J. Ethnopharmacol. = Journal of Ethnopharmacology; Interdisciplinary Journal Devoted to Bioscientific Research on Indigenous Drugs.

J. Genet. = Journal of Genetics.

J. Hort. Soc. London = Journal of the Horticultural Society of London.

J. Jap. Bot. = Journal of Japanese Botany.

J. Kentucky Acad. Sci. = Journal of the Kentucky Academy of Science.

J. Linn. Soc., Bot. = Journal of the Linnean Society. Botany.

J. Nat. Prod. (Lloydia) = Journal of Natural Products (Lloydia).

J. Pl. Res. = Journal of Plant Research. [Shokubutsu-gaku zasshi.]

J. Proc. Linn. Soc., Bot. = Journal of the Proceedings of the Linnean Society. Botany.

J. Range Managem. = Journal of Range Management.

J. Syst. Evol. = Journal of Systematics and Evolution.

J. Torrey Bot. Soc. = Journal of the Torrey Botanical Society.

J. Wash. Acad. Sci. = Journal of the Washington Academy of Sciences.

Jacobsen, E. 2000. *Retama monosperma*. In: C. C. Bossard et al., eds. 2000. Invasive Plants of California's Wildlands. Berkeley. Pp. 266–268.

Jacquin, N. J. 1760. Enumeratio Systematica Plantarum, Quas in Insulis Caribaeis Vicinaque Americes Continente Detexit Novas.... Leiden. (Enum. Syst. Pl.)

Jacquin, N. J. 1763. Selectarum Stirpium Americanarum Historia.... Vienna. (Select. Stirp. Amer. Hist.)

Jacquin, N. J. 1770–1776. Hortus Botanicus Vindobonensis.... 3 vols. Vienna. (Hort. Bot. Vindob.)

Jacquin, N. J. 1781–1793[–1795]. Icones Plantarum Rariorum. 3 vols. in fascs. Vienna etc. [Vols. paged independently, plates numbered consecutively.] (Icon. Pl. Rar.)

Jacquin, N. J. 1786[1787]–1796[1797]. Collectanea ad Botanicam, Chemiam, et Historiam Naturalem Spectantia.... 5 vols. Vienna. (Collectanea)

Jacquin, N. J. 1797–1804. Plantarum Rariorum Horti Caesarei Schoenbrunnensis Descriptiones et Icones. 4 vols. Vienna, London, and Leiden. (Pl. Hort. Schoenbr.)

Jacquin, N. J. [1800–]1809. Fragmenta Botanica, Figuris Coloratis Illustrata.... 6 fascs. Vienna. (Fragm. Bot.)

James, L. F. et al., eds. 1989. Swainsonine and Related Glycoside Inhibitors. Ames.

James, L. F. et al., eds. 1992. Poisonous Plants. Proceedings of the Third International Symposium. Ames.

James, L. F. and S. L. Welsh. 1992. Poisonous plants of North America. In: L. F. James et al., eds. 1992. Poisonous Plants. Proceedings of the Third International Symposium. Ames. Pp. 94–103.

Janick, J. and A. Whipkey. 2002. Trends in New Crops and New Uses. Alexandria.

Jansen, P. C. M. 2005. *Mucuna sloanei* Fawc. & Rendle. In: P. C. M. Jansen and D. Cardon, eds. 2005. Dyes and Tannins. Text + CD-ROM. Wageningen. Record from Protabase.

Jansen, P. C. M. and D. Cardon. 2005. Dyes and Tannins. Text + CD-ROM. Wageningen. [Pl. Res. Trop. Africa 3.]

Janzen, D. H. and P. S. Martin. 1982. Neotropical anachronisms: The fruits the Gomphotheres ate. Science, ser. 2, 215: 19–27.

Jawad, J. T., D. S. Seigler, and J. E. Ebinger. 2000. A systematic treatment of *Acacia coulteri* (Fabaceae, Mimosoideae) and similar species in the New World. Ann. Missouri Bot. Gard. 87: 528–548.

Jepson, W. L. 1909–1943. A Flora of California.... 3 vols. in 12 parts. San Francisco etc. [Pagination consecutive within each vol.; vol. 1 page sequence independent of part number sequence (chronological); part 8 of vol. 1 (pp. 1–32, 579–index) never published.] (Fl. Calif.)

Jepson, W. L. [1923–1925.] A Manual of the Flowering Plants of California.... Berkeley. (Man. Fl. Pl. Calif.)

Johnston, I. M. 1924. Taxonomic records concerning American spermatophytes. 1. *Parkinsonia* and *Cercidium*. Contr. Gray Herb. 70: 61–68.

Joly, S. and A. Bruneau. 2004. Evolutionary significance of the multiple origins of triploidy in *Apios americana* Medik. as revealed by genealogical analysis of the H3-D histone gene. Evolution 58: 282–295.

Jones, M. E. 1923. Revision of North-American Species of *Astragalus*. Salt Lake City. (Rev. N.-Amer. Astragalus)

Jorgensen, J. L. et al. 2003. Implications of ITS sequences and RAPD markers for the taxonomy and biogeography of the *Oxytropis campestris* and *O. arctica* complexes in Alaska. Amer. J. Bot. 90: 1470–1480.

Jurtzev, B. A. 1986. *Oxytropis*. In: A. I. Tolmatchew, ed. 1960–1987. Flora Arctica URSS. 10 vols. in 12. Moscow and Leningrad. Vol. 9(2), pp. 61–146.

Jurtzev, B. A. 1993b. *Oxytropis tananensis*, a new species of section *Baicalia* (Fabaceae) from the interior of eastern Alaska. Bot. Zhurn. (Moscow & Leningrad) 78: 59–65.

Kajita, T. and H. Ohashi. 1994. Chloroplast DNA variation in *Desmodium* subgenus *Podocarpium* (Leguminosae): Infrageneric phylogeny and infraspecific variations. J. Pl. Res. 107: 349–354.

Kalmia = Kalmia; Botanic Journal.

Kansas Univ. Sci. Bull. = Kansas University Science Bulletin.

Karrenberg, S. et al. 2003. Patterns in woody vegetation along the active zone of a near-natural alpine river. Basic Appl. Ecol. 4: 157–166.

Karron, J. D. 1989. Breeding systems and levels of inbreeding depression in geographically restricted and widespread species of *Astragalus* (Fabaceae). Amer. J. Bot. 76: 331–340.

Karron, J. D. et al. 1988. Genetic structure of populations of geographically restricted and widespread species of *Astragalus* (Fabaceae). Amer. J. Bot. 75: 1114–1119.

Kartesz, J. T. and K. N. Gandhi. 1992b. *Pediomelum ockendonii* sp. nov.: Correct name for *P. palmeri* Grimes (Fabaceae). Sida 15: 137–138.

Kartesz, J. T. and C. A. Meacham. 1999. Synthesis of the North American Flora, ver. 1.0. Chapel Hill. [CD-ROM.]

Kartzinel, R. Y. et al. 2016. Divergence and isolation of cryptic sympatric taxa within the annual legume *Amphicarpaea bracteata*. Ecol. & Evol. 6: 3367–3379.

Käss, E. and M. Wink. 1995. Molecular phylogeny of the Papilionoideae (family Leguminosae): *rbc*L gene sequences versus chemical taxonomy. Bot. Acta 108: 149–162.

Kaul, A. D. and D. Combes. 1986. *Lathyrus* and Lathyrism. New York.

Kearney, T. H. and R. H. Peebles. 1951. Arizona Flora. Berkeley.

Kearney, T. H. and R. H. Peebles. 1960. Arizona Flora, ed. 2. Berkeley.

Keeler, R. F. et al. 1977. Lupine-induced crooked calf disease and a management method to reduce incidence. J. Range Managem. 30: 97–102.

Keener, B. R. 2013. Two vascular plant species new to the Alabama flora. Phytoneuron 2013-61: 1–4.

Keil, D. J. 2019. *Trifolium albopurpureum* var. *columbinum* (Fabaceae), a new combination for a California clover. Phytologia 101: 131–133.

Kellogg, A. 1861. Presidential address. Proc. Calif. Acad. Sci. 2: 115–117.

Kellogg, A. 1877. Notes and descriptions of some California plants. Proc. Calif. Acad. Sci. 7: 89–94.

Kenicer, G. J. et al. 2005. Systematics and biogeography of *Lathyrus* (Leguminosae) based on internal transcribed spacer and cpDNA sequence data. Amer. J. Bot. 92: 1199–1209.

Kennedy, P. B. and W. W. Mackie. 1925. Berseem or Egyptian clover *(Trifolium alexandrinum)*, a preliminary report. Bull. Calif. Agric. Exp. Sta. 389.

Kerridge, P. C. and B. Hardy, eds. 1994. Biology and Agronomy of Forage *Arachis*. Cali.

Kew Bull. = Kew Bulletin.

Kiger, R. W. and D. M. Porter. 2001. Categorical Glossary for the Flora of North America Project. Pittsburgh.

Kingsbury, J. M. 1964. Poisonous Plants of the United States and Canada. Englewood Cliffs.

Kirkbride, J. H., C. R. Gunn, and A. L. Weitzman. 2003. Fruits and Seeds of Genera in the Subfamily Faboideae (Fabaceae). Washington. [U.S.D.A. Agric. Res. Serv., Techn. Bull. 1890.]

Kirkia = Kirkia; Journal of the Federal Herbarium [Rhodesia].

Kleist, A. et al. 2014. Inferring the complex origins of horticultural invasives: French broom in California. Biol. Invasions 16: 887–901.

Klitgaard, B. B. and A. Bruneau, eds. 2003. Advances in Legume Systematics. Part 10. Kew.

Knapp, E. E. and P. G. Connors. 1999. Genetic consequences of a single-founder population bottleneck in *Trifolium amoenum* (Fabaceae). Amer. J. Bot. 86: 124–130.

Knaus, B. J., R. C. Cronin, and A. Liston. 2005. Genetic characterization of three varieties of *Astragalus lentiginosus* (Fabaceae). Brittonia 57: 334–344.

Knight, W. E. 1985. Crimson clover. In: N. L. Taylor, ed. 1985. Clover Science and Technology. Madison. Pp. 491–502.

Knight, W. E. 1985b. Miscellaneous annual clovers. In: N. L. Taylor, ed. 1985. Clover Science and Technology. Madison. Pp. 547–562.

Knowlton, C. H. and W. Deane. 1918. Reports on the flora of the Boston district—XXIX. Rhodora 20: 208–209.

Koch, K. H. E. 1869–1873. Dendrologie. Bäume, Sträucher und Halbsträucher, welche in Mittel- und Nord-Europa im Freien kultivirt werden. 2 vols. in 3. Erlangen. (Dendrologie)

Koch, W. D. J. [1835–]1837–1838. Synopsis Florae Germanicae et Helveticae.... 1 vol. in 2 sects. and index. Frankfurt am Main. [Index paged independently.] (Syn. Fl. Germ. Helv.)

Koehne, B. A. E. 1893. Deutsche Dendrologie. Stuttgart. (Deut. Dendrol.)

Komarov, V. L. et al., eds. 1963+. Flora of the U.S.S.R. (Flora SSSR). Translated from Russian. 30+ vols. Jerusalem etc.

Komarov, V. L., B. K. Schischkin, and E. Bobrov, eds. 1934–1964. Flora URSS.... 30 vols. Leningrad. (Fl. URSS)

Kosnik, M. A. et al. 1996. Natural hybridization among three sympatric *Baptisia* (Fabaceae) species in north central Texas. Sida 17: 479–500.

Kosterin, O. E. and V. S. Bogdanova. 2008. Relationship of wild and cultivated forms of *Pisum* L. as inferred from an analysis of three markers, of the plastid, mitochondrial and nuclear genomes. Genet. Resources Crop Evol. 55: 735–755.

Kral, R. et al. 2012. Alabama Plant Atlas. Livingston.

Kramina, T. E. 2006. A contribution to the taxonomic revision of the *Lotus angustissimus*-complex (Leguminosae, Loteae). Wulfenia 13: 57–92.

Krapovickas, A. and W. C. Gregory. 2007. Taxonomy of the genus *Arachis* (Leguminosae). Bonplandia (Corrientes) 16(suppl.): 1–205.

Kretschmer, A. E. and R. C. Bullock. 1980. *Aeschynomene* spp.: Distribution and potential use. Proc. Soil Crop Sci. Soc. Florida 39: 145–152.

Krukoff, B. A. and R. C. Barneby. 1973. Notes on species of *Erythrina*. VII. Phytologia 27: 108–114.

Krukoff, B. A. and R. C. Barneby. 1974. Conspectus of species of the genus *Erythrina*. Lloydia 37: 332–459.

Krüssmann, G. 1984–1986. Manual of Cultivated Broad-leaved Trees and Shrubs. 3 vols. Beaverton.

Kulakow, P. A. 1999. Variation in Illinois bundleflowers (*Desmanthus illinoensis* (Michaux) McMillan): A potential perennial grain legume. Euphytica 110: 7–20.

Kunth, C. S. 1819[–1824]. Mimoses et Autres Plantes Légumineuses du Nouvearu Continent.... 14 parts. Paris. [Parts paged consecutively.] (Mimoses)

Kuntze, O. 1891–1898. Revisio Generum Plantarum Vascularium Omnium atque Cellularium Multarum.... 3 vols. Leipzig etc. [Vol. 3 in 3 parts paged independently; parts 1 and 3 unnumbered.] (Revis. Gen. Pl.)

Kupicha, F. K. 1976. The infrageneric structure of *Vicia.* Notes Roy. Bot. Gard. Edinburgh 34: 287–326.

Kupicha, F. K. 1981. Vicieae. In: R. M. Polhill and P. H. Raven, eds. 1981. Advances in Legume Systematics. Parts 1 and 2. 2 vols. Kew. Vol. 1, pp. 377–381.

Kupicha, F. K. 1983. The infrageneric structure of *Lathyrus.* Notes Roy. Bot. Gard. Edinburgh 41: 209–244.

L'Héritier de Brutelle, C.-L. 1788[1789–1792]. Sertum Anglicum.... 4 fascs. Paris. [All text in fasc. 1; plates numbered consecutively.] (Sert. Angl.)

La Llave, P. de. 1837–1842. Mosiaco Mexicano. 7 vols. Mexico City. (Mosiaco Mex.)

Labillardière, J. J. H. de. 1804–1806[1807]. Novae Hollandiae Plantarum Specimen.... 2 vols. in parts. Paris. [Parts paged consecutively within vols., plates numbered consecutively throughout.] (Nov. Holl. Pl.)

Ladizinsky, G. et al. 1984. The biological species of the genus *Lens* L. Bot. Gaz. 145: 253–261.

Lady-slipper = The Lady-slipper.

Lamarck, J. 1778[1779]. Flore Françoise ou Description Succincte de Toutes les Plantes Qui Croissent Naturellement en France.... 3 vols. Paris. (Fl. Franç.)

Lamarck, J. et al. 1783–1817. Encyclopédie Méthodique. Botanique.... 13 vols. Paris and Liège. [Vols. 1–8, suppls. 1–5.] (Encycl.)

Lamarck, J. and A. P. de Candolle. 1805–1815. Flore Française, ou Descriptions Succinctes de Toutes les Plantes Qui Croissent Naturellement en France..., ed. 3. 5 tomes in 6 vols. Paris. [Tomes 1–4(2), vols. 1–5, 1805; tome 5, vol. 6, 1815.] (Fl. Franç. ed. 3)

Lamarck, J. and J. Poiret. 1791–1823. Tableau Encyclopédique et Méthodique des Trois Règnes de la Nature. Botanique.... 6 vols. Paris. [Vols. 1–2 = tome 1; vols. 3–5 = tome 2; vol. [6] = tome 3. Vols. paged consecutively within tomes.] (Tabl. Encycl.)

Lang, J. M. and D. Isely. 1982. *Eysenhardtia* (Leguminosae: Papilionoideae). Iowa State J. Res. 56: 393–417.

Larisey, M. M. 1940. A monograph of the genus *Baptisia.* Ann. Missouri Bot. Gard. 27: 119–244.

Larisey, M. M. 1940b. A revision of the North American species of the genus *Thermopsis.* Ann. Missouri Bot. Gard. 27: 245–258.

Lassen, P. 1989. A new delimitation of the genera *Coronilla, Hippocrepis,* and *Securigera* (Fabaceae). Willdenowia 19: 49–62.

Lassetter, J. S. 1975. Taxonomic status of *Vicia hassei* (Leguminosae). Madroño 23: 73–78.

Lassetter, J. S. 1978. Seed characters in some native American vetches. Sida 7: 255–263.

Lassetter, J. S. 1984. Taxonomy of the *Vicia ludoviciana* complex (Leguminosae). Rhodora 86: 475–505.

Lassetter, J. S. and C. R. Gunn. 1979. *Vicia menziesii* Sprengel (Fabaceae) rediscovered: Its taxonomic relationships. Pacific Sci. 33: 85–101.

Lau, C. P. Y., L. Ramsden, and R. M. K. Saunders. 2005. Hybrid origin of "*Bauhinia blakeana*" (Leguminosae: Caesalpinioideae), inferred using morphological, reproductive, and molecular data. Amer. J. Bot. 92: 525–533.

Lavin, M. 1988. Systematics of *Coursetia* (Leguminosae-Papilionoideae). Syst. Bot. Monogr. 21.

Lavin, M. 1990. The genus *Sphinctospermum* (Leguminosae): Taxonomy and tribal relationships as inferred from a cladistic analysis of traditional data. Syst. Bot. 15: 544–559.

Lavin, M. et al. 2001. The dalbergioid legumes (Fabaceae): Delimitation of a pantropical monophyletic clade. Amer. J. Bot. 88: 503–533.

Lavin, M. et al. 2001b. Africa, the odd man out: Molecular biogeography of dalbergioid legumes (Fabaceae) suggests otherwise. Syst. Bot. 25: 449–467.

Lavin, M. et al. 2003. Phylogeny of robinioid legumes (Fabaceae) revisited: *Coursetia* and *Gliricidia* recircumscribed, and a biogeographical appraisal of the Caribbean endemics. Syst. Bot. 28: 387–409.

Lavin, M. and J. J. Doyle. 1991. Tribal relationships of *Sphinctospermum* (Leguminosae): Integration of traditional and chloroplast DNA data. Syst. Bot. 16: 162–172.

Lavin, M. and H. Marriott. 1997. *Astragalus molybdenus* s.l. (Leguminosae): Higher taxonomic relationships and identity of constituent species. Syst. Bot. 22: 199–217.

Lavin, M. and M. Sousa S. 1995. Phylogenetic systematics and biogeography of the tribe Robinieae. Syst. Bot. Monogr. 45.

Lawless, P. J., J. M. Baskin, and C. C. Baskin. 2006. Scale-dependent classification of xeric limestone prairies: Annual or periennial grasslands? Ann. Missouri Bot. Gard. 93: 455–464.

Leafl. Alabama Agric. Exp. Sta. = Leaflet. Alabama Agricultural Experiment Station.

Leafl. Bot. Observ. Crit. = Leaflets of Botanical Observation and Criticism.

Leafl. W. Bot. = Leaflets of Western Botany.

Ledin, R. B. and E. A. Menninger. 1956. *Bauhinia*—The so-called orchid trees. Natl. Hort. Mag. 35: 183–200.

Ledingham, G. F. 1960. Chromosome numbers in *Astragalus* and *Oxytropis.* Canad. J. Genet. Cytol. 2: 119–128.

Ledingham, G. F. 1960b. Chromosome numbers in *Astragalus.* Proc. Genet. Soc. Canada 3: 15–18.

Lee, J. K. and T. Hymowitz. 2001. A molecular phylogenetic study of the subtribe Glycininae (Leguminosae) derived from the chloroplast DNA *rps*16 intron sequences. Amer. J. Bot. 88: 2064–2073.

Lee, Y. S., D. S. Seigler, and J. E. Ebinger. 1989. *Acacia rigidula* (Fabaceae) and related species in Mexico and Texas. Syst. Bot. 14: 91–100.

Leebens-Mack, J. and B. G. Milligan. 1998. Pollination biology in hybridizing *Baptisia* (Fabaceae) populations. Amer. J. Bot. 85: 500–507.

Legume Phylogeny Working Group. 2017. A new subfamily classification of the Leguminosae based on a taxonomically comprehensive phylogeny. Taxon 66: 44–77.

Legumes India—See: M. Sanjappa 1992

Leht, M. 2005. Cladistic and phenetic analysis of relationships in *Vicia* subgenus *Cracca* (Fabaceae) based on morphological data. Taxon 54: 1023–1032.

Leiden Bot. Ser. = Leiden Botanical Series.

Lesica, P. 2012. Manual of Montana Vascular Plants. Fort Worth.

Lesins, K. A. and I. Lesins. 1979. Genus *Medicago*. A Taxogenetic Study. The Hague.

Levings, C. K. 2006. A Monograph of the Genus *Maackia*. M.S. thesis. Miami University.

Lewis, G. P. 2005. Caesalpinieae. In: G. P. Lewis et al., eds. 2005. Legumes of the World. Kew. Pp. 127–161.

Lewis, G. P. et al., eds. 2005. Legumes of the World. Kew.

Lewis, G. P. and F. Forest. 2005. Cercideae. In: G. P. Lewis et al., eds. 2005. Legumes of the World. Kew. Pp. 57–67.

Lewis, Mer. and W. Clark. 2003 The Lewis and Clark Journals: An American Epic of Discovery..., ed. G. E. Moulton. Lincoln, Nebr.

Lewis, W. H. and M. P. F. Elvin-Lewis. 2003. Medical Botany: Plants Affecting Human Health, ed. 2. Hoboken.

Li, H. C. et al. 2019. Molecular phylogeny of the genus *Hylodesmum* (Fabaceae). Phytotaxa 403: 221–229.

Li, J. et al. 1993. Antitumor agents, 138. Rotenoids and isoflavones as cytotoxic constituents from *Amorpha fruticosa*. J. Nat. Prod. (Lloydia) 56: 690–698.

Li, J. H. et al. 2014. Molecular systematics and biogeography of *Wisteria* inferred from nucleotide sequences of nuclear and plastid genes. J. Syst. Evol. 52: 40–50.

Lievens, A. W. 1992. Taxonomic Treatment of *Indigofera* L. (Fabaceae: Faboideae) in the New World. Ph.D. dissertation. Louisiana State University.

Lima, L. C. P. et al. 2012. Proposal to conserve the name *Hedysarum incanum* Sw. against *H. incanum* Thunb. Taxon 61: 1122–1123.

Lima, L. C. P. et al. 2014. A taxonomic revision of *Desmodium* (Leguminosae, Papilionoideae) in Brazil. Phytotaxa 169: 1–109.

Link, J. H. F. 1821–1822. Enumeratio Plantarum Horti Regii Berolinensis Altera.... 2 parts. Berlin. (Enum. Hort. Berol. Alt.)

Link, J. H. F. 1829–1833. Handbuch zur Erkennung der nutzbarsten und am häufigsten vorkommenden Gewächse.... 3 vols. Berlin. (Handbuch)

Link, J. H. F., J. F. Klotzsch, and C. F. Otto. 1841–1844. Icones Plantarum Rariorum Horti Regii Botanici Berolinensis.... 2 vols. in 8 parts. Berlin. [Vols. and parts paged and plates numbered consecutively.] (Icon. Pl. Rar.)

Linnaea = Linnaea; ein Journal für die Botanik in ihrem ganzen Umfange.

Linnaeus, C. 1749[–1769]. Amoenitates Academicae seu Dissertationes Variae Physicae, Medicae Botanicae.... 7 vols. Stockholm and Leipzig. (Amoen. Acad.)

Linnaeus, C. 1753. Species Plantarum.... 2 vols. Stockholm. (Sp. Pl.)

Linnaeus, C. [1753.] Demonstrationes Plantarum in Horto Upsaliensi.... Uppsala. (Demonstr. Pl.)

Linnaeus, C. 1754. Genera Plantarum..., ed. 5. Stockholm. (Gen. Pl. ed. 5)

Linnaeus, C. 1754b. Herbarium Amboinense.... Uppsala. (Herb. Amb.)

Linnaeus, C. 1755. Centuria I. Plantarum.... Uppsala. (Cent. Pl. I)

Linnaeus, C. 1755b. Flora Suecica..., ed. 2. Stockholm. (Fl. Suec. ed. 2)

Linnaeus, C. 1758. Opera Varia...Fundamenta Botanica, Sponsalia Plantarum, et Systema Naturae.... Lucca. (Opera Var.)

Linnaeus, C. 1758[–1759]. Systema Naturae per Regna Tria Naturae..., ed. 10. 2 vols. Stockholm. (Syst. Nat. ed. 10)

Linnaeus, C. 1759. Plantarum Jamaicensium Pugillus.... Uppsala. (Pl. Jamaic. Pug.)

Linnaeus, C. 1762–1763. Species Plantarum..., ed. 2. 2 vols. Stockholm. (Sp. Pl. ed. 2)

Linnaeus, C. 1766–1768. Systema Naturae per Regna Tria Naturae..., ed. 12. 3 vols. Stockholm. (Syst. Nat. ed. 12)

Linnaeus, C. 1767[–1771]. Mantissa Plantarum. 2 parts. Stockholm. [Mantissa [1] and Mantissa [2] Altera paged consecutively.] (Mant. Pl.)

Linnaeus, C. f. 1762[–1763]. Decas Prima [Secunda] Plantarum Rariorum Horti Upsaliensis.... 2 vols. Stockholm. (Dec. Pl. Horti Upsal.)

Linnaeus, C. f. 1781[1782]. Supplementum Plantarum Systematis Vegetabilium Editionis Decimae Tertiae, Generum Plantarum Editionis Sextae, et Specierum Plantarum Editionis Secundae. Braunschweig. (Suppl. Pl.)

Linscott, T. M. 1994. Morphological and Genetic Diversity of *Trifolium virginicum* Populations Using Quantitative and Allozyme Studies. M.S. thesis. Miami University.

Liston, A. 1990. Taxonomic notes on *Astragalus* section *Leptocarpi* subsection *Californici* (Fabaceae). Brittonia 42: 100–104.

Liston, A. 1992. Isozyme systematics of *Astragalus* sect. *Leptocarpi* subsection *Californici* (Fabaceae). Syst. Bot. 17: 367–379.

Liston, A., L. H. Rieseberg, and O. Mistretta. 1990. Ribosomal evidence for hybridization between island endemic species of *Lotus*. Biochem. Syst. & Ecol. 18: 239–244.

Liston, A., K. St. Hilaire, and M. V. Wilson. 1995. Genetic diversity in populations of *Lupinus sulphureus* ssp. *kincaidii*, host plant of Fender's blue butterfly. Madroño 42: 309–322.

Little, E. L. Jr. 1971. Atlas of United States Trees. I. Conifers and Important Hardwoods. Washington. [U.S.D.A., Misc. Publ. 1146.]

Litvinov, D. I. 1898–1911. Schedae ad Herbarium Florae Rossicae.... 7 vols. St. Petersburg. (Sched. Herb. Fl. Ross.)

Lloydia = Lloydia; a Quarterly Journal of Biological Science.

London J. Bot. = London Journal of Botany.

London Med. J. = The London Medical Journal, by a Society of Physicians.

Long, R. W. and O. Lakela. 1971. A Flora of Tropical Florida: A Manual of the Seed Plants and Ferns of Southern Peninsular Florida. Coral Gables. [Reprinted 1976, Miami.]

Loudon, J. C. 1830. Hortus Brittanicus. A Catalogue of All the Plants Indigenous, Cultivated in, or Introduced to Britain. London. (Hort. Brit.)

Loureiro, J. de. 1790. Flora Cochinchinensis.... 2 vols. Lisbon. [Vols. paged consecutively.] (Fl. Cochinch.)

Love, R. M. 1985. Rose clover. In: N. L. Taylor, ed. 1985. Clover Science and Technology. Madison. Pp. 535–546.

Lowe, R. T. 1857–1872. A Manual Flora of Madeira and the Adjacent Islands of Porto Santo and the Desertas.... 2 vols. in parts. London. [Parts paged consecutively within volumes; Vol. 2, one part only.] (Man. Fl. Madeira)

Luckow, M. A. 1993. Monograph of *Desmanthus* (Leguminosae-Mimosoideae). Syst. Bot. Monogr. 38.

Luckow, M. A. 1996. The cultivated species of *Cassia, Senna,* and *Chamaecrista* (Leguminosae). Baileya 23: 195–241.

Luckow, M. A. 2005. Mimoseae. In: G. P. Lewis et al., eds. 2005. Legumes of the World. Kew. Pp. 163–183.

Luckow, M. A. and D. J. Du Puy. 2000. A new species of *Gagnebina* (Leguminosae: Mimosoideae) from Madagascar. Novon 10: 220–223.

Lundellia = Lundellia; Journal of the Plant Resources Center of the University of Texas at Austin.

Maass, B. L. et al. 2010. *Lablab purpureus*—A crop lost for Africa? Trop. Pl. Biol. 3: 123–135.

Mack, R. N. 2003. Plant naturalizations and invasions in the eastern United States: 1634–1860. Ann. Missouri Bot. Gard. 90: 77–90.

Macklin, B. and D. O. Evans, eds. 1990. Perennial *Sesbania* Species in Agroforestry Systems. Waimanalo.

Madroño = Madroño; Journal of the California Botanical Society [from vol. 3: a West American Journal of Botany].

Maekawa, M., Hasen, and F. Kita. 1991. Identification of reciprocal translocations observed in several *Melilotus* species (subgenus *Eumelilotus*) by interspecific triple crossings. Euphytica 54: 255–261.

Mag. Hort. Bot. = Magazine of Horticulture, Botany and All Useful Discoveries and Improvements in Rural Affairs.

Mag. Tosc. = Magazzino Toscano.

Mahler, W. F. 1965. The Pollen Morphology of the Tribe Psoraleae (Leguminosae). Washington. [Natl. Sci. Found. Res. Participation Rep.]

Man. Bot. ed. 2—See: A. Eaton 1818

Man. Bot. ed. 5—See: A. Eaton 1829

Man. Bot. ed. 8—See: A. Eaton and J. Wright 1840

Man. Bot. San Francisco—See: E. L. Greene 1894

Man. Fl. Madeira—See: R. T. Lowe 1857–1872

Man. Fl. Pl. Calif.—See: W. L. Jepson [1923–1925]

Man. Pl. Oregon—See: M. E. Peck 1941

Man. S.E. Fl.—See: J. K. Small 1933

Mancuso, M. 2001. The Status of *Trifolium owyheense* (Owyhee Clover) in Idaho. Boise.

Mant. Pl.—See: C. Linnaeus 1767[–1771]

Manual ed. 2—See: A. Gray 1856

Manual ed. 7—See: B. L. Robinson and M. L. Fernald 1908

Marazzi, B. et al. 2006. Phylogenetic relationships within *Senna* (Leguminosae, Cassiinae) based on three chloroplast regions: Patterns in the evolution of floral symmetry and extrafloral nectaries. Amer. J. Bot. 93: 288–303.

Marazzi, B. et al. 2006b. *Senna* (Cassiinae, Leguminosae) in Paraguay: Synopsis, conservation, ecologic role and ethnobotany. Candollea 61: 315–329.

Marazzi, B. et al. 2007. Diversity of anthers and stigmas in the buzz-pollinated genus *Senna* (Leguminosae, Cassiinae). Int. J. Pl. Sci. 168: 371–391.

Marazzi, B. et al. 2013. Diversity and evolution of a trait mediating ant-plant interactions: Insight from extrafloral nectaries in *Senna* (Leguminosae). Ann. Bot. (Oxford) 111: 1263–1275.

Marazzi, B. and P. K. Endress. 2008. Patterns and development of floral asymmetry in *Senna* (Leguminosae, Cassiinae). Amer. J. Bot. 95: 22–40.

Marazzi, B. and M. J. Sanderson. 2010. Large-scale patterns of diversification in the widespread legume genus *Senna* and the evolutionary role of extrafloral nectaries. Evolution 64: 3570–3592.

Marschall von Bieberstein, F. A. 1808–1819. Flora Taurico-Caucasica.... 3 vols. Charkow. (Fl. Taur.-Caucas.)

Marshall, H. 1785. Arbustrum Americanum: The American Grove.... Philadelphia. (Arbust. Amer.)

Martin, H. and M'P. Bindanda. 2008. Natural Medicine in the Tropics I: Foundation Text. Winnenden.

Martin, J. S. 1943. A Revision of the Native Clovers of the United States. Ph.D. dissertation. University of Washington.

Martin, W. C. and C. R. Hutchins. 1980. A Flora of New Mexico. 2 vols. Vaduz.

Martinez, M. L. and P. Moreno-Casasola. 1998 The biological flora of coastal dunes and wetlands: *Chamaecrista chamaecristoides* (Colladon) H. S. Irwin & Barneby. J. Coastal Res. 14: 162–174.

Martínez-Bernal, A., R. Grether, and R. M. González-Amaro. 2008. *Mimosa.* In: Instituto Nacional de Investigaciones sobre Recursos Bióticas. 1978+. Flora de Veracruz. 162+ fascs. Xalapa. Fasc. 147, pp. 9–127.

Martius, C. F. P. von, A. W. Eichler, and I. Urban, eds. 1840–1906. Flora Brasiliensis. 15 vols. in 40 parts, 130 fascs. Munich, Vienna, and Leipzig. [Vols. and parts numbered in systematic sequence, fascs. numbered independently in chronological sequence.] (Fl. Bras.)

Martyn, T. 1792–1794[–1795] Flora Rustica.... 4 vols. London. (Fl. Rust.)

Maschinski, J., H. D. Hammond, and L. Holter, eds. 1996. Southwestern Rare and Endangered Plants: Proceedings of the Second Conference: September 11–14, 1995, Flagstaff, Arizona. Fort Collins. [U.S.D.A. Forest Serv., Gen. Techn. Rep. RM-283.] (S.W. Rare Endang. Pl. 1995)

Maslin, B. R. 2008. Generic and subgeneric names in *Acacia* following retypification of the genus. Muelleria 26: 7–9.

Maslin, B. R., J. T. Miller, and D. S. Seigler. 2003. Overview of the generic status of *Acacia* (Leguminosae: Mimosoideae). Austral. Syst. Bot. 16: 1–18.

Mathesius, U., E. P. Journet, and L. W. Sumner, eds. 2006. The *Medicago truncatula* Handbook. Ardmore, Okla.

Matten, L. C., R. A. Gastaldo, and M. R. Lee. 1977. Fossil *Robinia* wood from the western United States. Rev. Palaeobot. Palynol. 24: 195–208.

Maxted, N. et al. 2004. An Ecogeographic Study. African *Vigna*. Rome.

Maxwell, R. H. 1979. Transfer of *Dioclea multiflora* to *Galactia* (Leguminosae). Castanea 44: 241–246.

Maxwell, R. H. and D. W. Taylor. 2003. Phylogenetic relationships of the Diocleinae with particular emphasis on the subgroups of *Dioclea*. In: B. B. Klitgaard and A. Bruneau, eds. 2003. Advances in Legume Systematics. Part 10. Kew. Pp. 325–353.

Mayer, M. S. and S. K. Bagga. 2002. The phylogeny of *Lens* (Leguminosae): New insight from ITS sequence analysis. Pl. Syst. Evol. 232: 145–154.

McCormick, C. A. 2007. The heartbreak of *Psoralea*. Ladyslipper 22(3): 4–5.

McDermott, L. F. 1910. An Illustrated Key to the North American Species of *Trifolium*. San Francisco.

McGuire, W. S. 1985. Subterranean clover. In: N. L. Taylor, ed. 1985. Clover Science and Technology. Madison. Pp. 515–534.

McMahon, M. 2005. Phylogenetic relationships and floral evolution in the papilionoid clade Amorpheae. Brittonia 57: 397–411.

McMahon, M. and L. Hufford. 2004. Phylogeny of Amorpheae (Fabaceae, Papilionoideae). Amer. J. Bot. 91: 1219–1230.

McMahon, M. and L. Hufford. 2005. Evolution and development the amorphoid clade (Amorpheae: Papilionoideae: Leguminosae): Petal loss and dedifferentiation. Int. J. Pl. Sci. 166: 383–396.

McNeill, J. and N. J. Turland. 2010. The conservation of *Acacia* with *A. penninervis* as conserved type. Taxon 59: 613–616.

McVaugh, R. 1987. Leguminosae. In: R. McVaugh and W. R. Anderson, eds. 1974+. Flora Novo-Galiciana: A Descriptive Account of the Vascular Plants of Western Mexico. 8+ vols. Ann Arbor. Vol. 5.

McVaugh, R. and W. R. Anderson, eds. 1974+. Flora Novo-Galiciana: A Descriptive Account of the Vascular Plants of Western Mexico. 8+ vols. Ann Arbor. (Fl. Novo-Galiciana)

Meded. Landbouwhoogeschool = Mededeelingen van de Landbouwhoogeschool te Wageningen.

Medikus, F. K. 1786. *Theodora speciosa....* Mannheim. (Theodora)

Meikle, R. D. 1950. Tropical African plants: XXI. Kew Bull. 5: 335–384.

Mém. Acad. Imp. Sci. Saint Pétersbourg, Sér. 7 = Mémoires de l'Académie Impériale des Sciences de Saint Pétersbourg, Septième Série.

Mém. Acad. Imp. Sci. St.-Pétersbourg Divers Savans = Mémoires Présentés à l'Académie Impériale des Sciences de St.-Pétersbourg par Divers Savans et Lus dans ses Assemblées.

Mém. Acad. Imp. Sci. St. Pétersbourg Hist. Acad. = Mémoires de l'Académie Impériale des Sciences de St. Pétersbourg. Avec l'Histoire de l'Académie.

Mem. Amer. Acad. Arts = Memoirs of the American Academy of Arts and Science.

Mem. New York Bot. Gard. = Memoirs of the New York Botanical Garden.

Mem. Reale Accad. Sci. Ist. Bologna = Memorie della R[eale]. Accademia delle Scienze dell' Istituto di Bologna.

Mém. Soc. Phys. Genève = Mémoires de la Société de Physique et d'Histoire Naturelle de Genève.

Mem. Torrey Bot. Club = Memoirs of the Torrey Botanical Club.

Mendenhall, M. G. 1994. Phylogeny of *Baptisia* and *Thermopsis* (Leguminosae) as Inferred from Chloroplast DNA and Nuclear Ribosomal DNA Sequences, Secondary Chemistry, and Morphology. Ph.D. dissertation. University of Texas.

Menon, S. R. et al. 1999. Structure-antimutagenic activity relationship study of plicatin B. J. Nat. Prod. (Lloydia) 62: 102–106.

Merrill, E. D. 1917. An Interpretation of Rumphius's Herbarium Amboinense.... Manila. (Interpr. Herb. Amboin.)

Mesquita, A. L. 1990. Revisão Taxonômica do Gênero *Enterolobium* Mart. (Mimosaceae) para a Região Neotropical. M.S. thesis. Universidade Federal Rural de Pernambuco.

Methodus—See: C. Moench 1794

Meyer, E. and J. F. Drège. 1836–1838. Commentariorum de Plantis Africae Australioris.... 2 fasc. Königsberg. (Comm. Pl. Afr. Austr.)

Meyer, G. F. W. 1818. Primitiae Florae Essequeboensis.... Göttingen. (Prim. Fl. Esseq.)

Meyer, Z. 2012. A Contribution to the Taxonomy and Phylogeny of *Oxytropis* Section *Arctobia* (Fabaceae) in North America. M.S. thesis. University of Alaska.

Michaux, A. 1803. Flora Boreali-Americana.... 2 vols. Paris and Strasbourg. (Fl. Bor.-Amer.)

Michener, D. C. 1986. Phenotypic instability in *Gleditsia triacanthos* (Fabaceae). Brittonia 38: 360–361.

Michigan Bot. = Michigan Botanist.

Micron = Micron; International Quarterly Journal of Electron Microscopy, Electron Probe Micro-analysis and Associated Techniques.

Miller, J. D. and H. D. Wells. 1985. Arrowleaf clover. In: N. L. Taylor, ed. 1985. Clover Science and Technology. Madison. Pp. 503–514.

Miller, J. T. and R. J. Bayer. 2000. Molecular phylogenetics of *Acacia* (Fabaceae: Mimosoideae) based on the chloroplast *trn*K/*mat*K and nuclear histone H3-D sequence. In: P. S. Herendeen and A. Bruneau, eds. 2000. Advances in Legume Systematics. Part 9. Kew. Pp. 181–200.

Miller, P. 1754. The Gardeners Dictionary.... Abridged..., ed. 4. 3 vols. London. (Gard. Dict. Abr. ed. 4)

Miller, P. 1768. The Gardeners Dictionary..., ed. 8. London. (Gard. Dict. ed. 8)

Miller, R. H. 1967. *Crotalaria* Seed Morphology, Anatomy, and Identification. Washington. [U.S.D.A. Agric. Res. Serv., Techn. Bull. 1373.]

Miller, V. M. 2004. Habitat Characterization of *Amorpha georgiana* var. *georgiana* Groups at Fort Bragg, North Carolina. M.S. thesis. North Carolina State University.

Mimoses—See: C. S. Kunth 1819[–1824]

Minissale, P. et al. 2013. *Bituminaria basaltica* (Fabaceae), a new species from Italy. Phytotaxa 98: 1–15.

Minnesota Bot. Stud. = Minnesota Botanical Studies.

Miquel, F. A. W. [1851–]1853–1855[–1857]. Plantae Junghuhnianae. Enumeratio Plantarum, Quas in Insulis Java et Sumatra, Detexit Fr. Junghuhn.... 5 parts. Leiden and Paris. [Parts paged consecutively.] (Pl. Jungh.)

Mitchell, R. S. and G. C. Tucker. 1997. Revised checklist of New York State plants. Bull. New York State Mus. Sci. Serv. 490.

Mito, T. and T. Uesugi. 2004. The status quo and the new regulation for prevention of their adverse effects. Global Envioronm. Res. 8:171–191.

Mitscher, L. A. et al. 1981. Amorfrutin A and B, bibenzyl antimicrobial agents from *Amorpha fruticosa.* Phytochemistry 20: 781–785.

Mitscher, L. A. et al. 1985. Amorphastibol, an antimicrobial agent from *Amorpha nana.* Phytochemistry 24: 1481–1483.

Moench, C. 1794. Methodus Plantas Horti Botanici et Agri Marburgensis.... Marburg. (Methodus)

Moerman, D. E. 1986. Medicinal Plants of Native America. 2 vols. Ann Arbor. [Univ. Michigan, Mus. Anthropol., Techn. Rep. 19.]

Moerman, D. E. 1998. Native American Ethnobotany. Portland.

Mohlenbrock, R. H. 1957. A revision of the genus *Stylosanthes.* Ann. Missouri Bot. Gard. 44: 299–355.

Mohlenbrock, R. H. 1961. A monograph of the leguminous genus *Zornia.* Webbia 16: 1–141.

Mohlenbrock, R. H. 1986. Guide to the Vascular Flora of Illinois, rev. ed. Carbondale.

Mohr, C. T. 1901. Plant life of Alabama. Contr. U.S. Natl. Herb. 6.

Molec. Ecol. = Molecular Ecology.

Molec. Ecol. Resources = Molecular Ecology Resources.

Molec. Phylogen. Evol. = Molecular Phylogenetics and Evolution.

Molina, G. I. 1782. Saggio sulla Storia Naturale del Chili.... Bologna. (Sag. Stor. Nat. Chili)

Molina, G. I. 1810. Saggio sulla Storia Naturale del Chili..., ed. 2. Bologna. (Sag. Stor. Nat. Chili ed. 2)

Monogr. Bot. = Monographiae Botanicae.

Moricand, M. E. 1833–1846[–1847]. Plantes Nouvelles d'Amérique.... 9 fascs. Geneva. [Fascs. paged consecutively.] (Pl. Nouv. Amér.)

Morton, J. F. 1989. Creeping indigo (*Indigofera spicata* Forsk.) (Fabaceae)—A hazard to herbivores in Florida. Econ. Bot. 43: 314–327.

Moscosoa = Moscosoa; Contribuciones Científicas del Jardin Botánico Nacional "Dr. Raphael M. Moscosa".

Mosiaco Mex.—See: P. de La Llave 1837–1842

Muelleria = Muelleria; an Australian Journal of Botany.

Muhlenbergia = Muhlenbergia; a Journal of Botany.

Munz, P. A. 1959. A California Flora. Berkeley and Los Angeles.

Murray, D. F. and H. F. Drury. 1974. The origin of *Trifolium lupinaster* (Leguminosae) in Alaska. Canad. J. Bot. 52: 277–278.

Murray, J. A. 1784. Caroli à Linné Equitis Systema Vegetabilium.... Editio Decima Quarta.... Göttingen. (Syst. Veg. ed. 14)

Musselman, L. J. 2007. Figs, Dates, Laurel, and Myrrh: Plants of the Bible and the Quran. Portland.

Muyskens, M. 2006. The fluorescence of lignum nephriticum: A flashback to the past and a simple demonstration of natural substance fluorescence. J. Chem. Educ. 83: 765–768.

N. Amer. Fl.—See: N. L. Britton et al. 1905+

N. Amer. Sp. Astragalus—See: S. L. Welsh 2007

Nabhan, G. P., J. W. Berry, and C. W. Weber. 1980. Wild beans of the Greater Southwest: *Phaseolus metcalfei* and *P. ritensis.* Econ. Bot. 34: 68–85.

Nachtr. Vollst. Lex. Gärtn.—See: F. G. Dietrich 1815–1824

Narr. Journey Polar Sea—See: J. Franklin et al. 1823

Nasir, E. and S. I. Ali, eds. 1970+. Flora of West Pakistan. 219+ nos. Karachi and Islamabad. [Title changed to Flora of Pakistan from No. 132, 1980.]

Nat. Areas J. = Natural Areas Journal; Quarterly Publication of the Natural Areas Association.

Nat. Arr. Brit. Pl.—See: S. F. Gray 1821[–1822]

Nat. Hist. Lepidopt. Georgia—See: J. E. Smith and J. Abbot 1797

Nat. Hist. Res. = Natural History Research; Journal of the Natural History Museum and Institute [Chiba]. [Chiba Kenritsu Chuo Hokubutsukan.]

Nat. Pflanzenfam.—See: H. G. A. Engler and K. Prantl 1887–1915

Nation, P. N. 1989. Alsike poisoning: A review. Canad. Veterin. J. 30: 410–415.

National Research Council [U.S.A.]. 1989b. Lost Crops of the Incas: Little Known Plants of the Andes with Promise for Worldwide Cultivation. Washington.

Native Natural. Legum. U.S.—See: D. Isely 1998

Native Pl. J. = Native Plants Journal.

Natl. Hort. Mag. = National Horticultural Magazine.

Naturaliste Canad. = Naturaliste Canadien. Bulletin de Recherches, Observations et Découvertes se Rapportant à l'Histoire Naturelle du Canada.

Naturw. Reise Mossambique—See: W. C. H. Peters [1861]1862–1864

Neilreich, A. [1857–]1859. Flora von Nieder-Oesterrich. 2 parts in fascs. Vienna. [Parts paged consecutively.] (Fl. Nied-Oesterr.)

Nelson, E. C. 1991. Shamrock—Botany and History of an Irish Myth. Aberystwyth.

Nelson, L. S. et al. 2007. Handbook of Poisonous and Injurious plants, ed. 2. Bronx.

Nelson, T. W. and J. P. Nelson. 1982. Noteworthy collections *(Astragalus tegetarioides).* Madroño 29: 58.

Nemoto, T. et al. 2010. Phylogeny of *Lespedeza* (Leguminosae) based on chloroplast *trn*L-*trn*F sequences. J. Jap. Bot. 85: 303–312.

Nemoto, T. and H. Ohashi. 1990. Organographic and ontogenetic studies on the inflorescence of *Lespedeza cuneata* (Dumont de Courset) G. Don (Leguminosae). Bot. Mag. (Tokyo) 103: 217–231.

Nemoto, T. and H. Ohashi. 1993. The inflorescence structure of *Kummerowia* (Leguminosae). Bot. J. Linn. Soc. 111: 281–294.

Nemoto, T. and H. Ohashi. 1996. The inflorescence structure of *Campylotropis* (Leguminosae). Amer. J. Bot. 83: 867–876.

Nene, Y. L., S. D. Hall, and V. K. Sheila. 1990. The Pigeonpea. Wallingford and Patancheru.

Nesom, G. L. 2009. Assessment of invasiveness and ecological impact of non-native plants of Texas. J. Bot. Res. Inst. Texas 3: 971–991.

Nesom, G. L. 2015. Taxonomy of *Galactia* (Fabaceae) in the USA. Phytoneuron 2015-42: 1–53.

Nesom, G. L. 2015b. Key to native and cultivated species of *Erythrina* (Fabaceae) in the USA and comments on the naturalization of *E. crista-galli*. Phytoneuron 2015-29: 1–8.

Nesom, G. L. 2016. *Erythrina herbacea* (Fabaceae) and two close relatives from Mexico. Phytoneuron 2016-40: 1–13.

Nesom, G. L. 2017b. *Galactia* (Fabaceae) in Florida: Comments on Franck's recent study. Phytoneuron 2017-39: 1–7.

Nesom, G. L. and J. L. Zarucchi. 2009. A new combination in North American *Tephrosia* (Fabaceae). J. Bot. Res. Inst. Texas 3: 157–158.

New Fl.—See: C. S. Rafinesque 1836[–1838]

New Mexico Bot. Newslett. = The New Mexico Botanist Newsletter.

New Phytol. = New Phytologist; a British Botanical Journal.

Newton, D. R. 2013. The vascular flora of the Eagletail Mountain region. Desert Pl. 29: 3–51.

Nicolson, D. H. 1978. Illegitimate "basionyms," impact on priority and author citations or, the rise of *Desmodium incanum* and fall of *D. canum* (Fabaceae). Taxon 27: 365–370.

Nielsen, I. C. et al. 1983. Studies in the Malesian, Australian and Pacific Ingeae (Leguminosae-Mimosoideae): The genera *Archidendropsis, Wallaceodendron, Paraserianthes, Pararchidendron* and *Serianthes* (part 2). Bull. Mus. Natl. Hist. Nat., B, Adansonia 5: 335–360.

Nielsen, I. C. and P. Guinet. 1992. Synopsis of *Adenanthera* (Leguminosae-Mimosoideae). Nordic J. Bot. 12: 85–114.

Nomencl. Bot. ed. 2—See: E. G. Steudel 1840–1841

Nordic J. Bot. = Nordic Journal of Botany.

Nores, M. J. et al. 2012. The phylogenetic relationships of four monospecific caesalpinioids (Leguminosae) endemic to southern South America. Taxon 61: 790–802.

Northington, D. K. 1976. Evidence bearing on the origin of infraspecific disjunction in *Sophora gypsophila* (Fabaceae). Pl. Syst. Evol. 125: 233–244.

Northington, D. K. and T. L. Burgess. 1979. Status of rare and endangered plant species of the Guadalupe Mountains National Park, Texas. In: H. H. Genoways and R. J. Baker, eds. 1979. Biological Investigations in the Guadalupe Mountains National Park, Texas. Washington. Pp. 55–77.

Northstrom, T. E. 1974. The Genus *Hedysarum* in North America. Ph.D. dissertation. Brigham Young University.

Northstrom, T. E. and S. L. Welsh. 1970. Revision of the *Hedysarum boreale* complex. Great Basin Naturalist 30: 109–130.

Not. Milit. Reconn.—See: W. H. Emory 1848

Notes Roy. Bot. Gard. Edinburgh = Notes from the Royal Botanic Garden, Edinburgh.

Notul. Syst. (Paris) = Notulae Systematicae, Herbier du Muséum de Paris. Phanérogamie.

Nov. Gen. Sp.—See: A. von Humboldt et al. 1815[1816]–1825

Nov. Holl. Pl.—See: J. J. H. de Labillardière 1804–1806[1807]

Nov. Pl. Descr. Dec.—See: C. G. Ortega 1797–1800

Nov. Pl. Sp.—See: A. W. Roth 1821

Novi Comment. Acad. Sci. Imp. Petrop. = Novi Commentarii Academiae Scientiarum Imperalis Petropolitanae.

Novon = Novon; a Journal for Botanical Nomenclature.

Nozzolillo, C. N. 1977. Identification of *Vicia* seedlings. Canad. J. Bot. 55: 2439–2462.

Nuovo Giorn. Bot. Ital. = Nuovo Giornale Botanico Italiano.

Nuovo Giorn. Lett. = Nuovo Giornale dei (de') Letterati.

Nutt. Pl. Ned.-Ind. ed. 2—See: K. Heyne 1927

Nuttall, T. 1813. A Catalogue of New and Interesting Plants Collected in Upper Louisiana.... London. (Cat. Pl. Upper Louisiana)

Nuttall, T. 1818. The Genera of North American Plants, and Catalogue of the Species, to the Year 1817.... 2 vols. Philadelphia. (Gen. N. Amer. Pl.)

Nuytsia = Nuytsia; Bulletin of the Western Australian Herbarium.

Obochi, G. O. et al. 2007. Efficacy and suitability of lectin from *Mucuna sloanei* seeds extract as a cell recptor signal inducer. Res. J. Biol. Sci. 2: 667–669.

Observ. Bot.—See: A. J. Retzius [1779–]1791; O. P. Swartz 1791

Ockendon, D. J. 1965. A taxonomic study of *Psoralea* subgenus *Pediomelum* (Leguminosae). SouthW. Naturalist 10: 81–124.

Ockendon, D. J. 1966. *Psoralea palmeri*. SouthW. Naturalist 11: 412.

Ocumpaugh, W. R. et al. 2004. Registration of 'BeeTAM-08' bundleflower. Crop Sci. (Madison) 44: 1861–1862.

Oesterr. Bot. Z. = Oesterreichische botanische Zeitschrift. Gemeinützige Organ für Botanik.

Ohashi, H. 2005. Desmodieae. In: G. P. Lewis et al., eds. 2005. Legumes of the World. Kew. Pp. 433–446.

Ohashi, H. and R. R. Mill. 2000. *Hylodesmum*, a new name for *Podocarpium* (Leguminosae). Edinburgh J. Bot. 57: 171–188.

Ohashi, H. and T. Nemoto. 1986. The branching system of *Desmodium triflorum* (Linnaeus) de Candolle (Leguminosae). J. Jap. Bot. 61: 15–21.

Ohashi, H. and T. Nemoto. 2014. A new system of *Lespedeza* (Leguminosae tribe Desmodieae). J. Jap. Bot. 89: 1–11.

Ohashi, H., T. Nemoto, and K. Ohashi. 2009. A revision of *Lespedeza* subgenus *Lespedeza* (Leguminosae) of China. J. Jap. Bot. 84: 143–166.

Ohashi, H. and K. Ohashi. 2016. A taxonomic revision of *Amphicarpaea* (Leguminosae), including a pollen morphological comparison with *Shuteria*. J. Jap. Bot. 91(suppl.): 231–249.

Ohashi, H. and K. Ohashi. 2018. *Grona*, a genus separated from *Desmodium* (Leguminosae tribe Desmodieae). J. Jap. Bot. 93: 104–120.

Ohashi, K. et al. 2018. Phylogenetic analyses for a new classification of the *Desmodium* group of Leguminosae tribe Desmodieae. J. Jap. Bot. 93: 165–189.

Ohashi, K. et al. 2018b. Phylogenetic analyses of the *Desmodium* group of Leguminosae 2. Two new genera separated from *Desmodium* and two new combinations in *Grona* and *Sohmaea*. J. Jap. Bot. 93: 293–306.

Oncology Rep. = Oncology Reports.

Opera Bot. = Opera Botanica a Societate Botanice Lundensi.

Opera Var.—See: C. Linnaeus 1758

Ortega, C. G. 1797–1800. Novarum, aut Rariorum Plantarum Horti Reg. Botan. Matrit. Descriptionum Decades.... 10 decades in 4 parts. Madrid. [Parts paged consecutively.] (Nov. Pl. Descr. Dec.)

Ottley, A. M. 1923. A revision of the California species of *Lotus*. Univ. Calif. Publ. Bot. 10: 189–305.

Ottley, A. M. 1944. The American loti with special consideration of a proposed new section *Simpeteria*. Brittonia 5: 81–123.

Owens, S. A. 2000. Secondary and tertiary pulvini in the unifoliate leaf of *Cercis canadensis* L. (Fabaceae) with comparison to *Bauhinia purpurea* L. Int. J. Pl. Sci. 161: 583–597.

Pacif. Railr. Rep.—See: War Department 1855–1860

Pacific Sci. = Pacific Science; a Quarterly Devoted to the Biological and Physical Sciences of the Pacific Region.

Palacios, R. A. 2006. Los mezquites Mexicanos: Biodiversidad y distribución geográfica. Bol. Soc. Argent. Bot. 41: 99–121.

Palaeontographica, B = Palaeontographica; Beiträge zur Naturgeschichte der Vorzeit. Abteilung B: Paläeophytologie.

Palanichamy, S. and S. Nagarajan. 1990. Antifungal activity of *Cassia alata* leaf extract. J. Ethnopharmacol. 29: 337–340.

Pallas, P. S. 1771–1776. Reise durch verschiedene Provinzen des russischen Reichs.... 3 vols. St. Petersburg. (Reise Russ. Reich.)

Pallas, P. S. 1800[–1803]. Species Astragalorum.... 13 parts. Leipzig. [Parts paged and plates numbered consecutively.] (Sp. Astragal.)

Palmer, E. J. 1931. Conspectus of the genus *Amorpha*. J. Arnold Arbor. 12: 157–197.

Panigrahi, G. and S. K. Murti. 1989. Flora of Bilaspur District, Madhya Pradesh. Calcutta. (Fl. Bilaspur Dist.)

Parker, M. A. 1995. Plant fitness variation caused by different mutualist genotypes. Ecology 76: 1525–1535.

Parker, M. A. 1996. Cryptic species within *Amphicarpaea bracteata* (Leguminosae): Evidence from isozymes, morphology, and pathogen specificity. Canad. J. Bot. 74: 1640–1650.

Parry, W. E. 1825. Appendix to Captain Parry's Journal of a Second Voyage for the Discovery of a North-west Passage...1821–22–23. London. (App. Parry J. Sec. Voy.)

Parsons, W. T. and E. G. Cuthbertson. 2001. Noxious Weeds of Australia. Victoria.

Parups, E. V. et al. 1966. A numerotaxonomic study of some species of *Trifolium*, section *Lupinaster*. Canad. J. Bot. 44: 1177–1182.

Pasquet, R. 2001. Notes on the genus *Vigna* (Leguminosae-Papilionoideae). Kew Bull. 56: 223–227.

Pasquet, R. 2001b. *Vigna*. In: Flora Zambesiaca Managing Committee. 1960+. Flora Zambesiaca.... 12+ vols. some in parts. London. Vol. 3, part 5, pp. 121–156.

Patterson, D. T. et al. 1989. Composite List of Weeds. Champaign.

Peck, J. H. and B. E. Serviss. 2011. *Neptunia oleracea* (Fabaceae) new to the continental United States, with new and noteworthy records of several angiosperms in Arkansas. J. Bot. Res. Inst. Texas 5: 321–326.

Peck, M. E. 1941. A Manual of the Higher Plants of Oregon. Portland. (Man. Pl. Oregon)

Pedley, L. 1978. A revision of *Acacia* Mill. in Queensland. Austrobaileya 1: 75–234.

Pedley, L. 1986. Derivation and dispersal of *Acacia* (Leguminosae), with particular reference to Australia, and the recognition of *Senegalia* and *Racosperma*. Bot. J. Linn. Soc. 92: 219–254.

Pennington, R. T. 2002. Proposal to change the authorship of *Andira*, nom. cons. (Leguminosae-Papilionoideae) and to conserve it with a conserved type. Taxon 51: 385–386.

Pennington, R. T. 2003. Monograph of *Andira* (Leguminosae-Papilionoideae). Syst. Bot. Monogr. 64: 1–143.

Pennington, R. T. et al. 2001. Phylogenetic relationships of basal papilionoid legumes based upon sequences of the chloroplast *trn*L intron. Syst. Bot. 26: 537–556.

Pérez-Laínez, D. et al. 2008. Bactericidal and fungicidal activities of *Calia secundiflora* (Ort.) Yakovlev. Z. Naturf., C 63: 653–657.

Persoon, C. H. 1805–1807. Synopsis Plantarum.... 2 vols. Paris and Tubingen. (Syn. Pl.)

Peters, W. C. H. [1861]1862–1864. Naturwissenschaftliche Reise nach Mossambique.... Vol. 6, Botanik. 2 parts. Berlin. (Naturw. Reise Mossambique)

Philipp. J. Sci. = Philippine Journal of Science.

Phillips, L. L. 1955. A revision of the perennial species of *Lupinus* of North America exclusive of southwestern United States and Mexico. Res. Stud. State Coll. Wash. 23: 161–201.

Phytogr. Lusit. Select.—See: F. Brotero 1816–1827

Phytologia = Phytologia; Designed to Expedite Botanical Publication.

Phytomedicine = Phytomedicine; International Journal of Phytotherapy and Phytopharmacology.

Phyton (Horn) = Phyton; Annales Rei Botanica.

Picasso, V. D. et al. 2011. Diverse perennial crop mixtures sustain higher productivity over time based on ecological complementarity. Renew. Agric. Food Systems 26: 317–327.

Pieters, A. J. et al. 1950. Sericea and Other Perennial Lespedezas for Forage and Soil Conservation. Washington. [U.S.D.A. Circ. 863.]

Piper, C. V. 1924. Native American forage plants. Agron. J. 16: 682.

Pittillo, J. D. 1963. Distribution and Ecology of *Cladrastis lutea*. M.S. thesis. University of Kentucky.

Pl. Baker.—See: E. L. Greene 1901

Pl. Bequaert.—See: É. A. J. De Wildeman 1921–1929

Pl. Coromandel—See: W. Roxburgh 1795–1820

Pl. Delavay.—See: A. R. Franchet 1889[–1890]

Pl. Ecol. = Plant Ecology.

Pl. Endem. Geoendem. Areas Utah ed. 2—See: S. L. Welsh and N. D. Atwood 2012

Pl. Genet. Resources Charact. Utiliz. = Plant Genetic Resources, Characterization and Utilization.

Pl. Hartw.—See: G. Bentham 1839[–1857]

Pl. Heermann.—See: E. M. Durand and T. C. Hilgard 1854

Pl. Hort. Schoenbr.—See: N. J. Jacquin 1797–1804

Pl. Jamaic. Pug.—See: C. Linnaeus 1759

Pl. Jungh.—See: F. A. W. Miquel [1851–]1853–1855[–1857]

Pl. Nouv. Amér.—See: M. E. Moricand 1833–1846[–1847]

Pl. Nov. Thurb.—See: A. Gray 1854

Pl. Physiol. (Lancaster) = Plant Physiology.

Pl. Syst. Evol. = Plant Systematics and Evolution.

Plukenet, L. 1691–1705. Phytographia sive Illustriorum & Miniis Cognitarum Icones Tabulis Aeneis Summâ Diligentiâ Elaboratae.... 7 parts. London. [Pars Prior, Pars Altera, 1691; Pars Tertia, 1692; [Pars Quarta], 1694; Almagestum, 1696; Almagesti...Mantissa, 1700; Almatheum, 1705.]

Podlech, D. and S. Zarre. 2013. A Taxonomic Revision of the Genus *Astragalus* L. (Leguminosae) in the Old World. 2 vols. Vienna.

Pojarkova, A. I. 1971b. *Caragana*. In: V. L. Komarov et al., eds. 1963+. Flora of the U.S.S.R. (Flora SSSR). Translated from Russian. 30+ vols. Jerusalem etc. Vol. 11, pp. 244–275.

Pokle, D. S. 2000. Synopsis of *Alysicarpus* Desv. (Fabaceae) in India. J. Econ. Taxon. Bot. 24: 128–132.

Pokle, D. S. 2017. Genus *Alysicarpus* Desv. in India. Aurangabad.

Polhill, R. M. 1982. *Crotalaria* in Africa and Madagascar. Rotterdam. (Crotalaria Afr. Madag.)

Polhill, R. M. and P. H. Raven, eds. 1981. Advances in Legume Systematics. Parts 1 and 2. 2 vols. Kew.

Polhill, R. M. and J. E. Vidal. 1981. Caesalpinieae. In: R. M. Polhill and P. H. Raven, eds. 1981. Advances in Legume Systematics. Parts 1 and 2. 2 vols. Kew. Vol. 1, pp. 81–95.

Pollich, J. A. 1776–1777. Historia Plantarum in Palatinatu Electorali.... 3 vols. Mannheim. (Hist. Pl. Palat.)

Porter, Ced. L. 1951. *Astragalus* and *Oxytropis* in Colorado. Univ. Wyoming Publ. 16: 1–49.

Porter, T. C. and J. M. Coulter. 1874. Synopsis of the Flora of Colorado.... Washington. (Syn. Fl. Colorado)

Powell, A. M. and R. D. Worthington. 2018. Flowering Plants of Trans-Pecos Texas and Adjacent Areas. Fort Worth.

Prakash, U. 1968. Miocene fossil woods from the Columbia basalts of central Washington, III. Palaeontographica, B 122: 183–200.

Prakash, U., E. S. Barghoorn, and R. A. Scott. 1962. Fossil wood of *Robinia* and *Gleditsia* from the Tertiary of Montana. Amer. J. Bot. 49: 692–696.

Pratt, R. C. and G. P. Nabhan. 1988. Evolution and diversity of *Phaseolus acutifolius* genetic resources. In: P. Gepts, ed. 1988. Genetic Resources of *Phaseolus* Beans.... Dordrecht and Boston. Pp. 404–440.

Prelim. Cat.—See: N. L. Britton et al. 1888

Prelim. Rep. U.S. Geol. Surv. Montana—See: F. V. Hayden 1872

Prenner, G. 2013. Papilionoid inflorescences revisited (Leguminosae - Papilionoideae). Ann. Bot. (Oxford) 112: 1567–1576.

Prescott-Allen, R. and C. Prescott-Allen. 1990. How many plants feed the world? Conservation Biol. 4: 365–374.

Prim. Fl. Esseq.—See: G. F. W. Meyer 1818

Proc. Acad. Nat. Sci. Philadelphia = Proceedings of the Academy of Natural Sciences of Philadelphia.

Proc. Amer. Acad. Arts = Proceedings of the American Academy of Arts and Sciences.

Proc. Arkansas Acad. Sci. = Proceedings of the Arkansas Academy of Science.

Proc. Biol. Soc. Wash. = Proceedings of the Biological Society of Washington.

Proc. Calif. Acad. Sci. = Proceedings of the California Academy of Sciences.

Proc. Genet. Soc. Canada = Proceedings of the Genetics Society of Canada.

Proc. Indiana Acad. Sci. = Proceedings of the Indiana Academy of Science.

Proc. Int. Seed Testing Assoc. = Proceedings of the International Seed Testing Association.

Proc. Iowa Acad. Sci. = Proceedings of the Iowa Academy of Science.

Proc. Natl. Acad. Sci. U.S.A. = Proceedings of the National Academy of Sciences of the United States of America.

Proc. Roy. Soc. Biol. Sci. Ser. B = Proceedings of the Royal Society. Biological Sciences Series B.

Proc. Soil Crop Sci. Soc. Florida = Proceedings of the Soil and Crop Science Society of Florida.

Proc. W. Sect. Amer. Soc. Anim. Sci. = Proceedings, Western Section, American Society of Animal Science.

Prodr.—See: A. P. de Candolle and A. L. P. P. de Candolle 1823–1873; O. P. Swartz 1788

Prodr. Fl. Ind. Orient.—See: R. Wight and G. A. W. Arnott 1834

Publ. Carnegie Inst. Wash. = Publications of the Carnegie Institution of Washington.

Publ. Field Mus. Nat. Hist., Bot. Ser. = Publications of the Field Museum of Natural History. Botanical Series.

Pursh, F. [1813]1814. Flora Americae Septentrionalis; or, a Systematic Arrangement and Description of the Plants of North America. 2 vols. London. (Fl. Amer. Sept.)

Quereshi, R. H., N. Ahamad, and M. Qadir. 2002. Amelioration of calcareous saline sodic soils through phytoremediation and chemical strategies. Soil Use Managem. 18: 381–385.

Radford, A. E. et al., eds. 1980+. Vascular Flora of the Southeastern United States. 2+ vols. Chapel Hill.

Radford, A. E., H. E. Ahles, and C. R. Bell. 1968. Manual of the Vascular Flora of the Carolinas. Chapel Hill.

Rafinesque, C. S. 1817. Florula Ludoviciana; or, a Flora of the State of Louisiana. Translated, Revised, and Improved, from the French of C. C. Robin.... New York. (Fl. Ludov.)

Rafinesque, C. S. 1836[–1838]. New Flora and Botany of North America.... 4 parts. Philadelphia. [Parts paged independently.] (New Fl.)

Rafinesque, C. S. 1836[1837–1838]. Flora Telluriana.... 4 vols. Philadelphia. (Fl. Tellur.)

Rafinesque, C. S. 1838b. Sylva Telluriana. Mantis. Synopt. ...Being a Supplement to the Flora Telluriana. Philadelphia. (Sylva Tellur.)

Raina, S. N., P. K. Srivastav, and S. Rama Rao. 1986. Nuclear DNA variation in *Tephrosia*. Genetics 69: 27–33.

Ralphs, M. H., J. D. Graham, and L. F. James. 2002. A close look at locoweed poisonings on shortgrass prairies. Rangelands 24: 30–34.

Ramawat, K. G. and J.-M. Mérillon, eds. 2013. Natural Products: Phytochemistry, Botany and Metabolism of Alkaloids, Phenolics and Terpenes. 5 vols. Berlin.

Randall, J. M. and J. Marinelli, eds. 1996. Invasive Plants: Weeds of the Global Garden. New York.

Randall, R. P. 2002. A Global Compendium of Weeds. Melbourne.

Randell, B. R. 1989. Revision of the Cassiinae in Australia. 2. *Senna* Miller sect. *Psilorhegma* (J. Vogel) Irwin & Barneby. J. Adelaide Bot. Gard. 12: 165–272.

Randell, B. R. and B. A. Barlow. 1998. *Senna*. In: R. Robertson et al., eds. 1981+. Flora of Australia. 32+ vols. Canberra. Vol. 12, pp. 89–138.

Rattan, V. 1887. Analytical Key to West Coast Botany.... San Francisco. (Anal. Key West Coast Bot.)

Raveill, J. A. 2002. Allozyme evidence for the hybrid origin of *Desmodium humifusum* (Fabaceae). Rhodora 104: 253–270.

Rebman, J. P. and M. G. Simpson. 2014. Checklist of Vascular Plants of San Diego, ed. 5. San Diego.

Rechinger, K. H. 1963+. Flora Iranica.... 175+ parts. Graz and Salzburg.

Rechinger, K. H. 1984b. Papilionaceae II. In: K. H. Rechinger. 1963+. Flora Iranica.... 175+ parts. Graz and Salzburg. Part 157.

Record, S. J. and R. W. Hess. 1943. Timbers of the New World. New Haven.

Record, S. J. and C. D. Mell. 1924. Timbers of Tropical America. New Haven.

Reed, C. F. 1964. A flora of the chrome and manganese ore piles at Canton, in the port of Baltimore, Maryland, and at Newport News, Virginia, with descriptions of genera and species new to the flora of eastern United States. Phytologia 10: 321–406.

Rees, A. [1802–]1819–1820. The Cyclopaedia; or, Universal Dictionary of Arts, Sciences, and Literature.... 39 vols. in 79 parts. London. [Pages unnumbered.] (Cycl.)

Rehder, A. J. 1922. New species, varieties and combinations from the herbarium and the collections of the Arnold Arboretum. J. Arnold Arbor. 3: 11–51.

Rehder, A. J. 1940. Manual of Cultivated Trees and Shrubs Hardy in North America..., ed. 2. New York.

Reichenbach, H. G. L. 1823–1832. Iconographia Botanica seu Plantae Criticae. 10 vols. Leipzig. [Vols. 6 and 7 each published in two half-centuries paged independently.] (Iconogr. Bot. Pl. Crit.)

Reise Russ. Reich.—See: P. S. Pallas 1771–1776

Renew. Agric. Food Systems = Renewable Agriculture and Food Systems.

Rep. (Annual) Arkansas Geol. Surv. = Report (Annual) of the Arkansas Geological Survey.

Rep. (Annual) Bur. Amer. Ethnol. = Annual Report of the Bureau of American Ethnology.

Rep. (Annual) Missouri Bot. Gard. = Report (Annual) of the Missouri Botanical Garden.

Rep. Colorado R.—See: J. C. Ives 1861

Rep. U.S. Mex. Bound.—See: W. H. Emory 1857–1859

Repert. Bot. Syst.—See: W. G. Walpers 1842–1847

Repert. Spec. Nov. Regni Veg. = Repertorium Specierum Novarum Regni Vegetabilis.

Res. J. Biol. Sci. = Research Journal of Biological Sciences.

Res. Stud. State Coll. Wash. = Research Studies of the State College of Washington.

Restorat. Ecol. = Restoration Ecology: the Journal of the Society for Ecological Restoration.

Retzius, A. J. [1779–]1791. Observationes Botanicae.... 6 vols. Leipzig. (Observ. Bot.)

Rev. N.-Amer. Astragalus—See: M. E. Jones 1923

Rev. Palaeobot. Palynol. = Review of Palaeobotany and Palynology; an International Journal.

Reveal, J. L. and F. R. Barrie. 1991. On the identity of *Hedysarum violaceum* Linnaeus (Fabaceae). Phytologia 71: 456–461.

Reveal, J. L., K. N. Gandhi, and D. H. Nicolson. 2004. The demise of the name *Astragalus tenellus* Pursh (Fabaceae). Taxon 53: 1055–1058.

Revis. Gen. Pl.—See: O. Kuntze 1891–1898

Revis. N. Amer. Lathyrus—See: C. L. Hitchcock 1952

Rheedea = Rheedea; Official Journal of Indian Association for Angiosperm Taxonomy.

Rhoads, A. F. and W. M. Klein. 1993. The Vascular Flora of Pennsylvania: Annotated Checklist and Atlas. Philadelphia.

Rhodora = Rhodora; Journal of the New England Botanical Club.

Rich, E. C. and A. A. Teixeira. 2005. Physical properties of *Mucuna* (velvet) bean. Appl. Engin. Agric. 21: 437–443.

Rico-Arce, M. L. and S. Bachmann. 2006. A taxonomic revision of *Acaciella* (Leguminosae, Mimosoideae). Anales Jard. Bot. Madrid 63: 189–244.

Rico-Arce, M. L., S. Gale, and N. Maxted. 2008. A taxonomic study of *Albizia* (Leguminosae: Mimosoideae: Ingeae) in Mexico and Central America. Anales Jard. Bot. Madrid 65: 255–305.

Riley-Hulting, E. T., A. Delgado-Salinas, and M. Lavin. 2004. Phylogenetic systematics of *Strophostyles* (Fabaceae): A North American temperate genus within a neotropical diversification. Syst. Bot. 29: 627–653.

Rios, R. S. et al. 2008. Population variation in plant traits associated with ant attraction and herbivory in *Chamaecrista fasciculata*. Oecologia 156: 577–588.

Ritter, N. 1917. Histology of *Astragalus mollissimus*. Kansas Univ. Sci. Bull. 20: 197–208.

Roark, R. C. 1947. Some promising insecticidal plants. Econ. Bot. 1: 437–445.

Robertson, K. R. 1977. *Cladrastis:* The yellow woods. Arnoldia (Jamaica Plain) 37: 137–150.

Robertson, R. et al., eds. 1981+. Flora of Australia. 32+ vols. Canberra.

Robinson, B. L. and M. L. Fernald. 1908. Gray's New Manual of Botany: A Handbook of the Flowering Plants and Ferns of the Central and Northeastern United States and Adjacent Canada, ed. 7. New York, Cincinnati, and Chicago. (Manual ed. 7)

Robyns, W., ed. 1948+. Flore du Congo Belge.... 9+ vols. Brussels. (Fl. Congo Belge)

Rodrigues, T. M. and S. R. Machado. 2007. Pulvinus functional traits in relation to leaf movements: A light and transmission electron microscopy study of the vascular system. Micron 39: 7–16.

Rogers, D. J. 1980. Lakota Names and Traditional Uses of Native Plants by Sicangu (Brulé) People in the Rosebud Area, South Dakota: A Study Based on Father Eugene Buechel's Collection of Plants of Rosebud around 1920. St. Francis, S.Dak.

Rogers, H. J. 1949. The Genus *Galactia* in the United States. Ph.D. dissertation Duke University.

Rollins, R. C. 1940b. Studies in the genus *Hedysarum* in North America. Rhodora 42: 217–239.

Roncal, J. et al. 2006. Propagation protocol for the endangered crenulate lead plant, *Amorpha herbacea* Walter var. *crenulata* (Rydberg) Isely. Native Pl. J. 7: 89–93.

Ross, J. H. 1974. A note on *Dichrostachys cinerea* in South Africa. Bothalia 11: 265–268.

Ross, M. D. and W. T. Jones. 1985. The origin of *Lotus corniculatus*. Theor. Appl. Genet. 71: 284–288.

Roth, A. W. 1788–1800. Tentamen Florae Germanicae.... 3 vols. in 5 parts. Leipzig. (Tent. Fl. Germ.)

Roth, A. W. 1821. Novae Plantarum Species Praesertim Indiae Orientalis.... Halberstad. (Nov. Pl. Sp.)

Rothfels, C. 2004. Significant vascular plant records from the Hamilton area, Ontario. Canad. Field-Naturalist 118: 612–615.

Roxburgh, W. 1795–1820. Plants of the Coast of Coromandel.... 3 vols. in parts. London. [Volumes paged independently, plates numbered consecutively.] (Pl. Coromandel)

Roxburgh, W. 1832. Flora Indica; or, Descriptions of Indian Plants. 3 vols. Serampore. (Fl. Ind. ed. 1832)

Rudd, V. E. 1955. The American species of *Aeschynomene*. Contr. U.S. Natl. Herb. 32: 1–172.

Rudd, V. E. 1956. A revision of the genus *Nissolia*. Contr. U.S. Natl. Herb. 32: 173–206.

Rudd, V. E. 1959. Supplementary studies in *Aeschynomene*. I. Series *Viscidulae*. J. Wash. Acad. Sci. 49: 45–52.

Rudd, V. E. 1967. *Oxyrhynchus* and *Monoplegma* (Leguminosae). Phytologia 15: 289–294.

Rudd, V. E. 1969. A synopsis of the genus *Piscidia* (Leguminosae). Phytologia 18: 473–499.

Rudd, V. E. 1972. Leguminosae-Faboideae-Sophoreae. In: N. L. Britton et al., eds. 1905+. North American Flora.... 47+ vols. New York. Ser. 2, part 7, pp. 1–53.

Rudd, V. E. 1981. Aeschynomeneae. In: R. M. Polhill and P. H. Raven, eds. 1981. Advances in Legume Systematics. Parts 1 and 2. 2 vols. Kew. Vol. 1, pp. 347–354.

Rural Herit. = Rural Heritage.

Ruskin, F. R. 1989. Basul. In: National Research Council [U.S.A.]. 1989b. Lost Crops of the Incas: Little Known Plants of the Andes with Promise for Worldwide Cultivation. Washington. Pp. 164–171.

Rutter, M. T. and M. D. Rauser. 2004. Natural selection on extrafloral nectar production in *Chamaecrista fasciculata:* The costs and benefits of a mutualism trait. Evolution 58: 2657–2668.

Rydberg, P. A. 1906. Flora of Colorado.... Fort Collins. (Fl. Colorado)

Rydberg, P. A. 1917. Flora of the Rocky Mountains and Adjacent Plains. New York. (Fl. Rocky Mts.)

Rydberg, P. A. 1919–1920. Fabaceae-Psoraleae. In: N. L. Britton et al., eds. 1905+. North American Flora.... 47+ vols. New York. Vol. 24, parts 1, 2, pp. 1–136.

Rydberg, P. A. 1924. Genera of North American Fabaceae. II. Tribe Galegeae (continued). Amer. J. Bot. 11: 470–482.

Rydberg, P. A. 1928. Genera of North American Fabaceae III. Tribe Psoraleae. Amer. J. Bot. 15: 195–203.

Rydberg, P. A. 1929. Fabaceae-Galegeae-Astragalaneae. In: N. L. Britton et al., eds. 1905+. North American Flora.... 47+ vols. New York. Vol. 24, pp. 251–462.

Rydberg, P. A. 1929b. Genera of North American Fabaceae VI. *Astragalus* and related genera (continued). Amer. J. Bot. 16: 197–206.

S. African J. Bot. = South African Journal of Botany.

S.W. Rare Endang. Pl. 1995—See: J. Maschinski et al. 1996

Sag. Stor. Nat. Chili—See: G. I. Molina 1782

Sag. Stor. Nat. Chili ed. 2—See: G. I. Molina 1810

Sales, F. and I. C. Hedge. 1993. *Melilotus* Miller (Leguminosae): Typification and nomenclature. Anales Jard. Bot. Madrid 51: 171–175.

Sanjappa, M. 1992. Legumes of India. Dehra Dun. (Legumes India)

Sargent, C. S. 1889. Notes upon some North American trees. V. *Parkinsonia*. Gard. & Forest 2: 388.

Sargent, C. S. 1922. Manual of the Trees of North America (Exclusive of Mexico), ed. 2. Boston and New York. [Facsimile edition in 2 vols. 1961, reprinted 1965, New York.]

Saskatchewan Agriculture and Food. 2006. Lentil in Saskatchewan. Regina.

Sauer, J. D. 1964. Revision of *Canavalia*. Brittonia 16: 106–181.

Savi, G. 1798. Flora Pisana.... 2 vols. Pisa. (Fl. Pis.)

Saxena, M. C. and K. B. Singh, eds. 1987. The Chickpea. Oxford.

Schaefer, H. et al. 2012. Systematics, biogeography, and character evolution of the legume tribe Fabeae with special focus on the middle-Atlantic island lineages. B. M. C. Evol. Biol. 12: 250.

Sched. Herb. Fl. Ross.—See: D. I. Litvinov 1898–1911

Schkuhr, C. [1787–]1791–1803. Botanisches Handbuch.... 3 vols. Wittenberg. (Bot. Handb.)

Schmelzer, G. H. and A. Gurib-Fakim, eds. 2008. Medicinal Plants. Wageningen. [Incl. CD-ROM database.]

Schmitt, A., H. Telikepalli, and L. A. Mitscher. 1991. Plicatin-B, the antimicrobial principle of *Psoralea juncea*. Phytochemistry 30: 3569–3570.

Schnabel, A., P. E. McDonel, and J. F. Wendel. 2003. Phylogenetic relationships in *Gleditsia* (Leguminosae) based on ITS sequences. Amer. J. Bot. 90: 310–320.

Schneider, C. K. [1904–]1906–1912. Illustriertes Handbuch der Laubholzkunde.... 2 vols. in 12 fascs. Jena. (Ill. Handb. Laubholzk.)

Schneider, C. K. 1907. Conspectus generis *Amorphae*. Bot. Gaz. 43: 297–307.

Schreber, J. C. 1771. Spicilegium Florae Lipsicae.... Leipzig. (Spic. Fl. Lips.)

Schubert, B. G. 1940. *Desmodium:* Preliminary studies-I. Contr. Gray Herb. 129: 3–31.

Schubert, B. G. 1950. *Desmodium:* Preliminary studies III. Rhodora 52: 135–155.

Schubert, B. G. 1950b. *Desmodium*. In: M. L. Fernald. 1950. Gray's Manual of Botany, ed. 8. New York. Pp. 915–923.

Schubert, B. G. 1970. *Desmodium*. In: D. S. Correll and M. C. Johnston. 1970. Manual of the Vascular Plants of Texas. Renner, Tex. Pp. 855–869.

Schubert, B. G. 1980. *Desmodium*. In: R. E. Woodson Jr. et al., eds. 1943–1981. Flora of Panama. 41 fascs. St. Louis. [Ann. Missouri Bot. Gard. 67: 622–662.]

Schultz-Kraft, R. 1990. *Centrosema:* Biology, Agronomy, and Utilization. Cali.

Schulz, E. D. 1928. Texas Wild Flowers.... Chicago and New York.

Schumacher, H. C. F. 1827. Beskrivelse af Guinddiske Planter.... Copenhagen. (Beskr. Guin. Pl.)

Sci. Stud. Montana Coll. Agric., Bot. = Science Studies, Montana College of Agriculture and Mechanic Arts. Botany.

Science = Science; an Illustrated Journal [later: a Weekly Journal Devoted to the Advancement of Science].

Scopoli, J. A. 1771–1772. Flora Carniolica..., ed. 2. 2 vols. Vienna. (Fl. Carniol. ed. 2)

Seabrook, J. A. E. 1973. A Biosystematic Study of the Genus *Apios* Fabricius (Leguminosae) with Special Reference to *Apios americana* Medikus. M.S. thesis. University of New Brunswick.

Sede, S. M. et al. 2008. Genetic relationships in the *Galactia-Camptosema-Collaea* complex (Leguminosae) inferred from AFLP markers. Pl. Syst. Evol. 276: 261–270.

Sede, S. M. et al. 2009. Phylogenetic relationships among southern South American species of *Camptosema, Galactia* and *Collaea* (Diocleinae: Papilionoideae: Leguminosae) on the basis of molecular and morphological data. Austral. J. Bot. 57: 76–86.

Seigler, D. S. and J. E. Ebinger. 2005. New combinations in the genus *Vachellia* (Fabaceae: Mimosoideae) from the New World. Phytologia 87: 139–178.

Seigler, D. S., J. E. Ebinger, and J. T. Miller. 2006. *Mariosousa,* a new segregate genus from *Acacia* s.l. (Fabaceae, Mimosoideae) from Central and North America. Novon 16: 413–420.

Seigler, D. S., J. E. Ebinger, and J. T. Miller. 2006b. The genus *Senegalia* (Fabaceae: Mimosoideae) from the New World. Phytologia 88: 38–93.

Select. Stirp. Amer. Hist.—See: N. J. Jacquin 1763

Senn, H. A. 1939. The North American species of *Crotalaria*. Contr. Gray Herb. 125: 317–370.

Sert. Angl.—See: C.-L. L'Héritier de Brutelle 1788[1789–1792]

Shaperenko, K. K. 1972. *Alhagi*. In: V. L. Komarov et al., eds. 1963+. Flora of the U.S.S.R. (Flora SSSR). Translated from Russian. 30+ vols. Jerusalem etc. Vol. 13, pp. 281–285.

Shelly, W. and R. P. Arthur. 1955. Mucunain, the active pruritogenic proteinase of cowhage. Science, ser. 2, 122: 469–470.

Shinners, L. H. 1958. Spring Flora of the Dallas-Fort Worth Area, Texas. Dallas. (Spring Fl. Dallas-Fort Worth)

Shinners, L. H. 1962e. Key to southeastern glabrous-styled *Tephrosia* (Leguminosae). Sida 1: 60–62.

Shreve, F. and I. L. Wiggins. 1964. Vegetation and Flora of the Sonoran Desert. 2 vols. Stanford. (Veg. Fl. Sonoran Desert)

Sibthorp, J. 1794. Flora Oxoniensis.... Oxford. (Fl. Oxon.)

Sida = Sida; Contributions to Botany.

Simpson, B. B. 1998. A revision of *Pomaria* (Fabaceae) in North America. Lundellia 1: 46–71.

Simpson, B. B. 1999. A revision of *Hoffmannseggia* (Fabaceae) in North America. Lundellia 2: 14–54.

Simpson, B. B. et al. 2004b. Phylogeny and character evolution of *Hoffmannseggia* (Caesalpinieae: Caesalpinioideae: Leguminosae). Syst. Bot. 29: 933–946.

Simpson, B. B. et al. 2006. Phylogeny and biogeography of *Pomaria* (Caesalpinioideae: Leguminosae). Syst. Bot. 31: 792–804.

Simpson, B. B. and E. A. Ulibarri. 2006. A synopsis of the genus *Hoffmannseggia* (Leguminosae). Lundellia 9: 7–33.

Singer, S. R. et al. 2009. Venturing beyond beans and peas: What can we learn from *Chamaecrista?* Pl. Physiol. (Lancaster) 151: 1041–1047.

Sinou, C. et al. 2009. The genus *Bauhinia* s.l. (Leguminosae): A phylogeny based on the plastid *trn*L-*trn*F region. Botany (Ottawa) 87: 947–960.

Širjaev, G. 1928–1934. Generis *Trigonella* L. revisio critica. Spisy Prír. Fak. Masarykovy Univ. 102, 110, 128, 136, 148, 170, 192.

Širjaev, G. I. 1932. Generis *Ononis* L. revisio critica. Beih. Bot. Centralbl. 49: 381–665.

Sist. Zametki Mater. Gerb. Tomsk. Univ. = Sistematicheskie Zametki po Materialam Gerbariya Imeni Tomskogo Universiteta.

Sketch Bot. S. Carolina—See: S. Elliott [1816–]1821–1824

Skr. Vidensk.-Selsk. Christiana, Math.-Naturvidensk. Kl. = Skrifter Udgivne af Videnskabs-Selskabet i Christiana. Mathematisk-Naturvidenskabelig Klasse.

Skvortsovia = Skvortsovia; International Journal of Salicology and Plant Biology.

Small, E. 1985. Morphological differentiation in *Medicago sativa* s.l. in relation to ploidy. Canad. J. Bot. 63: 1747–1752.

Small, E. 1987. Generic changes in Trifolieae subtribe Trigonellinae. In: C. H. Stirton, ed. 1987. Advances in Legume Systematics. Part 3. Kew. Pp. 159–181.

Small, E. 2011. Alfalfa and Relatives: Evolution and Classification of *Medicago*. Ottawa and Wallingford.

Small, E. et al. 1993. A systematic comparison of morphology and seed proteins of early- and late-flowering forms of *Medicago scutellata*. Canad. J. Bot. 71: 183–192.

Small, E. and B. S. Brookes. 1984. Taxonomic circumscription and identification in the *Medicago sativa-falcata* (alfalfa) continuum. Econ. Bot. 38: 83–96.

Small, E. and B. S. Brookes. 1990. A numerical taxonomic analysis of the *Medicago littoralis—M. truncatula* complex. Canad. J. Bot. 68: 1667–1674.

Small, E., B. S. Brookes, and E. J. Crawford. 1990. Intercontinental differentiation in *Medicago rigidula*. Canad. J. Bot. 68: 2607–2613.

Small, E. and M. Jomphe. 1989. A synopsis of the genus *Medicago* (Leguminosae). Canad. J. Bot. 67: 3260–3294.

Small, E., P. Lassen, and B. S. Brookes. 1987. An expanded circumscription of *Medicago* (Leguminosae, Trifolieae) based on explosive flower tripping. Willdenowia 16: 415–437.

Small, J. K. 1903. Flora of the Southeastern United States.... New York. (Fl. S.E. U.S.)

Small, J. K. 1913. Flora of the Southeastern United States..., ed. 2. New York.

Small, J. K. 1913b. Flora of Miami.... New York. (Fl. Miami)

Small, J. K. 1933. Manual of the Southeastern Flora, Being Descriptions of the Seed Plants Growing Naturally in Florida, Alabama, Mississippi, Eastern Louisiana, Tennessee, North Carolina, South Carolina and Georgia. New York. (Man. S.E. Fl.)

Smartt, J. 1990. Grain Legumes: Evolution and Genetic Resources. Cambridge and New York.

Smith, B. A. and D. L. Marsh. 1993. Occurrence of hybrid honey locust (*Gleditsia* ×*texana* Sarg.) in southwest Arkansas. Proc. Arkansas Acad. Sci. 47: 149–150.

Smith, B. W. 1950. *Arachis hypogaea.* Aerial flowers and subterranean fruit. Amer. J. Bot. 37: 802–815.

Smith, C. P. 1938–1953. Species Lupinorum. 44 fascs. Saratoga, Calif. (Sp. Lupinorum)

Smith, C. P. 1944. *Lupinus.* In: L. Abrams and R. S. Ferris. 1923–1960. Illustrated Flora of the Pacific States: Washington, Oregon, and California. 4 vols. Stanford. Vol. 2, pp. 483–519.

Smith, G. W., K. W. Allred, and D. E. Kiehl. 1992. Swainsonine content of New Mexico locoweeds. Proc. W. Sect. Amer. Soc. Anim. Sci. 42: 405–407.

Smith, Hu. H. 1928. Ethnobotany of the Meskawi Indians. Bull. Public Mus. Milwaukee 4: 175–326.

Smith, J. E. and J. Abbot. 1797. The Natural History of the Rare Lepidopterous Insects of Georgia. 2 vols. London. (Nat. Hist. Lepidopt. Georgia)

Smith, J. F. and J. C. Zimmers. 2017. New combination in *Astragalus.* Phytoneuron 2017-38: 1–3.

Smith, J. P. Jr. ed. 1984. Inventory of Rare and Endangered Vascular Plants of California, ed. 3. Berkeley.

Smithsonian Contr. Knowl. = Smithsonian Contributions to Knowledge.

Smithsonian Misc. Collect. = Smithsonian Miscellaneous Collections.

Smýkal, P. et al. 2011. Phylogeny, phylogeography and genetic diversity of the *Pisum* genus. Pl. Genet. Resources Charact. Utiliz. 9: 4–18.

Snyder, D. E. 1950. *Dalea alopecuroides* on Plant Island, Essex County, Massachusetts. Rhodora 52: 299.

Soil Use Managem. = Soil Use and Management.

Sokoloff, D. D. et al. 2007. Inflorescence and early flower development in Loteae (Leguminosae) in a phylogenetic and taxonomic context. Int. J. Pl. Sci. 168: 801–833.

Sokoloff, P. C. 2010. Taxonomic Status of the Narrow Endemic *Astragalus robbinsii* var. *fernaldii* (Fernald's Milkvetch—Fabaceae): Molecules, Morphology, and Implications for Conservation. M.S. thesis University of Ottawa.

Sokoloff, P. C. and L. J. Gillespie. 2012. Taxonomy of *Astragalus robbinsii* var. *fernaldii* (Fabaceae): Molecular and morphological analyses support transfer to *Astragalus eucosmus.* Botany (Ottawa) 90: 11–26.

Soltis, D. E. et al. 2011. Angiosperm phylogeny: 17 genes, 640 taxa. Amer. J. Bot. 98: 704–730.

Sommer, S. J. 1999. Genetic Diversity within and among Populations of *Trifolium lemmonii* S. Wats. M.S. thesis. Miami University.

Sonnante, G., I. Galasso, and D. Pignone. 2003. ITS sequence analysis and phylogenetic inference in the genus *Lens* Mill. Ann. Bot. (Oxford), n. s. 91: 49–54.

Sørensen, M. 1988. A taxonomic revision of the genus *Pachyrhizus* (Fabaceae-Phaseoleae). Nordic J. Bot. 8: 167–192.

Sørensen, M., ed. 1994. Proceedings of the First International Symposium on Tuberous Legumes, Guadeloupe, F.W.I., 21–24 April 1992. Copenhagen.

Sorrie, B. A. 1995. Status Survey of *Amorpha georgiana* var. *georgiana.* Asheville and Raleigh.

Sorrie, B. A. 2015. Notes on the morphology of *Acmispon helleri.* Phytoneuron 2015-44: 1–3.

Sousa S., M. and V. E. Rudd. 1993. Revisión del género *Styphnolobium* (Leguminosae: Papilionoideae: Sophoreae). Ann. Missouri Bot. Gard. 80: 273–280.

SouthW. Naturalist = Southwestern Naturalist.

Souza, É. R. et al. 2013. Phylogeny of *Calliandra* (Leguminosae: Mimosoideae) based on nuclear and plastid molecular markers. Taxon 62: 1200–1219.

Souza, É. R., M. Krishnaraj, and L. P. de Queiroz. 2016. *Sanjappa*, a new genus in the tribe Ingeae (Leguminosae: Mimosoideae) from India. Rheedea 26: 1–12.

Sp. Astragal.—See: P. S. Pallas 1800[–1803]

Sp. Lupinorum—See: C. P. Smith 1938–1953

Sp. Pl.—See: C. Linnaeus 1753; C. L. Willdenow et al. 1797–1830

Sp. Pl. ed. 2—See: C. Linnaeus 1762–1763

Spackman, S. et al. 1997b. Colorado Rare Plant Field Guide. Fort Collins.

Spaeth, J. P. and J. W. Thieret. 2004. Notes on "coffee" from the Kentucky coffeetree (*Gymnocladus dioicus*, Fabaceae). Sida 21: 345–356.

Span. J. Agric. Res. = Spanish Journal of Agricultural Research.

Spellenberg, R. 1974. Chromosome numbers as an indication of general relationship of *Astragalus*, section *Strigulosi* (Leguminosae) with notes on *A. altus*. SouthW. Naturalist 18: 393–396.

Spellenberg, R. 1976. Chromosome numbers and their cytotaxonomic significance for North American *Astragalus* (Fabaceae). Taxon 25: 463–476.

Spellenberg, R. 1981. Polyploidy in *Dalea formosa* (Fabaceae) on the Chihuahuan Desert. Brittonia 33: 309–324.

Spic. Fl. Lips.—See: J. C. Schreber 1771

Spisy Prir. Fak. Masarykovy Univ. = Spisy vydávané Přírodovědeckou Fakultou Masarykovy University.

Sprengel, K. [1824–]1825–1828. Caroli Linnaei...Systema Vegetabilium. Editio Decima Sexta.... 5 vols. Göttingen. [Vol. 4 in 2 parts paged independently; vol. 5 by A. Sprengel.] (Syst. Veg.)

Sprent, J. I. 2001. Nodulation in Legumes. Kew.

Spring Fl. Dallas-Fort Worth—See: L. H. Shinners 1958

St. John, H. 1937. Flora of Southeastern Washington and of Adjacent Idaho. Pullman. (Fl. S.E. Washington)

St. John, L., D. G. Ogle, and D. Tilley. 2010. Plant Guide for Strawberry Clover *(Trifolium fragiferum)*. Aberdeen, Md.

Stace, C. A. 1997. New Flora of the British Isles, ed. 2. New York and Cambridge.

Stafleu, F. A. et al. 1992–2009. Taxonomic Literature: A Selective Guide to Botanical Publications and Collections with Dates, Commentaries and Types. Supplement. 8 vols. Königstein.

Stafleu, F. A. and R. S. Cowan. 1976–1988. Taxonomic Literature: A Selective Guide to Botanical Publications and Collections with Dates, Commentaries and Types, ed. 2. 7 vols. Utrecht etc.

Standley, P. C. and J. A. Steyermark. 1946. Flora of Guatemala. Part V. Fieldiana, Bot. 24(5): 1–502.

Stansbury, H. 1852. An Expedition to the Valley of the Great Salt Lake of Utah.... Philadelphia. [Botanical appendix by J. Torrey, pp. 381–397, plates 1–9.] (Exped. Great Salt Lake)

Stebbins, G. L. 1971. Chromosomal Evolution in Higher Plants. London.

Steele, K. P. and M. F. Wojciechowski. 2003. Phylogenetic analyses of tribes Trifolieae and Vicieae, based on sequences of the plastid gene, *matK* (Papilionoideae: Leguminosae). In: B. B. Klitgaard and A. Bruneau, eds. 2003. Advances in Legume Systematics. Part 10. Kew. Pp. 355–370.

Steudel, E. G. 1840–1841. Nomenclator Botanicus Enumerans Ordine Alphabetico Nomina atque Synonyma tum Generica tum Specifica..., ed. 2. 2 vols. Stuttgart and Tübingen. (Nomencl. Bot. ed. 2)

Stevenson, G. A. 1969. An agronomic and taxonomic review of the genus *Melilotus* Mill. Canad. J. Pl. Sci. 49: 1–20.

Stevenson, M. C. 1915. Ethnobotany of the Zuñi Indians. Rep. (Annual) Bur. Amer. Ethnol. 30: 35–102. [Reprinted 1993, New York.]

Steyermark, J. A. 1963. Flora of Missouri. Ames.

Stirp. Austr. Fasc. ed. 2—See: H. J. N. von Crantz 1769

Stirton, C. H. 1981. Studies in the Leguminosae-Papilionoideae of southern Africa. Bothalia 13: 317–325.

Stirton, C. H. 1981b. The genus *Dipogon* (Leguminosae-Papilionoideae). Bothalia 13: 327–330.

Stirton, C. H. 1986. Notes on the genus *Ortholobium* (Psoraleae, Fabaceae). S. African J. Bot. 52: 1–6.

Stirton, C. H., ed. 1987. Advances in Legume Systematics. Part 3. Kew. (Advances Legume Syst. 3)

Stirton, C. H. and J. L. Zarucchi. 1989. Advances in Legume Biology. St. Louis. [Missouri Bot. Gard. Monogr. Syst. Bot. 29.]

Straub, S. C. K., S. M. Bogdanowicz, and J. J. Doyle. 2009. Characterization of twelve polymorphic microsatellite markers for Georgia false indigo (*Amorpha georgiana* Wilbur var. *georgiana*), an endangered species, and their utility in other dwarf *Amorpha* L. species. Molec. Ecol. Resources 9: 225–228.

Straub, S. C. K. and J. J. Doyle. 2014. Molecular phylogenetics of *Amorpha* (Fabaceae): An evaluation of monophyly, species relationships, and polyploid origins. Molec. Phylogen. Evol. 76: 49–66.

Strickland, W. 1801. Observations on the Agriculture of the United States of America. London.

Stritch, L. R. 1984. Nomenclatural contributions to a revision of the genus *Wisteria*. Phytologia 56: 183–184.

Suppl. Pl.—See: C. Linnaeus f. 1781[1782]

Svensk Bot. Tidskr. = Svensk Botanisk Tidskrift Utgifven af Svenska Botaniska Föreningen.

Swartz, O. P. 1788. Nova Genera & Species Plantarum seu Prodromus.... Stockholm, Uppsala, and Åbo. (Prodr.)

Swartz, O. P. 1791. Observationes Botanicae.... Erlangen. (Observ. Bot.)

Sweet, R. 1826. Hortus Britannicus.... 2 parts. London. [Parts paged consecutively.] (Hort. Brit.)

Sylva Tellur.—See: C. S. Rafinesque 1838b

Symb. Antill.—See: I. Urban 1898–1928

Symon, D. E. 1966. A revision of the genus *Cassia* in Australia. Trans. Roy. Soc. South Australia 90: 73–146.

Symon, D. E. 1998. *Senna phyllodinea:* A new combination in *Senna* (Caesalpiniaceae). J. Adelaide Bot. Gard. 18: 101–102.

Syn. Fl. Colorado—See: T. C. Porter and J. M. Coulter 1874

Syn. Fl. Germ. Helv.—See: W. D. J. Koch [1835–]1837–1838

Syn. Lupini—See: J. G. Agardh 1835

Syn. Pl.—See: D. N. F. Dietrich 1839–1852; C. H. Persoon 1805–1807

Syst. Biol. = Systematic Biology.

Syst. Bot. = Systematic Botany; Quarterly Journal of the American Society of Plant Taxonomists.

Syst. Bot. Monogr. = Systematic Botany Monographs; Monographic Series of the American Society of Plant Taxonomists.

Syst. Nat.—See: J. F. Gmelin 1791[–1792]

Syst. Nat. ed. 10—See: C. Linnaeus 1758[–1759]

Syst. Nat. ed. 12—See: C. Linnaeus 1766[–1768]

Syst. Veg.—See: K. Sprengel [1824–]1825–1828

Syst. Veg. ed. 14—See: J. A. Murray 1784

Tabl. Encycl.—See: J. Lamarck and J. Poiret 1791–1823

Tatnall, R. R. 1946. Flora of Delaware and the Eastern Shore: An Annotated List of the Ferns and Flowering Plants of the Peninsula of Delaware, Maryland and Virginia. [Wilmington.]

Taxon = Taxon; Journal of the International Association for Plant Taxonomy.

Taylor, D. W. 2010. Flora of the Yosemite Sierra.... LaVergne, Tenn. (Fl. Yosemite Sierra)

Taylor, N. L., ed. 1985. Clover Science and Technology. Madison.

Techn. Publ. North Carolina Agric. Exp. Sta. = Techincal Publication, North Carolina Agricultural Experiment Station.

Tekpinar, A. R. et al. 2016. Phylogenetic relationships between *Oxytropis* DC. and *Astragalus* species native to an Old World diversity center inferred from nuclear ribosomal ITS and plastid *mat*K gene sequences. Turk. J. Biol. (Ankara) 40: 250–263.

Tent. Fl. Germ.—See: A. W. Roth 1788–1800

Theodora—See: F. K. Medikus 1786

Theor. Appl. Genet. = Theoretical and Applied Genetics; International Journal of Breeding Research and Cell Genetics.

Thompson, R. L. 1980. Revision of the Genus *Lysiloma* (Leguminosae). Ph.D. dissertation. Southern Illinois University, Carbondale.

Thuillier, J. L. 1799. Flore des Environs de Paris..., ed. 2. Paris. (Fl. Env. Paris ed. 2)

Thulin, M. 1999. *Chapmannia* (Leguminosae-Stylosanthinae) extended. Nordic J. Bot. 19: 597–607.

Tidestrom, I. and T. Kittell. 1941. A Flora of Arizona and New Mexico.... Washington.

Tilley, D. 2012. Plant Guide for Frisco Clover *(Trifolium friscanum)*. Aberdeen, Md.

Tolmatchew, A. I., ed. 1960–1987. Flora Arctica URSS. 10 vols. in 12. Moscow and Leningrad. (Fl. Arct. URSS)

Tomooka, N. et al. 2001. The Asian *Vigna* Subgenus *Ceratotropis* Genetic Resources. Dordrecht

Tonne, P. 2000. Status Report for Chihuahua Scurfpea (*Pediomelum pentaphyllum;* Fabaceae). Albuquerque.

Török, K. et al. 2003. Invasion gateways and corridors in the Carpathian Basin: Biological invasions in Hungary. Biol. Invasions 5: 349–356.

Torrey, J. and A. Gray. 1838–1843. A Flora of North America.... 2 vols. in 7 parts. New York, London, and Paris. (Fl. N. Amer.)

Torreya = Torreya; a Monthly Journal of Botanical Notes and News.

Tournefort, J. P. de. 1700. Institutiones Rei Herbariae. 3 vols. Paris.

Trans. Amer. Philos. Soc. = Transactions of the American Philosophical Society Held at Philadelphia for Promoting Useful Knowledge.

Trans. & Proc. Roy. Soc. Victoria = Transactions and Proceedings of the Royal Society of Victoria.

Trans. Hort. Soc. London = Transactions, of the Horticultural Society of London.

Trans. Missouri Acad. Sci. = Transactions of the Missouri Academy of Science.

Trans. New York Acad. Sci. = Transactions of the New York Academy of Sciences.

Trans. Roy. Soc. South Australia = Transactions of the Royal Society of South Australia.

Trans. Sapporo Nat. Hist. Soc. = Transactions of the Sapporo Natural History Society. [Sapporo Hakubutsu Gakkai Kaiho.]

Trautvetter, E. R. von. 1878. Flora Terrae Tschuktschorum. St. Petersburg. [Preprinted from Trudy Imp. S.-Peterburgsk. Bot. Sada 6(1): 1–40. 1879.] (Fl. Terr. Tschukt.)

Travis, S. E., J. Maschinski, and P. Keim. 1996. An analysis of genetic variation in *Astragalus cremnophylax* var. *cremnophylax*, a critically endangered plant, using AFLP markers. Molec. Ecol. 5: 735–745.

Trelease, S. F. and O. A. Beath. 1949. Selenium. Burlington.

Trop. Pl. Biol. = Tropical Plant Biology.

Trudy Bot. Inst. Akad. Nauk S.S.S.R, Ser. 1, Fl. Sist. Vyssh. Rast. = Trudy Botanicheskogo Instituta Akademii Nauk S S S R. Ser. 1, Flora i Sistematika Vysshikh Rastenii.

Trudy Glavn. Bot. Sada = Trudy Glavnago Botanicheskago Sada.

Trudy Imp. S.-Peterburgsk. Bot. Sada = Trudy Imperatorskago S.-Peterburgskago Botanicheskago Sada.

Trudy Leningradsk. Khim.-Farm. Inst. = Trudy Leningradskogo Khimiko-Farmacevticheskogo Instituta.

Trusty, J. L. et al. 2007. Identity of naturalized exotic *Wisteria* (Fabaceae) in the south-eastern United States. Weed Res. 47: 479–487.

Tucker, S. C. 1988. Heteromorphic flower development in *Neptunia pubescens,* a mimosoid legume. Amer. J. Bot. 75: 205–224.

Tucker, S. C. 1996. Trends in evolution of floral ontogeny in *Cassia* sensu stricto, *Senna,* and *Chamaecrista* (Leguminosae: Caesalpinioideae: Cassieae: Cassiinae); a study in convergence. Amer. J. Bot. 83: 687–711.

Tucker, S. C. 2003. Floral development in legumes. Pl. Physiol. (Lancaster) 131: 911–926.

Turchi, G., G. Alagona, and V. Lubrano. 2009. Protective activity of plicatin B against human LDL oxidation induced in metal ion-dependent and -independent processes: Experimental and theoretical studies. Phytomedicine 16: 1014–1026.

Turk. J. Biol. (Ankara) = Turkish Journal of Biology. Ankara.

Turkington, R. and P. B. Cavers. 1979. The biology of Canadian weeds. 33. *Medicago lupulina* L. Canad. J. Pl. Sci. 59: 99–110.

Turkington, R. A., P. B. Cavers, and E. Rempel. 1978. The biology of Canadian weeds. 29. *Melilotus alba* Desr. and *M. officinalis* (L.) Lam. Canad. J. Pl. Sci. 58: 523–537.

Turland, N. J., N. Kirschner, and J. Štěpánek. 1996. Proposals to reject the names *Trifolium agrarium, T. filiforme* and *T. procumbens* (Leguminosae). Taxon 45: 549–551.

Turner, B. L. 1951. Revision of the United States species of *Neptunia* (Leguminosae). Amer. Midl. Naturalist 46: 82–92.

Turner, B. L. 1956b. Chromosome numbers in the Leguminosae. Amer. J. Bot. 43: 577–581.

Turner, B. L. 1959. The Legumes of Texas. Austin.

Turner, B. L. 1981. Thermopsidae. In: R. M. Polhill and P. H. Raven, eds. 1981. Advances in Legume Systematics. Parts 1 and 2. 2 vols. Kew. Vol. 1, pp. 403–407.

Turner, B. L. 1992. Taxonomic overview of the genus *Cologania* (Fabaceae, Phaseoleae). Phytologia 73: 281–301.

Turner, B. L. 1994e. Texas species of *Schrankia* (Mimosaceae) transferred to the genus *Mimosa*. Phytologia 76: 412–420.

Turner, B. L. 2000b. The Texas species of *Calliandra* (Leguminosae, Mimosoideae). Lundellia 3: 13–18.

Turner, B. L. 2006b. *Dalea austrotexana* (Fabaceae), a new species from southernmost Texas. Phytologia 88: : 288–293.

Turner, B. L. 2006c. Overview of the genus *Baptisia* (Leguminosae). Phytologia 88: 253–268.

Turner, B. L. 2008b. Revision of the genus *Orbexilium* (Fabaceae: Psoraleeae). Lundellia 11: 1–7.

Turner, B. L. 2012. New names in *Dermatophyllum* (Fabaceae). Phytoneuron 2012-3: 1–4.

Turner, B. L. 2013. Taxonomy of the *Dalea phleoides* (Fabaceae) complex. Phytologia 95: 274–276.

Turner, B. L. et al. 2003. Atlas of the Vascular Plants of Texas. 2 vols. Fort Worth. [Sida Bot. Misc. 24.]

Turner, B. L. and O. S. Fearing. 1964. A taxonomic study of the genus *Amphicarpaea* (Leguminosae). SouthW. Naturalist 9: 207–218.

Turner, N. J. and H. V. Kuhnlein. 1982. Two important "root" foods of the northwest coast Indians: Springbank clover *(Trifolium wormskioldii)* and Pacific silverweed (*Potentilla anserina* ssp. *pacifica*). Econ. Bot. 36: 411–432.

Turner, R. M., J. E. Bowers, and T. L. Burgess. 1995. Sonoran Desert Plants: An Ecological Atlas. Tucson.

Turrill, W. B. et al., eds. 1952+. Flora of Tropical East Africa. 152+ vols. London and Rotterdam. [Vols. by family, unnumbered, some in parts.]

Tutin, T. G. et al., eds. 1964–1980. Flora Europaea. 5 vols. Cambridge.

Tyndall, R. W. and P. L. Groller. 2006. Transplant survival, reproductive output, and population monitoring of *Desmodium ochroleucum* M. A. Curtis at Chicone Creek Woods in Maryland. Castanea 71: 329–332.

U.S.D.A. Farmers Bull. = U S Department of Agriculture. Farmers Bulletin.

U.S. Fish and Wildlife Service. 2004. Recovery Plan for Five Plants from Monterey County, California. Portland.

Univ. Calif. Publ. Agric. Sci. = University of California Publications in Agricultural Sciences.

Univ. Calif. Publ. Bot. = University of California Publications in Botany.

Univ. Wyoming Publ. = University of Wyoming Publications.

University of Chicago Press. 1993. The Chicago Manual of Style, ed. 14. Chicago.

University of Nebraska. 1895. Flora of Nebraska. Part 21. Rosales. Lincoln. (Fl. Nebr., Rosales)

Urban, I., ed. 1898–1928. Symbolae Antillanae seu Fundamenta Florae Indiae Occidentalis.... 9 vols. Berlin etc. (Symb. Antill.)

Utah Fl. ed. 3—See: S. L. Welsh et al. 2003

Vail, A. M. 1894. A study of the genus *Psoralea* in America. Bull. Torrey Bot. Club 21: 91–119.

Vail, A. M. 1895. A study of the genus *Galactia* in North America. Bull. Torrey Bot. Club 22: 374–378.

Valero, M. 1991. Discriminant alleles and discriminant analysis: Efficient characters to separate closely related species: The example of *Lathyrus latifolius* L. and *Lathyrus sylvestris* L. (Leguminosae). Bot. J. Linn. Soc. 107: 139–161.

van der Maesen, L. J. G. 1972. *Cicer* L., a monograph of the genus, with special reference to the chickpea (*Cicer arietinum* L.), its ecology and cultivation. Meded. Landbouwhoogeschool 72-10.

van der Maesen, L. J. G. 1985. Revision of the genus *Pueraria* de Candolle, with some notes on *Teyleria* Backer. Wageningen Agric. Univ. Pap. 85(1).

van der Maesen, L. J. G. 1986. *Cajanus* DC. and *Atylosia* W. & A. (Leguminosae). Wageningen Agric. Univ. Pap. 85(4): 1–225.

van der Maesen, L. J. G. 1987. Origin, history and taxonomy of chickpea. In: M. C. Saxena and K. B. Singh, eds. 1987. The Chickpea. Oxford. Pp. 11–34.

van der Maesen, L. J. G. 1990. Origin, history and taxonomy of pigeonpea. In: Y. L. Nene et al., eds. 1990. The Pigeonpea. Wallingford and Patancheru. Pp. 15–46.

van der Maesen, L. J. G. 1994. *Pueraria,* the kudzu and its relatives. In: M. Sørensen, ed. 1994. Proceedings of the First International Symposium on Tuberous Legumes, Guadeloupe, F.W.I., 21–24 April 1992. Copenhagen. Pp. 55–86.

van der Maesen, L. J. G. et al. 2007. Taxonomy of the genus *Cicer* revisited. In: S. S. Yadav et al., eds. 2007. Chickpea Breeding and Management. Wallingford and Cambridge, Mass. Pp. 14–46.

Varied. Ci. = Variedades de Ciencias, Literatura y Artes.

Vasc. Pl. Pacif. N.W.—See: C. L. Hitchcock et al. 1955–1969

Vasc. Pl. Wyoming—See: R. D. Dorn 1988

Vassilczenko, I. T. 1953. A review of the species of the genus *Trigonella* L. Trudy Bot. Inst. Akad. Nauk S.S.S.R, Ser. 1, Fl. Sist. Vyssh. Rast. 14: 124–269.

Vaughn, P. K. and D. B. Dunn. 1977. The *Lupinus latifolius* Agardh complex. Trans. Missouri Acad. Sci. 10: 89–106.

Veg. Fl. Sonoran Desert—See: F. Shreve and I. L. Wiggins 1964

Veg. Syst.—See: J. Hill 1759–1775

Vellozo, J. M. 1825–1827[1829–1831]. Florae Fluminensis, seu Descriptionum Plantarum Praefectura Fluminensi Sponte Nascentium.... 1 vol. text + 11 vols. plates + indexes. Rio de Janeiro. (Fl. Flumin.)

Ventenat, É. P. [1800–1803.] Description des Plantes Nouvelles et Peu Connues Cultivés dans le Jardin de J. M. Cels.... 10 parts. Paris. [Plates numbered consecutively.] (Descr. Pl. Nouv.)

Ventenat, É. P. 1808. Decas Generum Novorum.... Paris. (Dec. Gen. Nov.)

Verdcourt, B. 1970. Studies in the Leguminosae-Papilionoideae for the Flora of Tropical East Africa: II. Kew Bull. 24: 235–307.

Verdcourt, B. 1971. *Alysicarpus*. In: W. B. Turrill et al., eds. 1952+. Flora of Tropical East Africa. 152+ vols. London and Rotterdam. Leguminosae, part 3, pp. 491–501.

Verdcourt, B. 1979. A Manual of New Guinea Legumes. Lae.

Verdcourt, B. 2000. *Alysicarpus*. In: A. W. Exell and H. Wild, eds. 1960+. Flora Zambesiaca: Mozambique, Federation of Rhodesia and Nyasaland, Bechuanaland Protectorate. 12+ vols. in parts. London. Vol. 3, part 6, pp. 36–43.

Verh. Bot. Vereins Prov. Brandenburg = Verhandlungen des Botanischen Vereins der Provinz Brandenburg.

Verma, D. P. S. and J. Stanley. 1989. The legume-*Rhizobium* equation: A coevolution of two genomes. In: C. H. Stirton and J. L. Zarucchi, eds. 1989. Advances in Legume Biology. St. Louis. Pp. 545–557.

Vestal, P. A. and R. E. Schultes, R. E. 1939. The Economic Botany of the Kiowa Indians. Cambridge, Mass.

Vidensk. Meddel. Naturhist. Foren. Kjøbenhavn = Videnskabelige Meddelelser fra den Naturhistoriske Forening i Kjøbenhavn.

Villiers, J. F. 2002. *Viguieranthus*. In: D. J. Du Puy et al., eds. 2002. The Leguminosae of Madagascar. Kew. Pp. 271–275.

Villiers, J. F. 2002b. *Dichrostachys*. In: D. J. Du Puy et al., eds. 2002. The Leguminosae of Madagascar. Kew. Pp. 206–218.

Vincent, M. A. 1991. *Trifolium reflexum* L. (buffalo clover: Leguminosae) in Ohio, its history and present status. Michigan Bot. 30: 65–68.

Vincent, M. A. 2001. The genus *Trifolium* in Kentucky. J. Kentucky Acad. Sci. 62: 1–17.

Vincent, M. A. 2014. Neotypification of *Trifolium psoralioides* Walter (Fabaceae) and its transfer to *Orbexilum*. Phytoneuron 2014-36: 1–7.

Vincent, M. A. and D. Isely. 2012. *Trifolium*. In: B. G. Baldwin et al., eds. 2012. The Jepson Manual: Vascular Plants of California, ed. 2. Berkeley. Pp. 789–798.

Vincent, M. A. and R. Morgan. 1998. *Trifolium jokerstii* (Leguminosae, Papilionoideae), a new species from Butte County, California. Novon 8: 91–93.

Vines, R. A. 1960. Trees, Shrubs, and Woody Vines of the Southwest. Austin.

Viviani, D. 1808. Florae Italicae Fragmenta.... Genoa. (Fl. Ital. Fragm.)

Vogel, T. 1837. Generis Cassiae Synopsis. Berlin. (Gen. Cass. Syn.)

Vorles. Churpfälz. Phys.-Ökon. Ges. = Vorlesungen der Churpfälzischen Physicalisch-Ökonomischen Gesellschaft.

Voss, E. G. and A. A. Reznicek. 2012. Field Manual of Michigan Flora. Ann Arbor.

Voy. Bot. Espagne—See: P. E. Boissier 1839–1845

W. Amer. Sci. = West American Scientist.

W. N. Amer. Naturalist = Western North American Naturalist.

Wächter, G. A. et al. 1999. Antibacterial and antifungal flavanones from *Eysenhardtia texana*. Phytochemistry 52: 1469–1471.

Wageningen Agric. Univ. Pap. = Wageningen Agricultural University Papers.

Wagner, W. H. Jr. 1956. A natural hybrid, ×*Adiantum tracyi* C. C. Hall. Madroño 13: 195–205.

Wagstaff, D. J. 2008. International Poisonous Plant Checklist: An Evidence-based Approach. Boca Raton.

Waldron, G. E. 2003. Trees of the Carolinian Forest: A Guide to Species, Their Ecology and Uses. Erin.

Wallace, L. E. et al. 2017. Phylogeography and genetic structure of endemic *Acmispon argophyllus* and *A. dendroideus* (Fabaceae) across the California Channel Islands. Amer. J. Bot. 104: 743–756.

Walpers, W. G. 1842–1847. Repertorium Botanices Systematicae.... 6 vols. Leipzig. (Repert. Bot. Syst.)

Walter, K. S. and H. J. Gillett. 1998. 1997 IUCN Red List of Threatened Plants. Gland.

Walter, T. 1788. Flora Caroliniana, Secundum Systema Vegetabilium Perillustris Linnaei Digesta.... London. (Fl. Carol.)

Wang, H. C. et al. 2006. A phylogeny of Thermopsidae (Leguminosae: Papilionoideae) inferred from nuclear ribosomal internal transcribed spacer (ITS) sequences. Bot. J. Linn. Soc. 151: 365–373.

War Department [U.S.]. 1855–1860. Reports of Explorations and Surveys, to Ascertain the Most Practicable and Economical Route for a Railroad from the Mississippi River to the Pacific Ocean. Made under the Direction of the Secretary of War, in 1853[–1856].... 12 vols. in 13. Washington. (Pacif. Railr. Rep.)

Ward, D. B. 1971. Checklist of Legumes of Florida. Gainesville.

Ward, D. B. and D. W. Hall. 2004. Keys to the flora of Florida—10. *Galactia* (Leguminosae). Phytologia 86: 65–74.

Ward, D. E., R. Spellenberg, and D. Sutherland. 1993. Chromosome numbers for *Dalea* species (Fabaceae) from southwestern New Mexico and southeastern Arizona. Phytologia 75: 166–169.

Watson, S. 1871. United States Geological Expolration [sic] of the Fortieth Parallel. Clarence King, Geologist-in-charge. [Vol. 5] Botany. By Sereno Watson.... Washington. [Botanical portion of larger work by C. King.] [Botany (Fortieth Parallel)]

Watson, S. 1876. Descriptions of new species of plants, chiefly Californian, with revisions of certain genera. Proc. Amer. Acad. Arts 11: 121–148.

Weakley, A. S. et al. 2018. New combinations, rank changes, and nomenclatural and taxonomic comments in the vascular flora of the southeastern United States. III. J. Bot. Res. Inst. Texas 12: 27–67.

Wear, K. S. 1998. Hybridization between Native and Introduced *Lupinus* in Humboldt County. M.A. thesis. Humboldt State University.

Webb, C. J. et al. 1988. Naturalized pteridophytes, gymnosperms, dicotyledons. In: H. H. Allan et al. 1961–2000. Flora of New Zealand. 5 vols. Wellington, Christchurch, and Lincoln. Vol. 4.

Webb, P. B. and S. Berthelot. [1835–]1836–1850. Histoire Naturelle des Îles Canaries.... 3 vols. in 9. Paris. [Tome troisième, Botanique: Première partie, 1 vol; deuxième partie, 4 vols.] (Hist. Nat. Îles Canaries)

Webbia = Webbia; Raccolta di Scritti Botanici.

Weber, W. A. 1987. Colorado Flora: Western Slope. Boulder.

Weber, W. A. and R. C. Wittmann. 1992. Catalog of the Colorado Flora: A Biodiversity Baseline. Niwot, Colo.

Webster, G. T. 1955. Interspecific hybridization of *Melilotus alba* × *M. officinalis* using embryo culture. Agron. J. 47: 138–142.

Weed Res. = Weed Research.

Weed Sci. = Weed Science; Journal of the Weed Science Society of America.

Wei, Z. and M. A. Vincent. 2010. Fabaceae. Tribe Trifolieae. In: Wu Z. and P. H. Raven, eds. 1994–2013. Flora of China. 25 vols. Beijing and St. Louis. Vol. 10, pp. 547–559.

Weitemier, K. A. 2010. Phytogeographic Patterns and Intervarietal Relationships within *Lupinus lepidus:* Morphological Differences, Genetic Similarities. M.S. thesis. Portland State University.

Welsh, S. L. 1960. Legumes of the north-central states: Galegeae. Iowa State J. Sci. 35: 111–250.

Welsh, S. L. 1974. Anderson's Flora of Alaska and Adjacent Parts of Canada. Provo.

Welsh, S. L. 1989. *Astragalus* and *Oxytropis:* Definitions, distributions, and ecological parameters. In: L. F. James et al., eds. 1989. Swainsonine and Related Glycoside Inhibitors. Ames. Pp. 3–13.

Welsh, S. L. 1990. On the typification of *Oxytropis borealis* DC. Great Basin Naturalist 50: 355–360.

Welsh, S. L. 1995b. North American types of *Oxytropis* DC. (Leguminosae) at the Natural History Museum and Royal Botanic Gardens, England, with nomenclatural comments and a new variety. Great Basin Naturalist 55: 271–281.

Welsh, S. L. 2001. Revision of North American Species of *Oxytropis* de Candolle (Leguminosae). Orem.

Welsh, S. L. 2007. North American Species of *Astragalus* Linnaeus, a Taxonomic Revision. Provo. (N. Amer. Sp. *Astragalus*)

Welsh, S. L. et al., eds. 1987. A Utah flora. Great Basin Naturalist Mem. 9.

Welsh, S. L. et al., eds. 1993. A Utah Flora, ed. 2. Provo.

Welsh, S. L. et al., eds. 2003. A Utah Flora, ed. 3. Provo. (Utah Fl. ed. 3)

Welsh, S. L. et al., eds. 2008. A Utah Flora, ed. 4. Provo.

Welsh, S. L. et al., eds. 2015. A Utah Flora, ed. 5. Provo.

Welsh, S. L. and N. D. Atwood. 2012. Plant Endemism and Geoendemic Areas of Utah, ed. 2. Provo. (Pl. Endem. Geoendem. Areas Utah ed. 2)

Welsh, S. L. and M. H. Licher. 2010. *Pediomelum* Rydberg (Leguminosae) in Arizona and two previously undescribed species. W. N. Amer. Naturalist 70: 9–18.

Wemple, D. K. 1970. Revision of the genus *Petalostemon* (Leguminosae). Iowa State J. Sci. 45: 1–102.

Wendelberger, K. S., M. Q. N. Fellows, and J. Maschinski. 2007. Rescue and restoration: Experimental translocation of *Amorpha herbacea* Walter var. *crenulata* (Rydb.) Isely into a novel urban habitat. Restorat. Ecol. 16: 542–552.

Wendland, H. L. 1820. Commentatio de *Acaciis* Aphyllis.... Hannover. (Comm. Acac. Aphyll.)

Werdenda = Werdenda. Beiträge zur Pflanzenkunde.

Wetlands = Wetlands; Journal of the Coast and Wetlands Society (later Society of Wetlands Scientists).

Wexelsen, H. 1928. Chromosome numbers and morphology in *Trifolium.* Univ. Calif. Publ. Agric. Sci. 2: 355–376.

Wherry, E. T., J. M. Fogg, Jr., and H. A. Wahl. 1979. Atlas of the Flora of Pennsylvania. Philadelphia.

White, P. S. 1980. *Indigofera.* In: R. E. Woodson Jr. et al., eds. 1943–1981. Flora of Panama. 41 fascs. St. Louis. [Ann. Missouri Bot. Gard. 67: 706–714.]

Wiener Z. Kunst = Wiener Zeitschrift für Kunst, Litteratur, Theater und Mode.

Wight, R. and G. A. W. Arnott. 1834. Prodromus Florae Peninsula Indiae Orientalis.... 1 vol. only. London. (Prodr. Fl. Ind. Orient.)

Wilbur, R. L. 1963b. The Leguminous Plants of North Carolina. Raleigh.

Wilbur, R. L. 1963c. *Baptisia.* Techn. Publ. North Carolina Agric. Exp. Sta. 151: 41–52.

Wilbur, R. L. 1964b. A revision of the dwarf species of *Amorpha* (Leguminosae). J. Elisha Mitchell Sci. Soc. 80: 51–65.

Wilbur, R. L. 1975. A revision of the North American genus *Amorpha* (Leguminosae-Psoraleae). Rhodora 77: 337–409.

Willdenow, C. L. 1803–1816. Hortus Berolinensis.... 2 vols. in 10 fascs. Berlin. [Fascs. and plates numbered consecutively.] (Hort. Berol.)

Willdenow, C. L. 1809–1813[–1814]. Enumeratio Plantarum Horti Regii Botanici Berolinensis.... 2 parts + suppl. Berlin. [Parts paged consecutively.] (Enum. Pl.)

Willdenow, C. L., C. F. Schwägrichen, and J. H. F. Link. 1797–1830. Caroli a Linné Species Plantarum.... Editio Quarta.... 6 vols. Berlin. [Vols. 1–5(1), 1797–1810, by Willdenow; vol. 5(2), 1830, by Schwägrichen; vol. 6, 1824–1825, by Link.] (Sp. Pl.)

Williams, M. C. and R. C. Barneby. 1977. The occurrence of nitro-toxins in North American *Astragalus* (Fabaceae). Brittonia 29: 310–326.

Williams, W. M. et al. 2001. Evidence of three subspecies in *Trifolium nigrescens* Viv. Ann. Bot. (Oxford) 87: 683–691.

Windler, D. R. 1966. A revision of the genus *Neptunia* (Leguminosae). Austral. J. Bot. 14: 379–420.

Windler, D. R. 1973. Field and garden studies in *Crotalaria sagittalis* L. and related species. Phytologia 26: 289–354.

Windler, D. R. 1974. A systematic treatment of the native unifoliolate crotalarias of North America (Leguminosae). Rhodora 76: 151–204.

Wink, M., C. Meissner, and L. Witte. 1995. Patterns of quinolizidine alkaloids in 56 species of the genus *Lupinus*. Phytochemistry 38: 139–153.

Wochenschr. Vereines Beförd. Gartenbaues Königl. Preuss. Staaten = Wochenschrift des Vereines zur Beförderung des Gartenbaues in den königlich preussischen Staaten für Gärtnerei und Pflanzenkunde.

Wojciechowski, M. F. 2003. Reconstructing the phylogeny of legumes (Leguminosae): An early 21st century perspective. In: B. B. Klitgaard and A. Bruneau, eds. 2003. Advances in Legume Systematics. Part 10. Kew. Pp. 5–35.

Wojciechowski, M. F. 2005. *Astragalus* (Fabaceae): A molecular phylogenetic perspective. Brittonia 57: 382–396.

Wojciechowski, M. F. et al. 2000. Molecular phylogeny of the "temperate herbaceous tribes" of papilionoid legumes: A supertree approach. In: P. S. Herendeen and A. Bruneau, eds. 2000. Advances in Legume Systematics. Part 9. Kew. Pp. 277–298.

Wojciechowski, M. F., M. Lavin, and M. J. Sanderson. 2004. A phylogeny of legumes (Leguminosae) based on analysis of the plastid *mat*K gene resolves many well-supported subclades within the family. Amer. J. Bot. 91: 1846–1862.

Wojciechowski, M. F., M. J. Sanderson, and Hu J. M. 1999. Evidence on the monophyly of *Astragalus* (Fabaceae) and its major subgroups based on nuclear ribosomal DNA ITS and chloroplast DNA *trn*L intron data. Syst. Bot. 24: 409–437.

Wood, C. E. Jr. 1949. The American barbistyled species of *Tephrosia* (Leguminosae). Rhodora 51: 193–231, 233–302, 305–364, 369–384.

Woods, M. 2005. A revision of the North American species of *Apios* (Fabaceae). Castanea 70: 85–100.

Woods, M. and A. R. Diamond. 2014. The genus *Baptisia* in Alabama. Phytoneuron 2014-83: 1–11.

Woodson, R. E. Jr., R. W. Schery, et al., eds. 1943–1981. Flora of Panama. 41 fascs. St. Louis. [Fascs. published as individual issues of Ann. Missouri Bot. Gard. and aggregating 8 nominal parts + introduction and indexes.]

Wooton, E. O. and P. C. Standley. 1915. Flora of New Mexico. Contr. U.S. Natl. Herb. 19.

Wu, Z. and P. H. Raven, eds. 1994–2013. Flora of China. 25 vols. Beijing and St. Louis.

Wulfenia = Wulfenia; Mitteilungen des Botanischen Gartens des Landes Kärnten.

Wunderlin, R. P. 1998. Guide to the Vascular Plants of Florida. Gainesville.

Wunderlin, R. P. 2010. Reorganization of the Cercideae (Fabaceae: Caesalpinioideae). Phytoneuron 2010-48: 1–5.

Wunderlin, R. P. and B. F. Hansen. 2000+. Flora of Florida. 3+ vols. Gainesville.

Wunderlin, R. P. and B. F. Hansen. 2011. Guide to the Vascular Plants of Florida, ed. 3. Gainesville.

Wunderlin, R. P., K. Larsen, and S. S. Larsen. 1987. Reorganization of the Cercideae (Fabaceae: Caesalpinioideae). Biol. Skr. 28: 1–40.

Wyman, D. 1949. The wisterias. Arnoldia (Jamaica Plain) 9: 17–28.

Wyman, D. 1969. Shrubs and Vines for American Gardens. New York.

Wyman, D. 1977. Wyman's Gardening Encyclopedia. New York.

Wyoming Agric. Exp. Sta. Bull. = Wyoming Agricultural Experiment Station Bulletin.

Wyse Jackson, P. S. 2014. Ireland's Generous Nature. St. Louis.

Xu, B. et al. 2012. Analysis of DNA sequences of six chloroplast and nuclear genes suggests incongruence, introgression, and incomplete lineage sorting in the evolution of *Lespedeza* (Fabaceae). Molec. Phylogen. Evol. 62: 346–358.

Yadav, S. S. et al., eds. 2007. Chickpea Breeding and Management. Wallingford and Cambridge, Mass.

Yakovlev, G. P. 1968. The genus *Calia* Terán & Berl. (Sophoreae) in America. Trudy Leningradsk. Khim.-Farm. Inst. 26(5): 104–112.

Yakovlev, G. P. 1979. Notes on the taxonomy of the genus *Alhagi* Gagneb. (Fabaceae). Bot. Zhurn. (Moscow & Leningrad) 64: 1794–1799.

Yang, B. et al. 2003. Growth and metal accumulation in vetiver and two *Sesbania* species on lead/zinc mine tailings. Chemosphere 52: 1593–1600.

Yang, L. et al. 2015. Effect of bean extract of yabumame (*Amphicarpaea bracteata* (L.) Fernald subsp. *edgeworthii* (Benth.) H. Ohashi) on low-density lipoprotein oxidation in vitro. Food Sci. Technol. Res. 21: 589–596.

Young, J. P. W. and K. E. Haukka. 1996. Diversity and phylogeny of rhizobia. New Phytol. 133: 87–94.

Youngman, V. E. 1968. Lentils—A pulse of the Palouse. Econ. Bot. 22: 135–139.

Z. Naturf., C = Zeitschrift für Naturforschung. Teil C, Biochemie, Biophysik, Biologie, Virologie.

Zandstra, I. I. and W. F. Grant. 1968. The biosystematics of the genus *Lotus* (Leguminosae) in Canada. I. Cytotaxonomy. Canad. J. Bot. 46: 557–583.

Zhang, Y., Yang Ji, and Rao G. Y. 2006. Comparative study of the aerial and subterranean flower development in *Amphicarpaea edgeworthii* Benth. (Leguminosae: Papilionoideae), an amphicarpic species. Int. J. Pl. Sci. 167: 943–949.

Zimmers, J. C. et al. 2017. Species boundaries in the *Astragalus cusickii* complex delimited using molecular phylogenetic techniques. Molec. Phylogen. Evol. 114: 93–110.

Zoë = Zoë; a Biological Journal.

Zohary, D. and U. Plitmann. 1979. Chromosome polymorphism, hybridization and colonization in the *Vicia sativa* group (Fabaceae). Pl. Syst. Evol. 131: 143–156.

Zohary, M. and D. Heller. 1984. The Genus *Trifolium*. Jerusalem.

Index

Names in *italics* are synonyms, casually mentioned hybrids, or plants not established in the flora. Part numbers are shown in parentheses followed by a colon. Page numbers in **boldface** indicate the primary entry for a taxon. Page numbers in italics indicate an illustration. Roman type is used for all other entries, including author names, vernacular names, and accepted scientific names for plants treated as established members of the flora.

Index to Subfamilies, Tribes, and Genera Volume 11, Parts 1 and 2

The list below gives the part number and page on which each taxon is treated.

Flora of North America — Index to Families/Volumes of Vascular Plants

Boldface denotes published volume: page number, current as of October 2022.